D1448944

Illustrated Encyclopedia of
Applied and
Engineering Physics

Volume III
P–Z

Illustrated Encyclopedia of
Applied and
Engineering Physics

Volume III
P–Z

Robert Splinter, PhD

CRC Press
Taylor & Francis Group
Boca Raton London New York

CRC Press is an imprint of the
Taylor & Francis Group, an **informa** business

CRC Press
Taylor & Francis Group
6000 Broken Sound Parkway NW, Suite 300
Boca Raton, FL 33487-2742

© 2017 by Taylor & Francis Group, LLC
CRC Press is an imprint of Taylor & Francis Group, an Informa business

No claim to original U.S. Government works

Printed and bound in India by Replika Press Pvt. Ltd.

Printed on acid-free paper
Version Date: 20160831

International Standard Book Number-13: 978-1-4987-4083-8 (Hardback)

This book contains information obtained from authentic and highly regarded sources. Reasonable efforts have been made to publish reliable data and information, but the author and publisher cannot assume responsibility for the validity of all materials or the consequences of their use. The authors and publishers have attempted to trace the copyright holders of all material reproduced in this publication and apologize to copyright holders if permission to publish in this form has not been obtained. If any copyright material has not been acknowledged please write and let us know so we may rectify in any future reprint.

Library of Congress Cataloging-in-Publication Data

Names: Splinter, Robert, author.
Title: Illustrated encyclopedia of applied and engineering physics / Robert
Splinter.
Description: Boca Raton, FL : CRC Press, Taylor & Francis Group, [2016] |
"2016 | Includes bibliographical references and index.
Identifiers: LCCN 2015040711| ISBN 9781498740784 (alk. paper : v. 1) | ISBN
1498740782 (alk. paper : v. 1) | ISBN 9781498740821 (alk. paper : v. 2) |
ISBN 9781498740838 (alk. paper : v. 3) | ISBN 1498740839 (alk. paper : v.
3)
Subjects: LCSH: Physics--Dictionaries.
Classification: LCC QC5 .S65 2016 | DDC 530.03--dc23
LC record available at http://lccn.loc.gov/2015040711

Visit the Taylor & Francis Web site at
http://www.taylorandfrancis.com

and the CRC Press Web site at
http://www.crcpress.com

Contents

Preface   vii
Author   ix

P   1
Q   165
R   187
S   259
T   377
U   459
V   481
W   527
X   565
Y   569
Z   579

Appendix A   589
Appendix B   591
Appendix C   597
Index of Names   781
Index of Subjects   787

Preface

The purpose of this *encyclopedia* is to provide a single, concise reference that contains terms and expressions used in the study, practice, and applications of physical sciences. The reader will be able to quickly identify critical information about professional jargon, important people, and events. This encyclopedia gives self-contained definitions with essentials regarding the technical terms and their usages and information about important people in the following areas of physics:

- Acoustics
- Astronomy/astrophysics
- Atomic physics
- Biomedical physics
- Chemical physics
- Computational physics
- Condensed matter
- Dynamics
- Electromagnetism
- Electronics
- Energy
- Engineering
- Fluid dynamics
- General
- Geophysics
- High-energy physics
- Imaging
- Instrumentation
- Materials sciences
- Mechanics
- Meteorology
- Nanotechnology
- Nuclear physics
- Optics
- Quantum physics
- Relativistic physics
- Rheology
- Sensing
- Signal processing
- Solid-state physics
- Theoretical physics
- Thermodynamics
- Ultrafast phenomena

This reference differs from the standard dictionaries in its inclusion of numerous illustrations, including photographs, micrographs, diagrams, graphs, and tables, which support the textual definitions and draw the reader into the explanation to enhance didactic value. Together, these over 2500 entries will educate the reader about the current practice of physics and its applications in biomedicine, materials sciences, chemical engineering, electrical engineering, mechanical engineering, geology, astronomy, meteorology, and energy.

It is envisioned that novices and trainees, in addition to seasoned professionals, will find this resource useful, both for sustained reading and for taking a dip into the topics periodically. The contents are also designed to help the professionals who are new to a work environment and recently enrolled students who need to become more familiar with terminology and nuances relevant to certain research and applications. Moreover, it will assist in understanding the primary literature as well as technical reports and proposals. Finally, any student from the high school to graduate levels should be able to benefit from the broad and applied emphasis of this concise encyclopedia, which may support undergraduate courses in applied sciences for nonscience majors.

AUTHOR

Robert Splinter MSc PhD—University of North Carolina at Charlotte, North Carolina

MATLAB® is a registered trademark of The MathWorks, Inc. For product information, please contact:

The MathWorks, Inc.
3 Apple Hill Drive
Natick, MA 01760-2098 USA
Tel: 508-647-7000
Fax: 508-647-7001
E-mail: info@mathworks.com
Web: www.mathworks.com

Author

Robert Splinter, PhD, obtained his master of science degree in applied physics from the Eindhoven University of Technology, Eindhoven, the Netherlands, and his PhD from the VU University of Amsterdam. Dr. Splinter built his career as a scientist and technology manager in biomedical engineering. His work is dedicated to resolving issues in device development with a particular focus on medicine and biology through the development of novel diagnostic techniques and treatment methods using all multidisciplinary aspects of engineering and applied physics.

He cofounded several companies in biomedical engineering and worked for several established metrology and medical device companies. In addition, Dr. Splinter worked in clinical settings, prototyping, and validating devices using the full practical and theoretical knowledge of physics, engineering, electrical engineering, chemistry, and biology. He is an associate professor (Adj.) in the Department of Physics at the University of North Carolina at Charlotte.

p (linear momentum)

[general, mechanics] $p = mv$, where m is the mass of the object in MOTION with velocity v (*see* **MOMENTUM**).

Pacemaker

[biomedical] Biological or electronic unit providing the excitation mechanism that induces a self-sustained DEPOLARIZATION process in the HEART muscle. The biological unit in mammals is located in the atrium and consists of a small group of cells with a range of natural depolarization periods, presumably based on a cellular ionic leak that eventually generates a full cellular depolarization, generating an impulse that is transmitted to neighboring MUSCLE cells that will respond to the threshold exceeding voltage spike. Various cells have specific depolarization rates, thus allowing for a regulation mechanism of the heart rate. The depolarization rate can be influenced externally in limited amount by the autonomic nerve system and by hormonal influences. The artificial pacemaker is an electronic device that generates an electrical pulse that is conducted to the heart muscle by means of electrodes and is powered by a BATTERY. Artificial pacemakers have evolved of time from fixed rate to on demand. Additionally, bioelectricity is being investigated to power modern pacemakers, eliminating the need for surgical battery replacement. The on-demand pacemaker "measures" ACTIVITY and regulates the emission rate of the current spikes to longer or shorter intervals. The pacemaker's purpose is the general BLOOD supply to the body and brain as well as mitigation of external influences to maintain HOMEOSTASIS and accommodate the efficiency of the organs with respect to their particular functions. Artificial pacemakers are a major economic force in medical device design (see Figure P.1).

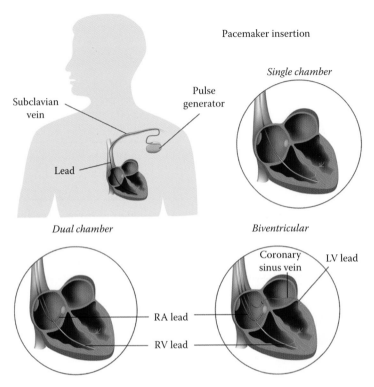

Figure P.1 Image of artificial pacemaker.

Packing fraction

[nuclear] The difference between the ATOMIC WEIGHT in nuclear mass units (standard atomic weight: M_a) and the mass number of an ELEMENT (A), divided by the mass number, multiplied by 10,000. Packing fraction $= \left[(M_a - A)/A \right] \times 10{,}000$. Packing fraction is used as an indicator of nuclear stability.

Pair annihilation

[atomic, nuclear] *See* ANNIHILATION.

Pair formation

[nuclear] The formation of an elementary PARTICLE and its antiparticle. The creation process involves the application of a trigger phenomenon (generally a BOSON; e.g., PHOTON) with high enough ENERGY to accommodate the formation of two particles that balance the energy in REST MASS and movement (i.e., kinetic energy content). Since the CONSERVATION LAWS apply, the two particles shall respectively have the inverse properties. The passage of gamma rays with energy greater than or equal to 1.022 MeV in the proximity of the atomic NUCLEUS of certain ELEMENTS will generate an electron and a positron pair. This process was first described by PAUL ADRIEN MAURICE DIRAC (1902–1984) in 1928 basing his premonitions on relativistic wave-mechanics theory, and was subsequently observed by CARL DAVID ANDERSON (1905–1991) in 1932. In the atomic annihilation process, under the influence of positron RADIATION two gamma photons with 511 keV are produced that are emitted in perfect opposite directions (±5°). POSITRON EMISSION TOMOGRAPHY uses this principle for imaging purposes. Another kind of pair formation is found in support of SUPERCONDUCTIVITY

called a "Cooper pair," consisting of two electrons (*see* COPPER PAIR *and* POSITRON EMISSION TOMOGRAPHY) (see Figure P.2).

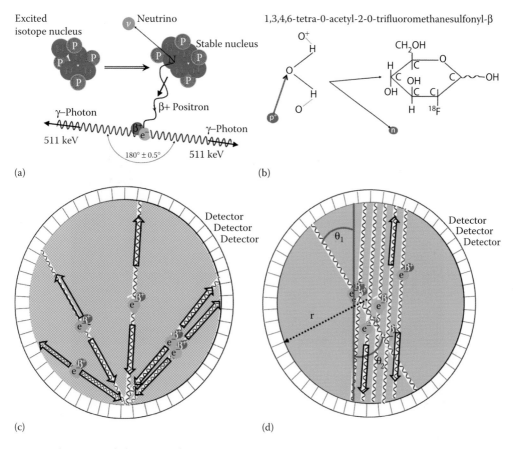

Figure P.2 (a–d) Process of photon pair formation in positron emission tomography.

Pairing energy (P_{pair})

[atomic, nuclear] In the event of the pairing of electrons, the SPIN pairing ENERGY refers to the energy required to accommodate two paired electrons to share one orbital and what the effects are on the molecules surrounding this orbit. The electron–electron interactions must be taken into account, which involves Hund's rule and PAULI EXCLUSION PRINCIPLES. For instance, Hund's rule predicts for $d^1 - d^3$ systems that the electrons will not pair and occupy the t_{2g}-set spin configuration. The electron configuration will largely depend on the difference between the pairing energy (P_{pair}) and the electron gap energy (Δ_0), providing a higher spin configuration energy when the pairing energy exceeds the electron band-gap. The pairing energy is expressed in cm^{-1}.

Paleomagnetism

[astrophysics/astronomy, energy, geophysics] Study of the historical development and evolution of the Earth's MAGNETIC field as permanently recorded in rocks, bricks, or clay. This study has revealed that the Earth's magnetic field has changed direction (North–South) on the order of every several thousand years on a regular basis over the history of the EARTH. The Earth's magnetic axis (magnetic North–South) can be described as having a "declination:" indicating the direction of MAGNETIC NORTH POLE with respect to the GEOGRAPHIC north pole; respectively "inclination:" the DISTANCE of the MAGNETIC AXIS to the geographic north pole.

$$\sin \lambda_p = \sin \lambda_\delta \cos p + \cos \lambda_\delta \sin p \cos D$$

$$\Phi_p = \Phi_s + \beta; \text{ for } \cos p > \sin \lambda_\delta \sin \lambda_p$$

$$\Phi_p = \Phi_s + 180 - \beta; \text{ for } \cos p < \sin \lambda_\delta \sin \lambda_p$$

where $\sin \beta = \sin p \sin D / \cos \lambda_p$. Additional information obtained shows that the MAGNETIC POLES are generally wandering, disturbing the presumed fixed MAGNETIC FIELD lines across the globe, thus influencing the global position through magnetic compass and guidance systems (*see* MAGNETIC POLE *and* MAGNETIC DRIFT) (see Figure P.3).

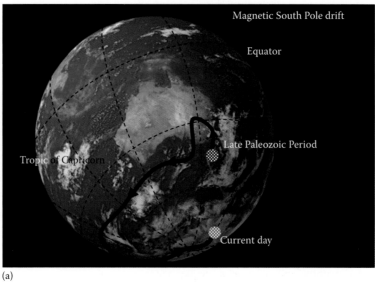

(a)

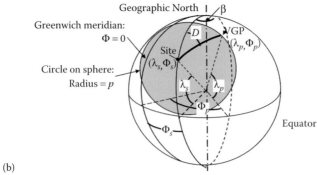

(b)

Figure P.3 (a) Documented drift of South Pole over the past ~250 million years (b) Illustration of the concept and study of paleomagnetism.

Papin, Denis (1647–1712)

[general, mechanics, thermodynamics] French physicist and mathematician. Forerunner of the concept of the steam ENGINE with his invention of the concept of the PRESSURE COOKER also called a digester. The ideas of Papin inspired THOMAS SAVERY (1650–1715) to pursue his collaborative efforts in the development of the steam engine (see Figure P.4).

Figure P.4 Denis Papin (1647–1712) in 1689.

Parabola

[biomedical, computational] Symmetric graphical representation of a variety of mathematical expressions, but the most well known is the quadratic equation, for instance, mathematically expressed as $y = ax^2 + bx + c$, or $x = y^2$, respectively, in general notation: $Ax^2 + Bxy + cy^2 + Dx + Ey + F = 0$, where x and y are CARTESIAN COORDINATES and the remaining letters are constants. The parabola has an axis of symmetry that intersects with the graphical representation of the parabola in the vertex. The parabola is in the family of conic intersects: circle, ellipse, parabola, and hyperbola. In MECHANICS, the parabolic trajectory is well known and can be defined by the vector sum of the gravitational attraction and the propulsion force, where PROPULSION will be in vertical and horizontal directions. A horizontally released PROJECTILE (e.g., bullet from a gun) will have a vertical dependence on gravity (GRAVITATIONAL ACCELERATION g) as a function of time (t), describing only one side of the parabolic track defined as $y = -(1/2)gt^2$ (see Figure P.5).

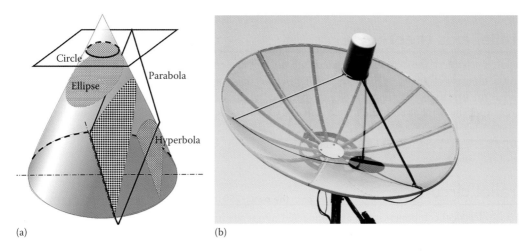

(a)   (b)

Figure P.5 (a) Parabola graph and (b) parabolic antenna.

Paracrine signaling

[biomedical, chemical, energy, general] Cellular uptake of signaling molecules, known as paracrine factors. Form of cellular communication, aimed at modifying the behavior of neighboring cells, short DISTANCE interaction only. Generally, the molecular constituents are self-terminating and have a short-lived impact.

This type of communication takes place in the early stage of cellular development. The following four specific communication pathways/receptor mechanisms can be identified: fibroblast growth factor (FGF) family, hedgehog family, TGF-β superfamily, and Wnt family. The concession is that the FGF family stimulates proliferation and differentiation, the hedgehog family of receptors affects protein assembly and other cellular process and has been shown to be instrumental in certain aspects of the proliferation of cancer processes, the TGF-β superfamily influences POLYPEPTIDE secretion and regulates cellular development, and the Wnt family of receptors has been shown to affect gene transcription, as well as influence the ACTIN and microtubular cytoskeleton next to the effects on transmembrane receptor function and the inhibition, respectively, assimilation of specific proteins (see Figure P.6).

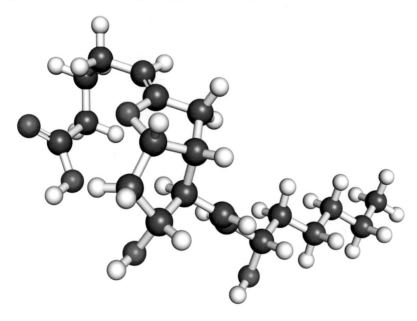

Figure P.6 Paracrine signaling function of prostacyclin hormone.

Parallel axis theorem

[general, mechanics] Theorem used to determine the moment of INERTIA of a rigid body about any axis, when the moment of inertia of the body about a parallel axis through the object's center of mass is known as well as the DISTANCE with respect to the perpendicular axes. Also known as the Huygens–Steiner theorem after the work of both the Dutch scientist CHRISTIAAN HUYGENS (1629–1695) and the Swiss mathematician Jakob Steiner (1796–1863). The MOMENT OF INERTIA (I) is now defined with respect to the distance between the off-center axis and the center of mass ($\square_{cm}$) axis, r, as $I = I_{cm} + mr^2$, where m is the mass of the object.

Parallel circuit

[general] Electrical components that are connected to operate in parallel to each other, groups of components that share at least one single common connection point. This stands in contrast to series circuits, where components operate in cascade. Electronic components are, for example, resistors, capacitors, inductors, diodes, transistors, operational amplifiers, and general INTEGRATED CIRCUITS (see Figure P.7).

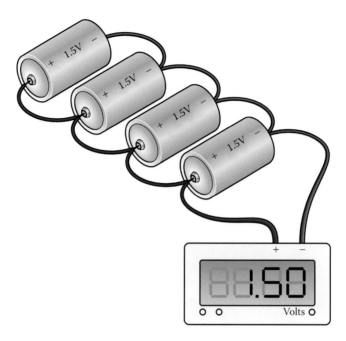

Figure P.7 Schematic of four dry-cell batteries in parallel circuit configuration, providing the same voltage as each individual battery.

Parallel processing

[acoustics, computational, theoretical] Functional process of simultaneously performing multiple operations or tasks. Parallel processing is used both for human cognition and in parallel computing by MACHINES. The brain in particular has the ability to simultaneously process multiple incoming stimuli, and respond to all or most of them. Parallel processing in the human brain has for instance particular relevance to VISION, HEARING, and touch. For other species, this may extend to smell just as much. In vision, the brain divides observations into four components: COLOR, depth, MOTION, and shape. These four perceptions are analyzed individually and compared to reference memories, in order to identify the observations. The brain then recombines all of this information into one image that you visually recognize and comprehend. Parallel processing of the brain may be been linked to what is referred to as the Stroop effect. The Stroop effect is a seamless operation that takes place on a continual basis. Computational parallel processing refers to having multiple algorithms work simultaneously, often splitting a program in its functional components. The computational processes will be run on individual separate electronic processors (central processing unit [CPU]). On a more elaborate level, several programs can run simultaneously in a single unit (i.e., computer) or on multiple computers electronically linked together in a cluster (cluster computing), which requires specialized software to function correctly, referred to as "distributed processing software." Concurrency is a term used in communications for operating systems and databases referring to the condition where multiple tasks remain logically active and simultaneously advancing in the process by interleaving the execution order of the tasks. Concurrency actually merely creates the illusion of simultaneously executing instructions.

Parallel-plate capacitor

[electronics, general] Two charge carrying plates, with area A, separated by a fixed DISTANCE d, at opposite and equal charge (charge density σ_{charge}) form a CAPACITOR with capacitance $C = \varepsilon_0 A/d$, where $\varepsilon_0 = 8.85419 \times 10^{-12} \, \mathrm{C^2/N\,m^2}$ is the permittivity of free space, which is altered when a medium is inserted with a different permittivity (ε), ignoring boundary effects. The electric field between the two plates is

$E = \sigma_{charge}/\varepsilon_0$. Parallel-plate capacitors provided a popular tuning mechanism for analog RADIO operation (*see* CAPACITOR) (see Figure P.8).

Figure P.8 Electrolytic parallel-plate capacitor rolled up into tuning capacitor (variable parallel-plate capacitor) that adjusts the resonant frequency of a circuit by means of changing the surface area of the capacitor when turning the dial.

Parallel-plate fluid flow

[fluid dynamics] Two-dimensional LAMINAR FLOW process that will exhibit primarily the effects of shear stresses. The shear stress at the wall (τ) can be derived from the Navier–Stokes equations and the CONTINUITY EQUATION: $\tau = 6Q\eta_{dyn}/wh^2$, where the FLOW rate (Q) and plate separation or height (h) are the determining factors as is the width of the flow chamber (w), where η_{dyn} is the DYNAMIC VISCOSITY. The flow velocity v_x can be used to solve for the Navier–Stokes and continuity equations: $-(dP/dx) + \eta_{dyn}\left(\partial^2 v_x/\partial y^2\right) = 0$; $-(dP/dy) + \rho g_y$; $-dP/dz = 0$, where P is the pressure and g_y the GRAVITATIONAL ACCELERATION. The volume flow rate follows from POISEUILLE'S LAW and can be derived as the integral over the cross-sectional area: $Q = -w\left(2h^3/\eta_{dyn}\right)\left(\partial P/\partial x\right)$. A special case is COUETTE FLOW, for instance relevant to LUBRICATION for a rotating axle in a housing (e.g., piston-bar on camshaft) (see Figure P.9).

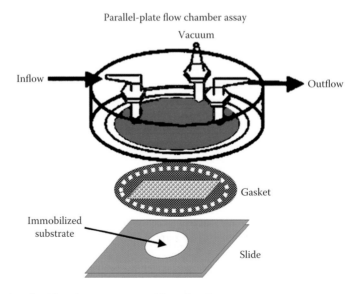

Parallel-plate flow chamber assay

Figure P.9 Parallel-plate fluid flow for an automated flow chamber assay.

Paramagnetic substances

[general] Magnetic material that under free space conditions has randomly oriented MAGNETIC dipoles, which can be aligned under the influence of an external MAGNETIC FIELD. The total magnetic field in the paramagnetic material under the influence of an external magnetic field $(\vec{B_0})$ is $B = B_0 + B_m = (1+\chi)\mu_0 nI$, where $B_m = \chi B_0$ is the induced field with χ the magnetic susceptibility for the paramagnetic medium in case the external field is provided by a SOLENOID, I is the current, n is the number of windings, and $\mu_0 = 4\pi \times 10^{-7}\,\mathrm{H/m}$ is the permeability of free space. For instance, for aluminum, $\chi_{Al} = 2.2 \times 10^{-5}$; for AIR, $\chi_{air} = 3.6 \times 10^{-7}$; and for water, $\chi_{water} = -9.12 \times 10^{-6}$.

Paramagnetism

[atomic, nuclear] The congruent lining up of the internal MAGNETIC FIELD within a solid body under the influence of exposure to an external magnetic field. The opposite is known as DIAMAGNETISM. Substances that have internal magnetic (DIPOLE) moment are sensitive to external magnetic fields as described by the MAGNETIC SUSCEPTIBILITY. The tendency of the internal magnetic dipoles to line up with an applied external magnetic field will generally be countered by the thermal agitation, which in turn continuously randomizes the individual magnetic dipoles. The partial alignment and resulting proportional increase in the total magnetic field was described by PAUL LANGEVIN (1872–1946).

Parametric acoustic array

[acoustics, computational] Directional transmitter and receiver configuration described based on WAVE propagation in an ideal FLUID that has no heat conduction and viscosity. The description involves nonlinear acoustical wave propagation described in accordance with the Lighthill equation as $(\partial^2 \rho / \partial t^2) - C_0^2 \nabla^2 \rho = -C_0^2 \,\square^2\, \rho = (\partial^2 / \partial x_i \partial x_j)\mathbb{T}_{ij}$, where $\mathbb{T}_{ij} = \rho u_i u_j + P_{ij} - C_0^2 \rho \delta_{ij} + D_{ij}$ (D_{ij} the respective viscous stresses, P the pressure, i and j the reference frame directional subscripts (orthogonal), ρ the density, u the velocity, and C_0 a constant related to the acoustic AMPLITUDE) and $\nabla^2 = \nabla \cdot \nabla = \sum_{i=1}^{n} \partial^2 / \partial x_i^2$ is the Laplace operator. The collected "INTERFERENCE" pattern for the ACOUSTIC INTENSITY as a function of ANGLE (θ) is now relatively similar to the atomic RUTHERFORD SCATTERING, observed as the scattered (Δ_s) ANGULAR FREQUENCY $\omega_s = \nu_s 2\pi$, with ν the acoustic frequency for a collimated beam with CROSS SECTION S_0, retrieved from DISTANCE R_0. The acoustic intensity distribution for the parametric array is described as $I_a = \omega_s^4 P_0^4 S_0^2 / 2(8\pi)^2 \rho_0^3 C_0^9 \left\{1 + (1/2)(\rho_0 / C_0^2)(d^2 P / d\rho^2)_{\rho=\rho_0}\right\}^2 * \left\{1/R_0^2 \left[\alpha^2 + k_s^2 \sin^4((1/2)\theta)\right]\right\}$, where $\omega_s = \omega_2 - \omega_1$, with ω_1 the incident and ω_2 the re-emitted wave frequency; $k_s = \omega_s / C_0$; and $\alpha \sim$ scattering probability the "attenuation coefficient" (*see* ULTRASOUND) (see Figure P.10).

Figure P.10 Example of a parametric acoustic ultrasound imaging probe array.

Parasympathetic nerve system

[biophysics, chemical, energy] The human autonomic nerve system is divided into two distinct functional areas: sympathetic and parasympathetic. The autonomic nerve system and the categorization into sympathetic, parasympathetic, and enteric systems managing the intestinal tract were introduced by John Newport Langley (1852–1925), a physiologist from Great Britain. The autonomic nerve system is the part of the nerve system that controls visceral functions: breathing, digestion, HEART function and heart rate, perspiration, pupillary dilation, respiratory rate, salivation, swallowing, sexual arousal, and urination, to name a few, and supports consciousness. The sympathetic nerve system controls the response to stimuli (e.g., "flight or fight") and maintains HOMEOSTASIS. The parasympathetic nerve system specifically manages the bodily maintenance such as defecation, digestion, salivation, sexual arousal, tear production (emotion), and urination (see Figure P.11).

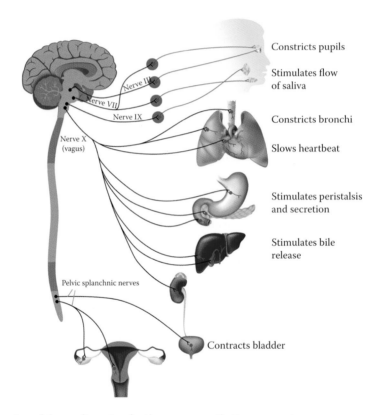

Figure P.11 Illustration of the configuration for the parasympathetic nerve system.

Paraxial approximation

[acoustics, computational, optics] Ray-tracing SOLUTION in the regime of small ANGLE with respect to the main axis, generally the following holds: $\sin \xi \approx \xi$; $\tan \vartheta \approx \vartheta$; $\cos \xi \cong 1$. In OPTICS, this is the Gaussian approach or first-order approximation, tracing the beam as quasiparallel paraxial rays. In ACOUSTICS, the paraxial approximation considers the ultrasound TRANSDUCER beam, emitted as a SPHERICAL WAVE, and approximates it as a quasiplanar WAVE assuming that the majority of SOUND is propagating in a fixed x-direction, and the AMPLITUDE profile can then be described by means of a diffraction correction term: $P = \partial v \nu_0 C \left(x, y, z, \omega \right) e^{i(kx-\omega t)}$, where v is the propagation velocity, $C \left(x, y, z, \omega \right)$ is the correction term, ANGULAR FREQUENCY $\omega_s = \nu_s 2\pi$, with ν the acoustic frequency, P is the pressure, $\partial = \sqrt{(y^2 + z^2)}$ is the average critical dimension, and $k = 2\pi\lambda$ is the wavenumber for wavelength λ (see Figure P.12).

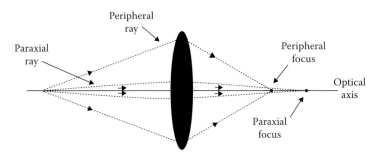

Figure P.12 Paraxial rays in image formation.

Parent nucleus

[atomic, biomedical, general] In biology, this refers to a NUCLEUS in CELL division, which divides and produces two or more daughter nuclei. In atomic PHYSICS, this refers to RADIOACTIVE DECAY, where the parent nucleus (parent RADIONUCLIDE or parent RADIOISOTOPE) is the originating nucleus that decays with emission of ENERGY or particles, for instance, ^{238}U, the uranium parent for ALPHA DECAY with thulium as the "daughter." More specifically, in nuclear decay the process refers to the components as nuclides (*also see* PARENT NUCLIDE).

Parent nuclide

[nuclear] In RADIOACTIVE DECAY, the parent nuclide can be long lived compared to daughter, or short lived. The parent can be naturally occurring or requires nuclear bombardment for formation. An ATOM is the smallest stable unit of an ELEMENT in existence. Each atom of the respective element consists of a certain number of electrons, protons, and neutrons, which define a nuclide and its chemical properties. These particles were discovered in the early 1900s and define modern atomic theory. Under the condition of decay, there are the following examples of naturally occurring long-lived parent nuclides: ^{86}Rb (rubidium), ^{100}Pd (palladium), ^{232}Th (thorium), ^{235}U (uranium), and ^{238}U (uranium); and artificially produced nuclides: ^{68}Ge (germanium; stable 270 days), $^{82}_{38}$Sr (strontium; stable 25.6 days), and $^{188}_{74}$W (tungsten; stable 69 days) all used in POSITRON EMISSION TOMOGRAPHY (PET). The NUCLIDE of certain atomic species are characterized by specific numbers of protons and neutrons (both called nucleons), representing the constitution of its NUCLEUS. The term nuclide was proposed in 1947 by Truman P. Kohman (1916–2010), referring to a species

P

of nucleus. Nuclides with the same atomic number (number of PROTON), but different NEUTRON numbers, are defined as isotopes of this element (*also see* PARENT NUCLEUS) (see Figure P.13).

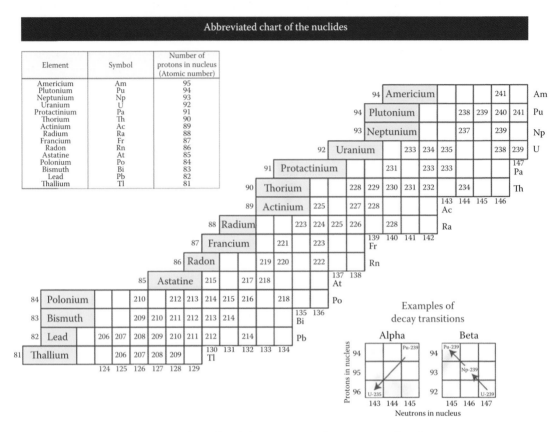

Figure P.13 Parent nuclide concept: chart of nuclides. (Courtesy of American Nuclear Society.)

Parity

[atomic, computational, nuclear, quantum, solid-state] Property describing the characteristic state of a phenomenon, specifically the equality between conditions or the condition being odd or even, particularly referencing the quantum-mechanical state. The scientific implications of parity range from ELEMENTARY PARTICLES to the NUCLEUS and the wavefunction. For elementary particles, the "intrinsic parity" defines the conditions for conservation. The intrinsic parity conforms to an integer number +1 or −1, which is assigned to each individual elementary PARTICLE in such a way that the product of the parities of all the particles in a system, multiplied by the parity of the wavefunction, which describes the entire system, remains unchanged when particles are formed (created) or annihilated. For elementary particles (BARYONS, antibaryon, QUARK, antiquark), both strangeness (QUANTUM NUMBER: strangeness: S) and parity are conserved under strong (nuclear) interaction; however, weak interactions are exempt. Quarks have a defined intrinsic parity +1 and a defined antiquark parity −1. Nucleons, in general, have a defined intrinsic parity +1. In a complex system of a MESON with quark ("q") and antiquark ("$\bar{q}$"), assuming antiparallel spins ($s = 0$), yields for parity $P = P_q P_{\bar{q}} (-1)^{\ell}$, where ℓ is the orbital angular quantum number. The meson parity is defined as $P = -(-1)^{\ell} = (-1)^{\ell+1}$. For the nucleus, parity is associated with the TOTAL ANGULAR MOMENTUM quantum number (I), generally provided as superscript to the total angular momentum quantum number in denomination "+" or "−" (or "+1" associated with even orbital quantum number, and "−1" associated with odd orbital quantum number), as a multiplicative quantum number. Nuclear DECAY involving beta emission generally does not conserve parity. Nuclear states are identified as having both an intrinsic SPIN and a well-defined parity, which is a function of the wavefunction for all the nucleons. The behavior of wavefunction of the nucleons under reversal of their coordinates, taking the origin at the center of the nucleus, will define the parity of the nuclear system. The parity of the WAVEFUNCTION (Ψ), which also applies to photons, is a property of symmetry as well, positive parity: $\Psi(x) = \Psi(-x)$, and negative parity: $\Psi(x) = -\Psi(-x)$. The wavefunction parity can be traced to the Hermite polynomials as a SOLUTION to the quantum-mechanical problem of the harmonic oscillator, using the PRINCIPAL QUANTUM NUMBER (n). Parity violation comes into play based on the fact that conservation of nuclear parity relies on the assumption that potentials involved in nuclear transitions are MIRROR symmetric. Nuclear conditions that are not symmetric and have loss of parity are considered to possess helicity, since a helix is not mirror symmetric (e.g., a human is not MIRROR symmetric on the MACROSCOPIC scale). Purely mathematically, parity is the fact whether an observation or a quantity is odd or even. Mesons have a specific parity, referred to as G-PARITY (see Figure P.14).

Figure P.14 Illustration of the concept of parity as a "condition" with opposite configuration.

Parity conservation rule

[atomic, nuclear, quantum, solid-state] In beta DECAY, the change in PARITY is $\Delta\pi_P = (-1)^{L\beta}$ and the parity conservation rule accounts for this as $\pi_P = \pi_D (-1)^{L\beta}$.

Partial pressure, Dalton's law of

[thermodynamics] *See* **DALTON'S LAW**.

Partial pressure of a constituent

[thermodynamics] The pressure of a GAS in a GAS MIXTURE (P_i) or as dissolved in LIQUID. In atmospheric AIR, there are several gasses with nitrogen the dominant component at 1 atmosphere (1 atm = 1.01325×10^2 kPa) and normal temperature (293 K) holding 0.78 atm = 7.90335×10^1 kP. For BLOOD, the partial pressure of oxygen is important for biological and physiological functions and efficacy of the metabolic reactions. One specific example is in the binding of oxygen to hemoglobin. The binding of oxygen to the protein LIGAND in hemoglobin can be described by the HILL EQUATION (*also see* **DALTON'S LAW** [of partial pressures]) (see Figure P.15).

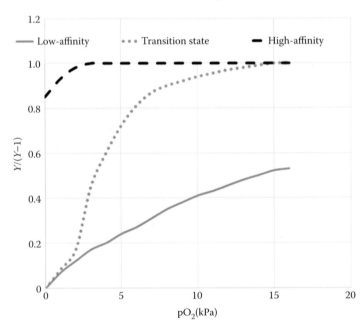

Figure P.15 Graphical representation of the partial pressure concept.

Particle

[atomic, general, solid-state] Any MACROSCOPIC or MICROSCOPIC unit that is considered to be one piece. On a macroscopic scale, dust particles and RAIN drops are examples of a broad scale of presumably solid items, which specifically move as one object with respect to the external observer. The relative size of the object defines it as either a particle or an object; generally particles are less than a millimeter in diameter. On a microscopic scale, the particles range from molecules to atoms, electrons, protons, neutrons to elementary particles of leptons, mesons and BARYONS, as well as respective antiparticles. Technically, a PHOTON is also considered a particle for a range of interactions (see Figure P.16).

Figure P.16 Concept of particles in air.

Particle accelerator

[atomic, general, nuclear] CYCLOTRON developed by ERNEST LAWRENCE (1901–1958) in 1934. Device for acceleration of charged particles such as protons, deuterons, and alpha particles under the influence of a MAGNETIC FIELD. The conduit used for the PARTICLE trajectory consists of a METAL tube that has two halves that are formed in the shade of opposite facing Ds, called "Dees," where the path forms a continuous loop. Particles are injected under the influence of an external electric field, after which they experience a magnetic field inside the D-shaped tube. The maximum velocity (v_{max}) obtained is a function of the radius of the cyclotron (R), the magnetic field strength (B), the respective particle charge (q), and the MASS (m) of the particle: $v_{max} = q(BR/m)$, which will be ejected from the cyclotron, for instance to initiate a collision, with kinetic ENERGY: $(1/2)mv^2 = (1/2)q^2\left(B^2R^2/m\right)$, which can reach or exceed 30 MeV, above which relativistic effects start being introduced, for instance an increase of the period of the phenomenon as a function of radius. The classical MECHANICS period is $T = 2\pi m/qB$, for a particle moving in a circle with radius: $r = mv/qB$. Cyclotrons are nuclear colliders, for instance producing radioactive isotopes, next to FISSION and FUSION experimentation. The cyclotron in Batavia, IL, USA, has a diameter of 1.5 km, supporting research at the Fermi Laboratories. Other LINEAR ACCELERATORS (SYNCHROTRON) are also used for similar experimentation, for instance the Stanford, CA, USA accelerator is 3.3 km long and relies on an electric field along the length of the accelerator, harmonically fluctuating over the length of the evacuated tube, providing kinetic energies up to 50 GeV (see Figure P.17).

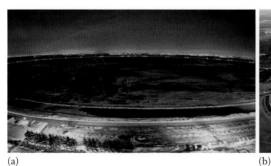

(a) (b)

Figure P.17 (a) Areal view of a particle accelerator and (b) large hadron collider particle accelerator aerial view.

Particle accelerators, linear

[atomic, nuclear] *See* SYNCHROTRON.

Particle imaging velocimetry (PIV)

[fluid dynamics] Noninvasive optical laser imaging technique used in research and diagnostics of combustion processes, flow, MICROFLUIDICS, spray atomization as well as TURBULENCE. The PARTICLE concept relies on the use of "tracer" particles for tracking, combined with LIGHT delivery and imaging in a "single sheet" within the flow. The imaging process relies on a cross-correlation technique for "particle tracking." Standard, MACROSCOPIC PIV uses imaging arrays and particularly "time-resolved" CMOS cameras in combination with laser scanning, while lab-on-a-chip devices are used in MICROSCOPIC imaging. PIV measures whole velocity fields by taking multiple consecutive images within approximately 6–10 ns time frame. The IMAGE processing calculates the DISTANCE and trajectory of individual particles within the image interval time. Based on the measured displacement over the time difference, the localized velocity can be calculated. Because of the anticipated fast flow, blurring needs to be avoided, which requires the use of fast laser pulses. Additionally, laser light can be focused into a thin light sheet, allowing only particles in a single plane to be imaged. The use of a high-speed CAMERA can rapidly store the first frame to subsequently acquire additional exposures (see Figure P.18).

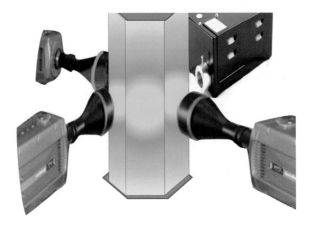

Figure P.18 Particle imaging velocimetry design of experiment. Flow created in a transparent water channel is seeded with light-reflecting particles. The particulate solute are illuminated by a laser and the images of migration is captured by means of a high-resolution camera. The collected tracks of the particle flow derived from sequential images are processed to yield the volumetric instantaneous flow velocity measurements.

Particle in potential well

[nuclear] *See* SHELL MODEL.

Particle theory of light

[general, optics] Documented model of LIGHT by SIR ISAAC NEWTON (1642–1727) in 1704, describing light as small particles. The concept itself actually dates back to early Greek and Persian descriptions, specifically REFLECTION. In Newton's description, refraction is also captured as the interaction of a PARTICLE at the surface of a medium, where it experiences a brief attractive force towards the medium, increasing the vertical component of the particle's velocity. Since the particle is not exposed to any net horizontal forces, the resulting horizontal vector component of the velocity will remain constant. On the COLOR aspects, Newton also hypothesized that the mass of the light particle varied with color. RED light particles are heavier than violet. In refraction the red particle will experience a greater attractive force; hence the refraction ANGLE will be greater, thus explaining the workings of a PRISM. In order to account for POLARIZATION effect, Newton postulated that light particles cannot be spherical. In order for polarization to be possible, the particles should either be plate-like or at least have "sides," deviating from spherically symmetric (see Figure P.19).

Figure P.19 Illustration supporting the particle theory of light; a male "Great Tit" from the Paridae family of birds observing itself in the reflection from the water as we see both bird and image. The reflection can be described through the path of photons acting as tennis balls interacting with the reflective surface.

Particle tracking velocimetry (PTV)

[fluid dynamics] Technique to measure PARTICLE velocity, specifically applied to fluid-dynamic applications. This kind of IMAGE analysis algorithm is available in the tool kits of several commercial SIGNAL analysis software packages, often based on a Lagrangian reference frame (*also see* PARTICLE IMAGING VELOCIMETRY).

Partition coefficient

[biomedical, chemical] The ratio of the respective concentrations of a compound in an amalgam of two immiscible phases (e.g., two liquids, or a mobile with respect to a stationary PHASE, generally pertaining to the solubility of one LIQUID in another) while maintained at an EQUILIBRIUM STATE.

Partition function

[computational, mechanics, thermodynamics] Simple systems can be partitioned based on their respective quantum or energy states (E_i), which will follow the partition function: $Z_{part} = \sum_i e^{-\beta_T E_i}$, where $\beta_T = 1/k_b T$ is the "inverse temperature," with $k_b = 1.3806488 \times 10^{-23}$ m^2 kg/s^2 K the Boltzmann coefficient, and T the temperature in kelvin. For the harmonic oscillator, this becomes, based on the energy $E = [n + (1/2)]\hbar\omega$, $Z_{part} = e^{-(1/2)\beta_T \hbar\omega}/1 - e^{-\beta_T \hbar\omega}$, where $\hbar = h/2\pi$, $h = 6.62606957 \times 10^{-34}$ m^2 kg/s is PLANCK'S CONSTANT, $\omega = 2\pi\nu$ the ANGULAR VELOCITY, ν the frequency, and n the QUANTUM NUMBER. On a mathematical basis, specifically in PROBABILITY theory, this also refers to a configuration integral, as a generalization, using the Hamiltonian (H) representing the potential function (which is measurable, is an observable): $Z_{part}(\beta_T) = \int \exp - \{\beta_T H(x_1, x_2, x_3, \ldots)\} dx_1, dx_2, \ldots$. Specific applications are in information science, SIGNAL processing, and pertaining to dynamical systems. In statistical MECHANICS, the free entropies of a system can frequently be expressed as the LOGARITHM of a partition function, specifically for the ONSAGER RECIPROCAL RELATIONS. In thermodynamic systems, the Onsager reciprocal relations are used to express the equality of particular ratios between forces and flows that are not specifically in equilibrium; however, local equilibrium may exist under strict boundary conditions.

Pascal (Pa)

[fluid dynamics, general] unit of pressure $1\,\text{Pa} = 1\,\text{N/m}^2$, named in honor of the groundbreaking work for standardizing pressure assessment by BLAISE PASCAL (1623–1662).

Pascal, Blaise (1623–1662)

[fluid dynamics, thermodynamics] Scientist, physicist, and mathematician from France. The work of Pascal is primarily known in FLUID DYNAMICS with respect to pressure, to which he lend his name as the unit for pressure. Other works of Pascal in the mathematical field are his contributions to the principle of probability as a contribution to the work of PIERRE DE FERMAT (1601–1665) (see Figure P.20).

Figure P.20 Blaise Pascal (1623–1662), engraved by H. Meyer.

Pascal, law of

[thermodynamics] *See* LAW OF PASCAL.

Pascal's law

[fluid dynamics] Mechanism of pressure operating in all directions. When in any point in a confined fluid there is an increase in pressure, there is an immediate and equal increase in pressure at every other point within the FLUID in the container that holds the fluid.

Pascal's principle

[fluid dynamics, general] The pressure applied to a FLUID is transferred equally and uniformly throughout the entire fluid. (described in the treatise of BLAISE PASCAL [1623–1662] "On the Equilibrium of Liquids," approximately 1651). In his treatise, Pascal recognized that with force applied to a liquid, the DISTANCE traveled by the LIQUID and the applied force were linearly proportional irrespective of the surface area. In this manner, force can be scaled in a similar manner to a LEVER, using the hydraulic force applied over a larger area to be transferred proportionally to the ratio of the respective surface areas. The hydraulic LIFT provides the most common example for this (fluid examples: water, OIL). Hydraulic systems use incompressible fluids, whereas pneumatic systems use compressible fluids (e.g., AIR or gasses in general) (see Figure P.21).

Figure P.21 Hydraulic lift (automobile jack) working based on the Pascal principle, transferring force based on the surface area of the fluid column.

Paschen, Friedrich (1865–1947)

[atomic, nuclear, quantum] Physicist from Germany, dedicated to electro-optics. The PASCHEN LINES for hydrogen discharge (1908) are a key result of his work as well as other theoretical descriptions for electrical IONIZATION effects (see Figure P.22).

Figure P.22 Friedrich Paschen (1865–1947).

Paschen law

[atomic, nuclear] *Also* **Paschen's Law**. The breakdown voltage ($V_{\text{excitation}}$) for a GAS in a pressurized vessel exposed to electrical discharge will reduce in MAGNITUDE proportional to the gap (d) between the ANODE and CATHODE and the partial PRESSURE (p): $V_{\text{excitation}} = f(p, d)$, described by FRIEDRICH PASCHEN (1865–1947) in 1889. PASCHEN'S LAW reflects the atomic breakdown described by JOHN SEALY TOWNSEND (1868–1957). Townsend's work involved the analysis of the cascade effect of colliding electrons in an electrical discharge in gas between two electrodes, where the secondary electrons are gaining ENERGY under the influence of the applied electric field resulting in additional excitation effects induced by collision, providing enhanced IONIZATION (see Figure P.23).

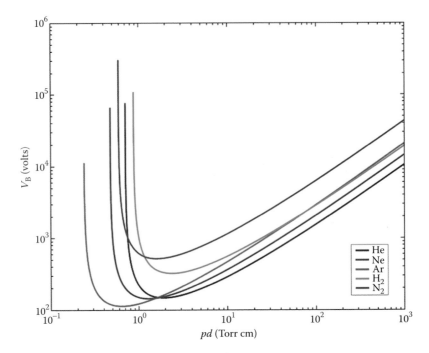

Figure P.23 Paschen curves representative of the Paschen law.

Paschen lines

[atomic, general] *See* **PASCHEN SERIES**.

Paschen series

[atomic, general, nuclear] ATOMIC EMISSION wavelengths (λ), respectively, FREQUENCY (ν), as derived by FRIEDRICH PASCHEN (1865–1947), in particular for hydrogen, based on the BOHR ATOMIC MODEL transitions between electron orbits (n_i): $\nu = m_e e^4 Z^2 / 8\varepsilon_0^2 h^3 \left[(1/n_1^2) - (1/n_2^2) \right]$, for $n_1 = 3$, where $m_e = 9.10939 \times 10^{-31}$ kg is the electron mass, $e = 1.60217657 \times 10^{-19}$ C the charge equivalence of an electron [–] (or respectively, PROTON [+]), the permittivity of free space $\varepsilon_{\text{EM0}} = 8.85419 \times 10^{-12} \text{C}^2/\text{N m}^2$, PLANCK'S CONSTANT $h = 6.62606957 \times 10^{-34} \text{ m}^2 \text{ kg/s}$, Z the number of charges in the NUCLEUS, and n_2 the respective originating electron orbits. Note that $n_1 = 1$ represents the LYMAN SERIES, $n_1 = 2$ is the BALMER SERIES, $n_1 = 4$ yields the Brackett series, and $n_1 = 5$ the Pfund lines, where $n_2 > n_1$ (see Figure P.24)

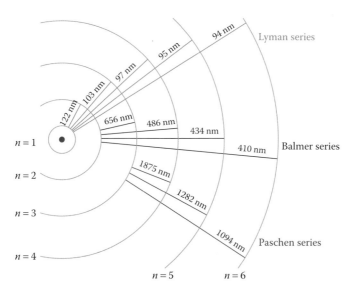

Figure P.24 Paschen line emission spectrum.

Paschen–Back effect

[atomic, general, nuclear, quantum] The coupling of the L-vector (total orbital momentum) and the S-vector (spin angular momentum) (i.e., RUSSELL–SAUNDERS COUPLING) regarding atomic transitions under the influence of very strong external MAGNETIC FIELD. In contrast, the absence an external magnetic field provides the "normal ZEEMAN EFFECT," whereas a weak magnetic field induces the anomalous Zeeman effect. The Paschen–Back effect only affects changes in the L and m_L, completely neglecting the SPIN influences, as described by FRIEDRICH PASCHEN (1865–1947) and ERNST EMIL ALEXANDER BACK (1881–1959). The Paschen–Back effect resembles the normal Zeeman effect under restrictions of the "LANDE's G-FACTOR" being 1: $\Delta E = \left(e\hbar/2m_e\right)m_J B$, where $e = 1.60217657 \times 10^{-19}$C is the electron charge equivalent, $\hbar = h/2\pi$, with PLANCK's CONSTANT $h = 6.62606957 \times 10^{-34}\,\mathrm{m^2\,kg/s}$, electron mass $m_e = 9.10939 \times 10^{-31}$kg, m_J the QUANTUM NUMBER for the TOTAL ANGULAR MOMENTUM, and B the external magnetic field (*also see* ZEEMAN EFFECT).

Passenger car, drag coefficient

[fluid dynamics, mechanics] Automobile, two axles and four wheels propelled by gasoline, diesel, ELECTRICITY, natural GAS, or fuel cells. The DRAG COEFFICIENT of an automobile pertains to its AERODYNAMICS, and interrelated to its fuel economy (fuel consumption). Items that influence the aerodynamic properties are deviations from a perfectly smooth surface, such as a roof rack, curvature on the front and rear, as well as door-handle grips and windshield wipers, next to mudflaps behind the wheels and the encasing of the wheels, and also the definition of a front and rear "spoiler" makes an impact. The final design components that influence the drag are the length, height and width of the car, and the inherent frontal surface area (A), next to the velocity of both the independent airflow and the automobile PROPULSION, combined (v_{flow}); note that turbulent or LAMINAR FLOW will influence the final interaction, providing lower drag under turbulent flow. The drag coefficient (C_d) is derived from the resisting force $\left(F_d = C_d\left(A\rho v_{flow}^2/2\right)\right)$ as $C_d = 2F_d/A\rho v_{flow}^2$, where ρ represents the density of the FLUID in which the object is moving (i.e., AIR). The smaller the number the more aerodynamic the object. The power (e.g., horsepower) required to overcome the drag is $W = F_d v_{flow}$. In addition to these factors, the REYNOLDS NUMBER also contributed to the final outcome of the influence of flow on the MOTION: $\mathrm{Re} = v_{flow}L/\eta_{visc}$, where η_{visc} is the viscous RESISTANCE and L the characteristic length, meaning that the longer the automobile the more likely the flow along the body will be laminar. For $\mathrm{Re} > 47$, BOUNDARY LAYER separation will take place, hence influencing the fluid resistance experienced by the body. Lowest COEFFICIENT OF DRAG on record for a production automobile at the time of assembly of this record is the Mercedes CLA with $C_d = 0.23$, compared to that for a Ford Model T that resembles the drag of a cube at $C_d = 0.80$. Note that nonproduction automobiles may have superior values for drag coefficients in the front and side direction, but these are special cases, such as Formula One race cars (see Figure P.25).

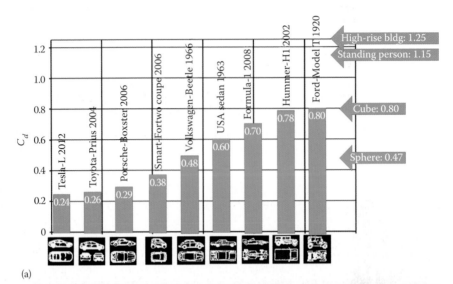

(a)

(b)

Figure P.25 (a) Automobile drag coefficient and (b) Formula One race car with adjustable drag coefficient through adjustment of flaps and airfoils by means of remote control based on the on-the-fly measured road and air-flow conditions.

Passive resistance

[thermodynamics] States of equilibrium and the associated settings can respond to a change while meeting with a certain RESISTANCE, which has been termed passive resistance, based on the direction in which it acts. These equilibrium situations can generally be unstable. This instability will cause a potentially violent response and a respective change to an often very small disturbance. The disturbance in this case is small compared to the quantities within the system (*also* "inertia resistance").

Passive state

[thermodynamics] Thermodynamic state that does not produce work (*also see* CANONICAL STATE).

Pauli, Wolfgang Ernst (1900–1958)

[atomic, computational, general, nuclear] Scientist and theoretical physicist from Austria. His work contributed to the understanding of the BOHR ATOMIC MODEL, and also to the formation and understanding of the WAVE MECHANICS principles in QUANTUM MECHANICS, associating wave theory with electron orbits (sometime referred to as "electron optics"), yielding stability conditions for electron orbits, limiting the number of electrons occupying a certain ENERGY level. The work of Pauli started out in 1925 in sync with the work of WERNER KARL HEISENBERG (1901–1976), ERWIN SCHRÖDINGER (1887–1961), and PAUL DIRAC (1902–1984). He is most known for his "EXCLUSION PRINCIPLE" pertaining to electron orbit occupation. Additionally, he introduced two new quantum numbers in 1924: the MAGNETIC QUANTUM NUMBER (m_ℓ) and the spin quantum number (m_s). He is one of the pioneers in quantum PHYSICS and received the Nobel Prize for his work in 1945 (see Figure P.26).

Figure P.26 (a) Wolfgang Ernst Pauli (1900–1958) at the 1933 Solvay Conference Structure et propriétés des noyaux atomiques: Structure and properties of the atomic nucleus; Chair Paul Langevin (1872–1946) (Courtesy of US Department of Energy (DOE) Washington, DC); (b) Wolfgang Pauli. (Courtesy of ETH-Bibliothek Zürich, Bildarchiv.)

Pauli exclusion principle

[atomic, nuclear] No two electrons in orbit in a single ATOM can exist in the same ENERGY and spin state. For instance, in helium the two electrons in the lowest energy state (with PRINCIPAL QUANTUM NUMBER $n = 1$) must have opposite SPIN states, with quantum numbers $\ell = 0$, $m_\ell = 0$ and $m_s = \pm(1/2)$. Electrons with the same principal quantum number will occupy the same "shell" (*also see* EXCLUSION PRINCIPLE).

Pauli spin matrix

[atomic, energy] Expression satisfying the commutator requirements describing the ELECTRON SPIN, represented as

$$\sigma_x = \begin{bmatrix} 0 & 1 \\ 1 & 0 \end{bmatrix}, \sigma_y = \begin{bmatrix} 0 & -i \\ i & 0 \end{bmatrix}, \text{ and } \sigma_x = \begin{bmatrix} 1 & 0 \\ 0 & -1 \end{bmatrix}.$$

The commutator requirement expressions are based on the angular momentum expressions: $L_x = \hbar/i\left[y(\partial/\partial z) - z(\partial/\partial y)\right]$, where $\hbar = h/2\pi$ with PLANCK'S CONSTANT $h = 6.62606957 \times 10^{-34}$ m^2 kg/s, and $L_y = \hbar/i\left[z(\partial/\partial x) - x(\partial/\partial z)\right]$, providing the commutators: $\left[L_x, L_y\right] = \hbar^2\left[x(\partial/\partial y) - y(\partial/\partial x)\right] = i\hbar L_z$, $\left[L_y, L_z\right] = i\hbar L_x$, $\left[L_z, L_x\right] = i\hbar L_y$, and $\left[L_x, L_y\right] = i\hbar L_z$.

Paxillin

[biomedical, chemical, mechanics, signal] A 68 kDa neurofilament antibody cytoskeletal SIGNAL transduction adaptor protein involved in cellular organization as well as functioning of focal cellular adhesions. Paxillin adaptor proteins are critical in CELL ADHESION as well as in cellular migration.

PDT

[biomedical, chemical, optics] *See* PHOTODYNAMIC THERAPY.

Péclet, Jean Claude Eugène (1793–1857)

[energy, fluid dynamics] Physicist from France. He is most known for his contributions to FLUID dynamic definition and the PÉCLET NUMBER(s) (see Figure P.27).

Figure P.27 Jean Claude Eugène Péclet (1793–1857).

Péclet number (Pe)

[energy, fluid dynamics, thermodynamics] Dimensionless number used in HEAT TRANSFER representing the bulk heat transfer over the conductive heat transfer: $Pe = vL/\alpha = Lv\rho c_p/\kappa = Re \times Pr$, with v the velocity, L the characteristic length, α the thermal DIFFUSIVITY, κ the THERMAL CONDUCTIVITY, ρ density, c_p the heat capacity, Re the REYNOLDS NUMBER, and Pr the PRANDTL NUMBER. Generally used in forced convection and universal heat transfer. Named after the originator JEAN CLAUDE EUGÈNE PÉCLET (1793–1857).

Péclet number, mass transfer (Pe$_m$)

[energy, fluid dynamics, mechanics, thermodynamics] Dimensionless number used in mass transfer representing the bulk mass transport over DIFFUSIVITY of a constituent: $Pe_m = vL/D_{dif}$, with v the velocity, L the characteristic length, α the thermal diffusivity, D_{dif} the DIFFUSION coefficient, based on the work of JEAN CLAUDE EUGÈNE PÉCLET (1793–1857). The mass transfer PÉCLET NUMBER is sometimes also referred to as the "SHEAR PÉCLET NUMBER," specifically in SHEAR FLOW, such as in MICROFLUIDICS.

Peierls, Rudolf Ernst, Sir (1907–1995)

[acoustics, mechanics, solid-state] Scientist and physicist from Germany. His work on nuclear PHYSICS provided many theoretical insights, specifically treating the ATOM as having an electron cloud with discreet wavefunctions, different from the Schrödinger model (see Figure P.28).

Figure P.28 Rudolf Peierls (1907–1995), 1937 picture.

Peierls transition

[acoustics, mechanics, solid-state] Density WAVE in one-dimensional electron GAS. The ENERGY transfer takes place by exchanges between states, PARTICLE to particle transitions (Cooper channel), or particle to hole transitions (Peierls channel). The particle–hole transitions will exhibit periodic variations in charge density or SPIN density; as such these transitions are referred to as charge-density or spin-density wave GROUND states.

Peierls–Fröhlich–Kuper ground state

[acoustics, computational, mechanics, solid-state, thermodynamics] CHARGE DENSITY WAVE as a result of electron–phonon interaction in a partially filled electron band. Periodic lattice distortions create a single PARTICLE gap at the FERMI LEVEL. This transition forms an INSULATOR condition, known as the PEIERLS TRANSITION. The influence of an external electric field (nearby atoms or applied field creates a periodic instability as suggested by RUDOLF PEIERLS (1907–1995) in 1955, with theoretical support by Charles Goethe Kuper (twentieth century), and with independent contributions from HERBERT FRÖHLICH (1905–1991) in 1954 on a theoretical thermodynamic level. Under the particle gap migration, an electric current is generated on atomic level, specifically under the influence of an external electric field.

P

Peltier, Jean Charles Athanase (1785–1845)

[energy, thermodynamics] Physicist from France. He described the electrical potential resulting from placing two dissimilar materials in direct contact with each other—the PELTIER EFFECT (see Figure P.29).

Figure P.29 Jean Charles Athanase Peltier (1785–1845).

Peltier coefficient

[energy, thermodynamics] Representation of the heat quantity transferred per unit charge for a specific material, placed in contact with another material $(_j)$: Π_i. This concept relates to the PELTIER EFFECT.

Peltier effect

[energy, thermodynamics] Electrochemical effect, describing the thermoelectric principles involved in the thermocouple ACTIVITY of two metals joined together. The two metals will absorb heat at the METAL junction that is at a higher temperature and emit heat at the lower temperature junction. This was described by JEAN CHARLES ATHANASE PELTIER (1785–1845) in 1834. Respectively, when an electrical source is connected in the THERMOCOUPLE circuit in the inverse direction, heat will be generated at the high-temperature junction and heat will be absorbed (cooling effect) at the colder junction. The Peltier effect is generally associated with electric heating and cooling. One specific example is the electric heating stove-top. The scientific description is defined as the rate of heat generated or removed as a function of ELECTRIC CURRENT (I): $\dot{Q} = \left(\Pi_A - \Pi_B \right) I$, where Π_A, respectively, Π_B, are the PELTIER COEFFICIENTS for the respective conductors joined together. A similar principle was described earlier in 1826 by THOMAS JOHANN SEEBECK (1770–1831), but is primarily credited to Peltier (see Figure P.30).

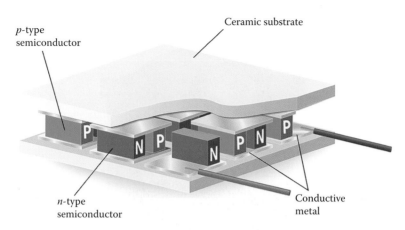

Thermoelectric module

Ceramic substrate

p-type
semiconductor

n-type
semiconductor

Conductive
metal

Figure P.30 Peltier element that cools based on the Peltier effect.

Pendulum

[general] Physical body that will rotate around a fixed axis when an external force is applied to initiate the removal from EQUILIBRIUM STATE; the device will produce a simple periodic MOTION. The first pendulum-based clock was constructed in 1657 by the scientist from the Netherlands: CHRISTIAN HUYGENS (1629–1695), who also developed the mathematical formulation for the pendulum. The pendulum will have a harmonic period (T) that is a function of the length from the axis of rotation to the center of mass (ℓ), the mass at the center of mass (m), the GRAVITATIONAL ACCELERATION (g), as well as the generalized MOMENT OF INERTIA (I_{inertia}), expressed as $T_{\text{period}} = 2\pi\sqrt{I_{\text{inertia}}/mg\ell}$. The pendulum, for small angular displacement ($\sin\theta = \theta$, where $\theta = A\sin(\omega t + \varphi)$, with φ an arbitrary initial PHASE of motion (depending on the time of initiation of observation) and ω the ANGULAR VELOCITY, $\omega = \sqrt{(g/\ell)} = \sqrt{(mg\ell/I_{\text{inertia}})}$) as a function of time (t), without friction obeys the WAVE EQUATION $(\partial^2\theta/\partial t^2) + (g/\ell)\sin\theta = 0$. When considering that the pendulum experiences friction at the movement around the axis, the wave equation incorporates dampening as $I_{\text{inertia}}(\partial^2\theta/\partial t^2) + mg\ell\theta = \pm\tau_{\text{friction}}$, where τ_{friction} represents the torque resulting from the rotational friction with respect to the center of mass. The SOLUTION then yields a dampened angular swing, with decreasing displacement: $\theta(t) = [\theta_0 - (4t\tau_{\text{friction}}/\omega_0{}^2 I_{\text{inertia}} T_{\text{period}})]$. When the pendulum is submerged in a viscous fluid, the wave equation incorporates dampening as $I_{\text{inertia}}(\partial^2\theta/\partial t^2) + b_{\text{visc}}(\partial\theta/\partial t) + mg\ell\theta = 0$, where b_{visc} represents the viscous friction with respect to the center of mass, with ensuing DAMPING term $b(\partial\theta/\partial t)$. The fluid-dampened OSCILLATION has the solution $\theta(t) = \theta_0 e^{-b_{\text{visc}}t/2I_{\text{inertia}}}\cos(\omega't + \varphi)$, where the oscillation period decreases, expressed as $\omega' = \sqrt{((mg\ell/I_{\text{inertia}}) - \{b_{\text{visc}}/2I_{\text{inertia}}\}^2)}$, and $\gamma_{\text{damp}} = b_{\text{visc}}/2I_{\text{inertia}}$ is the dampening constant. GALILEO GALILEI (1564–1642) also worked on the pendulum concept, dating back to 1582, but never constructed a clock mechanism, nor defined the rhythmic motion aspects. Generally, a pendulum

is driven by a weight mechanism to maintain motion. The FRICTION from liquids will result in a dampened motion, except for in VACUUM; however, the gear and sliding friction also reduce the ENERGY content (see Figure P.31).

Figure P.31 Pendulum of a clock, ensuring proper time keeping. Sometimes adjustments to the length of the pendulum of a clock are required for calibration purposes.

Penumbra

[biomedical, general, geophysics] PHASE in "shadow" pattern created by an OPAQUE object irradiated from behind. The source can be a PARTICLE source or emit ELECTROMAGNETIC RADIATION. The three phases recognized are umbra, penumbra, and antumbra. During a penumbra only a portion (edge) of an emission source is obscured by the object, casting a shadow resembling a finger-nail clipping, as seen during the onset of a total eclipse of the SUN or generally a partial eclipse. The umbra represents a total blackout of the source on a projected surface, or when observed straight on (*Note:* Not advisable during the observation of a solar eclipse, since when the Sun peaks back out the radiance can literally be blinding.) and the antumbra has LIGHT passing around the object. Note that for a POINT SOURCE, only the umbra is produced. In biomedical applications, this applies to RADIATION THERAPY, where the penumbra represents the biological space in the periphery of the spot irradiation location, and is generally defined as the tissue volume receiving only a partial dose, between 80% and 20% of the therapeutically intended isodose (see Figure P.32).

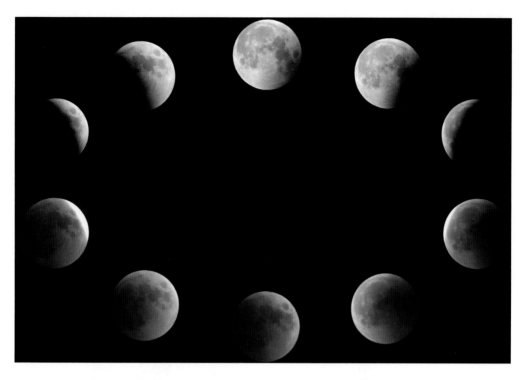

Figure P.32 Lunar eclipse, penumbra.

Perception

[biomedical, chemical, mechanics, optical, theoretical] Parameter of sensation. A sensation is quantified and qualified by several attributes and parameters, also defined as dimensions. One "quality" of a sensation is the subjective value that provides a name. The clinical classification of the senses is as follows. Special senses are VISION, auditory, taste, olfactory (smell), and vestibular (balance, equilibrium, spatial orientation; located in the vestibular system of the INNER EAR). Other superficial or cutaneous senses are touch/pressure, warmth, cold (separate from warmth), and pain (most overstimuli can produce pain in any of the sensing neurons with sensor specialization). Deep sensations are muscle/tendon/joint and position, deep pressure, and deep pain. Visceral sensations served by the autonomic nervous system are hunger and nausea for instance and visceral pain. Senses can also be organized by "location." Somatic ("body") senses are for instance temperature, either warm or cold; touch pressure; pain, next to "deep sensibility." Deep sensibility is an indication of the knowledge and awareness to the relative position of the extremities (arms/legs; i.e., "muscle sense") and the perception of the direction of MOTION with eyes closed. Generally, a power function can be attached to the sensation that links the MAGNITUDE of the stimulus ($\mathbb{S}$) to the psychological magnitude ($\mathcal{M}$): $\mathcal{M} = K_{\text{sens}}\mathbb{S}^2$, where K_{sens} represents a "personal" factor ("sensitivity," "numbness"). Sensors can also be classified by their function: chemoreceptor, mechanoreceptor, and optical sensor. The sensation is ultimately a function of the type of nerve-fiber/sensor combination that is stimulated, not the ENERGY of the stimulus itself. The magnitude of the stimulus of the sense is encoded in a binary frequency train, which is logarithmically linked to the strength of the excitation. The fine free nerve-ending in hairy SKIN as well as nerve-baskets around the hair roots are serving a variety of sensations, ranging from touch, to warm and cold. Specialized sensors are constructed of encapsulated nerve-endings, with various configurations and designs for specific applications; RODS and CONES for the RETINA of the EYE for instance. The RESOLUTION of a sense is a function of the number of sensors per unit area (sensor density); the fingertips of a mammal can gauge submillimeter resolution, whereas the palm spans several millimeters. Another highly innervated area is the lips. Since the lips are close to the brain, and conversely fast conducting nerves (i.e., myelinated nerves) are formed only slowly after birth, the lips are the most direct link to the brain for babies, most likely the reason why they touch everything with their mouth since the fingertips are not fully developed. Generally, several neurons carry information from different locations to the same functional area in the brain. Under normal conditions the brain can identify exactly where the sensation originates (potentially imbedded in other types of encoding, possibly "PHASE ENCODING," which for a binary system is different than for an analog system, for instance using a phase shift for a "marker" pulse segment), whereas under overstimulus (very strong stimulus) the sensation is "projected" to the most distal point on the perception branch (see Figure P.33).

Figure P.33 Cartoon representation for sensory perception. Hearing, smell, taste, and sight; not specifically included: touch; however the lips have the highest density of sensors, providing resolution of better than 0.05 mm.

Perceptron

[biomedical, computational] Computational algorithm used in machine learning. The algorithm is designed to detect a linear threshold for an event or data trend. The linear function in vector components can be represented as $a_1x_2 + a_1x_2 + \cdots + a_ix_i + \cdots + a_nx_n > 0$ and in vector format as $\vec{a}^1 \cdot \vec{x} > 0$, threshold at zero, where $\vec{a}^1$ is a unit length vector. In a sequence (S_{seq}) of data with potential mistakes (M_{mis}), the "margin" (γ_{marg}) in the mistakes for the perceptron algorithm is $\gamma_{marg} = \min_{x \in S_{seq}} |\vec{a}^1 \cdot \vec{x}|/\vec{x}$, with the number of mistakes in the order of $\left(1/\gamma_{marg}\right)^2$. This is one of the early concepts in machine learning, introduced in the early 1960s.

Percolation

[chemical, computational, geophysics] In chemical applications percolation references the filtration system, while in computational theory this defines the interrelation of data clusters in a graph that are connected ("neighbors"). Additionally, in geology, percolation refers to the CIRCULATION of water and the inherent filtration of water through the soil of the mantle as well as permeable rocks. The percolated water seeps to groundwater storage (i.e., aquifer). One particular mathematical use of percolation refers to the probabilistic interactions during PHASE transitions. The phase transitions are outlined in graphical representation (e.g., PV-DIAGRAM) for a region in the medium; percolation can describe the PROBABILITY (p) that the "edges" of the segment are open to the neighboring vertices (faces and edges; intersection in geometric space). Image and SIGNAL percolation generally involves finite ELEMENT analysis (Monte Carlo simulation) (see Figure P.34).

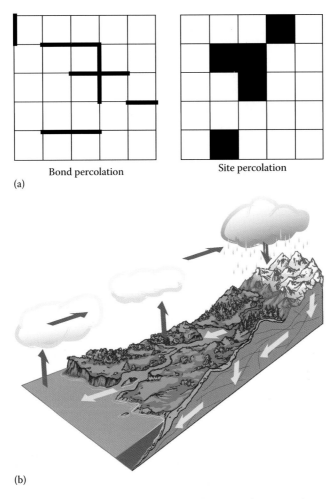

Bond percolation   Site percolation

(a)

(b)

Figure P.34 (a) Image analysis percolation and (b) percolation of water in the atmospheric circulation and drainage to aquifer to be stored underground, ultimately with the opportunity to be used as drinking water due to the cleaning from the seepage.

Perfect diamagnetism

[general] Generally DIAMAGNETISM is the result of atomic current loop in response to an applied external MAGNETIC FIELD. The induced currents result in a magnetization within the diamagnetic material with a direction that opposes the applied field. When the external field is removed the magnetization disappears. The relationship between magnetization (M_{mag}) and the magnetic field (B) is expressed as a function of the volume MAGNETIC SUSCEPTIBILITY (χ_m) as $M_{mag} = \chi_m B$. In superconductor material, the magnetic field is zero and hence there will be no magnetization, that is, perfect diamagnetism (*also see* **MEISSNER EFFECT** *and* **DIAMAGNETISM**).

Perfect gas

[fluid dynamics, thermodynamics] An IDEAL GAS that has simplified stable equilibrium conditions (specifically behaving with a weak), dependence of the SPECIFIC HEAT on the temperature (in most cases negligible; i.e., c_p = constant [constant pressure: P] and c_v = constant [constant volume: V]), yielding $c_p - c_v = R$, where $R = 8.3144621(75)$ J/K mol is the gas constant, and $c_p/c_v = \gamma_p$ a constant within a specific temperature range. The specific INTERNAL ENERGY of a perfect gas is defined as $U(T) - U_0 = (1/\gamma_p - 1)(PV - P_0V_0) = c_v(T - T_0)$, Δ_0; $V_0 = R(T_0/P_0)$ denoting the GROUND STATE or initial state. The specific enthalpy is defined by $h(T) - h_0 = \left[\gamma_p/(\gamma_p - 1)\right](PV - P_0V_0) = c_p(T - T_0)$. And finally the specific entropy as a function of combinations of respectively temperature, pressure, and volume: $S(T, P) - S_0 = c_p \ln(T/T_0) - R \ln(P/P_0)$, S_0 at P_0, T_0, V_0 (similarly for h_0 and U_0); $S(T, V) - S_0 = c_v \ln(V/V_0) + R \ln(P/P_0)$; $S(V, P) - S_0 = c_p \ln(V/V_0) - c_v \ln(P/P_0)$. Additionally, for the perfect gas along any ISENTROPIC the following holds: $TP^{-\gamma_p - 1/\gamma_p} = \text{Constant}$; $TV^{\gamma_p - 1} = \text{Konstant}$; and $PV^{\gamma_p} = \text{KonStant}$ (*also see* **IDEAL GAS**); however, the ideal gas is not necessarily equal to the perfect gas.

Perfect incompressible behavior

[fluid dynamics, geophysics, mechanics, thermodynamics] Poisson's ratio for incompressible media is $\nu_p = 0.5$. Incompressible VISCOELASTIC behavior has as boundary condition that the strain is finite. The MAGNITUDE of allowable finite strain is a function of the medium. Theoretically, media can have perfect incompressible behavior for several phases (solid, LIQUID, or gas). The equation of MOTION for perfect INCOMPRESSIBLE FLUID behavior assuming the absence of internal FRICTION was described by LEONARD EULER (1707–1783). Examples of materials that approach prefect incompressible behavior are several polymers: polystyrene, polycarbonate, polyvinyl acetate; as well as vulcanized natural rubber. Generally, the bulk modulus will decrease for a medium approaching $\nu_p \rightarrow 0.5$, and mathematically the ratio of bulk modulus to shear modulus will trend to infinity. Incompressible flow is described by the Euler equations.

Perfusion

[biomedical, fluid dynamics] Integral network of BLOOD vessels supplying nutrients and oxygen to bulk tissues and organs and removing waste and carbon dioxide. Vessels consisting of arteries, arterioles, capillaries, venules, and veins (see Figure P.35).

P

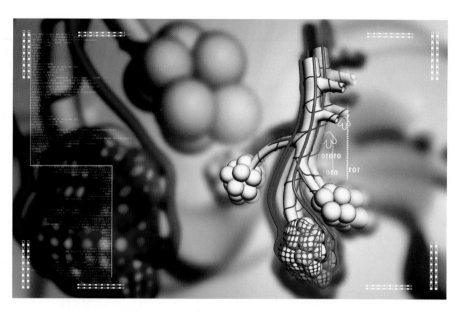

Figure P.35 Blood perfusion of lung tissue around the alveoli exchanging oxygen and carbon dioxide.

Pergrinus, Petri, a.k.a. Pierre de Maricourt (1220–1290)

[electromagnetism] Scientist from France, accredited with the first documented description of the use of the Earth's magnetism using a needle to map the MAGNETIC fields produced by magnetic objects as well as the Earth's MAGNETIC FIELD line patterns. Magnetic fields introduced by objects/particles and the Earth's magnetic field were known as far back as the thirteenth century before Christ. The work by Pergrinus postdates the early recording by almost 24 centuries (see Figure P.36).

Figure P.36 Plaque commemorating Petrus Peregrinus de Maricourt; a.k.a. Petri Pergrinus (1220–1290), a.k.a. Pierre de Maricourt.

Period doubling

[biomedical, computational] Sudden doubling of the frequency of a (PENDULUM) event. This may be graphically illustrated as a bifurcation in a POINCARÉ SECTION of an orbital plot in a QUALITY FACTOR versus v-coordinate ($v = d\theta/dt$, where θ represents the angular path of a pendulum). In the statistical analysis of animal population as a function of time, on average the population will persistently gyrate between two values as a function of time with no consistent equilibrium. The rate of growth is a function of the fertility, which is a function of environmental and seasonal factors. Considering the dependence of an animal population as a function of its rate of growth will display a "bifurcation" for the population value as a function of growth. At a certain value of the rate, there is no established equilibrium in the population, and the number alternates between two values. This process of "bifurcation" continues, and the population will subsequently dissolve into chaos (see Figure P.37).

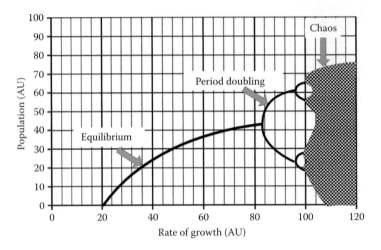

Figure P.37 Period doubling in population growth estimation based on graphical representation.

Period of a cycle (T)

[acoustics, general, mechanics, optics] The time frame (t) required to bring a period event back to a well-defined prior state (MAGNITUDE of displacement, field strength) with the same change of state configuration, primarily associated with a sinusoidal phenomenon such as a WAVE: $A = A_0 \sin\left[(t/T)2\pi\right]$ (see Figure P.38)

Figure P.38 Period, time to complete one sequence of events to the point where everything repeats itself, as in the revolution of a Ferris wheel, once around within a certain timespan.

Periodic law

[solid-state] Description of the perceived regular pattern in ATOM structural configuration with respect to electron structure as the basis for the PERIODIC TABLE OF ELEMENTS, introduced by DMITRI MENDELEEV (1834–1907).

Periodic table of elements

[atomic, nuclear] Discrete pattern of atomic configurations, nuclides, and electron orbits for the ELEMENTS as introduced by DMITRI MENDELEEV (1834–1907). The table designed by Dmitri Mendeleev listed the elements according to ATOMIC WEIGHT. In 1913 amateur theoretical physicist and economist Anton van den Broek (1870–1926) from the Netherlands suggested that the ordering principle for the periodic table should be based on ordinal numbers, i.e., the NUCLEAR CHARGE of each ATOM. This principle was validated by HENRY GWYN JEFFREYS MOSELEY (1887–1915) from Great Britain shortly thereafter, providing the final structure for the current use of the periodic table (see Figure P.39).

P

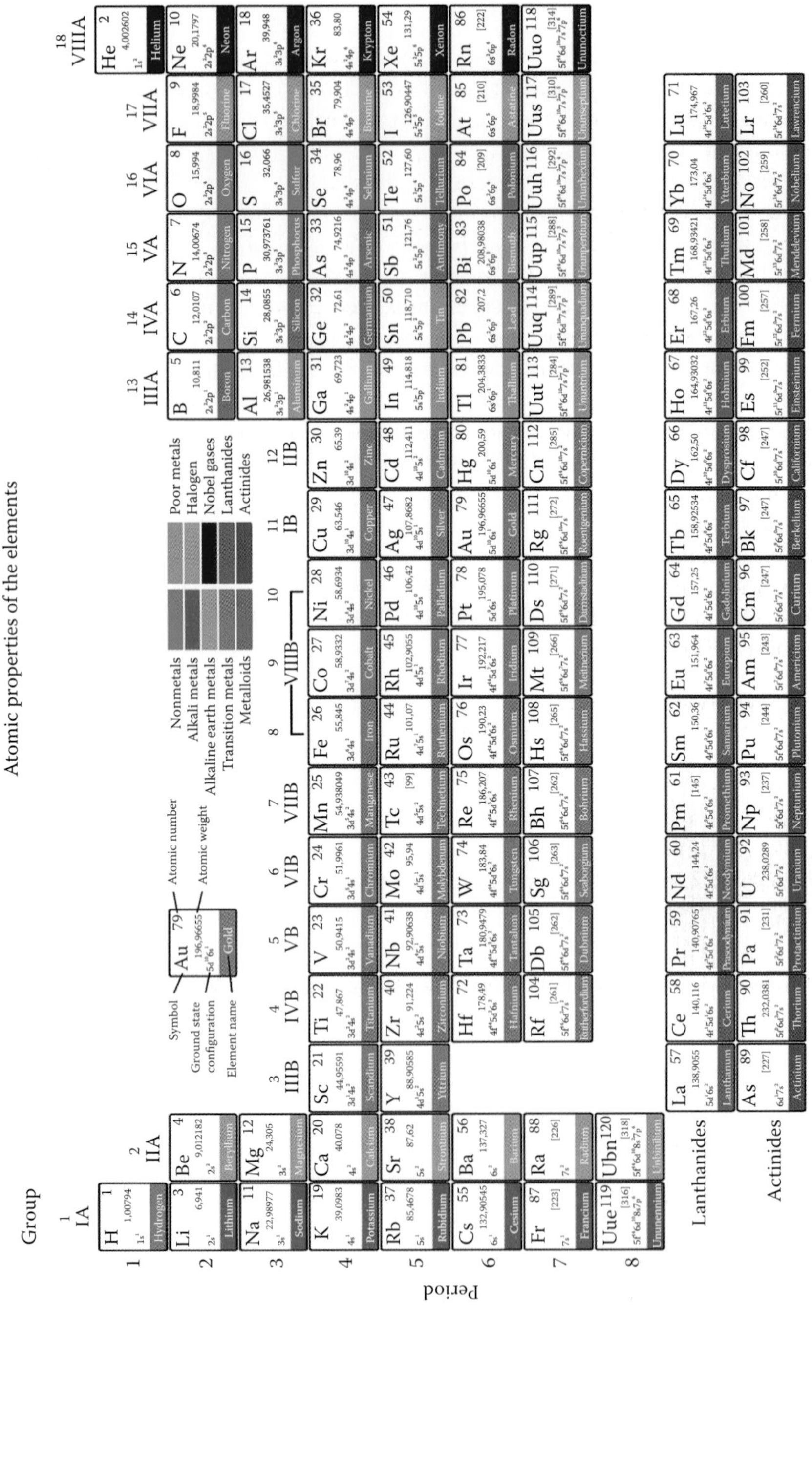

Figure P.39 Periodic table of the elements.

Periodic waves

[general] Harmonic principle of ENERGY flow, where the MAGNITUDE of the representative phenomenon (e.g., mechanical deflection, electric or MAGNETIC FIELD strength, etc.) fluctuates with a fixed rhythm, indicated by the period of the WAVE (T), or the FREQUENCY ($\nu = 1/T$, expressed in Hertz [Hz]).

Periodogram

[acoustics, astronomy, computational, mechanics, optics] Periodogram is the statistical analysis of a time series of events that are not always periodic in nature. The events can be objects placed in a two-dimensional space (e.g. telephone poles) or sound AMPLITUDES, respectively light (ELECTROMAGNETIC RADIATION). One item of particular interest to the analysis by means of periodograms is in the occurrence of sunspots. Generally, a FOURIER TRANSFORM may not capture all the frequency data due to the unique and unevenly distributed nature of the events. The concept of the periodogram was introduced in the late 1800s. The periodogram concept can be in principle attributed to Sir Franz Arthur Friedrich Schuster (1851–1934), published in 1897. The periodogram analysis uses the discrete Fourier transform (DFT) as a basis, but requires several stages of averaging: *smoothing*. The periodogram uses the squared modulus of the DFT at selected frequencies, applied in asymptotic approximation. The FREQUENCY SPECTRUM analysis for the periodogram is primarily a statistical estimation process. It is the MAGNITUDE and span approximation for the spectral density of a periodic or discrete SIGNAL. A mathematical and statistical concept used to break down a complicated object of data stream, for instance a time series, into a sum of objects (e.g., spectral or temporal components) with reduced simplicity: $x(t) - x = \sum_{k=2}^{(n/2)+1} \gamma_k \{ a_k \cos[2\pi(t-1)\omega_k] + b_k \sin[2\pi(t-1)\omega_k] \}$, where ω_k represents the frequency components, $\gamma_k = 2$ unless $k = 1$, and a_k, b_k respectively the real and imaginary components of the Fourier transform of the data series. The individual components can then be studied separately. The less important components (low probability of impacting the overall outcome) can potentially be discarded to form a general approximation of the original phenomenon or object (also see FAST FOURIER TRANSFORM [FFT]) (see Figure P.40).

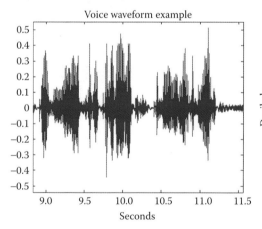
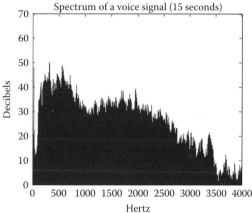

Figure P.40 Periodogram for the sound from voice over a time frame of 15 seconds, showing an amplitude graph for a section of 2.8 seconds only, with the calculated voice frequency on the right spectrum. Calculations performed by Matlab-MathWorks, Natick, MA, US. http://www.mathworks.com/help/signal/ref/periodogram. html?requestedDomain=www.mathworks.com. (Courtesy of National Center for Supercomputing Applications (NCSA) at the University of Illinois, Urbana, IL; Fortner Software, Unidata Program Center (netCDF), Boulder, CO; , The Independent JPEG Group (JPEG), Jean-loup Gailly and Mark Adler (gzip), and Digital Equipment Corporation (DEC), Maynard, MA.

Periphractic region

[fluid dynamics] Region in an irrotational segment of a moving FLUID, or electric respectively magnetic FLUX, which is defined by one or more closed surfaces. Also see APERIPHRACTIC, as found pertaining to Maxwell theory, where a closed surface may be contracted down to a point without losing the confinement for the region.

Peristaltic motion

[biomedical, mechanics] Sequential relaxation and subsequent contraction of circular muscles in antero-grade MOTION to form a WAVE-like propagation that mechanically transports the content within a biological tube, as found in the gastrointestinal track. The MUSCLE structure is smooth muscle. Certain worms also use this mechanism for in-line advancement on the exterior (see Figure P.41).

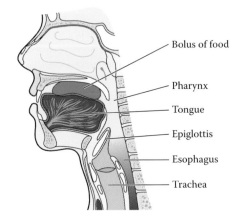

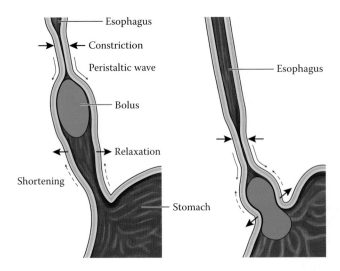

Figure P.41 The peristaltic motion of the esophagus as a result of swallowing food.

Perkins, Donald Hill (1925–)

[high-energy, nuclear] Physicist from Great Britain. He is best known for his contributions in PARTICLE physics, specifically the discovery of the negative PION in cosmic RADIATION (see Figure P.42).

Figure P.42 Donald Hill Perkins (1925–). (Courtesy of Physics Institute of the University of Bonn, Bonn, Germany.)

Permanent magnet

[general] *See* MAGNET.

Permeability (μ_{mag})

[biomedical, electromagnetism, energy, general, thermodynamics] $\mu_0{}^{mag} = 4\pi \times 10^{-7}\ \mathrm{H\,m^{-1}}$ for free space. Material property describing the ratio of the MAGNITUDE of magnetization (i.e., magnetic intensity) under the influence of a current through the material in a annular shape to the intensity of magnetization produced by the same current through a nonferromagnetic material with the same configuration of windings and dimensions. The permeability is an indication of the ability of the material to sustain the MAGNETIC FIELD. Generally, the permeability is a function of the magnetization itself, specifically for ferromagnetic media.

Permittivity (ε_{elec})

[biomedical, energy, general, thermodynamics] The electric field response of a medium under the influence of an applied external electric field. Measure of electric RESISTANCE of a medium under the process of forming an electric field within the medium. Note that the electric field is the electric potential per unit length resulting from separation of charges; how easily are the charges in a medium polarized under the influence of an external electric field. In a related definition, the electric susceptibility is an indication of the degree of POLARIZATION for a medium under the influence of an external electric field, the ease at which charges can be reorganized. The permittivity is the product of the RELATIVE PERMITTIVITY (ε_r) and the permittivity of free space ($\varepsilon_0 = 8.85419 \times 10^{-12}\,\mathrm{C^2/N\,m^2}$).

P

Pérot, Jean-Baptiste Alfred (1863–1925)

[electronics, optics] Also PEROT French physicist most known for his work on interferometry with CHARLES FABRY (1867–1945). In spectroscopic analysis, the team developed the FABRY–PÉROT INTERFEROMETER (see Figure P.43).

Figure P.43 Jean-Baptiste Alfred Pérot (1863–1925).

Perpetual motion

[general] Any finite system by definition has finite INTERNAL ENERGY. In case a machine, or a system in general, performs work, energy is exchanged with the external system and the mechanism will have a decrease in internal energy by definition of CONSERVATION OF ENERGY (FIRST LAW OF THERMODYNAMICS). In case of perpetual motion, the system is supposedly crating more energy than it is producing allowing it to operate indefinitely without fuel (i.e., externally added energy). The system that operates for infinite period of time without contribution of external energy is referred to as the hypothetical case of perpetual motion of the first kind, which is theoretically and practically impossible. Perpetual motion of the second kind is claiming the possibility of extracting energy from the outside system without the requirements of a thermal gradient towards the system. This phenomenon would not violate the FIRST LAW OF THERMODY-NAMICS; however, since it would supposedly effortlessly extract energy from the environment, this will violate the SECOND LAW OF THERMODYNAMICS, which prescribes a thermal gradient in order for heat to FLOW. The perpetual motion of the second kind presumably could extract energy against the gradient, that is, from a colder system, which is a practical and theoretical impossibility. The perpetual motion of the second kind however does not claim an infinite lifetime of operation, nor does it generate more energy than it consumes, but is still highly improbable and unrealistic (see Figure P.44).

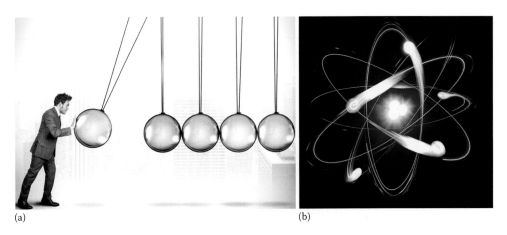

(a)   (b)

Figure P.44 (a) Apparent perpetual motion, the fact that a significant amount of energy was required to produce the "bouncing ball" device (i.e., Newton Cradle) and the fact that one ball needs to be pulled away initially by means of an external force by definition disqualify this device as a perpetual motion machine and (b) atomic motion is the closest system satisfying the perpetual motion theorem; still energy was added to this system during the primordial creation mechanism.

Perrin, Jean Baptiste (1870–1942)

[atomic, general, nuclear] Physicist from France who described the PHOTOELECTRIC EFFECT. Additional work by Perrin involved the BROWNIAN MOTION. He employed the description of Brownian motion provided by Einstein to derive the value of the Avogadro number. His work provided the following values for Avogadro's number 68.2×10^{22} mol^{-1} under the investigation of vertical velocity distribution; 68.8×10^{22} mol^{-1} for translational displacement; 65×10^{22} mol^{-1} under rotational DIFFUSION; and 69×10^{22} mol^{-1} under diffusion MEASUREMENT in the early 1900s, with respect to the established value (est. 2011; based on the work of LORENZO ROMANO AMEDEO CARLO AVOGADRO [1776–1856] in 1811) $N_a = 6.02213678 \times 10^{23}$ mol^{-1}. His work on CATHODE RAYS proved that their nature consisted of negatively charged particles. He also studied the effect on conductivity of gasses under the influence of X-RAY RADIATION. In addition, his work encompassed FLUORESCENCE, the disintegration of the radium isotope, next to the general phenomenon of emission and transmission of acoustic ENERGY (i.e., SOUND) (see Figure P.45).

Figure P.45 Jean Baptiste Perrin (1870–1942).

Persistence time

[biomedical, computational, energy, general, mechanics] The average time frame between MOTION occurrences of significant influence relating CELL MOTILITY, for example, change in direction or MAGNITUDE: $\tau_{\text{persistance}} = \left\{ \theta_T \left(1 - \sin \phi \right) \right\}^{-1}$, where θ_T is the average time interval between two changes in direction and ϕ is the ANGLE between the prior direction and the new direction.

Perturbation theory

[atomic, computational] In wave MECHANICS the eigenfunctions of an applicable operator, such as the Hamiltonian ($H\Psi$), can be expanded in series. For certain cases, in atomic PHYSICS an exact NUMERICAL solution to the SCHRÖDINGER EQUATION may not be attainable. The case of perturbations in the Hamiltonian pertaining to fluctuations in the local potential can be difficult to ascertain. On a MACROSCOPIC scale, the same principles have been applied to the definition of PLANETARY ORBITS, first assumed to be circular, later found to be *approximating* elliptical tracks, due to various external influences. The process for the PLANETARY MOTION uses the following perturbation mechanism: first assume a single PLANET in an elliptical orbit, next add additional planets, and implement their influences (assuming that they also only move in an elliptical orbit; first perturbation). This allows the approximation of the velocity and the displacement of the planet. In the second-order approximation, the other planets will be calculated for their deviations on a recursive method, and the respective influence on the primary planet of interest. In the quantum-mechanical approach, generally the perturbations will proceed past the first order for initial investigations. The Hamiltonian can be enriched by a perturbing term (H', perturbing Hamiltonian between quantum states): $H^* = H_0 + H'$, which is subsequently used in the Schrödinger equation: $H^*\Psi_k = E_k\Psi_k$, where E_k is the primary ENERGY distribution, and the solutions have the associated orthonormal eigenvalues (u_i). In first order, this yields only the direct influences, canceling out interactions between states $m \neq n$, at the perturbation $\square_m$: $\sum_{n=1}^{\infty} a_{kn}H'_{mn} = \left(E_k - E_{0m} \right) a_{km}$, where $H'_{mn} = \int u_m^* H' u_n d\tau$ is the matrix ELEMENT of the perturbing Hamiltonian H' between states m and k, with u_m^* the complex conjugate EIGENVALUE, $E_k = \sum_{n=1}^{\infty} a_{kn}u_n$, a_{kn} the EXPANSION coefficient (which are all zero except for a_{kk}), and $a_{km} \cong H'_{mk}/\left(E_{0k} - E_{0m} \right)$ under the approximation $E_k \approx E_{0k}$. The simple example is for a square POTENTIAL WELL. A time-dependent version will apply to photon emission, gamma DECAY, beta and alpha emission as well as atomic and NUCLIDE collisions; this process involves a change of state, for instance from excited to GROUND STATE under photon emission. In this case, the state is defined as $\Psi = \psi_m e^{-(E_m/h)t}$, with PLANCK's CONSTANT $h = 6.62606957 \times 10^{-34}\,\text{m}^2\,\text{kg/s}$, which in this case will be required to satisfy the Schrödinger time-dependent equation: $H^*\Psi = i\hbar \left(\partial\Psi/\partial t \right)$, where $\hbar = h/2\pi$, and t denotes time. This provides a SOLUTION that yields the transition rate (λ_{trans}) from state ψ_m to all other states as $\lambda_{\text{trans}} = 2\pi/\hbar \left| H'_{km} \right|^2 \left(dN/dE \right)$, with N representing the accessible final states, and dN/dE the accessible final states per unit energy. The exact final state itself after transition can in general not be determined or experimentally derived. This last part is often referenced as "golden rule number two" (in the first-order perturbation approximation). The first-order probability of finding the system in state ψ_k is found to be $P_{\psi_k} = \left\{ (1/i\hbar)\int_0^t H'_{km}e^{-i\omega_{km}t} dt \right\}^2$, where $\omega_{km} \equiv \left(E_k - E_n \right)/\hbar$. (*Note*: "golden rule number one" applies to second-order perturbations, specifically where the matrix ELEMENTS H'_{km} will vanish under exchanges that do not violate the CONSERVATION LAWS.)

PET tracer

[biomedical, imaging] Radioisotopes that are used to TRACE specific metabolic or biological events in combination with POSITRON EMISSION TOMOGRAPHY (PET) imaging. For instance, $\left[^{18}\text{F} \right]$—fluorodeoxyglucose has a half-life of 110 min, becomes part of the GLUCOSE, and is used to track tissue ACTIVITY (used in cancer research, neurology, and cardiology), $\left[^{18}\text{F} \right]$—fluoride has a half-life of 110 min and is used in bone imaging, $\left[^{11}\text{C} \right]$—PK11195 has a half-life of 20 min and is used for determining microglial activation, specifically associated with various neuroinflammatory and neurodegenerative diseases. Many more TRACERS are available to monitor physiological and anatomical features ranging from BLOOD flow, hypoxia, CELL binding studies, to dopamine receptor binding characteristics (e.g., drug efficacy), and cerebral ischemia as well as behavior studies based in viral infections (linking to the virus).

Peters, Bernard (1910–1993)

[atomic, geophysics, nuclear] Scientist from Poland (Prussia), contributor to the determination of the primary cosmic ray FLUX of nuclei with atomic number $Z \geq 2$, some in collaboration with Helmut L. Bradt (–1950). Peters and Bradt collected a significant amount of data during a balloon flight in 1948. This work provided essential information with regard to the ionizing potential with respect to the Earth's ATMOSPHERE (see Figure P.46).

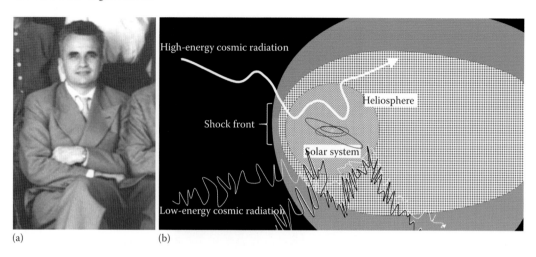

(a)   (b)

Figure P.46 (a) Bernard Peters (1910–1993) in 1959 (Courtesy of Niels Bohr Archive, Copenhagen, Denmark.) and (b) outline of atmospheric ionization based on the work of Bernard Peters.

Petit, Alexis Thérèse (1791–1820)

[thermodynamics] Physicist from France. His work provided significant insight into the efficiency of steam engines. Additional work was his discovery of the combustible nitrogen trichloride in 1813. Several efforts in his thermodynamic field were with PIERRE LOUIS DULONG (1785–1838) (*see* LAW OF DULONG AND PETIT) (see Figure P.47).

Figure P.47 Alexis Thérèse Petit (1791–1820).

Pfaff, Johann Friedrich (1765–1825)

[computational] Mathematician from Germany. His main focus was on special differential equations; specifically, he developed a method to solve series of complex interrelated functions, known as Pfaffian equations, which generally cannot be solved through normal mathematical mechanisms. One person particularly interest in Pfaff's work was Johann Carl Friedrich Gauss (Gauß) (1777–1855), pertaining to solving complex geometries for the derivation of the specific shape of magnetic field lines (see Figure P.48).

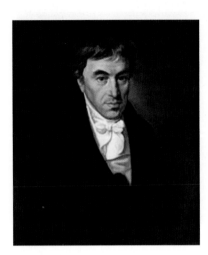

Figure P.48 Johann Friedrich Pfaff (1765–1825).

Pfaffian

[computational, thermodynamics] Differential equation with specific geometric configuration: $df = \sum_{i=1}^{n} X_i dx_i$, where the functions/phenomena X_i are dependent on individual or all the independent variables x_i. This equation is generally not considered to be a normal differential equation. The Pfaffian equation is for the specific condition: $df = \sum_{i=1}^{n} X_i dx_i = 0$. This process was developed by Johan Pfaff (1765–1825). These types of special differential equations often come into play in the field of axiomatic thermodynamics, based on the work of the German mathematician Constantin Carathéodory (1873–1950) published in 1909, on an axiomatic approach to thermodynamics.

Pfund, August Herman (1879–1949)

[atomic, nuclear] Physicist and spectroscopist from the United States. Additional work by Pfund involved the invention and creation of a specialized spectroscopic telescope: the Pfund telescope. The mechanism of action of the Pfund telescope applies a method for realizing a fixed focal point regardless of the positioning of the line of sight of the telescope. Other work by Pfund was the creation of a special compass in 1944 in the investigation of POLARIZATION by the sky, called the Pfund sky compass (see Figure P.49).

Figure P.49 August Herman Pfund (1879–1949). (Courtesy of Johns Hopkins University, Baltimore, MD.)

Pfund series

[atomic, nuclear] Atomic transition LINE SPECTRUM for hydrogen described by AUGUST PFUND (1879–1949) in 1924. The observed ATOMIC EMISSION wavelengths (λ), respectively FREQUENCY (ν), were found to adhere to a very pragmatic equation. The paradigm is based on the BOHR ATOMIC MODEL transitions between electron orbits (n_i): $\nu = \left(m_e e^4 Z^2 / 8\varepsilon_0^2 h^3 \right)\left[\left(1/n_1^2\right) - \left(1/n_2^2\right) \right]$, for $n_1 = 5$, where $m_e = 9.10939 \times 10^{-31}$ kg is the electron mass, $e = 1.60217657 \times 10^{-19}$ C is the charge equivalence of an electron [–] (or respectively PROTON [+]), the permittivity of free space $\varepsilon_{EM0} = 8.85419 \times 10^{-12}$ C^2/N m^2, PLANCK'S CONSTANT $h = 6.62606957 \times 10^{-34}$ m^2 kg/s, Z the number of charges in the NUCLEUS, and n_2 the respective originating electron orbits (*also see* PASCHEN SERIES for additional detail) (see Figure P.50).

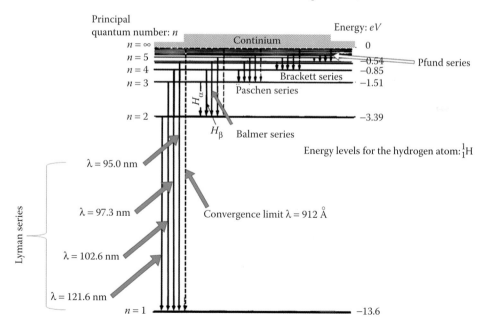

Figure P.50 Pfund series.

pH

[biomedical, chemical] Parameter defining the level of acidity or alkaline exchange of hydrogen ions (H^+) for a substance. A pH less than 7 generally indicates acidic and greater than or equal to 7 alkaline. The scale stretches from 0 to 14. pH is defined as the LOGARITHM of the hydrogen ion ACTIVITY (a_{H^+}) in SOLUTION: $pH = -\log_{10} a_{H^+}$, where the hydrogen ion activity represents $a_{H+} = f^*[H^+]$, where f represents the activity coefficient, this describes the hydrogen ion mibility. The pH was originally defined by the Danish chemist SØREN SØRENSEN (1868–1939) based on the hydrogen ion concentration ($[H^+]$): $pH = -\log_{10} H^+$. The pH of certain liquids for instance ranges from; urine: pH → 6.5–7 range; BLOOD: pH = 7.38–7.42 range.

pH VALUE	H+ CONCENTRATION	
–1	Hydrochloric acid (found in the stomach for digestion); also known as muriatic acid	Acid
0	Battery acid	
1	Concentrated sulfuric acid	
2	Lemon juice, vinegar	
3	Orange juice, soda	
4	Tomato juice, acid rain	
4.5–6.5	Black coffee	
5	Bananas	
6	Urine, milk	
7	Pure water	Neutral
7.40 ± 0.05	Blood	Alkaline
8	Seawater, eggs	
9	Baking soda	
10	Great Salt Lake, milk of magnesia	
11	Ammonia solution	
12	Soap solution	
13	Bleach, oven cleaner	
14	Liquid drain cleaner	

The acidity of the blood plasma is tightly regulated between pH = 7.38 and 7.42. The body's pH HOMEOSTASIS is essential to the proper progress of chemical reactions, survival of the cells, and ultimately survival of the organism. The pH is tightly monitored through chemoreceptors measuring the H^+ concentration in both the blood plasma and the cerebrospinal FLUID. Two organs of particular importance to tight control of acidity are the lungs and the kidneys. Central and peripheral pH sensors are located throughout the mammalian body, in particular in the internal and external carotid (neck, leading to the brain), the aortic arch (right after the egress from the left ventricle of the HEART), and in the medulla of the brain. Even though the blood–brain BARRIER provides poor permeability to H^+, the acidity of the brain is influenced by means of carbon dioxide (cellular METABOLISM waste product): $CO_2 + H_2O \rightleftharpoons H_2CO_3 \rightleftharpoons H^+ + HCO_3^-$, carbolic ACID. Note that the brain cells are perfused by an extracellular fluid (ECF) that is independent from the blood flow. The function of the chemoreceptors is to mitigate changes to the pH by influencing the RESPIRATION, through inducing the release of buffer solutions, and by means of KIDNEY function as a residual effort. Buffers are for instance $H_2PO_4^{2-}$ and HCO_3^-, which bind to H^+ and can be released from cells and ECF. In all these mechanisms contradictions can arise, for instance the increase of carbon dioxide (partial pressure of CO_2;

subsequent lower pH) subsequently decreases the binding of oxygen to hemoglobin. The latter results in the release of additional oxygen in regions that are rich in carbon dioxide, the BOHR EFFECT (see Figure P.51).

Figure P.51 Litmus paper used to indicate the acidity of a substance.

Phagocyte

[biomedical, mechanics] Specialized biological CELL that uses PHAGOCYTOSIS for the removal of extracellular material that may be considered harmful (see Figure P.52).

Figure P.52 Illustration of how a phagocyte captures the content of, for instance, medication (i.e., pill).

Phagocytosis

[biomedical, mechanics] The active mechanism for biological CELL to ingest solid items. The CELL MEMBRANE forms a vesicle that wraps around the material on the exterior of the cell membrane and subsequently transports the encapsulated material to the interior of the cell. The consumption process is part of the classification of ENDOCYTOSIS, which also includes consumption of LIQUID defined as PINOCYTOSIS. Generally, the PARTICLE size is larger than 1 mm. Specialized cells call phagocytes uses phagocytosis for the removal of pathogens. On the MECHANICS of the selective restructuring of the lipid-protein bilayer (*also see* CELL MEMBRANE) (see Figure P.53).

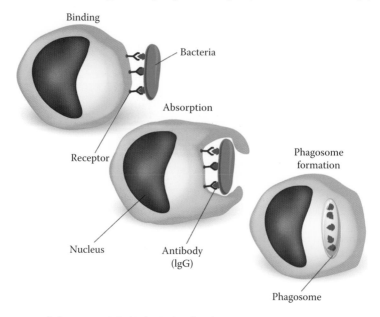

Figure P.53 The process of phagocytosis in biological cells. This is an active cellular deformation process. The local surface tension is adjusted actively to "open-up" the wall for consumption.

Phantom

[acoustics, computational, electromagnetism, optics] Artificially constructed medium that has most of the essential characteristics representative of the real object that needs to be investigated, specifically with respect to the ENERGY in question; ELECTROMAGNETIC RADIATION, particle beam, acoustic WAVE. For instance, a tissue phantom for PHOTODYNAMIC THERAPY dosimetry investigations can be constructed of a watery solution with SCATTERING particles (e.g., lipid [soy] or POLYMER [polyester; or other materials, including metals] of specific size; scatterer dimension determines both the scattering coefficient and the scattering anisotropy factor) and absorbing particles (e.g., Indian ink) (see Figure P.54).

Figure P.54 The use of a phantom medium to illustrate the concept of a physics phenomenon, in this situation steam formation that is boiling water.

Phase

[acoustics, chemical, electromagnetism, fluid dynamics, general, geophysics, mechanics, quantum, solid-state, thermodynamics] Several particular definitions of phase are in use; geophysical phenomena, mechanics, material sciences, logistic processes, and thermodynamic processes. In material science and general PHYSICS, the phase indicates a location in a region of time and space, within which all physical characteristics of a medium, or a material, are fundamentally unvarying and uniform. In MECHANICS, the phase represents the angular fraction during a periodic process (e.g., sinusoidal) with respect to equilibrium at a chosen start time (i.e., the phase constant (ϕ) and the progression over time ωt), pertaining to a rhythmic, HARMONIC MOTION: $\Phi = \Phi_0 \sin(\omega t + \phi)$, where $\omega = 2\pi\nu$ is the ANGULAR VELOCITY and $\nu = v/\lambda$ the frequency for a wave with wavelength λ under propagation velocity v. The frequency of the observation, WAVE, is of critical importance when comparing the respective phases. Two phenomena that are operating almost at the same frequency will experience INTERFERENCE at certain time frames when the respective wave crests match up, and this will generate a BEAT FREQUENCY of the combined phenomena. The beat frequency will be observable at the difference of the two frequencies: $\nu_{beat} = \nu_2 - \nu_1$, with respective AMPLITUDE $A_R(t) = (A_1 + A_2)\cos\left\{2\pi\left[(\nu_2 - \nu_1)/2\right]t + \phi_i\right\}$; note that this only holds true for a deviation in the order of less than 0.25%, respectively less than 1 to several Hz, depending on several boundary conditions, including the MAGNITUDE of either wave phenomenon. A similar concept applies to the tuning fork used to tune a musical instrument. The phase of a wave phenomenon has a 360° or 2π recurrence, where 0 or 2π, respectively 360°, indicates complete in-phase, versus a phase difference between two events of 180° or π represents totally out-off phase, or opposite phase. For waves the concept of superposition applies under all conditions.

Wave phenomena that are totally in-phase will provide a condition of RESONANCE, or amplification of the magnitude of the phenomenon, whereas totally out-off phase characterizes cancelation. The phase difference is an indication how much difference there is in the "location" (in time and/or space, depending on the phenomenon or the specific ENGINEERING interests) of the respective crests of two waves of identical frequency. Generally, the phase of a wave will allow synchronization of events as well as imaging applications—coherence. Laser LIGHT by nature is coherent and hence in phase over the entire path of the emitted beam, extending over light-years. The phase of ELECTROMAGNETIC RADIATION is essential in the process of OPTICAL COHERENCE TOMOGRAPHY for instance. Other applications of phase related detection/ sensing are based on the correlation between emitted and retrieved reflected waves in radar imaging of weather phenomena and objects in flight (e.g., airplanes), nondestructive testing (using electronic, optical, and acoustic mechanisms of action), ULTRASOUND imaging (MEDICINE), and radar detection of the velocity of an object, for instance used by law-enforcement agencies. In ACOUSTICS, the phase of a wave is predominantly determined by the dimension of the source, for instance a sting on a cello or alternatively a PIPE organ. In THERMODYNAMICS, the phase represents the state of a medium: solid, LIQUID, gas, or plasma. In that regard, phase transitions refer to changes from liquid to VAPOR (vaporization) and solid to liquid (melting) and respectively for the reverse processes (condensation: vapor to liquid; FREEZING/congealing: liquid to solid), as well as solid to vapor (SUBLIMATION), and deposition: from gas to solid. Freezing is the phase change as a substance changes from a liquid to a solid. A PHASE DIAGRAM in thermodynamics illustrates the behavior of a medium as a function of pressure, temperature, and volume, specifically with respect to the exchange of heat. The PHASE DIAGRAMS usually illustrate the condition of a medium in a graph with the horizontal axis outlining the units of the independent variable considered in the study (abscissa, x-axis; Cartesian), either temperature or pressure, and the vertical axis the units of either the dependent variable in the study or in this case a second independent variable (ordinate, y-axis; Cartesian), the pressure. The angular phase of the process describes the stage in a distinct period of change or forming during the development of something; either a logistic course of action or a device design/manufacturing sequence of events. In a geophysical concept, the lunar phase describes the relative location of the MOON with respect to the EARTH under illumination by the SUN from a coordinate in space, providing a sequence of views of the Moon ranging from dark new moon to full disk full moon. The lunar phases range in appearance during eight key stages for its revolution around the Earth: new moon, waxing crescent, first quarter, waxing gibbous, full moon, waning gibbous, third quarter, and finally waning crescent (see Figure P.55).

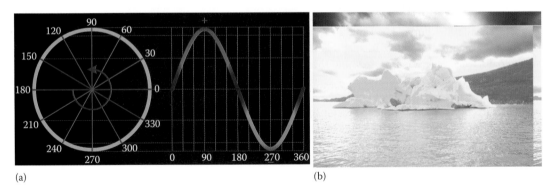

(a)   (b)

Figure P.55 Scientific use of the definition of phase (a) in wave formation and (b) in material characteristics liquid, solid, and gas.   *(Continued)*

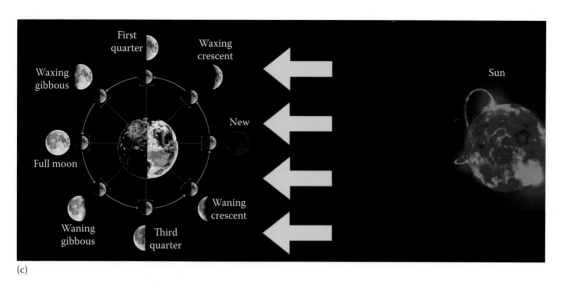

(c)

Figure P.55 (Continued) Scientific use of the definition of phase (c) in illumination stages for the Moon.

Phase cancellation

[acoustics, electromagnetism, fluid dynamics, general, mechanics, quantum, thermodynamics] The moment at which two periodic phenomena that operate at the same frequency are in opposite PHASE with each other and cancel each other out in its entirety (see Figure P.56).

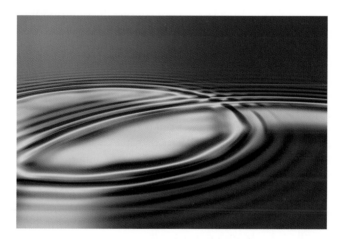

Figure P.56 Surface waves resulting from two perturbations in two different locations will result in merging waves where locations with opposing phase will cancel each other out yielding zero surface displacement.

Phase diagram

[chemical, computational, general, thermodynamics] Graphical representation of conditions used to illustrate at which point thermodynamically distinct phases can exist during equilibrium. The thermodynamic phase diagrams illustrate the phases of a medium under variable conditions of pressure, volume, and temperature, indicating the TRIPLE POINT (coexistence of LIQUID, VAPOR, and GAS phases at certain combination of pressure and temperature) and the critical point (the threshold temperature, when exceeded will result in a GAS PHASE for the medium regardless of the pressure) between vapor, liquid, and solid. More generally, the phase diagram illustrates the processes of FREEZING (SOLIDIFICATION)/melting, and vaporization/condensation, while under certain circumstances the conditions for the formation of a plasma may also be included. Also referred to as PV-DIAGRAM, for pressure versus volume outline of the state of the medium, and as PT-DIAGRAM with respect to temperature (see Figure P.57).

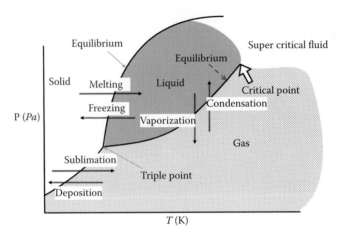

Figure P.57 Phase diagram.

Phase encoding

[biomedical, computational, theoretical] Signals that carry information can be encrypted with encoding mechanisms ranging from AMPLITUDE, phase to frequency, in both analog and digital SIGNAL transmission. The process of amplitude modulation is found in AM-RADIO, whereas frequency encoding is used in FM-radio and television to name a few. In order to create a greater discrimination and added security to avoid accidental "listing-in" or "hijacking" personal information, additional mechanism of encoding need to be implemented, including the highly configurable phase encoding. The phase encoding can be embedded with a preprogrammed phase DRIFT that is geared to the "receiver" conditions, such as that used in mobile phones. In imaging the process of phase encoding is for instance applied in magnetic resonance imaging (MRI), where the phase of a MAGNETIC FIELD is configured through altering the phase of spins in one dimension by pulsing the *magnetic field gradient* along the intended dimension of interest prior to the acquisition of the signal. The magnetic field has three components in a Cartesian system, where under imaging conditions the three respective vectors will have the same chemical frequency shift, and will subsequently possess the same Larmor frequency when exposed to a uniform magnetic field. If the applied gradient in the magnetic field is directed along the x-direction, the three magnetic field vectors will precess at a frequency given by the RESONANCE equation, with respect to the direction of the applied external magnetic field. On the other hand, the phase ANGLE (i.e., phase encoding) of each respective vector is not identical. The phase angle in this case represents the angle between a reference axis, either the x- or z-axis. Note that the magnetization vector will need to be discontinued at the time the phase encoding gradient takes place to avoid convolution of information. There are three distinct phase angles in this example. The subsequent spatial reconstruction can be explicitly and precisely located by means of FOURIER TRANSFORM analysis. The ensuing MRI spatial RESOLUTION is a direct function of the number of phase encoding levels applied to the respective field gradients. In telecommunications, specifically data transfer and data storage, phase encoding uses a clock frequency to provide a tuning mechanism for the collection of the signal. One other application is also found in card-key reader and access code using RFID (radio-frequency identification). Phase encoding on a digital basis uses a line code that has no DC-components, in which the encoding can be identified by means of ensuring that each data bit has at least one transition that occupies the same time. The clock signal can in this manner be recovered from the encoded data. Phase encoding is also used in 10BASE-T Ethernet (IEEE 802.3 standard). Digital phase encoding can apply highly configured phase trains, with a phase pattern repeater for imbedding many different sources of information. Temporal phase encryption disqualifies the coherent addition of various pulses in the frequency domain. This in itself provides a platform for reducing the signal power spectral density. Hence eliminating the need to transmit the signal within the bandwidth used by the handler in order to conceal information within the signal spectrally. Spectral phase encoding provides a mechanism for temporal spreading of the pulse sequence, resulting in a stealth-like temporal and spectral transmission. This process applied for instance to optical communications by means of fiber-optics. On a biomedical level, phase encoding is potentially used to indicate the location of the source of a signal transmitted through the nerves, nervous system and identified by the brain (phase encoding for a binary system is different than for an analog system, for instance using a phase shift for a "marker" pulse segment). Further decoding is with respect to the digitally encoded characteristics of the observation, such as COLOR, taste, etc., MAGNITUDE as well as the physical characteristic itself (touch versus pain, brightness versus pin/threat, etc.) where the encoding will first allow only the appropriate receptor (brain function segment, special dedicated functional areas in the brain for sensation, MOTION control and thought, in addition to lobes for "mood/character") to collect the relevant data. The intensity/magnitude of any sensation is represented in the frequency aspect of the binary signal; higher frequency pulse train indicates stronger sensation. For instance, the EYE has three CONES for RED, green, and blue, but the communication process through many branches and matrices of nerve cells, synaptic junctions, and amplifier stations (one nerve exciting multiple downstream nerves) does provide an accurate PERCEPTION after an elaborate signal processing network. Furthermore, after damage to the nerve system, respectively the brain, under certain conditions other nerve paths and respective brain segment can "learn" to acquire the data and encode it, which may initially be flawed but can grow to a highly accurate representation varying per individual since biology is by far not an exact science and has a wide range of boundary conditions that influence the final outcome. Respectively, sometimes the biological encoding may not be intact or "perfect" by nature, for instance resulting in reduced perception or "signal confusion," such as certain forms of colorblindness or the often learned behavior for flavor (e.g., dislikes, thresholds). Phase encoding is also known as Manchester encoding, developed by the University of Manchester, Manchester, United Kingdom (see Figure P.58).

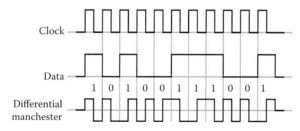

Figure P.58 Conceptual representation of phase encoding.

Phase noise

[acoustics, electromagnetism, mechanics] Noise in general is SIGNAL that deviates from a well-defined spectral and AMPLITUDE configuration. Noise can be generated as the result of the phenomenon itself, creating harmonics and specifically harmonics that are not in sync with the primary WAVE, or have fluctuating amplitude for the respective orders as a function of time. Other sources of NOISE originate from the medium in which a signal is generated or through which it will travel, providing DISPERSION next to dampening effects, with different MAGNITUDE for different frequencies and spatially diverse. Specifically, crystals produce inherent noise due to the source properties pertaining to freedom of movement of the oscillator; mechanical constraints will automatically induce harmonics and dispersion effects. Thermal effects also provide a main cause for noise, due to collision interactions. Since noise contains components at multiple frequencies, the respective phases will have a random distribution, as well as the amplitudes will be randomly distributed over time and spectrally. Noise is described in statistical terms because its magnitude is constantly and randomly changing. However, one can assign an average amplitude (A) that can be expressed in root-mean-square (RMS) value. Phase noise has implication in both the FREQUENCY (v) and TIME (t) domain. In particular, in the time domain it causes jitter in the acquired signal. In the frequency domain, the phase noise contributes to a PHASE shift (ϕ_{random}): $A = \{A_0 + A_{noise}(t)\}\sin(2\pi v_0 t + \phi_{random})$. The signal will appear as a primary component with sidebands (*also see* NOISE) (see Figure P.59).

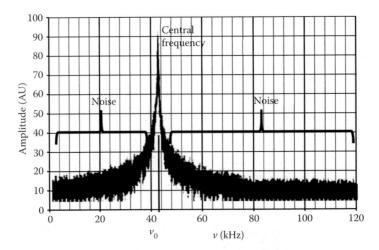

Figure P.59 Graphical representation of the phase noise spectral profile.

Phase rotation

[acoustics, computational, mechanics, theoretical, thermodynamics] In a polyphase system, the order of waveform sequences. In electrical applications, the power supply will have a specific PHASE associated with the alternating current $\left(I_i = I_{i,0}\sin(\omega t + \phi)\right)$. In a three-phase system (high-voltage, high-power consumption electric motor design, e.g., crane), the three power supplies will have their own respective phases that will interact with each other inside the electric motor, allowing the MOTOR to rotate one way and when switching two of the phases it will reverse the direction. Operational process for three-phase alternator: PHASE SEQUENCE for proper operations; clockwise: Also described as phase "sequence." Alternatively, in acoustic communications with one TRANSDUCER and multiple receivers, the collected phase at the respective receivers can be subject to DOPPLER shift or DISPERSION, creating a SIGNAL processing complexity due to the various signal phases related to the information transmitted for the single source, specifically pertaining to imaging (communications, scanner array). In particular, the use of a PHASED ARRAY in ULTRASOUND imaging relies on phase rotation to systematically build a three-dimensional IMAGE (see Figure P.60).

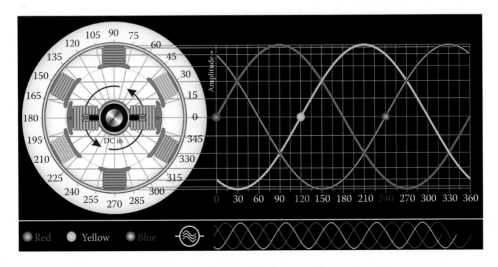

Figure P.60 Phase rotation for a three-phase generator, Crane using a three-phase electromotor.

Phase rule

[thermodynamics] Mechanism to determine the MAGNITUDE of the number of DEGREES OF FREEDOM (DF), respectively the variance of a chemical system, proposed by JOSIAH WILLARD GIBBS (1839–1903) in 1875: $DF = 2 + C_n + P_{chem}$, with C_n the number of constituents in the chemical mixture and P_{chem} the respective number of phases present within the system. The PHASE is defined as the part of a system that is chemically and physically homogeneous. The region confined to certain phase is bounded by a distinct interface with respect to other phases and can be physically separated from other phases. The phase rule defines the possible number of equilibrium situations for a system or chemical reaction. The phase rule has particular application in PHASE DIAGRAMS. For instance at triple points, all phases must coexist in the adjacent stability fields as well as at equilibrium lines (see Figure P.61).

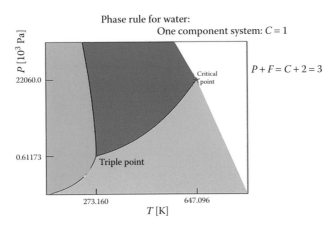

Figure P.61 Graphical representation of the phase rule principles.

Phase sequence

[acoustics, computational, mechanics, thermodynamics] *See* PHASE ROTATION.

Phase space

[atomic, computational, nuclear] A graphical statistical representation space in which all possible physical and thermodynamic states of a system are outlined. Each possible state of the system in the phase space will have an assigned unique point. One example is the representation of location and respective momentum ($p = mv$, with the mass m at location x, traveling at velocity v) for all coordinates of the constituents of a system. The Hamilton operator (H) connects the location to the momentum, which can be observed dynamically, creating what can be considered a Hamiltonian flow in phase space. The VOLUME (V) in this phase space ($dV = dp_x dx$) is conserved: $(1/V)(dV/dt) = \nabla \cdot f\left(\eta_{phase}\right) = \partial/\partial x \left(\partial H/\partial p_x\right) + \left(\partial/\partial p_x\right)\left(-\partial H/\partial x\right) = 0$, where $\eta_{phase} = \left(x, p_x\right)$ represent the location (phase point) in phase space, and $\partial \eta_{phase}/\partial t = f\left(\eta_{phase}\right) = \left[\left(\partial H/\partial p_x\right), \text{and} -\left(\partial H/\partial x\right)\right]$ is known as the Liouvile theorem. The mathematical concept of phase space was unknowingly introduced by the French mathematician JOSEPH LIOUVILLE (1809–1882) in 1838. Liouville's work was further refined approximately in 1842 by the German mathematician Carl Gustav Jacob Jacobi (1804–1851), without a direct reference to space or phase, but with a consistent and working mathematical treatment. Additional work by Ludwig Eduard Boltzmann (1844–1906) in 1866 also references the concept of phase space with respect to his theory of gasses, introducing a new field of statistical mechanics (see Figure P.62).

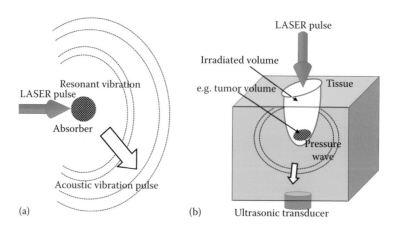

Figure P.62 (a,b) Phase space for electroencephalogram (EEG) monitoring. Courtesy of Michel Le Van Quyen.

Phase transition

[computational, thermodynamics] Conversion between the three states of solid, liquid, and gas. The following phase transitions are recognized: liquid to vapor: vaporization; vapor to liquid: condensation; solid to liquid: melting; liquid to solid: freezing/congealing; solid to vapor: sublimation, and gas to solid: deposition. Additional phase transitions are recognized as conducting-to-superconducting, fluid-to-superfluid, as well as solid-to-solid transitions. With any phase transition, a latent heat is associated defining the total heat (Q) required to transform a mass (m); for instance for solid to liquid or vice versa the latent heat of fusion L_f, providing $Q_f = mL_f$, respectively for vaporization L_v. Note that all these transitions are reversible. Two phases of the same single-component system in equilibrium have equal Gibbs free energy ($G = H - TS$, where H represents the system enthalpy, T the temperature, and S the entropy). Phase transitions are categorized by the Ehrenfest classification. The order of the phase transition is defined based on the order of the lowest order derivative at the phase boundary involved in the transition, which changes discontinuously (*also see* second-order phase transition).

ORDER	GIBBS DIFFERENTIAL		CORRESPONDING CHARACTERISTICS		
First	S	V	S	V	
Second	$(\partial S/\partial T)_P$	$(\partial V/\partial T)_P$	c_p	β	K_p
	$(\partial S/\partial P)_T$	$(\partial V/\partial P)_T$			
Third	$(\partial^2 S/\partial T^2)_P$	$(\partial^2 V/\partial T^2)_P$	$(\partial c_p/\partial T)_P$ $(\partial c_p/\partial P)_T$	$(\partial \beta/\partial T)_P$ $(\partial \beta/\partial P)_T$	$(\partial K_p/\partial T)_P$ $(\partial K_p/\partial P)_T$
	$\partial^2 S/\partial T\partial P$	$\partial^2 V/\partial T\partial P$			
	$(\partial^2 S/\partial P^2)_T$	$(\partial^2 V/\partial P^2)_T$			
S, Entropy	P, Pressure	V, Volume	c_p, specific heat under constant pressure	$\beta = 1/k_b T$ $k_b = 1.3806488 \times 10^{-23}$ $m^2 kg/s^2 K$, the Boltzmann constant	K_p, equilibrium constant: $\ln(K_p(T))$ $= -(1/RT)\sum v_i \mu_i^0(T)$; $R = 8.3144621(75) J/K\,mol$ The gas constant; v_i the stoichiometric coefficient $\mu_i^0(T)$ the chemical potential for component $\square_i$

Phase velocity

[acoustics, atomic, mechanics, nuclear, optics] Speed at which any fixed PHASE of the cycle of a WAVE is displaced: $v_p = \omega/k = \lambda v$, where $\omega = 2\pi v$ is the ANGULAR VELOCITY of a single wave form operating at frequency v, $k = 2\pi/\lambda$ the wavenumber, and λ the associated wavelength. This stands in comparison to "group velocity" and "wave velocity." For a composite waveform, the individual frequencies will experience DISPERSION, causing deformation in the wave pattern.

Phase-locked loop

[electromagnetism, theoretical] A closed-loop phase-based frequency control feedback mechanism, locking in on the primary WAVE. The phase-locked loop (PLL) is an electronic circuit designed for PHASE sensitive detection, for instance in communication (e.g., RADIO), of electrical phase difference between the received input signals and the output signals of a tunable oscillator. The tuning mechanism relies on continuously adjusting the oscillator frequency of the receiver tuner to match the phase of the frequency of the input SIGNAL, hence reconstituting the acquired signal with reduced NOISE. In communications, the PLL modulates and respectively demodulates the collected signal to provide uninterrupted reception with few distortions (breaks in communication) and low noise. The PLL can be voltage controlled or current driven, using the CARRIER frequency of the source as the control mechanism for accurately matching up the receiver signal. The tuning oscillator (e.g., crystal-controlled reference oscillator; voltage controlled oscillator: VCO) is approximately tuned to the intended frequency by means of component value selection (e.g., RC value for recovery time). With the help of a phase comparator circuit the receiver seeks out the frequency and will lock onto the desired frequency. The phase detector produces a voltage that is proportional to the phase difference between the input and reference signal, where it is used to provide a reduction in difference feedback in the loop filter. In radio reception, this principle is achieved by the DEMODULATOR (FM-radio). The combination of PLL, VCO, reference oscillator, and phase comparator (phase detector that compares the phase of the signal derived from the oscillator to the input signal) forms what is called a frequency synthesizer.

Phase-only imaging

[acoustics, imaging, optics] Imaging technique based on using only the PHASE information of the AMPLITUDE in a complex formation of a WAVE. One specific application of phase-only imaging is applied to HOLOGRAPHY. Phase-only imaging has a reduced bit rate over conventional imaging and requires less data storage. It will still provide high-resolution images.

Phased array

[acoustics, biomedical, computational, electronics, geophysics, imaging] Source (e.g., piezoactuator and ANTENNA) composed of a multitude of radiating ELEMENTS each equipped with a PHASE shifter to provide a predetermined phase difference between respective, individually wired, elements. The consecutive phase shift between elements can turn the direction of a plane WAVE without physically changing the location of the emitters, and provide a focusing mechanism: BEAM FORMING. The beam steering ANGLE (θ_s) is directly based on the phase difference ($\Delta\varphi$), the intersource spacing (d), and the source wavelength (λ): $\Delta\varphi = 2\pi\left(\sin\theta_s/\lambda\right)d$. When performing a scan, a sweep may be performed by changing the phase according to $\exp\left[i2\pi\left(\sin\theta_s/\lambda\right)d\right]$. The detection mechanism uses the original phase difference to exclude detection from other respective sources, and additionally relies on INTERFERENCE for contrast enhancement. In ULTRASONIC IMAGING (nondestructive testing, medical imaging), this device operation can be used in sweep mode, where the phase angle is altered in a predetermined pattern to perform a sector scan. The sweeps are performed at high frequency (kHz). Because of the inherent semi empirical approach the decoding will require a look-up table for IMAGE reconstruction (see Figure P.63).

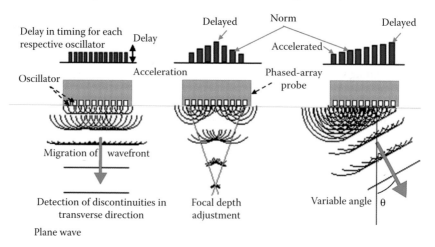

Figure P.63 Diagram of phased array, such as those used in ultrasonic imaging.

Phasor

[atomic, computational, general] Graphical representation of two quantities that are linked by a time-dependent relationship (e.g., alternating, harmonic), potentially resulting in a delay in PHASE between the two oscillatory phenomena (e.g., current in an electronic circuit versus voltage; presented as a function of the phase ANGLE between the two). Alternatively, the depiction of a rotating vector from a sinusoidal phenomenon as a function of ANGULAR VELOCITY (ω) with AMPLITUDE A. A phase vector. Also described as the Smith chart in electronic design.

Phosphorescence

[atomic, optics, solid-state] The ability of a substance to semi autonomously emit light (photoluminescence), without the requirement of excitation by ELECTROMAGNETIC RADIATION as under FLUORESCENCE. Phosphorescence may be fueled by chemical processes. During biological emission of light, such as that found in bacteria, squids, blooming phytoplankton, and certain fish, the pigment flavin, LUCIFERIN, is oxidized in the presence of an enzyme luciferase. The luciferase is also produced by the organism itself. One particularly well-known form of BIOLUMINESCENCE is found for the fire-fly. Phosphorescent substances have the ability to store up light and release it gradually. The notion of a metastable state explains this. If the molecules of the substance can get from the GROUND STATE to a metastable state, and if the metastable state can slowly DECAY back to the ground state via PHOTON emission, then we have phosphorescence. The mechanism of action of phosphorescence relies on the excited metastable triplet state, with respect to the ground state that is a SINGLET STATE. The TRIPLET STATE is defined for a MOLECULE containing two unpaired electrons that can migrate between three spin-states. Each of the electrons is subject to spin–orbit coupling; however, each with respective strengths s_1 and s_2, which will subsequently precess at different rates. A SPIN triplet consists of a set of three QUANTUM states, each with respective total spin $S = 1$. The MAGNITUDE of the resultant spin vector, $s_1 + s_2$, will tip back and forth between quantum states $S = 0$ and $S = 1$. Hypothetically, the system could consist of just a solitary elementary "spin 1" PARTICLE, of undefined size. The active molecules can be raised from the ground state by ENERGY absorption (chemical, electrical, electromagnetic) to excited singlet states. Most frequently, they will immediately return to the ground state, emitting a photon (fluorescence). Under certain conditions (chemical, external fields, etc.), a nonradiative processes will raise the state to a less energetic triplet state. Once these molecules reach the lowest triplet state, they will remain in this state for an undetermined time. Under the low-probability triplet–singlet conversion processes, the molecules will emit LIGHT. The total energy stored in the molecule includes nuclear processes including VIBRATION and rotation of the nuclides as well. Under the assumption that the excited singlet state is close in energy to a triplet state, the molecule can make a singlet–triplet transition, exchanging energy with the environment through the vibrational modes (i.e., vibrational relaxation). After that it will decay to the bottom triplet state, followed by a triplet–singlet transition. The triplet–singlet and singlet–triplet transitions, in fact, both violate the $\Delta S = 0$ SELECTION RULE, AND are hence relatively slow (seconds–minutes, compared to a nanosecond scale and less for fluorescence). However, the $\Delta S = 0$

selection rule applies only to DIPOLE transitions, meaning that the phosphorescent, "glow-in-the-dark" objects in fact do not violate any laws (see Figure P.64).

Figure P.64 Phosphorescent jelly fish.

Phosphorus (phosphor) ($^{30}_{15}$P)

[atomic, chemical, nuclear, solid-state] ELEMENT described first in 1669. Nonmetal, polyatomic. Phosphorus is found primarily in three forms: white, violet, and red, but is never discovered as pure substance due to its highly reactive nature (always bound, oxidized). Phosphorus is particularly known for its ability to emit visible LIGHT under the influence of incident short-wavelength ELECTROMAGNETIC RADIATION as well as certain energetic PARTICLE radiation. Electron bombardment provides the mechanism of action for visible light emission in photographic X-RAY detectors as well as the IMAGE formation on the face of the old-fashioned CRT (CATHODE ray tube) television/monitor screens (also found in oscilloscopes). Phosphorus is used in many everyday chemicals, ranging from cleaning supplies to pesticides to nerve agents and in matches. Note: only the white phosphorus can oxidize and form light, not the red or violet phosphorus (see Figure P.65).

Figure P.65 Phosphorus as used in matches.

Photinus-luciferin 4-monooxygenase

[biomedical, chemical, optical, thermodynamics] Biological enzyme that is closely linked to the formation of ADENOSINE TRIPHOSPHATE (ATP, cellular biological renewable ENERGY form in macromolecule) that emits LIGHT at a very narrow bandwidth of around 562 nm. One particular form of emission is under chemical OXIDATION excitation: Photinus luciferin $+O_2+$ATP $\overrightarrow{\text{Mg}}$ oxidized Photinus luciferin $+CO_2+$AMP$+$diphosphate$+562$ nm light, where Mg is a magnesium cofactor (chemical catalyst), and AMP represents adenosine monophosphate.

Photoacoustic microscopy

[acoustics, biomedical, imaging, optics] Hybrid imaging technique that relies on the excitation of phonons inside a medium by means of selective absorption of photons, photoacoustic effect. Photoacoustic imaging is nondestructive, high RESOLUTION, and has deep penetration. The acquired spatially resolved acoustic spectrum will yield information about the configuration of the local elastic moduli (also known as PHOTO-ACOUSTIC IMAGING). Photoacoustic imaging is based on the principle of LIGHT absorption that will generate elevated temperatures. Based on the Boyle–Gay–Lussac law, higher temperatures will lead to increased pressure, and from this it can be seen that a net increase in local volume can also be expected. Under pulsed laser irradiation, the short duration temperature rise can produce mechanical longitudinal shock waves. Combining the fact that light will penetrate deep into a medium and the localized generation of acoustic SHOCK WAVE, will produce an imaging system that may surpass the attributes and characteristics of both optical and acoustical imaging. The photoacoustic effect is described based on three equations, each with a range of unknowns. The first equation is the EQUATION OF RADIATIVE TRANSFER, describing the light distribution inside the target medium resulting from the pulsed light irradiation and the potentially nonlinear optical effects under these conditions. The resulting temperature generation and associated thermal effects (damage) are described by the heat equation. Finally, the EXPANSION with rising temperature and resulting acoustic wave propagation is defined through the WAVE EQUATION; in three dimensions with changing boundary conditions due to the thermal effects and transient nature of the compression. Solving this problem analytically relies on clever choices for approximations, when possible. Generally during pulsed laser photoacoustic imaging the light is delivered over periods in the nano or femtosecond time frame, which creates several theoretically advantageous conditions. The equation of radiative transfer will incorporate the source function $S(\vec{r}, \vec{s})$, defining the laser bean incident on the medium under investigation, assuming standard Gaussian characteristics: $S(\vec{r}, \vec{s}) = I_0 \text{EXP}\left[-2r^2/w^2\right]$, where I_0 is the radiance at the center of the beam, w the beam waist, and r the radius from center of the beam. The time-dependent equation of radiative transfer can generally be solved by separating the anisotropic radiance in a direction-dependent term next to a diffuse term: $L(\mathbf{r}, \hat{\mathbf{s}}, t) = (1/4\pi)\Psi(\mathbf{r}, t) + (3/4\pi)\varpi F(\mathbf{r}, \hat{\mathbf{s}}')$. Here, the symbol F defines the direction-dependent (i.e., diffuse) radiance. The fraction of ENERGY scattered to that removed from the radiance stream is indicated by the albedo: ϖ, for pure absorption $\varpi = 0$, while for totally elastic, conservative SCATTERING $\varpi = 1$, which is a function of optical depth. The diffuse fluence rate can be calculated based on the DIFFUSION approximation of the equation of radiative transfer as $(1/c)\left(\partial L(\mathbf{r}, t)/\partial t\right) - \vec{s} \bullet \nabla L(\mathbf{r}, t) + \left[\mu_a(\vec{r}) + \mu_s(\vec{r})\right]L(\vec{r}, t) - \mu_s(\vec{r})\int_{4\pi} p(\hat{\mathbf{s}}, \vec{s}')L(\vec{r}, t)d\Omega' = S(\vec{r}, \vec{s}')$. Under the preferential short pulse conditions, the source $S(\vec{r}, \vec{s}', t)$ function for the laser pulse can be written as $S(\vec{r}, \vec{s}', t) = \delta(\vec{r})\delta(\vec{s})\delta(t)$; this is specifically allowed due to the fact that the thermal RELAXATION TIME is much longer than the pulse duration. Additionally, the SOLUTION for the equation of radiative transfer can be found under these conditions as a FOURIER SERIES. For example, using the speed of light ($v = 299792458/n_2$ m/s, n_2 the index of refraction for the medium [$n_2 = 1.35$ water]), within a laser pulse duration of 100 fs, the cluster of irradiating photons can travel approximately 22 µm. Generally, in a turbid medium there will be isotropic scattering, resulting in a significant DISPERSION. However, due to nonlinear effects and long wavelength (in the RED and near INFRARED), the scatter will be primarily in the forward direction with a scattering anisotropy factor of $g > 0.95$, providing only a slightly diverging beam. On the thermal aspects, assuming an output energy of only 9 nJ (commonly found for Q-switched lasers), the peak energy density will be 0.0076 J/cm^2, or 760 kW/m^2, heating up a focal volume. Generally, under these short-pulse conditions, only a slight temperature rise will be seen, avoiding vaporization and, depending on Young's modulus of the medium, also cracking can be avoided. In rigid media such as teeth, the potential for cracking under "long" pulse duration may still exist. The heat resulting from the laser light absorption will flow in the direction of any temperature gradient inside the sample. The steeper the temperature gradient, the more efficient the conversion from optical to acoustical energy. The instantaneous local temperature rise of the medium under the absorption of light is given by $\Delta T = \mu_a L/\rho C_p$. The temperature rise is directly proportional to the absorbed local light fluence rate $\mu_a L(\vec{r}, \vec{s}, t)$ divided by the local SPECIFIC HEAT C_p times the density ρ, where $\vec{L}(\vec{r}, \vec{s}, t)$ is the local radiance of light, and $\mu_a(\vec{r}, \vec{s}, t)$ is the optical absorption coefficient for the medium as a function of location, direction of propagation, and time. The temperature development $T(\vec{r}, t)$ can be calculated from the heat equation, ignoring the influence of flow of the medium itself, or through the presence of irrigation channels (which will be BLOOD vessels in biological media). The heat equation is written as $\nabla\left(k\nabla T(r, t)\right) = \rho C_p\left[\left(\partial T(r, t)/\partial t\right) + \tau\left(\partial^2 T(r, t)/\partial t^2\right)\right] - \mu_a L(r, t)$, where κ is the THERMAL CONDUCTIVITY and $\alpha_T = \kappa/C_p\rho$ is the thermal DIFFUSIVITY. In order to assess the full impact of the thermal LONGITUDINAL WAVE the thermal relaxation time $\tau = 1/4k\mu_a^2$ needs to be considered. For ultrashort laser pulses the thermal relaxation is in the order of $\tau_T \approx 1$ µs. Any event shorter than the thermal relaxation time can be considered QUASI-STEADY STATE, which is the case for femtosecond laser pulses allowing the time component of the source function to be approximated by a Delta distribution. As a result the second-order terms in the mathematical description, with respect to time, become negligible. The temperature distribution can hence be modeled by the HEAT TRANSFER equation as $\nabla^2 T(\vec{r}, t) - a^2\left[\partial T(\vec{r}, t)/\partial t\right] = -\left[S(\vec{r}, t)/\kappa\right]$, with boundary conditions $T(\vec{r}, 0) = T_0(\vec{r})$. The temperature solution follows in terms of GREEN'S FUNCTION ($G(x, t; \xi, \tau)$): $T(\vec{r}, t) = \int_0^t \int_V G(x, t; \xi, \tau) f(\xi, \tau) d\tau dV(\xi) - a^2 \int_V G(x, t; \xi, 0) T_0(\xi) dV(\xi)$, where $f(\xi, \tau)$ represents the heat source, modeled as a spatial GAUSSIAN DISTRIBUTION $f(\xi, \tau) = -\left[(1-R)/\kappa\tau_P\right]\mu_a J \exp[-\mu_a z] \exp\left[-2\rho^2/\omega^2\right]\delta(t)$, where $\omega(z) = \omega_0 \left[1 + \left(\lambda(z - z_0)/\pi\omega_0^2\right)^2\right]^{1/2}$, R is the surface reflectivity, J is the laser FLUX (J/cm^2), ω is the beam radius (cm), z_0 is the location of the minimum waist, λ is the wavelength, and τ_p is the laser pulse width. Under the short time approximation, the heat source is a POINT SOURCE with solution for the Green function: $G(x, t; \xi, \tau) = -\left[a^2/4\pi(t-\tau)\right]^{3/2}\left(1/a^2\right)\exp\left[-a^2|\vec{r} - \vec{\rho}|/(t-\tau)\right]$, where $\vec{\rho}$ is the radius in the

"Greens-medium." This yields the solution for the temperature under femtosecond laser-pulse RADIATION as $T = T_0 + \left(c_2\sqrt{\pi}d_1/4b_1^{3/2}\right)\exp\left[d_1^2/4b_1\right]$, using the following abbreviations: $b_1 = \left(a^2/4t\right) + \left(2/\omega^2\right)$, $d_1 = a^2r/2t$ and $c_2 = (1-R)\mu_a Je^{-az}\exp\left\{-a^2r^2/4t\right\}/2\sqrt{\pi}t\,ar\kappa\tau_p$. Two particular cases can be distinguished for the conditions of the media: (1) absorption > scattering (black-body); (2) scattering > absorption. For a "black-body," all the light emitted by the laser will be absorbed on the surface of the medium, negating the need for solving the RADIATIVE TRANSFER equation. Introducing the thermal relaxation length: $\ell_T = \tau_T v_{th}$, where v_{th} is the thermal propagation velocity of the medium; the thermal DIFFUSION LENGTH $\ell_D = \sqrt{2\left(\alpha_T/v_{laser}\right)}$, where v_{laser} is the laser repetition rate. All these conditions provide the platform for a confined process, both spatially and temporally. It can be shown that under confinement the THERMAL EXPANSION length will be much smaller than the diffusion length. Additionally, the thermal diffusion length is also smaller than the thermal relaxation length. These conditions provide the simplification that the second-order derivatives in most equations will become zero. This can be verified by making Taylor expansions for all the parameters, which yields infinitesimally small second- and higher-order terms. As a result the thermal diffusion/propagation can be neglected in the heat equation, which can be shown to hold true after the Fourier expansion of the quadratic initial heat equation. The heat equation hence reduces to $\rho C_p\left(\partial T/\partial t\right) = \mu_a L(\mathbf{r},t)\delta(t)$. The third declaration describing the temperature impact on the displacement and as such the longitudinal pressure WAVE is defined based on the medium parameters, including Young's modulus E and the cubic expansion coefficient β (which is three times the linear expansion coefficient: 3α) delivering the displacement u as $\rho\left(\partial^2 u/\partial t^2\right) - \left[E/2(1+\upsilon_p)\right]\nabla^2 u - \left[E/2(1+\upsilon_p)(1-2\upsilon_p)\right]\nabla\left(\nabla u\right) = -E\beta/3(1-2\upsilon_p)\nabla\theta$. The parameter υ_p represents the Poisson ratio, the ratio of the transverse contraction strain to the longitudinal extension strain in the direction of the stretching force: $\upsilon_p = -\varepsilon_{trans}/\varepsilon_{longitudinal}$. The Poisson ratio is a material constant. In the "far-field" theoretical analysis of the ULTRASOUND photoacoustic IMAGE formation, the following assumptions will be made. These conditions will subsequently be adjusted and refined based on the observed deviations from these approximations (requiring an iteration process based on the lack of knowledge of the real local parameters; deviating from the assumed conditions): (1) All calculations are performed in the Fraunhofer region, that is, in the far field; (2) in the far field the waves can be treated as plane waves; (3) the square of the received acoustic AMPLITUDE is directly linearly proportional to the scattered energy; (4) the scattered acoustic longitudinal pressure wave pattern is weak relative to the "photothermal" generated instantaneous pressure. The pressure wave may be converted into displacement, since the pressure is directly proportional to the square of the displacement. The medium will oscillate with a local RESONANCE FREQUENCY (ν) that is defined by the characteristic length of the confined segments under consideration, the value of Young's modulus (E_Y), and the local density distribution can be expressed as $\upsilon = C\sqrt{E_Y/\rho}\left(d/w \times h\right)$, with d the depth, w the width, and h the height of the structure of the medium. C denotes a constant that is a function of the MOMENT OF INERTIA (I) of the structure; alternatively, $\nu = A\sqrt{\left(E_Y I/m_\ell L^4\right)} \cong A'\sqrt{\left(E_Y/\rho L^2\right)}$, where L represents the length of the sides of a cube of the medium, m_ℓ is the mass per unit length, and A is a constant that depends on the mode of excitation. The use of the moment of inertia is justified since during the tissue expansion process a VORTEX will be formed. With respect to the vortex formation, there will be strain due to the change in volume (ΔV) with respect to the initial volume (V): $\varepsilon = \Delta V/V$. This is inherently linked to the temperature jump, as described by the volume expansion coefficient: β, $\Delta V = \beta V \Delta T$, giving $\varepsilon = \beta\Delta T$. The stress in the medium equals the force per unit area, which by definition describes pressure. Hence the pressure associated with this strain is expressed as $P = -K_{bulk}\varepsilon$, where K_{bulk} represents the bulk modulus that specifies the pressure per unit strain. The photoacoustic wave equation in the medium resulting from the light absorption can be derived from the momentum equation, the EQUATION OF CONTINUITY, and the EQUATION OF STATE. The three equations reduce to the following three conditions: $\left[\partial\rho(r,t)/\partial\tau\right] + \nabla \bullet\left[\rho V(\mathbf{r},t)\right] = -\int_{t_0}^{t_1} S(\mathbf{r},t)/\mathbf{r}^2\delta\tau$, $\left[\beta(\mathbf{r})/\rho_0 C_0^3\right]\rho\left[\partial V(\mathbf{r},t)/\partial\tau\right] - \left(V(\mathbf{r},t) \bullet \nabla\right)V(\mathbf{r},t) + \nabla \bullet P(\mathbf{r},t) = \nabla S(\mathbf{r},t)$, and $P(\mathbf{r},t) = K\rho^i$. Here, $V(\vec{\mathbf{r}},t)$ is the displacement velocity and $P(\vec{\mathbf{r}},t)$ is the acoustic pressure amplitude of the primary (ultrasonic) wave. The acoustic propagation resulting from photoacoustic excitation and the associated imaging aspects are very similar to ULTRASONIC IMAGING. The main difference with ultrasound imaging is that under photoacoustic imaging the acoustic source is less well defined and requires specialized sensory placement and SIGNAL acquisition design techniques to gain access to the three-dimensional information. The initial pressure $P_0(\vec{\mathbf{r}},t)$, resulting from laser absorption is defined as $P_0(\vec{\mathbf{r}},t) = G_r K\beta\left[\mu_a \vec{L}(\vec{r},\vec{s},t)/\rho C_p\right]$. Using the correction factor, G_r, which expresses the fraction of thermal energy from the absorbed light that is converted into mechanical expansion. With photoacoustic imaging, soft biological media such as blood vessels can be mapped. Frequently, ultrasonic imaging of soft tissues in biology required the use of a chemical being inserted into the patient as a contrast enhancement that may become obsolete under photoacoustic imaging. Other diagnostic applications are in thin-film thickness determination and associated quality control in semiconductor manufacturing and the automobile and airplane industry.

Photobiological process

[biomedical, chemical, optics, thermodynamics] Light mediated biological/biochemical effect including the PHOTOSYNTHESIS in plants and animals, as well as photoperiodism, phototaxis, and phototropism. A very special class is VISION. Other extended applications are found under LOW-LEVEL-LIGHT THERAPY (LLT).

Photobleaching

[biomedical, chemical, optics] The optical modification of the electromagnetic characteristics of a MOLECULE. Often photobleaching involves the destruction of dyes, or the SATURATION of the absorption with resulting decrease in SCATTERING of LIGHT or specifically the reduction or extinction of fluorescent transitions. Photobleaching indicates the temporary loss of a fluorophore to fluoresce as a result of PHOTON-induced chemical damage and on a molecular level the covalent modification. The covalent modification consists of the saturation of the transition from an excited SINGLET STATE to the excited TRIPLET STATE. During the FLUORESCENCE process, fluorophores may be induced to interact with another molecule and inadvertently produce irreversible covalent modifications. The triplet state is relatively long-lived with respect to the energetic singlet state. Hence excited molecules will experience a much longer time frame to endure chemical reactions with environmental constituents. The average number of excitation and emission cycles allowed for a particular fluorophore is generally dependent on the molecular structure as well as the local environment. Certain fluorophores may bleach rapidly after emitting merely a few photons. Other molecules can perform millions of fluorescence cycles before bleaching. The deliberate extinction of fluorescence with the ensuing fluorescent recovery is one particular application of photobleaching used for physiological imaging in biological applications, specifically with respect to the protein binding analysis for the CELL MEMBRANE; called fluorescence recovery after photobleaching (FRAP) imaging (*also see* "FADING").

Photocathode

[electronics, imaging] Light sensitive negatively charged ELECTRODE that releases electrons when ELECTROMAGNETIC RADIATION is incident, such as that used in the design of a PHOTOMULTIPLIER TUBE. The electrode may be treated with specific materials to increase the sensitivity to LIGHT and encourage the PHOTOELECTRIC EFFECT on the surface, releasing an electron in free space.

Photochemical effect

[biomedical, chemical, optics] In VISION it has been shown that in contrast to the slow overall phenomenological mechanism of vision there are events in ROD and CONE sensibility that take place in the femtosecond and even picosecond range. The vision experience itself is however in the 20–100 Hz range for the various species. The physiochemical process of the PHOTOCHEMICAL EFFECT in the RETINA is in the same range as the PHOTOELECTRIC EFFECT.

Photochemical reaction

[biomedical, chemical, optics, thermodynamics] *See* LOW LEVEL LIGHT THERAPY.

Photocoagulation

[biomedical, optics] The conversion of PHOTON energy into MECHANICAL ENERGY (i.e., THERMAL ENERGY). The process describes the thermal denaturation of proteins to kill cells, either unwanted or potentially harmful, by means of destruction of the cellular membrane or the NUCLEUS of the CELL. The initial attempts of the clinical use of photocoagulation can be traced back to the eighteenth century, by means of reflecting sunlight. Sunlight was channeled from the roof of the hospital in the operating rooms by means of mirrors and lenses. Prior to that, the healing potential of LIGHT was used by the Egyptians and Greek around the beginning of the western calendar. Other use of bright broad-band light such as the incandescent light or even still sunlight for clinical applications was in use for welding detached retina in the EYE, specifically in response to retinal detachment in diabetics in the early twentieth century. Other applications, also in the eye (primarily lending itself due to its optical transparency), were for the treatment of intraocular tumors. With the introduction of laser light, optical treatment procedures became more proficient due to the potential for selecting the most appropriate wavelength, resulting in minimized peripheral damage. The photocoagulation process specifically relies on the conversion of photon energy in thermal energy. The light absorption in the medium is a direct function of the light distribution as a function location with a tissue volume on a three-dimensional pattern, calculated using the TRANSPORT EQUATION or EQUATION OF RADIATIVE TRANS-FER. Examples of other specific application of photocoagulation are wrinkle reduction/removal, tattoo removal, hair removal, and the removal of port-wine stains on human SKIN, and thermal superficial cancer tissue removal next to nonthermal deep cancer treatment (*see* PHOTODYNAMIC THERAPY), while minimizing the formation of scar tissue resulting from thermal burns to the peripheral tissues. Other applications are in tissue welding, providing an elegant manner for wound closure. Tissue welding is gaining popularity in the treatment of vascular diseases by a transcatheter approach. One particular application of vascular tissue welding is in anastomosis, joining vessels together that re-route the BLOOD flow, for instance in solving poor CIRCULATION in the legs or for SHUNT application in the arm, to be used during the process of connecting a patient to an external filtration system during KIDNEY dialysis. There are a number of ways to perform tissue welding: (1) through photothermal heating of the tissue itself, (2) by means of a solder or a photoactivated adhesive, or (3) by combining a LIQUID solder and a solid solder. Commonly used LIQUID solder agents are ALBUMIN and blood. Solid solders include insertion of biodegradable POLYMER thin films. To enhance the photoselective coagulation process, dyes can be used to achieve wavelength selective absorption. Direct laser welding relies on coagulating tissue proteins. The main advantage is that the tissues repair fast, with little or no foreign body reaction, and generally the seals are watertight. Disadvantages may be low acute strength, compared to a suture, and thermal damage to the tissue. The use of CHROMOPHORE-enhanced protein "solders" can augment the welding process, improving acute wound strength. Solders include polymers such as the biodegradable PLGA (polylactic-co-glycolic acid) as well as a liquid albumin solder. Additionally, the protein cross-linker genipin added to albumin solder results in a stronger tissue weld. Other welding agents are indocyanine green doped albumin (derived from bovine serum colored green to enhance absorption at the near INFRARED wavelengths used). Especially in vascular welding there is a frequent need for solder. Other factors involved in the welding efficiency are the thickness of the media d and the absorbed laser energy over the duration of exposure t. Before getting into the photothermal concepts, two definitions need to be introduced: enthalpy and entropy. Enthalpy H defines the energy of the chemical bonds between the atoms that constitute the molecules within the system. The entropy of the system is defined by the change in INTERNAL ENERGY divided by the temperature of the system at the time, as $dS = dQ/T$. The FIRST LAW OF THERMODYNAMICS postulates that energy cannot be destroyed nor generated. The work done on a system combined with the administered heat hence r is the temperature in kelvin and esults in a change in internal energy: $dU = dQ - dW$. The laser/light energy deposited in the tissue will be absorbed and hence raise the local temperature. The energy deposition as well as the temperature rise can induce chemical reactions by means of changing the enthalpy of a system. The biological system consists of the atoms that form the complex molecules providing the building blocks of amino acids, carbohydrates, fats, and proteins. The deposited light energy is considered the reaction enthalpy, where the change in enthalpy is the final system enthalpy minus the enthalpy of the initial state of the system. TEMPERATURE EFFECTS OF LIGHT-TISSUE INTERACTION: the amount of photon energy conversion into thermal energy in the propagation process for the light in tissue is based on the absorption coefficient and the total attenuation coefficient. The locally generated temperature rise will result in heat flow due to a thermal gradient. The HEAT TRANSFER Q can be calculated at any given point in the tissue based on the local temperature gradient

$\Delta T/\text{length} = \left[(d/dx) + (d/dx) + (d/dx)\right]T = \nabla T$, yielding $Q = -k_T\left[(d/dx) + (d/dx) + (d/dx)\right]T = -k_T\nabla T$,

where T is the temperature in kelvin and k_T is the THERMAL CONDUCTIVITY, on average 0.5 W m^{-1} K^{-1} for water-based tissue. This heat transfer process is time dependent: $\rho c_V \left(\partial T / \partial t \right) = \nabla \left(k_T \nabla T \right)$, where ρ is the tissue density, for most tissues it is $1.04 \times 10^3 \, \mathrm{kg \, m^{-3}}$, and c_V is the heat capacity, approximately on average $3.7 \times 10^3 \, \mathrm{J \, kg^{-1} \, K^{-1}}$. Incorporating the laser heat source q resulting from the light absorption gives $\rho c_V \left(\partial T / \partial t \right) = \nabla \left(k_T \nabla T \right) + q$, where q equals the rate of energy deposited in a volume of tissue cells, which is the local fluence rate (i.e., the location- and time-dependent light distribution) times the local absorption coefficient $\mu_a L(r, \theta, z)$. Additionally, in a full analysis the heat transfer resulting from blood PERFUSION should be included due to the abundance of blood vessels in all living tissues. Including blood perfusion in the energy balance for heat will incorporate the flow rate of the blood ω_b, in $\mathrm{m^3 \, kg^{-1} \, s^{-1}}$; the density of the blood ρ_b; the SPECIFIC HEAT of blood c_b; and the heat exchange between the heated tissue and blood is based on the temperature difference between the blood and the surrounding tissue: $T - T_b$, to yield a blood flow heat loss as $-\omega_b \rho_b c_b \rho (T - T_b)$. Combining all the characteristics and phenomena describing the tissue temperature evolution as a function of time an expression can be obtained, known as THE HEAT EQUATION, respectively bioheat equation: $\left(\partial T / \partial t \right) = \left(1 / \rho c_V \right) \left[q + k_T \left[\left(\partial^2 / \partial x^2 \right) + \left(\partial^2 / \partial y^2 \right) + \left(\partial^2 / \partial z^2 \right) \right] T - \omega_b \rho_b c_b \rho (T - T_b) \right] = \left(1 / \rho c_V \right) \left[k_T \nabla^2 T - \omega_b \rho_b c_b \rho (T - T_b) + q \right]$. In the process of raising the tissue temperature, other phenomena will take place, such as coagulation and EVAPORATION, which are both heat sinks that need to be accounted for. The coagulation process encompasses both a temperature rise and a PHASE TRANSITION. The phase transition for coagulation has a LATENT HEAT that is tissue specific: h_{coag} and is expressed in $\mathrm{J \, kg^{-1}}$. The heat loss due to coagulation, Q_{coag}, is a direct function of the coagulated tissue volume V_t and the tissue density ρ_t, providing the coagulated tissue mass, defining $Q_{coag} = h_{coag} \rho_t V_t$. The heat loss due to evaporation is defined by the rate of water loss. Note that for cosmetic surgery the material under consideration may be either partially composed of fat or solely, with its own thermodynamic characteristics. The heat loss due to evaporation is the rate of evaporation multiplied by the latent heat of evaporation (water $h_{ev,W} = 2.26 \times 10^6 \, \mathrm{J \, kg^{-1}}$), which yields $Q_W = V_W \left(\rho_{W,\infty} - \rho_{W,S} \right) h_{ev,W}$, where V_W is the volume of evaporated water, $\rho_{W,S}$ is the mass density of saturated water VAPOR at the surface of the evaporation surface (e.g., vapor BUBBLE), and $\rho_{W,\infty}$ is the vapor mass density outside the biological tissue (i.e., cell). Because of the fact that evaporation inside the cell with the CELL MEMBRANE intact changes the internal pressure (sometime reaching several hundred ATMOSPHERE), thus affecting the thermodynamic parameters in the process as a dynamic system. The local metabolic heat generation can generally be neglected. Integration of the heat equation over a volume of tissue yields $V \rho c_V \, \partial T / \partial t = \iint_s k_T \nabla^2 T * \vec{n} \bullet d\vec{s} - V \omega_b \rho_b c_b \rho (T - T_b) + qV - \dot{Q}_W - \dot{Q}_{coag}$, where the volume of heated tissue has a surface area s, $\vec{n}$ is the normal to the surface of the area over which heat is radiated out, and $\dot{Q}_W$ and $\dot{Q}_{coag}$ are the rate of heat loss due to coagulation as well as evaporation (i.e., dehydration), respectively. Because of the DYNAMICS of the local light distribution and the changing thermodynamic parameter, the heat equation generally requires solving numerically by stepwise integration over time to produce the temperature distribution within the full length of the duration of laser irradiation. The tissue is therefore divided into volumetric units that are homogeneous and in steady state during the integration step duration. These volume ELEMENTS are called voxels. The VOXEL dimensions close to the laser impact will need to be smaller than that at large diffusion DISTANCE. This is referred to as a finite ELEMENT method in mathematical procedures. In the tissue, the volume element, voxel v_{ijk}, will yield a finite time description for the temperature, assuming in first-order noncompeting processes in three dimensions as $\partial^2 T / \partial x^2 = \left(T_{i+1} - T_i + T_{i-1} \right) / \left[(i+1) - i \left(i - (i-1) \right) \right]; \partial^2 T / \partial y^2 = \left(T_{i+j1} - T_j + T_{j-1} \right) / \left[(j+1) - j \left(j - (j-1) \right) \right]$; and $\partial^2 T / \partial z^2 = \left(T_{k+1} - T_k + T_{k-1} \right) / \left[(k+1) - k \left(k - (k-1) \right) \right]$. Stepping through the NUMERICAL process will provide the change in temperature due to energy deposition by laser irradiation in tissue while accounting for all inherent losses. The next stage in the determination of thermal damage is the calculation of the degree of tissue degeneration as a function of local temperature MAGNITUDE and exposure time.

photocoagulation: coagulation can be reversible or irreversible. Whether a process is reversible or not depends on the total amount of energy delivered and the time frame over which the total amount of energy is administered. In general, chemical reaction takes place in infinitesimally small temporal steps and the ensuing changes in chemical composition take place gradually and can be considered reversible. In a reversible process, the system is always at equilibrium, and will revert to the starting conditions when no additional energy deposited, subsequently releasing the energy that was initially deposited. REVERSIBLE

PHOTOCOAGULATION: in a REVERSIBLE PHOTOCOAGULATION process the changes to the molecular bond configuration can revert back to the original state without resulting in a change in entropy. Histological examination may under these conditions reveal changes that are not classified as denaturation. Reversible damage constitutes cell membranes that are still intact and a surviving nucleus. Under normal conditions the reversibly damaged region will be equivalent to normal healthy tissue after a healing period. Typical proteins have an energy range in which they are stable. For instance, the range of stability between folded and unfolded protein strands is resilient from 7 to 15 kcal/mol of added heat at 37°C. This stability energy level is defined as the (Gibbs) free energy of the protein. IRREVERSIBLE PHOTOCOAGULATION: the process of IRREVERSIBLE PHOTOCOAGULATION is defined by either or both the destruction of the cell membrane and/or nucleus. Including the SECOND LAW OF THERMODYNAMICS it will follow that for an irreversible process in an ISOLATED SYSTEM the entropy will by definition increase: $\Delta S = S_{final} - S_{innitial} > 0$. The molecular disorder associated with the increase in ENTROPY (S) has been defined by LUDWIG EDUARD BOLTZMANN (1844–1906) as the natural log of the number of all possible configurations within a system ω_c, multiplied by the Boltzmann constant: $S = k \ln \omega_c$. An equilibrium condition corresponds to $\partial S = 0$, where S represents the maximum attainable entropy. In order to describe the process of photocoagulation providing irreversible damage, the internal energy of the molecules that constitute the tissue needs to be considered. The change in internal energy of a system exposed to external influences is defined as the change in enthalpy for the molecular system $\Delta H = U + \Delta(PV)$, incorporating the work done by changing volume and/or pressure $\Delta(PV)$, which, under constant pressure, becomes the volume labor: $P\Delta V$. Incorporating the IDEAL GAS LAW ($PV = nRT$), this transforms to a chemical reaction: $\Delta H = U + \Delta nRT$, where Δn equals the change in molecules resulting from the (thermally induced) chemical reaction, and $R = 8.3144621\,\mathrm{J/mol\,K}$ is the universal gas constant. The temperature of the system (T) is measured in kelvin. The enthalpy change in an EXOTHERMIC REACTION of a system is considered to be negative, which entails that the chemical reaction produces heat. PHOTOCOAGULATION will constitute an endothermic reaction, where heat is absorbed, rendering the change in enthalpy for the system positive. The change in free energy of the system (Gibb's free energy: G) combining the enthalpy and entropy and yields $\Delta G = \Delta U - T\Delta S - S\Delta T + \Delta nRT + nR\Delta T$. Building on this the chemical process of denaturation is described as follows: $\Delta G_{den} = \Delta H_{den} - T\Delta S_{den}$, which applying the chemical process $aA + bB = cC + dD$ $\Delta G = xJ$ yields $\Delta G_{den} = \Delta G_{native} + RT \ln \left[[C]^c [D]^d / [A]^a [B]^b \right]$, where $[A]$ and $[B]$ represent the respective native molecular concentrations, and $[C]$ and $[D]$ are the concentrations of the denatured states for the molecules involved in the respective processes. Using the fact that the entropy change ΔS_{den} will be positive, it can be shown that $\Delta S_{den} = k \ln \left(\omega_{c,denatured} / \omega_{c,native} \right)$, where $\omega_{c,native}$ is the fraction of native (protein) molecules and $\omega_{c,denatured}$ the fraction of ensuing denatured molecules resulting from the administered heat. The fact that the entropy change will be positive is the result of the fact that denatured proteins will have more configurations available than the native proteins: $\omega_{denatured} / \omega_{native} \gg 1$. In comparison, when the temperature is high enough, the change in free energy will be negative, implying that the denatured state is stable at high temperature and that the native state is stable at low temperature. In the process of photocoagulation, the energy deposited by the laser light is the activation energy used by the denaturation process. An example of the reaction process with hypothetical energy levels. The standard Gibbs energy difference between the transition state from GROUND STATE to product for the reactants is calculated from the experimental rate constant k_r based on the conventional form of the Eyring absolute rate equation. The EYRING ABSOLUTE RATE EQUATION relies on the fact that the energy for each reaction is subject to QUANTUM THEORY due to the discrete nature of the chemical reactions: $\Delta G = RT \left[\ln(k/h) - \ln(k_r/T) \right]$, where k is the Boltzmann constant and h the PLANCK CONSTANT ($k/h = 2.08358 \times 10^{10}\,\mathrm{K^{-1}\,s^{-1}}$). The values of the rate constants, and hence Gibbs energies of activation, will depend on the choice of concentration units, and the choice of thermodynamic ground state of the chemical medium. The standard enthalpy of activation for the process is $\Delta^{\ddagger}H^0$, which represents the enthalpy change in the rate equation obtained from conventional transition state theory. Alternatively, the quantity $\Delta^{\ddagger}S^0$ represents the standard entropy of activation. Solving the chemical process for change in molecular quantity, Δn yields an expression for the PROBABILITY of conversion between the native protein state and the denatured state k_r, defined as $k_r = \left(kT/h \right) e^{\Delta^{\ddagger}S^0/R} e^{-\Delta^{\ddagger}H^0/(RT)}$, also written as $k_r = A' e^{-E^*/(RT)}$.

The empirical reaction constants A' and E^* can be defined based on the fact that the rate of change for the transition from the native protein state to the denatured state takes place at kT/h; this provides $A' = (kT/h)e^{\Delta S/R}$ and $E^* = \Delta H$. Generally, these constants are experimentally determined since there is not merely a single MOLECULE involved in the denaturation process for a biological specimen. The denaturation process is verified either by functional analysis (in situ) or by identified of histological markers of nuclear destruction. DAMAGE INTEGRAL: the numerical expression for achieving irreversible tissue damage can be derived from the so-called damage integral. The damage integral calculates the loss of normal tissue based on a standard reaction equation, transforming into the denatured state:

$$\Omega(t) = \ln\left[N_{\text{total}}\right]/\left(\left[N_{\text{total}}\right] - \left[N_{\text{denatured}}\right]\right) = A'\int_0^t \exp\left(-E^*/RT\right)dt,$$ where $\left[N_{\text{total}}\right]$ defines the total number of cells in the tissue volume that is subject to irradiated by light and $\left[N_{\text{denatured}}\right]$ the number of denatured cells post laser irradiation. On a more complex scale, this is defined as follows. When there are initially N_0 molecules of one molecular species in a volume of tissue, the number of surviving molecules is proportional to the native number, and the rate of denaturation dN obeys the heuristic equation $dN = k_r N dt$. The number of surviving native molecules as part of the denaturation process as a function of time is defined as $N(t) = N_o e^{-\Omega(t)}$, where $\Omega(t) = \int_0^t k_r(t')dt' = \int_0^t \left[kT(t)/h\right]e^{\Delta S/R}e^{-\Delta H/(RT(t))}dt'$. The expression $\Omega(t)$ is called the damage integral for the coagulation process. At any time during the photocoagulation process, the number of denatured molecules, $N_{\text{denatured}}(t)$, equals $N_0 - N(t)$. Thus, the damage integral incorporates the average values of all molecules involved in the denaturation process but specified by tissue section. The rate value k_r depends on the temperature of exposure and the values of ΔS and ΔH, which are characteristic for most measurable transitions in the chemical processes for the respective tissue. Examples of chemical transitions are the coagulation of egg white (cooking an egg, which may be performed by MICROWAVE ELECTROMAGNETIC RADIATION), the irreversible loss of enzymatic ACTIVITY that involves denaturation of labile proteins, and the whitening of soft tissues such as MUSCLE or LIVER during cooking (grilling out, frying pan, or using electromagnetic radiation: INFRARED lamps, laser, microwave). Each of these processes involves denaturation as well as the AGGREGATION process for proteins. The coagulation of collagenous tissue will yield gelatin, which involves the loss of collagen fiber bundle structure, such as that used for wrinkle removal. The rate constant kr at a given temperature will have a value that is specific for different transitions. For example, second-degree burns can be captured by a value $\Omega > 10$, and for third-degree burns the value $\Omega > 10\,000$ is generally accepted. The more complex the molecular structure that is involved in the denaturation process, the steeper the change in rate constant with temperature. This change is due to the fact that the change in entropy (ΔS) is greater in addition to the fact that the number of bonds are being broken concurrently at a larger number (ΔH). The rate constant k_r for each tissue will vary as a function of temperature. In the denaturation process, generally the exposure time (t_Ω [s]) required to achieve $\Omega = 1$ is one of the parameters of interest. This exposure time is by definition $k_r = 1/t_\Omega$. When denaturing a less structured tissue, the chemical matrix will DECAY more gradually, with an associated change in rate constant due to the less vigilant changes in ΔS and ΔH in response to the temperature changes. The molecular structure involved in an irreversible thermal transition (denaturation) has in first-order approximation an entropy ΔS release linearly related to the enthalpy change ΔH for that particular transition. The enthalpy change ΔH describes an independent variable that is conceptually integral to the energy of all bonds that cooperatively provide the cohesive force for a molecular structure. The increase in entropy is generally considered to be a dependent variable, associated with the bond-breaking energy change. Examples of published average empirical values for tissues are skin $E^* = 627$ kJ mol^{-1}, $A' = 3.10 \times 10^{98}$ s^{-1}; and collagen $E^* = 89$ kJ mol^{-1}, $A' = e^{130}$ s^{-1}. The DAMAGE STATE: the damage region $0 \le \Omega(t) \le 0.53$ is generally considered to be reversible, or rather will not cause any (permanent) damage whatsoever to the tissue. The damage range $0.53 < \Omega(t) < 5$ will provide tissue coagulation. Generally, $\Omega(t) < 1$ can be used to define reversible tissue damage. A value of $\Omega(t) = 4.6$ represents the condition providing 99% probability of tissue denaturation. At $\Omega(t) > 5$, the tissue is susceptible to carbonization. Based on this, the following timelines can be projected for exposure to extreme solar energy (desert conditions): a second-degree burn resulting from skin

exposure to 135°C yields a time exposure of approximately 2.5 min, while a third-degree burn can be expected after exposure lasting in excess of on the order of 1 day and 18 h. The time–temperature correlation associated with final irreversible damage is one critical factor in the assessment process with respect to the thermal damage (see Figure P.66).

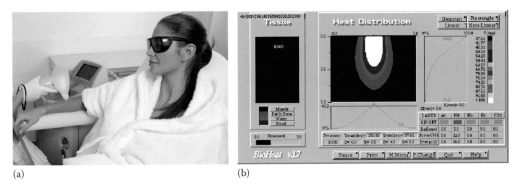

(a) (b)

Figure P.66 (a) Port-wine stain removal. (b) Photocoagulation process for port-wine stain computational model.

Photocopy

[general] Process that transfers a charge density image of a real paper image over on role that is coated with ink, with ink density proportional to charge density, from which the ink is transferred to paper in a printing process: rolled over the paper (Xerox process). The charge distribution is achieved through a corona process, which generates an intense flash of LIGHT that ionizes the photographic role or alternatively the paper directly. Alternatively, the paper itself is ionized and the ink (toner) is directly transferred to the paper (electrostatic process). The charge density is the result of an ionic transfer process based on a flash discharge (corona) in the early devices. The process is used to generate a gray-scale/black and white copy of an illustration or object. The photocopy process has evolved to the use of laser scanners to scan original paper or object that is targeted for image formation on paper. The transfer of ink to regular paper has an efficiency of better than 90%. Dry paper can hold a charge distribution for several seconds, allowing the charged toner (ink) to adhere in a proportional fashion. The fusing process following the deposition will make the IMAGE permanent. Fusing can be accomplished by pressure, which is generally achieved by running the paper between two hot rollers. The FUSION process with the paper takes place at around 130°C. Thermal fixation with radiant heat alone is not very efficient due to the reflectivity of most paper materials. In a more elaborate process, the use of a spray-on fixative (e.g., EVAPORATION) is applied prior to the pressure roller process. The same process is used to transfer an image into a two-dimensional digital array for FAX transmission. The machine that performs the process is called a photocopier. Photocopy MACHINES are also known as Xerox machine, based on the success of the largest manufacturer, and patent holder, in the early glory days. The dry photocopy process was first introduced in 1938 by the physicist Chester Carlson (1906–1968), working for the Haloid Photographic Corporation, renamed to the Xerox Corporation in 1961. The dry process stands in contrast to wet printing used in the early days of newspaper printing where an etched plate is wetted with ink that is transferred to paper. The etched plate is mounted on a roller, which allows multiple prints with the identical image to be generated without the need for elaborate technology. The earliest form of physical paper printing from a

carved plate (wood plate to be exact) is documented to have been performed in China around the year 200. The automated printing press dates to 1453 (*also see* LITHOGRAPHY) (see Figure P.67).

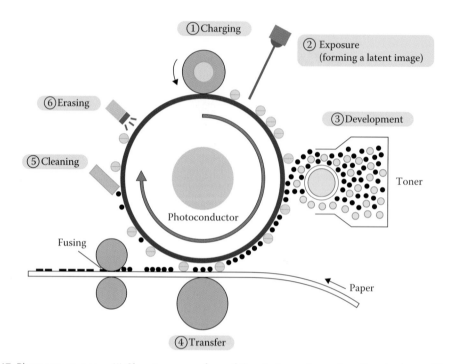

Figure P.67 Photocopy process: (1) Charging—e surface of the photoconductor is uniformly charged by the charging device; (2) Exposure—e document to be copied is illuminated and its image projected onto the photoconductor to form a latent image; (3) Development—e charged toner particles are attracted to the latent image, forming a visible image on the photoconductor; (4) Transfer—e toner image is transferred to the paper. In other step, the toner image is permanently fused to the paper; (5) Cleaning—Any remaining toner is removed from the photoconductor surface; (6) Erasing—e photoconductor surface is exposed to light to remove any remaining electrostatic charge. (Courtesy of Fuji Xerox.)

Photocurrent

[general] Electron current resulting from interaction of ELECTROMAGNETIC RADIATION with a material. The material can be artificial or natural. Examples are zinc as a natural material or silicone and germanium as a man-made medium (*see* PHOTOELECTRIC EFFECT).

Photodetector

[electronics, optics] Device that converts ELECTROMAGNETIC RADIATION into electrical current by either releasing valence electrons (i.e., PHOTOCURRENT) or by generating an electrical potential (electromotive force) that will generate a flow of electrons when a circuit is completed. Examples of photodetectors are photoconductors, junction photodetectors, and avalanche photodetectors. Photoconductors will change resistance under the influence of electromagnetic RADIATION, moving additional electrons to the VALENCE BAND. Junction photodetectors are for instance the SCHOTTKY DIODE, respectively layered Positive-Intrinsic-Negative doped (PIN) diodes, and Metal-Semiconductor-Metal (MSM) stacked diode. Avalanche photodetectors operate based on ionization efficiency, more specifically the difference in ionization between two materials. The IONIZATION process is the result of the quantum-well mechanism (see Figure P.68).

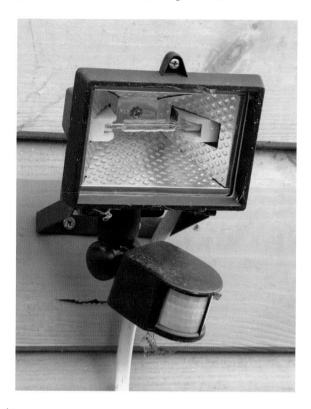

Figure P.68 Microchip light sensor.

Photodisintegration

[atomic, nuclear] High-energy electromagnetic interaction on a NUCLEON level. The interaction cross-section can be described using Lorentz invariance as $\int_0^\infty \left[\sigma^p(k) - \sigma^A(k) \right] dk/k = 2\pi^2\alpha S_t \left[K_t / m_t \right]^2$, where $\sigma^p(k)$ is the inelastic photon CROSS SECTION for polarized LIGHT parallel interacting with the target spin (S_t), $\sigma^p(k)$ is the inelastic PHOTON cross section for polarized light on antiparallel interacting with the target spin, K_t the anomalous MAGNETIC moment of the target, m_t the target mass, $k = 2\pi/\lambda$ the wave-number, λ the wavelength, and α a condition constant. One specific interaction is described for the photo-disintegration of a DEUTERON.

Photodynamic therapy (PDT)

[biomedical, chemical, energy, optics] The use of LIGHT to affect biological properties. The use of light to treat medical conditions and general SKIN disorders has been documented as far back as approximately 1550 BC in the Ebers papyrus to treat pigmentation disorders assumed to be associated with leprosy. The PDT applications for clinical use on smallpox was described by the physician HENRI DE MONDEVILLE (1260–1320). More in-depth work on photodynamics interaction was described by OSCAR RAAB (1876–1986) and his work under the guidance of Hermann von Tappeiner (1847–1927) based on the PHOTOTOXICITY by Marcacci in 1888. In cancer treatment, photodynamic therapy uses a chemical mediator that produces unstable and aggressive singlet oxygen, which rapidly oxidizes cells and effectively kills the cell. The efficacy of the photodynamic therapy is dependent on the wavelength of the light used with respect to the activation biochemical as well as the tissues the light is required to pass through to reach the target locations below the surface of the biological medium. The photosensitizer must adhere to several criteria to ensure efficiency: selective uptake in the tumor, activation by specific wavelengths that will penetrate deep into the tissue. The photochemical cannot be toxic by itself, and it has to have the capability to destroy malignant tissue growths once activated. The effectiveness of the photosensitizer depends largely on the localization of the drug in the tumor, and the light transmittance of the tissue that surrounds the tumor, at the activation wavelength. The PDT treatment is hence a function of the SOLUTION to the EQUATION OF RADIATIVE TRANSFER, as well as the conversion efficiency on a chemical level. One particularly important clinical application of PDT is in brain tumor. Generally, the spear and uptake of the photosensitive dyes (i.e., photoporphyrins) are not selective and will easily be distributed wherever BLOOD flow is available, thus using the local perfusion as an indication of the local photoporphyrin concentration. Certain photoporphyrins are designed to selectively bind to brain tumors, taking advantage of certain modifications in the blood–brain BARRIER due the tumor presence. Under normal/healthy conditions the photochemical will not be allowed to pass the blood–brain barrier based on the PHYSIOLOGY of this particular part of the CIRCULATION (see Figure P.69).

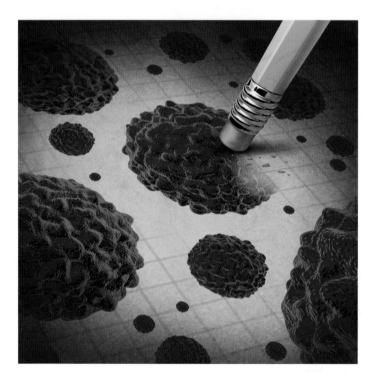

Figure P.69 Photodynamic laser therapy for cancer treatment using deep penetrating light and photoactivated chemicals that are concentrated in the cancer tissue volume.

Photoelasticity

[optics, mechanics] A material property with respect to the optical characteristics of an anisotropic medium wherein incoming single beam of unpolarized LIGHT enters into an medium where at the interface it is split into two rays traveling in different directions. The primary ray (called the ordinary ray) will be transmitted through the medium unchanged. A second ray is also formed in the BIREFRINGENCE process called the extraordinary ray, which is refracted at an ANGLE and will emerge at a different angle and location from the opposite side of the medium. Examples of materials that are naturally birefringent are calcite crystal, frozen water (ice), sapphire, QUARTZ, and a wide selection of PLASTICS. Under the concept of *photoelasticity* optically transparent materials that are ordinarily not double refracting (birefringent) can be made to be birefringent under influence of applied stress. Examples of such materials are certain types of GLASS (BK7), CELLOPHANE, lucite and BAKELITE. The optical change, specifically the mechanically induced photoelasticity, can be used for quality control issues, highlighting location-specific discontinuities in the transparent patterns, specifically the spectral distribution, and potentially the changes in POLARIZATION angle of the transmitted light. These discontinuities will be cause for rejection or will require additional investigation for mechanical consistency. In this field, the following terms are used to define the optical characteristics of the medium: linear birefringence, circular birefringence, uniaxial, biaxial, and chiral birefringence. A special form of birefringence is Brillouin SCATTERING in birefringent media. Additionally, gyrotropic media become isotropic media under the influence of an external constant MAGNETIC FIELD. Examples are Earth's IONOSPHERE (furthermore, various plasma conditions), semiconductor materials, ferrites, and specialty fiber-optics. Additionally, the POCKELS EFFECT (after the German physicist FRIEDRICH CARL ALWIN POCKELS [1865–1913]), who in 1893 discovered that a steady electric field or a varying electric field applied to certain materials will induce birefringence by causing the refractive index to vary (*also see* **KERR EFFECT**). The practical application of the Pockels effect is applied to Pockels cells providing the mechanism of operation for Q-switched lasers (*also see* **BIREFRINGENCE**) (see Figure P.70).

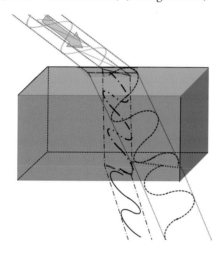

Figure P.70 Photoelasticity.

Photoelectric cells

[atomic, nuclear] Device for which the electrical characteristics are a function of incident LIGHT, providing electromotive force. Specifically, the conversion of ELECTROMAGNETIC RADIATION into electric ENERGY, producing a voltage (V_{EMF}) as a function of radiance. The mechanism of action depends on the PHOTOELECTRIC EFFECT. Additionally, the electrical RESISTANCE may change linearly with the incident radiance, hence providing a mechanism of measuring the MAGNITUDE when connected to a voltage source and a GALVANOMETER (VOLTMETER). As was described in 1897 by JOSEPH JOHN THOMSON (1856–1940), who showed that the increased electrical sensitivity of material was caused by "light pushing on electrons" (also referred to as PHOTOCELL) (see Figure P.71).

Figure P.71 Photocell, semiconductor device relying on photoelectric effect (i.e., photovoltaic effect) to generate electricity, c.q. electrical potential.

Photoelectric effect

[biomedical, energy, nuclear, optics] The conversion of ELECTROMAGNETIC RADIATION ENERGY into kinetic energy of a loosely bound electron (i.e., VALENCE electron) culminating in the emission of a free electron from the ATOM providing the opportunity to initiate the flow of electrons and hence produce current. The PHOTON ENERGY will need to exceed the WORK FUNCTION (ϕ_{elec}, in electron volt eV) of the material in question. The relationship between the work function of the material/metal exposed to LIGHT (with energy $h\nu$, where $\nu = c/\lambda$ is the frequency of electromagnetic radiation with wavelength λ traveling at the speed of light: c and $h = 4.13567 \times 10^{15}$ eV $= 4.1356692 \times 10^{-15}$ Js is PLANCK'S CONSTANT) and the electron energy (KE_e) is expressed as $h\nu = KE_e + \phi_{elec}|_{Metal}$. Hence the threshold for the photoelectric effect is provided by $\nu_0 \geq \phi_{elec}/h$. The PROBABILITY of photon-electron interaction increases with: $h\nu \xrightarrow{\text{approaches}} E_B$, or : $\nu \xrightarrow{\text{approaches}} \nu_0$, where $\nu_0 = E_B/h$ is the frequency of the ABSORPTION EDGE resulting from resonant interaction with the orbiting electron, revolving with NATURAL FREQUENCY: ν_0 at BINDING ENERGY E_B. Under certain specific conditions the simultaneous capture of more than one photon, each at below threshold energy levels, can still result in a multiphoton photoelectric effect. The cumulative energy of multiple photons will exceed the threshold conditions. This is primarily reserved for ultra-short pulsed LASER irradiation, with inherently high RADIATIVE EMISSION per pulse (RADIANCE in order of MW per pulse) (see Figure P.72).

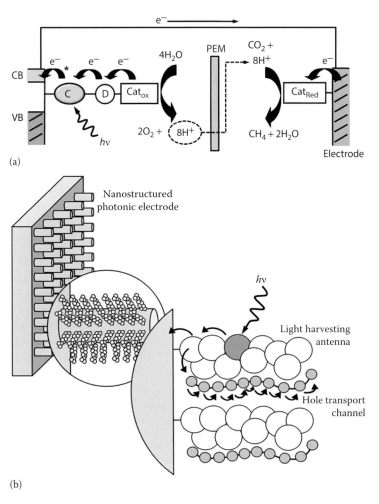

(a)

(b)

Figure P.72 Work performed at the University of North Carolina at Chapel Hill in biological photovoltaics. (a) Schematic showing a modular approach to a process termed artificial photosynthesis. The "artificial photo-synthesis relies on similar principles as used by plants, absorbing sunlight and using those photons to split water that provides the protons and high-energy electrons needed to reduce CO_2 to make plant parts (carbohydrates). Modifying the photovoltaic mechanism of action of nature with dye-sensitized solar cell technology to make a dye-sensitized photoelectrosynthesis cell (DSPEC) is shown in schematic form. PEM stands for proton exchange membrane, C stands for chromophore (a.k.a. light absorber), D stands for donor, Cat_{ox} stands for catalyst designed for oxidation (e.g., water oxidation catalyst), Cat_{Red} stands for catalyst designed for reduction (e.g., CO_2 reduction catalyst), CB stands for conduction band, and VB stands for valence band. Strictly speaking, D is not a requirement, just might help the device to separate redox equivalents at the two catalysts. (b) Schematic show-ing a new approach to photovoltaics by incorporating a light-harvesting antenna capable of very rapid energy transfer down to the surface of the electrode. The nanostructured photonic electrode also serves to trap light for higher efficiency, capturing much light as in comparison to the structure and working function of a butterfly's wing. (Courtesy of Kyle Brennaman, University of North Carolina Chapel Hill; Chapel Hill, NC.)

Photoelectric equation

[general] Definition of the kinetic ENERGY (E_k) of an electron emitted from a METAL as a result of the absorption of a radiation QUANTUM as a function of the electromagnetic FREQUENCY (ν): $E_k = h\nu - \omega_w$, where $h = 6.62606957 \times 10^{-34}\,\mathrm{m^2\,kg/s}$ is PLANCK'S CONSTANT, and ω_w the work function of the metal, as introduced by ALBERT EINSTEIN (1879–1955) in 1905. The PHOTOELECTRIC EFFECT was first observed by HEINRICH HERTZ (1857–1894) in 1887 during his experimental work on RADIO receivers with a spark-gap GENERATOR.

Photoelectric nuclear effect

[nuclear] In nuclear PHYSICS, it can be annihilated by means of gamma radiation. The condition is that the photon ENERGY $E_{photon} = h\nu$ needs to exceed the BINDING ENERGY of the PARTICLE involved. One specific example is the disintegration of DEUTERON, $_2^1 D + h\nu \rightarrow {}_1^1 H + {}_1^0 n$, producing hydrogen and a NEUTRON. Additionally, this phenomenon has been recreated for beryllium. An additional phenomenon describes the pair production under the passage of a GAMMA RAY close to the NUCLEUS; a PHOTON with energy $E_{photon} = h\nu > 1.022$ MeV can produce two "electron particles:" electron and positron, each traveling in perfectly opposite direction, with respective energy $E_{positron} = 511$ keV, which is the mechanism of action for pair production in POSITRON EMISSION TOMOGRAPHY (PET).

Photoelectron

[general] Electron released from METAL under influence of ELECTROMAGNETIC RADIATION (*see* PHOTOELECTRIC EFFECT).

Photographic plate

[chemical, general, optics] Surface coated with a light-sensitive emulsion that changes its transparency or REFLECTION after exposure to LIGHT, primarily resulting from oxidation, for example, silver chloride, which is converted to. The principle of chemical photographic (i.e., light-sensitive oxidation) sensitivity was discovered by the chemist (alchemist) Georg Fabricius in 1556; that is, LUDOLF GEORG GOLDSCHMIED, Prussian-German chemist (1526–1581) in his publication "De Rebus Metallicis" related to the darkening of "horn silver" [silver chloride] under exposure to light. Another photographic emulsion is silver nitrate with calcium. In 1777, the Swedish scientist and chemist CARL WILHELM SCHEELE (1742–1786) discovered that silver chloride has wavelength-dependent light sensitivity, primarily related to the difference between OXIDATION resulting blue light with respect to the longer wavelengths of the visible light (see Figure P.73).

(a) (b)

Figure P.73 (a) Old-style studio camera with objectives and a framework for viewing photographic plate and (b) Georg Fabricius (Goldschmidt: 1526–1581).

Photography

[biomedical, imaging, optics] The process of producing an IMAGE on a plate based on incident ELECTRO-MAGNETIC RADIATION originating from a set of real objects, respectively transmitted through a real object (e.g., X-RAY radiation). The imaging system can be analog, using silver halide crystals as the image-forming medium (photographic film; CELLULOSE ACETATE film), or digitally based on charge-coupled device technology PIXEL array (digital CAMERA). The word "photographie" was first used by the French scientists Joseph Nicéphore Niépce (1765–1833) in 1826 and is known for his pioneering efforts in the development of photography with the first photograph displayed in 1825. The great deal of effort was contributed by the scientist and inventor from the United States, GEORGE EASTMAN (1854–1932) commercialized by the Eastman-Kodak corporation, known as Kodak (see Figure P.74).

Figure P.74 The art of photography exemplified by a high-speed frame capture ("freeze-frame") of tea being spilled from a cup.

Photomultiplier tube

[atomic, nuclear] VACUUM tube that uses a cascade system to increase the number of electrons released from the incident PHOTON by means of the PHOTOELECTRIC EFFECT. Several plates positioned in a sequence are under a potential difference, which accelerates the initial PHOTOELECTRON to the second plate where additional electrons are released by collision impact. $E_k = h\nu - \omega_w$, where $h = 6.62606957 \times 10^{-34} \, \text{m}^2 \, \text{kg/s}$ is PLANCK'S CONSTANT and ω_w the work function of the METAL (specific for photon interaction), as introduced by ALBERT EINSTEIN (1879–1955) in 1905, which is primarily a function of the electromagnetic FREQUENCY (ν) of the incident RADIATION. The number of secondary electrons released by the collision is a direct function of the electron kinetic ENERGY, which depends on the electrical potential between the plates: $E_k = k_e \left(e^2 / r \right) - \omega_{w,c}$, where $k_e = 1/4\pi\varepsilon_0$ is the Coulomb constant with $\varepsilon_0 = 8.85419 \times 10^{-12} \, \text{C}^2 / \text{N} \, \text{m}^2$ the permittivity of free space, $e = -1.60217657 \times 10^{-19} \, \text{C}$ is the electron charge, r is the separation between the subsequent plates in the photomultiplier (dynodes), and $\omega_{w,c}$ is the release energy of the metal under collision. Generally, a single photoelectron can generate up to 10^7 secondary electrons, finally detected on the terminal ANODE, which are quantified by a GALVANOMETER (VOLTMETER). PHOTOMULTIPLIER TUBES have an inherent high internal gain and are extremely sensitive detectors for low-radiance detection applications;

P

however, they are relatively large and require an elaborate power supply, operating at a high negative voltage, typically ranging from −500 to −1500 V (see Figure P.75).

Figure P.75 Photomultiplier tubes inside a drum scanner.

Photon

[atomic, general, optics, quantum] Quantity of ENERGY emitted in the form of ELECTROMAGNETIC RADIATION with a value that is the product of its FREQUENCY (ν) and PLANCK'S CONSTANT ($h = 6.62606957 \times 10^{-34} \, m^2 \, kg/s$): $E = h\nu$ (quantum of LIGHT), this has a continuous distribution spectrum. The photon is the result of a charge OSCILLATION, where the ELECTRIC CHARGE (q) carries an electric field (E_{elec}), while the MOTION of the charge generates an alternating current (I, with the same frequency as the oscillation; FARADAY LAW): $I = I_0 \sin \omega t = dq(\vec{r})/dt$, where $\omega = \nu 2\pi$ is a function of charge location $\vec{r}$, which is the essential component to induce an associated and frequency matching alternating MAGNETIC FIELD ($\vec{B}$) (AMPÈRE'S LAW: $\oint \vec{B} \cdot d\vec{\ell} = \mu_0 I$, where the integral is taken over a loop around the current, and $\mu_0 = 4\pi \times 10^{-7} \, H/m$ the permittivity of free space). The energy of the photon is expressed by the Pointing vector. The vector direction of the electric field defines the POLARIZATION of the electromagnetic radiation. Photons are generally described by the WAVE–PARTICLE DUALITY principle. Sometime treating the photon as a PARTICLE provides the essential mechanism for the process, for instance REFLECTION. Whereas the wave phenomenon is more suitable for several other interactions, for instance diffraction and INTERFERENCE. The particle theory dates back to the ancient Greek philosophers (starting as far back as Aristotle [384–322 BC]), but SIR ISAAC NEWTON (1642–1727) formally introduced his corpuscular hypothesis. The first formal introduction of the wave theory of light was introduced by the Dutch scientist CHRISTIAAN HUYGENS (1629–1695). Photons span the entire ELECTROMAGNETIC SPECTRUM (see Figure P.76).

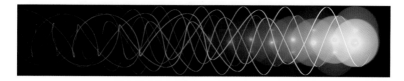

Figure P.76 The elusive photon.

Photopic vision

[biomedical, optics] Part of the three main modes of human vision: photopic, scotopic, and mesopic. Photopic vision represents VISION under brightly lit conditions. Photopic has COLOR perception, encompassing all functions associated with the cone cells in the retina of the EYE. Scotopic vision is black and white vision ("intensity" [magnitude] only. *Note:* intensity is technically not appropriate for ELECTROMAGNETIC RADIATION due to the duplicity of the nature of LIGHT, intensity is the AMPLITUDE squared) under low-light radiance conditions, attributed to the rod cells in the RETINA. Mesopic vision combines the low-level rod vision and bright cone vision, a combination of photopic vision and scotopic vision (see Figure P.77).

(a)　　　　　　　　　　　　　　　　　　　(b)

Figure P.77 (a) Photopic vision under bright sunlight and white reflecting buildings and (b) in comparison mesopic vision under artificial lighting in a grocery store.

Photosphere

[astrophysics/astronomy, geophysics] Solar layer, consisting of a PLASMA-nuclear reaction medium, primarily responsible for the LIGHT emission, the corona. The photosphere of our SUN is approximately 600 km thick. While brighter and hotter stars will have a thicker photosphere, it is estimated that the thickness is generally 1/1000 of the total radius of the solid STAR. The composition of the photosphere s generally inferred from the emitted Fraunhofer spectrum (see Figure P.78).

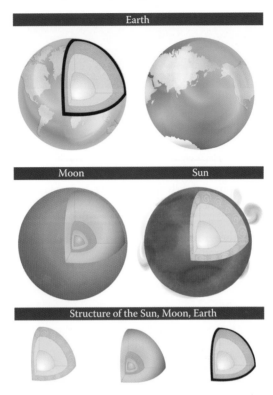

Figure P.78 Layers of the Sun, outlining the photosphere.

Photosynthesis

[biomedical, geophysics, thermodynamics] The phenomenon of the conversion of carbon dioxide to oxygen by plants as postulated in 1779 by a scientist from the Netherlands: JAN INGENHOUSZ (1730–1779).

Even though the discovery of the molecule oxygen (O_2) was only recent in these days of discovery in 1774, by JOSEPH PRIESTLEY (1733–1804) (see Figure P.79).

Leaf anatomy

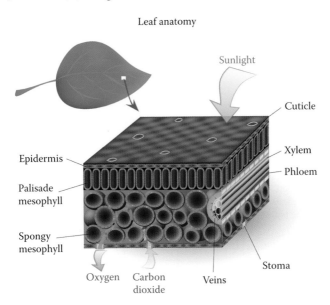

Figure P.79 Process of photosynthesis, primarily known for its action through the chloroplasts in the leaves of plants; however, the skin of various mammals also has photosynthesis capabilities. The skin photosynthesis also produces a necessary hormone and chemical catalyst for cellular function: vitamin D, in addition to a rudimentary supply of oxygen. During exposure to sunlight, high-energy ultraviolet light (specifically in the range 290–315 nm) is absorbed in melanin that is part of the tissue structure directly underneath the epidermis of the skin and the photon energy is used to photolyze provitamin D3 (7-dehydrocholesterol) to previtamin D3. Once previtamin D3 is formed, it undergoes an isomerization process that is thermally induced and forms vitamin D3. The isomerization process takes 2–3 days to reach completion. Additionally, certain algae and seaweed and certain organisms, such as the *Euglena* species (found in both fresh- and saltwater), also provide a significant contribution to the conversion of carbon dioxide into oxygen. Some scientists claim that algae and seaweed combined provide the lion's share of oxygen production, exceeding that of surface plants. The true respective contributions remain difficult to quantify accurately due to a broad range of ill-defined and transient boundary conditions.

Phototoxicity

[biomedical, chemical, optics] Inflammatory toxic response, primarily associated with the SKIN, under the influence of LIGHT exposure of surface areas that have been in contact with certain chemicals. Photoxicity may sometimes be misdiagnosed as sunburn but is a different dermal response on a chemical and cellular level.

Photovoltaic effect

[atomic, nuclear] Electric current generated as the result of light irradiance of a junction between two media of different chemical composition in direct contact. The effect was first observed by ANTOINE HENRI BECQUEREL (1852–1908) in 1839. The photovoltaic effect can also be applied in combination with an externally induced potential difference (V), providing a CURRENT (I) as a function of the irradiance (I_{rad}) and temperature at the junction (T): $I = I_{reverse}\{\exp(eV/kT)-1\} - I_{rad}$, where $e = 1.60217657 \times 10^{-19}$C is the electron charge and $k_b = 1.3806488 \times 10^{-23}\,\text{m}^2\,\text{kg/s}^2\,\text{K}$ is the BOLTZMANN CONSTANT (*also* **PHOTOVOLTAICS or PHOTOELECTRIC EFFECT**) (see Figure P.80).

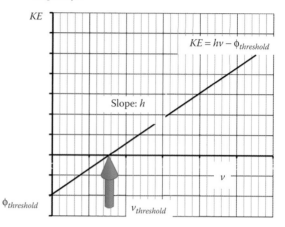

Kinetic energy (*KE*) of emitted electron vs. light frequency: *v*

Higher-frequency photons (i.e, shorter wavelength) represent greater effective kinetic energy ($KE = hv - \phi_{threshold}$; *h* Planck's constant), resulting in greater efficiency for the photoelectric effect. At fixed frequency and increasing radiance will emit a greater number of electrons proportional to the increase in radiant energy of the photon stream.

One application in particular is in night vision goggles

$KE = hv - \phi_{threshold}$

Slope: *h*

$\phi_{threshold}$

$v_{threshold}$

v

Figure P.80 Graphic representation of the photovoltaic effect.

Physics

[general] (Ancient Greek: φύσις physis "nature;" the Knowledge of Nature, in principle the knowledge of how things work and how phenomena originate. Latin: physica, plural, "natural science") A natural science that involves the study of MATTER, phenomena, the MOTION of object and phenomena through both space and time, as well as all related force and ENERGY concepts. More broadly, the general hypothetical description and analysis of nature, with associated laws of conservation and rules and laws of conduct. The study of physics postulates rules about the conduct of events and phenomena in order to understand, and predict how the UNIVERSE behaves and how matter and energy interact. Most laws and definitions in physics are proven within certain boundary conditions and are correct until new observations require adjustments to the theory, one example is the special relativity concepts, following classical Newtonian physics. The first known use of the "physics concept" was 1715. The broad spectrum of physics has been further subdivided into the following topics: classical, high energy, nuclear, relativistic, THERMODYNAMICS, FLUID DYNAMICS, hydrodynamics, fluid mechanics, dynamics, statics, MECHANICS, OPTICS, photonics, QUANTUM MECHANICS, electromagnetism, BIOPHYSICS, theoretical physics, GEOPHYSICS, ASTROPHYSICS, ACOUSTICS, high-pressure, low-temperature, PLASMA physics, particle physics, and many new subdisciplines being demarcated on a continual basis. The list of areas of interest in physics is not intended to be all encompassing, various topics

will overlap between the nomenclature and also depend on the respective execution-group interests (see Figure P.81).

Archimedes principle

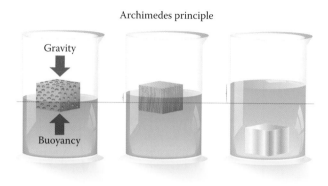

Gravity

Buoyancy

Figure P.81 Physics as a technology platform.

Physics constants

[general] Broad range of constants used in the various definitions within the integral field of PHYSICS, ranging from the electron charge to the speed of LIGHT, found in many description throughout the encyclopedia.

Physics laws

See LAWS OF PHYSICS.

Physiologic dead space

[biomedical, fluid dynamics] Physiologic dead space is defined as the volume of expired AIR per breath that does not receive any CO_2 from the BLOOD flow through that part of the lung. In RESPIRATION, the volume capacity of the lung is measured using this as one of the characteristics for the individual examined. Physiologic dead space quantifies the volume of the trachea, bronchi, and bronchioles, which is not involved in the exchange of oxygen with blood (i.e., anatomic dead space), in addition to the volume of "damaged" alveoli that have vascular constraints that limit the blood flow and hence limit the exchange of oxygen with blood (i.e., alveolar dead space). The method specifically determines the physiological dead space of the lung total expired volume. In certain regions of the lung, there can be a very high ventilation-to-perfusion ratio, with an associated wasted VENTILATION, which acts as physiologic dead space. Physiologic dead space can be measured using the Bohr method. The Bohr method collects all expired air is over several breaths. The expired partial pressure for those breaths (P_{eCO_2}) is measured. Concurrently, a sample of alveolar air (i.e., end-tidal air; with volume V_t) is collected, the air that is exiting at the end of expiration during forced expiration. This end-tidal air does not contain a significant amount of dead space air, hence serves as a representative of alveolar air. From the end-tidal breath, the alveolar P_{aCO_2} is measured. The total expired CO_2 per breath is by definition from the expired alveolar air. Dead space volume (V_d) can be

derived from the fact that the total amount is concentration multiplied by volume:
$V_d/V_t = \left(P_{aCO_2} - P_{eCO_2}\right)/P_{aCO_2}$ (Bohr equation; defined by the Danish physician CHRISTIAN BOHR [1855–1911]) (see Figure P.82).

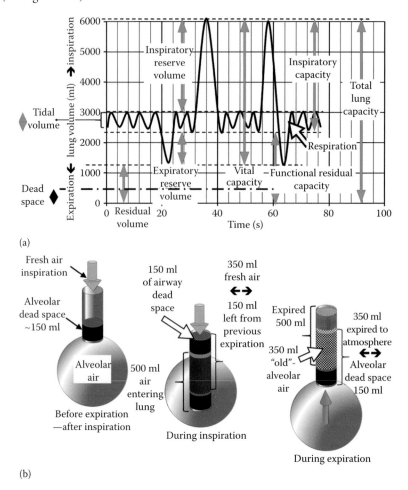

(a)

(b)

Figure P.82 Physiologic dead space in the process of respiration. (a) Normal respiration and (b) volume diagram for the lungs.

Physiology

[biomedical, chemical, general] Study of the activities involved in biological entities. Description and QUANTIFICATION of the operational functionality of organs, cells as well as on a molecular level, including enzyme interactions and hormones. A general study of how biological organism function, with associated ENERGY, balances and ENGINEERING interactions. The first recorded principles of physiology date back to

Hippocrates (approximately 470–377 BC) in 420 BC, hence known as the father of modern medicine (see Figure P.83).

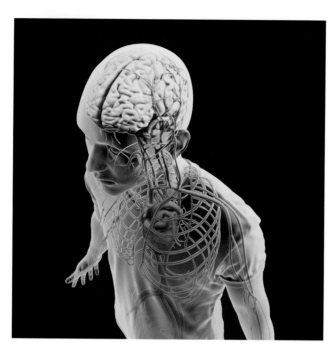

Figure P.83 Brain regulating the activities of a person that is performing an activity and hence has cells that perform a physiological activity.

Physisorption

[atomic, biomedical, energy, thermodynamics] The process of electron interaction on a Van der Waals attraction level, describing the adsorption while the electron structure remains unaffected. The adsorption process refers to the chemical hybridization of electrons in a molecular surface. The electrons in orbit can be considered electron clouds. In contrast during chemisorption the electrons are affected, performing a perturbation of the chemical bonds. Under helium beam interaction with helium the scattering process is described as physisorption with very low energy content (order of meV).

Piano

[acoustics, computational] Acoustical string instrument used to produce music by tapping strings with blocks attached to the keys on the front of the instrument. There are two particular kinds of pianos: upright and grand-piano. The grand piano has gained popularity from the manufacturer Steinway for over 160 years. The history of the piano dates back to the harpsichord of the beginning of the eighteenth century, evolving to the pianoforte. The Harpsichord was invented by the Italian musician and craftsman Bartolomeo Cristofor (1655–1731). This was the equivalent of what is now known as the "grand piano." The composer Beethoven was writing music for the piano when the instrument was close to one hundred years old. The upright piano was designed in 1780 by the Austrian Johann Schmidt (late eighteenth century). The "hammer" design of the piano creates a sound by actuating the string in a time segment of milliseconds, the duration will largely depend on the force with which the key stroke is played. The key stroke affects the harmonic spectrum of the string as well as the loudness. The tone spectrum of the piano generally covers better than six octaves, ranging approximately from 25.5 to 4186 Hz for the fundamental frequencies with harmonics spanning from 2 to 12 kHz. The sound spectrum is influenced by the string material, the string tension as well as the reverberations in the mechanical device housing the strings, with its inherent material properties and stresses and strains (see Figure P.84).

Figure P.84 Grand piano.

Picard, Jean-Félix (1620–1682)

[astronomy] French astronomer. He equipped a TELESCOPE with Vernier-type gauge lines that could be used for MEASUREMENT and laid the foundation for angular division of the globe in longitude and latitude scales for cartography.

Pickering, Edward Charles (1846–1919)

[astrophysics/astronomy, atomic] Physicist and astronomer from the United States. He is best known for his derivation of the spectral line series: PICKERING SERIES (see Figure P.85).

Figure P.85 Edward Charles Pickering (1846–1919) by Sarah Gooll Putnam (1851–1912). (Courtesy of Harvard University Portrait Collection.)

Pickering series

[atomic, nuclear] Helium absorption lines for helium fond in hot stars. The Pickering lines are for a special IONIZATION state of helium (He^+, singly ionized, instead of He^{2+}) involving a transition to the $n = 4$ QUANTUM STATE. The Pickering lines closely resemble the transition lines for the BALMER SERIES to the $n = 2$ quantum state.

Pickup reaction

[nuclear] The reverse of a single NUCLEON transfer reaction, in this case a nucleon is removed from the target NUCLEUS.

Picture

[general] Two-dimensional IMAGE captured on a canvas (painting), paper (drawing), digital array, or on PHOTOGRAPHIC PLATE (photographic film), representing a visual PERCEPTION of an object or event. Photographic film, or digital array (digital CAMERA) is the prominent mechanism for capturing a picture and preserving the experience for posterity. In digital image capture, the picture ELEMENTS are referred to as pixels, the individual array elements with the gray-scale respectively COLOR coding information of one location in the total reconstituted display (see Figure P.86).

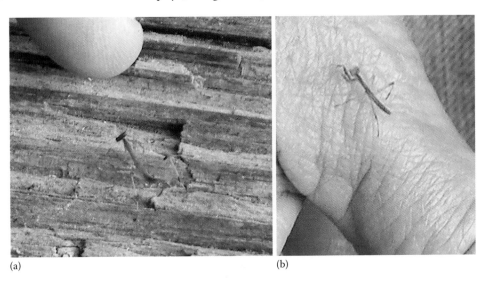

(a)   (b)

Figure P.86 (a,b) Picture of baby "praying mantis" ("walking stick," since it resembles a tiny branch), insect: *Carausius morosus* of the order Phasmatodea. The population consists virtually exclusively of females. The females are able to lay fertile eggs, without the requirement of mating or for that matter the presence of males. The eggs hatch and also develop into females.

Piezoelectric effect

[acoustics, atomic, energy, fluid dynamics, general, mechanics, quantum] Electromechanical process (i.e., strain) in certain materials. The materials that can produce this effect have specific symmetry features, LATTICE structure related for instance. Additional effects producing the piezoelectric effect include the stress induced in a material by an applied electric field. The piezoelectric effect was discovered in 1880 by PAUL-JACQUES CURIE (1856–1941) and PIERRE CURIE (1859–1906). Example materials that possess the piezoelectric effect are quarts, ferroelectric ceramics, and certain salts. Rochelle SALT (potassium sodium tartrate: $KNaC_4H_4O_6 \cdot 4H_2O$ first known preparation in the late 1600s by Pierre Seignette (1660–1719), an apothecary of La Rochelle, France; used as a laxative); discovered to have pyroelectric properties by SIR DAVID BREWSTER (1781–1868) in 1824 later to show piezoelectric properties by the Curie brothers.

One specific example of the practical use of the piezoelectric effect is in a quartz-based timing mechanism used in clocks, a battery-operated quartz resonator (*also see* ULTRASOUND) (see Figure P.87).

Figure P.87 Piezoelectric effect applied for ignition of a gas stove-top flame.

Piezoelectric resonance

[acoustics, atomic, electromagnetism, fluid dynamics, general, mechanics, quantum] Certain materials will develop mechanical stress under the influence of electrical voltage. The crystal structure is polarized by the external application of the potential difference creating an electrical DIPOLE. The crystal will have one dominant axis of mechanical ACTIVITY. The process can also be reversed, where mechanical stress will provide an electrical potential across the crystal proportional to the MAGNITUDE of the applied stress. The electronic OSCILLATION results from the electronic configuration as described under oscillation, with a frequency: $\nu = 1/2\pi\sqrt{LC}$ and this frequency will ideally match the mechanical boundary conditions with resonance frequency: $\nu_r = 1/2\ell_1\sqrt{\rho s_{11}^E}$, where ℓ_1 is the fundamental length of compression (generally, the crystal will have three sides: $\ell_1 > \ell_2 > \ell_3$), ρ is the material density of the piezoelectric crystal, and s_{11}^E is the elastic COMPLIANCE under a constant electric field resulting from a constant electrical potential. Under ideal conditions the mechanical and electronic RESONANCE FREQUENCY will be match for optimal ENERGY conversion. Piezoelectric resonance can for instance be used in tweeter speakers for high-frequency acoustic SOUND emission (*also see* OSCILLATION *and* RESONANCE) (see Figure P.88).

Figure P.88 Tweeter with piezoelectric resonance-driven transverse wave emission.

Piezoelectric transducer

[acoustics, atomic, energy, fluid dynamics, general, mechanics, quantum] Around 1880 Pierre Curie (1859–1906) and Paul-Jacques Curie (1856–1941) discover the electromechanical properties of specific ceramic crystals. One of the best known crystals is PZT: lead (Pb) zirconate (Zr) titanate (Ti): $Pb[Zr_xTi_{1-x}]O_3$, oxygen (O), a ceramic perovskite (see Figure P.89).

P

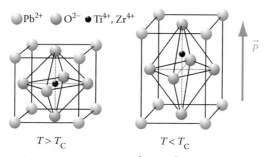

Figure P.89 Chemical structure of ceramic PZT crystal: $Pb[Zr_xTi_{1-x}]O_3$.

Piezoelectricity

[acoustics, atomic, energy, fluid dynamics, general, mechanics, quantum] The mechanism providing the means of transferring stress and strain into electrical SIGNAL, reversible electromagnetic process. Applying an electrical potential to certain materials will deform the material. Piezoelectricity is applied for microphones, pressure transducers, and ULTRASONIC IMAGING devices (both as source and detector) (*also see* PIEZOELECTRIC EFFECT).

Pinch effect

[atomic, nuclear] PLASMA effect that constricts the electric current due to the narrowing of an electric field, causing the charges to increase per cross-sectional area representative of the kinks in sausage links. Lightning bolts are a visual example of pinched plasma filaments. The pinch effect can also occur in liquid CONDUCTOR (LIQUID metal) or solid conductors. The process is the result of MAGNETIC FIELD lines. Experimentally the pinch effect is produced in Tokamak systems (plasma) with respect to NUCLEAR FUSION (see Figure P.90).

Figure P.90 Lightning "pinch."

Pinch temperature

[thermodynamics] Smallest temperature difference in a steam TURBINE between the temperature profile for AIR and water, analytically equivalent to the smallest temperature difference between the cold curve and the hot curve (e.g., steam) for a heat-exchange process. The heating medium can be of any kind: GAS (propane, methane, etc.), gasoline, electric, coal and so forth (see Figure P.91).

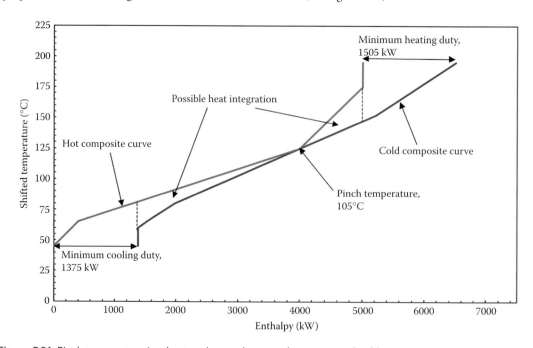

Figure P.91 Pinch temperature in a heat exchanger between hot steam and cold steam.

Pinocytosis

[biomedical] The active process of LIQUID transport from the outside of the CELL MEMBRANE to the interior of the CELL by means of the formation of a vesicle. This process is part of cellular ingestion classified as ENDOCYTOSIS, which also includes solid consumption defined as PHAGOCYTOSIS. On the MECHANICS of the selective restructuring of the lipid-protein bilayer (*also see* CELL MEMBRANE) (see Figure P.92).

Role of an antigen-presenting cell

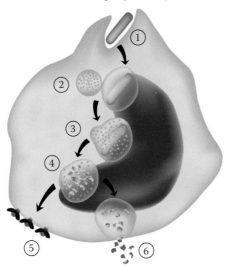

Figure P.92 Pinocytosis, would be similar to phagocytosis except for the cell consumption is liquid instead of solids. (1) Phagocytosis of enemy cell (antigen); (2) Fusion of lysosome and phagosome; (3) Enzymes start to degrade enemy cell; (4) Enemy cell broken into small fragments; (5) Fragments of antigen presented on APC surface; (6) Leftover fragments released by exocytosis.

Pion

[astrophysics/astronomy, atomic, energy, general, nuclear, quantum, thermodynamics] Elementary PARTICLE in the category of MESON. The pion was discovered in 1947, and has a mass equivalent ENERGY of $E = mc^2 = 135$ MeV (*also see* PI-MESON).

Pipe

[computational, fluid dynamics] Fluid conduit. Flow in pipes will generally obey the Bernoulli equation and Poiseuille's equations. Pipes will provide LAMINAR FLOW under steady state relatively low flow velocity. A straight pipe with uniform diameter has no particular geometric configurations that will provide conditions that are conducive for flow other than laminar. Junctions connecting pipes with different diameters or pipes with curvature will however provide the boundary conditions that can result in turbulent flow. Computational FLUID DYNAMICS will describe the flow in curved pipes with discrete or continuous changes in diameter due to the complex nature of the boundary conditions as a function of axial and radial location. Pulsatile flow will generate complex conditions that are not easily solved by analog means and will require in-depth computational simulation. Compliant pipe describes the flow in BLOOD vessels and has time-dependent boundary conditions and well as involves PULSATILE FLOW. For a flexible tube, the COMPLIANCE is defined as $C_{compliance} = \partial A/\partial P$, where A is the cross-sectional area of the tube and P the local pressure; this translates into a distensibility: $D_{dist} = (1/A)(\partial A/\partial P) \xrightarrow{thin\ wall} (2r/d)\left[\left(1-v_p^2\right)/Y_n\right]$, with Y_n the Young's modulus of the tube material, v_p the Poisson ratio, r the tube radius, and d the wall thickness. The flow (Q) in the flexible tube is approximated by the "windkessel" model as $Q = C_{compliance}\left(\partial P/\partial t\right) + \left(P/R_p\right)$, where R_p represents the peripheral RESISTANCE and t is time. This can be developed in a FOURIER SERIES for pulsatile flow with ANGULAR FREQUENCY $\omega = 2\pi\nu$, ν the frequency: $\hat{Q} = \left[i\omega C_{\text{compliance}} + (1/R_p)\right]\hat{P}$. Because of the BOUNDARY LAYER the flow at the wall is generally stagnant and the material transport close to the boundary can be discarded by rejecting the boundary flow by applying an ORIFICE (syphoning off the boundary layer; for instance applied to transcontinental FLUID transportations). This way the flow medium may be changed but the output consistency can be pure and consistent at the core (see Figure P.93).

Figure P.93 Pipe.

Pipeline parameter ($\rho'' = \varpi_{\text{gr}}\varpi_0/2gH$)

[fluid dynamics, mechanics] Dimensionless number used in MOMENTUM transfer associated with the WATER-HAMMER phenomenon, where ν_{gr} is the GROUP VELOCITY of the WAVE phenomenon, ν_0 is the initial VELOCITY, g is the GRAVITATIONAL ACCELERATION, H is the STATIC HEAD. One area of interest in this is for mining and OIL drilling with regard to slurry and oil transportation. The pipeline parameter provides a metric for the hydraulic characteristics of a flow system. For instance, a value of $\rho'' > 1$ may require the use of a reflux VALVE bypassing the system's PUMP. The pipeline parameter is a means of predicting problematic circumstances and safety concerns.

Pitch

[general] Human perceptual response to frequency of acoustic ENERGY, a bass is low pitch and a flute has a high pitch. Pitch is primarily associated with the zero-order harmonic of the instrument or source of the SOUND. A related expression is from the French word "TIMBRE." The timbre denotes the base frequency as well as the spectrum, the "COLOR" of the sound of the device producing the sound (*see* FREQUENCY *and* WAVELENGTH) (see Figure P.94).

Figure P.94 French horn emitting a "rainbow" of sound i.e. frequency spectrum; analoguos to an optical spectrum.

Pitot, Henri (1695–1771)

[fluid dynamics] Scientist and hydraulic engineer from France. The PITOT TUBE for measuring flow velocity was named after him. He also gained fame for the design of the aqueduct in Montpellier, France; the aqueduct saint Clément de Montpellier also called the aqueduct Pitot (see Figure P.95).

Figure P.95 Henri Pitot (1695–1771).

Pitot theorem

[computational] The opposite sides of a quadrilateral (four-sided closed outline of regular or irregular shape; special case rectangle) enclosing a circle are equal to the sum of the remaining sides: $AB + CD = BC + DA$. Proposed by the French engineer and mathematician HENRI PITOT (1695–1771) in 1725 (see Figure P.96).

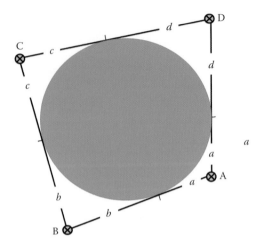

Figure P.96 Pitot theorem.

Pitot tube

[fluid dynamics] Tube invented by the French scientist and engineer HENRI PITOT (1695–1771), later modified by the French engineer Henry Darcy (1803–1858) and is widely used to measure flow velocity, specifically for airflow around the WING of a plane or water flow speed for a boat as well as TURBINE generators/engines. The Pitot tube is relatively narrow, open on one side, facing upstream and is connected to a MANOMETER on the opposite side, providing the stagnation pressure (P_t) also referred to as the total pressure. The principle relies on Bernoulli's theorem. In a modified form, the static pressure (P_s) is measured by placing small perforations in the WALL of the tube. The flow velocity (v) is defined as $v = \sqrt{\{2(P_t - P_s)/\rho\}}$, where ρ is the density of the flow medium. The flow velocity is an indirect means of determining the velocity of the craft. Ice formation in the Pitot tube could have been the cause of several airplane accidents in the past, and nowadays it is hence heated (see Figure P.97).

Figure P.97 Pitot tube on the nose of the plane.

Pixel

[imaging, theoretical] Smallest unit area on sensor array with uniform intensity of all spectral lines due to the fact that it is a self-confined single ELEMENT as part of a larger detector or display raster assembly. Generally, the pixel is part of a two-dimensional arrangement, forming a component of an IMAGE: a picture element. Pixels are describing the sensor ELEMENTS of a CAMERA as well as the display elements of a screen. The sensing elements can be components of a CCD CAMERA, alternatively the RGB-LED (red-green-blue–light emitting diodes) clusters or LCD (LIQUID crystal display) sections on a visual display unit (see Figure P.98).

Figure P.98 Images constructed for low-resolution pixels, each individual single-colored square.

Planck, Maxwell Karl Ernst Ludwig (1858–1947)

[atomic, computational, energy, general, nuclear, thermodynamics] German scientist. Introducer of the concept of QUANTUM THEORY in 1900. The theoretical concept of the fact that ELECTROMAGNETIC

RADIATION has a discrete ENERGY SPECTRUM was derived from Planck's experimental and theoretical work on BLACK-BODY RADIATION. In 1905, ALBERT EINSTEIN (1879–1955) substantiated the work of Max Planck by his introduction of the PHOTON-PARTICLE DUALITY theory (see Figure P.99).

Figure P.99 Maxwell Karl Ernst Ludwig Planck (1858–1947).

Planck's Constant *h*

[atomic, computational, electromagnetism, energy] A natural constant of proportionality relating the frequency of a quantum of ENERGY to the total energy of the QUANTUM, $h = 4.1356692 \times 10^{-15}$ Js. Often the derived Planck's constant "h-bar:" $\hbar = h/2\pi$, introduced by PAUL ADRIEN MAURICE DIRAC (1902–1984) is used in simplified equation format.

Planck's law

[atomic, nuclear] *See* PLANCK'S RADIATION LAW.

Planck's radiation law

[atomic, nuclear] Black-body RADIATION spectral definition by MAX PLANCK (1858–1947) in response to a challenge by Kirchhoff in follow-up on the Kirchhoff radiation law: $\varepsilon_\lambda / \alpha_\lambda = I_\lambda$, where ε_λ represents the radiated ENERGY as a function of the wavelength (λ), α_λ the fraction of absorbed energy, and I_λ the energy incident on the "black-body." Combining this with the WIEN'S DISPLACEMENT LAW and the energy (E) quantization: $E = h\nu$, with $h = 4.1356692 \times 10^{-15}$ Js the PLANCK CONSTANT, and $\nu = c/\lambda$ the frequency

(c the speed of light). This led Planck to derive the spectral energy distribution: $I_\lambda = 2\pi hc^2 / \lambda^5 \left(e^{hc/\lambda k_b T} - 1\right)^{-1}$, with $k_b = 1.3806488 \times 10^{-23}$ m² kg/s² K Boltzmann's constant, and T temperature (see Figure P.100).

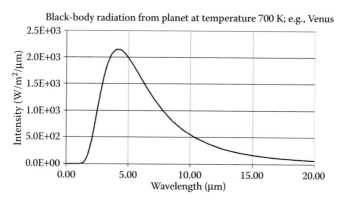

Figure P.100 Planck's radiation law.

Plane of incidence

[general] The local surface area with the normal vector indicating the largest congruent area with equal vector representation. The plane of incidence makes an ANGLE with the vector of the direction of propagation of the incident ENERGY form (PARTICLE or WAVE).

Plane of polarization

[general] The plane in which the direction of the electric field of ELECTROMAGNETIC RADIATION is directed (*see* POLARIZATION) (see Figure P.101).

Figure P.101 The light reflected from the seawater is polarized in the horizontal direction, which is suppressed when viewing through the polarizer filter, reducing the glare.

Plane wave

[general, optics] $U(\vec{r}) = Ae^{ik\vec{r}}$, where $k = 2\pi/\lambda$ is the wavenumber, $\vec{r}$ the vectorial DISTANCE to the source, and A a constant (i.e., AMPLITUDE). The plane wave SOLUTION follows from the Euler theorem.

Plane-polarized waves

[general] ELECTROMAGNETIC RADIATION with the electric field in a fixed single direction. Generally, ordinary light-sources emit unpolarized light, with POLARIZATION direction that is continually changing with no fixed pattern of direction, or for a single time frame, the LIGHT will be a combination of photons that form a ray that can be considered to consist of elliptically (circularly) polarized light with a random combination of electric field directions (see Figure P.102).

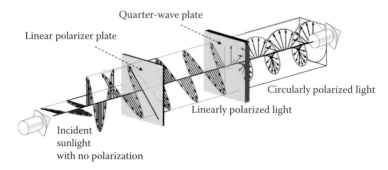

Figure P.102 Plane wave.

Planet

[general] In general, galactic material in our SOLAR SYSTEM has to satisfy the following three criteria in order to classify as planets: (1) the material needs to orbit around the SUN in a regular pattern, (2) the material needs to have enough mass to generate a cohesive gravitational force that constrains the orbiting mass into a spherical geometry, and (3) the mass in orbit needs to be cohesive, collecting all mass in the same orbiting pattern (i.e., no debris in the same path), as defined by the International Astronomical Union (IAU). As a result Pluto was recently discarded as a qualified planet leaving only 8 planets in our Solar system; from the Sun outward: Mercury, VENUS, EARTH, MARS, JUPITER, SATURN, Uranus, and Neptune. Two additional dwarf planets at the outer edge of our Solar system have been recognized in orbit but with debris: Pluto and Eris, where Eris and Pluto are relatively close and Eris was discovered fairly recently. The ASTEROID Ceres also meets those requirements postulated by the IAU and hence is a dwarf planet as well (see Figure P.103).

Figure P.103 Planets.

Planetary data

[astrophysics/astronomy, computational] The SOLAR SYSTEM consists of the SUN in the center with planets orbiting around it from the inside to the outside, conventionally: Mercury, VENUS, EARTH, MARS, JUPITER, SATURN, Uranus, Neptune and Pluto; with Jupiter the largest (about 11 times the diameter of Earth). However, certain philosophies are considering Pluto to be a dwarf PLANET (size one-fifth the diameter of Earth, our MOON has a diameter that is one quarter of Earth's diameter on average) and may not be counted as a full planet, making Neptune the outermost planet. Most recently another planet (dwarf) at the outer extremity has been added, for instance Eris. Additionally, Pluto has a substantial size moon: Charon, which makes the orbit of Pluto go inside the orbit of Neptune for nearly 20 years (total solar orbit 248 earth-years). Pluto's moon, Charon, makes it a double planet. Pluto has a total of three moons, two of which very small (*also see* **SOLAR SYSTEM**, *and respective planets*) (see Figure P.104).

Figure P.104 Planetary system and galactic objects.

Planetary motion

[astrophysics/astronomy, general, geophysics] The planets in orbit around the SUN primary are responding to the gravitational attraction by the Sun, which represents 99.9% of all the mass in our SOLAR SYSTEM. The orbiting planets do however influence the ORBITS of neighboring planets under a perturbation effect, making the orbits deviate from the perfect ellipsoidal pattern. The orbital velocity (v_o) of each planets results in first-order approximation on the CENTRIPETAL FORCE balancing the gravitational force: $v_o = \sqrt{(GM_{sun}/r)}$, where G is the gravitational constant, M_{sun} the mass of the Sun, and r the respective planetary DISTANCE to the Sun. Please note that the orbits are not perfectly circular (*see* **KEPLER'S LAW**) (see Figure P.105).

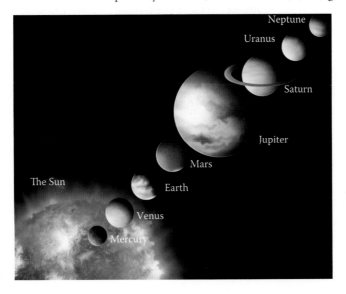

Figure P.105 Graphical representation of the relative size within our Solar system.

Planetary motion, Kepler's laws of

[astronomy/astrophysics, general, geophysics] *See* **KEPLER'S LAWS**.

Planetary orbits

[computational, geophysics] *See* **KEPLER'S LAW**, as described by **JOHANNES KEPLER** (1571–1630).

Planetary precession

[astrophysics/astronomy, general, geophysics] Precession of a planet's SPIN axis, in addition to the "wobble" of the Earth's axis every 26 000 years. For the EARTH, the precession angular tilt (ϕ) with respect to the normal to the INVARIABLE PLANE (the Laplace plane), which is inclined to the planetary equator by ϑ. The spatial orientation of the planetary orbit can be described by the EULER ANGLES for the ecliptic and EQUINOX position (respectively: φ, ω, Ω). This PRECESSION can be described under the assumption that the variations induced by the MOTION resulting from the SUN and its own satellites (planetary perturbations, as well as our own MOON) is given as $\partial \phi / \partial t = -(3/2)\left(MR_e^2/I_c \omega_s\right) J_n n^2 \{\cos \epsilon_e + \sum_j [(n_j/n)^2 [M_j/(M_j + M)]\cos(\epsilon_e - \vartheta_j)]\}$, where M is the mass of the PLANET in precession, R_e is the planetary radius, J_n are harmonic coefficients (also referred to as zonal coefficients; derived from the Legendre polynomials [Legendre functions: P_{nj}; for instance, $P_{00} = 1$, $P_{10} = x$, $P_{20} = \left(3x^2 - 1\right)/2$, etc.]), ω_s is the angular spin of the planet, I_c is the moment of INERTIA for the polar axis, M_j is the mass of adjacent planets and satellites (SATELLITE is a term introduced by JOHANNES KEPLER [1571–1630]), $n = d/dt\left(\varphi + \omega + \Omega\right)$ is the orbital mean displacement motion for the planet with respect to the Sun, and ϵ_e is the inclination of the equator with respect to its orbit. Note that the seasons on Earth are the result of the orbital position of the Earth with respect to the Sun and the ANGLE of the Earth's axis in the rotational plane creating the seasons: summer, autumn, winter, and spring. The presumably fixed angle of the Earth's axis in the solar orbit is however affected by the Earth's precession and will cause the seasons to shift.

Planetary vorticity

[dynamics, general, geophysics] *See* **CORIOLIS FREQUENCY**.

Plasma

[atomic, biomedical, general, nuclear] One of the four states: solid, LIQUID, vapor/gas, and plasma. A plasma is a condition of a medium where the electrons of a significant number of atoms have been removed and flow freely, mixture of atoms, ions, and electron clouds, existing predominantly at high temperature, however, with a high density that does not correspond to the otherwise "gaseous" behavior of the plasma medium. Plasma generally has a luminous behavior, for instance a sodium lamp, fluorescent lamp, or "neon" lamp are plasma LIGHT sources. The SUN is also a plasma as well as a NUCLEAR FUSION reactor. Additionally, BLOOD is composed of plasma as the main fluid, with red and white blood cells and dissolved proteins, next to GLUCOSE, clotting factor (providing the means to congeal/coagulate blood—forming a "scab;" also provides the mechanism to form blood clots [thrombus]) and electrolytes, dissolved carbon dioxide (carbolic ACID) and hormones and enzymes and more (see Figure P.106).

Figure P.106 Plasma.

Plasma frequency

[atomic, nuclear] Oscillations within a PLASMA resulting from the electron thermal velocity (v_e). The wavelength of the OSCILLATION (λ_D) has the Debye length $\lambda_D = v_e/2\pi v_{pe}$, with frequency dominated by the free electron density (n_e): $v_{pe} = \omega/2\pi = \sqrt{(n_e e/\pi m_e)} = 8.97\sqrt{n_e}$ Hz, where m_e is the electron mass and e is the electron charge. The plasma oscillation phenomenon was observed by the American chemist and physicist IRVING LANGMUIR (1881–1957) in 1929.

Plasmon

[atomic, nuclear] Quantum of OSCILLATION energy in a PLASMA, defined as $E_{pl} = \hbar\sqrt{(4\pi n_e e^2/m_e)}$, with $\hbar = h/2\pi$ ($h = 4.1356692 \times 10^{-15}$ Js the PLANCK'S CONSTANT), n_e the free electron density, m_e the electron mass, and e the electron charge.

Plastic strain

[geophysics, mechanics] Permanent deformation in shape or size of an entity without resulting in destructive fracture, which may accumulate over time as the result of a sustained stress that exceeds the elastic yield point for the constitution of the material. Plastic strain can be expressed as a POWER LAW defined as the strain rate ($e_s = \dot{\epsilon}_s$), linking applied stress (σ_s) to the activation ENERGY for deformation (Q_{ac}), the prevalent temperature (T) as $e_s = A\sigma_s{}^n \exp(-Q_{ac}/RT)$, where n is the heuristic power function constant, which is derived from experimental data, A is an arbitrary material constant, and $R = 8.3144621(75)\, \mathrm{J/K\,mol}$ the GAS constant. For an perfect viscous fluid, $n = 1$. Beyond plastic behavior the material will rupture. Materials can be "hardened" or "softened" to modify the plastic strain behavior. In GEOPHYSICS, the elastic–plastic behavior applies to the crust and mantle of the EARTH. Rheological stratification of the continental crust under stress can be defined with integral application of brittle friction and plastic flow. Deformation can occur in several ways: plastic, ductile, and brittle. Ductile materials will accumulate any permanently applied stress without macroscopically visible signs of fracture until the ELASTIC LIMIT is reached, at which point the material will disintegrate. Brittle deformation will experience MICROSCOPIC deformations, where grains of material will slide along each other and will break (crumble) past the yield point of the material. Viscoplasticity, in particular, is used to describe the flow of lave (*also see* CREEP) (see Figure P.107).

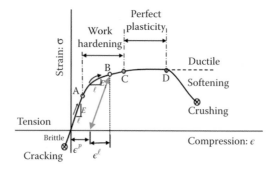

Figure P.107 Plastic strain.

Plasticity

[biomedical, chemical, mechanics] Process of irreversible deformations that are presumably based on an atomic scale, in biology on a cellular composition scale (in reference to stem cells). The deformations are formed when a threshold level or ELASTIC LIMIT is exceeded. The applied stress under plastic deformation is referred to a flow STRESS (see Figure P.108).

Figure P.108 Plasticity of an automobile, absorbing the external forces in deformation.

Plasticizers

[biomedical, chemical, mechanics] "Weak-makers," phthalates. Chemical additives that will makes PLASTICS more pliable and maneuverable.

Plastics

[chemical, mechanics] Chemical grouping of organic polymers that are deformable, generally derived from both plant-based (e.g., CELLULOSE, from cotton; vegetable oils from seeds), naptha (natural gas) or oil-based ingredients. The ingredients are called resins. Plastics are for instance polypropylene and polyethylene. The building blocks are, for instance, propylene, ethane, and ethane (monomers), which are constructed into polymers. Polymerization can be accomplished either by means of addition or in condensation reactions; sometimes the POLYMER is formed at the interface of two LIQUID layers of different media. Plastics are frequently manufactured as composite materials. Not all plastics formed from plant-based ingredients are biodegradable, since the same monomers are formed in comparison to oil-based plastics. Plastics are usually formed into shape by injection molding or pressing/stamping (see Figure P.109).

Figure P.109 Plastics.

Plato (427–347 BC)

[general] Original name "Aristocle," Greek scientist and philosopher, and founder of the modern concepts of optics and sight, contradicting the EXTRAMISSION theory of VISION of his peers. However, his work was not recognized millennia latesr, after the publications by LEONARDO DA VINCI (1452–1519). Other work by Plato involves the description of MAGNETISM (*also see* LOADSTONE) in support of the work by Socrates

(469–399 BC). In MECHANICS, Plato had postulated the CONSERVATION OF ENERGY concept in his description of the exchange between heat and ACTIVITY (i.e., kinetic ENERGY) (see Figure P.110).

Figure P.110 Plato (427–347 BC), artistic impression statue at the Louvre in Paris, France.

Plücker, Julius (1801–1868)

[atomic, general, nuclear] Scientist from Germany (Prussian empire). Plucker realized that when the pressure in a CATHODE ray tube is low, the GLASS wall at the opposite side can be made to emit light. The location where LIGHT is emitted can be altered by applying a MAGNET to the side WALL of the tube.

He interpreted the light emission and MAGNETIC manipulation with the presence of ELECTRIC CHARGE and indirectly indicated the discovery of the electron in 1858 (see Figure P.111).

Figure P.111 Julius Plücker (1801–1868).

Plutonium ($^{244}_{94}$Pu)

[atomic, nuclear] Artificially produced radioactive ELEMENT. Plutonium-244 is very stable with a half-life of 82 000 000 years, decays into $^{240}_{92}$U by ALPHA DECAY. Plutonium ($^{238}_{94}$Pu, plutonium isotope) was first made at the University of California in 1941 by high-speed collision of deuterons on uranium-238. Plutonium-238 is used as nuclear fuel on space ships. The Cassini probe and the Galileo probe are powered under thermo-nuclear reactors from plutonium-238. Another ISOTOPE, plutonium-239 has a FISSION reaction mechanism and used in nuclear weapons and certain NUCLEAR REACTOR power generators (see Figure P.112).

P

Figure P.112 Plutonium.

Plutonium Project

[general] *See* MANHATTAN PROJECT.

PMM1

[thermodynamics] PERPETUAL MOTION machine of the first kind. A hypothetical system with a cyclic process that does not endure an internal change in state (no ENERGY transfer); however, it produces work. There is a theoretical impossibility of such a device in existence or ever being developed since there is no energy produced but work would follow nonetheless.

PMM2

[thermodynamics] PERPETUAL MOTION machine of the second kind. A lossless mechanism based on a cyclic change in state that results in work. The number of constituents in the system will not change from state to state. This system is impossible to achieve. Assuming that there are different ways of achieving this process, one process is from one stable equilibrium, performing work, and reaching a new equilibrium with lower ENERGY. After subsequent work performed on the system, the new state will reach a NONEQUILIBRIUM STATE, which should be equivalent to the starting state but cannot be equivalent since the first state was an EQUILIBRIUM STATE and the third state is not.

Pneumotachometer

[biomedical, fluid dynamics] Device for measuring GAS flow in addition to the pressure difference over the device from input (pressure at the source) to output (external, ambient pressure). One particular application is in measuring the exhaled and inhaled breath and deriving the associated lung-volume (see Figure P.113).

Figure P.113 Pneumotachometer.

pn-junction

[electronics, general] Junction of a *p*-type material and an *n*-type material, forming a DIODE. The *p*-type material has a shortage of electrons (holes), while the *N*-TYPE SEMICONDUCTOR material has been treated to have a permanent surplus of electrons. The *pn*-junction forms a semiconductor diode. The SCHOTTKY DIODE is a metal–semiconductor *pn*-junction diode that uses the work function between the METAL and the semiconductor material to yield a SCHOTTKY BARRIER. The Schottky diode has RECTIFIER characteristics, with current profile: $I = I_r \left\{ \exp\left(qV/nk_bT \right) \right\} - 1$, where I_r represents the reverse leak current, q the charge, V the applied voltage, qV represents the bias potential, n is a factor that represents the idealistic character ($n = 1$ would be a perfect diode, $k_b = 1.3806488 \times 10^{-23}\,\mathrm{m}^2\,\mathrm{kg/s}^2\,\mathrm{K}$ the Boltzmann coefficient, and T the temperature at the junction. Step recovery diodes are *p-n* diodes with extremely fast recovery time due to the designed graded FERMI-LEVEL drop at the junction, thus minimizing the dwell time of the minority charge carriers. A Zener diode is a *p-n* diode with a well-defined and sharp reverse bias breakdown voltage (up to several hundred volt). Another type of *p-n* diode is the tunnel diode. The tunnel diode has greater than average DOPING of both *n-* and P-TYPE SEMICONDUCTOR materials resulting in a Fermi level that is in the valance band for the *p*-type material and for the *n*-type material the Fermi level is in the CONDUCTION BAND (see Figure P.114).

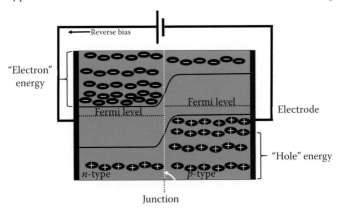

Figure P.114 *pn*-junction.

PNP transistor

[general] Semiconductor sandwich with N-TYPE SEMICONDUCTOR material has been treated to have a permanent surplus of electrons electronically positioned between two *p*-type materials with respective permanent shortage of electrons (holes). One *p*-type material is the "collector" while the other is the "emitter" and the *n*-type material provides the current quenching mechanism as the "base." Transistors can be used to make rudimentary amplifier circuits with power supplies and resistors. The current gain for the TRANSISTOR is the collector current (ΔI_C) to base current (ΔI_B) ratio: gain = $\Delta I_C/\Delta I_B$, and similarly for the voltage gain (see Figure P.115).

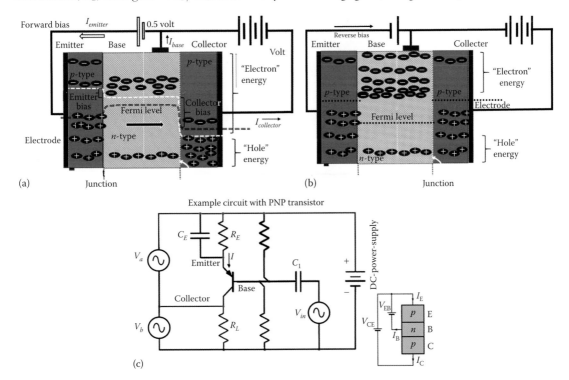

Figure P.115 (a–c) PNP transistor.

Po₂

[biomedical, chemical, fluid dynamics, general] Partial pressure of oxygen in a system, mixture of gasses. Gasses can be freely dispersed in liquids or chemically dissolved in fluids. In biomedical applications, this is used to determine the oxygen SATURATION of BLOOD with a PULSE OXIMETER (*see* RESPIRATION *and* PULSE OXIMETRY) (see Figure P.116).

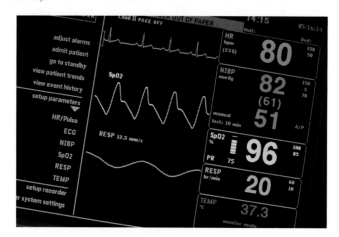

Figure P.116 Graphical representation of the partial pressure of oxygen, in particular, relevant to respiration.

Pockels, Friedrich Carl Alwin (1865–1913)

[general, optics] Physicist from Italy. Pockels is best known for his research how in certain birefringent materials the refractive index can be altered under the influence of an externally applied electric field (see Figure P.117).

Figure P.117 Friedrich Carl Alwin Pockels (1865–1913). (Courtesy of Technische Universität Dresden, Germany.)

Pockels effect

[electromagnetism, energy, general, optics, thermodynamics] Change in the optical axis of a medium linear to the MAGNITUDE of an externally applied electric field, observed and described by FRIEDRICH CARL ALWIN

Pockels (1865–1913) in 1893. Also considered to be part of the BIREFRINGENCE phenomenon. The local INDEX-OF-REFRACTION (n) can be described in a first-order Taylor series to depend on the local magnitude (location $\vec{r}$) of the ELECTRIC FIELD (E) as a function of time expressed as $n\left(E,\vec{r},t\right)=n\left(\vec{r},t\right)+\left[dn\left(\vec{r},t\right)/dE\right]E\left(\vec{r},t\right)$. The effect is used in the Pockels CELL for modulation of a beam of LIGHT, specifically in laser design, used in the MODE-LOCKED LASER (*also see* **KERR EFFECT**) (see Figure P.118).

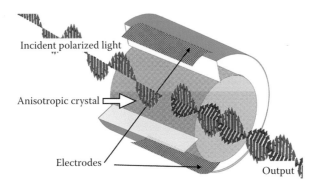

Figure P.118 The use of the Pockels effect in the Pockels cell, used to temporarily interrupt laser emission, creating a mode-locked laser beam.

Poincaré, Jules Henri (1854–1912)

[computational, general, thermodynamics] Theoretical physicist from France. Additionally, he was a mathematician and engineer. His computation work describes the shape of a rotating sphere turning into a "pear shape" in correlation with the momentum $L = I\omega$, where ω represents the ANGULAR VELOCITY and I the MOMENT OF INERTIA (which is a direct function of the shape of the revolving body). His most well-known work describes the MECHANICS of a rotating FLUID published in 1885: *Sur l'équilibre d'une masse fluide animée d'un mouvement de rotation*, in the *Acta Mathematica*. This work appears to be in follow-up of the work by CARL JACOBI (1804–1851) and COLIN MACLAURIN (1698–1746). The main reference of this work relates to the swing of a PENDULUM (see Figure P.119).

P

Figure P.119 Jules Henri Poincaré (1854–1912).

Poincaré section

[computational] Mechanism designed to discover structure in an attractor. The attractor for a dynamic system is the outlined CONTINUUM of physical parameter that the system tends to achieve irrespective of the starting conditions by physical evolution. The attractor can be plotted in a multidimensional graph. The Poincaré section follows from placing an arbitrary plane in the attractor graph and the orbit of the evolution of the attractor mechanism will intersect with the plane on several locations, which provides the marking outline for the Poincaré plane or section, providing an indication of structure of the attractor and hence the processes involved. Part of "chaos" theory.

Poinsot, Louis (1777–1859)

[mechanics] Physicist and mathematician from France. Poinsot is considered the father of geometrical MECHANICS. He was a contemporary, and colleague of French mathematician AUGUSTIN LOUIS CAUCHY (1789–1857) and the Italian mathematician JOSEPH-LOUIS LAGRANGE (1737–1813), all working at the École Polytechnique in Palaiseau near Paris, France (see Figure P.120).

POINSOT,
(Louis)
Membre de la Légion d'honneur.

Figure P.120 Louis Poinsot (1777–1859), engraved by Julien-Leopold Boilly.

Poinsot motion

[mechanics] Phenomenon in the Euler equation of MOTION calculations where two PRINCIPAL MOMENTS of inertia have the same value and direction, while only one force is present. Examples of Poinsot motion are found in gyroscopes and a spinning top. The Poinsot method was developed by LOUIS POINSOT (1777–1859) in 1809, which uses graphical interpretations of a body in MOTION based on conservation of KINETIC ENERGY and conservation of momentum. The KINETIC ENERGY (KE) of a rotating body with MOMENT OF INERTIA (I) and ANGULAR VELOCITY ω can be written, using the coordinate substitution $\vec{\rho}_m = \vec{\omega} / \sqrt{(2KE)}$, as $KE = (1/2)\left(I_1\omega_1^2 + I_2\omega_2^2 + I_3\omega_3^2\right)$, which yield: $I_1\rho_{m1}^2 + I_2\rho_{m2}^2 + I_3\rho_{m3}^2 = 1$, which is a description of an ellipsoid. The rotating ellipsoid in the graph represents the force-free motion, and the tangent plane is called the invariable plane (see Figure P.121).

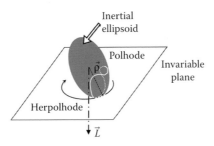

Figure P.121 Poinsot motion.

Point charges

[computational, general] Mathematical approximation for a geometry that is much larger than the source to allow for disregarding the boundary effects of the phenomenon in the SOLUTION of the situation. All charges are clumped together on an object of infinitesimal small size, or the charge itself is a single electron or PROTON charge. When the DISTANCE to the collection of charges is much greater than the diameter of the charge cloud the local effects of the charges are experienced as if they originate from the center of the charge collection. The point charge ($Q = \sum_i q_i$) will generate a Coulomb field at distance r resulting from Gauss' law expressed as $E_{\text{elec}} = \left(Q/4\pi\varepsilon r^2\right)\vec{r}$, where $\varepsilon = \varepsilon_r\varepsilon_0$, with $\varepsilon_0 = 8.85419\times10^{-12}\,\mathrm{C}^2/\mathrm{N\,m}^2$ the permittivity of free space and ε_r the RELATIVE PERMITTIVITY of the medium.

Point source

[acoustics, mechanics, optics] Any ENERGY representation that is considered to be located in an infinitesimally small volume at a single location in three-dimensional space. The size of the source often is taken with respect to the observed phenomena. The source will be isotropic and produce a SPHERICAL WAVE pattern. In certain approximations, the SUN can be considered a point source. In ACOUSTICS, a point source is for instance the emission from a piezoelectric device or SPEAKER, for this the ACOUSTIC INTENSITY will DECAY with $I \,\hat{=}\, 1/r^2$, whereas the pressure will decay as $P(r) \,\hat{=}\, 1/r$ with r the DISTANCE to the source. A point source can also be referenced as a mono-pole (monopole). The emitted wave front over TIME (t) will obey the WAVE EQUATION: $\left[\Delta - \left(n'/c^2\right)\left(\partial^2/\partial t^2\right)\right]V\left(\vec{r},t\right) = 0$, where $\Delta = \left(\partial^2/\partial x_1^2\right)+\left(\partial^2/\partial x_2^2\right)+\left(\partial^2/\partial x_3^2\right)+\cdots+\left(\partial^2/\partial x_m^2\right)$ is the Laplace operator for m-dimensional space, $V\left(\vec{r},t\right)$ the phenomenon (in which case this represents harmonics the function becomes FREQUENCY ($\nu = \omega/2\pi$) dependent: $V\left(\vec{r},t,\omega\right)$; acoustic electromagnetic etc., $n' > 1$ a constant, and c the speed of propagation of the phenomenon (e.g., speed of sound, speed of LIGHT). The spatial components of the wave equation will satisfy the Helmholtz equation. For an acoustic point source, the INTENSITY (I) over a period (T) is the average from the pressure and the PARTICLE motion ($\nu\left(\vec{r}\right)$) expressed as $I = (1/T)\int_0^T P\left(\vec{r},t\right)\nu\left(\vec{r},t\right)dt$

Point vortex

[computational, fluid dynamics] In FLUID DYNAMICS the calculation of the CIRCULATION ($\Gamma = \oint_c \nu dl = \int_s \left(\Delta\times\vec{v}\right)\cdot d\vec{s}$, where v is the velocity at the boundary of the tube generating the vortex, $\Delta = \left(\partial^2/\partial x_1^2\right)+\left(\partial^2/\partial x_2^2\right)+\left(\partial^2/\partial x_3^2\right)+\cdots+\left(\partial^2/\partial x_m^2\right)$ the Laplace operator for m-dimensional space and $\vec{s}$ the surface with circumference c) associated with for instance a RANKINE vortex tube can be approximated for vanishing CROSS SECTION to provide the point vortex $\Gamma = \pi a^2\omega_0 = \text{Constant}$, with ω_0 the angular velocity of rotation and $a \downarrow 0$ the vanishing radius (at which $\omega_0 \to \infty$) (see Figure P.122).

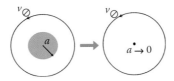

Figure P.122 Point vortex.

Poise (*P*)

[fluid dynamics, general, mechanics] Unit for DYNAMIC VISCOSITY, specifically in reference to liquids. One poise is equal to one-tenth pascal-second: $1P = 0.1\,\mathrm{Pa\,s}$. The poise is named after the French physiologist POISEUILLE, JEAN LEONARD MARIE (1799–1869).

Poiseuille, Jean Leonard Marie (1799–1869)

[fluid dynamics] Scientist and physiologist from France. Jean Poiseuille introduced a range of flow concepts with wide ranging implications (see Figure P.123).

Figure P.123 Jean Leonard Marie Poiseuille (1799–1869).

Poiseuille flow

[fluid dynamics] Laminar flow in a horizontal tube with diameter D, with PRESSURE (P) drop in direction z that can be described by the POISEUILLE LAW, with flow velocity ($v(r)$) profile as a function of radius (r): $v(r) = (1/16\eta)(dP/dz)(D^2 - 4r^2)$, where η is the viscoscity of the LIQUID in flow.

Poiseuille number ($Ps = v_{ph}\eta / gd_p^2 (\rho_s - \rho_f)$)

[fluid dynamics] Dimensionless number indicating the ratio of the net viscous force to the gravitational force, where v_{ph} is the PHASE VELOCITY of the WAVE phenomenon, η the KINEMATIC VISCOSITY, g GRAVITATIONAL ACCELERATION, d_p the (average) PARTICLE diameter, and ρ_s and ρ_f the respective density of the solid and the FLUID. The Poiseuille number applies primarily to LAMINAR FLOW conditions, and is mainly a function of the duct shape (e.g., circular, parallel plates).

Poiseuille's law

[biomedical, fluid dynamics] (also known as the Poiseuille equation) Expression for the flow rate through a horizontal tube as a function of the radius to the fourth power expressed by JEAN LEONARD MARIE POISEUILLE (1799–1869) in 1840. The average flow rate (Q_{flow}) is represented with respect to the radius of the tube (R) over a characteristic length (L) with a pressure gradient ($P_1 - P_2$) as

$Q_{\text{flow}} = (\pi R^4/8\eta)[(P_1 - P_2)/L]$, where η is the VISCOSITY of the LIQUID in flow. The use of Poiseuille's law to define BLOOD flow has limited validity due to the nonlaminar behavior and the fact that the vascular walls are compliant, next to the influences of the direction of flow in an upright body, which may also be in MOTION. Also found under HAGEN-POISEUILLE LAW, with the independent contributions of the Prussian (now his birthplace is in Russia) scientist GOTTHILF HEINRICH LUDWIG HAGEN (1797–1884).

Poisson, Siméon Denis (1781–1840)

[astrophysics/astronomy, biomedical, computational] Physicist and mathematician from France, with additional training in MEDICINE. Poisson was a pupil of GIUSEPPE LUIGI COMTE DE LAGRANGE (1737–1813), ADRIEN-MARIE LEGENDRE (1752–1833) and PIERRE-SIMON DE LAPLACE (1749–1827). Poisson contributed to the interpretation and development of differential equations and partial differential equations. Siméon Poisson elaborated on the work by JOHANNES KEPLER (1571–1630) on the perturbations by planets and provided elaborate descriptions of charge migration as well as DIFFUSION characteristics and properties next to HEAT TRANSFER in association with SADI NICOLAS LÉONARD CARNOT (1796–1832). Siméon Poisson replaced ÉTIENNE LOUIS MALUS (1775–1812) on his death at the École Polytechnique in 1812. His mathematical work under Laplace also influenced the work of GEORGE GREEN (1793–1841) (see Figure P.124).

Figure P.124 Siméon Denis Poisson (1781–1840).

Poisson brackets

[computational] Recursive process of differentiation, extending out over partial differential equations; for instance applied to two functions f and g with variables p and q, this yields $\{f(p,q), g(p,q)\} = \left[(\partial f/\partial p)(\partial g/\partial q)\right] - \left[(\partial f/\partial q)(\partial g/\partial p)\right]$. In differential equations, the Poisson brackets provide a Hamiltonian operation (H) in MECHANICS as a binary operation. The connection with the Hamiltonian in mechanics is as follows: $\dot{p} = \{p, H(p,q)\}$, respectively, $\dot{q} = \{q, H(p,q)\}$. The Poisson brackets are an integral part of the Hamiltonian EQUATIONS OF MOTION. Specific rules associated with the Poisson brackets in differential expressions are $\{f,g\} = -\{g,f\}$; $\{f,f\} = 0$; $\{f,gh\} = g\{f,h\} + \{f,g\}h$; and $\{f,\{g,h\}\} + \{h,\{f,g\}\} + \{g,\{h,f\}\} = 0$, which are all natural properties of QUANTUM operators.

Poisson distribution

[computational] PROBABILITY theory describing the distribution of obtaining exactly n successes in N trials, as the limit of a binomial distribution $P_\chi = \lim_{n \to \infty}\left\{[N!/n!(N-n)!]\,p^n(1-p)^{N-n}\right\}$, where P represents the probability and $\chi = Np$ the expected number of successes. The Poisson distribution is maximized under the condition $dP_\chi(n)/dn = 0$. The Poisson distribution was the brain child of SIMÉON DENIS POISSON (1781–1840).

Poisson equations

[biomedical, chemical] DIFFUSION of charges. $\nabla \cdot \vec{J} = d\rho_{charge}/dt = \nabla \cdot \gamma_{cond}\vec{E} = \gamma_{cond}\left(\nabla \cdot \vec{E}\right) = -\gamma_{cond}\left(\nabla^2\Phi\right)$, where the first part expresses the continuity of charge, $\nabla^2\Phi = \rho_{charge}/\varepsilon = \nabla \cdot \vec{J}/\gamma_{cond}$, $\vec{E}$ the electric field, γ_{cond} the electrical conductivity of the medium, $\vec{J}$ the charge FLUX (per unit area), Φ the potential difference across the BARRIER, which is the CELL MEMBRANE in biology, ∇^2 the Laplace operator, ρ_{charge} the charge density, and $\varepsilon = \varepsilon_r\varepsilon_o$, with $\varepsilon_0 = 8.85419 \times 10^{-12} C^2/N\,m^2$ the permittivity of free space and ε_r the RELATIVE PERMITTIVITY of the medium, introduced by SIMÉON DENIS POISSON (1781–1840).

Poisson noise

[biomedical, electronics, electromagnetism] Random SIGNAL fluctuations in the registered detector value resulting from a limited PHOTON count. The source may be powerful enough, however, due to attenuation in a medium the photon count can be drastically reduced. The limited photon count may not reach threshold values for conversion into an electrical signal, but cumulative events may provide electron release. Photon emission during X-RAY RADIATION provides an example of the random generation of the X-ray photons in the emission process. Poisson noise stands in comparison to GAUSSIAN NOISE. Poisson noise is based on the initial efforts and conclusions by SIMÉON DENIS POISSON (1781–1840) on general phenomenological description.

Poisson's ratio (v_p)

[fluid dynamics, geophysics, mechanics] Quotient of extensions normal to the PRINCIPAL STRESS vector over extensions parallel to the principal stress vector: $v_p = -\epsilon_x/\epsilon_z$, where ϵ_i is the strain in direction i. Note that Young's modulus is stress over strain. Poisson's ratio can, in geological applications, be derived from SEISMIC WAVE-velocity vector comparison. For a compressible medium $v_p < 0.5$, whereas for an incompressible medium $v_p = 0.5$.

Polar coordinates

[biomedical, computational, fluid dynamics, mechanics] Two-dimensional outline with two references; the DISTANCE with respect to a fixed origin, conveniently chosen, and the angular dependency with respect to a conveniently chosen reference line through the origin. This is superseded in three dimensions by cylindrical coordinates or alternatively spherical coordinates (see Figure P.125).

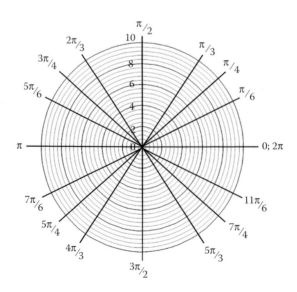

Figure P.125 Polar coordinates.

Polar moment of inertia

[biomedical, computational, mechanics] Geometrical outline of the distribution of the points within an arbitrary area (A) for a two-dimensional "object" in relation to an axis of choice: $J_{axis} = \int_A r_\rho^2 dA \xrightarrow{to\ x\text{-}axis} \iint_A y_\rho^2 dxdy$, where r_ρ represents the DISTANCE to the axis of choice. This is also known as the MOMENT OF INERTIA of a plane area, or the second moment area.

Polar nature of a medium

[biomedical, chemical, fluid dynamics, mechanics, thermodynamics] Materials (especially liquids) can on a molecular level be inertly polarized or can be induced to shift their ELECTRIC CHARGE concentration to create the equivalence of a DIPOLE. Water is a clear example of the natural polarity due to the arrangement of the two hydrogen atoms with respect to the single oxygen ATOM, where the hydrogen is arranged asymmetrically, with both atoms approximately at 120° with each other. Oils on the other hand are nonpolar. Both alcohols and the general classification of detergents are a special case that can mix with both water and OIL due to the induced polarity when in contact with water and the nonpolar behavior under a zero net charge exposure. Detergents are large molecules with a polar and a nonpolar end, which makes them ideal for MIXING with both water and oil (see Figure P.126).

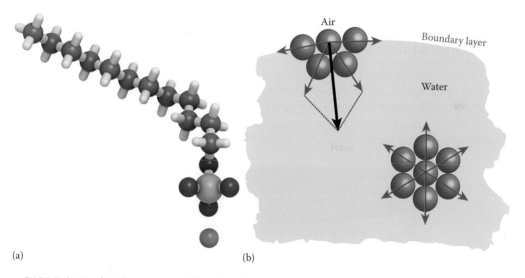

(a)   (b)

Figure P.126 Polarity of (a) detergent and (b) surface force of a polar medium.

Polarity of emf (electromotive force)

[electronics, general] The potential due to a surplus or deficiency of electron charges. For instance, a BATTERY has a positive and negative side, current flows per definition from positive to negative polarity.

Polarization

[general, nuclear, optics] Property of ELECTROMAGNETIC RADIATION, indicating the predominant angular direction of the electric field vector in a plane that is outlined by the direction of propagation coalescing with the normal to the plane, generally measured with respect to an arbitrary horizontal reference line. Certain animals can observe polarization, for instance the pygmy octopus, and it may communicate this way as well. The dung beetle and the field cricket for instance use the polarization of the LIGHT reflected by the MOON for navigation. Light reflecting from a surface will have a polarization direction that is outlined by the orthogonal of the direction of propagation in the plane of the reflecting surface and the direction of propagation of the reflected WAVE (see Figure P.127).

Figure P.127 Dung beetle navigating the ball of dung for her breeding housing, at night under light as polarized when reflected by the Moon.

Polarization of light

[general] A transverse electromagnetic WAVE is plane polarized when the electric field oscillates in a single plane outlined by the direction of propagation, whereas a circularly polarized beam of LIGHT has the electric field perform a rotation around the axis of propagation in a circular pattern with DISTANCE traveled repeatedly per wavelength. Light generated by various sources, including the SUN and an incandescent lamp is unpolarized also referred to as NATURAL LIGHT (*also see* **MALUS' LAW**) (see Figure P.128).

Figure P.128 Sunlight by its nature is unpolarized. The reflection from the windshield of an automobile.

Polarization selective film

[chemical, general] Transparent sheet that facilitates the preferred transmission of LIGHT with a single angle of polarization. Iodine is linked to the POLYMER chain in a polyvinyl alcohol (PVA) sheet, which is stretched under raised temperature, forming aligned long chains of hydrocarbon molecules. The POLARIZATION angle lining up with the polymeric molecules will be transmitted. The concept was introduced in 1928 by EDWIN HERBERT LAND (1909–1991).

Polaroid™ film

[chemical, general] Light-sensitive POLYMER film constructed of NITROCELLULOSE (transparent) with embedded iodoquinine sulfate crystals invented by EDWIN HERBERT LAND (1909–1991) in 1928. Produced by the Polaroid Corporation® (with founder Edwin Land). Polaroid film produces a virtually instantaneous hard-copy photograph after a brief fixation process inside the CAMERA. The principle of the polaroid film was initially a polarizer, a sheet that allows only LIGHT with a single POLARIZATION direction to pass through. The initial synthetic polarizer sheet was clear polyvinyl alcohol that was heated and stretched. Subsequent DOPING with iodine formed a MICROSCOPIC wire structure that allowed only light with an electric field that lines up with the molecular chains of iodine to pass through. The first camera was the Polaroid Land Camera Model 95 loaded with the first Polaroid Land Film Type 40, which were first offered to the public in late 1948. The polaroid photographic film works as follows. Once the special light-sensitive film has been exposed the "PICTURE" rolls between two rollers that crack a pouch with chemicals that covers the exposed film and fixes the chemical processes so that they are no longer light sensitive. A short heating process fixes the chemicals to prevent any further chemical interactions. The ejected photograph was only in black and white for the first camera (using a single-layer silver compound), later converted to operate in COLOR by including three layers of RED, green, and blue emulsion that are all light activated, and the process takes approximately 45 s (see Figure P.129).

Figure P.129 Polaroid® camera.

Poles

[general, geophysics] Poles have various meanings, mainly indicating the fact that there are opposite properties involved with respect to location. Geographic poles of the EARTH indicate the connecting points on opposite sides of the world through which the axis of rotation passes, whereas the MAGNETIC poles are an indication of the beginning and end points on either side of the world where MAGNETIC FIELD lines connect; the two are not in identical locations. Moreover, the magnetic north and south poles DRIFT and have switched location several times in traceable history. The poles of a PERMANENT MAGNET are on opposite sides of the magnetic object, generally also referenced as NORTH and south poles. The MAGNETIC POLES were first described in 1267 by the French engineer PIERRE PELERIN DE MARICOURT (a.k.a. Peter Peregrine) (c. 1220–1270); however, MAGNETISM was known for centuries prior to that. Poles that are equal will repel, whereas opposite poles attract. The poles on a BATTERY are the respective positive and negative terminals (*also see* DIPOLE) (see Figure P.130).

Figure P.130 Compass indicating the orientation with respect to the Earth's magnetic poles.

Pollio, Marcus Vitruvius (c. 80 BC–c. 15 AD)

[general] Roman scientist, engineer, and architect. According to Pollio (actually known as Vitruvius), nature is the inspiration to architecture. Birds and squirrels built nests; likewise humans erect housing from NATURAL MATERIALS. The Greek initiated architectural orders that linked biology to man-made structures: Doric, Ionic, and Corinthian. The order described in this culminated in understanding the HUMAN BODY,

perceived as the greatest ENGINEERING feat. This symbiosis led Vitruvius Pollio to define the Vitruvian Man, which was adopted and later drawn by LEONARDO DA VINCI (1452–1519) (see Figure P.131).

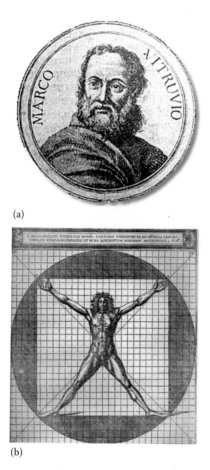

(a)

(b)

Figure P.131 (a) Artist representation of the likeness of Marcus Vitruvius Pollio (c. 80 BC–c. 15 AD) and (b) Vitrivius man. (Courtesy of De Architectura by Marcus Vitruvius Pollio [Como, 1521]. Shelfmark: 60.g.4. Copyright The British Library Board.)

Polonium ($_{209}^{84}$Po)

[atomic, nuclear] Radioactive, unstable "metallic" chemical ELEMENT, primarily found in uranium ores. Polonium was discovered by Marie (Manya)SKLODOVSKA CURIE (1867–1934) and her husband PIERRE CURIE (1859–1906) in 1898.

Polycrystalline solids

[general] Organized internal structure medium, often associated with metallic objects. A material that has no definite internal structure is amorphous, in contrast. Ordinary objects such as METAL spoons and metal cases are polycrystalline solids.

Polydimethylsiloxane (PDMS)

[biomedical, chemical] Chemical ELASTOMER, $CH_3\left[Si\left(CH_3\right)_2 O\right]_n Si\left(CH_3\right)_3$. PDMS is a nontoxic semipermeable material (gas permeable) that is also transparent to LIGHT down to 300 nm. PDMS is often referred to as an organosilicon, but is less expensive than silicon-based materials ("silicones"). Polydimethylsiloxane is an organic POLYMER that is used in many different applications, several in biomedical design; for instance contact lenses. Other consumer application is as a coating in shampoo, to make the hair slick and glossy.

Polymer

[biomedical, chemical] Synthetic compound, macro MOLECULE. The polymer matrix consists of repeated monomers (small molecular chains). In biomedical context, bone is considered a polymer, consisting of collagen and inorganic salts, comprised of carbonates and phosphates; alternatively, CELLULOSE is a polymer as well. Other biological polymers are proteins, starches, and latex. One of the most well-known and simple chemical polymers is polystyrene $(-(C_8H_8)_n)$ {MONOMER: C_8H_8}, next to polyethylene $(-(CH_2-CH_2)_n)$. Other common consumer polymers are POLYDIMETHYLSILOXANE (PDMS), POLY(VINYLIDENE) FLUORIDE (PVDF), and PVC (POLYVINYL CHLORIDE: $(-(CH_2=CHCl)_n)$ (*also see* MONOMER) (see Figure P.132).

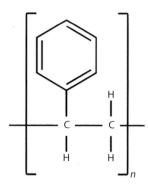

Figure P.132 Chemical structure of polystyrene polymer.

Polymethylmethacrylate (PMMA)

[biomedical, chemical, general] Transparent POLYMER, often used in place of GLASS, high strength making it shatterproof. Also known as acrylic glass; synthetic emulsion polymerization of methyl methacrylate, developed in 1928. Trade names include (but not limited to) Lucite®, Plexiglas®, and Perspex® (see Figure P.133).

Figure P.133 Plexiglas chairs.

Polypeptide

[biomedical, chemical] Amino-ACID monomers linked by peptide bonds to form a POLYMER structure. Often related to the formation of a polypeptide chain (see Figure P.134).

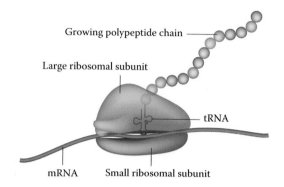

Figure P.134 Polypeptide in biological configuration.

Polytropic process

[astrophysics/astronomy, thermodynamics] Process that follows the CONTINUITY EQUATION for the linked properties for PRESSURE (P) and specific volume (V_s) as $PV_s^{n_p} = $ Const, where n_p is the polytropic index; alternatively, with respect to ENTROPY (S) as a function of TEMPERATURE (T) it can be described as $T(dS/dT) = $ Konstant. The polytropic index ($n_p = (c_p - \text{Konstant})/(c_v - \text{Konstant})$), where c_p and c_v are the SPECIFIC HEAT under constant pressure or constant volume respectively, defines and characterizes the specifics of process. The concept of polytropic mechanism relies on the process path in the state diagram (i.e., P-V diagram; respectively T-S diagram), where several paths are possible and they intersect (polytropic path). Any closed system for GAS or VAPOR that involves HEAT TRANSFER and work can be described by a polytropic path. Polytropic process describes heat transfer, specifically associated with EXPANSION and contraction. In ASTROPHYSICS, this applies to fluids where the pressure is a function of the density, in solutions to the LANE–EMDEN EQUATION.

Polyvinyl chloride (PVC)

[biomedical, chemical, mechanics] Polymer chemical that has a wide range of applications, made by polymerization of vinyl chloride. PVC is a plastic that is a solid under normal conditions. PVC forms the basis for products such as pipes, vinyl siding, BLOOD bags, drink bottles, HEART bypass tubing, etc. It is the third most popular polymer after polyethylene and polypropylene. PVC poses significant health risks, primarily when exposed to incineration fumes and in dust form, specifically due to the high chlorine content. Chemicals known as dioxins are released during the manufacturing, or incineration of PVC.

P

Dioxins exposure can lead to problems in reproductive, respiratory (asthma), and developmental health as well as provide carcinogenic properties (see Figure P.135).

Figure P.135 Applications of polyvinyl chloride (PVC) in the formation of plumbing pipes.

Poly(vinylidene) fluoride (PVDF)

[acoustics, biomedical, chemical, mechanics] Thermoplastic polymer $-\left(C_2H_2F_2\right)_n-$. Versatile fluoropolymer used in biomedical applications to attract proteins (ADHESION) and in consumer applications for instance in the manufacturing of bottles and insulation on wiring. PVDF is a very strong material, as well as flexible, that can be electrically polarized and can withstand temperatures up to 149°C and down to –62°C and remain stable. Because of its electrical POLARIZATION (ferroelectric polymer, recognized in the 1970s), it has piezoelectric properties and is used in ULTRASOUND transducers and extremely small and thin pressure sensing devices. The PVDF TRANSDUCER can operate at frequencies above 15 MHz with low acoustic impedance and low residual electrical impedance. PVDF pressure transducers can be made in film format with minimal mass and size.

Pool, M. L.

[atomic, nuclear] (twentieth century) Scientist from the United States involved in the description of nuclear processes in 1935. One specific area of research by Pool was in monokinetic electron sources.

Population inversion

[general] Atomic or molecular artificial excitation with respect to GROUND STATE for the majority of excitable atoms/molecules. Population inversion is the essential and critical process in the mechanism of action for LIGHT amplification by STIMULATED EMISSION of radiation (LASER). The concept of population inversion was hypothesized by ALBERT EINSTEIN (1879–1955) in 1917. The Einstein theory of population inversion defines the phenomenological relations between external electric and/or MAGNETIC fields, interacting with a group of atoms. This interaction forms the elementary foundation when "laser" conditions can be accomplished. The primary condition to achieve the laser mechanism of action is the atomic/molecular population inversion. This situation is defined by the fact that a greater number of excited atoms are present in the laser medium than there are atoms in the ground state. In order to achieve this, the following conditions need to be analyzed. There will be a minimum amount of ENERGY required to raise the majority of atoms to the excited state. For this, the zeroth-order assumption is that all energy injected into the laser medium (the medium that has an ELECTRON DECAY process with an associated particular electromagnetic emission energy, i.e., single wavelength; in most cases, some lasers make use of a broad-band source, such as dye lasers)

provided to raise electrons to the excited state is 100% effective. In the case of 100% stimulation efficiency, only the electron energy lost due to light emission, resulting from stimulated emission in particular, will need to be replaced. The excited state is not necessarily a single energy band; most likely, the atomic structure will be composed of several bands that can be filled by supplying external energy excitation. Furthermore, those multiple excitation energy levels can be split further in modes. These excited energy modes will have their own associated characteristic lifetimes. The energy modes describing one single energy band can be referenced by the notation N_m, each individual mode with respective average lifetime τ_c. A relationship defining the MINIMUM ENERGY requirements for exciting (pumping) the laser medium to EXCITED STATES can be developed based on a range of assumptions. In zeroth-order approximation, the idealized situation of a system with simply two energy levels can be considered, consisting of the GROUND state energy and the excited state. The energy supplied as input for the excitation of a two-level system raises the ground state condition to an excited state in an acceptable first-order description for the process. The supplied energy is assumed to be provided by an external ELECTROMAGNETIC FIELD; however, also an ELECTRIC field alone or MAGNETIC FIELD or chemical reaction can satisfy the energy requirements. The electromagnetic input satisfies the Planck relationship $W = h\upsilon = h(c/\lambda)$. The additional assumption is that the supplied photon energy W matches exactly the difference in energy between the excited energy level E_2 and the ground level: E_1: $E_2 - E_1 = h\upsilon_0 = h\left(c/\lambda_0\right)$. Because of the fact that this is a two-energy level system, the emissions will also only be composed of one single wavelength λ_0 or frequency $\upsilon_0 = \lambda_0/c$, with $c = 2.997\,924\,58 \times 10^8\,\mathrm{m/s}$ the speed of light. The resulting boundary conditions for the "pumping" POWER (P) of the excitation source is hence: $P = N_m hc/\lambda_0 \tau_c$, where N_m is the necessary number of atoms to be promoted to an excited state. The rate of stimulated emission that fuels the process of laser emission is directly proportional to the absolute value of the difference between the number of atoms raised to the excited state N_2, to the number of atoms sustaining the ground state N_1, defined as $N_2 - N_1$. This difference between the excited state and the ground state (two [2] level system) is linearly proportional to the ratio of the average lifetime with respect to the PHOTON emission associated with the decay process τ_e, in reference to the average lifetime that belongs to the excited state τ_c, defined as $\Delta N = N_2 - N_1 = N_m \tau_e/\tau_c$. Although spontaneous emission is not a consideration, it will initially be the driving "force" for the decay process and is defined as $dN_2/dt = -A_{21}N_2$, where A_{21} is the PROBABILITY coefficient defining the spontaneous emission process, also known as the Einstein A_{21} coefficient, and has the dimension of time^{-1}. The light energy absorption process for stimulation will adhere to the same principles, outlined as $dN_1/dt = -R_{12}N_1 = -B_{12}U(\upsilon_0)N_1$, where B_{12} is defined as the absorption coefficient, and also has the dimension of time^{-1}. Similarly, the stimulated emission process can be described as $dN_2/dt = -R_{21}N_2 = -B_{21}U(\upsilon_0)N_2$, where B_{21} is defined as the stimulation probability, where B_{21} also has the dimension of time^{-1} to remain consistent in the phenomenological description. The stimulation probability coefficient B_{21} depends on the energy-level transition only, and is hence a function of the particular ATOM used in the "laser medium," thus providing the unique emission wavelength for each medium. The decay of the respective energy occupation populations N_1 and N_2 also depends on the radiance of the incident light, that is, the MAGNITUDE of the incident excitation photon FLUX, and additionally depends on the cross-sectional area representing the stimulation excited atom—target: $R_{21} = \sigma_{21}\Phi$, where R_{21} is the rate of stimulated emission, Φ is the incident electromagnetic flux, and σ_{21} represents the "target area" stimulated emission CROSS SECTION. In this process, the coefficients A_{12}, B_{21}, and B_{12} are referred to as the Einstein coefficients. In the population inversion process, there is a requirement for achieving a Metastable state. The metastable state is a function of the interaction of various ELEMENTS in the laser medium in the presence of other elements (i.e., the base medium matrix, doped with the excitable atoms used for the stimulated emission process), and one is required to account for the interaction of this atomic matrix with the energy structure of the neighboring atoms. This will be part of the second-order approach. Still back to the two-level system, the decay processes as a function of time (i.e., decay rate) for the energy levels N_1 and N_2 are defined by the following rate equations: $dN_2/dt = -A_{21}N_2 + B_{12}U(\upsilon_0)N_1 - B_{21}U(\upsilon_0)N_2$; $dN_1/dt = -dN_2/dt$. Once again employing the Planck's black-body radiation equation (known as PLANCK'S LAW) for a BLACK BODY presumably at "virtual" temperature T, the emission of ELECTROMAGNETIC RADIATION with spectral profile $U(\nu)$ can be defined as $U(\upsilon_0)d\nu = \left(\upsilon^2/c^3\right)h\upsilon\left\{1/\left(\exp[h\upsilon/kT]-1\right)\right\}d\upsilon = e'h\upsilon < n > d\upsilon$, where e' represents the EIGENVALUE for the RESONANCE energy density associated with the emitted photons, per photon, and n represents the average number of photons present in each respective resonance energy density.

The occupation of the respective energy levels N_1 and N_2 while operating under thermal equilibrium, satisfies the condition: $N_2/N_1 = \left(g_1/g_2\right)\exp[-h\upsilon/kT]$, where g_1 and g_2 are representing the respective RADIATION weight for the various energy levels. By definition, under thermal equilibrium the decay rate from level 1 is equal to the decay rate from level 2, and hence neither level will experience no decay what so ever: $dN_1/dt = dN_2/dt = 0$. As a result of this particular boundary condition the following can be derived: $-A_{21}N_2 + B_{12}U(\upsilon_0)N_1 = B_{21}U(\upsilon_0)N_2$ R. This can be rewritten as $[A_{21}N_2 + B_{21}U(\upsilon_0)]N_2 = B_{12}U(\upsilon_0)N_1$, providing the electromagnetic field condition during population inversion: $U(\upsilon_0) = A_{21}/\left[B_{12}\left(N_1/N_2\right) - B_{21}\right]$. Based on the conditions of thermal equilibrium between the two energy levels, and including the Planck black-body radiation, the Einstein coefficients can be shown to be correlated to each other as $B_{12}\left(g_1/g_2\right) = B_{21}$, and $\left(\upsilon^2/c^3\right)B_{21} = -A_{21} = U_e(\upsilon_0)B_{21}$. The condition $U_e\left(\nu_0\right) = \left(n^3/c^3\right)$ defines the spectral energy density for the situation of one (1) photon in each respective eigenvalue OSCILLATION, under the condition that the average number of photons present in each eigenvalue oscillation equates to only one single photon. This condition represent the fact that under an external field during stimulated emission this process equates to spontaneous emission, where only one single photon is allowed in each energy configuration. This condition is by definition satisfied based on the PAULI EXCLUSION PRINCIPLE as well as Schrödinger conditions and the de Broglie orbital constraints. The fact that in a real atomic energy configuration, the electron energy levels are split up due to the orbital constraints imposed by the BOHR ATOM model, the laser emission will not necessarily consist of a single wavelength, but rather be composed of spectral emission with a linewidth. This linewidth will be confined and defined by the choice in elements used to construct the LASER excitation medium. To summarize: the stimulated emission will dominate under population inversion $n > 1$, while for $n < 1$ the prevailing mechanism of light emission will be based on spontaneous emission. In order to harness the photons in the LASER medium, the laser medium has an optical construction known as a cavity that is confined by mirrors on either side, one side with slightly less than perfect reflectivity allowing laser light emission. The mirrors on opposite sides of the laser medium create an oscillator, or under specific boundary conditions a resonator (*also see* LASER).

Porphyrins

[biomedical, chemical] Sensitizer organic chemicals, which are neutral and nontoxic in their GROUND STATE but become chemically active when excited by a reagent medium, either chemical or energetic (e.g., photon energy). The porphyrin structure forms a macrocyclic structure, consisting of four pyrrole rings with joining molecular segments, primarily $= CH -$. Porphyrins consist of conjugate acids that are forming ligands that bind to metals (e.g., IRON in "heme"). The two most well-known porphyrins are chlorophyll (oxygen process in plant leaves) and heme as cofactor to the hemoglobin protein in BLOOD, used to acquire and loosely bind oxygen and carbon dioxide in the RESPIRATION system. One particular biomedical application is in PHOTODYNAMIC THERAPY to treat cancer through light-mediated chemical process that results in CELL death. Other chemical integrations are by means of for instance pheoporphyrin, also known as a petroporphyrin. Pheoporphyrin is a geologic porphyrin found in coal, crude OIL, sedimentary rocks, or oil shale (see Figure P.136).

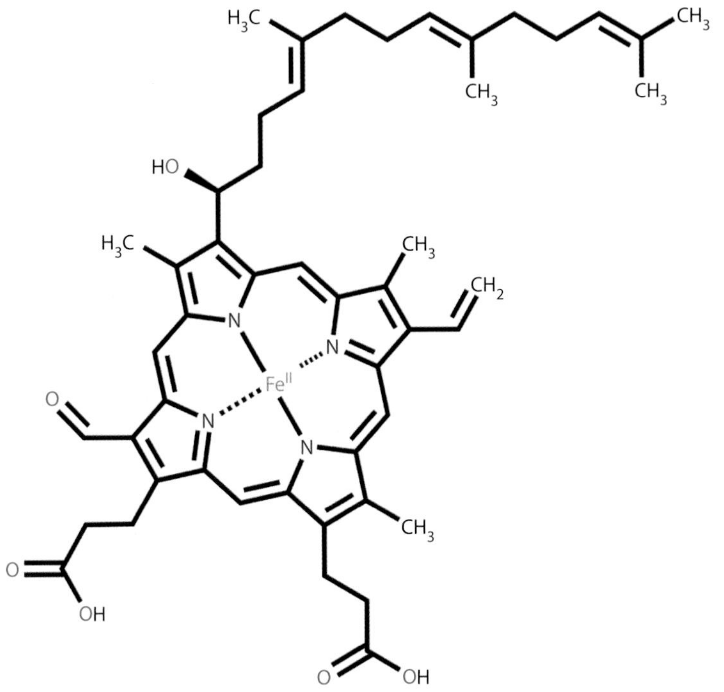

Figure P.136 Heme porphyrin, cofactor, and integral part of the hemoglobin protein, used for the transport of oxygen by red blood cells.

Positive charge

[general] Net charge with value that has opposite sign of the charge of an electron; alternatively, with a charge that repels protons. Charge is quantized, on an atomic level by PROTON value and as a material based on the amount of missing electrons with respect to a neutral electric state. An object made from GLASS that is rubbed with silk or flannel will become positively charged, transferring electrons from the glass to the cloth. The existence of charges can be dated back to the rubbing of AMBER with fur, as described by PLATO (427–347 BC). The nomenclature of positive and NEGATIVE CHARGE (introducing the hypothesis that there are only two types of charges) was introduced by the scientist and statesman (founding father) from the United States BENJAMIN FRANKLIN (1706–1790), and was based on the presumed transfer of positive charge, later found to be a misinterpretation. Franklin's proposition was based on the observations by the scientist and astronomer from Great Britain STEPHEN GRAY (1666–1736) in 1730.

Positive displacement pump

[fluid dynamics] Machine that has as the mechanism of action for flow the reduction of volume of a chamber holding the liquid (see Figure P.137).

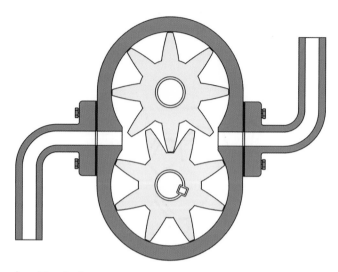

Figure P.137 Example of positive displacement pump: gear pump.

Positive ions

[atomic, nuclear] Atom or MOLECULE that is missing one or more electrons (see Figure P.138).

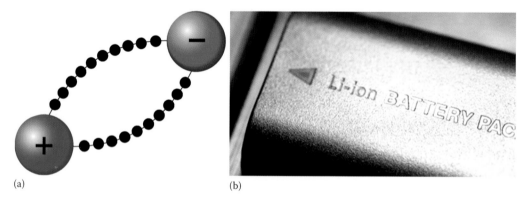

(a)   (b)

Figure P.138 (a) Positive ion interacting with negative ion, attraction and (b) lithium ion battery, popular rechargeable battery in most electronic portable devices.

Positive lens

[general] Lens that has a positive focal length and generally produces a magnified IMAGE with magnification greater than one (1) and produces a real image, providing the boundary conditions that are supporting the application. A positive lens is a converging LENS. Keep in mind that a converging lens with the object

placed at a DISTANCE closer than the FOCAL POINT will create a virtual image. The most well-known example of a positive lens is a loop (see Figure P.139).

Figure P.139 Example of positive lens, or loupe.

Positive rays

[atomic, nuclear] During the CATHODE ray experiments in 1886 by JOSEPH JOHN THOMSON (1856–1940), the observation was made that on the opposite side of the side of the tube where the ANODE is positioned and the CATHODE RAYS are fitting the GLASS window, other emissions were recorded that could be deflected by MAGNETIC fields, however, responding in opposite manner to the cathode rays. Thompson named them positive rays. The cathode ray tube from the late 1900s was preceded by the CROOKES TUBE, invented by the physicist and chemist from Great Britain SIR WILLIAM CROOKES (1832–1919) in 1870, resembling the modern neon-gas-discharge tube. This phenomenon was predated by observed and documented low-pressure discharges in a BAROMETER by the French astronomer JEAN PICARD (1620–1682) in 1675; however no conclusive evidence of the mechanism of action in both cases, or the values of the charges were involved.

Positron (β^+)

[astrophysics/astronomy, atomic, general, nuclear, quantum, thermodynamics] Positive counterpart of the electron, also sometimes referred to as the antielectron. The positron was predicted by the DIRAC EQUATION. The positron was discovered in 1932, and has an equivalent ENERGY of $E = \mathrm{mc}^2 = 0.511$ MeV. The positron resulted from investigations into the COSMIC RAYS.

Positron annihilation

[atomic, biomedical, solid-state] Particle emitted by a radionucleotide ISOTOPE after a relatively short half-life. The positron will be emitted from a nucleotide during DECAY and subsequently annihilated after a relatively short lifetime (examples of RADIONUCLIDE half-life and inherent ENERGY are $^{18}\mathrm{F} : 110$ min, $E = 0.64$ MeV; $^{11}\mathrm{C} : 22.4$ min, $E = 0.96$ MeV; $^{15}\mathrm{O} : 2.1$ min, $E = 1.72$ MeV, where fluoride [$^{18}\mathrm{F}$] is in a RADIOPHARMACEUTICAL: fludeoxyglucose [FDG]) with any of the many free electrons in the medium, specifically applied to biological media for imaging purposes in POSITRON EMISSION TOMOGRAPHY (PET). The annihilation process generally releases energy in excess of $E > 1.2$ MeV. The annihilation energy is released as two identical gamma (Γ) quanta with $E_\gamma = 511$ keV. These QUANTA are emitted in perfectly opposite directions. The energy balance for the positron annihilation process and the gamma pair production is described as $E_{\mathrm{positron}} + E^{\mathrm{kinetic}} + E_{\mathrm{electron}} \geq 2E_\gamma$. The rest energy is derived from the difference in energy of the isotope and the annihilation product. In addition to the rest energy of the electron (E_{electron}) and the positron (E_{positron}) respectively, there can be positron or electron MOTION with respective kinetic energy E^{kinetic}. The nuclear energy of the decay reaction follows from the quantum PHYSICS using the mass-energy equivalence, providing the REST MASS energy as $E = mc^2$, where m is the mass of the object and $c = 2.99792458 \times 10^8$ m/s the speed of LIGHT. The photon energy follows $E = h\nu$, where $h = 6.626068 \times 10^{-34}$ m^2 kg/s is PLANCK's CONSTANT and ν the frequency of the PHOTON. This yields $m_p c^2 + m_e c^2 = 2h\nu_\gamma$, where m_p is the mass of the positron and m_e the electron mass. Filling in the mass equivalent energy for each respective component yields $511\,\text{keV} + E_{positron}^{kin} + 511\,\text{keV} \geq 1.022\,\text{MeV}$. Only concurrent emission of two 511 keV gamma quanta is considered an indication of positron release (*also see* ANNIHILATION) (see Figure P.140).

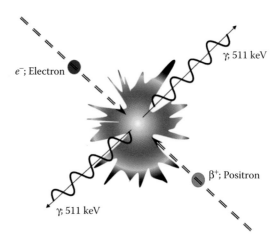

Figure P.140 Positron annihilation and gamma pair emission.

Positron decay

[nuclear] *See* BETA DECAY.

Positron emission tomography (PET)

[atomic, biomedical, energy, general, imaging, nuclear, solid-state] Nuclear imaging technique that produces images by means of introduction of radioactive isotopes that will emit a positron at a relatively short half-life. This imaging technique offers the capabilities to determine METABOLIC ACTIVITY of living organisms through incorporation of a Trojan horse ISOTOPE in the cellular METABOLISM obtained through radioactive labeling. The short-lived positron-emitting radionucleotide can be detected noninvasively for imaging purposes by specialized equipment. Specific crystals, for instance bismuth germanate (BGO), convert the high-energy gamma photons into lower ENERGY photons. The visible light photons can subsequently be collected by a semiconductor array, such as a CCD (charge-coupled device) ELEMENT. The CCD array converts the PHOTON energy into electrical data, registered and located in three-dimensional space by the tomograph ELECTRONICS. The RADIOPHARMACEUTICAL that is administered contains radioactively labeled chemical substances using constituents that are identical, or chemically equivalent, to naturally occurring ELEMENTS in the body. Radioactive labeling pertains to the fact that one ATOM in a MOLECULE is replaced by a radioactive equivalent, a radionucleotide. Examples of radioisotopes used in PET imaging are, for instance, ^{11}C, ^{18}F, ^{13}N, and ^{15}O. All the short-lived radioisotopes used in PET scans DECAY by positron emission. Positrons ($\beta+$) are positively charged electrons. Positrons hence have the same mass and rest energy as an electron. Positron emission isotopes are introduced in the BLOOD stream to finally be incorporated in the organ or tumor of interest. Imaging is made possible by the positron–electron annihilation process, which emits two gamma rays in opposite direction. A specially designed detection mechanism in a tomograph detecting the MAGNITUDE and detection sequence of the gamma photons and subsequently derives the isotope's location and concentration by interpolation, transforming the received SIGNAL in a three-dimensional IMAGE. The PET visualization provides the tools to identify normal and abnormal activity in living tissue. This is in contrast to X-RAY computed tomography (CT), which principally renders anatomical images. PET measures chemical changes in the tissue that can be used to identify metabolic activity that is not consistent with normal healthy tissue. Analogously, MAGNETIC RESONANCE IMAGING (MRI) can also measure specific metabolic activity with the specific limitation to blood oxygenation consumption. In the annihilation process of the constituent as an example, fluoride is stabilized by removing a POSITIVE CHARGE from the NUCLEUS through the conversion shown in the chemical reaction: $^{18}_{9}F \rightarrow \, ^{0}_{+1}e + \, ^{18}_{8}O$. A special version of PET is SINGLE-PHOTON EMISSION COMPUTED TOMOGRAPHY (SPECT) (see Figure P.141).

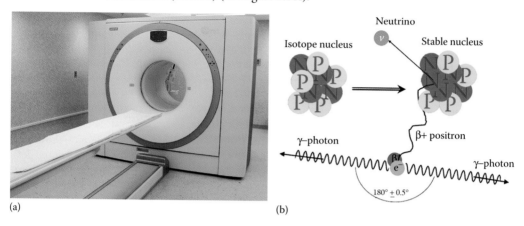

(a)   (b)

Figure P.141 (a) Positron emission tomography equipment (PET) and (b) PET mechanism of action.

Positronium

[atomic, nuclear] Metastable, ISOLATED SYSTEM consisting of an electron and the antiparticle: positron, bound as a single hypothetical atomic structure, predicted in 1932, detected in the 1950s. The positronium energetically resembles a HYDROGEN ATOM; however, positronium does not have the positron as the NUCLEUS but as a partner in orbit. The positronium decays with the emission of two gamma QUANTA, each at 511 keV. Positronium is referred to as an "exotic" atom, which defines an altered atom in which one or more nuclides have been substituted by other type particles of the same charge in different ENERGY setting, not necessarily with same total energy (see Figure P.142).

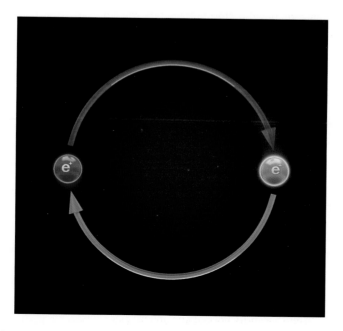

Figure P.142 Positronium.

Potassium ($^{19}_{39}$K)

[biomedical, chemical] Mineral, ALKALI METAL. In biology, potassium is one of the essential constituents of cells and tissues. Potassium performs a critical function in most muscular functions and is in integral part of the MEMBRANE POTENTIAL.

Potassium chloride (KCl)

[biomedical, chemical] SALT. In many facets similar to SODIUM CHLORIDE (conventional table salt: NaCl).

Potential (V)

[general] Referring the electrical potential that is associated with a charge accumulation and the work requirements for transporting a charge to or from the charge cluster. The potential is the POTENTIAL ENERGY (PE) of a charge in the vicinity of a charge grouping per unit charge: $V = (\text{electrical} - \text{PE})/\text{charge}$. The potential energy results from the electric field emanating from the charge cluster. The potential difference between two locations is equal to the work performed moving a charge between the two locations, per value of the moving charge. The work (W) performed is the force on the charge multiplied by the DISTANCE traversed (d): $W = Fd$, where the FORCE (F) is the charge to be moved multiplied by the ELECTRIC FIELD (E), $F = dE$. The electric field is the potential over the distance $E = Vd$ (also see COULOMB LAW and VOLTAGE).

Potential barrier

[atomic, energy, quantum] A potential ENERGY discontinuity, or slope (BARRIER) expressed as electrical potential, that influences the SOLUTION to the SCHRÖDINGER EQUATION for the transportation of a charged particle (NUCLIDE, electron) through a charge cloud. The energy barrier can be the difference between GROUND STATE and excited state of an atomic electron. The PROBABILITY of crossing the barrier will be a function of the kinetic energy of the PARTICLE with respect to the barrier "height" (MAGNITUDE). The probability (P_{chance}) of passing a mass (m_o) with charge through the barrier (over a DISTANCE $x_2 - x_1$) can be written as proportional to the potential magnitude as $P_{\text{chance}} \approx e^{-\gamma_{\text{barrier}}}$, where $\gamma_{\text{barrier}} = (2/\hbar)\int_{x_1}^{x_2} \{2m_o [V(x) - \text{KE}]\}^{1/2} dx$, with $\hbar = h/2\pi$ ($h = 6.62606957 \times 10^{-34}\,\text{m}^2\,\text{kg/s}$ PLANCK's CONSTANT) (also see BARRIER PENETRATION and TUNNELING) (see Figure P.143).

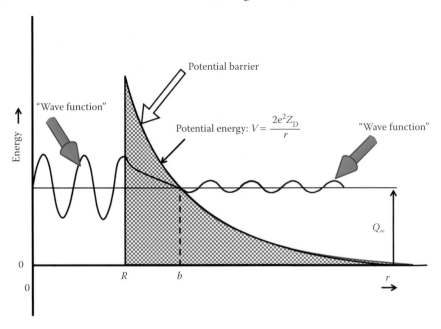

Figure P.143 Potential barrier as part of a nuclear or atomic energy model. The probability of escape from the nucleus, respectively atom is proportional to the "height" of the barrier.

Potential difference

[biomedical, energy, general] The difference in potential between any two points in a circuit; the work required to carry a unit POSITIVE CHARGE from one point to another (*see* POTENTIAL *or* ELECTRICAL POTENTIAL *as well as* VOLTAGE) (see Figure P.144).

Figure P.144 Potential difference for a battery.

Potential energy (PE)

[general, mechanics, nuclear] The ENERGY that a body possesses by virtue of its location, external exposure, or mechanical attachments that it can potentially release in another form of energy (*Note*: CONSERVATION OF ENERGY). The potential to release energy can be made in reference to any point in space, where the work performed (W) to bring an object from one point to another point in space is the difference in potential energy between those two points: $W_{21} = PE_2 - PE_1$. Potential energy is expressed for location as $PE(x, y, z) = \rho V g s(x, y, z)$, where ρ is the density, V is the volume of the object, $\rho V = m$ is the mass of the object at rest, and $s(x, y, z)$ is the location of the object with respect to a point of reference, primarily height. One form of external exposure is a DIPOLE in an external MAGNETIC FIELD ($\vec{B}$), which has the potential of generating a TORQUE. The potential energy of the dipole (e.g., current loop) with MAGNETIC DIPOLE moment ($\overrightarrow{M_{current}} = NIA\vec{n}$) is expressed as $PE = -\overrightarrow{M_{current}} \cdot \vec{B}$, where I is the current in the loop, N the number of loops in the device carrying the current, A the area outlined by the loop, and $\vec{n}$ a unit vector in direction perpendicular to the plane of the loop, whose direction can be found by applying the right-hand rule. Additionally, for a spring, the mechanical attachment of an elastic device has the potential to release energy when the object is removed from the state of equilibrium, expressed as $PE = (1/2)ks^2$, where k is the spring constant and s is the displacement from equilibrium. Another form of potential energy is the potential of becoming engaged in a chemical reaction or nuclear degeneration (e.g., breaking down of isotopes). The potential energy stored in a SOLENOID with a magnetic field B may depend on the location within the solenoid and is frequently defined as energy density per unit VOLUME (V) as $PE/V = B^2/2\mu_0$, where μ_0 is the DIELECTRIC permeability of VACUUM. Similarly, the potential energy of a CAPACITOR with electric field E

P

between the plates is defined per unit volume as $PE/V = (1/2)\,\epsilon_0\,E^2$, where ϵ_0 is the dielectric permittivity of vacuum (see Figure P.145).

Figure P.145 Example of potential energy resulting from elevation converted into hydroelectric energy.

Potential energy of a liquid surface

[biomedical, chemical, fluid dynamics, mechanics, thermodynamics] Molecules in the main body of a LIQUID are subject to thermal agitation and the internal forces on the molecules from neighboring molecules, and gravity will fluctuate but on average have zero balance, while the surface molecules are subject to an attractive force that maintains the molecules in the liquid. The molecules at the surface hence are considered to possess a potential ENERGY greater than the internal molecules of the liquid. The SURFACE TENSION provides the foundation for the SURFACE POTENTIAL ENERGY. The surface will continuously seek a condition of minimal potential energy, meaning that the surface will tend to shrink if allowed to assume minimum surface area with lower potential energy since the work needed to stretch the surface is counteracted by the potential energy. This also explains that a droplet in AIR will tend to take on a spherical shape, having the smallest area for any mass and volume. The surface potential is directly linked to the surface tension, however, with a correction for the MENISCUS curvature at the edge of the surface. The ANGLE of the surface with the WALL is represented by θ measured with respect to the wall above the liquid surface, giving the ratio of surface tension (σ_{surface}) to surface potential energy (γ_{surface}) as $\cos\theta = -\gamma_{\text{surface}}/\sigma_{\text{surface}}$ (*see* SURFACE TENSION).

Potential flow

[fluid dynamics] In FLUID DYNAMICS a "potential function" $\phi(x_1, x_2, t)$ can be defined that outlines the conformation to the CONSERVATION LAWS, with $\nabla \times \nabla\phi = 0$, while for IRROTATIONAL FLOW the average VELOCITY ($\bar{v}$) is defined by $\bar{v} = \nabla\phi$. Lines of $\phi = \text{Constant}$ describe the velocity field, also called potential lines of flow. The velocity profile is defined with respect to orientation (x_1, x_2) as $d\phi = u'dx_1 + v'dx_2$, where $u' = \partial\phi/\partial x_1$ and $v' = \partial\phi/\partial x_2$. For the potential flow, it yields $dx_2/dx_1 = -u'/v'$, representing the potential lines that are by definition perpendicular to the streamlines. The streamlines are defined by the STREAM FUNCTION ψ, $u' = \partial\phi/\partial x_1 = \partial\psi/\partial x_2$. Note that irrotational flow is best defined by ϕ, while incompressible flow adheres to ψ; for incompressible, irrotational flow both parameters apply. With the potential function, the flow definition reduces to one parameter instead of three velocity components: (u', v', w'). The VELOCITY POTENTIAL satisfies the LAPLACE EQUATION. The potential function for flow can be used to rewrite the Bernoulli equation as $\rho[(\partial/\partial t)\nabla\phi + (1/2)(\nabla\phi)^2] + \nabla P + \rho g\nabla x_3$, with P the pressure, ρ the local density, and g the GRAVITATIONAL ACCELERATION. The CIRCULATION (Γ_{circ}) for a free VORTEX in irrotational flow is described as $\Gamma_{\text{circ}} = \oint_C \vec{\omega}(\vec{r}, t)\,d\vec{s} = \oint_C \nabla \times \vec{v}(\vec{r}, t)\,d\vec{s} = \oint_C \nabla\phi(\vec{r}, t)\,d\vec{s}$, where $\vec{\omega}$ represents the vorticity (*also see* CAUCHY–RIEMANN EQUATIONS).

Potential head

[fluid dynamics] The head in FLUID DYNAMICS relates to the height of a LIQUID column; combining this with applied pressure, the potential head becomes the pressure head plus the elevation head. Expressed in ENERGY, the potential head is the potential energy per unit weight of the FLUID. The pressure head is the PRESSURE (P) per DENSITY (ρ): $P/\rho g$; the elevation head is height of the column y. For dynamic systems, the total head is the kinetic head plus the potential head, where the kinetic head (KH) is $KH = v^2/2g$, with v the flow velocity and g the GRAVITATIONAL ACCELERATION (see Figure P.146).

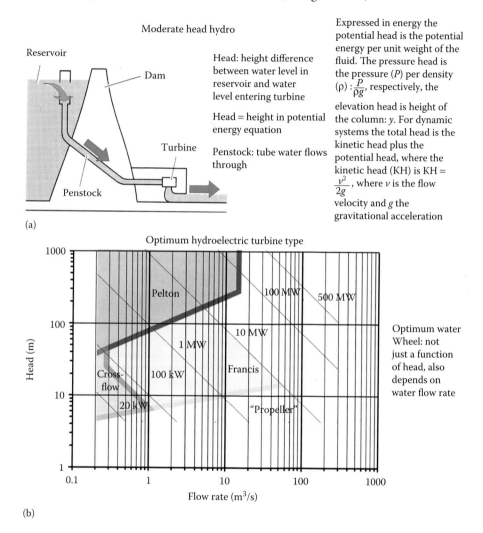

Moderate head hydro

Head: height difference between water level in reservoir and water level entering turbine

Head = height in potential energy equation

Penstock: tube water flows through

Expressed in energy the potential head is the potential energy per unit weight of the fluid. The pressure head is the pressure (P) per density (ρ) : $\frac{P}{\rho g}$, respectively, the elevation head is height of the column: y. For dynamic systems the total head is the kinetic head plus the potential head, where the kinetic head (KH) is KH = $\frac{v^2}{2g}$, where v is the flow velocity and g the gravitational acceleration

(a)

Optimum hydroelectric turbine type

Optimum water Wheel: not just a function of head, also depends on water flow rate

(b)

Figure P.146 (a,b) Potential head.

Potential well

[atomic, chemical, computational, nuclear, quantum, thermodynamics] In atomic PHYSICS, the ENERGY function for a nucleon in motion ("orbit") can be described by the SCHRÖDINGER equation, specifically in spherical coordinates only the radial part (r) remains: $-\left(\hbar^2/2m_0\right)\left(d^2u/dr^2\right) + \left\{\left[\ell\left(\ell+1\right)\hbar^2/2m_0r^2\right] + V\left(r\right)\right\} = Eu$, where $V\left(r\right)$ represents the potential that confines the nucleon, ℓ the ORBITAL QUANTUM NUMBER, u the (radial-) wavefunction, a polynomial function, $\hbar = h/2\pi$, with $h = 6.62606957 \times 10^{-34}\,\mathrm{m}^2\,\mathrm{kg/s}$ PLANCK'S CONSTANT, m_0 the nucleon mass, and E the total energy of the process (kinetic and potential energy). Under the boundary conditions, u will be a finite polynomial when $r \to \infty$. For an INFINITE SQUARE WELL with radius R, the potential function becomes $V(r) = 0$ for $r < R$; $V(r) = \infty$ for $r = R$. Alternatively, for a harmonic oscillator potential, the well is defined as $V(r) = (1/2)m_0\omega_0 r^2$ for $r < R$, where ω_0 is the oscillator angular frequency. More realistic cases are $V(r) = -V_0$ for $r \leq R$ and $V(r) = 0$ for $r > R$; alternatively, $V(r) = -V_0 + br + cr^2$ for $r \leq R$, a "rounded" or parabolic well (see Figure P.147).

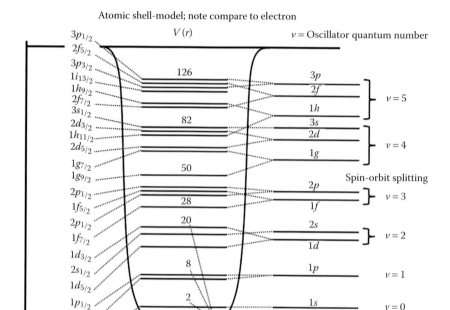

(a)

For: $\ell = 0,1,2,3,4,5$
The spectroscopic letters are assigned as follows:
s, p, d, f, g, h

Notation: $n\ell_j$

Quantum number: n
Angular momentum: vh
Nuclear spin: j

$j^2 = \ell^2 + s^2 - 2(\vec{\ell}\cdot\vec{s})$

(b)

Figure P.147 (a,b) Potential well.

Potentiometer

[general] Variable, continuously adjustable RESISTOR. Generally, the potentiometer has three poles, between two the RESISTANCE increases (using the "center" connection as a reference) as the dial is turned clockwise; alternatively, switching the outer connectors makes the resistance decrease with increasing ANGLE (see Figure P.148).

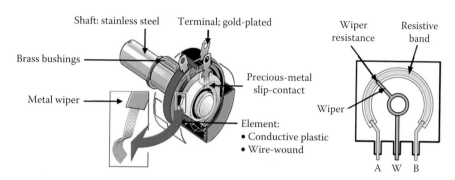

Figure P.148 Potentiometer.

Pound (lb)

[general] Unit of mass in the English unit system. One pound in SI UNITS equals 453.592 g. Most units in the system of measurements used in the United States are based on the British Imperial Units; however, in 1824 the British units were adjusted and there are now differences with the American units; for instance, the imperial gallon equals in SI units 4.54609 liters, whereas the US Gallon is 3.785411 liters.

Pound, Robert Vivian (1919–2010)

[atomic, imaging, nuclear] Scientist form Canada who was instrumental in the discovery and development of nuclear magnetic resonance imaging (MRI), while at Harvard University. The MAGNETIC RESONANCE work coincided with the independent work of the Swiss scientist FELIX BLOCH (1905–1983). He gained

P

additional fame with his experimental verification of general relativity concepts in the Pound–Rebka experiment, in collaboration with Glen Anderson Rebka, Jr. (1931–) in 1959 (see Figure P.149).

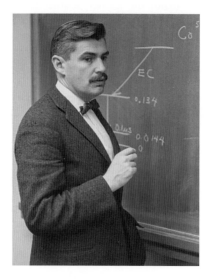

Figure P.149 Robert Vivian Pound (1919–2010). (Courtesy of Harvard University; Cambridge, MA. Image reference: UAV 605.270.5p, Box 7, Pound, Robert V., Harvard University Archives.)

Pound–Rebka experiment

[relativistic] Experimental verification of the special relativistic gravitational REDSHIFT and general relativistic blueshift under DOPPLER circumstances. The experiment performed by ROBERT VIVIAN POUND (1919–2010) and his student Glen Anderson Rebka, Jr. (1931–2015) in 1959 at Harvard University, Boston, MA, USA, combined the special relativistic redshift with the general relativistic blueshift. The special relativity (($\square_s$)) Doppler shift is given by $\Delta v_{d,s} = \sqrt{\{1+(v^2\cos^2\theta/c^2)/[1-(v^2/c^2)]\}}v_0$, where θ is the ANGLE between the relative velocity and the direction of MOTION of the source, v the relative velocity between the source and the observer, and c the speed of LIGHT. The blueshift predicted by general relativity resulting from gravitational influences (($\square_g$)) is defined as $\Delta v_{d,g} = \sqrt{\{(1-[2GM/(R+h)c^2])/[1-(2GM/Rc^2)]\}}v_0 \overset{R \gg h}{=} (MGh/R^2c^2)v_0$, with G the gravitational constant, R the radius of curvature, and M the gravitational mass (i.e., Earth's mass). In superposition, this yields for the observation made by the detector: $\Delta v_{d,s,g}/v_0 = \sqrt{\{[1+(v^2\cos^2\theta/c^2)]/[1-(v^2/c^2)]\}\{1-[2GM/(R+h)c^2]/1-(2GM/Rc^2)\}}$. At the time, measuring the influence of the gravitational attraction from the top of the Harvard Jefferson building with a height of $h = 21.6$ m, resulting in a [*measured*] Doppler shift of $\Delta v_{d,s,g}/v_0 = 2.46 \times 10^{-15}$ for a 14 400 eV gamma ray produced by the Fe^{57} ISOTOPE, quite extraordinary.

Poussin, Baron Charles-Jean Étienne Gustave Nicolas de la Vallée (1866–1962)

[computational] Mathematician and physicist from Belgium. Charles de la Vallée Poussin is known for proving the Prime number theorem in 1896. Other work included the study of approximation theory (see Figure P.150).

Figure P.150 Baron Charles-Jean Étienne Gustave Nicolas de la Vallée Poussin (1866–1962).

Powell, Cecil Frank (1903–1969)

[atomic, nuclear] Scientist and physicist from Great Britain. Cecil Powell developed an innovative method using a photographic film to elucidate SUBATOMIC PARTICLES. The COSMIC RAYS at high altitude appeared to interact with the nuclei within the emulsion of the film. Discoverer of the π-meson, also known as the ; in 1946 (see Figure P.151).

Figure P.151 Cecil Frank Powell (1903–1969).

Power (*P*)

[general, nuclear, thermodynamics] The TIME (*t*) rate of doing work ($W = \vec{F} \cdot \vec{d}$, the force *F* applied to move an object over a DISTANCE *d*): $P = dW/dt$; alternatively, the time rate of expenditure of ENERGY: $P = dE/dt$; units Watt (W). Also the force applied to a moving object in the direction of MOTION to maintain a constant velocity: $P = \vec{F} \cdot \vec{v}$, for instance to overcome resistive forces such as friction (sliding or rolling). In electrical applications, the power is the consumed or generated power from the CURRENT (*I*) and voltage (*V*), combined with OHM'S LAW with respect to RESISTANCE *R* (or more generally impedance *Z*), also referred to as apparent power $P = VI = V^2/Z = I^2 Z$. Some examples of power equivalencies: $1(\text{BTU}/s) = 1054$ W, 1 horsepower $(\text{HP}) = 745.7$ W, $1(\text{gallon of oil}/\text{minute}) = 2.5$ MW, and $1(\text{J/s}) = 1$ W. The average power exerted by the human HEART can be estimated based on the contractile force, expressed as the ventricular PRESSURE (*P*) times the area of the aortic VALVE (*A*) multiplied by the flow velocity (*v*): $P = PAv$, which per beat is approximately 1.2 W. The power produced by the SUN (as a "NUCLEAR REACTOR") is approximately 4×10^{26} W. The power produced by a waterwheel is on the order of 1–75 kW; the output depends on the head difference, flow rate, and the efficiency that is a function of the design and how well the water FLOW is "captured" to generate the torque. The power output of an undershot wheel is a function of the total area of the paddles that are exposed to flow (*A*), the flow velocity (v_{flow}), and the conversion efficiency (η_{conv}), expressed as $P = 100\eta_{\text{conv}} A v^3$; while for an "overshot" or breast shot wheel, the power results from the flow (*Q*) times the "bucket" size (volume *V* [i.e., the weight]; the head of the wheel [b_{head}]) as $P = 4\eta_{\text{conv}} Q V b_{\text{head}}$. The efficiency is the result of the way water is captured as well as the electric GENERATOR attached or the mechanical gear to produce the work. The work can for instance be making paper, cutting wood, or lifting water (see Figure P.152).

Figure P.152 Waterwheel performing work and generating the power to perform other work.

Power cycle

[thermodynamics] Cyclic change of state in a thermodynamic system, such as a Carnot machine, Sterling cycle, OTTO CYCLE, Rankin cycle, DIESEL CYCLE, JOULE–BRAYTON CYCLE, cooling (refrigeration), or heating cycle, transforming ENERGY at a high- or low-temperature source to work. An additional power cycle is the LINDE–HAMPSON LIQUEFACTION CYCLE.

Power factor

[general] Real power consumption in an electrical circuit based on the PHASE shift (θ) between the current and the voltage resulting from the complex impedance: $P = VI \cos\theta$, where $\cos\theta$ represents the power factor for the alternating current circuit configuration. Note that $\cos\theta = 1$ for a purely resistive system.

Power law

[computational] Mathematical expression that has one parameter as a function of another parameter expressed to the order of a fixed or variable mathematical expression; for instance, in the most rudimentary form, $f(x) = ax^n$. The expression is the result of a causal dependency that influences the output by a certain MAGNITUDE or function. WIEN'S DISPLACEMENT LAW is one of many examples.

Power method

[computational] Computational mechanism of deriving eigenvalues for the solutions to a function. One interpretation is that the eigenvalues are the matrix ELEMENTS of a polynomial EXPANSION. The base matrix is used to derive the subsequent terms in an iteration method, substituting the last derived output to derive the subsequent term.

Power number ($N_p = c_{Np} (P_w/\omega_N{}^3 \rho L^5)$)

[energy, fluid dynamics, mechanics] Dimensionless number indicating the ratio of the net DRAG FORCE to the net INERTIAL FORCE pertaining to rotational systems, where $P_w = \Delta W/\Delta t$ (i.e., rate of change in WORK) is the POWER consumed or produced by the device, ω_N the rotational rate of change, c_{Np} a dimensional constant, ρ DENSITY, and L characteristic length. The Power number relates to MOMENTUM transfer in for instance agitators, pumps, and fans as well as power consumption.

Power spectrum

[acoustics, computational, optics] The ENERGY distribution per frequency range ("bin"), converting the SIGNAL distribution in a discrete format. This has particular value for the situation where there are limited frequencies, for example, harmonics only. The power spectrum generally can be derived by taking the FOURIER TRANSFORM. Note that the Fourier transform of a product is the convolution of the respective Fourier transforms and that the Fourier transform of a convolution is the product of the respective Fourier transforms.

Poynting, John Henry (1852–1914)

[electromagnetism, energy, general] Physicist from England. John Poynting was the theoretical resource behind the development of the general description of CONSERVATION OF ELECTROMAGNETIC ENERGY, in particular the flow of ELECTROMAGNETIC ENERGY and hence he was the eponym of the POYNTING VECTOR (see Figure P.153).

Figure P.153 John Henry Poynting (1852–1914).

Poynting correction

[thermodynamics] Expression used in the fugacity of LIQUIDS as a correction to LIQUID–VAPOR EQUILIBRIUM of a non-IDEAL GAS. The expression for the FUGACITY itself is $\pi_f(T,P) = \pi_f(T,P_0)\exp\left[\mu_f(T,P) - \mu_f(T,P_0)/RT\right]$, a slight deviation from the IDEAL GAS LAW: $PV = nRT$. The exponential term rewrites as $\exp\left[\mu_f(T,P) - \mu_f(T,P_0)/RT\right] = \exp\left\{(v_f/RT)\left[P_f(T,P) - P_{sat}(T)\right]\right\} \cong 1 + (v_f/RT)\left[P_f(T) - P_{sat}(T)\right]$, which is known as the Poynting correction. For ordinary media, the ideal gas law will be adhered to and the Poynting correction is close to unity, with the inherent condition that the fugacity is independent of the pressure and approximately equates $\pi_f(T,P) \cong P_{sat}(T)$.

Poynting vector ($\vec{S}$)

[atomic, electromagnetism, general] Vector indicating the direction and rate of passage through a unit area in the direction of propagation of the transport of ELECTROMAGNETIC ENERGY from the combined effects of an electric field ($\vec{E}$) and a MAGNETIC FIELD ($\vec{B}$), defined as $\vec{S} = (1/\mu_0)(\vec{E} \times \vec{B}) = \vec{E} \times \vec{H}$ (where $\vec{B}$ is the magnetic field measured in Tesla, and H is the MAGNETIC field expressed in N/mA), units: W/m^2, where $\vec{S} = (\sqrt{\varepsilon_0\mu_0}/4\pi)(\vec{E} \times \vec{B})$ is the Poynting vector and $c = \sqrt{\varepsilon_0\mu_0}$ is the speed of LIGHT.

Praetorius, Michael (original name: Michael Schultheiß) (1571–1621)

[acoustics, mechanics] Composer and scientist from Germany. Praetorius used a particular musical analysis and organization and provided a rhythm "template" for sacred music in particular (cantus and hymns) (see Figure P.154).

Figure P.154 Michael Praetorius (1571–1621).

Prandtl, Ludwig (1875–1953)

[astrophysics, computational, fluid dynamics, thermodynamics] German mathematician and physicist that pioneered the development of a rigorous mathematical description of flow patterns and the influence of forces. He introduced the BOUNDARY LAYER in 1905. The boundary layer consists of a thin section of the flowing medium where the interaction with an object or other medium is expressed. The pioneering work by Archimedes (287–212 BC) only provided basics on statics for fluids. Additional anecdotal details of flow were presented by LEONARDO DA VINCI (1452–1519) by graphical interpretation. While LEONARD EULER (1707–1783) described the flow of a medium conceptualized as a CONTINUUM of small fluid ELEMENTS, the boundary effects were still not well defined in his days. The work of DANIEL BERNOULLI (1700–1782) was more generalized that of Euler. The internal FRICTION with respect to fluid FLOW was introduced by CLAUDE-LOUIS NAVIER (1785–1836) in 1822 and later refined (presumably independently) by GEORGE STOKES (1819–1903) in 1845 to culminate in the Navier–Stokes equations for flow. He hypothesized that FLUID elements (Euler's concept) directly in contact with a surface, which was moving at a different velocity, would experience attraction, and hence friction. The boundary layer is very different for a pure LIQUID in comparison to a colloid solutions (e.g., BLOOD), where the boundary effects will extend for the particulates. The body (or liquid) inside a flowing fluid will experience pressure on its surface and shear tangentially to the surface. The boundary layer will display a velocity profile that is dependent on the DISTANCE to the surface. Elaborating on Prandtl's concept, PAUL RICHARD HEINRICH BLASIUS (1883–1970) expanded on the boundary layer problem in 1908 illustrating the separation of a boundary layer. Prandtl postulated a hypothesis on MIXING length for fluid-mechanic layers in 1925. The MIXING LENGTH (ℓ_m) is the distance along the shear layer at a surface, it takes for the fluid to reach the time average of an assumed sinusoidal velocity fluctuation starting out from turbulent, expressed as a function of the eddy viscosity η_T, the turbulent velocity (u_T), the velocity profile as a function of the STREAM FUNCTION (ψ) expressed as $U_y = \partial\psi/\partial y$; respectively $U_x = -\partial\psi/\partial x$, defined by $u_T \sim \ell_m |\partial U_y/\partial y| = \ell_m |\partial^2\psi/\partial y^2|$ as a function of the distance to WALL (y). Far from the wall, the mixing length can also be approximated as a function of the von Kármán constant (κ_K) as $\ell_m = \kappa_K y$; however, this does not apply to the viscous sublayer. The known values for the mixing length for certain flow conditions are for instance for a regular emission JET: $\ell_m = 0.09\ell_s$, where ℓ_s is the half-width of the shear layer; and for a circular jet: $\ell_m = 0.075\ell_s$ (see Figure P.155).

Figure P.155 Ludwig Prandtl (1875–1953).

Prandtl number (Pr = ($\eta/\propto_{dif}$) = c$_p\eta/\kappa$)

[fluid dynamics] Dimensionless number expressing the ratio of the DIFFUSIVITY of momentum to thermal DIFFUSION, where η the KINEMATIC VISCOSITY, α the THERMAL DIFFUSIVITY, c_p the HEAT CAPACITY, and κ the THERMAL CONDUCTIVITY. This number shows the relation between HEAT TRANSFER and MECHANICS in both free and forced convection.

Prandtl–Meyer expansion

[fluid dynamics] Mathematical approach for SUPERSONIC FLOW, describing the ISENTROPIC expansion of a MACH WAVE through a series of Mach waves, where the CENTRAL wave portion is referred to as the Prandtl–Meyer expansion. The EXPANSION is divergent. This phenomenon is in particular related to the propagation of a supersonic flow through a shock. Under these conditions, for normal flow the flow velocity normal to the shock is expected to increase; however, this will violate the SECOND LAW OF THERMODYNAMICS.

Prandtl–Meyer function

[fluid dynamics] Mathematical approach for SUPERSONIC FLOW, describing the ISENTROPIC expansion of a MACH WAVE through a series of Mach waves, where the central WAVE portion is referred to as the PRANDTL–MEYER EXPANSION. The Prandtl–Meyer function describes the flow expansion (fan type) as a function of the changing MACH NUMBEr (Ma) as a function of ANGLE with the line of propagation: $dw/w = (d\text{Ma}/\text{Ma}) + (dv_s/v_s)$, where $w = \sqrt{u_x^2 + u_y^2}$, u_x and u_y respectively the orthogonal flow-velocity components, $v_s = (\partial P/\partial \rho)_s$ the speed of sound, P the pressure, and ρ the local density. Expressed as a function of angle (ϑ_{PM}) as the Prandtl–Meyer function:
$$\vartheta_{PM}(\text{Ma}) = \sqrt{[(\gamma_b+1)/(\gamma_b-1)]} \tan^{-1}\left(\sqrt{[(\gamma_b+1)/(\gamma_b-1)][\text{Ma}^2-1]}\right) - \tan^{-1}\left(\sqrt{(\text{Ma}^2-1)}\right),$$ where $\gamma_b = c_p/c_v$ is the ratio of SPECIFIC HEAT at constant pressure (c_p) to specific heat at constant volume (c_v). Generally, the parameter ϑ_{PM} is listed in tabular form for the specific flow conditions.

Precession

[atomic, biomedical, mechanics, nuclear, quantum] Rotation of the axis of SPIN around a reference axis. The precession of the Earth's rotational axis is slow with a period of approximately 26 000 years. The rotation of the EARTH around the SUN provides the seasonal changes. A spinning top will "wobble" with its axis of rotation around the perfect vertical axis, normal to the gravitational plane. The angular velocity of the precession (ω_p) is the result of the MOMENT OF INERTIA (I_m), and the spinning ANGULAR VELOCITY (ω) around the object's axis of symmetry is expressed as $\omega_p = (d\phi/dt) = rmg/I_m\omega$, with r the DISTANCE from the intersect of the axis of rotation with the vertical reference axis (frame of reference; i.e., the pivot point) to the center of mass of the object in rotation with mass m, g the GRAVITATIONAL ACCELERATION, and ϕ is the ANGLE of rotation. Precession is used to give a GYROSCOPE a very stable frequency (*also see* LARMOR PRECESSION) (see Figure P.156).

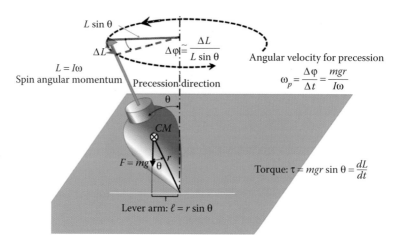

Figure P.156 The process of precession.

Pressure (P)

[biomedical, fluid dynamics, general, material, mechanics] Force (F) per unit area (A), expressed in all directions with equal MAGNITUDE: $P = \lim_{\Delta A \to 0}(\Delta F/\Delta A)$. Pressure has no direction and is hence a SCALAR quantity. The pressure of a LIQUID column with density ρ is directly proportional to the height (h) of the column above the point of interest, in addition to the pressure above the liquid from the GAS column (e.g., ATMOSPHERIC PRESSURE): $P = \rho g h + P_0$, where g is the GRAVITATIONAL ACCELERATION. Pressure can be used to transfer force by means of changing the area as used in hydraulic systems. At the "critical pressure" in the PHASE DIAGRAM, the liquid phase and the VAPOR phase become identical. The units for pressure are PASCAL (Pa); colloquial use is ATMOSPHERE, or PSI (pounds per square inch) (see Figure P.157).

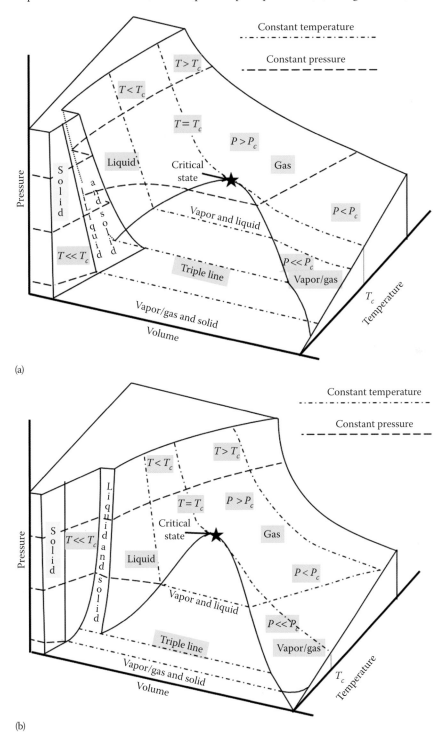

(a)

(b)

Figure P.157 Phase diagram including the influence of pressure on the physical conditions and state of a medium: (a) medium that has a lower density at temperature below the liquid–solid phase transition, for instance water, and (b) medium with decreasing density with decreasing temperature.

Pressure coefficient $(Pt = (P - P_\infty)/(1/2)\rho_\infty v_\infty^2)$

[astrophysics, fluid dynamics] Dimensionless number describing the ratio of the relative PRESSURES throughout a FLOW field to the KINETIC ENERGY density, also referred to as INERTIAL FORCES. In a FLUID FLOW field, every point will have a unique respective pressure coefficient. In the definition, the following parameters are used: P the pressure, P_∞ the pressure in the main body/volume of the fluid medium, ρ_∞ the bulk DENSITY, and v_∞ the VELOCITY of flow in the main part of the medium or main free flow. The pressure coefficient applies to flow over an AIRFOIL as well as BOUNDARY LAYER effects in fluid flow and RHEOLOGY.

Pressure cooker

[general] Device that is sealed in order to increase the PRESSURE (P) with respect to the ambient pressure in the closed VOLUME (V) with the direct consequence of an increase in temperature (T) of the boiling point of the LIQUID in the container based on the Boyle–Gay–Lussac law: $PV/T = $ Constant. The concept of the pressure cooker was invented by DENIS PAPIN (1647–1712) in the late 1600s. For food, the chemical denaturation process increases by approximation over every 10°C, while the modern pressure cooker is designed to operate at approximately 121°C; the processing time is dramatically reduced. Alternatively, when living at high elevation, for instance in Denver, CO, USA, mile-high city (elevation approx. 1600 m), the cooking temperature is dramatically reduced under regular conditions, requiring longer cooking times. The autoclave is another example used for sterilization of medical equipment based on this principle (see Figure P.158).

Figure P.158 Pressure cooker.

Prévost, Pierre (1751–1839)

[general, nuclear, thermodynamics] Scientist and clergyman from Switzerland with a minor interest in law. Primarily known for his contributions on heat (thermodynamics) and MAGNETISM (see Figure P.159).

Figure P.159 Pierre Prévost (1751–1839). (Courtesy of *Journal Officiel Illustré De L'Exposition Nationale Suisse Genève 1896.*)

Prévost theory of heat exchange

[atomic, nuclear] Matter at constant temperature is in perfect equilibrium, proposed by PIERRE PRÉVOST (1751–1839) in 1791.

Priestley, Joseph (1733–1804)

[chemistry] English chemist and theologian attributed with the discovery of the colorless and reactive GAS oxygen (O_2; although it was named by the French chemist ANTOINE LAURENT LAVOISIER [1734–1794]). Priestley's breakthrough observation was that AIR was not a single substance but a mixture of elementary components, that is, gasses, as published in 1774. Additionally, Priestley invented several items such as the rubber eraser and carbonated water (see Figure P.160).

Figure P.160 Joseph Priestley (1733–1804) in 1794. (Courtesy of Ellen Sharples [1769–1849]. Scan of a print. Original at the National Portrait Gallery, London, England.)

Primary colors

[general] Based on human perception the following three colors can be used to make up in access of 10 million colors as defined by the base colors RED, green, and blue (RGB), as outlined by the CIE CHROMA-TICITY diagram. The RGB mechanism is for instance applied to monitors as well as digital cameras. The documented first observation of the eye's response to three colors was by THOMAS YOUNG (1773–1829) in the early 1800s (see Figure P.161).

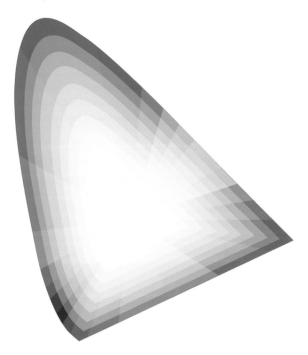

Figure P.161 Color chart as defined by the CIE 1931 (Commission internationale de l'éclairage; "International Commission on Illumination") with primary colors defining the corners of the map.

Primary cosmic ray particles

[atomic, nuclear] Various SUBATOMIC PARTICLES reach the Earth's ATMOSPHERE from outer space, ranging from protons (~89%) to helium nuclei (10% of total), up to uranium nuclei (1% heavy nuclei). In the upper atmosphere, these particles will collide and generate reactions, primarily generating pions.

Primary electron

[solid-state] The electron ejected from an ATOM by an initial ionizing event, as caused by a PHOTON or BETA PARTICLE.

Principal moments

[atomic, mechanics, solid-state] The MOMENT OF INERTIA associated with a rigid molecule. The MOLECULE has three principal moments, which follow from the diagonalization of the moment of inertia matrix:

$$
\mathrm{II} = \begin{bmatrix} \sum_i m_i \left(y_i^2 + z_i^2 \right) & -\sum_i m_i x_i y_i & -\sum_i m_i x_i z_i \\ -\sum_i m_i y_i x_i & \sum_i m_i \left(x_i^2 + z_i^2 \right) & -\sum_i m_i x_i z_i \\ -\sum_i m_i z_i x_i & -\sum_i m_i z_i y_i^0 & \sum_i m_i \left(x_i^2 + y_i^2 \right) \end{bmatrix} = C \begin{bmatrix} I_A & 0 & 0 \\ 0 & I_B & 0 \\ 0 & 0 & I_C \end{bmatrix},
$$

where in case all three moments are equal the molecule is referred to as a spherical rotor (e.g., CH_4); in case only two are equal the molecule is a symmetric rotor (e.g., CH_3CL); and if all three are different the molecule is an asymmetric rotor (e.g., H_2O).

Principal plane

[mechanics] The plane to which the stress in the direction of the normal is at extreme (maximal/minimal).

Principal quantum number

[atomic, nuclear] QUANTUM NUMBER defining the binding states of electrons: n. For the ENERGY states of the electron with mass m_e and charge $e = 1.60217657 \times 10^{-19}$ C, this provides for a NUCLEUS with cumulative proton charge Z: $E_n = -m_e e^4 Z^2 / 8\varepsilon_0^2 h^2 n^2$, with $\varepsilon_0 = 8.85419 \times 10^{-12}$ $C^2/N\,m^2$ the permittivity of free space and $h = 6.62606957 \times 10^{-34}$ m^2 kg/s PLANCK's CONSTANT. In the Bohr model, this yields $E_n = -\left(13.6 / n^2 \right)$ eV for each level, $= 1, 2, 3, \ldots$. Note that in some cases, the "REDUCED MASS" need to be used: $m' = m_e M / \left(m_e + M \right)$, where M is the total mass of the protons.

Principal stress

[biomedical, mechanics] Stress in the PRINCIPAL PLANE.

Principia of Newton

[general] Published in 1687 by SIR ISAAC NEWTON (1642–1727) on the laws of MOTION as well as the wave-particle duality of light: the first law is the LAW OF INERTIA; the SECOND LAW is the force law; and the third is the law of reciprocity. The WAVE characteristic of LIGHT was not readily accepted for almost 150 years, until resurrected by THOMAS YOUNG (1773–1829) and AUGUSTIN FRESNEL (1788–1827).

Principle of complementarity

[general] Fundamental principle that applies to quantum-mechanical phenomena, specifically with respect to the BOHR ATOMIC MODEL as described by Niels Henrik David Bohr (1885–1962) in 1913. The principle of

complementarity states that in quantum-mechanical phenomena the outcome of experimental observations is directly correlated to the instruments used to analyze the mechanism of action, which is related to the Schrödinger "cat" (both alive and dead) as well as the double slit that appears to describe that a single PHOTON can be in two place simultaneously. Based on the "complementarity," the basic mathematical formalisms of QUANTUM MECHANICS were developed autonomously by both WERNER HEISENBERG (1901–1976) and ERWIN SCHRÖDINGER (1887–1961) in 1926. The consequence of the principle of complementarity was the Copenhagen interpretation of quantum mechanics.

Principle of conservation of mass

[fluid dynamics] *See* CONSERVATION OF MASS.

Principle of corresponding states

[fluid dynamics, solid-state] Theorem introduced by JOHANNES DIEDERIK VAN DER WAALS (1837–1923) in 1873 concerning the similar (identical) behavior of all fluids at the scaled parameters for temperature ($T_s = T/T_c$), volume ($V_s = (V/V_c)$), and pressure ($P_s = P/P_c$) with the same compressibility factor $Z_c = P_c V_c / n_c k_b T_c$, which is taken at the critical point ($\square_c$), where n_c is the number of particles (molecules/atoms) and $k_b = 1.3806488 \times 10^{-23} \, \text{m}^2 \, \text{kg/s}^2 \, \text{K}$ is the Boltzmann coefficient. The fluids can be considered to act under the same deviation (adjustment/offset) from the IDEAL GAS LAW, as if they are ideal gasses.

Principle of highest entropy

[thermodynamics] A system that is in stable equilibrium will have a higher entropy than any other system state with the same constituent and ENERGY parameters. Alternatively, this configuration will have the lowest energy.

Principle of least action

[general, mechanics] In follow-up on NEWTONIAN MECHANICS, the concepts of equation of MOTION can be derived from perturbations to stationary situations. The least action principle considers the path of an object with mass m and potential ENERGY $U(\vec{r})$ that leads from beginning to end as a function of time (t), instead of the start and end points, assigning a SCALAR that defines the action as a function of location ($\vec{r}$): $S[\vec{r}(t)] = \int_{t_1}^{t_2} [(1/2)m\dot{\vec{r}}^2 - U(\vec{r})]$, where the path holds an extremum of the "action" performed, $\dot{\vec{r}} = d\vec{r}/dt$.

Principle of lowest energy

[thermodynamics] A system that is in stable equilibrium will have the lowest ENERGY in comparison to the identical system in any other state.

Principle of relativity

[general] Relativity is subdivided into general relativity and special relativity; see the respective descriptions for additional details. The concepts of relativity were introduced by ALBERT EINSTEIN (1879–1955) in 1905. Based on Newtonian physics, as introduced by SIR ISAAC NEWTON (1642–1727), GRAVITY was constant, but with new knowledge adjustment had to be made. The traditional gravitational potential (ϕ_G) linked by the Poisson equation to gravity was $\nabla^2 \phi_G = \nabla \cdot \nabla \phi_G = \left[(\partial^2/\partial x^2) + (\partial^2/\partial y^2) + (\partial^2/\partial z^2) \right] \phi_G = 4\pi G\rho$, where ∇^2 is the Laplace operator, G is the gravitational constant, and ρ is the density of MATTER, which was changed to include a time-dependent aspect as the d'Alembertian operator ($\square_{d'A}$): $\square_{d'A} \phi_G = \left\{ \left[(1/c^2)(\partial^2/\partial t^2) \right] + \nabla^2 \right\} \phi_G = 4\pi G\rho$, where $c = 2.99792458 \times 10^8 \, \text{m/s}$ is the speed of LIGHT. The first postulate by Albert Einstein with respect to relativity is that all laws of PHYSICS are valid and identical for observers moving in uniform motion, even though they may be in separate reference frames. The second postulate states that the speed of light, in free space, will be constant and independent of the MOTION of the source. Relativity is split between the fields of "classical physics" and "modern physics." Relativistic

concepts are the result of Einstein's postulate that gravity is curved, in both space and time, as part of general relativity under classical physics, while the postulates of Einstein are part of modern physics.

Prism

[optics] Transparent body with specifically two surfaces at an ANGLE. The medium of the optical body will have an index of refraction different from the ambient medium, generating refraction at both surfaces, resulting in an angular deviation from the ray incident with an angle to the normal on the first surface, incident in the plane outlined by the normal and the axis of the plane normal to the line mating the adjoining plane (see Figure P.162).

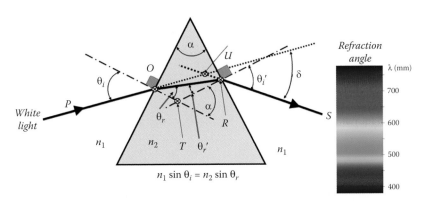

$$n_1 \sin \theta_i = n_2 \sin \theta_r$$

Figure P.162 Prism- and color-based refraction (i.e., wavelength).

Probability

[atomic, computational, nuclear, thermodynamics] Branch in mathematical analysis that studies the likelihood of the occurrence of an event. The probability is the specific outcome divided by the total number of events. The probability ranges from 0 to 1, or respectively 0% to 100% likelihood. Specifically, with respect to other events in a probability distribution. The probability is often weighed against a null hypothesis, as proposed in 1931. The null hypothesis is the definition that the event is related to the most-likely phenomenon, at "zero change;" in contrast to the "alternate hypothesis" that everything is different. The most well-known probability is for a coin toss; "heads–tails," with 50% probability for "heads," provided a large enough number of tosses are performed. Probability is frequently used to prove or disprove a hypothesis, when the number of occurrences yields a fit less than a certain "p-value," chosen based on preferences: $p < 0.05$, $p < 0.01$, $p < 0.005$; the smaller the p-value the better the argument that the alternate to the null hypothesis is *rejected*; hence the event is true in comparison to a standard. The p-value is an indication of the significance of obtaining a test value with statistical MAGNITUDE at least as high in comparison as actually observed, under the assumption that the null hypothesis is true. Alternatively, the p-value is an indication of getting a different answer than the null hypothesis; hence a small p-value means low likelihood and null hypothesis stands correct. Probability can be distributed over opportunities. Several probability distributions are available from a mathematical foundation: POISSON DISTRIBUTION, NORMAL DISTRIBUTION, GAUSSIAN DISTRIBUTION, multinormal distribution, iniform distribution, delta function, bionomial distribution, Bernoulli distribution, gamma distribution, Student's t-distribution, and several more. Note that the "normal" distribution is not the most likely probability distribution for every phenomenon; the name does not represent the causality. The choice of distribution has to do with the sample size, the phenomenon, and the representation of "outliers" (failed events) (*also see* **BAYESIAN ANALYSIS**) (see Figure P.163).

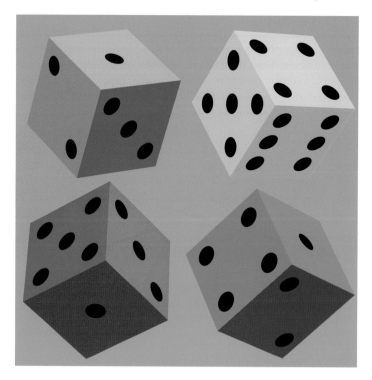

Figure P.163 Concept of probability.

Probability, theory of

[computational, mechanics]: fundamental concept of PHYSICS in the description of the opportunities and chances for an event or ENERGY configuration the form and the path the process will follow based on the available options of energy distribution as initially described by BLAISE PASCAL (1623–1662) and PIERRE DE FERMAT (1601–1665). Theoretical analysis pertaining to random phenomena. The nondeterministic events in physics and engineering that are either discrete, unique in occurrence, or have a pattern of evolution that does not follow a path that can be defined by strict conditions (i.e., STOCHASTIC PROCESS). The probability theory dates back to the teachings of PIERRE DE FERMAT (1601–1665), BLAISE PASCAL (1623–1662), and PIERRE-SIMON MARQUIS DE LAPLACE (1749–1827) with further refinements by for instance ALEKSANDR MIKHAILOVICH LYAPUNOV (1857–1918). The formulation of these events has its primary foundation in statistical methods. In biomedical aspects, this relates to BAYES' THEOREM. The other side of PROBABILITY is in QUANTUM MECHANICS and HEISENBERG'S UNCERTAINTY PRINCIPLE. Examples of stochastic processes are BROWNIAN MOTION, thermal collisions, and the DOUBLE-SLIT EXPERIMENT. An additional feature of a wave representation of an object in MOTION provides a mechanism of outlining the probability of an objects location, in particular the location of an electron. This provides a concept known as the probability flux. The probability FLUX is associated with solutions to the SCHRÖDINGER WAVE EQUATION, outlining the momentum associated with the eigenvalues of the solutions that can be used to define a "particle density" (*also see* **PROBABILITY**).

Projectile

[general, mechanics] Object moving in two or three dimensions. GALILEO GALILEI (1564–1642) was one of the first documented scientists that recognized that the projectile MOTION can be segregated in two independent motions: horizontal and vertical. The horizontal motion is the result of the applied force, whereas the vertical motion is defined by gravitational interaction. A ballistic projectile is an object that is launched to target something (see Figure P.164).

Figure P.164 Ballistic projectile.

Prompt neutron

[atomic, nuclear] During NUCLEAR FISSION, in excess of 99% of NEUTRON are emitted within a "brief" delay (10^{-12} s), with respect to the FISSION event and are referred to as prompt neutrons. Several neutron may be emitted as long as minutes later and these are called delayed neutrons. However small the fraction of delayed to prompt neutron may be, the delayed neutrons form an essential control mechanism for the nuclear reaction.

Propeller

[fluid dynamics] Circular symmetric three-dimensional mechanical design with discrete sections that are twisted to perform a specific fluid dynamic function during rotation around the central axis. Blades on a propeller will convert rotational MOTION into thrust, either moving the object the propeller is attached to or making the propeller rotate under an applied flow to for instance generate ELECTRICITY. Propellers are founds on airplanes and boats in particular for PROPULSION, and on wind turbines for generating electrical power. The THRUST (T_b) provided by a propeller is a function of the ANGLE of the blade (ϕ) and the LIFT of the blade from the plane of attachment (α) as well as the ENERGY from the torque on the blade as a function of location (L) and shear energy over the blades (w, at widest segment): $T_b = dL\cos(\phi+\alpha) - dw\sin(\phi+\alpha)$, with associated TORQUE (τ_b), as a function of the radius to the axis (r), approached by discrete incremental steps over the radial DISTANCE along the length of the propeller: $\tau_b = r\{dL\cos(\phi+\alpha) - dw\sin(\phi+\alpha)\}$, where $dL = (1/2)\rho|\vec{v}_e|^2 c^* C_\ell dr$ (with ρ the fluid density, $\vec{v}_e$ the exit flow velocity, c^* a fractional factor (representative of the performance efficacy), C_ℓ the surface) and $dw = (1/2)\rho v_e^2 c^* C_d dr$ (with C_d the surface area carved out by the rotating propeller). Propeller efficiency (η_{propel_p}) with respect to propulsion is the ratio of the kinetic energy of the flow ($P_{\text{flow}} = \dot{m}[(u_e^2/2) - (u_0^2/2)]$), where $\dot{m} = \partial m/\partial t$, $u_e = \vec{v}_e \cdot \vec{n}$ the normal flow velocity through the propeller, and u_0 the background FLOW velocity (i.e., flight velocity), and with respect to the propulsive power ($P_{\text{propel}_p} = $ thrust × flight velocity): $\eta_{\text{propel}\_p} = 2[1 + (u_e/u_0)]^{-1}$, which is equivalent or the efficiency of a jet engine. Alternatively, the FLUID dynamic efficiency for a GENERATOR is rather complex, depending on the fluid FLOW (e.g., water, AIR, combustion), and only the power (P_{turbine}) and efficiency (η_{turbine}) for a wind TURBINE is provided. The power of a wind turbine in approximation is a function of the rotor swept area (A_{swept}), the density of the air (ρ), the wind velocity (v_w), the generator efficiency ($\eta_{\text{generator}}$), the gear transfer efficiency (η_{gear}), as well as a general coefficient of performance (c_{perf}): $P_{\text{turbine}} = 0.5\rho A_{\text{swept}}\eta_{\text{gear}}\eta_{\text{generator}}\eta_{\text{perf}}v_w^3$; the efficiency is now: $\eta_{\text{generate}\_p} = (P_{\text{out}}/P_{\text{turbine}}) = (VI/0.5\rho A_{\text{swept}}\eta_{\text{gear}}\eta_{\text{generator}}\eta_{\text{perf}}v_w^3)$, where P_{out} is the electrical output power, based

P

on CURRENT (I) and voltage (V), which requires corrections for PHASE losses (the generator is a multiphase generator, ideally all need to be in phase), specifically when multiple generators are connected together. Wind turbines generally do not effectively generate electricity at wind velocity below 8 km/h (see Figure P.165).

Figure P.165 Range of propellers used for the generation of electricity. Specialty propeller designs for wind turbines. (Courtesy of Helix Wind.)

Propulsion

[general, mechanics, thermodynamics] Push forward, mechanism of THRUST that makes an object move, operationally based on NEWTON'S THIRD LAW. Propulsion is specifically associated with JET engines, whereas PROPELLER engines provide propulsion as well. The force is exerted in several directions, while a remaining net force exerted on one surface that will result in a MOTION of that surface with radial forces canceling out and the force in the direction opposite to the surface in motion discarded. Thrust is a force (F), specifically the change in momentum ($p = mv$, where m is the mass and v the velocity; note that the combustion mass changes over time as well: $\dot{m} = dm/dt = \rho v A$ as a function of DENSITY (ρ), and cross-sectional area (A)) over time (t): $F = (dp/dt)$. The propulsion of a jet engine can be expressed as $F_T = \dot{m}_e v_e - \dot{m}_0 v_0 + (P_e - P_0)A_e$, where the respective subscripts denote the exit ($\square_e$) and ambient ($\square_0$) conditions, and the PRESSURE (P) plays a role as well. The rocket engines for the space shuttle for instance produce 1.8 MN thrust. The propulsion from a propeller engine with propeller area (A_{prop}) can be expressed as $F_T = 2\rho A_{prop}(v_\infty + v)v$, where v_∞ is the fluid velocity, v the velocity "induced" to the medium (e.g., increase in AIR flow, water flow), and ρ the FLUID density (*also see* PROPELLER) (see Figure P.166).

Figure P.166 Water propulsion.

Proton

[atomic, nuclear] Nuclear particle (BARYON, HADRON) with a positive ELECTRIC CHARGE equal numerically to the charge of the electron and having a mass of $m = 1.673 \times 10^{-27}$ kg $= 1.007575$ mu and charge $q = +1.60217657 \times 10^{-19}$C. FERMION with SPIN of one half unit: $s = (1/2)\hbar = (1/2)(h/2\pi)$ ($h = 6.62606957 \times 10^{-34}$ m^2 kg/s PLANCK'S CONSTANT). The PROTON is composed of three quarks, two quarks in the "up" direction and one in the "down" orientation (classification: uud). Theoretically, a proton can DECAY with emission of a PION or positron; however, experimentally to date there is no evidence that a proton will decay, and the lifetime of a proton has been established at 10^{31} years.

Prout, William (1785–1850)

[atomic, biomedical, nuclear, thermodynamics] Physician, chemist, and scientist from Great Britain. William Prout proposed that based on the current knowledge of the periodic table all ELEMENTS were composed of constituents resembling the HYDROGEN ATOM, called "protyle" by William Prout, although never observed by him. His concepts of nuclear structure predate the Bohr model and verified detection of specific particles by almost one hundred years. Additionally, Prout made statements about the biological system, such as the METABOLIC ACTIVITY, that could not be verified at the time but hold great value for current biological knowledge. The unit of NUCLEAR BINDING ENERGY was named after him, the Prout, which is (1/2) binding energy of the DEUTERON = 185.5 keV. He also made several contributions to the theoretical description of HEAT TRANSFER. Based on William Prout's rudimentary but essential contributions to the understanding of the nuclear construction, the discovery of the PROTON was named in his honor by ERNEST RUTHERFORD (1871–1937) during its discovery in 1920 (see Figure P.167).

Figure P.167 William Prout (1785–1850).

Prout's hypothesis

[nuclear] Proposition that all chemical ELEMENTS are constructed with base building blocks resembling the helium ATOM, referred to as "protyle." Suggested by WILLAM PROUT (1785–1850) in 1815. Using the protyle as the building block for ISOTOPE, atomic mass description is accurate within 1%.

Pseudo plastics

[biomedical, fluid dynamics] SHEAR-THINNING FLUID, FLUID that decreases in SHEAR FORCE with increasing flow velocity. The associated viscous phenomena also decrease with a reduction in viscosity per se, in contrast with a NEWTONIAN FLUID or dilatant fluid (see Figure P.168).

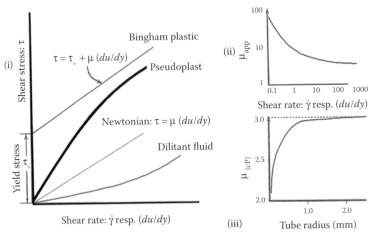

Alterations in viscosity: (i) Non-newtonian fluids, (ii) apparent viscosity, and (iii) the Fahraeus–Lindqvist effect.

(a)

(b)

Figure P.168 (a) Shear-thinning and (b) slurry, liquid manure.

Psychrometry

[thermodynamics] Energetic study of MOIST AIR. The mixture of air and water VAPOR in the Earth's ATMOSPHERE may generally be considered as an IDEAL GAS, not accounting for foggy conditions. Also referred to as hydrometry. The graphic outline of the relationship between RELATIVE HUMIDITY, specific humidity, molar fraction, and total mass of water vapor is represented by a psychrometric chart, also known as MOLLIER Chart (*see* MOLLIER CHART).

Ptolemaeus, Claudius (approximately 90–168 AD)

[astrophysics/astronomy, geophysics] Astronomer, mathematician, and geophysicist from Greece. Author of a comprehensive work on all the information available in his time on the SOLAR SYSTEM and astronomical phenomena: Μεγαλη Συυταξιζ (i.e., summary), mostly based on the work of HIPPARCHUS (190–125 BC). He is also known for his detailed tabulation of trigonometrical data with greater detail and more elaborate incremental steps than most current mathematical handbooks (*also* PTOLEMY) (see Figure P.169).

Figure P.169 Ptolemy (approximately 90–168 AD), rendering produced in the early sixteenth century.

Ptolemy (approximately 90–168 AD)

[general, optics] Scientist from Greece. Ptolemy described the ANGLE of incidence and refraction for water and made attempts to relate them mathematically (*also* CLAUDIUS PTOLEMAEUS).

p-type doping

[atomic, electronics, general] Intrinsic SEMICONDUCTORS that have had impurities introduced are considered to be doped, impurities consisting of foreign atoms into a crystal lattice structure. The crystal lattice structure provides the conduction and ENERGY platform for a stable structure. Certain semiconductors have VALENCE electrons that can easily be moved to the CONDUCTION BAND, sometimes spontaneously under slightly elevated temperatures. The ultimate release of the conduction electron (electron deficiency) creates a "hole" in the semiconductor lattice that can travel as if it were a POSITIVE CHARGE, hence the nomenclature *p*-type doping; positive. Introduction of an impurity with three valence electrons generally results in the formation of a "hole" in the lattice. The lattice may for instance consist of germanium or silicon. The FERMI LEVEL for intrinsic semiconductor materials is generally in the middle between the VALENCE BAND and the conduction bands in the energy level diagram. For the P-TYPE SEMICONDUCTOR, the valence band will have "hole energy" whereas the conduction band comprises "electron energy." Joining a *p*-type semiconductor with an N-TYPE SEMICONDUCTOR creates an PN-JUNCTION that can be influenced to modulate electron transmission between the two semiconductor materials, creating on an elementary level a DIODE. The addition of more *n*-type and/

or *p*-type junctions will form transistors and more complex integrated circuit designs (*also see* N-TYPE, DIODE, *and* TRANSISTOR) (see Figure P.170).

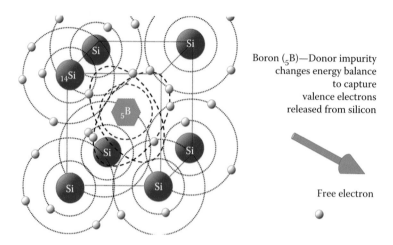

Boron ($_5$B)—Donor impurity changes energy balance to capture valence electrons released from silicon

Free electron

Figure P.170 *p*-type doping, semiconductor energy configuration.

p-type semiconductor

[electronics, general] Semiconductor material with an electron deficiency, permanently imbedded "holes" (*see* P-DOPING) (see Figure P.171).

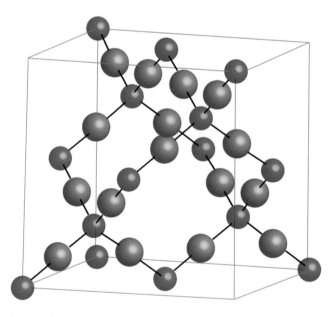

Figure P.171 Silicon oxide crystal design as the basis for certain semiconductor platforms.

Pulley

[general, mechanics] System of wheels with v-shape or u-shape channel along the outside track of the wheel to fit a belt or rope (chain) to run over the outside circumference. The pulley acts as a force multiplier depending on the number of up–down loops used for hoisting a mass upwards, or alternatively for a horizontal force and direction. Hanging a mass on the pulley and attaching a rope to a location above the pulley will require half the force applied to raise the object when applying tension on the free distal end of the rope. This is due to the fact that both ends of the rope have equal tension, combinedly yielding the gravitational force on the object; thus the free end only has half the tension, requiring half the force (see Figure P.172).

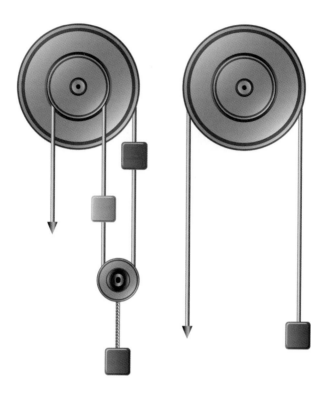

Figure P.172 Pulley.

Pulmonary system

[biomedical, fluid dynamics] Biological system consisting of the lungs and vasculature, providing RESPIRATION function. The GAS exchange in the lungs between AIR and BLOOD is based on HENRY'S LAW that states that the gas volume, and therefore the concentration ([Gas]) dissolved in a LIQUID is directly proportional to its partial PRESSURE (P), defined as $[\text{Gas}] = K_{sol}P$, where K_{sol} is a solubility constant. The thin alveolar and pulmonary CAPILLARY walls provide a minimal BARRIER, allowing for swift DIFFUSION of oxygen and carbon dioxide, yielding a rapid equilibrium for the respective partial pressures of the constituents. This equilibration diffusion is described by Fick's law, relating the rate of diffusion to the concentration gradient as well as surface area for gas exchange, while being inversely related to the thickness of the WALL of the exchange surface; alveolar membrane. Pulmonary CIRCULATION is the flow from the HEART to the lungs and back. One specific biomedical complication in FLUID DYNAMICS is a pulmonary EMBOLISM, a blockage due to plaque or blood clot that reduces the flow to zero. At this point, the local VENTILATION/PERFUSION ratio becomes large, while reducing it for the "healthy" part of the lung. The remaining functional perfused segment of the lungs will result in large arterial to alveolar P_{O_2}, difference with an associated increase in PHYSIOLOGICAL DEAD SPACE (see Figure P.173).

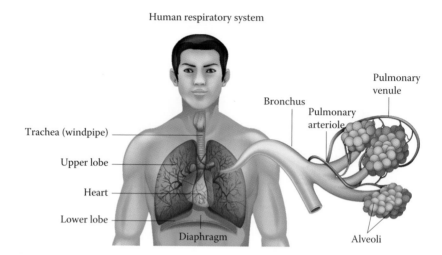

Human respiratory system

Trachea (windpipe)

Upper lobe

Heart

Lower lobe

Diaphragm

Bronchus

Pulmonary arteriole

Pulmonary venule

Alveoli

Figure P.173 Pulmonary system.

Pulsar

[astrophysics/astronomy, general] Collapsing spinning STAR, "end of life," resulting in increased density with decreasing angular momentum and associated increasing ANGULAR VELOCITY (ω) (resembling a figure skater performing a pirouette, pulling in the arms and legs). The rotational ENERGY of the pulsar follows from Newtonian physics as $E_{rot} \sim (1/2)MR^2\omega^2$, with R the radius of the pulsar and M its mass. One known pulsar in the CRAB NEBULA has a mass equivalent to our SUN, however only at a 25 km diameter due to the collapse. The Crab Nebula pulsar ("Crab pulsar") rotates at $\omega = 60\pi$ rad/s, emitting X-RAY and gamma radiation at pulsating intervals. The pulsar emission is generally erratic and irregular in both frequency and MAGNITUDE, as well as spectral profile, but will generally resemble the angular period (see Figure P.174).

Figure P.174 Supernova remnant and pulsar wind nebula in the constellation of Taurus.

Pulsatile flow

[biomedical, fluid dynamics] Many systems have a periodic flow pattern based on the mechanism of action of the device providing the ENERGY for the flow. In biological applications, the pulsatile flow is provided by the beating HEART. The flow process in biological systems is very complex due to the COMPLIANCE of the system (vascular dilation/stretch), and downstream RESISTANCE that can be influenced by mechanical and hormonal functions (e.g., muscle contraction and adrenaline). Other mechanical pulsatile systems are piston pumps, rotary pumps, and for instance windmills with a paddle system operating with ANGULAR VELOCITY ($\omega = \nu 2\pi$, where ν represent the alternation frequency). The flow in mechanical systems can be analyzed using the (time-dependent) Navier–Stokes equation ($\rho(\partial u/\partial t) = -\left(\partial P/\partial z\right) + \mu\left\{\left(\partial^2 u/\partial t^2\right) + [(1/r)(\partial u/\partial r)]\right\}$), with the boundary condition ($\partial u/\partial z = 0$) assuming that the FLUID is incompressible (constant density ρ); the tubes are rigid with constant radius r, for LAMINAR FLOW at flow velocity u, driven by an applied PRESSURE (P) gradient as a function of the axial direction z. Developing the pressure gradient in a series will prove to be beneficial: ($\partial P/\partial z) = \sum_{n=1}^{N} C_n e^{in\omega t}$, disregarding the steady-state background flow that can be incorporated in various ways (e.g., $n = 0$) and the velocity is directly in line with the pressure fluctuations (*also see* BLOOD FLOW) (see Figure P.175).

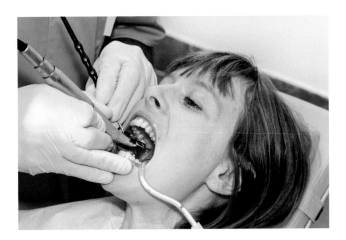

Figure P.175 Pulsatile flow used during a tooth-cleaning procedure.

Pulse oximeter

[biomedical, optical] Optical sensor device used to determine the partial oxygen SATURATION of BLOOD circulating in a biological system. The pulse oximeter relies on two aspects: PULSATILE FLOW and differential absorption between oxyhemoglobin (HbO_2) and deoxyhemoglobin (hemoglobin Hb). Hemoglobin has a much higher absorption in RED, at approximately 660 nm, while oxygenated hemoglobin has a slightly higher attenuation in the INFRARED (IR) 940–960 nm bandwidth. The pulsating nature brings fresh oxygenated blood in the tissue region on a period interval matching the heartbeat. Comparing the attenuation at two or more wavelengths as a function of time allows the oxygenated portion to be segregated out and yields the expression for the percentile oxygen saturation (SpO_2) as
$$SpO_2 = \left\{\mu_{a\lambda=\text{red}}\left(Hb\right)/\left[\mu_{a\lambda=\text{red}}\left(Hb\right) - \mu_{a\lambda=\text{red}}\left(HbO_2\right)\right]\right\} - \left\{\mu_{a\lambda=\text{IR}}/\left[\mu_{a\lambda=\text{red}}\left(Hb\right) - \mu_{a\lambda=\text{red}}\left(HbO_2\right)\right]\right\}*$$

P

$\left[\ln\left(\psi_{\lambda=\text{red}}\right)-\ln\left(\psi_0{}'_{\lambda=\text{red}}\right)\right]\Big/\left[\ln\left(\psi_{\lambda=\text{IR}}\right)-\ln\left(\psi_0{}'_{\lambda=\text{IR}}\right)\right]\Big\}$, where μ_a represent the spectral attenuation coefficient and ψ the radiance of the LIGHT at the respective wavelength (see Figure P.176).

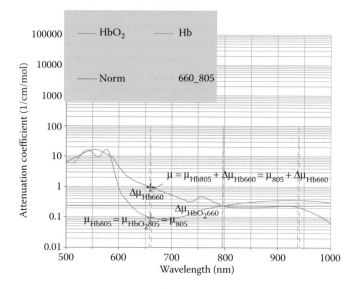

Figure P.176 Optical background in pulse oximetry for the determination of the oxygen saturation of blood.

Pump

[fluid dynamics, thermodynamics] Mechanical device designed to move fluids. The fluids can include PARTICLE solutions (slurry, waste). Many different mechanism apply to the pumping action, ranging from a diaphragm, pistons to screws and also peristaltic action. The peristaltic action is known for the transport of emulsions in the esophagus and intestinal tract for mammals. The lobe pump is generally used for transporting cooling FLUID in automobiles. Old-fashioned plunger-operated hand pumps for water displacement are found to very effective and require no other ENERGY source than MUSCLE action. Another low-energy pump operating on a similar mechanism is the bobbing oil-pump found at OIL wells. A pump that requires no power to operate, except to initially get the process started is the siphon. The siphon requires a negative pressure to fill the tube, and gravitational pull will maintain flow as long as the distal end of the siphon (hose) is lower than the entry point and the entry point remains submerged at all times to prevent AIR from entering into the system, hence defeating the VACUUM. Pumps satisfy the Bernoulli and Navier–Stokes equations (see Figure P.177).

(a)　　　　　　(b)

Figure P.177 (a) Water pump and (b) oil pump.

Purcell, Edward Mills (1912–1997)

[astrophysics/astronomy, atomic, biomedical, nuclear] Physicist from the United States who won a Nobel Prize for his discovery of the nuclear MAGNETIC RESONANCE effects of certain LIQUID and solid media in 1952. Additional efforts of Purcell were in RADIOASTRONOMY and microwave technology (see Figure P.178).

Figure P.178 Edward Mills Purcell (1912–1997).

p-wave

[biomedical] In the ELECTROCARDIOGRAM (ECG) of the HEART the DEPOLARIZATION wavefront starts in the atrium that excites the ventricle, where the QRS-complex is representative of the depolarization of the ventricular cardiac MUSCLE. The p-wave is the depolarization of the atrium resulting from the SA-node trigger (natural PACEMAKER; sinus node or sino-atrial node [sino-auricular]; located on the right atrium) (see Figure P.179).

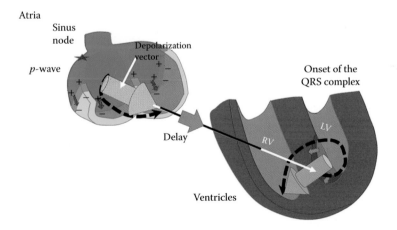

Figure P.179 Atrial p-wave and its relevance in the electrocardiogram (ECG). The QRS-complex is the main segment for ventricular electrical cell-membrane depolarization and repolarization activity.

Pyroelectricity

[acoustics, atomic, electromagnetism, fluid dynamics, general, mechanics, quantum, solid-state, thermodynamics] Electrical potential generated by heating certain crystalline structures. The thermal effect results in a LATTICE structure reorganization that produces a permanent ELECTRIC DIPOLE structure that aligns, forming a polarized structure.

Pythagoras (c. 570–c. 495 BC)

[computational, general] Pythagoras of Samos was a scientist and mathematician from Greece. Supposedly, a great deal of his mathematical knowledge was influenced by Babylonian scientists during his captivity in what is now known as the Persian Empire. Apart from the introduction of the PYTHAGOREAN THEOREM, Pythagoras is known for his work on astronomy and discovered the OCTAVE aspect of VIBRATION frequencies for string instruments. Pythagoras and his followers also introduced the principle that the SUN was the center of our planetary system based on certain mathematical principles of PLANETARY MOTION as observed with rudimentary devices. However, this concept was not generally accepted until the late fifteenth century, NICOLAUS COPERNICUS (1473–1543) (see Figure P.180).

Figure P.180 Artist impression of what Pythagoras (c. 570–c. 495 BC) may have looked like.

Pythagorean theorem

[computational, general] Geometric analysis of a triangle linking the lengths of the three edges with respect to the longest edge (c) as to the remaining edges (respectively a and b): $c = \sqrt{(a^2 + b^2)}$. The Pythagorean theorem was defined by the Greek mathematician PYTHAGORAS (approx. 570–490 BC).

PZT

[acoustics, biomedical, electromagnetism, general, mechanics] Specifically the material: lead (Pb)-zirconate (Zr)-titanate (Ti) (PZT; $Pb\left[Zr_m Ti_{1-m}\right]O_3$, where $0 \leq m \leq 1$), a synthetic ceramic material used as an acoustic TRANSDUCER. PZT in its indigenous state exhibits no piezoelectric properties of its own. When the PZT material is heated past the Curie point in temperature, the ceramic material can have the internal dipoles to be aligned be means of an externally applied electric field. The PZT is in this manner used to create ACOUSTIC WAVES resulting from an alternating electric field, usually in the MHz range for ULTRASOUND imaging. The speed of sound in the artificial ceramic PZT material is approximately 4000 m/s. The operating frequency of the medium is determined by the combined conditions of the speed of sound and the thickness of the medium. The half wavelength of the SOUND pulse will need to match the dimension of the ceramic, the thickness; for a 5 MHz (i.e., center frequency) pulse the wavelength is $\lambda = v_{sound}/v = 4000/5\times10^6 = 0.8\,\text{mm}$, which yields for the thickness 0.4 mm. The RESONANCE FREQUENCY of the PZT block is achieved from a short block-WAVE voltage spike in the μs range (*see* PIEZOELECTRIC TRANSDUCER).

Q Equation

[atomic, chemical, nuclear] Reaction quotient, describing the transposition of states and ENERGY configurations. The reaction quotient for a chemical process is defined as the ratio of the concentration of products to the concentration of reactants, for instance in a reaction with ingredients $A; B; C; D$ at relative quantities $a; b; c; d$ in reaction $aA + bB \rightleftharpoons cC + dD$, with respective (molar-) concentrations $[A]; [B]; [C]; [D]$, proceeding as $a[A] + b[B] \rightleftharpoons c[C] + d[D]$, which yields the reaction quotient $Q_c = C^c D^d / A^a B^b$. This can provide the change in Gibbs free energy (ΔG) as ($\Delta G = \Delta G^0 + RT \ln Q_c$), at temperature T with $R = 8.3144621(75)$ J/kmol the GAS constant, applied to SOLUTION (see Figure Q.1).

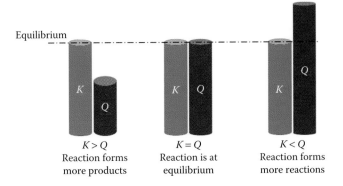

Figure Q.1 Diagram representing the implication of the Q equation. Reaction example: $CO(g) + H_2O(g) \rightleftharpoons CO_2(g) + H_2(g)$ (g: gas) in molar quantities: $CO = 1.00$ mol, $H_2O = 1.00$ mol; $CO_2 = 2.00$ mol, $H_2 = 2.00$ mol, with $Q_c = [CO_2][H_2] / [CO][H_2O] = 2 \times 2/1 \times 1 = 4$, while the (gas-) equilibrium constant is defined in relative quantities as follows: 1 unit CO reacts with 1 unit H_2O yielding 1 unit CO_2 and 1 unit H_2 with equilibrium constant $K = (CO_2)(H_2)/(CO)(H_2O) = 1 \times 1/1 \times 1 = 1$.

Q Factor

[acoustics, biomedical, computational, electronics, mechanics, nuclear] QUALITY FACTOR, dimensionless parameter used as an indicator for the mechanical or electronic dampening of the MAGNITUDE pertaining to an oscillatory phenomenon. The Q factor is an indication of the inflicted AMPLITUDE reduction with respect to the free OSCILLATION. In ULTRASOUND scanning, for instance, low Q is required pertaining to DOPPLER imaging, and does not imply any value judgment of the material used to generate the specific acoustic frequency band. An ultrasound probe (for instance, made from PZT material) will have a dampening efficiency that is expressed as $Q = \nu_0 / \Delta \nu$, where ν_0 is the center frequency of the material or RESONANCE FREQUENCY and $\Delta \nu$ the bandwidth of the mechanism with enclosure and materials in close contact with the walls of the piezoelectric structure, acting as dampeners. A high Q factor is an indication of a narrow resonance peak. In nuclear reactions the Q VALUE has a different meaning from the Q factor, in that case indicating the net gain in kinetic ENERGY. Alternatively, in MECHANICS it relates to the length of the crank arm for a bicycle paddle. The bicycle paddle DISTANCE between the attachment to the axis through the gear sprocket (chain ring) for the chain and the platform bicycle pedal (*also see* QUALITY FACTOR) (see Figure Q.2).

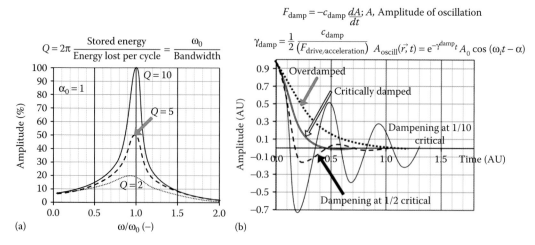

Figure Q.2 (a,b) Damping effect for amplitude of oscillation (either mechanical or electronic) for conditions defining specific Q factors.

Q of reaction

[atomic, nuclear] *See* Q VALUE.

Q Phase

[thermodynamics] Heterogeneous state, composite system of phases that are in MUTUAL STABLE EQUILIBRIUM. For alloys, the Q-phase designates a condition of specific structure. In the aluminum–copper–magnesium–silicon alloy for instance, the Q phase is the compound $Al_5Cu_2Mg_8Si_6$. This alloy Q phase is formed during the SOLIDIFICATION process and has inferior mechanical properties. The alloy Q phase can be predicted and subsequently avoided by a computational thermodynamic approach, using isothermal phase diagrams with regard to the PHASE stability (see Figure Q.3).

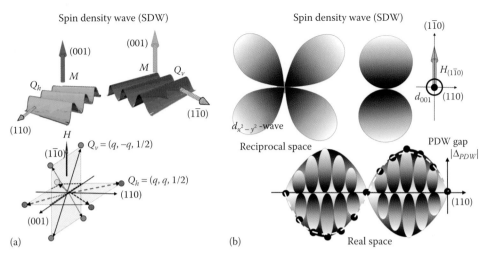

Figure Q.3 (a,b) Electronic matrix with respect to the Q phase of Cooper pair electrons in an alloy structure describing the superconductivity conditions under the influence of an applied external magnetic field, where the magnetic field direction controls the complex quantum state with respect to the Q phase. The Q-phase diagram illustrates the Q vectors associated with the spin-density waves for the alloy CeCoIn$_5$ (cerium–cobalt–indium), describing the magnetic Bragg positions corresponding to the magnetic field direction in reciprocal space. In this situation, the Q phase illustrates the quantum critical point defining magnetically induced superconductivity.

Q Space

[computational, condensed matter] Q space analysis in computational data analysis provides an alternative to diffusion-weighted imaging (DWI). Q space provides an estimation of maximum likelihood of processes and events, for instance the SCATTERING of RADIATION by particles or discontinuities. Q space analysis involves plotting the scattered wavefunction (and respective PHASE function) magnitude versus the MAGNITUDE of the scattering WAVE vector: $q = (4\pi/\lambda) \sin(\theta/2)$, using a double log plot. The Q space analysis allows for the estimation of the probability density function (PDF) for molecular DIFFUSION without the need for assumptions with regard to a specific Gaussian shape. One particular application is in the IMAGE analysis for magnetic resonance imaging (MRI). Q space represents wavelength (λ) (long wavelength corresponding to small q) with respect to displacement (location: r). It is a transform from the diffusion TENSOR (see Figure Q.4).

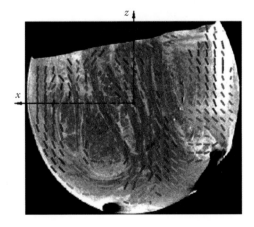

Figure Q.4 Q-space map obtained by magnetic resonance imaging. Quantitative analysis of Q-space (QUAQ) data for a section of a human pons acquired on a 14.1T VARIAN NMR imager with 90 Q vectors (corresponding diffusion gradients with 3 strengths × 30 directions): estimated distribution of neuronal bundles illustrated by cylinders superimposed over a high-resolution spin-echo image of a transverse section of a human rostral pons. The predominant orientation of the neuronal bundles is indicated in blue for the z-direction, green for the x-direction, and red for the y-direction (out of plane axis). (Courtesy of L. Guy Raguin.)

Q Switching

[optics, quantum] Pulsing mechanism used to form an extremely high radiance laser pulse with an extremely short duration, that is, Q-switched laser. Q-switched laser pulses are convenient in tattoo removal based on the short thermal interaction, preventing thermal DIFFUSION, which would result in ambient damage. Q-switched laser pulses are in the order of nanosecond duration. The pulsation is achieved by influencing the losses in the cavity, diminishing the laser emission process while gaining on INVERSION. The reduction in "emission" of the LASER acronym can be achieved by any of the following means: rotating MIRROR, SATURATION of a programmable absorbing medium, acousto-optic modulation of the path within the cavity, and electro-optic modulation of the path within the laser cavity, for instance, by means of a Pockels CELL. The Q switching modulates the rate equation of the LASER action mechanism on an atomic level within Einstein's population inversion process, with a time constant embedded in the DECAY constant of the cavity, indicative of the depletion of the EXCITED STATES. The loss is virtually instantaneously switched to "low" to release all the stored inverted state ENERGY as a short PHOTON pulse for the duration of the low loss. The pulse duration (τ_c) is a function of the IONIZATION decay rate as $dn(t)/dt = K\{N_i - N_{th}\}n(t) \approx (r_i - 1)/\tau_c$, where $r_i = N_i/N_{th}$ is the initial inversion ratio, with N_i the POPULATION INVERSION directly after switching and N_{th} the threshold inversion immediately after switching, and $n(t)$ is the cavity photon number (~number of excited states). Q-switched lasers generally operate in a pulse sequence range of hundreds of hertz to megahertz with below nanosecond pulse duration (e.g., picosecond laser pulse duration used for tattoo removal with minimal peripheral thermal damage, due to the short thermal diffusion time) at output energy levels exceeding J. In 1958, GORDON GOULD (1920–2005) proposed the concept of Q switching, but the practical implementation was applied in the state-of-the-art ruby laser of the day by Robert W. Hellwarth (1930–) and Fred J. McClung (1907–2014) in 1961 by means of a Kerr cell shutter, operating based on electrical switching placed within the laser cavity (see Figure Q.5).

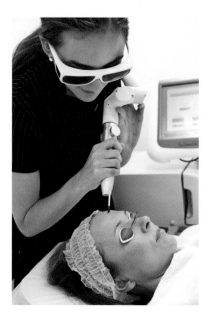

Figure Q.5 Beautician applying a Q-switch laser for cosmetic skin modification based on photocoagulation processes.

Q Value

[chemical, nuclear, solid-state] In nuclear reactions, the Q value is an indication of the net gain in kinetic ENERGY (KE), standing with respect to the rest energy: $Q = \sum \left(Mc^2 \right)_{before} - \sum \left(Mc^2 \right)_{after} = \sum \sum KE_{after} - \sum \sum KE_{before}$, where $c = 2.99792458 \times 10^8$ m/s is the speed of LIGHT and M the respective masses in the processes. In PARTICLE physics, the Q value represents the DECAY of a particle; for instance, the decay for a NEUTRON is described in relativistic energy as $Q = \left(m_n - m_p - m_{\bar{v}} - m_e \right) c^2$, with m_n the neutron mass, m_p the proton mass, $m_{\bar{v}}$ the mass for the antineutrino, m_e the electron mass, and $c = 299792458$ m/s the speed of light. Not to be confused with the Q FACTOR (see Figure Q.6).

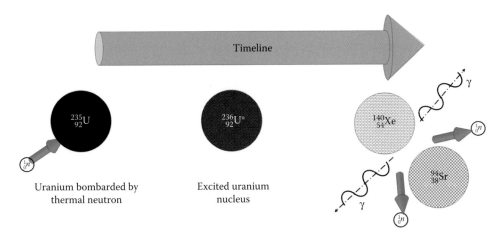

Figure Q.6 Diagram illustrating the mass equivalence with respect to the Q value for a nuclear fission process.

Q–T Interval

[biomedical] Time interval for each heart beat, defining the ventricular DEPOLARIZATION (Q; in the QRS segment of the EKG) with respect to the subsequent atrial depolarization (T) for the next contraction of the atrium, lowed by the ventricular contraction, perfusing the body with BLOOD (see Figure Q.7).

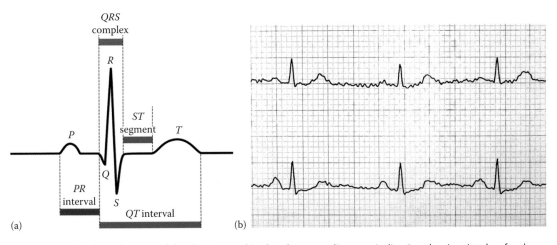

Figure Q.7 (a,b) The relevance of the Q–T interval in the electrocardiogram, indicating the time it takes for the heart to contract and subsequently refill with blood before initiating the next contraction. The Q–T interval is a function of exercise history, the age, and gender of the individual, as well as the regularity and frequency of the standard heart rate. A long Q–T interval represents the deviations in the heart's electrical recharging system from the mean with respect to the overall population, and can be genetically defined or have correlation with a broad range of diseases, not necessarily heart related.

Quadrupole moment

[atomic] Description of the deviation from a spherical charge distribution in the NUCLEUS with respect to the nuclear moment, defined as $Q_e = (1/e)\int r^2 \left(3\cos^2\theta - 1\right)\rho d\tau$, where θ is the azimuth ANGLE in reference to the projection of the total SPIN of the charge ELEMENT $\rho d\tau$ in the direction where this is maximized for QUANTUM NUMBER $m = I$ (I is the TOTAL ANGULAR MOMENTUM for the spin) at location r, and $e = 1.60217657 \times 10^{-19}$ C is the ELECTRIC CHARGE. The quadrupole moment provides the expectation value for the charge distribution and respective spin angular momentum configuration. Note that the quadrupole moment is nonzero for nuclei that have the total angular momentum greater than or equal to one ($I \geq 1$). The quadrupole momentum can provide details about the internuclear forces. The quadrupole moment is negative for nuclei with a closed (spherical) shell and that possess an additional positive PARTICLE. A nearly closed shell will yield a quadrupole moment that has a positive denomination (prolate nuclear shape). The electric quadrupole moment for a nucleus can also be described in TENSOR format as a function of the wavefunction for the respective nuclear states (ψ_N), for the corresponding Cartesian components x_i: $Q_e = \sum_{k=1}^{Z} e\left(3x_i x_j - \delta_{ij} r^2\right)_k \left|\psi_N\right|^2 d\tau$, where δ_{ij} is the KRONECKER DELTA FUNCTION (see Figure Q.8).

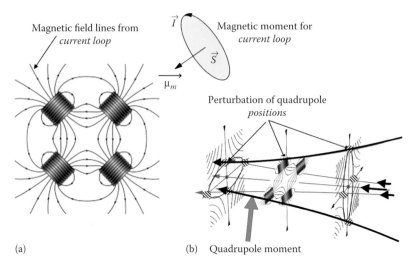

Magnetic field lines from *current loop*

$\vec{I}$

Magnetic moment for *current loop*

$\vec{S}$

$\vec{\mu}_m$

Perturbation of quadrupole *positions*

(a)

(b) Quadrupole moment

Figure Q.8 (a) Macroscopic quadrupole rods of an analyzer from a triple quadrupole mass spectrometer, and (b) diagram of the associated field distribution under the wavefunction affected changes in nuclear states with a perturbation in magnetic field distribution and associated quadrupole moment. The magnetic moment is a direct function of the magnetic strength of each of the poles and the respective separation between the various poles, constructing a complex vector summation subject to recursive influences from the "other" poles performed in a perturbation analysis.

Quality factor

[nuclear, optics] The quality factor is used in several locations in PHYSICS; ionizing radiation and laser radiation are two specific scientific designations of interest. With respect to ionizing radiation the quality factor is an equivalence indicator for RADIATION in comparison to human risk during exposure of X-RAY radiation. The following quality factor applies to the respective sources of radiation: γ, $Q = 1$; β, $Q = 1$; α, $Q = 20$; NEUTRON, $Q = 10$, proton (high energy), $Q = 10$. In laser design the quality factor dictates the efficiency of a laser cavity: $Q_f = \omega t_{out}/\delta_c = \left(4\pi L/\lambda\right)\left(1/\delta_c\right)$, for a WAVE with wavelength λ of a cavity with time of flight at the output mirror $t_{out} = 2L/c$ ($c = 2.99792458 \times 10^8$ m/s is the speed of LIGHT and L is the laser cavity length), with δ_c the "loss coefficient" expressing the fractional loss over the

REFLECTION–transmission path. In this case the quality factor determines the line width, $\Delta\omega = 2\pi\Delta\nu$ ($\nu = c/\lambda$ the frequency), of the laser beam (see Figure Q.9).

Type of radiation	Rad	Q Factor	Rem
X-ray	1	1	1
Gamma ray	1	1	1
Beta particles	1	1	1
Thermal neutrons	1	5	5
Fast neutrons	1	10	10
Alpha particles	1	20	20

Figure Q.9 Quality factor with respect to dose equivalence for radiation exposure.

Quanta

[atomic, general, mechanics, optics, photons, quantum] Discrete quantities of ENERGY or charge, or mass. The QUANTUM of charge was named by George Johnstone Stoney (1826–1911) in 1891 as the electron. The quantum for electromagnetic RADIATION is the PHOTON, named in 1926 by Frithiof Wolfers (1890–1971) and Gilbert N. Lewis (1875–1946).

Quantification

[acoustics, computational, image] Mechanism used in ULTRASONIC IMAGING applied to boundary detection. The acoustic quantification provides a regional analysis.

Quantized Dirac equation

[computational, energy, general, thermodynamics] Mathematical description that applies to the interaction of the electric field resulting from the electron current density of a system, with associated ELECTRO-MAGNETIC FIELD configuration (atomic, or generalized QUANTUM–mechanical particles) as well as the photons entering and leaving the system on the electron "self-field" expression. The electron current density for a flow of charges with net charge q: $J^\mu(x) = iq/2\left[\Psi(x), \gamma^\mu\Psi(x)\right]$ ([,] the commutator; γ^μ the set of four 4×4 Dirac matrices defined by $\{\gamma^\mu, \gamma^\nu\} = 2g_m^{\mu\nu}$, where $g_m^{\mu\nu} = \text{diag}(-1, +1, +1, +1)$ is the matrix diagonal and $\{,\}$ is the anticommutator). The adjoint wavefunction $\Psi(x)$ is defined through the Hermitian conjugate: $\gamma^{\mu*} = -\mathbb{A}\gamma^\mu\mathbb{A}^{-1}$, as $\Psi(x) = \mathbb{A}\Psi^*(x)$, where $\mathbb{A}$ is the 4×4 Hermitian matrix. This provides the function of the WAVEFUNCTION ($\Psi(x)$) SOLUTION to the SCHRÖDINGER EQUATION as $\left[\gamma^\mu\partial_\mu + iq\gamma^\mu\left(A_\mu(x) + A_\mu^{\text{ext}}(x)\right) + m_0\right]\Psi(x) = 0$, with

$$\partial_\mu = \left(\left.\frac{\partial}{\partial x}\right|_0, \nabla\right)$$

(∇ the Laplace second derivative matrix) the differential operator, $A_\mu^{\text{ext}}(x)$ the (classical) external electromagnetic field, $A_\mu(x)$ the field from the entering photons combined with the "virtual photons" of the electron self-field, and m_0 the charge mass associated with q.

Quantum

[nuclear, quantum] A discrete quantity of radiative (electromagnetic) ENERGY equal to the product of its frequency and Planck's constant. The equation is $E = h\nu$ (see Figure Q.10).

Figure Q.10 Postage stamp dedicated to the quantum concept, specifically pertaining to light, dedicated to Max Planck (1858–1947).

Quantum chromodynamics

[general, high-energy] COLOR identification of GLUON exchange with respect to the interaction between quarks. The color QUANTUM gluon has a spin 1 and is a massless VECTOR BOSON. The vector boson is described by means of a four-dimensional wavefunction. The GLUON offers eight different coupling mechanisms that are represented by color-GAUGE THEORY as eight massless gluons. The color denominations are approximately as follows: green versus antigreen: magenta; RED versus antired: cyan; blue versus antiblue: yellow; and so on, less well defined in some cases.

Quantum concentration

[energy, thermodynamics] The number of particulate constituents per unit volume with a separation DISTANCE that is equal to the DE BROGLIE WAVELENGTH, defined as $n_Q = \left(mk_b T / 2\pi\hbar^2 \right)^{3/2}$, with $\hbar$ the Planck constant h divided by 2π, $k_b = 1.3806488 \times 10^{-23}\,\mathrm{m^2\,kg/s^2\,K}$ the Boltzmann coefficient, and m the mass of the elementary unit forming the system or GAS.

Quantum dot (QD)

[biomedical, quantum, solid-state] Macromolecular crystalline structure that has QUANTUM mechanical properties. The quantum dot concept is frequently associated with nanoparticles. In many cases, the quantum dot has a semiconductor material base. The quantum dot can have photoluminescent properties. QDs are also used for biological and chemical marking and tracking due to the highly configurable nature. The name originates from the discovery by ALEXEI EKIMOV (1945–) in a GLASS matrix, published in 1975, and independently in colloidal solutions by Louis E. Brus (1943–) in 1980. The term "quantum dot" was coined by Mark Reed (1955–) in. Quantum dots have an ability to convert LIGHT into ELECTRICITY and vice versa. They have found applications in a range of scientific device designs, ranging from quantum computers, solar panels, light emitting devices, cellular imaging, to siRNA delivery, next to target tumor detection and therapeutic targeting (see Figure Q.11).

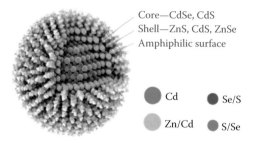

Figure Q.11 Graphical representation of the quantum dot principle. (Courtesy of RusNano, Moscow, Russia.)

Quantum electrodynamics (QED)

[atomic, computational, energy, general, thermodynamics] Relativistic QUANTUM THEORY-based physics principles introduced by Dirac. Electromagnetic phenomena where the electric field is mathematically considered to be ruled by the laws of QUANTUM MECHANICS. One specific quantum phenomenon is the PHOTON. In theoretical physics the merger of the MAXWELL EQUATIONS with SPECIAL RELATIVITY formed the relativistic quantum theory known as QUANTUM ELECTRODYNAMICS (QED). The mathematical treatment of charged particles will range from classic, nonrelativistic to relativistic. QED has its roots in the revelation of the quantum hypothesis for LIGHT (i.e., photons with ENERGY $E = h\nu$) by Max Planck in 1900. Additional fundamental atomic interactions such as ANNIHILATION and PAIR PRODUCTION require a quantized energy format as well as relativistic theory. The first use of QED was by WERNER KARL HEISENBERG (1901–1976) and WOLFGANG ERNST PAULI (1900–1958) when they introduced a spinless relativistic PARTICLE in 1929. Around the same time a relativistic particle with spin $\hbar/2$ was introduced that relies on PAUL ADRIEN MAURICE DIRAC's (1902–1984) relativistic WAVE EQUATION, where $\hbar = h/2\pi$ is derived from MAX KARL ERNST LUDWIG PLANCK's (1858–1947) constant h. The ELECTRON SPIN is described perfectly well in the Dirac interpretation of the special relativistic approach to quantum mechanics known as quantum electrodynamics. One notable example of QED is the QUANTIZED DIRAC EQUATION. QED applies to electrons, electromagnetic RADIATION, and ELEMENTARY PARTICLES such as muons, except for hadrons that are governed by strong interaction, which makes the QED theoretical approach more a phenomenological exercise. QED also allowed for the introduction of ANTIMATTER, which helped balance the energy scales in nuclear physics. It forms the basis for the theoretical description in high energy physics.

Quantum field theory

[computational, energy, general, thermodynamics] Interaction of MATTER with each other based on the hypothesis that each object or phenomenon is based on PARTICLE interaction, where each particle has a GRAVITATIONAL FIELD surrounding it that decays with DISTANCE. Generally, all forces between objects are maintained by particle stream, where GRAVITATION is enforced by the hypothetical massless GRAVITON particle. The quantum field theory attempts to portray forces and fields as a physical presence. This concept followed the description of the PHOTON as the "particle" carrying the ENERGY of the electric and MAGNETIC FIELD fluctuations. When enough energy $E = mc^2$ is present in any form, theoretically a real particle can be created to replace the virtual one. Quantum field theory has four assumptions: (1) quantum fields are the essence (there are no other parameters); (2) all quantum fields obey the laws of QUANTUM MECHANICS as well as special relativity; (3) field MAGNITUDE in any location is the likelihood of interacting with a particle at a specific location; and (4) the field QUANTA provide an interaction that is equivalent to the general concept of classical field theory. In quantum field theory, the concept of DEGREES OF FREEDOM is replaced by operators, where one example is the HAMILTONIAN. Another switch is the exchange of POISON BRACKETS in general quantum mechanics by commutators. The way quantum field theory is formulated offers a mechanism to describe and explain the FOUR FORCES of nature: GRAVITY, weak, electromagnetic, and strong.

Quantum fluids

[computational, energy, fluid dynamics, general, thermodynamics] Fluids that have the apparent property of remaining LIQUID at ABSOLUTE ZERO temperature and zero pressure. By definition, a quantum fluid has a ZERO-POINT ENERGY that is comparable with the potential energy associated with the interparticle forces. This property is the definition of fluid, while the THERMAL ENERGY brings it into the quantum field. These fluids have a remarkably large zero-point energy while possessing extremely small interatomic forces. Both factors contribute to the prevention of forming a solid. Examples of quantum fluids are electron "GAS" in sodium, nuclear MATTER in general, NEUTRON matter, and helium: ^{3}He and ^{4}He.

Quantum gas

[energy, thermodynamics] Gas or LIQUID solution that has a concentration (n_{gas}) that is greater than or equal to the QUANTUM CONCENTRATION: $n_{gas} \geq n_Q = \left(mT/2\pi\hbar^2 \right)^{3/2}$. The quantum gas can be either fermions or bosons, but in contrast with the GAS in the classical regime the FERMI GAS behaves significantly different from the Bose gas.

Quantum jump

[general] The transition of an electron in a high ENERGY (initial energy state: E_i) orbit to a low energy orbit (final energy state: E_f), or ultimately GROUND STATE. The electron orbits are defined in the BOHR ATOMIC MODEL, described by NIELS HENRIK DAVID BOHR (1885–1962). The change in ENERGY LEVEL in the atomic model is associated with a change in the kinetic energy of the ELECTRIC CHARGE; hence, the electron will accelerate. The accelerated charge with an associated electric field will generate a changing MAGNETIC FIELD and hence produce electromagnetic RADIATION, that is, LIGHT, with frequency ν expressed by $h\nu = E_i - E_f$, where $h = 4.1356692 \times 10^{-15}$ Js is the Planck constant.

Quantum level

[general] ENERGY level of an electron or of any atomic system, distinct from any other of its energy levels by discrete quantities dependent on Planck's constant.

Quantum liquid

[astrophysics/astronomy, computational, energy, fluid dynamics, mechanics, quantum, thermodynamics] Concept introduced by LEV LANDAU (1908–1968), specifically for "Bose" type liquids (*also see* BOSE LIQUID).

Quantum magnet

[astro, biomedical, electric, quantum, solid-state] Magnet based on the MEISSNER EFFECT. MAGNETIC FIELD resulting from the transition of a superconductor to the superconducting state.

Quantum mechanics

[computational, electric, energy, general, nuclear, thermodynamics] Theoretical approach to phenomena that are fundamentally discrete in operation; changes occur in increments. Examples of quantized phenomena are angular atomic and subatomic momentum, charge transfer, electromagnetic interactions (e.g., photons), PARTICLE interaction (e.g., COLLISION), virtual particles (QUANTUM ELECTRODYNAMICS), and SPIN (specifically ELECTRON SPIN). One specific phenomenon that falls under quantum mechanics is the description of object MOTION by DE BROGLIE WAVES, specifically for electrons orbiting around a NUCLEUS. One specific application of the de Broglie wave theorem is in ELECTRON MICROSCOPY. The early twentieth century work of Heisenberg on the matrix theory, and the theoretical approach introduced by PAUL ADRIEN MAURICE DIRAC (1902–1984) on the transformation theory and the WAVE MECHANICS from ERWIN RUDOLF JOSEF ALEXANDER SCHRÖDINGER (1887–1961) all converged to the principle of QUANTUM MECHANICS. Under certain conditions, quantum mechanics is also referred to as wave mechanics, specifically in reference to the electron obit described by de Broglie waves. The de Broglie wave can be considered as prescribing a standing wave for the electron in an orbit, which can be shown to follow the format of the electron packing sequence in orbital layers as described by NIELS HENRIK DAVID BOHR (1885–1962) due to the discrete nature of the boundary conditions for a standing wave. The science of description of atomic systems in terms of discrete quantum states (*also see* SCHRODINGER WAVE EQUATION, WAVE MECHANICS, QUANTUM THEORY, QUANTUM PHYSICS, *and* QUANTUM NUMBER) (see Figure Q.12).

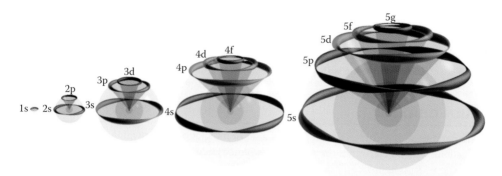

Figure Q.12 Quantum mechanical aspect of electron orbits, in particular the application of the Schrödinger wave function probability distribution for the alleged position of the electron or respectively the physical de Broglie wave aspect to satisfy the boundary conditions for electron orbits presented by PRINCE LOUIS DE BROGLIE (1892–1987) in 1924 as part of his PhD dissertation. (Courtesy of Kenneth Snelson, http://kennethsnelson.net/.) Artist representation of the quantum model for electron orbital filling based on the energy levels with reference to the de Broglie wave model from Louis de Broglie. Louis de Broglie proposed that—in equivalence to how ALBERT EINSTEIN (1879–1955) had shown light to have a dual nature—acting both as light waves and particle photons, moving matter may also be represented by a dual character. De Broglie hypothesized that the electron can act as a wave as well as a particle. As an example de Broglie used the electron in Bohr's hydrogen atom. De Broglie provided evidence that his "matter waves" fits perfectly in velocity and wavelength around Bohr's hydrogen atom model's quantized concentric orbits. In the first shell, closest to the nucleus, a single wave could fit resembling a snake biting its own tail. In shell two, there would be two waves; three waves would fit in shell three, and so on. Two years after the publication of the de Broglie dissertation, in 1926, Erwin Schrödinger (1887–1961) adapted the de Broglie's matter wave idea to create the Schrödinger wave equation, which soon became one of the principle tools of quantum physics. In the following year, that is 1927, the Davisson–Germer experiment (CLINTON JOSEPH DAVISSON [1881–1958] and LESTER HALBERT GERMER [1896–1971]) proved that there are indeed electron matter waves, providing evidence for de Broglie waves. The concepts expressed by Louis de Broglie are in this illustration interpreted on an artistic level. In de Broglie model an object comprising the following requirements and, respectively, properties: (1) As with Bohr's quantized electron, a de Broglie orbital wave remains at a single energy shell and can move from one shell to another only by absorbing or transmitting energy, in the form of light (i.e., accelerated charge motion). (2) The electron's negative electric charge is distributed evenly over the orbital circle's circumference. (3) The de Broglie orbit is defined both by orbital magnetism and top-like angular momentum. (4) The orbit incorporates the electron particle's intrinsic spin (as presented by George Uhlenbeck [1900–1988] and Samuel Abraham Goudsmit [1902–1978] in 1925) with the North and South Poles either adding to the orbit's magnetism or, by inverting, subtract from it. (5) De Broglie matter waves are matter-like. In similarity to macro pieces of matter, de Broglie waves occupy exclusive space. Several respective orbits cannot be in the same space at the same time. When the speed of an electron increases, the de Broglie wavelength shrinks by a quantized unit and vice versa. This process may be thought of as resembling striking different notes on a piano, but unlike a glissando for playing a slide-trombone. At each higher shell or orbit the electron slows down and increases its de Broglie wavelength by one notch. This quantization describes the main feature of the atom model described by NIELS BOHR (1885–1962) in 1913 and the associated orbital jumps matching the energy changes indicated in the hydrogen's spectrograph. On initial interpretation the wave for the first orbit is only half the size, unable to surround the equator, the one-wave orbit inherently takes up space on a small meridian of the sphere and hence becomes a 2p electron. Because the electron completes its circle in half the time of the 2s state and because, as illustrated by its transparent cone, the orbit extends outward with respect to the nucleus. At the third shell, de Broglie's original three-wave equatorial orbit complex is represented by the 3s state. When reduced to a two-wave orbit, this will become the 3p state. The final one-wave orbit is identified by the 3d state. The velocity and wavelength for the respective 3s, 3p, and 3d are the same. The smaller the orbit fitting the electron shell, the farther it will project distal to the nucleus. The far-right illustration represents the full range of orbits available to hydrogen atom's electron, from the first shell through the fifth. The s, p, d, f ... electron orbit labels are derived from of the old quantum theory and the ellipsoidal orbit model described by Arnold Sommerfeld (1968–1951) in 1916, which were intended to satisfy the azimuthal quantum number symbolized by (lowercase L). The quantum number describes the electron's angular momentum for orbits at each shell. Sommerfeld's ellipsoidal shapes ranged from true

(Continued)

Figure Q.12 (Continued) circles, to ovals, progressing to straight lines. The de Broglie's matter waves represented a distinctly different interpretation from Bohr's orbiting electron. Alternatively, despite Sommerfeld's ellipsoids extending out from the nucleus, both physicists' atoms were only two-dimensional, that is, flat as a pancake. Irving Langmuir (1841–1957) defined a list of eleven postulates describing the Lewis–Langmuir atom model (*see* LANGMUIR). Postulate 1: there is symmetry in the atomic configuration. Postulate 2: the electrons in any given atom are distributed through a series of concentric (nearly) spherical shells, all of equal thickness. Hence, the mean radii of the shells formulate an arithmetic series 1, 2, 3, 4, and the respective effective orbital areas are in the ratios 1: 22; 32; 42. Postulate 3: each shell is divided into cellular spaces, respectively cells, each occupying equal areas in their respective shells and are distributed over the surface of the shells according to the symmetry suggested in Postulate 1. As a result, the first shell contains 2 cells, the second 8, third 18, and the fourth cell holds 32.

Quantum number

[atomic, computational, nuclear, quantum] One of a set of integral or half-integral numbers, one for each degree of freedom, which determines the state of an atomic system in terms of the constants of nature.

A QUANTUM MECHANICS approach to determining the ENERGY of electrons in an ELEMENT or ION is based on the results obtained by solving the SCHRÖDINGER WAVE EQUATION for the HYDROGEN ATOM. The various solutions for the different energy states are characterized by the three main quantum numbers: n, ℓ, and m_ℓ. Each orbital has an associated characteristic shape, which reflects the MOTION of the electron pertaining to that particular orbital. This motion is hence characterized by an angular momentum defined by the angular velocity of the electron revolving around the NUCLEUS in its orbit. Electrons in an atom reside in shells characterized by a particular value of n, the PRINCIPAL QUANTUM NUMBER. Within each shell an electron can occupy an orbital that is further characterized by an ORBITAL QUANTUM NUMBER, ℓ, which can take all values in the range $\ell = 0,1,2,\ldots,(n-1)$; these conditions are traditionally termed "s," "p," "d," "f," and so on orbitals. Other quantum states are in the description of orbital momentum and orbital spin, where L represents the ORBITAL ANGULAR MOMENTUM of the electron, S represents the SPIN (which cannot change, since that would mean a reversal of rotation direction), J represents the TOTAL ANGULAR MOMENTUM, with M_L the MAGNETIC moment and M_S the spin moment, and in reference $n = 1,2,3,4,\ldots$ is the primary quantum number, $\ell = 0,1,2,\ldots(n-1)$ the orbital quantum number, and $m_\ell = \ell, \ell-1,\ldots,0,\ldots-\ell+1,-\ell$ the MAGNETIC QUANTUM NUMBER. Similar to an electron moving in its orbital revolution around a nucleus, the electron spinning about its axis has associated with its rotation a well-defined angular momentum. The quantum number m_ℓ is a subset of the quantum number ℓ, where there are $(2\ell+1)$ values associated with each m_ℓ for each value of ℓ, representing the configuration for the s-orbital ($\ell = 0$), three p-orbitals ($\ell = 1$), five d-orbitals ($\ell = 2$), and so on. Furthermore, $m_S = -(1/2), +(1/2)$ represents the spin quantum number for the electrons that identifies the orientation of the spin of one electron relative to those of other electrons in the system. The spin quantum number is associated with the fact that a single electron in free space has a fundamental property, called spin. The spin of the electron represents an inhomogeneous asymmetrical charge distribution spinning around its own axis. Each electron in its orbital configuration (e.g., Bohr model, Rutherford model) is characterized by four base quantum numbers (see Figure Q.13).

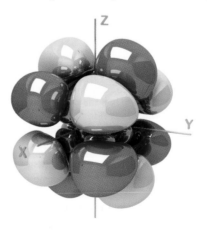

Figure Q.13 Graphical representation of the atomic orbital configuration based on quantum number preferences.

QUANTUM NUMBERS		
SYMBOL	DESCRIPTION	RANGE OF VALUES
n	Principal quantum number: describes the "proximity" to the nucleus, i.e., the range of orbital motion and associated energy levels	1, 2, 3, etc.
ℓ	Azimuthal/orbital quantum number: largely determines the shape of subshell 0 for the s orbital, 1 for the p orbital, etc.	$(0 \leq \ell \leq n-1)$; for instance under the condition $n = 3$; $\ell = 0, 1, 2$ with associated "levels" (s, p, d)
m_ℓ	Magnetic quantum number: defines the orientation of a subshell's shape. Examples are p_x, p_y, and p_z.	$-\ell \leq m_\ell \leq \ell$, for instance under the condition $\ell = 2$, $m_\ell = -2, -1, 0, 1, 2$
m_s	Spin quantum number	Only two possible values for a single electron: +1/2 or −1/2

Quantum of action (*h*)

[general] The oscillatory "wavefunctions" in NIELS HENRIK DAVID BOHR's (1885–1962) atomic model (influenced by LOUIS DE BROGLIE [1892–1987]) could only be satisfied if the WAVE would fit a "circumference," and hence the closed wave turned out to have discrete values that had a constant with the units of ENERGY multiplied by time (*Js*), which was the equivalent of momentum multiplied by the traversed DISTANCE, a parameter known as "action" in classical MECHANICS. The constant was derived by MAX PLANCK (1858–1947) as PLANCK'S CONSTANT: $h = 6.62606957 \times 10^{-34}$ m^2 kg/s, which he referred to as the "quantum of action," due to the discrete nature of the phenomenon. The orbital momentum in classical terms had the following condition for an electron orbit with mass m_e at radii r_n, traveling with discrete velocity v_n: $m_e r_n v_n = n(h/2\pi)$, with n the ordinal for the discrete ORBITS.

Quantum optics

[computational, energy, optics] QUANTUM THEORY pertaining to the bandwidth of optical wavelengths (i.e., visible LIGHT). The processes of detection of light, and propagation as well as generation are all subject to the QUANTUM effects; one specific example is in the coherence of laser light. The topic of "squeezed states" has special significance for the quantum optical approach.

Quantum orbital angular momentum

[atomic] The orbital angular momentum is subject to classical theory based on the fact that there are no external forces; hence, no torque acting and conservation rules apply. The ORBITAL ANGULAR MOMENTUM (*L*) is quantified as spherical harmonic functions as a SOLUTION to the SCHRÖDINGER WAVE EQUATION with discrete values for the MAGNITUDE expressed as a function of the angular quantum number (ℓ): $L = \hbar\sqrt{\ell(\ell+1)}$, where $\hbar = h/2\pi$, with $h = 6.62606957 \times 10^{-34}$ m^2 kg/s the Planck constant. Similarly, the z-component of the angular momentum has eigenvalues: $L_z = m_\ell \hbar$, with m_ℓ the discrete MAGNETIC QUANTUM NUMBER (*also see* QUANTUM NUMBER).

Quantum physics, electron shells

[atomic, general, mechanics, nuclear, quantum] The field of PHYSICS that specializes in the theoretical description of events and phenomena that are discrete in nature, specifically pertaining to atomic and nuclear procedures and processes. Quantum physics made its introduction in the 1920s. Quantum physics encompasses, but not limited to, de Broglie waves (introduced by LOUIS DE BROGLIE [1892–1987]), QUANTUM ELECTRODYNAMICS (as introduced by PAUL DIRAC [1902–1984]), the PAULI EXCLUSION PRINCIPLE (as introduced by WOLFGANG PAULI [1900–1958]), relativistic QUANTUM THEORY, the HEISENBERG UNCERTAINTY PRINCIPLE (introduced by KARL HEISENBERG [1901–1976] in 1927), Schrödinger's work (ERWIN SCHRÖDINGER [1887–1961]), and the description of ANTIMATTER (first experimental indication, the "antielectron," the positron, by CARL ANDERSON [1905–1991] in 1932 (with postulation records dating back to 1928), followed by the antiproton in 1955 and the ANTINEUTRON in 1956). The ZEEMAN EFFECT is another aspect of quantum physics as well (*also see* QUANTUM NUMBER, QUANTUM MECHANICS, *and* QUANTUM THEORY).

Quantum randomness

[general] The fact that under probability theory IDENTICAL PARTICLES, or ENERGY packages (e.g., photons), subjected to identical circumstances (i.e., identical boundary conditions) do not necessarily act in an identical manner.

Quantum spin angular momentum

[atomic] ELECTRON SPIN angular momentum belonging to the Dirac relativistic WAVE mechanical phenomenon (PAUL DIRAC [1902–1984]) as a component of the atomic angular momentum, defined by the SPIN quantum number s, as $L_s = \sqrt{s(s+1)}\hbar$, where $\hbar = h/2\pi$, with $h = 6.62606957 \times 10^{-34}\,\mathrm{m}^2\,\mathrm{kg/s}$ the Planck constant. The z-component of the electron spin is linked with the MAGNETIC moment by Dirac as having an intrinsic spin with a $g_s = 2$, value that is twice as large as for the corresponding ORBITAL ANGULAR MOMENTUM: $L_{s,z} = m_s\hbar$, with $m_s = \pm(1/2)$ the magnetic spin quantum number. The g-factor introduces a correction for the relationship between the magnetic momentum and the angular momentum, based on the difference in charge density with respect to mass density (note that for the orbital MOTION the charge density matches the mass density and yields alternatively $g_s = 1$ with respect to the orbital angular momentum). The spin vector will precess with a Larmor frequency, different from the orbital angular momentum vector PRECESSION frequency.

Quantum state

[atomic, general, nuclear] Term defining the way in which an atomic system exists at any specific time. This state is often described by means of a complex mathematical function. *see* QUANTUM LEVEL (see Figure Q.14).

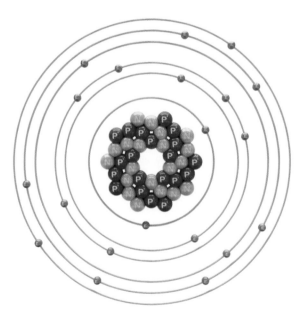

Figure Q.14 Atomic quantum states for calcium: the diagram illustrates one particular orientation only for a specific quantum number configuration.

Quantum theory

[atomic, general, nuclear, relativistic] The concept that ENERGY is radiated intermittently in discrete units of definite MAGNITUDE called QUANTA, under conditions that may be subject to a relativistic approach. The basic principles of quantum theory date back to BLACK BODY radiation concepts from 1859 by the German scientist GUSTAV ROBERT KIRCHHOFF (1824–1887). This was followed by the hypothesis published in 1900 by MAX PLANCK (1858–1947) that energy can only be emitted or absorbed in discrete quantities. On the basis of the experiential observations in 1911 by ERNEST RUTHERFORD (1871–1937) leading to the nuclear model of the ATOM, NIELS HENRIK DAVID BOHR (1885–1962) developed the atom model in 1913, providing additional building blocks that illustrated that classical MECHANICS does not apply on an atomic level. The theoretical transition was fully made by the contributions of ERWIN SCHRÖDINGER (1887–1961) in 1925, partially based on the work of LOUIS DE BROGLIE (1892–1987) published in 1924. Additional components forming the complete story resulted from the HEISENBERG UNCERTAINTY PRINCIPLE introduced in 1927 by WERNER WEISENBERG (1901–1976). Over the years many refinements and additions followed, but the foundation evolved over a time span stretching out over more than 60 years. Also see QUANTUM MECHANICS (*also see* QUANTUM PHYSICS *and* QUANTUM NUMBER).

Quantum total angular momentum

[atomic, quantum] The superposition of the orbital angular quantum effect and the SPIN quantum effect. Under conditions there may be coupling of the spin and ORBITAL ANGULAR MOMENTUM, specifically under the influence of a weak external MAGNETIC FIELD (*also see* L–S COUPLING, QUANTUM NUMBER, TOTAL ANGULAR MOMENTUM, *and* ZEEMAN EFFECT).

Quantum tunneling

[computational, quantum] QUANTUM mechanical phenomenon where a PARTICLE migrates through an ENERGY BARRIER described as a tunnel that under classical PHYSICS would not be attainable. The *quantum tunneling* process was observed by ANTOINE HENRI BECQUEREL (1852–1908) in 1896 and later theoretically defined by GEORGIY ANTONOVICH (GEORGE) GAMOW (1904–1968) around 1928. The "transmission coefficient (T_Q)" for the PROBABILITY of a particle (mass m) with energy $E_{particle}$ traveling through a POTENTIAL BARRIER with height $V_{barrier}(x)$, which is a function of DISTANCE (r) to the core of the MOLECULE/ATOM, is given as

$$T_Q = \exp\left(-2\int_{r_1}^{r_2}\sqrt{\left\{\left(2m/\hbar^2\right)\left[V(r)-E\right]\right\}}\right) \Bigg/ \left\{1+(1/4)\exp\left(-2\int_{r_1}^{r_2}\sqrt{\left(2m/\hbar^2\right)\left[V(r)-E\right]}\right)\right\}^2,$$

Q

where $\hbar = h/2\pi$, with $h = 6.62606957 \times 10^{-34} \, \mathrm{m^2 \, kg/s}$ Planck's constant. Also found described as *tunneling*. (see Figure Q.15).

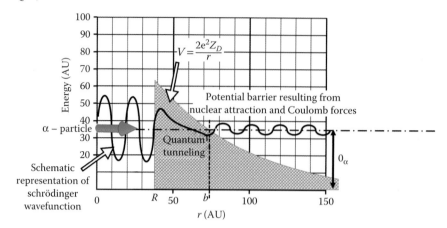

Figure Q.15 Quantum tunneling with respect to the energy configuration of the nucleus of an atom, respectively an atomic model.

Quark

[atomic, general, high-energy] Elementary PARTICLE with the following energetic and momentum designations: first generation: "up" and "down;" second generation: "CHARM" or "strange;" and third generation: "top" and "bottom or beauty." The subgroup of three varieties of quarks, up, down, and strange, have a fractional charge of $(1/3)e$ and $(2/3)e$, where e represents the standard electron charge. Quarks have standard half spin: $s = 1/2$. They are the latest in FUNDAMENTAL PARTICLES that are known and verified based on the state-of-the-art technology of MEASUREMENT as well as what can be mathematically validated. All "higher order" particles, such as neutron and proton, are constructed of quarks, referred to as hadrons. Electrons (LEPTON) are seemingly stand-alone particles, based on the knowledge at the time of this description. Nonetheless, there are indications that electrons themselves also exhibit quark equivalent "flavors." Quarks are never found as isolated particles; they are always part of the collective of quarks in the HADRON. A PROTON is composed of two "up" quarks and a "down" quark; a NEUTRON is constructed from the GLUON "strong-force" COHESION between one "up" quark and two "down" quarks. Another particle is, for instance, the PION, constructed from an "up" with an "antidown" quark, or a "down" quark, combined with an "antiup" quark. In turn, electrons, neutrons, and protons form atoms that constitute the building blocks for MATTER as we know it and work with on a daily basis. The quark concept was introduced in 1964 by both MURRAY GELL-MANN (1929–) and GEORGE ZWEIG (1937–), as independent hypotheses and experimentally verified starting in 1968 by experimental observations at the Stanford Linear Accelerator Center (now known as SLAC National Accelerator Laboratory). The "top" quark was verified as the last in a sequence as recent as 1995 (see Figure Q.16).

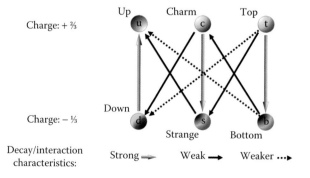

Figure Q.16 The concept of quark illustrated in nonrelativistic terms.

QUARK AND ANTIQUARK CHARACTERISTICS

FLAVOR	SYMBOL	CHARGE	SPIN	BARYON NUMBER	CHARM	STRANGENESS	BOTTOMNESS	MASS RANGE (MeV/c²)	GENERATION
Quarks									
Up	u	$+\frac{2}{3}e$	$\frac{1}{2}h$	$\frac{1}{3}$	0	0	0	$1.7 \leftrightarrow 3.1$	1st
Down	d	$-\frac{1}{3}e$	$\frac{1}{2}h$	$\frac{1}{3}$	0	0	0	$4.1 \leftrightarrow 5.7$	1st
Bottom	b	$-\frac{1}{3}e$	$\frac{1}{2}h$	$\frac{1}{3}$	0	0	+1	172900 ∓ 600	3rd
Top	t	$+\frac{2}{3}e$	$\frac{1}{2}h$	$\frac{1}{3}$	0	0	0	$4190 {+180}/{-60}$	3rd
Strange	s	$-\frac{1}{3}e$	$\frac{1}{2}h$		0	−1	0	$100 {+30}/{-20}$	2nd
Charmed	c	$+\frac{2}{3}e$	$\frac{1}{2}h$	$\frac{1}{3}$	+1	0	0	$1290 {+50}/{-110}$	2nd
Antiquarks									
Antiup	$\bar{u}$	$-\frac{2}{3}e$	$\frac{1}{2}h$	$-\frac{1}{3}$	0	0	0	$1.7 \leftrightarrow 3.1$	1st
Antidown	$\bar{d}$	$+\frac{1}{3}e$	$\frac{1}{2}h$	$-\frac{1}{3}$	0	0	0	$4.1 \leftrightarrow 5.7$	1st
Antibottom	$\bar{b}$	$+\frac{1}{3}e$	$\frac{1}{2}h$	$-\frac{1}{3}$	0	0	−1	172900 ∓ 600	3rd
Antitop	$\bar{t}$	$-\frac{2}{3}e$	$\frac{1}{2}h$	$-\frac{1}{3}$	0	0	0	$4190 {+180}/{-60}$	3rd
Antistrange	$\bar{s}$	$+\frac{1}{3}e$	$\frac{1}{2}h$	$-\frac{1}{3}$	0	+1	0	$100 {+30}/{-20}$	2nd
Anti-charmed	$\bar{c}$	$-\frac{2}{3}e$	$\frac{1}{2}h$	$-\frac{1}{3}$	−1	0	0	$1290 {+50}/{-110}$	2nd

Q

Quark, color of

[energy, general, quantum, relativistic] *See* COLORS OF QUARKS *and* QUARK.

Quark, flavor of

[energy, general, quantum, relativistic] *See* FLAVORS OF QUARKS *and* QUARK.

Quartz

[biomedical, optics, solid-state] Optically transparent crystalline lattice structure. Quartz materials are optically active, resulting in a rotation of the POLARIZATION direction of transmitted LIGHT. Quartz has its special features derived from the polarized electronic state of the LATTICE structure. The OPTICAL ACTIVITY of quartz is attributed to the helical molecular structure of the quartz crystal. Quartz can be electrically excited to oscillate, acting as a RADIO WAVE emission source or tuning receptor for oscillating electric and electronic signals. Quartz can also be made to expand and contract under electrical excitation, forming an ULTRASOUND emission source. The chemical base for quartz is silicon and oxygen (SiO_2) (see Figure Q.17).

Figure Q.17 Raw white quartz; other color quartz crystals are also found. The color of the quartz is the result of "pollution" or doping by other elements, some of which are considered semiprecious gemstones (e.g., amethyst). Most common inclusions are metals as well as phosphorous compounds. Quartz is the second most abundant mineral found on the Earth's surface. The pure quartz crystal is constructed from SiO_4 (silicon and oxygen).

Quasar

[astrophysics/astronomy] Acronym for "quasi-stellar radio source." Star-like objects in the UNIVERSE that are outside the MILKY WAY. Quasars emit a broad range of electromagnetic RADIATION, with the most abundant amount of frequencies in the "radio" band of the spectrum. Quasars are presumably galactic cores (assemblies of many stellar sources), hypothetically incorporating "black holes." The RADIO emissions are supposedly a secondary effect resulting from high-energy photons interacting with material outside the quasar space, originally resulting from excessive high-temperature-based interaction for instance with the BLACK HOLE. The spectral lines of quasars form part of the verification process supporting the "BIG BANG THEORY," based on the DOPPLER redshift, indicating the general EXPANSION of the universe (*also see* HUBBLE EFFECT) (see Figure Q.18).

Figure Q.18 Artist impression of the format describing the mechanism of operation for a quasar.

Quasicrystalline solid

[general, solid-state] Molecular or atomic configuration in a regular orderly three-dimensional pattern that is different from crystalline or amorphous (noncrystalline), while being nonrepetitive (not a regular LATTICE) forming a solid that is quasicrystalline.

Quasimonochromatic light

[general, optics] Whereas the term MONOCHROMATIC LIGHT indicates an extremely narrow linewidth of less than 0.5 nm, quasimonochromatic would be the accurate term for this, since the true meaning of mono-chromatic will described deep into the decimal aspect of the source definition, technically indicating an infinitely duration source. The shorter duration would indicate a lower number of harmonics, an extremely short pulse such as for a *Q*-switched laser renders a broad linewidth, approaching several nanometers.

Quasiparticle

[atomic, high-energy, optics] Many-body system that possesses excitation levels resembling those of free ELEMENTARY PARTICLES, but may have a convoluted interparticle interaction. One specific example is the Fermi liquid in the LANDAU THEORY, where the electrons of a medium at extremely low temperature (e.g., Helium) can essentially behave as free fermions, although bound (i.e., quasiparticle); this also forms one of the basics of SUPERCONDUCTIVITY and superfluidity. The main complication lies in the distribution function for the "PARTICLE" momentum with respect to the Fermi momentum, which for the ideal particle is a delta function; however, this may not hold true throughout all theoretical processes. In general, the FERMION forms the base for the quasiparticle; however, under special boundary conditions, bosons (term coined by PAUL DIRAC [1902–1984]; e.g., phonon, PLASMON, COOPER PAIR, SPIN WAVE, etc.) may also be considered quasiparticles.

Quasi-steady state

[astrophysics/astronomy, fluid dynamics, geophysics, mechanics, meteorology, thermodynamics] Intermediate states of a system that progress linearly in response to temperature, pressure, and volume changes. The EQUATION OF STATE for the system is well defined, specifically conforms to the IDEAL GAS LAW over discrete steps in time, and changes gradually between incremental episodes. Also known as the quasistatic process. When applied to the UNIVERSE, the Hubble constant would yield a fixed number under quasi-steady-state approximation; however, under longer period examination it will not, since then the process becomes transient. The quasi-steady-state approach is a linearization process with very specific boundary conditions, pertinent to the system under consideration. The considerations for when to label a process quasi-steady state rely on the characteristic time frame for the phenomena within the system; in particular, the processes with the shortest time frame are critical in the analysis. Additionally, the required accuracy of the analysis forms a major scaling factor in the assumption what may be considered quasi-steady state. In first order approximation, one may find that the accuracy is proportional to the relevant time scale (observation time divided by the time frame of the shortest event), and exhibits an exponential behavior. In first-order analysis, when observations are stationary within a time frame that is minimally five (5) times the shortest process of all the processes that define the system, then they can be considered quasi-steady state, with less than 0.7% error in the outcome. However, it will be incorrect to assume that all processes are independent from each other; hence, the exact error will be a convoluted calculation procedure, integrating all factors and interactions. Alternatively, when the consequences of a process are at least ten (10) times the duration of the initiating phenomenon (first-order), then those events can be considered quasi-steady state as well, and since this forms a recursive relation, the dependency may be more quadratic than exponential. These conditions may require one to be more strict due to the fact that they change the boundary conditions, as well as the process itself. One example is that heat DIFFUSION for a femtosecond (Q-switched) laser pulse is negligible within the time frame of interest, and hence the process and fallout for ultrashort laser delivery is frequently quasi-steady state. NUMERICAL solutions to time-dependent equations are always performed under quasi-steady-state conditions, where the boundary conditions need to be adjusted at specified intervals, or dynamically, to account for changes resulting from external influences or due to the processes themselves (see Figure Q.19).

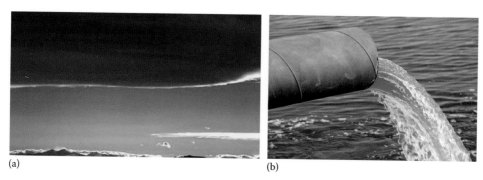

(a)   (b)

Figure Q.19 (a) Quasi-steady state for meteorological events: the big block of clouds remains steady while a remote steady flow of mountain air provides a backdrop of an active event. The event is still very stable and will not interfere with the contiguous cloud formation in the foreground that is apparently at a distance that remains unaffected by the boundary conditions from the flow pattern. The cloud concentration may move under the influence of atmospheric pressure and bring the clouds close enough to the mountain wave to disturb the equilibrium. (b) Drainage pipe flow that is considered steady state within a broad time frame; however, the flow rate and flow patter are for instance influenced by the position of the Moon next to the water level in the back country, which in turn will be a function of precipitation and runoff from regional population concentrations and industrial complexes.

Raab, Oscar (1876–1986)

[biomedical, optics] Medical student from Germany who described the principle of PHOTOTOXICITY as the light-mediated enhanced cytotoxicity of eosin on SKIN in 1898/1899 and named it photodynamic action. He reported that paramecia cells injected with the dye acridine orange resulted in CELL death when exposed to LIGHT. The discovery of phototoxicity led to medical applications in cancer treatment and was named photodynamic therapy (PDT). These pioneering efforts in BIOMEDICAL OPTICS used the phototoxic effect of the combination of certain dyes with light to treat skin cancer reportedly starting in the period from 1903 through 1907 and this was rapidly followed by the treatment of EYE tumors. An illustration of the importance of light in photodynamic therapy applications is specifically in a particularly hard to treat anatomical section: the brain. More easily and more frequently treated oncology conditions are in skin cancer and other superficial tumors, including but not limited to the urinary bladder and intestines (see Figure R.1).

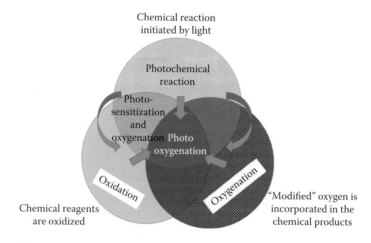

Figure R.1 Diagram of Oscar Raab's (1876–1986) phototoxicity concept. Despite the significant influence on modern medicine, unfortunately no known images exist of Oscar Raab.

Rabi, Isidor Isaac (1898–1988)

[atomic, nuclear] Physicist from Austria (Prussian empire)/(Poland). Rabi is most known for his contributions to the understanding of the MAGNETIC RESONANCE and general magnetic properties of the atomic NUCLEUS and the evolution of magnetic resonance imaging (MRI), for which he received the Nobel Prize for Physics in 1944. Isidor Rabi's work on the magnetic moments of nuclei involved his prediction and verification that absorbed ENERGY from an externally applied electromagnetic WAVE, at the appropriate (RESONANCE) frequency, would flip the magnetic orientation of the recently discovered protons and neutrons. The SPIN would subsequently emit the identical amount of energy when reverting back to the lower energy orientation. Rabi coined the term "MOLECULAR BEAM magnetic resonance" for this phenomenon. Rabi's work also lead to the development of the atomic clock (see Figure R.2).

Figure R.2 Isidor Isaac Rabi (1898–1988). (Courtesy of Columbia University Libraries; University Archives, Columbia University in the City of New York.)

Radial quantum number

[nuclear] As applied to a harmonic oscillator applied to Laguerre–Gauss modes. Although not used in general nuclear QUANTUM MECHANICS the radial quantum number (n_r) provides insight in the number of radial nodes of the (radial; in cylindrical coordinates) WAVE function and is tied to the PRINCIPAL QUANTUM NUMBER (n) as $n = n_r + \ell + 1$, where ℓ is the ORBITAL ANGULAR MOMENTUM quantum number, the azimuthal quantum number. In this context the radial quantum number defines the DISTANCE of the electron from the NUCLEUS in the Bohr model. Alternatively, the principal quantum number may also be found referred to as the radial quantum number (*see* PRINCIPAL QUANTUM NUMBER).

Radial wave equation

[nuclear] *See* SCHRÖDINGER EQUATION.

Radial wave function

[nuclear] *See* WAVE FUNCTION.

Radiance ($\Phi(\vec{r},\vec{s})$)

[biomedical, electromagnetism, general, nuclear, optics] Radiant ENERGY; power emitted, transferred, or received as radiation (W). The radiance has an angular dependence that can be developed in a truncated series of polynomials. In most cases the function that is part of the differential equation can be developed in a series of power series solutions: Legendre polynomials, BESSEL FUNCTIONS, and Laguerre polynomials. Using Cauchy theorem, the expression can be developed in series of orthogonal polynomials: $f(x) = \sum_{k=0}^{\infty} A_k x^k$, as

$$\Phi(\vec{r},\vec{s}) = \sum_{n=0}^{1} \sum_{m=-n}^{n} Y_n^m(\vec{s}) \Phi_n^m(\vec{r})$$

$$= Y_0^0(\vec{s}) \Phi_0^0(\vec{r}) + Y_1^{-1}(\vec{s}) \Phi_1^{-1}(\vec{r}) + Y_1^0(\vec{s}) \Phi_1^0(\vec{r}) + Y_1^1(\vec{s}) \Phi_1^1(\vec{r}) + Y_2^0(\vec{s}) \Phi_2^0(\vec{r}) + \cdots$$

Also found identified by the parameter $L(\vec{r},\vec{s})$ (see Figure R.3).

Figure R.3 The difference in radiance from several floodlights with adjustable focal points.

Radiant energy fluence rate ($E^0(\vec{r},t)$)

[astrophysics/astronomy, biomedical, energy, thermodynamics] Total radiant power incident on a surface from all directions per unit surface area. The fluence per unit time: $E^0(\vec{r},t) = dH^0(\vec{r},t)/dt = d\Psi(\vec{r},t)/dt$. Also the integrated radiance $\left(L(r,\theta,\varphi,t)\right)$ over full SOLID ANGLE: $E^0(r,t) = \int_{4\pi} L(r,\theta,\varphi,t)d\Omega$. Also known as fluence rate. In comparison, the ENERGY per unit area incident on a small sphere is the fluence ($\Psi(\vec{r},t)$; also found as $H^0(\vec{r},t)$). For a parallel, none scattered beam incident on a surface the radiant energy fluence rate reduces to "Irradiance," for example, laser beam on clear semi-infinite medium (no reflective boundaries).

Radiant flux

[general] *See* RADIATIVE POWER.

Radiation

[atomic, general, optics, quantum] Method of transmission of ENERGY. Specifically, (1) any electromagnetic wave (QUANTUM), (2) any moving electron or nuclear particle, charged or uncharged, emitted by a radioactive substance, (3) acoustic pressure waves, and (4) GRAVITATION WAVE extension of gravitational attraction force through gravitational radiation. The elementary form of radiation is found as electromagnetic radiation, which is the result of an accelerated charge. The ELECTROMAGNETIC THEORY was delineated by JAMES CLERK MAXWELL (1831–1879) in 1861. The concept of electromagnetic radiation resulting from accelerated charges was described by JOSEPH LARMOR (1857–1942) in 1897. In 1903 ERNEST RUTHERFORD (1871–1937) and FREDERICK SODDY (1877–1956) realized that radioactive ELEMENTS (now known as isotopes; introduced by Francis William Ashton [1877–1945] in 1919) spontaneously transform from one chemical substance to another accompanied by the emission of radiation of particulate (e.g., electron [JOSEPH THOMPSON (1856–1940) 1897], PROTON [identified/postulated by WILHELM WIEN (1864–1928) in 1898, named by ERNEST RUTHERFORD in 1920], NEUTRON [discovered by JAMES CHADWICK (1891–1974) in 1932], helium ion: ALPHA PARTICLE) or electromagnetic radiation (e.g., X-RAY, gamma radiation, and visible LIGHT as well as INFRARED radiation). At the time of Rutherford's and Soddy's declaration, the ATOM concept was known, however, the NUCLEUS was not discovered as of yet. Natural ACTIVITY resulting in radiation is one mechanism, specific examples are uranium and thorium; artificial radiation is the result of

R

the application of an external source on a stable ELEMENT, such as the production of X-ray resulting from the impact of fast electrons on metals such as tungsten. Radiation can be classified in ionizing (PARTICLE, high-energy electromagnetic) and nonionizing (mid- to long-wave electromagnetic) (*also see* WIEN'S DISPLACEMENT LAW, PLANCK'S RADIATION LAW, *and* RAYLEIGH–JEAN LAW) (see Figure R.4).

(a)

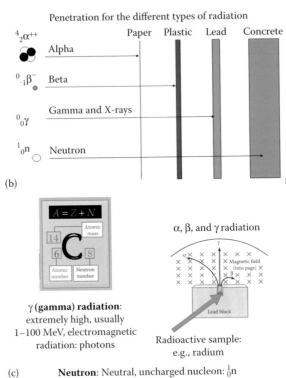

(b)

(c)

Figure R.4 Radiation: (a) antennas with simulated electromagnetic radiation, (b) penetration for different types of radiation, and (c) radiation physics showing the properties of α, β, and γ radiations.

Radiation belt

[astrophysics/astronomy, general] Partial shell of charged particles in orbit around EARTH, maintained by the earth's MAGNETIC FIELD. Several radiation belts are suspected, but the Van Allen radiation belts are verified and well described (*see* VAN ALLEN RADIATION BELTS; *also see* AURORA BOREALIS [i.e., NORTHERN LIGHTS]) (see Figure R.5).

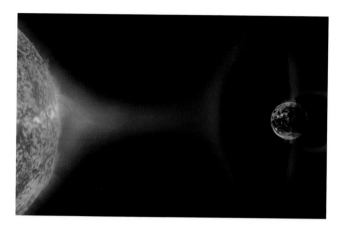

Figure R.5 Diagram of what a radiation belt around the Planet Earth may look like; with one of the consequences: the auroras.

Radiation coupling

[acoustics, optics] Coupling of acoustic or optical WAVE respectively. A principle that operates as a LINEAR FILTER which describes the transition between two lumped mechanical or optical components (see Figure R.6).

Figure R.6 Radiation coupling for acoustic waves. Relatively high-energy ultrasound is coupled into the skin for the disintegration of the mixture of fatty and connective tissue (e.g., collagen) in the treatment of cellulite. In order to avoid "burning" the skin a medium is applied between the transducer and the skin to maximize the transfer of acoustic energy to penetrate deep below the surface of the skin to perform the restructuring of the tissue based on radiation absorption at a location that is remote from the point of entry.

R

Radiation dose

[biomedical, nuclear] The emitted dose of PARTICLE and electromagnetic RADIATION resulting from ISOTOPE DECAY. The kind of radiation and respective ENERGY content will determine the biological impact, known as dosimetry and biological hazard. Radiation dose is generally measured in rem or millirem, accepted as a standard by the Nuclear Regulatory Commission (*see* DOSIMETRY; *also see* CARBON DATING) (see Figure R.7).

Figure R.7 Radiation dose meter, that is, Geiger counter, providing the exposure in Rads per hour.

Radiation force

[acoustics] Acoustic radiation force represents the interaction of an acoustic WAVE (longitudinal pressure wave) with an obstacle in its path. The MAGNITUDE of the FORCE (F) is directly correlated to the local AMPLITUDE (and respective intensity: I; in $\left[\mathrm{W/cm^2}\right]$) as $|F| = 2\alpha_{\mathrm{abs}}I/v_s$, where v_s is the speed of SOUND in the medium with localized acoustic attenuation α_{abs}. The absorption coefficient is expressed in Neper per CENTIMETER $\left(\mathrm{Np/cm}\right)$ (see Figure R.8).

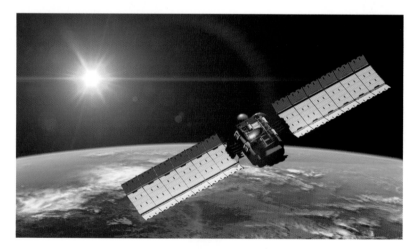

Figure R.8 Conceptual representation of solar wind, applying radiation force, acting on a long-range probe with large panels acting as solar sails. Note that for the solar radiation force to be effective the "sails" will need to be substantial since the effect is minimalistic, especially at expanding distance (diminished effect from the solar radiation pressure inversely proportional to the radius square).

Radiation hazards

[atomic, nuclear] Various kinds of radiation have different ENERGY content with specific biological and material consequences. The radiation ACTIVITY is one of the means of determining the potential for the energy content; disintegration rate. Another concept related to the energy content is the half-life. The originally adopted standard for radiation consequences is the number of ionizations produced by X-RAY or gamma rays, since then replaced by the number of disintegrations per SECOND for a RADIOACTIVE ISOTOPE, measured in Becquerel ([Bq]). The biological damage potential is generally based on the ABSORBED DOSE, measured in Gray (old unit Rad). The risk for modifications to the genetic material: DNA, or causing burns resulting from a specific kind of exposure is expressed by the QUALITY FACTOR. The quality factor provides the dose equivalent exposure, which is a more quantifiable risk identifier for human risk. The quality factor (Q_r) for specific types of RADIATION is defined as follows: X-ray, gamma rays, and beta radiation $Q_r = 1$; high-energy photons have $Q_r = 10$; exposure to neutrons of unknown energy has a quality factor $Q_r = 10$; while ALPHA PARTICLES are considered to be the most hazardous with $Q_r = 20$. The following heuristic values for biological damage have been determined; absorbed dose and biological effect: 100 Gy results in virtually instantaneous death (hours); 12 Gy results in death within days; 6 Gy results in death within weeks; 1 Gy may be treated and the person may recover and survive (with residual biological damage); 0.5 Gy has no discernible biological effects; 0.25 Gy results in changes to the BLOOD structure; and at 0.05 Gy the first changes to blood are observed. Note that radiation exposure is cumulative. (*Note*: MARIE SKŁODOWSKA CURIE [1876–1934] suffered the consequences of her work with radiation, dying from radiation-inflicted damage to her biological functions.) In reference an average day yield exposure of 3 mSv/year; while a chest X-ray provides 6 mRem, and a lumbar spine CT 16 mSv. Background radiation exposure to every person on the PLANET results from the following sources: COSMIC RAYS; natural phenomena (e.g., ^{14}C {carbon dating} and radon); terrestrial sources (^{235}U); therapeutic devices (X-ray, etc.); various consumer products hold radioactive isotopes (e.g., tobacco: ^{210}Po; welding rods: ^{222}Th; certain mechanical watches have the dial "illuminated" by tritium or radium (old style); and smoke detectors: ^{241}Am), fall-out from nuclear weapons tests, radiation leaks from nuclear power plants; and the following sporadic and low importance (small MAGNITUDE) effects ISOTOPE research and AIR travel (*also see* RADIATION UNITS) (see Figure R.9).

(a)　　　　　　　　　　　　　　　　　　　　　　　　(b)

Figure R.9 (a) Radiation hazard warning sign near a nuclear power station and (b) graphical representation of how high-energy radiation may modify the genetic structure, resulting in cancer and/or death. Section of the abandoned city of Pripyat near Chernobyl in Ukraine (then Russia; as a matter of fact: CCCP/USSR) after a nuclear meltdown in the nuclear power plant.

Radiation therapy

[biomedical, energy, thermodynamics] Clinical, therapeutic procedures involving various types of RADIATION: charged particles (e.g., protons and electrons), X-ray, and gamma rays to selectively cause the eradication of undesirable cells, specifically malignant cells of tumor structures. The radiation may be applied externally or internally. The external radiation is provided by specialized devices, whereas the internal radiation may be provided either from a confined RADIOACTIVE ISOTOPE (brachytherapy) or from the systemic release from an ISOTOPE introduced by ingestion or injection (e.g., radioactive iodine). The mechanism of action of generating CELL death as a therapeutic goal is in the restructuring of DNA form external to the cell, or by means of creating secondary free radicals inside the cell without actual penetration subsequently resulting in cell death. The treatment of hypo- or hyper thyroidism by means of radioactive iodine is one of the most common and well-known methods. The thyroid treatment is relatively selective due to the affinity of the thyroid for iodine. Most cancer treatments are not selective about the targeted cells, and subsequently have a consequence of damaging and killing healthy cells as well, specifically in the direct vicinity of the tumor during external radiation, but more systemic (whole body) for isotope reagents released in the bloodstream (primary) or ingested for absorption in the BLOOD stream through the digestive system (secondary system). Radiation therapy may also be used for benign cancer when the cancer is causing secondary effects, for instance, causing pressure on vital organs due to the rapidly expanding cell volume, such as esophagus and spine. Therapeutic radiation to the brain may destroy the brain but the metastases of cancer spreading into the brain can potentially be regressed by radiation. One particularly specific and selective external means of radiation therapy is currently achieved by the CyberKnife. Brachytherapy may require special tools, such as catheters and needles and nanoparticles (see Figure R.10).

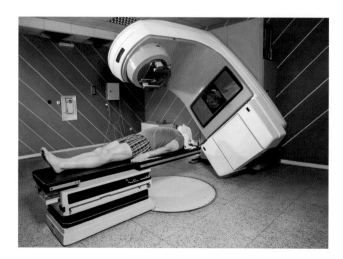

Figure R.10 Patient undergoing radiation therapy.

Radiation units

[atomic] The number of decaying nuclei per unit of time (disintegrations per SECOND) is measured in Becquerel ([Bq]; SI unit), alternatively the Curie is also found: $1 \text{ Cu} = 3.7 \times 10^{10} \text{ Bq}$. The ENERGY of radiation is measured in electronvolt, ([eV]); the energy of an electron under a potential difference of 1 V. Examples are the electrons emitted from the carbon ISOTOPE ^{14}C have an energy of $157 \text{ keV} = 0.157 \text{ MeV}$ (beta radiation); gamma radiation form cesium (^{137}Cs) has an energy of 662 keV, and alpha radiation from Americium (^{241}Am) has an energy of 5.485 MeV. The ABSORBED DOSE is measured in Gray ([Gy]); old unit Rad. The conversion from Rad to Gray is $1 \text{ Rad} = 0.01 \text{ Gy}$. The exposure is measured in Coulombs per kilogram (SI: [C/kg]), with the old unit the Röntgen ([R]). The conversion equivalence from the Röntgen is $1 \text{R} = 2.58 \times 10^{-4} \text{ C/kg}$. The dose equivalent has the quantity in Sievert (SI: [Sv]), while the old unit is Rem.

The Rem converts to the Sievert as $1\,\text{Rem} = 0.01\,\text{Sv}$. The "dose equivalent" exposure incorporates the type of radiation, expressed by the QUALITY FACTOR. The dose equivalent is a more quantifiable risk identifier for human risk (for instance, resulting in modifications to the genetic material: DNA, or causing burns) from exposure. For X-RAY RADIATION one Röntgen of radiation is approximately equivalent to 1 Rad with respect to human tissues. Under the old units gamma radiation yields $1\,\text{R} \cong 1\,\text{Rad} \sim 1\,\text{Rem}$ (see Figure R.11).

Radiation activity units of measure

- The number of decaying nuclei per unit of time
- The Systéme International (SI) unit of radioactivity is the becquerel (Bq)

    - One Bq = 1 disintegration per second
- Non-SI unit of radioactivity is the Curie (Ci)
    - One Ci = 3.7×10^{10} transformations per s
    - One millicurie (mCi) = $3.7 \times 10^{7}\,\text{s}^{-1}$
    - One microcurie (µCi) = $3.7 \times 10^{4}\,\text{s}^{-1}$
    - 1 Bq = 2.7×10^{-11} Ci

(a)

Quantities and units

Quantity	Conventional	SI
Exposure	roentgen (R)	coulomb/kg
Absorbed dose	rad	gray (Gy)
Dose equivalent	rem	sievert (Sv)

(b)

Activity

- Activity is the number of transformations (or disintegrations) per time occurring in a radioactive material
- Conventional unit: curie (Ci)
    - 1 Ci = 3.7×10^{10} disintegrations per second
- International System (SI): Becquerel (Bq)
    - 1 Bq = 1 disintegration per second
- 1 Ci = 3.7×10^{10} Bq

(c)

Activity—units: conventional vs. SI

Conventional system	SI system
• 1 milliCi = 1/1000 Ci	• 1 kiloBq = 1000 Bq
• 1 microCi = 1/1,000,000 Ci	• 1 megaBq = 1,000,000 Bq
• 1 kiloCi = 1000 Ci	• 1 gigaBq = 1,000,000,000 Bq
• 1 megaCi = 1,000,000 Ci	

(d)

Energy units for measuring radiation

Radiation energies are typically measured in units of keV (1000 electron volts) or MeV (million electron volts)

Examples:
C-14 beta   0.157 MeV or 157 keV
Cs-137 gamma   662 keV
Am-241 alpha   5.485 MeV

(e)

Figure R.11 (a–e) Radiation unit configuration.

Radiative capture

[atomic] Capture of a low-energy proton (p) or NEUTRON (n) by the atomic nucleus, transforming the NUCLEUS into a RESIDUAL NUCLEUS in a highly excited state. The capture PARTICLE may not be expelled, leaving the nucleus to emit the excess ENERGY as gamma radiation (γ), while changing the ISOTOPE value. An example is the conversion of magnesium to aluminum through proton capture: $^{26}\text{Mg} + p \rightarrow {}^{26}\text{Al} + \gamma$. Eventually, the (unstable) converted state will regress to the "GROUND" state when bombarded by gamma radiation during a process called PHOTODISINTEGRATION: $^{26}\text{Al} + \gamma \rightarrow {}^{26}\text{Mg} + p$ (see Figure R.12).

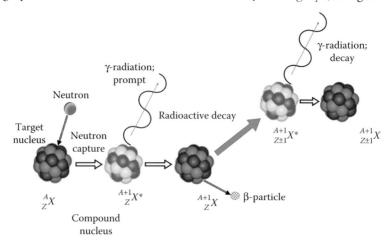

Figure R.12 Example of the process with respect to radiative capture for a neutron.

Radiative power

[biomedical, general] ENERGY transfer from one location to another. Calculated by the number of photons per SECOND ($\dot{n}$) at wavelength λ this yields: $P_{\text{radiative}} = (\dot{n}h/\lambda)c$, where with $h = 6.62606957 \times 10^{-34}$ m^{2}kg/s the PLANCK'S CONSTANT, and $c = 2.99792458 \times 10^{8}$ m/s the speed of LIGHT. Also known as RADIANT FLUX.

Radiative transfer

[astrophysics/astronomy, biomedical, energy] The transfer of ENERGY through the medium of electromagnetic RADIATION, also known as the radiative transfer equation (*see* **EQUATION OF RADIATIVE TRANSFER**).

Radio

[electronics, general] Device for receiving radio waves, which are emitted from radio stations. Sometimes also referring to the functional unit emitting the radio waves, the RADIO STATION (building with record players). Radio is subdivided in AMPLITUDE MODULATION (AM) and frequency modulation (FM). AM RADIO waves imply a perturbation applied to a CARRIER WAVE, where the perturbation encodes a selected portion of the audible frequency range (20 Hz–20 kHz), AM radio does not provide STEREO reception. In FM electromagnetic transmissions, the frequency of the carrier WAVE is changed within a narrow band to provide encoded embedded signals that can be decoded at the radio receiver. AM stations can be subdivided into short waves and long waves; operate in the frequency range 153 kHz to 26.1 MHz. Specifically, AM radio as found on the receiver operates from 535 to 1605 kHz. Long-wave radio SIGNAL as well as most AM signals across the frequency band will reflect off the IONOSPHERE, resulting in a long span of reception, long-wave radio specifically (153–279 kHz) can be received from the opposite side of the world under the appropriate weather conditions. FM radio primarily relies on line-of-sight reception (the tip of the ANTENNA is in theoretical view by the receiving location), this can extend in a flat topography for the geographic location for up to 30 km (primarily as a function of the radiant power supplied by the emitting station), apart from SATELLITE transmission. FM radio generally operates in the frequency range 88–108 MHz. Due to the intricate process of FM and decoding process at the receiver, two signals can be transmitted simultaneously, offering stereo audio when two separate SPEAKER units are available and attached to the radio entity (see Figure R.13).

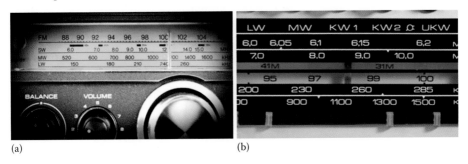

(a)   (b)

Figure R.13 (a) Analogue radio, showing the various wavebands: short wave (SW), medium wave (MW), long wave (LW), and frequency modulated (FM) and (b) analog radio display tuning panel which includes ultrashort wave band (UKW), primarily used in FM transmission.

Radio frequency (RF)

[biomedical, electronics] EMISSION SPECTRUM with the electromagnetic phenomenon. Radio frequency is in the wavelength range beyond INFRARED and microwave and in the same spectrum as RADIO and television waves, while shorter in wavelength than alternating power supplies/generators. The established spectral range is 3 kHz to 300 GHZ, where the high frequencies generally fall under microwave, it may still qualify as radio frequency. The Federal Communications Commission classifies radio frequency as the range of 9 to 275 kHz. Radio frequency RADIATION can be transmitted through cable more easily than the shorter wavelengths in the MICROWAVE regime, and is used for interstitial heal in biological therapeutic applications to provide elevated temperature-induced CELL death. Radio frequency is also used for navigation purposes as well as wireless communication (see Figure R.14).

Figure R.14 Radio frequency: radio-controlled remote operating helicopter.

Radio receiver

[general] There is a fundamental difference between analog and digital RADIO signal production and reception. The mechanism of action in analog modulation is continuous frequency modulation. In digital electromagnetic transmission and reception the encoding and decoding will still occur at the principal frequency, but the encoding will involve discrete pulse trains. With current technology the use of digital

mechanisms are more prevalent due to the reduced risks for distortion and NOISE compared to analog SIGNAL processing (*see* **RADIO**) (see Figure R.15).

Figure R.15 Radio receiver. Edwin Howard Armstrong (1890–1954) and his wife Esther Marion MacInnis on the beach with the "portable" radio designed and built for his wife, on Palm Beach, Florida, in 1923. The radio was Edwin Armstrong's portable superheterodyne. Earlier "portable radios" are on record.

Radio station

[electronics, general] Building with record players, CD-players (MP3, MP4, etc.), digital storage devices (computer hard drives, memory sticks, etc.), and one or more microphones, that are connected electronically to an encoding device that embeds the audio signals in electromagnetic RADIATION that is conveyed to an ANTENNA that radiates the electromagnetic SIGNAL in all directions; alternatively routed to SATELLITE stations for satellite transmission. The first RADIO operation was in 1906, only AM. The FM radio principle was patented in 1933 by Edwin Howard Armstrong (1890–1954), an electrical engineer from the United States, followed in 1937, the first experimental radio station (W1XOJ) in the United States providing the first frequency modulated radio transmission, followed in 1948 with FM TRANSMISSIONS in Germany under newly implemented waveband plans. In 1958 English radio transmissions were experimentally used for STEREO transmissions. Note that the first two-channel audio system had already been introduced in 1881 by Clément Ader (1841–1925) in Paris (see Figure R.16).

Figure R.16 Example of a radio station in the United States.

Radioactive decay

[atomic, computational, energy, general, nuclear] Radioactive decay will depend on the original state of the ISOTOPE or unstable NUCLEUS. The determining factor is relying on PROTON or NEUTRON deficiency. The kinds of DECAY recognized are the following. ALPHA PARTICLE decay [α], the PARTICLE emitted during decay resembles a helium nucleus consisting of two neutrons and two protons: $^A_Z X \rightarrow ^{A-4}_{Z-2} Y + ^4_2 He$. The second form is BETA PARTICLE decay [β⁻]: $^A_Z X \rightarrow ^A_{Z+1} Y$, where the beta particle is in all characteristics identical to an electron. The other mechanism of decay is represented by beta-plus radiation (also referred to as positron emission) [β⁺]: $^A_Z X \rightarrow ^A_{Z-1} Y$. Gamma radiation is another form of radioactive decay due to annihilation, where a positron (beta-plus particle) and an electron (equivalent beta particle) collide and form a pair of gamma photons that are emitted at perfectly opposite directions. Each gamma PHOTON has an ENERGY of 0.511 MeV. ELECTRON CAPTURE is a form of RADIATION where an electron is captured by an unstable nucleus that does not have enough energy to spontaneously decay by positron emission. The convergence of a proton and the captured electron are transformed into a neutron and a NEUTRINO: $p_{proton} + e^- = n_{neutron} + \bar{v}$. The resulting vacancy in the electron shell will result in X-RAY emission. The CHARACTERISTIC X-RAY radiation associated with the removal of the electron will with great PROBABILITY come from K-shell decay. In the electron capture process gamma radiation may also occur. In certain cases, depending on the energy configuration the release of gamma energy will be captured by an orbital electron, which is internally released, indicated by the mechanism of action of INTERNAL CONVERSION (see Figure R.17).

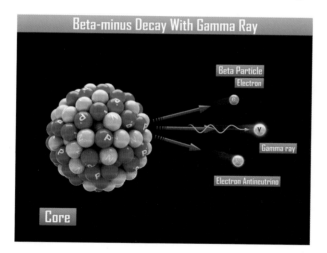

Figure R.17 Radioactive decay example.

Radioactive decay chain

[nuclear] RADIOACTIVITY was discovered by ANTOINE HENRI BECQUEREL (1852–1908) in 1896, but the phenomenon was named by MARIE SKŁODOWSKA CURIE (1876–1934) around 1903. Chain of discrete isotopes that are formed during the RADIOACTIVE DECAY process. The chain represents the series of events and

product from naturally radioactive of artificially produced RADIOACTIVE ISOTOPE to the final stage over the extended time duration of the cumulative half-life intervals of all the intermediate steps (see Figure R.18).

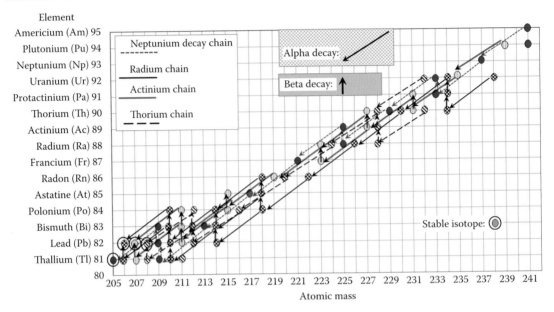

Figure R.18 Radioactive decay chain.

Radioactive decay constant (λ_{decay})

[atomic, nuclear] Constant indicating the rate of isotope DECAY, representing the proportional reduction in ISOTOPE ($N_{isotope}$) with respect to the original quantity, or ACTIVITY at initiation of isotope (N_0) over time of activity (t): $dN = -\lambda_{decay} N dt$, or $N(t) = N_0 e^{-\lambda_{decay} t}$. The HALF-LIFE ($\tau_{decay}$, also found as $T_{1/2}$) of the isotope follows directly from the time lapse to decay to half the original quantity $N(\tau_{decay}) = (1/2)N_0$, yielding $\tau_{decay} = T_{1/2} = \ln 2/\lambda_{decay} = 0.693/\lambda_{decay}$ (see Figure R.19).

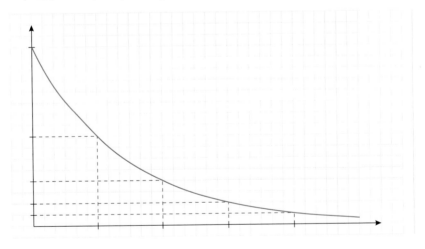

Figure R.19 Graphical interpretation of the radioactive decay constant in the time lapse for disintegration.

Radioactive decay law

[atomic, biomedical, energy, nuclear] *see* RADIOACTIVE DECAY CONSTANT *and* RADIOACTIVE TRANSFORMATION.

Radioactive isotope

[atomic, nuclear] Atom with identical chemical behavior as a known ELEMENT but with a different mass. Isotopes are generally radioactive with an associated half-life. The most well-known radioisotope is carbon-14, the ISOTOPE of carbon-12. Carbon-14 occurs naturally in all carbon-based life forms due to the chemical exchange during the lifetime of the biological entity, for example, consumption of carbohydrates. Carbon-14 is specifically known for determination of the AGE of the "deceased" biological object, based on the RADIOACTIVE DECAY. The half-life of ^{14}C is 5,730 years with electron emission, which limits the use for age determination to approximately 50,000 years; with potential enhancements in the detection technique stretching the span to 100,000 years (e.g., accelerator technique). The ratio of ^{14}C to ^{12}C is a relative constant at 1.3×10^{-12} in a living environment. Other examples of naturally occurring isotopes, with respective HALF-LIFE ($\tau_{1/2}$) and decay process are uranium-238, $\tau_{1/2} = 4.5 \times 10^{9}$ years, alpha-particle (α_d); tritium-3, $\tau_{1/2} = 12.26$ years, ELECTRON (e^-); cobalt-60, $\tau_{1/2} = 5.24$ years, e^-; iodine-131, $\tau_{1/2} = 8$ days, e^-; and radon-222, $\tau_{1/2} = 3.82$ days, α_d. It is also known as RADIOISOTOPE, or ISOTOPE (see Figure R.20).

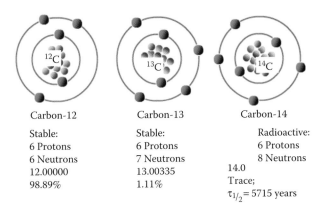

Carbon-12   Carbon-13   Carbon-14

Stable: Stable: Radioactive:
6 Protons   6 Protons   6 Protons
6 Neutrons   7 Neutrons   8 Neutrons
12.00000   13.00335   14.0
98.89%   1.11%   Trace;
                                              $\tau_{1/2} = 5715$ years

Figure R.20 Carbon isotopes.

Radioactive transformation

[atomic, nuclear] The random process of nuclear transmutations of ELEMENT, subject to the WEAK FORCE. The transformation process can be expressed as a STOCHASTIC PROCESS describing the overall likelihood of the occurrence of a change in elemental structure over TIME (t) expressed as $N(t) = N_0 e^{-t/\tau_{1/2}}$, with $\tau_{1/2}$ the RADIOACTIVE DECAY half-life, and N_0 the initial quantity of radioactive material; known as the LAW OF RADIOACTIVE TRANSFORMATION. The following transformation processes are available: ELECTRON DECAY, POSITRON DECAY, ALPHA DECAY, gamma decay, orbital ELECTRON CAPTURE, nucleon energy transfer to GROUND STATE, INTERNAL CONVERSION (NUCLEON to electron), next to spontaneous FISSION, double BETA DECAY (specifically related to ^{92}Mo and ^{100}Mo), and cluster decay (*see* RADIOACTIVITY).

Radioactive waste

[atomic, nuclear] Refuse resulting from the commercial use of radioactive isotopes. Radioactive waste is produced by hospitals during cancer therapy, in the production of several consumer goods and the generation of ELECTRICITY by means of nuclear power plants. A byproduct of coal burning factories is slurry (ash) that is also radioactive due to the uranium and thorium content in coal (see Figure R.21).

Figure R.21 Radioactive waste handling and disposal.

Radioactivity

[atomic, nuclear, quantum] The process whereby certain nuclides undergo spontaneous atomic disintegration in which ENERGY is liberated, generally resulting in the formation of new nuclides. The process is accompanied by the emission of one or more types of RADIATION, such as ALPHA PARTICLES, BETA PARTICLES, and gamma radiation (*also see* URANIUM *and* ISOTOPE) (see Figure R.22).

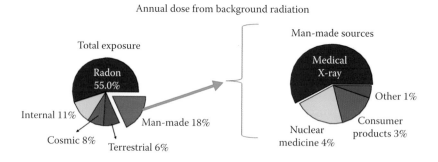

Figure R.22 Some commonly occurring low-level emission radioactive consumer goods.

Radioastronomy

[astrophysics/astronomy, atomic] Branch of astronomy that uses the coherent aspects of electromagnetic RADIATION from galactic bodies for identification and determination of location. Generally, the sensing mechanism involves a RADIO telescope arranged in an INTERFEROMETER setting. Next to several multi-dish ANTENNA stations in discrete locations all over the world, the independent locations are collaborating to form a global-sized interferometer. One of the independent antenna arrays is the very large array on the plains of San Agustin, between the towns of Datil and Magdalena in New Mexico, consisting of 27 antennas, each with a diameter of 25 m, configured in a Y-setting with arm length of 21 km. The very large array has a spatial RESOLUTION of 0.08 arcsec (see Figure R.23).

Figure R.23 Examples of radio telescopes searching the universe for radiographic (electromagnetic) information about structural composition of remote galactic objects next to potential radio emissions from artificial sources indicating the existence of extraterrestrial life. In the United States, the search for extraterrestrial life is categorized under SETI: search for extraterrestrial intelligence, in which the United States is executed by groups at, for instance, Harvard University, Cambridge, Massachusetts; the University of California, Berkeley, California, and the SETI Institute in Mountain View, California.

Radiography

[imaging] Transcorporal imaging technique using X-RAY RADIATION. It is also known as radiographic analysis and radiography imaging (*also see* **CT-IMAGING** *and* **X-RAY IMAGING**) (see Figure R.24).

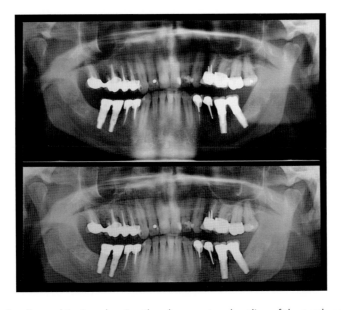

Figure R.24 Extra-oral radiographic view showing the placement and outline of the teeth, sometimes to be used for identification purposes. Sometimes also referred to as fluoroscopy, based on the scintillation elements recording the transmitted X-ray radiation and converting it in electromagnetic radiation that can be detected by electronic sensor units. The collected signals as a function of location and time of detection are ordered by computational techniques to render a reconstructed image based on attenuation for line of flight.

R

Radioisotope

[atomic, biomedical, general, nuclear] *See* ISOTOPE.

Radionuclide

[atomic, biomedical, nuclear] *See* NUCLIDE.

Radiopharmaceutical

[biomedical, chemical] RADIOACTIVE ISOTOPE used for tagging and imaging of physiological and anatomical features and phenomena, primarily applied in positron emission TOMOGRAPHY. One of the most used radiopharmaceuticals is fludeoxyglucose (FDG: $C_6H_{11}{}^{18}FO_5$) used in gauging the METABOLIC ACTIVITY related to cancer, HEART disease as well as epilepsy due to its equivalence with standard dietary GLUCOSE (see Figure R.25).

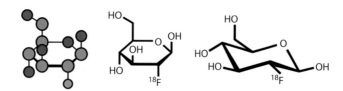

Figure R.25 Chemical diagram of radiopharmaceutical: fludeoxyglucose ^{18}F.

Radium ($^{226}_{88}$Ra)

[atomic, general, nuclear] Radioactive ELEMENT discovered by MARIE (MANYA) SKŁODOWSKA CURIE (1867–1934) and her husband PIERRE CURIE (1859–1906) approximately in 1902. Radium, generally found in the GROUND, decays to radon in the ground.

Radius of gyration (R_g)

[atomic, biomedical, fluid dynamics, solid-state] Parameter used to describe the characteristic dimension that apply to a POLYMER chain in polymer PHYSICS, defined as

$$R_g = \sqrt{\left[(1/n) \sum_{i=1}^{n} (r_i - r)^2 \right]} = \sqrt{\left[(1/2n^2) \sum_{i,j}^{n} (r_i - r_j)^2 \right]},$$

where r_i signifies the DISTANCE to the "central axis" of the polymer; representing the center of mass as a function of longitudinal location for location i, and r the mean radius to the central axis for the collective assembly of monomers; also with respect to the interspatial distance for the respective monomers (defined in the root mean square for $r_i - r_j$). Alternatively, in fluid-dynamic applications of buoyance the radius of gyration signifies the configuration of a floating object, given by the root mean square distance for a representative number of locations on the surface of the objects and associated parts with respect to the CENTER OF GRAVITY over the length of the object: $R_g = \sqrt{(I/A)}$, where I is the MOMENT OF INERTIA of the object in the direction of roll (predominantly perpendicular to the long axis of the body), and A the surface area of the buoyant object under the LIQUID surface.

Radon ($^{222}_{86}$Rn)

[atomic, general, nuclear] Radioactive ELEMENT formed by ALPHA DECAY of radium. Radon GAS is often found in the basement of houses due to the way radon is formed in the GROUND. Radon radiates by alpha decay and provides approximately 55% of all background RADIATION (see Figure R.26).

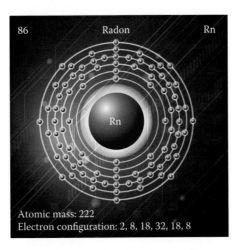

Figure R.26 The element radon and the theoretical electron configuration.

Rain

[energy, fluid dynamics, general, geophysics] Precipitation in LIQUID form, droplets of condensate water from clouds; the condensate water VAPOR reaches a volume that becomes subject to gravitational attraction, overcoming the BUOYANCY (see Figure R.27).

Figure R.27 Liquid precipitation.

Rain gauge

[energy, fluid dynamics, general, geophysics] Device used to determine a physical phenomenon in the lower part of EARTH's ATMOSPHERE directly related to LIQUID precipitation (see Figure R.28).

Figure R.28 Rain gauge.

Raisin-pudding atom

[general] *See* **BOHR ATOM MODEL**.

Raman, Chandrasekhara Venkata, Sir (1888–1970)

[energy, optics] Indian scientist and philosopher. Sir Raman received Nobel Prize for Physics with regard to his work on the molecular SCATTERING of LIGHT in 1930. In 1921 Professor Chandrasekhara V. Raman and his students discovered that an incident light beam transmitted through a LIQUID resulted in a spectrum that not only included the original light but also secondary radiation at shifted wavelengths. The original experimental setup passed sunlight through an optical filter to produce a polarized incident light beam that was then transmitted through the sample material. The emerging scattered light beam was then passed through a second optical filter and the resulting spectrum was observed visually. From these initial experiments it was determined that the intensity of the resulting secondary RADIATION was dependent on both the frequency and the POLARIZATION of the light beam incident to the sample (see Figure R.29).

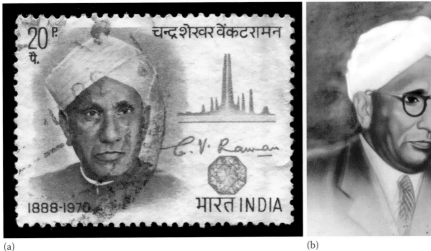

(a)   (b)

Figure R.29 (a,b) Sir Chandrasekhara Venkata Raman (1888–1970).

Raman scattering

[nuclear, optics, solid-state] Inelastic SCATTERING of photons, first described in a LIQUID turbid medium by SIR CHANDRASEKHARA VENTAKA RAMAN (1888–1970) and Kariamanickam Srinivasa Krishnan (1898–1961) in liquid in 1921. The effect was confirmed for scattering in crystals by Grigory Samuilovich Landsberg (1890–1957) and Leonid Isaakovich Mandelshtam (1879–1944) in 1928. In contrast to ELASTIC SCATTERING, where the ENERGY is conserved, in Raman scattering portion of the PHOTON energy is transferred to the molecular bindings, thus revealing details about the energy of the atomic–molecular structure based on the emitted INFRARED spectrum. For the constituents of a CHEMICAL COMPOUND with N atoms, there are a total of $3N$ DEGREES OF FREEDOM with respect to rotation, stretch, and bend (scissor action) for the motions of the MOLECULE. For a linear molecule the total number of vibrational modes is $3N-5$, whereas for a complex structure the vibrational modes add up to $3N-6$. This principle is applied to gas CHROMATOGRAPHY for molecular analysis. The spectral profile will be composed of Rayleigh scatter, Stokes and anti-Stokes scatter frequency shifts (cm^{-1} scale), and is referred to as the Raman spectrum. The shifts in spectral peaks are indications of the energy changes with respect to GROUND STATE of the molecule, and define the BINDING ENERGY profile and can be used to identify the chemical structure with the help of look-up tables.

R

Also known as the Raman effect. Also described as RAMAN SPECTROSCOPY with respect to the physical detection of the transition processes (see Figure R.30).

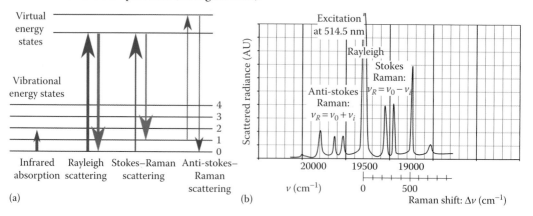

(a)　　　　　　　　　　　　(b)

Figure R.30 (a,b) Raman scattering and associated Raman spectroscopy. The Raman spectrum is composed of sharp and narrow peaks. The peaks are on either side of the excitation line resulting from laser irradiation (excitation). The peaks are referred to as Stokes and anti-Stokes lines. The graph represents the Stokes and anti-Stokes Raman spectral lines for the chemical compound CCl_4, under excitation irradiation by a 514.5 nm argon ion laser line. The frequency differences between the excitation radiation and the Raman scattered radiation are called the Raman shift. Raman shifts are reported in units of wavenumber (cm^{-1}) and are defined by the Raman shift: $\Delta = (1/\lambda_0) - (1/\lambda_R)$ $[cm^{-1}]$ resulting from laser irradiation with wavelength λ_0, with the resulting Raman radiation at wavelength: λ_R.

Raman spectroscopy

[atomic, nuclear, optics] *See* **RAMAN SCATTERING**. Also known as RAMAN SPECTRA.

Ramsay, William Mitchell, Sir (1852–1916)

[general] Scientist from Scotland (Great Britain), known for his discovery of helium on EARTH, specifically in uranium bearing minerals as well as the description of noble gases (inorganic chemistry) starting in approximately 1885. His work and the work of FREDERICK SODDY (1877–1956) showed that the helium originated from radium, produced in a DECAY process. They however did not describe the atomic structure of helium just yet. Sir Ramsay received the Nobel Prize in Chemistry for his work on noble gases in 1904. Sir Ramsay discovered and defined argon, helium, krypton, neon, and xenon (see Figure R.31).

Figure R.31 Sir William Mitchell Ramsay (1852–1916).

Random walk

[biomedical, computational] Stochastic principle in discrete PROBABILITY distribution with respect to the SCATTERING of photons in a turbid medium such as tissue. The concept of random walk is most frequently approached through computer simulation mechanisms using a principle called "Monte Carlo" analysis, relying on a probability distribution of the scattering events in this case using THEORY OF LARGE NUMBERS. Compare to FINITE ELEMENT ANALYSIS (see Figure R.32).

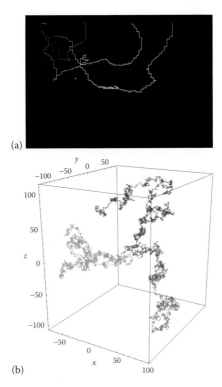

Figure R.32 Representation of the principle of random walk (a) in two-dimensional projection for 5 photons and (b) for three events (e.g., photons, molecules, etc.) in three-dimensional diagram, generated by means of computer simulated ray-tracing.

Rankine

[biomedical, thermodynamics] Unit of measure of ABSOLUTE TEMPERATURE designed by WILLIAM RANKINE (1820–1872). In comparison the Kelvin and degrees Celsius are relative scales.

Rankine, William John Macquorn (1820–1872)

[general, solid-state, thermodynamics] Scottish scientist (physicist/engineer), who made significant contributions to the development of the thermodynamic theoretic base (see Figure R.33).

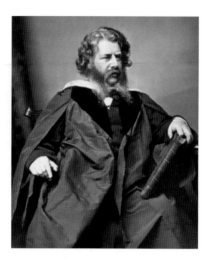

Figure R.33 William John Macquorn Rankine (1820–1872). (Courtesy of University of Glasgow, Glasgow; "Memorials of the Old College of Glasgow"—http://encore.lib.gla.ac.uk/iii/encore/record/C__Rb1168827?lang=eng.)

Rankine cycle

[thermodynamics] Process that is fundamentally reversible pertaining to the temperature-specific entropy loop for a system of bulk flow states. The process consists of four segments; the first segment is isobaric heating, followed by an ISENTROPIC interval of EXPANSION to the two-phase system, the third segment involves the isobaric condensation under constant temperature, with the final stage returning to the original format under isentropic compression under MECHANICAL ENERGY resulting from the compression by piston with work rate $\dot{W}_c^{\leftarrow}$. The efficiency (η_{eff}) of the Rankine cycle is a function of the specific enthalpy (h_i) of the various stages (4) in the process: $\eta_{\text{eff}} = \left[\left(h_4 - h_5\right) - \left(h_1 + h_6\right)\right]/\left(h_4 - h_1\right) = 1 - \left[\left(h_5 - h_6\right)/\left(h_4 - h_1\right)\right]$, introduced based on the work of WILLIAM RANKINE (1820–1872) (see Figure R.34).

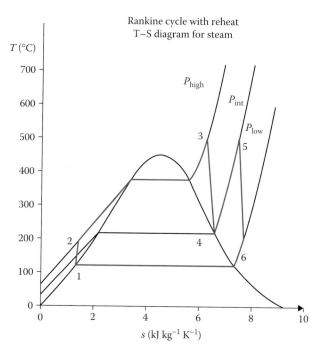

Figure R.34 Graphical representation of the Rankine cycle.

Rankine–Hugoniot equations

[fluid dynamics] Equation describing the physical properties during a SHOCK WAVE propagating with shock WAVE velocity v_s, undergoing volumetric changes (specific volume V_{sp}), and velocity of the mechanism of expansion (e.g., piston, breaking plate, moving surface) v, with $\square_0$ describing the initial state, pertaining to CONSERVATION OF MASS: $\left(V_{sp,0} - V_{sp}\right)/V_{sp,0} = \left(v - v_0\right)/v_s$; as well as the conservation of momentum under PRESSURE (P) change: $P - P_0 = v_s\left[\left(v - v_0\right)/V_{sp,0}\right]$; and the CONSERVATION OF ENERGY, where the EXPANSION provides kinetic ENERGY (KE), combined with the potential energy (U) as total energy $\left(E\right)$: $E - E_0 = \left(V_{sp,0} - V_{sp}\right)\left(P + P_0\right)/2$. The Rankine–Hugoniot equations define the respective final states of the shock compression for the medium with an initial state. The graphic representation of the pressure versus the volume for the shock wave is referred to as the "Hugoniot." With the use of the Rankine–Hugoniot equations the shock wave can be determined when the initial conditions are known and any two of the other five components in the equation can be measured. The expansion velocity is most commonly measured. Related to the shock wave the following relationships apply. For the expansion the correlation to the MACH NUMBER (M), SPECIFIC HEAT (c_p; respectively c_v), and respective specific heat ration: $\gamma_s = c_p/c_v$, provides $P/P_0 = \left[2\gamma_s M^2 - \left(\gamma_s - 1\right)\right]/\left(\gamma_s + 1\right)$. For the specific volume this yields $V_{sp}/V_{sp,0} = \left[\left(\gamma_s - 1\right)M^2 + 2\right]/\left[\left(\gamma_s + 1\right)M^2\right]$. Whereas the IDEAL GAS LAW provides the TEMPERATURE (T) relation during a shock-wave as $T/T_0 = PV/P_0V_0$.

R

Raoult, François-Marie (1830–1901)

[chemical, thermodynamics] A chemist from France. François-Marie Raoult defined the MIXING of gases (and this may under strict conditions also apply to solutions) as RAOULT'S LAW. Additional work by Raoult described the lowering of the freezing point (T_{freeze}) as a result of adding a SOLUTE to a LIQUID, proportional to the molecular concentration: $T_{freeze} = MA_{temp}$, where M is the MOLECULAR WEIGHT of the dissolved component and A_{temp} the molecular lowering of the FREEZING temperature; sometimes referred to as the general law of the freezing of solutions (see Figure R.35).

Figure R.35 François-Marie Raoult (1830–1901). (Courtesy of Zeitschrift für Physikalische Chemie, Vol. 27, 1898.)

Raoult's law

[thermodynamics] The partial VAPOR PRESSURE for each of the components in a mixture is equal to the vapor pressure of the individual constituent at that temperature multiplied by the respective MOLE fraction in the mixture. Introduced by FRANÇOIS-MARIE RAOULT (1830–1901) in 1882.

Rapid prototyping

[biomedical, general, mechanics] The process of "printing" a three-dimensional design with composite material in a rapid process without the requirements for a mold, such as those used in injection molding, generally based on a VOXEL-based construction using incremental steps of micrometers or millimeters; however, single molecular construction is also being developed for medical device and nanoscale intervention. Rapid-prototyping uses computer aided design (CAD-drawings) as the input for the process to "write" the construction in a stereolithographic format. The composite material is selectively positioned in pre-designated locations in three-dimensional space and cured by a process that depends on the material choice, sometime requiring laser LIGHT, sometimes OXIDATION or EVAPORATION by means of outside AIR. Rapid prototyping is used to create either scale models for show-and-tell or full-sized working devices, on small profile, in mass production up to several CENTIMETER in size. The size of rapid-prototyping designs is rapidly increasing to construct devices in meter size and larger. Several different techniques are available, ranging from laser sintering to epoxy molding. The initial introduction of rapid-prototyping was in the late 1980s. Also known as 3D printing, since the process has outgrown the "prototyping" stage. This rapid-prototyping is gently replacing computer NUMERICAL control machining since composite materials are approaching and exceeding METAL strengths (see Figure R.36).

Figure R.36 Rapid prototyping machine made out of LEGO® bricks, fully functional, connected to a computer and supplied with polymer substrate.

Rarefaction

[general] Reduction in molecular or PARTICLE density, or alternatively for a solid in space this may equate to an EXPANSION of the material, respectively stretch of a spring. Opposite of compression. For gases rarefaction is the opposite to condensation (see Figure R.37).

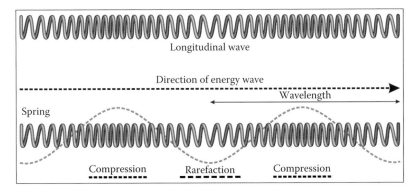

Figure R.37 Rarefaction.

Rasmussen, John (1926–)

[nuclear] Chemist from the United States. John Rasmussen provided significant details to the understanding of the nuclear structure from both experimental and on theoretical basis (see Figure R.38).

Figure R.38 John Rasmussen (1926–).

Rayleigh, Lord, a.k.a. John William Strutt (1842–1919)

[general, optics] Scientist from Great Britain. Lord Rayleigh's work describes the interaction of LIGHT with small particles, providing scatting at wavelengths generally smaller than the PARTICLE size. The Rayleigh scatting explains the spectral profile for the colors of the sky with respect to the position of the SUN and the pollutants and water droplet size in the ATMOSPHERE. The work of Lord Rayleigh was based on the experimental observations from JOHN TYNDALL (1820–1893), resulting is the RAYLEIGH SCATTERING theory in 1871. The Rayleigh scattering theory compares to the MIE SCATTERING from long wavelengths, described by GUSTAV MIE (1868–1957) in 1908 (see Figure R.39).

Figure R.39 Lord Rayleigh, a.k.a. John William Strutt (1842–1919).

Rayleigh criterion

[acoustics, optics] The angular separation ($\sin\theta \cong \theta$) that allows for independent recognition of two closely spaced objects or LIGHT sources (primary or secondary) as a function of wavelength (λ) as observed through an APERTURE with diameter D defined as $\theta = 1.22(\lambda/D)$, with corrections for edge effect of a circular opening ($\theta = \lambda/D$ for straight edges) (*see* ABBE CRITERION *and* AIRY DISK) (see Figure R.40).

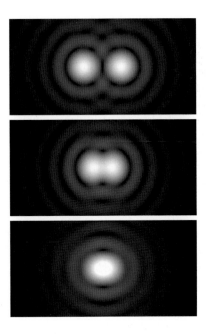

Figure R.40 Rayleigh criterion.

Rayleigh emission law

[general, optics] Black-body RADIATION as a function of wavelength (λ) or FREQUENCY (ν): $I_{\nu,T}(T,\nu) = \left(2\pi c/\lambda^4\right)k_b T = \left(2\pi\nu^2/c^2\right)k_b T$, where $\lambda = c/\nu$ is WAVELENGTH, ν the frequency, c the speed of LIGHT, k_b is the BOLTZMANN CONSTANT, T the TEMPERATURE (in Kelvin). Also known as the Rayleigh–Jeans emission Law (see Figure R.41).

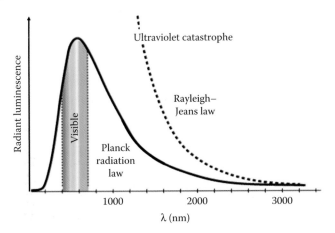

Figure R.41 Rayleigh (Rayleigh–Jeans) emission law.

Rayleigh flow

[fluid dynamics, thermodynamics] Flow condition with respect to adiabatic flow in a tube with constant cross-sectional area under flow velocity approaching or exceeding the MACH NUMBER. The flow under these conditions is subject to the stagnation temperature (T_s) and the Mach number (Ma) changes as described by $dM^2/M^2 = \left[\left(1+\gamma_s \text{Ma}^2\right)/\left(1-\text{Ma}^2\right)\right]\left(1+\left[(\gamma_s-1)/2\right]\text{Ma}^2\right)\left(dT_0/T_0\right)$, where $\gamma_s = c_p/c_v$ is the SPECIFIC HEAT ratio; for the specific heat (c_p at constant pressure; respectively c_v at constant volume). The associated change in ENTROPY (S) is $\Delta S = \Delta s/c_p = \ln\left\{\text{Ma}^2\left[(\gamma_s+1)/(1+\gamma_s M^2)\right]^{(\gamma_s+1)/\gamma_s}\right\}$, which is frequently plotted against the dimensionless entropy ($H = b/b^*$, with entropy at static temperature b^*). which yields the RAYLEIGH LINE.

Rayleigh line

[fluid dynamics, thermodynamics] Graphical representation of a flow condition with respect to adiabatic flow in a tube with constant cross-sectional area represented the enthalpy (S, respectively change: ΔS: $\Delta S = \Delta s/c_p = \ln\left\{\text{Ma}^2\left[(\gamma_s+1)/(1+\gamma_s \text{Ma}^2)\right]^{(\gamma_s+1)/\gamma_s}\right\}$; see RAYLEIGH FLOW plotted against the dimensionless entropy ($H = b/b^*$, with entropy at static temperature b^*) (see Figure R.42).

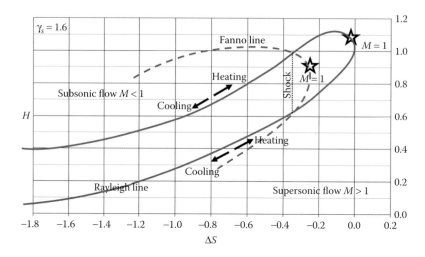

Figure R.42 Rayleigh line.

Rayleigh number (Ra = $L^3\rho^2 g\alpha_{exp}\Delta T c_p/\eta\kappa$ = GrPr)

[fluid dynamics, thermodynamics] Dimensionless number applying to convective and general HEAT TRANSFER, where L is the characteristic length (e.g., thickness of layer), ρ the density, g GRAVITATIONAL ACCELERATION, α_{exp} THERMAL EXPANSION coefficient, ΔT the temperature gradient across the phenomenon, c_p heat capacity, η the VISCOSITY, κ THERMAL CONDUCTIVITY, and Gr the GRASHOF NUMBER and Pr the PRANDTL NUMBER. The Rayleigh number can be used in BOUNDARY LAYER effects during surface heating and provide the thermal gradient.

Rayleigh scattering

[biomedical, general, nuclear] ELASTIC SCATTERING (compare to RAMAN SCATTERING) of LIGHT of a certain wavelength (λ) under interaction with objects smaller than the wavelength as described by English mathematician John William Strutt, also known as LORD RAYLEIGH (1842–1919) in 1871. The scattering CROSS SECTION ($\sigma_R(\lambda)$) is defined as $\sigma_R(\lambda) = \left(128\pi^5\alpha_R^2/3\lambda^4\right)\left(6+3\delta/6-7\delta\right)$, with α describing the function to the index of refraction(n) as $\alpha_R = (n-1)/2\pi N_0$, where N_0 is the PARTICLE density ("concentration") and δ the DEPOLARIZATION factor. The scattered light will be polarized (as can be observed by applying a POLARIZATION filter to a CAMERA lens, or polaroid sunglasses) With respect to the angular distribution (θ) of scattered radiance L, at a DISTANCE ℓ from the scatterer this rewrites as $L = L_0 \left(\pi^4 \alpha_R^2 / 3\lambda^4 \ell^2 \right) \left(1 + \cos^2 \theta \right)$. Rayleigh scattering provides an explanation to the sky looking blue, since beyond the ATMOSPHERE there is darkness. At great angular distance from the SUN the blue light is remaining form the solar spectrum, whereas closer to the incident ray of the Sun the entire spectrum scatters and provides a COLOR tending to white near the Sun. White clouds, on the other hand, are the result of MIE SCATTERING (see Figure R.43).

Figure R.43 Blue sky over Mont Michel in France due to Rayleigh scattering of white light emitted by the Sun.

Rayleigh screening

[biomedical, imaging, optics] Screening method for determination of molecular separation while applying the ULTRACENTRIFUGE principle. In this method TRANSILLUMINATION of the sample vial with SOLUTE sediment generates an INTERFERENCE FRINGE pattern. The separation of the fringes has a direct correlation with the concentration of molecular aggregate, which will correlate to the DISTANCE to the axis of rotation.

Rayleigh–Bénard flow

[fluid dynamics] Convection flow. Discrete convective turbulent flow cells occur in a horizontal layer of a FLUID heated from below. Named based on the contributions by the French physicist Henri Bénard (1874–1939) and LORD RAYLEIGH (1842–1919), defined in 1900.

Rayleigh–Gans theory

[computational, optics] SCATTERING approximation for a scattering medium that has an index of refraction close to unity ($n \approx 1$), which shifts the weight to zero scattering ANGLE. The Rayleigh–Gans scattering is described for the condition $\alpha_R = (n-1)/2\pi N_0 \cong n^2 - 1/4\pi N_0$, see **RAYLEIGH SCATTERING**. Also known as RAYLEIGH–GANS SCATTERING.

Rayleigh–Gans–Debye scattering

[computational, optics] Transition SCATTERING regime for Rayleigh and Mie scattering under index of refraction of scattering compound close to one (1). Scattering theory based on the contributions from LORD RAYLEIGH (1842–1919), Richard Martin Gans (1880–1954), and PETER DEBYE (1884–1966) (*see* RAYLEIGH–GANS THEORY).

Rayleigh–Jeans equation

[atomic, nuclear, optics] RADIATION law describing the BLACK-BODY radiant power emitted per unit solid angle within a frequency range ($\Delta\nu$), in the limit $h\nu/kT \ll 1$: $P_{BlackBody/unitSolidAngle} = \left(2k_bT/\lambda^2\right)\Delta\nu$ where $\lambda = c/\nu$ is WAVELENGTH, ν the frequency, c the speed of LIGHT, k_b is the BOLTZMANN CONSTANT, T the TEMPERATURE (in Kelvin). This law was the result of the combined efforts of LORD RAYLEIGH (1842–1919) published in 1900 and Sir James Hopwood Jeans (1877–1946) published in 1905. The validity of the Rayleigh–Jeans is identified by the Raleigh–Jeans limit which is defined as $\lambda \gg \left(hc/k_bT\right)$ beyond this point PLANCK'S LAW is approximately equal to the Rayleigh–Jeans law (*also see* BLACK-BODY EMISSION, RAYLEIGH EMISSION LAW, *and* ULTRAVIOLET CATASTROPHE).

Rayleigh–Sommerfeld diffraction

[acoustics] Diffraction theory approached in plane WAVE, in contrast to the SPHERICAL WAVE Huygens–Fresnel diffraction (near-field), modified by GUSTAV ROBERT KIRCHHOFF (1824–1887) as the Fresnel–Kirchhoff diffraction theory. Modifications by the German (Prussia) physicist and mathematician ARNOLD JOHANNES WILHELM SOMMERFELD (1868–1951) of the work by LORD RAYLEIGH (1842–1919) expressed with respect to the Fresnel–Kirchhoff approximation: $A(\vec{q}) = \int_S \kappa(\vec{r},\vec{q})\left[A(\vec{r})/|\vec{q}-\vec{r}|\right]e^{-i\kappa|\vec{q}-\vec{r}|}dS$, where dS is a surface ELEMENT, $\vec{q}$ a location on the screen, $\vec{r}$ a location of the surface ELEMENT, $A(\vec{r})$ the real value of the complex field AMPLITUDE in location $\vec{r}$, respectively $\vec{q}$; with the coefficient: $\kappa_{RS} = \cos\alpha/i\lambda$, where λ the wavelength under angular DISPERSION α for the angular position of the surface element; compared to Kirchhoff's interpretation: $\kappa_{RS} = (1-\cos\alpha)/2i\lambda$.

Rayleigh–Taylor instability

[astrophysics/astronomy, computational, energy, fluid dynamics, thermodynamics] As part of thermo-nuclear instabilities with a solar flame the flare propagation becomes unstable when the density of the fuel (ρ_{fuel}) becomes greater than the density of the ash (ρ_{ash}) as described in $\tau_{decay}^2 = kg\Delta\rho/2\rho_{avg}$, where τ_{decay} represents the DECAY rate of the combustion, g is the GRAVITATIONAL ACCELERATION on the STAR, $\Delta\rho = \rho_{ash} - \rho_{fuel}$ the gradient in density between fuel and ash, and ρ_{avg} the average density of the mixture.

R–C Circuits

[electronics, general] Electronic circuit composed of resistors (R) and capacitors (C).

Reabsorption

[biomedical, chemical] The process of lysis (enzymatic or osmotic process in reference to a cellular condition) and assimilation of a substance which is produced by a biological entity as the end result of the cellular breakdown which has been secreted. In biology this describes a process in the KIDNEY.

Reactance (χ_L)

[electronics, general] Electronic parameter pertaining to inductance: L (e.g., coil): $\chi_L = \omega L$, where $\omega = 2\pi\nu$ the ANGULAR VELOCITY and ν the frequency of the alternating current through the "coil," that is, INDUCTOR.

Reactor

[nuclear] *See* NUCLEAR REACTOR.

Réaumur, René-Antoine Ferchault de (1683–1757)

[general, thermodynamics] Scientist from France who introduced the Réaumur temperature scale with respect to his research in METEOROLOGY. The Réaumur scale used the FREEZING point of water as the zero degree mark, but in contrast to his later scientific follower ANDERS CELSIUS (1701–1744) with the CELSIUS SCALE, set the second calibration point on the scale for the boiling point of water at 80°, also making his scale in segments of 8, "octogesimal." The Réaumur temperature gauge had significant initial popularity, but was soon replaced by the Fahrenheit scale (by DANIEL GABRIEL FAHRENHEIT, 1686–1736) in the United Kingdom and the United States and the Celsius scale in the rest of the world and is now only of historic value (see Figure R.44).

Figure R.44 René Antoine Ferchault de Réaumur (1683–1757). (Courtesy of Galerie des naturalistes de J. Pizzetta, Ed. Hennuyer, 1893.)

R

Reciprocal space

[computational, condensed matter, imaging] Graphic representation using imaginary coordinates that are configured to represent vector orientation that coincide with the normal to the vector in the real space. Real space identifies the locations of atoms in a structural setting, whereas the reciprocal space represents the MAGNITUDE and direction of momentum of the wavevector for the LATTICE structure. In this setting the special DISTANCE between the imaginary coordinates represents the reciprocal of the real interplanar distance. The reciprocal lattice configuration that provides the outline to display the FOURIER TRANSFORM for the wavefunction within the original lattice structure (prevalent lattice configuration: Bravais). The general mode of operations defines the reciprocal lattice vector as the reciprocal of the real interplanar distance multiplied by 2π, placing it in Fourier space, with units radians per unit length; which yield the units of the WAVE vector ($k = 2\pi/\lambda$) used for spectroscopic analysis (cm^{-1}). The reciprocal lattice defines the slopes and planes of the crystal planes in a lattice structure. The reciprocal lattice can be made "visible" through illumination of a real lattice by X-RAY imaging. Also referred to as Fourier space or k-SPACE (see Figure R.45).

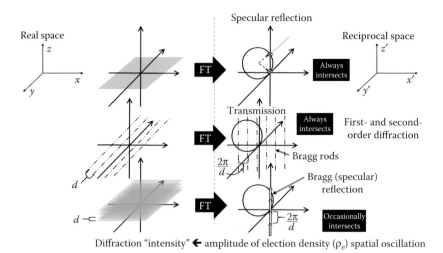

Diffraction "intensity" ← amplitude of election density (ρ_e) spatial oscillation

Figure R.45 Diagram representing the transition between real space and reciprocal space. Objects imaged in real space (left) are transformed to reciprocal space using Fourier transformation (FT). In reciprocal space (right-side) the representation may or may not have intersections with the Ewald sphere. The Ewald sphere defines the monochromatic radiation, illustrated as a two-dimensional project in the right-hand side (circle). The narrow-band (monochromatic) radiation is diffracted by the object in the direction that corresponds to the respective intersection of the Ewald sphere with the representation of the object in reciprocal space. For a planar interface there will be specular reflection. Specular reflection is represented by the intersection at the origin, which in turn corresponds to transmission. When assuming a line grating there will be additional intersections, each respectively corresponding to first-order and second-order diffraction within the object. The middle right diagram represents both orders in reflection, as well as in transmission. When imaging a set of planes, similar to what is, for instance, found in a crystal that is diffracting X-rays, the reciprocal space intersection may in actuality be absent. The definition of the orientation of the Ewald sphere is provided by the Bragg equation, which yields the intersect representing the reflections.

Reciprocity rule

[chemical] *See* BUNSEN–ROSCOE RULE.

Recoil energy

[nuclear, quantum] Interaction of an energetic PARTICLE (elementary, alpha, etc.) with a NUCLEUS, transferring some or all of its momentum without changing the DEGREES OF FREEDOM of the nontranslational states. A specific recoil effect is induced during the emission of ALPHA DECAY. In contrast to resonant absorption of gamma RADIATION by the nucleus of atoms without loss to recoil described by Rudolf Mössbauer (1929–2011) in 1958, used in spectroscopic analysis pertaining to the nuclear ENERGY configuration. Rudolf Mössbauer along with Robert Hofstadter (1915–1990) received the Nobel Prize in Physics for their electron SCATTERING (and related alpha decay) in the nucleus with the recoil energy defining the nuclear energy configuration in 1961 (*also see* MÖSSBAUER EFFECT).

Rectifier

[electronics, general] Device used for conversion of ALTERNATING CURRENT (AC) ENERGY and rotating or three-phase current energy into direct current (DC) energy. This can be done in single-phase or multiphase modes. The mechanism of action can be either single-phase rectification or multiple-phase rectification.

The duty cycle of single-phase rectification is only 50%, whereas multiple phases can approach 100% duty cycle, depending on the number of phases involved and the level and participation of multiphase suppression.

Red

[electromagnetism] COLOR in the longer wavelength range for the visible ELECTROMAGNETIC SPECTRUM, considered to be one of the PRIMARY COLORS, in comparison to blue and green. The red color spectrum is at the extreme end of the visible spectrum, ranging from approximately 600 to 650 nm. On the shorter wavelengths LIGHT is yellow and on the longer wavelength side light is invisible INFRARED.

Red dwarf

[astrophysics/astronomy] Galactic STAR, classification that includes the definition for the approximate size of our SUN but much cooler, less than 4000 K (compared to 5800 K for our Sun). The mass of a red dwarf is less than 40% of the mass of our Sun, down to as little as 7.5% of the mass of our Sun. The emission of the red dwarf places it in the late K-spectral type or M-spectral type. The spectral type system for stars was devised by the Danish astronomer Ejnar Hertzsprung (1911–1967) in 1908, which was complemented by the astronomer from the United States HENRY NORRIS RUSSELL (1877–1957), which led to naming the classification the Hertzsprung–Russell diagrams. Red dwarfs presumably have no active nuclear reactions at the surface, the heat primarily emanates by convection. Due to the minimalistic nuclear reaction, remixing hydrogen and helium, these stars can live extremely long, hundreds of billions of years. In comparison, our Sun has an anticipated lifetime of 11 billion years before it reaches the WHITE DWARF stage, of which approximately 4.5 billion years has passed (no prospects for direct changes to the sun's luminosity and temperature at this point) (see Figure R.46).

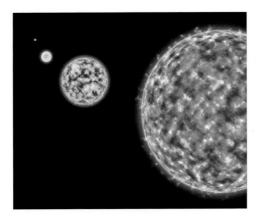

Figure R.46 Red dwarf representation; Stellar evolution of the Sun from yellow dwarf expand into huge red giant (left to right).

Red giant

[astronomy/astrophysics] Galactic star that passes through an evolutionary stage toward its demise (process of millions of years). The red giant evolves from a STAR that is low in mass, less than eight times the mass of our SUN. Due to hydrogen burn-up in the center the diameter of the star will grow to a diameter that is in the order of 100 times the size of our Sun, with associated lower ENERGY content, thus cooler and hence emitting at longer wavelength peak emission, creating the red glow. As it continues its growth process it becomes a red super giant with diameter in the order of 500 times that of our Sun, extending past the location of the earth's orbit. Our Sun is anticipated to eventually grow to a red giant with an anticipated increase in luminosity of 10,000 times the current radiance, while it cools to a temperature of 4,000 K with an approximate core temperature of 10^8 K. In the evolutionary process the red giant may progress to

R

become a WHITE DWARF once the hydrogen has been consumed with its final stage once the helium has been consumed, forming a black dwarf (see Figure R.47).

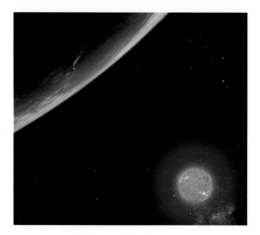

Figure R.47 Red giant representation in the vicinity of a planet.

Redox potential

[biomedical, chemical, energy] QUANTIFICATION of the potential to acquire electrons, forming a reduction process (*see* **REDOX REACTION**). The tendency that a chemical species will acquire electrons is measured in volts, the redox potential (*see* **NERNST POTENTIAL**).

Redox reaction

[biomedical, chemical, energy] Classification of a grouping of chemical reactions that have the OXIDATION reduction as the basis, transferring electrons between chemical species. The chemical interaction basis is either the reduction of electronic charge, either from negative ION to neutral or from neutral to a positive ion known as oxidation; respectively the gain of electrons is known as reduction generating a negatively charged ion (see Figure R.48).

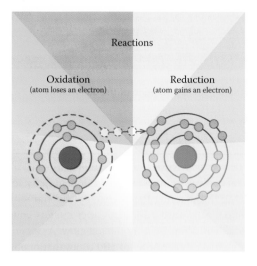

Figure R.48 Illustration comparing redox reaction with oxidation.

Redshift

[astrophysics/astronomy, computational] DOPPLER shift in spectral emission lines in the direction of longer wavelength due to the fact that the emission source is moving away from the observer, primarily observed on astronomic scale due to movement of stars. The spectral redshift was described in 1848 by HIPPOLYTE FIZEAU (1819–1896) for the first time. The emission lines are recognized transition lines for specific ELEMENTS, specifically hydrogen, helium, and certain metals. The redshift supports the "BIG BANG THEORY;" outlining the continual EXPANSION of the UNIVERSE (*also see* **DOPPLER EFFECT**) (see Figure R.49).

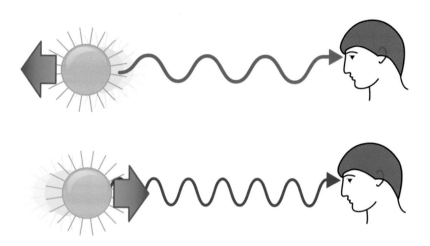

Figure R.49 Redshift diagram on top for a emitting source moving away with respect to the location of the observer. Doppler shift resulting from moving source. (Courtesy of Aleš Tošovský, Czech Republic.)

Reduced mass

[general] Mass measured when an object placed on a scale is submerged in water. This equates to the mass of the object in water from the mass of the object in AIR: $m_r = m - m_w$.

Reflectance

[atomic, general, optics] Image formed by reflection (see Figure R.50).

(a) (b)

Figure R.50 (a) Object may be closer than they appear in the convex mirror and (b) reflection of a bald eagle in flight reflected by the undisturbed surface of the water, where the eagle broke the surface tension to capture a fish that was observed from the sky accounting for the refraction with respect to the underwater location of the fish as observed from air. (Courtesy of Ray Hennessy, http://www.rayhennessy.com.)

Reflecting telescope

[general] Telescope using curved mirrors for rays forming and associated magnification in addition to lenses (see Figure R.51).

Figure R.51 Reflection telescope design.

Reflection

[atomic, general, nuclear, optics] Redirection of ENERGY wave stream that conforms to PARTICLE characteristics, resembling a ball bouncing of a WALL. The path of the WAVE propagation will form an ANGLE with an interface, where the path equates to the rectilinear propagation of a PROJECTILE. The angle of incidence of LIGHT measured with respect to the normal to the surface equals the angle of reflection. Electromagnetic RADIATION is redirected at a boundary that has different optical density from the adjacent medium, pertaining to the DIELECTRIC properties: permittivity and permeability. ACOUSTIC WAVES reflect from a boundary with different density, as do mechanical waves (i.e., water waves). Also described as specular or diffuse reflectance. Specular reflectance creates a real or virtual IMAGE that generally has the outline of the object reversed in the plane of reflection and remains crisp and clearly visible, whereas diffuse reflectance mixes the reflected rays in random directions due to the interaction from a surface or interface that is not perfectly smooth; hence the outline of the image does no longer match the object. Reflection also applies to waves of electrons, using the DE BROGLIE WAVELENGTH as the wave phenomenon next to the particle characteristics, both applied to electron microscopy imaging (see Figure R.52).

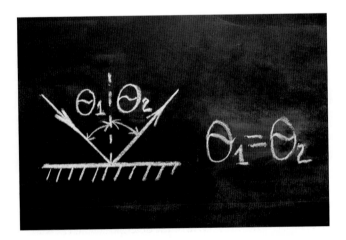

Figure R.52 Principle of reflection: equal angles with respect to normal to the surface.

Refraction

[acoustics, general, nuclear, optics] Redirection of wave of ENERGY at an interface with a change in direction that has a diminished vector component in the direction of the incident ray; the ray proceeds in the second medium with a direction that is a function of the density and obeys the equivalent of SNELL'S LAW for all forms of energy. In OPTICS the refraction is coupled to the characteristics of the medium identified as the index of refraction; linking the velocity of propagation to the definition of the medium. Refraction also applies to waves of electrons, using the DE BROGLIE WAVELENGTH as the WAVE phenomenon with respect to electron microscopy imaging (see Figure R.53).

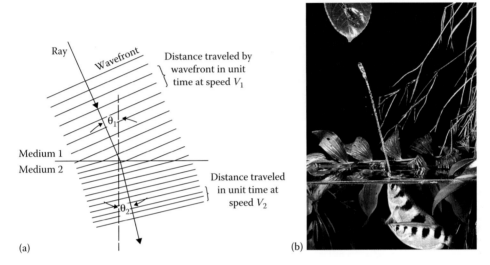

Figure R.53 (a) Principle of refraction. (b) Archerfish "spitting" at insect above the waterline, compensating for the refraction, hitting the insect and capturing it for consumption. Apparently the archerfish is able to modulate the jet-phase flow velocity (dispersion, frequency modulation, etc.) to shape the jet providing higher efficiency in disabling the prey. Note that the jet is a wave phenomenon.

Refraction, index of (n)

[general, optics] *See* INDEX OF REFRACTION.

Refraction, law of

[general] *See* SNELL'S LAW.

Refrigeration cycle

[thermodynamics] Compression cycle leading to a reduction in temperature. This principle applies to refrigeration: refrigerator and air-conditioning (*also see* RANKINE CYCLE).

Reines, Frederick (1918–1998)

[astrophysics/astronomy, general, nuclear] Physicist from the United States. Discoverer of the NEUTRINO and antineutrino, in collaboration with the American physicist Clyde Lorrain Cowan (1919–1974) in 1956. The equivalent mass of the antineutrino has been derived to be less than $27\,\mathrm{eV/c^2}$, with c the speed of LIGHT in 1986. Additional efforts of Frederick Reines were in the description and the workings of SUPERNOVA stars.

R

Reines received the Nobel Prize in Physics with Martin Lewis Perl (1927–) in 1995 for the discovery of the TAU LEPTON (see Figure R.54).

Figure R.54 Frederick Reines (1918–1998).

Relative density

[general] The nondimensional expression for the density of an object expressed as the ratio of the mass-in-air to the difference of the mass-in-air and the mass-under-water: relative density = $\rho/\rho_w = (m/V)/(m_w/V) = m/m_w = m/(m - m_r)$ = specific gravity, which is equivalent to the specific gravity. The quantity is the density while the subscripts respectively represent the mass of displaced FLUID and REDUCED MASS (or APPARENT MASS). The concept was first introduced by AL-BIRUNI (973–1048) in approximately 1025, while he was a philosopher and scientist in the Persian Empire.

Relative humidity (RH)

[thermodynamics] Measure of the ratio of water VAPOR content, measured as partial pressure (P_i), in a volume of a mixture of gases at a specific temperature with respect to the partial pressure of saturated water vapor in equilibrium with a LIQUID water bath, where saturated water vapor defines 100% percent. RH = (actual vapor density at a certain temperature/saturated vapor density at the same temperature) × 100% = $(P_{H_2O,T}/P_{SatH_2O,T}) \times 100\%$.

Relative permeability

[fluid dynamics, thermodynamics] In a cyclic thermodynamic process, the FLUID saturation will reveal HYSTERESIS with respect to PHASE transitions between the various phases in the mixture, specifically under conditions of a porous medium. The absolute permeability of a porous medium defines the ability to transmit fluids. The effective permeability relates the permeability of a particular phase in the context to other phases present. The relative permeability is the ratio of the effective permeability to the baseline permeability of the porous medium (e.g., rock). Permeability has its relevance in fracturing (fracking), where there is a presence of water, OIL, and other fluid media (including gases) in porous and semiporous rock or rock that will need to be made more permeable.

Relative permittivity

[thermodynamics] The DIELECTRIC permittivity can generally be considered as independent of the external MAGNETIC and electric fields provided the respective magnitudes are low. The permittivity can be described as dependent on both temperature and density, expressed relative to the permittivity of VACUUM as follows: $\epsilon = \epsilon_0 + (\rho/M)\left[\alpha + \left(d^2/3kT\right)\right]$, where k is the Boltzmann constant, d the ELECTRIC DIPOLE MOMENT of the respective molecules in the volume, ρ the density, M the MOLECULAR WEIGHT, and α the molecular POLARIZATION.

Relaxation time

[biomedical, computational, mechanics, nuclear, solid-state] Time period in which a phenomenon decreases to a value that is a fraction e^{-1} times the initial value. This may relate to, for instance, temperature effects, SPIN (ELECTRON SPIN under excited conditions), MAGNETIC RESONANCE (ref. MRI), electronic circuit current fluctuations (CAPACITOR discharge), mechanical (stress/strain) as well as NUCLEON and electron transitions, however, not limited to these alone.

Renaldini, Carlo {Rinaldini} (1615–1698)

[general] Engineer and nobleman from Italy who was one of the first scientists to suggest the use of the PHASE transitions of water as calibration points for a temperature scale (i.e., THERMOMETER) and provided experimental proof of the concepts in 1654. Note that the originators of several temperature scales, such as ANDERS CELSIUS (1701–1744), DANIEL GABRIEL FAHRENHEIT (1686–1736), RENÉ ANTOINE FERCHAULT DE RÉAUMUR (1683–1757), and WILLIAM THOMSON, 1ST BARON KELVIN (1824–1907) all lived after Renaldini (see Figure R.55).

Figure R.55 Carlo Renaldini (1615–1698).

Rényi, Alfréd (1921–1970)

[imaging, theoretical, thermodynamics] Mathematician and physicist from Hungary. Alfréd Rényi is known for his contributions to PROBABILITY theory, graph theory, and combinatorics as well as number theory. His contributions to the stochastic nature of thermodynamic process is expressed by the RÉNYI ENTROPY (see Figure R.56).

Figure R.56 Alfréd Rényi (1921–1970). (Courtesy of Hungarian Foreign Ministry, Hungary.)

Rényi entropy

[computational, imaging, theoretical, thermodynamics] Theoretical analysis of the additive effects of independent events. Practically, it is the derivative of the (Gibbs) free energy (G) with respect to the functional parameter for the system, introduced by ALFRÉD RÉNYI (1921–1970). The entropy is defined by this parameter; assume the spatial factor "q," describing the state of an "event," with respect to the TEMPERATURE (T) of the system, described as $\left(dG/d(1/q)\right)_T$. Rényi's approach uses the stochastic influences and improves on the Shannon entropy model, which is a linear approximation on averaging. The entropy approach incorporates an exponential function to describe the PROBABILITY (p) aspect of achieving certain states (j) expressed as the "information" (information potential ($I(p)$)) in under certain conditions for a multidimensional system consisting of a range of independent events: $I(p) = \mathcal{G}^{-1}\{\sum_{j=1}^{N} p_j \mathcal{G}\left(I_j(p)\right)\}$, where $\mathcal{G}$ provides the format of interaction for independent events, which is $\mathcal{G} = c_* q$ for Shannon's model, and in the model by Rényi this is replaced by $\mathcal{G} = c_*^{-2(1-\alpha)q}$, with $I_j(p)$ the information potential estimator for the respective states (j), c_* a coefficient for the system, q the localization factor, α a scaling parameter, and I-norm designated as the NORMALIZATION of the maximum likelihood distribution. The Rényi entropy reduces to $I_\alpha(p) = [1/(1-\alpha)]\log\left(\sum_{j=1}^{N} p_j^{\alpha}\right)$, defining a family (plural) of information measures (Rényi entropies).

Reproduction factor

[atomic, nuclear] *See* MULTIPLICATION FACTOR.

Reserve volume (RV)

[biomedical, fluid dynamics] Classification of lung volumes, consisting of INSPIRATORY RESERVE VOLUME and expiratory reserve volume. The vital capacity of the lung is the sum of the inspiratory reserve volume, the expiratory reserve volume, and the TIDAL VOLUME; where the combination inspiratory reserve volume and tidal volume constitutes the INSPIRATORY CAPACITY. The expired reserve volume refers to the lung volume that can be forcefully exhaled what is remaining after normal expiration (see Figure R.57).

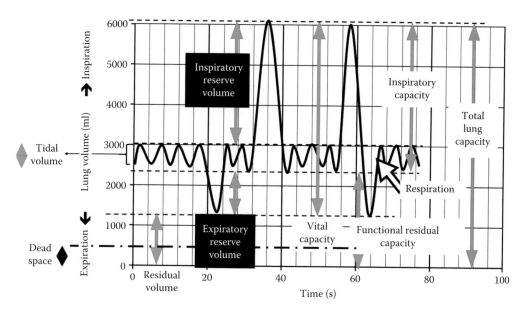

Figure R.57 Diagram of respiration and the two kinds of reserve volume involved.

Residual nucleus

[atomic, nuclear] The residue of a nuclear disintegration from the base atomic structure, where a different kind of PARTICLE is emitted resulting from an incident particle interaction, or more than one particle is emitted. The process is referred to as the reaction of transmutation, indicating that the NUCLEUS is transmuted into another nuclear species.

Residual volume

[biomedical, fluid dynamics] The lingering quantity of GAS remaining in the lungs after exhalation to the maximum effort. Residual volume and other TIDAL BREATHING parameters can be measured with a spirometer. The volume of AIR occupied in the lung remaining after normal expiration is called the functional residual capacity, which constitutes the expired reserve volume and the residual volume (*see* RESPIRATION *and* PHYSIOLOGIC DEAD SPACE).

Residuals

[computational, fluid dynamics] Method of solving for the Navier–Stokes equation using "weighted residuals." The weighted residuals are the statistical distributions with regard to the error in the order of termination for the polynomial development of the SOLUTION function.

Resistance

[biomedical, electronics, fluid dynamics, mechanics] Reactance to a phenomenon, diminishing the MAGNITUDE of a physical parameter that defines the system. In ELECTRONICS either the current or the voltage is reduced due to resistance, while flow in general is reduced as a result of resistance, specifically pertaining to fluid-dynamic conditions. Under mechanical translation, the resistance is embodied by frictional forces or general hindrances such as unevenness in the surface or a wedge between two surfaces. Under biomedical conditions the resistance is also offered through the presence of an ANTAGONIST muscle with respect to the intended MOTION. In electronics the electrical resistance follows from OHM's LAW, relating the voltage drop (V) over a resistance (R) due to a CURRENT (I) as $V = IR$.

Resistor

[electronics, general] Physical device in electronic circuit that obeys OHM's LAW and provides a voltage drop between the two poles when a current is applied (*see* RESISTANCE) (see Figure R.58).

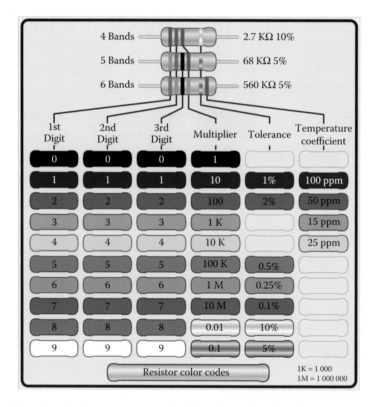

Figure R.58 Electrical resistor in electronic circuit and color code used to identify the ohmic values for conventional resistors.

Resolution

[general] Due to the DISTANCE factor between the object under observation and the viewing device resolution is expressed by the angular limit of the separation resolution between two points on an object. The resolution is provided by the Raleigh criterion, or alternatively the ABBE CONDITION (*also see* AIRY DISK).

Resolving power

[general, nuclear] The ability to distinguish between two events or two locations on an object, respectively identify the minimum separation between two objects. Newspaper print in particular takes advantage of this phenomenon, relying on an observation DISTANCE that will blend the half-tone dots in the printed images into a grayscale, or COLOR, smooth visual interpretation (see Figure R.59).

Figure R.59 Resolving power.

Resonance

[acoustics, atomic, computational, electromagnetism, fluid dynamics, general, mechanics, quantum]
Three types of resonant systems can be identified: (1) mechanical (e.g., ACOUSTICS), (2) electromagnetic, and (3) electronic. A mechanical system under temporal fluctuating external force will come to resonance when the driving frequency matches the mechanical boundary conditions of the system, either dimensions in multiples of half (e.g., closed box, solid stick, closet with door closed, etc.) or quarter wavelengths (e.g., open box, flute). Alternatively, an electronic system will come to resonance when the applied external alternating electrical potential matches the circuit conditions for the characteristic frequency of the system, for instance, the free-running frequency: $v = 1/2\pi\sqrt{LC}$ for an undamped CAPACITOR (C) and INDUCTOR (L) circuit, respectively, adding DAMPING by including a RESISTANCE in the circuit. In electronic circuits, there are three resonant configurations: series, parallel, and two branch. A resonant electromagnetic system refers to a PHOTON, which by definition has an infinite lifetime (*also see* OSCILLATION, MASS-SPRING SYSTEM, FREQUENCY, RESONANT, *and* Q-FACTOR [quality factor]) (see Figure R.60).

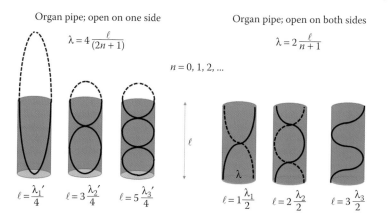

Figure R.60 Resonance.

Resonance absorption

[atomic] Electromagnetic absorption that matches the wavefunction of an atomic orbit, hence in RESONANCE with the electron ENERGY for excitation to the next energy level. A particular example of resonance absorption are the Lyman lines of hydrogen in the far ULTRAVIOLET.

Resonance frequency

[acoustics, biomedical, imaging] Frequency of oscillatory ENERGY field that matches the autonomic frequency of one of the parameters that define a system. In ACOUSTICS the frequency of a structure is directly dependent on the dimensions of the device, where at least one of the dimensions will need to match a quarter or a half wavelength multiplied by an integer, depending on whether the ends are loose (free to move independently) or fixed, respectively. In magnetic resonance imaging (MRI and NMR, respectively) the RADIO frequency perturbation of the MAGNETIC FIELD will need to match a oscillatory frequency of the NUCLEAR MAGNETIC MOMENT spin, usually in the radio frequency range. A structure exited at the resonance frequency and continuously stimulated will acquire a significant amount of energy which may eventually result in failure of the structure. Microwave ovens (i.e., magnetron) apply MICROWAVE electromagnetic RADIATION to bring water to its resonant VIBRATION relying on DIPOLE interaction, hence raising the local temperature and thus heating the food (i.e., water) (*also see* FREQUENCY, RESONANT) (see Figure R.61).

Figure R.61 Bell ringing at its resonance frequencies. Due to the shape of the bell there are a multitude of vibrational characteristic dimensions, which provide the spectrum of the sound of the bell, the "color" of the sound. Vibrating string with frequency determined by the tension and the length of the string as defined by "father" Marin Mersenne (1588–1648), *see* "MERSENNE."

Resonance potential

[atomic] The ENERGY required to raise an electron from its GROUND STATE to an excited state with certain associated freedom of movement, hence dissociating the ATOM. On an atomic level this requires traversing a potential energy BARRIER, the resonance potential. This concept was validated by JAMES FRANCK (1882–1964) and HEINRICH HERTZ (1857–1894) in 1913, who verified the dissociation energy of mercury vapor under 4.9 eV applied energy, the resonance potential for mercury, a single atom GAS. Mercury has an IONIZATION POTENTIAL of 10.4 eV, however at the resonance potential the electrons are in direct interaction with the CATHODE ray electrons in the VACUUM tube. The RESONANCE of the exited

electrons and the ballistic electrons results in a direct decrease in the current in the vacuum tube (*also see* IONIZATION) (see Figure R.62).

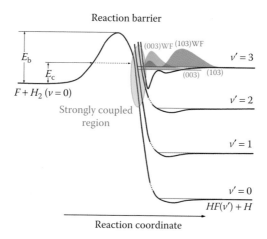

Figure R.62 Resonance potential, graphical representation of the Feshbach resonances in the $F + H_2 \rightarrow HF + H$ chemical reaction. (Courtesy of Dalian Institute of Chemical Physics, Chinese Academy of Sciences; Group 1102: Laboratory of Reaction Dynamics; Dalian, Liaoning, China.)

Resonance reactions

[nuclear] In the process of nuclear interaction resulting from PROJECTILE particles there are opportunities for population of EXCITED STATES by PARTICLE capture (e.g., NEUTRON or charged particle), where RESONANCE is induced supporting a constant reaction rate resulting from capture at the appropriate ENERGY (see Figure R.63).

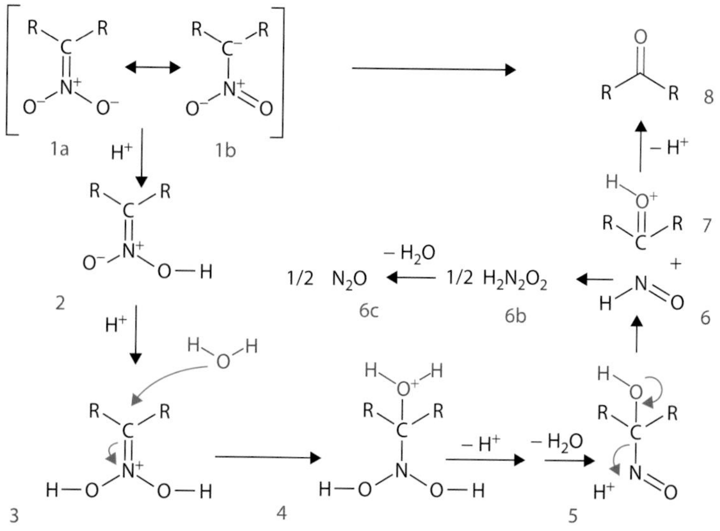

Figure R.63 Resonance reaction: chemical reaction with recursive energy exchanges.

Resonance states

[atomic, condensed matter] Peak in the ENERGY density for subatomic particle interaction with nuclides (e.g., BARYON, upsilon mesons) resulting in an excited state that is a function of the CROSS SECTION of the PARTICLE interaction providing the RESONANCE peak: $\Gamma_r = \hbar/\tau$, where $\hbar = h/2\pi$, with $h = 6.62606957 \times 10^{-34}\,m^2kg/s$ the PLANCK'S CONSTANT and τ is the lifetime of the excited state of the particle or the lifetime of the particle itself. The resonance state is an indication of the energetic width of the excited state, indicating the PROBABILITY of interaction.

Respiration

[biomedical] The process of oxygen intake by means of exchanging AIR by exhaling low SATURATION PRESSURE oxygenated fluids and inhaling high saturation pressure fluids. In the same process the carbon dioxide exchange is from high to low due to CARBOHYDRATE oxidation in the biological medium producing carbon dioxide as a metabolic waste product. The air intake/outflow is generally comprised of the following constituents and relative values with variable water VAPOR PRESSURE depending on RELATIVE HUMIDITY. Intake $20\%\,O_2 - 7\%\,N_2 - 60\%\,CO_2$; outflow $16\%\,O_2 - 7\%\,N_2 - 64\%\,CO_2$. Respiration efficiency is directly correlated to the exchange in volumes and the total volume of the respiration device (i.e., lung) (*see* RESIDUAL VOLUME, TOTAL LUNG VOLUME, EXPIRED VOLUME, INHALED VOLUME, *and* VITAL CAPACITY). The oxygen—carbon dioxide exchange takes place in the Alveoli of the lung under a blood–gas BARRIER (*see* ALVEOLI, HEMOGLOBIN, *and* LUNG) (see Figure R.64).

The movements of the chest during breathing

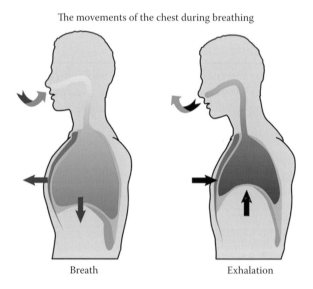

Breath

Exhalation

Figure R.64 Human respiration.

Rest energy (E_0)

[general, relativistic] The ENERGY of a system with mass m in a particular state, consisting of momentum and velocity under relativistic conditions has a rest energy $E_0 = mc^2$, where $c = \sqrt{\mu_0\varepsilon_0}^{-1} = (\mu_0\varepsilon_0)^{-1/2} = 2.99792458 \times 10^8\,m/s$ is the speed of LIGHT in VACUUM.

Rest mass

[atomic, nuclear] Relativistic mass for a system containing a mass m_0 that consists of movement with velocity v with respect to an observer in a reference frame, defined as $m_r = m_0 \big/ \sqrt{\left[1 - \left(v^2/c^2\right)\right]}$, where $c = \sqrt{\mu_0 \varepsilon_0}^{-1} = \left(\mu_0 \varepsilon_0\right)^{-1/2} = 2.99792458 \times 10^8$ m/s is the speed of LIGHT in VACUUM.

Resting potential

[biophysics, chemical, electromagnetism, energy] *See* MEMBRANE POTENTIAL.

Retina

[biomedical, chemical, optics] Cellular layer on the inside WALL of the EYE on the opposite side with respect to the LENS. The retina has two types of CELL for the detection of light: RODS and CONES. The retina of the HUMAN EYE contains approximately 120 to 130 million rods and 6.5 to 7 million cones (the cones are concentrated primarily in the FOVEA of the eye). The rod cells are primarily geared to the detection of radiance, and provide black and white (grayscale) vision. The cones are diversified in three specific sensitive wavelength ranges, respectively RED, green, and blue with a broad sensitive range, largely overlapping. The cones of the eye are sensitive approximately from 330 to 660 nm, which varies with AGE and depending on the applied radiance from the source. The retina has a pigment layer that can reduce the MAGNITUDE of light that will be collected at the rods or cones. The LIGHT incident on the lens of the eye will traverse the VITREOUS HUMOR before reaching the retina. At the retina the pigment layer is encountered first; next the light traverses the choroid respectively (vascular layer), before the light is reflected from the sclera (the white part of the eye), after which the light returns back through the pigmented layer before detection is possible in the rods and cones. The macula provides high-resolution COLOR and black and white vision in a spot of approximately 5.5 mm diameter (depending on the size of the eye), with the central fovea (diameter of approximately 1.5 mm) which contains only cones. The rods are spread out over a large surface and yield dark vision as well as peripheral vision. (*also see* EYE) (see Figure R.65).

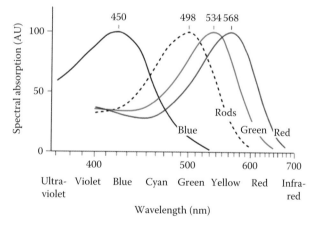

Figure R.65 Retina. Including a representation of the area of the retina where the optic nerve leads off to the rain, with nerve fibers instead of rods and cones leaving a proverbial and true "blind spot." Illustration of the three color vision cone sensitivity yielding ultimate white color by signal analysis integration.

Reverberation

[acoustics, fluid dynamics, general] The compounded cumulative effect of multiple reflections of SOUND waves within an enclosure. The characteristics of reverberation created in an enclosed environment are affected by the materials of which the enclosure is constructed as well as the material construction (geometry and materials) of any object and partitions in the enclosure and the size and shape of the enclosure. Materials can both selectively dampen a spectral profile and reflect (see Figure R.66).

Figure R.66 Reverberation: cymbal, triangle, and drum skin vibrating under percussion by hand.

Reverse osmosis

[biomedical, chemical, general] Water purification process that uses a SEMIPERMEABLE MEMBRANE to filter out potentially harmful, and generally unwanted constituents and ingredients from unknown source or unreliable quality water supply. Osmosis itself is the process of influencing the flow of a SOLUTE, primarily water, to pass across a (semipermeable) membrane between two different concentration solutions, with an inherent partial pressure gradient, forcing the SOLVENT flow to further dilute the higher solute concentration on one side of the membrane. One specific application is the removal of SALT from seawater (desalinization) for drinking purposes. Reverse osmosis applies external pressure, thus modifying the chemical potential, which will force the solvent flow to counterbalance the OSMOTIC PRESSURE resulting from the solutes. The mechanism of action thus retains the solute on the pressurized side of the membrane and the solvent will pass through (see Figure R.67).

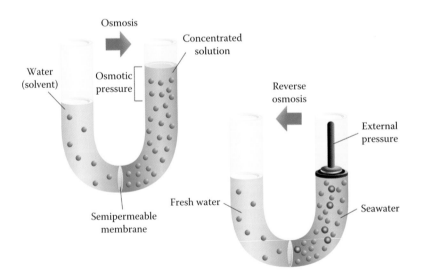

Figure R.67 Reverse osmosis process, as well as used in desalinization.

Reverse-biased diode

[electronics, general] Semiconductor DIODE that is placed in a circuit in conductive direction that is opposite the favored conduction. The general definition of the diode is an electrical device that allows current to move through it in one direction preferred over the opposite direction (*see* DIODE *and* **pn**-JUNCTION; *also see* ZENER DIODE).

Reynolds, Osborne (1842–1912)

[biomedical, fluid dynamics, thermodynamics] Scientist from Ireland. Osborne Reynolds is known for his contributions to scaling of flow and the definition of boundary conditions in a flow system. Specific contributions were in the understanding and conditions affecting the onset and persistence of turbulent flow. Additional work by Reynolds was in the HEAT TRANSFER between solids and fluids. The work of Osborne Reynolds has provided the Reynolds numbers for flow and for heat transfer and helped in the design of objects to influence the aerodynamic aspects, such as the dimples on the GOLF BALL. The dimples in the surface of the golf ball enhances TURBULENCE. This turbulence narrows the WAKE (concurrently reduces the flow RESISTANCE) and will result in an increase of the trajectory DISTANCE of the ball by up to 50%. The dimples in the golf ball result in a specific REYNOLDS NUMBER for flow, which provides the theoretical conditions for minimal velocity to induce turbulence. On an anecdotal note, Reynolds described the phenomenon of wet sand drying out when one steps in the sand locally. Reynolds recognized that lapping waves bring sand to an optimal packing. The granular packing yields sand grains as close together as they can get. Under the influence of external compaction resulting from the footprint more empty space is created, allowing the water to flow into the sand mass, temporally draining the water from the surface (see Figure R.68).

Figure R.68 Osborne Reynolds (1842–1912) in 1903, painted by John Collier.

Reynolds experiment

[fluid dynamics] Experimental design to illustrate LAMINAR FLOW, turbulent flow, and the progression (transitional flow) from laminar to fully turbulent flow.

Reynolds number

[biomedical, fluid dynamics] $Re = (D \times \rho \times v)/(\eta \times g)$, dimensionless number portraying the ratio of the net inertial force to the viscous force, where η is the VISCOSITY, D the core length of the phenomenon (i.e., length of the tube of object, e.g., automobile, train, plain, etc.), ρ the DENSITY (also SPECIFIC WEIGHT) of the FLUID, v the average relative flow velocity, and g is the GRAVITATION due to acceleration.

Reynolds number, magnetic ($Re_m = \mu\sigma v_{fl}L$)

[fluid dynamics, geophysics] Dimensionless number applying to magnetic field–fluid DYNAMICS describing the interaction of MAGNETIC FIELD and FLUID flow (e.g., magma), where μ is the DIELECTRIC permeability, σ the electrical conductivity, L the characteristic length, and v_{fl} the FLUID FLOW VELOCITY. The MAGNETIC REYNOLDS NUMBER can indicate when MAGNETIC convection over the RELAXATION TIME is small with respect to the size of the phenomenon. For large magnetic Reynolds number ($Re_m \gg 1$), the electromagnetic (i.e., the electric current and magnetic field) response can be $180°$, or π rad out of PHASE with the flow, resulting in abrupt changes in the local MAGNETIC FIELD with associated ENERGY surges and shock waves.

Reynolds stress

[fluid dynamics] Terms in the Navier–Stokes equation related to FLUID shearing stresses, as expressed by the term $-\overline{u_i u_j}$ for the velocity components with respect to all the DEGREES OF FREEDOM in $U_j\left(\partial u_i/\partial x_j\right) = \left(\partial P/\partial x_i\right) - \left(\partial/\partial x_j\right)\left(\overline{u_i u_j}\right) + \eta_{kin}\nabla^2 U_i$, where u_i is the perturbation and u_i the mean MAGNITUDE of the $\square_j$ component of the velocity profile in direction x_i, $\nabla^2 = \sum\left(d^2/dx_i^2\right)$ the Laplace operator, η_{kin} the KINEMATIC VISCOSITY, and P the mean pressure.

Rheobase

[biomedical, chemical, electronics] *See* RHEOBASIC CURRENT.

Rheobasic current

[biomedical, chemical, electronics] The smallest ION exchange measured as current across the biological CELL MEMBRANE that has the capability to induce DEPOLARIZATION and hence activate the cell to perform its function. It is also known as RHEOBASE.

Rheological diagram

[fluid dynamics] Diagram outlining the flow classification of Newtonian versus non-Newtonian, as well as defining PLASTICITY; plotting the shear stress against the rate of deformation for a FLUID (see Figure R.69).

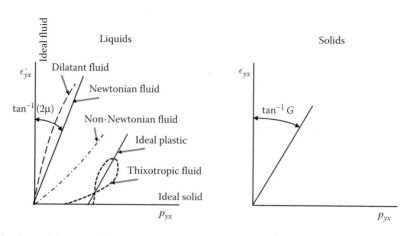

Figure R.69 Rheological diagram: illustrating the plastic flow (e.g., Bingham medium) under fluid-dynamic conditions response, rather than deforming elastically in response to an applied shear stress.

Rheology

[biomedical, computational, fluid dynamics, geophysics, mechanics, thermodynamics] Flow of inelastic condensed MATTER, also described as Bingham PLASTICS. The viscosity of the FLUID is flow velocity dependent and can be time dependent. Due to the nonlinear and inelastic nature this flow process is usually irreversible, the exception is generally for BLOOD flow, as a colloid SOLUTION flow. Blood flow changes with tube dimension (artery, arteriole, CAPILLARY, venule, VEIN, etc.) aspect ratio to the red blood CELL diameter. The flow of media that are subject to nonlinear behavior of shear stress and strain, also described by the Herschel–Bulkley model. Blood is the most recognized rheological LIQUID, other media include toothpaste, volcanic lava/magma flow, and make-up to name but a few.

Riccati, Jacopo Francesco; Count (1676–1754)

[computational, fluid dynamics] Mathematician from Italy. Count Riccati devised several expressions to perform differential equations with respect to quadratic expressions in an unknown function, the most well-known is the Riccati equation (see Figure R.70).

Figure R.70 Count Jacopo Francesco Riccati (1676–1754).

Riccati equations

[acoustics, computational, fluid dynamics, quantum] Mathematical first-order differential equation designed by COUNT JACOPO FRANCESCO RICCATI (1676–1754). The equation is quadratic in the unknown function that needs to be solved for. The general convoluted expression for the Riccati equation is given as $dy/dx = a^*(x) + b^*(x) y(x) + c^*(x) y^2(x)$, where $a^*(x)$, $b^*(x)$ and $c^*(x)$ are system-defining parameters, with respect to location-specific conditions. The Riccati equation reduces to the Bernoulli equation under certain conditions, and another example applies to the WAVE EQUATION in acoustic propagation in a geometry with curved walls. Other specific applications are found for solving the wave propagation for the SCHRÖDINGER EQUATION, respectively with respect to wave propagation in layered inhomogeneous media.

Richardson, Owen Willans, Sir (1879–1959)

[computational, solid-state] Physicist from Great Britain, known for his work on THERMIONIC EMISSION and the RICHARDSON'S EQUATION. Sir Richardson received the Nobel Prize in Physics for his thermionic emission work in 1928 (see Figure R.71).

Figure R.71 Sir Owen Willans Richardson (1879–1959) at the 1929 Solvay Conference; Fifth Solvay International Conference on Electrons and Photons under chair Hendrik Lorentz (1853–1928), far right front row.

Richardson–Dushman equation

[thermodynamics] Relationship between the "free electron," respectively ION thermionic emission with respect to the current density (J_s) through a CONDUCTOR and the work function (ϕ_w) of the emitting material as a function of temperature (T): $J_s = A_{RD} T^2 \exp(-\phi_w/kT)$, where $A_{RD} = 4\pi m e k_b^2/h^3$ the Richardson–Dushman coefficient (an indication of the PROBABILITY for release of charges per unit CROSS SECTION), and $k_b = 1.3806488 \times 10^{-23}$ m^{2}kg/s^{2}K the Boltzmann coefficient, m the electron mass, $e = 1.60217657 \times 10^{-19}$ C the electron equivalent charge and $h = 6.62606957 \times 10^{-34}$ m^{2}kg/s the PLANCK'S CONSTANT. Described by SIR OWEN WILLANS RICHARDSON (1879–1959), one particular application is in CATHODE emissions. The THERMIONIC EMISSION as initially described by the British scientist Frederick Guthrie (1833–1886) in 1873, later attributed to the scientist and statesman from the United States THOMAS ALVA EDISON (1847–1931) based on his published work in 1880. It is also known as Richardson equation.

Richardson's equation

[atomic, computational, nuclear] See RICHARDSON–DUSHMAN EQUATION. It is also known as RICHARDSON'S LAW.

Rician noise

[acoustics, biomedical, imaging, quantum] PROBABILITY distribution with respect to random signals generated as a result of nonlinear effects, providing a deviation from standard GAUSSIAN NOISE distribution. The Rician distribution specifically applies under MAGNETIC RESONANCE excitation and detection. Additionally, in ULTRASOUND imaging the random secondary resonance resulting from vibrational excitation is considered Rician noise. Rician noise takes into consideration the frequency distribution as well as the PHASE differences in the collected WAVE patterns with respect to the incident source, including the angular redistribution resulting from scatter. The Rician noise distribution is written as a function of the standard Gaussian distribution as $p_{\mathrm{R}}\left(I_{\ell}(\vec{r})\right) = \left[I_{\ell}(\vec{r})/\sigma_{\mathrm{sd}}\right]\exp-\left[\left(I_{\ell}(\vec{r})^2 + A(\vec{r})^2\right)/2\sigma_{\mathrm{sd}}^2\right] \times J_0\left(I_{\ell}(\vec{r})A(\vec{r})/\sigma_{\mathrm{sd}}^2\right)$, where $I_{\ell}(\vec{r})$ is the location-specific collected (noisy) SIGNAL magnitude, σ_{sd} the standard deviation with respect to the GAUSSIAN DISTRIBUTION, $A(\vec{r})$ the noise-free signal magnitude as a function of location (in approximation: $I_{\ell}(\vec{r}) = \sqrt{\{A(\vec{r})^2 + \sigma_{\mathrm{sd}}^2\}}$; where the signal-to-noise ratio is defined as SNR $= A(\vec{r})/\sigma_{\mathrm{sd}}$), and $J_0\left(I_{\ell}(\vec{r})A(\vec{r})/\sigma_{\mathrm{sd}}^2\right)$ a modified zero-order Bessel function of the first kind (see Figure R.72).

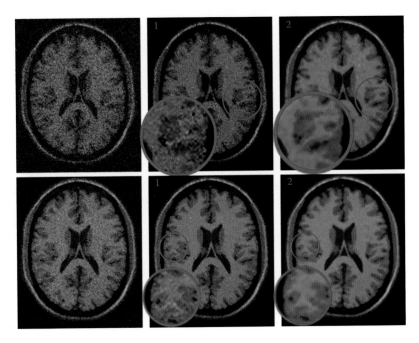

Figure R.72 Rician noise in MRI image outlined in detail focal areas. (Courtesy of Antonio Tristán Vega, submitted at Mathworks.)

Right-hand current rule

[general] *Also see* RIGHT-HAND FORCE RULE, which describes a different aspect. The direction of the MAGNETIC FIELD resulting from a current (virtual flow of positively charged particles) is indicated by the direction of the fingers when the hand grabs (encloses) the POSITIVE CHARGE flow (i.e., wire with current) and the thumb points in the direction of the current flow (see Figure R.73).

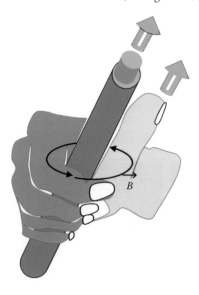

Figure R.73 Right-hand current rule.

Right-hand force rule

[general] The FORCE (F) applied on a current resulting from a moving charge (expressed as the charge q with velocity $\vec{v}$) in a MAGNETIC FIELD (B) follows the direction of the "lifted middle finger," when the charge moves in the direction of the extended thumb and the MAGNETIC field point in the direction of the extended index finger, defined by $\vec{F} = q\vec{v} \times \vec{B}$. *Also see* RIGHT-HAND CURRENT RULE, which describes a different aspect (see Figure R.74).

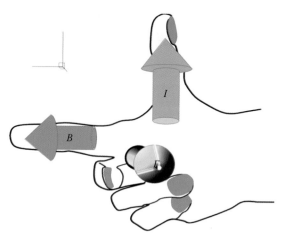

Figure R.74 Right-hand rule.

Ripple

[fluid dynamics] *See* WAVE.

Ritter, Johann Wilhelm (1776–1810)

[astrophysics/astronomy, general, optics] Discoverer of ULTRAVIOLET RADIATION in 1801 based on the work by the Swedish researcher CARL WILHELM SCHEELE, published in 1777. The work by Scheele describes the discoloration of paper coated with silver chloride when exposed to sunlight. Ritter also described the GALVANIC MECHANISM under the influence of LIGHT and he described the ELECTROLYSIS of water. Observations of current distributions in branched wires predate the publications by GEORG OHM (1789–1854) and GUSTAV KIRCHHOFF (1824–1887) (see Figure R.75).

Figure R.75 Johann Wilhelm Ritter (1776–1810), as he would have looked in 1804.

Riva-Rocci, Scipione (1863–1937)

[fluid dynamics] Physician from Italy. Inventor of the mercury SPHYGMOMANOMETER in 1896, device used to measure BLOOD PRESSURE (see Figure R.76).

Figure R.76 Scipione Riva-Rocci (1863–1937). (Courtesy of photographer Hans Christophersen and the Danish National Archive.)

Riva-Rocci cuff

[biomedical, fluid dynamics] Pressure cuff on the device introduced by SCIPIONE RIVA-ROCCI (1863–1937) for the BLOOD PRESSURE detection in the arm. The cuff is inflated and hence compresses the tissue surrounding the artery in the arm (brachial artery), thus restricting the blood flow. When the pressure is diminished the flow of blood in the artery intermittently, creating a VIBRATION of the vascular WALL similar to the RESONANCE of the an inflated balloon that is squeezed at the opening as AIR is escaping. The pressure in the cuff is raised above the known highest pressure recorded for any human heart before gradually reducing the pressure in the cuff over time. As the external pressure drops, instantly the blood will begin intermittent flow under the equilibrium condition where the applied pressure is equal to the SYSTOLIC PRESSURE applied by the HEART, not accounting from differences in height between the heart and the location of the pressure cuff and any inherent and residual flow RESISTANCE between the heart and the location of the pressure cuff, based on Bernoulli's law. Further reduction in pressure will eventually drop below the DIASTOLIC PRESSURE, at which point this will cause a cessation of the flow-induced vascular vibrations. In this manner the equivalent systolic and diastolic pressure for the individual is derived with relative accuracy. The device uses the ACOUSTICS resulting from the restricted and lack of blood flow using the vascular vibration identified by the Russian scientist NIKOLAI SERGEYEVICH KOROTKOV (1874–1920: Николай Сергéевич Коротков), known as the Korotkov sounds (see Figure R.77).

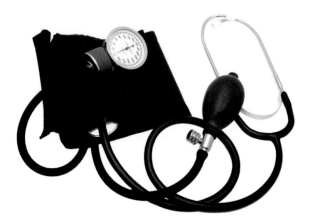

Figure R.77 Riva-Rocci cuff and Littmann stethoscope.

RMS value

[general] Root mean square, averaged value of MAGNITUDE of parameter using the weighted average of the square of all data points (n_i), by addition and divided by the number of data points, subsequently the square root is taken to yield the root-mean-square average: $\text{RMS} = \sqrt{\sum_{i=1}^{N} n_i^2 / N}$.

Roberval, Gilles Personne de (1602–1675)

[computational, general] Mathematician from France. The work of Gilles de Roberval was a prelude to modern mathematics ("infinitesimal calculus"), Additionally, the work of de Roberval supported the Copernican HELIOCENTRIC system; the SUN as the center of our planetary system, which was not fully accepted. The prior work of NICOLAUS COPERNICUS (1473–1543) also provided supporting evidence.

Gilles Personier (Personne) de Roberval was a contemporary of René Descartes (1596–1650), and they supported joint scientific beliefs (see Figure R.78).

Figure R.78 Gilles Personne de Roberval (1602–1675). Gilles de Roberval was a founding member of the French Academy of Sciences and the portrait was made during the inauguration in 1666; originally painted by Charles le Brun.

Robot

[acoustics, computational, electronics, fluid dynamics, mechanics, optics] Autonomous wired or wirelessly controlled device, respectively (*see* ROBOTICS) (see Figure R.79).

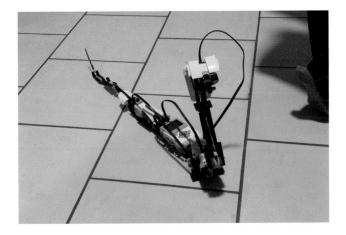

Figure R.79 Example of robots. Robot created by Zoe Crider.

Robotics

[acoustics, computational, electronics, fluid dynamics, mechanics, optics] Technological manifestation of mechanical devices that can operate by either remote control or independently under computer or MICROPROCESSOR (microchip) supported actuation, that is, ROBOT. Robots are devices that result from the integration of multifaceted aspects of a range of diverse technologies and ENGINEERING efforts, including but not limited to

MOTOR control, sensory PERCEPTION, information technology, cause-and-effect response autonomous "learning," IMAGE acquisition, and data processing. The word "robot" originates from the play R.U.R. (Rossum's Universal "Robots;" original title: Rossumovi Univerzální Roboti), by the Czechoslovakian writer Karel Čapek (1890–1938) published in 1920. The word robot originates from the Slavic word robota (and similarly also found in neighboring Cyrillic languages), which means "work" or "labor" (see Figure R.80).

Figure R.80 House robot developed by Honda.

Rock salt

[condensed matter, solid-state] Mineral form of SODIUM CHLORIDE (NaCl, i.e., table SALT) and is also known as halite. The halite crystalline structure is primarily symmetric (see Figure R.81).

Figure R.81 Rock salt.

Rods

[biomedical, chemical, optics] Anatomical feature in the EYE responsible for the electrochemical conversion of the luminous intensity (i.e., radiance) of electromagnetic RADIATION in the PERCEPTION of shades of gray (see Figure R.82).

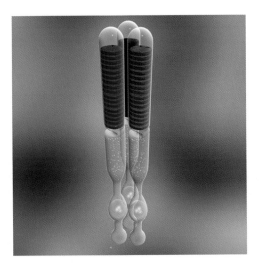

Figure R.82 Radiance sensor: rods of the retina in the eye.

Roemer {Rømer, also Römer}, Olaus (Ole) (1644–1710)

[astronomy, general, optics] Astronomer from Denmark. Ole Roemer concluded that the speed of LIGHT was finite and provided experimental proof with rudimentary equipment of this in 1675, the value obtained was $c = 2.0 \times 10^8$ m/s against the currently accepted value $c = 2.99792458 \times 10^8$ m/s. Roemer used the eclipse one of the largest observable moons of JUPITER, Io, based on the known distance between EARTH and Jupiter at that time. The MEASUREMENT of the speed of light was improved by ARMAND FIZEAU (1819–1896) in 1849 (see Figure R.83).

Figure R.83 Olaus Rømer {Ole Roemer} (1644–1710). (Courtesy of Leonardo Moledo, and portrait by Jacob Coning [circa 1647–1724 dated 1700]; Niels Bohr Institute, Denmark.)

Roentgen, Röntgen

[atomic, nuclear] X-RAY unit. The quantity of X-ray RADIATION which produces 1 esu positive or negative ELECTRICITY cm^{-3} or 3 2.083 × 10^9 ion pairs/cm^3 of AIR at standard temperature and pressure.

Roentgen, W. C.

[atomic, nuclear] *See* RÖNTGEN, WILHELM CONRAD.

Roentgen rays

[nuclear] *See* X-RAY.

Rolling friction

[general] RESISTANCE resulting from deformation of the object or the surface under rolling MOTION. The bulging of automobile tires is a common phenomenon of FRICTION, resulting in an increase in fuel consumption for the automobile, in contrast to solid rubber or low-profile tires. It is also known as "rolling resistance" (see Figure R.84).

Figure R.84 Rolling resistance examples.

Röntgen, Wilhelm Conrad {Roentgen} (1845–1923)

[atomic, biomedical, general, nuclear, solid-state] Physicist from Germany who described the discovery of X-RAY RADIATION. The discoveries by Röntgen made a remarkable and long lasting impact on solid media imaging, in particular medical imaging. Wilhelm Röntgen observed that the electron beam from a CROOKES TUBE generated other emissions when the electrons collided with the GLASS shell. The released particles were subsequently observed as FLUORESCENCE when exciting the barium platinocyanide coating. Röntgen subsequently recognized that the emitted radiation was capable of traversing paper, aluminum, wood, and other materials, and it would also form a chemical reaction with the photographic plates used for IMAGE formation using visible LIGHT. The new "undefined" *X-ray* was used to make images of the inside of several objects, including his wife's hand, showing the bone structure outline on the imprint on the PHOTOGRAPHIC PLATE consisting of silver chloride. Wilhelm Röntgen received the Nobel Prize in Physics for his discovery in 1901 (see Figure R.85).

Figure R.85 Wilhelm Conrad Röntgen {Roentgen} (1845–1923).

Rotational (divergence-free) vector field

[computational, fluid dynamics] A fundamental component of HELMHOLTZ DECOMPOSITION in vector calculus. In three-dimensional space, the vector field composed of sufficiently smooth, rapidly decaying vectors can be decomposed into the sum of two "orthogonal" components, one consisting of an IRROTATIONAL (CURL-FREE) VECTOR FIELD and the second segment composed of rotational (divergence-free) or solenoidal vector field (see DIVERGENCE-FREE VECTOR FIELD).

Roughness

[fluid dynamics, mechanics] See SURFACE ROUGHNESS.

Roughness, relative

[fluid dynamics, mechanics] See SURFACE ROUGHNESS.

R

Rouleaux formation

[biomedical, fluid dynamics] Plural for the French word for roll (i.e., roll of coins) rouleau, representative of the forming and maintaining of a stacked red BLOOD CELL in CAPILLARY FLOW (see Figure R.86).

Figure R.86 Rouleaux formation: stack of red blood cells in small vessel flow.

Rumford, Count (1753–1814)

[general] *See* BENJAMIN THOMPSON.

Runge, Carl David Tolmé (1856–1927)

[computational, general] Mathematician from Germany, known for his collaboration with another German mathematician MARTIN WILHELM KUTTA (1867–1944), both involved in the development of the RUNGA–KUTTA METHOD (see Figure R.87).

Figure R.87 Carl David Tolmé Runge (1856–1927).

Runge–Kutta method

[computational, theoretical] Numerical method for integrating nonlinear differential equations and hence providing means to solve them. The mechanism of action uses a conveniently chosen point in the coordinate system that allows integration to minimize the impact of lower order error terms. The method was designed by two mathematicians from Germany (Prussian Empire) CARL DAVID TOLMÉ RUNGE (1856–1927) and MARTIN WILHELM KUTTA (1867–1944) around 1900.

Russell, Bertrand Arthur William (1872–1970)

[general] Mathematician from Great Britain (see Figure R.88).

Figure R.88 Honorable Bertrand Russell (1872–1970) in 1916.

Russell, Henry Norris (1877–1957)

[nuclear] Astronomer from the United States (see Figure R.89).

Figure R.89 Henry Norris Russell (1877–1957). (Courtesy of The World's work; published by Doubleday Page, Garden City, New York.)

Russell–Saunders coupling

[atomic, computational, nuclear, quantum] In the orbital MECHANICS of the atomic structure the TOTAL ANGULAR MOMENTUM (J) for the electrons is the result of direct interaction between the ELECTRON SPIN angular momentum (S) and the orbital momentum (L) for that electron. The theoretical description of this phenomenon was developed by HENRY NORRIS RUSSELL (1877–1957) and FREDERICK ALBERT SAUNDERS (1875–1963). The angular momenta associated with the orbital MOTION as well as the SPIN motion can be combined in various manners. The integration of all aspects of these orbital and rotational states for atoms defined by a many electron configuration (Bohr model, Rutherford model) and how they contribute to the ENERGY state definition in a many-electron-atoms depends on three types of interactions: (1) spin–spin coupling, (2) orbit–orbit coupling, and (3) spin–orbit coupling. The two principal coupling schemes identified on a computational level are Russell–Saunders (or L–S) coupling and J–J COUPLING. Under Russell–Saunders coupling it is assumed that the following holds true: spin–spin coupling exceeds the influence over orbit–orbit coupling, which in turn trumps spin–orbit coupling. This approximation holds well for the first column in the table of ELEMENTS, where spin–orbit (J) coupling is relatively small and can be neglected. When the atomic number exceeds thirty (30) the j–j coupling takes precedent due to the fact that spin–orbit coupling becomes more influential. The overall electron spin QUANTUM NUMBER S is the sum of all individual SPIN quantum numbers m_s for the respective electrons, providing spin–spin coupling (first mechanism). The total ORBITAL ANGULAR MOMENTUM quantum number L defines the energy state described by the system composed of electrons, represented by the following terms (second mechanism):

TOTAL ORBITAL MOMENTUM						
L	0	1	2	3	4	5
	S	P	D	F	G	H

The third mechanism of spin–orbit coupling is defined by the resultant of the spin and orbital momenta of each electron which gives yields of the total angular momentum quantum number J. The interaction includes the concept of multiplicity, describing the closely spaced energy levels, defined by the term $(2S+1)$. The Russell–Saunders expression associated with this coupling is $^{(2S+1)}L$, which can be described, for instance, using a d^1 electron configuration, where $S = +1/2$, $(2S+1) = 2$, with respectively $L = 2$ and associated GROUND term ^2D. The Russell–Saunders description for the remaining three "ION" configurations are represented as:

TERMS FOR THE RESPECTIVE 3d^n "FREE" ION CONFIGURATIONS				
CONFIGURATION	NUMBER OF ENERGY LEVELS	NUMBER OF QUANTUM STATES	GROUND TERM	WITH RESPECTIVE EXCITED TERMS:
$d^1; d^9$	1	10	^2D	–
$d^2; d^8$	5	45	^3F	$^3P; {}^1G; {}^1D; {}^1S$
$d^3; d^7$	8	120	^4F	$^4P; {}^2H; {}^2G; {}^2F; 2\times {}^2D; {}^2P$
$d^4; d^6$	16	210	^5D	$^3H; {}^3G; 2\times {}^3F; {}^3D; 2\times {}^3P; {}^1I; 2\times {}^1G; {}^1F; 2\times {}^1D; 2\times {}^1S$
d^5	16	252	^6S	$^4G; {}^4F; {}^4D; {}^4P; {}^2I; {}^2H; 2\times {}^2G; 2\times {}^2F; 3\times {}^2D; {}^2P; {}^2S$

From this it can be seen that there is congruence between energy levels: d^n gives the same configuration term as d^{10-n}. The ground terms for the electron configurations are derived from Hund's rules: (1) ground term configuration will have maximum value for "multiplicity" and (2) when more than one term with maximum "multiplicity" is available, the ground term will be assigned the largest value for L. Outline of the interpretation of Hund's rule is as follows:

d^n	2	1	0	−1	−2	L	S	GROUND TERM
d^1	↑					2	1/2	^2D
d^2	↑	↑				3	1	^3F
d^3	↑	↑	↑			3	3/2	^4F
d^4	↑	↑	↑	↑		2	2	^5D
d^5	↑	↑	↑	↑	↑	0	5/2	^6S
d^6	↑↓	↑	↑	↑	↑	2	2	^5D
d^7	↑↓	↑↓	↑	↑	↑	3	3/2	^4F
d^8	↑↓	↑↓	↑↓	↑	↑	3	1	^3F
d^9	↑↓	↑↓	↑↓	↑↓	↑	2	1/2	^2D

In order to derive S the values associated with the unpaired electrons need to be summarized using a value of ½ for each. In order to derive L the labels in the respective columns are used to calculate the L value associated with that particular CELL in the table. Subsequently, summarize all respective cells. For instance, for the d^7 configuration the following applies. The +2 box has 2 electrons, yielding for that cell $L = +2 \times 2 = +4$; while the +1 box occupies 2 electrons, with respectively $L = +1 \times 2 = +2$, henceforth the 0 box has 1 electron: $L = 0$, the −1 box is 1 electron with $L = -1$, and finally the −2 box with 1 electron yields $L = -2 \times 1 = -2$, respectively $L = +4 + 2 + 0 - 1 - 1 = 3$. Note under the configuration of 5 electrons with 1 electron in each cell $L = 0$. The latter entails that the L-value for a d^1 configuration has the same configuration as for a d^6. Alternatively, substitution of electrons with "holes" provides a platform to equate alternative electron configurations, such as conforming a d^1 configuration to a d^9 condition, where the d^1 case has one (1) electron and the d^9 case has a hole (i.e., absence of electron). From the L–S table it can be derived that there are 4D ground terms configurations (d^1, d^4, d^6, d^9). Similarly the F ground term has four configurations: (d^2, d^3, d^7, d^8), while the d^5 configuration provides for an S ground term (*also see* **L–S COUPLING**) (see Figure R.90).

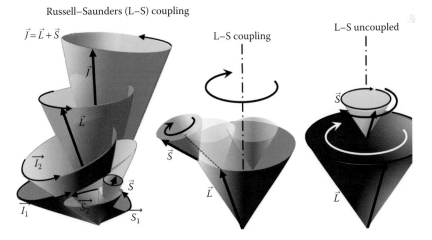

Russell–Saunders (L–S) coupling

$\vec{J} = \vec{L} + \vec{S}$

L–S coupling

L–S uncoupled

Figure R.90 Diagram representing Russell–Saunders coupling.

Rutherford, Ernest (1871–1937)

[general, nuclear, solid-state, thermodynamics] Scientist from New Zealand, apprentice of JOSEPH JOHN THOMSON (1856–1940); 1st Baron Rutherford of Nelson, Lord Rutherford of Nelson. Recipient of the Nobel Prize in Chemistry in 1908. During his research in BECQUEREL RADIATION (the phenomenological description of radioactivity as discovered by HENRI BECQUEREL, 1852–1908, in 1896) he discovered the ALPHA PARTICLE (α) and defined the BETA PARTICLE (β). Rutherford is generally recognized as the leader in experimental nuclear PHYSICS. The PROTON was identified/postulated by WILHELM WIEN (1864–1928) in 1898, and named by Ernest Rutherford in 1920. The major contributions of Ernest Rutherford are the description of the nuclear HALF-LIFE and the conversion from one ELEMENT to another during NUCLEAR DECAY (see Figure R.91).

(a)

(b)

Figure R.91 Ernest Rutherford (1871–1937); in 1905: (a) United States Library of Congress's Prints and Photographs division under the digital ID ggbain.36570, (b) at the 1933 Solvay Conference; Structure et propriétés des noyaux atomique: Structure and properties of the atomic nucleus; Chair Paul Langevin (1872–1946). (Courtesy of Department of Energy, Office of the Chief Financial Officer.)

Rutherford cross section

[atomic, nuclear] Respective scattering CROSS SECTION (finite size $d\sigma_s$) into a SOLID ANGLE ($d\Omega$) for the interaction with a PROJECTILE charged PARTICLE with a NUCLEUS with "size" (charge distribution related, the atomic number [Z] multiplied with the proton charge [e]: Ze) with respect to an incident charge particle with atomic number Z_1 and velocity v_0: $d\sigma_s/d\Omega = \left(Z_1 Z_2 e^2/8\pi\varepsilon_0 m_\alpha v_0^2\right)^2 \csc^4\left(\theta/2\right)$, with the electron charge: $e = 1.60217657 \times 10^{-19}$C, the permittivity of free space: $\varepsilon_0 = 8.85419 \times 10^{-12}$C^2/Nm^2, m_α the mass of the incident particle, the ALPHA PARTICLE, at deflection angle θ.

Rutherford scattering

[atomic, quantum] Based on the PARTICLE scattering distribution of Ernest Rutherford's (1871–1937) bombarding of a gold foil with ALPHA PARTICLES, described as the ANGLE between the incident velocity of an alpha particle and the respective scattered velocity. The SCATTERING probability distribution as a function of the size of the NUCLEUS under target (i.e., the total charge; determined from the atomic number ["proton number"]: Z) for a charged PROJECTILE traveling with incident velocity v_0, and mass m_α is presented in an angular (scattering angle: θ) representation as $P(\theta) = n(\theta)/n_0 = \left[Z_\alpha^2 Z^2 e^4/4(4\pi\varepsilon_0)^2 m_\alpha^2 v_0^4\right]\left[1/\sin^4(\theta/2)\right]$, with the unit "electron" charge (identical for the PROTON, but opposite sign): $e = 1.60217657 \times 10^{-19}$C, the permittivity of free space: $\varepsilon_0 = 8.85419 \times 10^{-12}$C^2/Nm^2, m_α the mass of the alpha particle (or in general the incident particle, with number of negative charges: Z_α), and v_r the recoil velocity of the nucleus. For the preverbal gold foil with thickness d_f and n_g gold atoms per unit volume, this translates into the angular probability $(N(\theta))$ for the collection of the number of scattered alpha particles $(N(\theta))$ at a return angle (θ), from a DISTANCE to the target nucleus (r), with respect to the incident beam of N_i alpha particles, each with kinetic ENERGY (KE$_\alpha$ = $(1/2)m_\alpha v_0^2$) as $N(\theta) = \left(N_i n_g d_f Z^2 k_C^2 e^4/4r^2 KE_\alpha^2\right)\left[1/\sin^4(\theta/2)\right]$, with the Coulomb's constant: $k_C = 1/4\pi\varepsilon_0$, where: $\varepsilon_0 = 8.85419 \times 10^{-12}$C^2/Nm^2 the permittivity of free space. The scattering concept provide a means to derive the size of the nucleus based on the "closest approximation distance" (d_0) for the incident charge with respect to the nucleus. At the closest approach the kinetic energy will be totally converted in potential energy for a brief moment, where the potential energy is the Coulomb energy: $U_p = (1/4\pi\varepsilon_0)\left(Z_\alpha Z e^2/d_0\right)$, which yields: $d_0 = (1/4\pi\varepsilon_0)\left(Z_\alpha Z e^2/m v_0^2\right)$. The closest distance of approach revealed deviations from a pure proton nucleus, and in 1920 the NEUTRON was introduced hypothetically by Rutherford, which was verified in 1932 and generally accepted in 1935 (see Figure R.92).

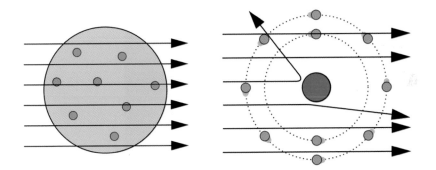

Figure R.92 Diagram representing the early concept of Rutherford scattering from the early 1900s.

Rutherford's atom

[general, nuclear, solid-state, thermodynamics] The ATOM consists of two main components: the NUCLEUS and orbiting "PLANET" electrons. This model was developed in parallel with the BOHR ATOMIC MODEL (see Figure R.93).

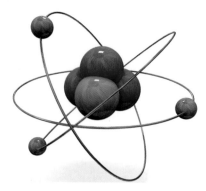

Figure R.93 Rutherford's "planetary" atom model.

Rydberg, Johannes Robert (1854–1919)

[atomic, nuclear] Physicist from Sweden. Johannes Rydberg provided elementary details about atomic structure and ENERGY configuration. Rydberg specifically introduced a constant that labeled the energy transitions used by various experimentalists, the RYDBERG CONSTANT. The Rydberg constant is used in the RYDBERG SERIES, and the BALMER SERIES, Humphreys series, LYMAN SERIES, PASCHEN SERIES, and PFUND SERIES (see Figure R.94).

Figure R.94 Johannes Robert Rydberg (1854–1919).

Rydberg constant

[atomic, general, nuclear, solid-state, thermodynamics] Fundamental constant describing the relationship between WAVELENGTH and ATOMIC NUMBER of an ATOM in the ELECTRON ENERGY TRANSITIONS occurring at the inner level of the BOHR ATOMIC MODEL, generating CHARACTERISTIC X-RAY RADIATION: $R_{Ry} = 1.097373 \times 10^7 \, m^{-1}$. The value was derived by the Swedish scientist JOHANNES ROBERT RYDBERG (1854–1919) around 1890.

Rydberg series

[atom] Atomic ELECTRON DECAY introduced in 1888 by JOHANNES ROBERT RYDBERG (1854–1919) in general denomination, but primarily geared to hydrogen as

$$\left. \frac{1}{\lambda} \right|_{vacuum} = R_{Ry} \left[(1/n_1^2) - (1/n_2^2) \right] \overset{generalized}{\Rightarrow} R_{Ry} Z^2 \left[(1/n_1^2) - (1/n_2^2) \right],$$

describing the decay RADIATION with wavelength λ emitted by the ENERGY lapse for an electron traversing from orbit n_2 to orbit n_1 ($n_1 < n_2$), with higher "BINDING" ENERGY, with RYDBERG CONSTANT $R_{Ry} = 2\pi^2 k_b^2 e^4 m_e Z^2 / h^3 c = 1.097373 \times 10^7 \, m^{-1}$ $Z = 1$ for (Boltzmann coefficient $k_b = 1.3806488 \times 10^{-23} \, m^2 kg/s^2 K$, electron charge: $e = 1.60217657 \times 10^{-19} \, C$, electron mass: m_e, PLANCK'S CONSTANT: $h = 6.62606957 \times 10^{-34} \, m^2 kg/s$, and c the speed of LIGHT), and Z the charge of the hydrogen-like ATOM (see Figure R.95).

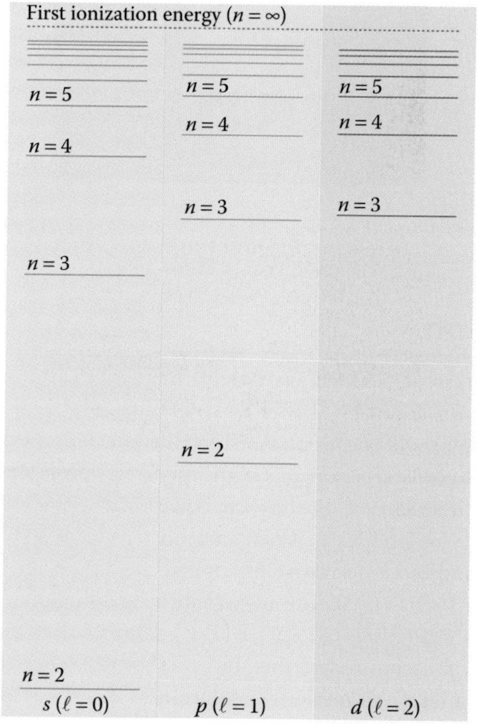

Figure R.95 Rydberg series for lithium. (Courtesy of DJ Indica.)

Rydberg state

[atomic, general, solid-state] Excited electron state in an ATOM or MOLECULE that provides an isolated energetic condition for that electron, resembling the state of an electron an a HYDROGEN ATOM. The electron acting as if it were a free electron has DECAY stages that have an ENERGY transfer resembling the RYDBERG SERIES.

Rytov, Sergei M. [Рытов, Сергей Михайлович] (1908–1996)

[acoustics, computational, mechanics] Mathematician from the United Soviet Republic (USSR; now Russia). Sergei Rytov was best known for his PERTURBATION THEORY and WAVE propagation description with respect to nonuniform media (see Figure R.96).

Figure R.96 Sergei M. Rytov (1908–1996). (Courtesy of Kotel'nikov Institute of Radio Engineering and Electronics, Russian Academy of Sciences, Moscow, Russian Federation.)

Rytov approximation

[acoustics, computational] Ultrasonic TOMOGRAPHY algorithm using a perturbation of the PHASE of the WAVE in the WAVE EQUATION. Introduced by SERGEI RYTOV (1908–1996). This is of importance based on the assumption that wave transport will suffer DISPERSION due to inhomogeneities, specifically what is providing information about the acoustic parameters of the media in transit for the pressure wave ($P(\vec{r},\nu)$), as a function of location $\vec{r}$ and frequency ν. In the wave equation the phase ($\phi(\vec{r},\nu)$) of the pressure wave field is defined as $\phi(\vec{r},\nu) \equiv \log_{10} P(\vec{r},\nu)$. When an acoustic source $w(\vec{r}'',\nu)$ (acoustic perturbation with respect to location in second-order derivative) is applied the dispersion is captured as the reciprocal speed of propagation: $\vec{s}(\vec{r},\nu) = 1/\vec{v}(\vec{r},\nu)$. The acoustic propagation adheres to the wave equation: $[1/\vec{v}(\vec{r},\nu)^2](\partial^2/\partial t^2)P(\vec{r},\nu) - \nabla^2 P(\vec{r},\nu) = w(\vec{r},\nu)$, $w(\vec{r},\nu)$ defining the VELOCITY POTENTIAL and DIVERGENCE. The unperturbed situation is described by $[1/\vec{v}(\vec{r},\nu)^2](\partial^2/\partial t^2)P_0(\vec{r},\nu) - \nabla^2 P_0(\vec{r},\nu) = 0$. The wave equation has standard Green's functions as solutions: $G(\vec{r},\vec{r}'',\nu)$; respectively $G(\vec{r},\vec{r}',\nu)$ and $G(\vec{r}',\vec{r}'',\nu)$, in locations $\vec{r}$; $\vec{r}'$; $\vec{r}''$. The phase perturbation ($\partial\phi(\vec{r},\nu)$) is now defined as $\partial\phi(\vec{r},\nu)/\partial\vec{s}(\vec{r},\nu) = \iiint 8\pi^2\nu^2\vec{s}(\vec{r},\nu)G(\vec{r},\vec{r}',\nu)G(\vec{r}',\vec{r}'',\nu)w(\vec{r}'',\nu)d^3\vec{r}'' / \iiint G(\vec{r},\vec{r}'',\nu)w(\vec{r}'',\nu)d^3\vec{r}''$. This yields for the pressure wave: $P(\vec{r},\nu) = [1/\vec{v}(\vec{r},\nu)^2](\partial^2/\partial t^2)\iiint \eta_c P_0(\vec{r}',\nu)G_0(\vec{r}',\vec{r}'',\nu)d^3\vec{r}'''$, with η_c the "susceptibility" of the medium ("COMPLIANCE") and $G_0(\vec{r}',\vec{r}'',\nu) = G_0(\vec{r}' - \vec{r}'',\nu)$ the Greens function SOLUTION to the unperturbed situation, in first-order approximation. In contrast the Born approximation uses perturbation of the AMPLITUDE.

S

[general] DISTANCE vector used in description of displacement [$\vec{s}$]. The absolute value is the SCALAR value of displacement, while the imaginary part describes the direction (see Figure S.1).

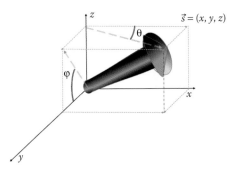

Figure S.1 s-vector.

S, M, and L responses of the human eye

[biomedical, general, optics] Layman's description of the COLOR vision by three sets of CONES: Short (-wavelength), Medium (-wavelength) and Long (-wavelength) representing the blue, green and RED cones (*also see* VISION *and see* RETINA).

Saberian number (Sa =)

[fluid dynamics] Dimensionless number signifying the LIQUID fraction applying to two-phased flow. The Saberian number is an indication of the "ease" with which a drop can be formed. Also applies to SIGNAL processing in neural networks.

Sabine equation

[acoustics, biomedical] Theoretical description of the time scale (reverberation time: RT) to allow a SOUND reverberating in a closed environment (volume V) to reduce by 60 dB while reflecting of walls with attenuation $\mu_{s,a}$, defined as $RT = k_s \left(V / \mu_{s,a} \right)$, where k_s is the temperature dependence for the WAVE interaction. The temperature coefficient has been established to be $k_s = 0.161$ for a room temperature of 22°C.

Saccade

[biomedical, electronics, theoretical] Short deliberate movement across the field of view outlined by the azimuthal and the polar ANGLE in a spherical coordinate system. The saccade MOTION is regulated by the brain but is not necessarily something that is controlled by the desire of the subject. The duration of these EYE movement generally ranges from 100 to 300 ms and ranges over several degrees of rotation. The movement is both voluntary and involuntary, in contrast to the solely involuntary MICROSACCADE. The saccade can be a response to an incident in the peripheral VISION that makes the brain aware of a change in the status-quo that deserves attention, which can be considered a defense mechanism but also falls under the deliberate focusing of attention during a quick survey of one's perimeter. The main reason for saccade motion is avoiding "burn-in," where a group of RODS and CONES may get saturated from continued exposure and as a result will adjust their sensitivity down (sometime to the point of not detecting LIGHT anymore). In case SATURATION of the RETINA is induced the rods and cones become insensitive to exposure and form a risk of not being able to detect threats or challenges. Under strict concentration one can force the eyes to stay targeted without performing saccade motion (*also see* **MICRO-SACCADE**) (see Figure S.2).

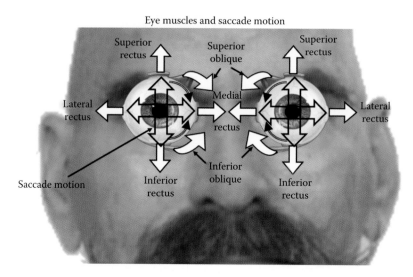

Figure S.2 Saccade motion of the eye. One way of observing this saccade motion yourself is with the use of an older model LED display calculator (*Note*: LCD screens do not blink and the visual aspect is hence not obvious). Looking straight forward (not following the calculator itself) move the calculator with at least one single display light-up in a straight up and down motion and the blinking lights will trace-out a curvy path up-down.

Saha, Meghnad (1893–1956)

[electronics, nuclear, thermodynamics] Indian astrophysicist. Saha's work describes the chemical and electronic balance in compounds as well as stellar structures including galactic dust. The ENERGY balance is defined by the Saha equation (see Figure S.3).

Figure S.3 Meghnad Saha (1893–1956).

Saha ionization equation

[astrophysics, electronics, nuclear, thermodynamics] Also Saha ionization equation, or Saha-Langmuir equation, developed by the Indian physicist MEGHNAD SAHA (1893–1956) in 1920. The Saha-equation describes the ratio of free charges to the number of electrons bound in atomic form, the IONIZATION fraction: $[\rho_e(x)\rho_i(x)]/\rho_a(x) = (1/nh^3)(2\pi m_e kT)^{2/3} e^{-[I/(kT)]}$, with $\rho_*(x)$ the ELECTRIC CHARGE density for the electrons ($* = e$), atoms ($* = a$) and ions ($* = i$) respectively and $I = (Z/n^2)(-13.6eV)$ the IONIZATION ENERGY, n the electron level in the BOHR ATOMIC MODEL, $k = 1.3806503 \times 10^{-23}$ m^{2}kgs^{-2}K^{-1} the Boltzmann constant, T temperature in Kelvin, m_e electron mass, and $h = 6.626068 \times 10^{-34}$ m^{2}kgs^{-1} PLANCK'S CONSTANT.

S

Sahl, Ibn (Arabic: سهل ابـن) (Abu Sa'd al-'Ala'ibn Sahl) (940–1000)

[mathematics, optics] Physicist and mathematician from Iraq, at the time known as Persia. The work of Ibn Sahl describes the LAW OF REFRACTION in a similar manner as attributed to WILLEBRORD SNEL (SNELLIUS) VAN ROYEN (1591–1626) (see Figure S.4).

Figure S.4 Artist impression of what Abu Sa'd al-'Ala' ibn Sahl (940–1000) may have looked like.

Saint-Elmo's fire

[atomic, energy] CORONA or charge streamer from a narrow pointy object (needle-like) such as the mast of a ship. It has also been observed on planes and in particular on helicopters, during the war in Afghanistan and was named Kopp–Etchells effect by the photographer in honor of two soldiers who lost their lives there (see Figure S.5).

Figure S.5 Saint-Elmo's fire on top of a roof. (Courtesy of Joe Thomissen.)

Salt

[chemical, general] Chemical binding between a METAL and a halogen occurring in crystalline form as a solid and dissolves as ions in water. The most well-known salt is sodium chloride, or kitchen salt: NaCl.

SAM

[acoustics, biomedical] Imaging device based on the probing by focused MECHANICAL WAVE patterns. The propagation of SOUND through solids is a function of the local elastic properties, specifically the acoustic impedance which is a function of the wavelength of the density wave and the temperature next to the medium itself. The pressure wave or stress-wave propagation is indicated by the AMPLITUDE of the pressure at a point in the path of the WAVE. The migration of the stress wave is confined by the mechanical attributes of the media, that is, localized COMPLIANCE ($C = \partial V/\partial P$) or Young's modulus ($E_{mech}$) as a function of location. The time factor describing the propagation is called stress confinement or stress RELAXATION TIME, $\tau_s = \delta/V_a$, where V_a is the speed of sound in tissue. The acoustic transmission through the tissue layers is governed by the acoustic impedance, Z, a quantity defined as a product of density, ρ (tissue, temperature) and sound velocity, $v(\nu) = \sqrt{E_{mech}/\rho}$, yielding $Z = \rho v$ for the acoustic impedance. The acoustic impedance has a dispersive relation in inhomogeneous tissue, providing one of the elementary tools for diagnostic sensing. The RESOLVING POWER is directly proportional to the half wavelength of the probing sound wave. The sound is reflected from boundaries and dispersed and scattered to be analyzed by means of path reconstruction by means of time of flight measurements from array type sensor configurations (*see* SCANNING ACOUSTIC MICROSCOPE) (see Figure S.6).

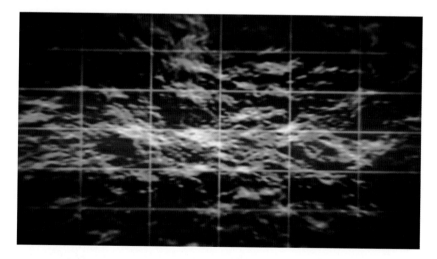

Figure S.6 Intensity profile image obtained by scanning acoustic microscope. (Courtesy of Ronald D. Kriz.)

Sampled delay focusing

[acoustics, computational] Ultrasonic BEAM-FORMING technique used with PHASED ARRAY pressure source which enables the emission of the SOUND WAVE to be confined within a narrow SOLID ANGLE (*see* PHASED-ARRAY).

Sampling

[acoustics, computational, electromagnetism, optics] The process of collecting data points. The sample data collection may be continuous or event-triggered. The limiting factor for discrete, periodic events (both spatial and temporal) is the minimum sampling rate, which is defined by the Nyquist sampling rate, or NYQUIST-SHANNON SAMPLING THEOREM. The minimum sampling rate used for a periodic event was defined

S

by HARRY NYQUIST (HARRY THEODOR NYQVIST; 1889–1976) and CLAUDE SHANNON (1916–2001) to be twice that of the minimum limit on the occurrence of an event within an observation composed of several events. The Nyquist sampling rate will provide two data-points for the definition of the location (i.e., spatial) or duration (resp. temporal) of a single event.

Sampling depth

[acoustics, computational, electromagnetism, optics] The depth from which SIGNAL is collected that has a signal to NOISE (background) ratio that provides useful information for accurate signal processing, meaning the phenomenon that is probed can be identified with scientific and clinical diagnostic limits of acceptance. Depending on the probing source configuration the sampling depth can range from micrometers to meters.

Sarcomere

[biomedical, chemical, mechanics] Elementary contraction unit in skeletal and HEART muscle. A MUSCLE fiber (e.g., SKELETAL MUSCLE) is a thin elongated cylinder with rounded ends and may extend the full length of the muscle. Beneath its sarcolemma (CELL MEMBRANE), the cytoplasm or sarcoplasm of the fiber contains many small, oval nuclei and MITOCHONDRIA. Within the sarcoplasm are numerous threadlike myofibrils that lie parallel to one another. They play an important role in muscle contractions. The myofibrils contain two kinds of protein filaments, thick ones composed of the protein MYOSIN and thin ones composed of the protein ACTIN. The arrangement of these filaments in repeated units are called sarcomeres, which produce the characteristic alternating LIGHT and dark striations of muscles. Light areas are the I-bands and the darker areas are A-bands. Z-lines are where adjacent sarcomeres come together and thin myofilaments of adjacent sarcomeres overlap slightly. Thus, a sarcomere can be defined as the area between Z-lines. Myosin filaments are located primarily within the dark portions of the sarcomeres, while actin filaments occur in the light areas (*see* MUSCLE) (see Figure S.7).

Figure S.7 Light microscopy magnified image of sarcomere in muscle.

Satellite

[astrophysics/astronomy, general] Word for artificial object launched from EARTH in orbit or at least in PROJECTILE motion horizontal to the earth's surface. The word "satellite" was introduced by JOHANNES KEPLER (1571–1630). Kepler's initial description of satellite MOTION were based on a model of a flat Earth, yielding a parabolic trajectory. With current knowledge and verified ORBITS this is showing that all motions in space are primarily ellipsoids. The first EARTH SATELLITE defined as an electronic medium relaying signals from space to the Earth or from one location on Earth to another location beyond the horizon, was the Newton. Probably the most well-known satellite is the Russian (then USSR) space communication device Sputnik. Other applications are in observation (spy satellite, and METEOROLOGY). Satellites generally have no means of correction and are presumably placed in a geo-stationary or GEOSYNCHRONOUS ORBIT. However, due to gravitational pull and interaction with space debris the satellite may eventually return to Earth (see Figure S.8).

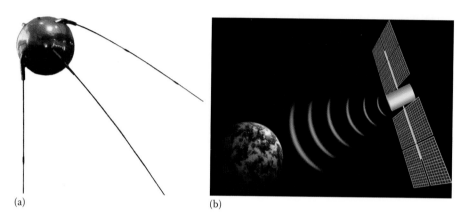

(a) (b)

Figure S.8 Satellite: (a) Sputnik and (b) detail of general satellite in orbit around Earth.

Saturable nuclear force

[general, nuclear] One NUCLEON particle can only influence a limited number of closely neighboring particles, primarily based on the fact that the nucleon is totally surrounded by other nucleons, except for the nucleons at the "surface" of the NUCLEUS of the ATOM. This phenomenon is part of the short-range NUCLEAR FORCE.

Saturated state

[thermodynamics] A condition where the conditions would under normal conditions result in condensation (GAS) or AGGREGATION (dissolved SOLUTE) but due to the absence of condensation points refrains from changing state. For instance low temperature steam derived from cooling SUPERHEATED STEAM. The saturated state can be formulated by the EQUATION OF STATE for the equilibrium.

Saturated vapor pressure

[general] Situation where the GAS pressure of a medium is greater than the pressure in the LIQUID form of the medium at the boiling point. This condition may be achieved in a closed container. VAPOR PRESSURE increases with temperature, until at equilibrium the liquid comes to a boil. The liquid-GAS PHASE diagram as a function of volume of the container and the pressure at various temperatures is expressed in the Van der Walls diagram, supported under the Van der Waals equation (*see* PHASE DIAGRAM).

Saturation

[biomedical, chemical, mechanics, optics, thermodynamics] Critical range or point above which there is no linear increase of the parameter, identifying a maximum in the distribution function. In SOLUTION once saturation is reached the solutes start to crystallize and dissociate from the SOLUTE. When a force is in saturation there will be no increase in velocity. Under magnetization when saturation is reached there is no further increase in the MAGNETIC FIELD of the magnetic material. Soil acting as a sponge can only contain a

S

certain amount of LIQUID, where saturation sets in, above this point additional liquid will drain from the sponge, resulting in flooding. In visual PERCEPTION saturation of COLOR will indicate the "richness" of the perceived spectral profile of a source, which may be due to either illumination or pigment quantity content. A saturated GAS will precipitate a condensate, most well-known is fog and associated RAIN. In an IONIZATION chamber the production of ions can be saturated once the applied voltage captures all the produced ions without inducing additional ionization. In semiconductor operations an NPN TRANSISTOR can become saturated when the collector voltage is set at a level that is lower than the base voltage, hence making the collector change to emitter and the function of the TRANSISTOR is saturated. In a gas discharge the type of discharge will be regulated by the applied current, switching from GLOW-DISCHARGE to ARC DISCHARGE when a threshold is exceeded. In thermodynamic terms for instance water VAPOR at a certain temperature can be out of equilibrium with water, creating super-heated steam, or yielding condensation. Additional saturation in chemistry pertains to the maximum of chemical bonds created, or the maximum number of molecular products (see Figure S.9).

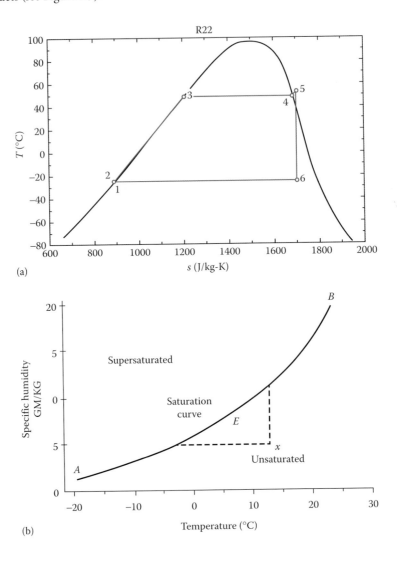

(a)

(b)

Figure S.9 (a–b) Saturation.

(Continued)

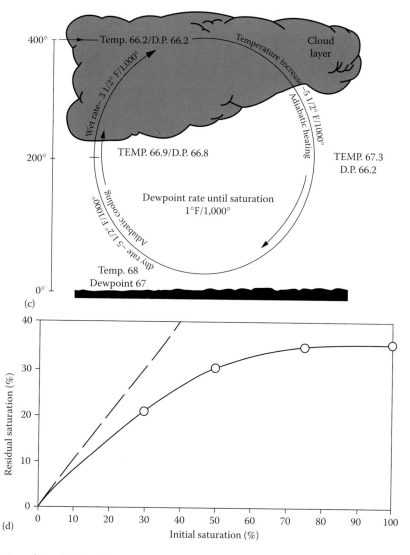

Figure S.9 (Continued) (c–d) Saturation.

Saturation curve

[biomedical, mechanics, meteorology, thermodynamics] The SATURATION vapor curve describes the equilibrium between LIQUID and VAPOR in the T-S diagram, where T represents the temperature and S the entropy of the system. Alternatively the Michaelis-Menten saturation curve describes the chemical interaction in an enzymatic reaction, illustrating the plateau reached in the chemical reaction rate after a certain chemical quantity has been converted, resembling the charge curve of a CAPACITOR with an exponential/logarithmic temporal response. In biology the Oxygen binding to hemoglobin has a saturation leveling-off as a function of the partial pressure of the SOLUTE oxygen transferred in the alveoli of the lung into the blood-stream. The oxygen saturation is indicated by the Hüfner's constant ($\xi_{Hüfner} = 1.34$). BLOOD has a theoretical maximum capacity of binding oxygen of $= 1.39$ mL/gr. Additionally STRAIN-GAUGES have a response time that saturates when plotting the deformation (i.e., DISTANCE or arc) versus time. In geothermal applications the formation of fog follows the RELATIVE HUMIDITY and the local temperature with respect to the rate in which fog is formed. In ELECTRONICS the response of an electronic circuit is plateauing as a function of frequency in alternating current drives such as RADIO frequency, radio, or television where the output at a certain point does no longer increase linearly with the driver input. A related principle applies to the charge accumulation on a capacitor as a function of time. An entirely different saturation is found in hydrocarbon AGGREGATION in the EARTH'S CRUST subsurface terrain. Hydrocarbon gasses and liquids are confined in four modes in particular: (1) GAS or OIL in volume storage, (2) oil or gas droplets in isolated form (e.g., suspended in gasses or on a surface, for instance through SURFACE TENSION), (3) hydrocarbon as solute in various liquids, and (4) suspended in kerogenous (porous) rocks. Specifically the dissolved and aggregated form of hydrocarbon content has a saturation curve per unit medium (see Figure S.10).

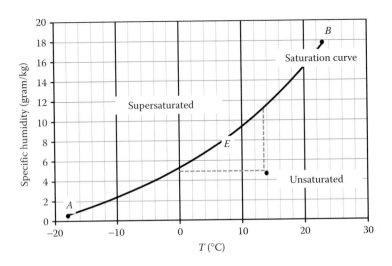

Figure S.10 Saturation curve diagram.

Saturation dome

[thermodynamics] Dome shaped relationship for the liquid-vapor equilibrium in a pressure–volume diagram (P–V diagram) with respect to temperature (see Figure S.11).

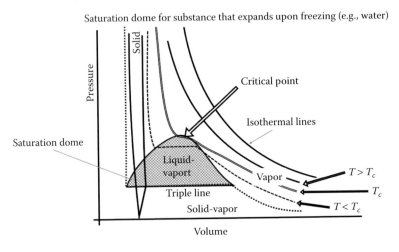

Figure S.11 Graphical representation of a saturation dome.

Saturation pressure

[thermodynamics] The optimal equilibrium pressure between LIQUID and saturated VAPOR in a confined environment (e.g., sealed container). The saturation pressure is a function of temperature, and volume as well as quantity of liquid (*see* PHASE DIAGRAM).

Saturn

[astrophysics/astronomy, general, mechanics] Sixth planet orbiting the SUN in our SOLAR SYSTEM, and second largest. The PLANET Saturn is the only planet with a seemingly infinite number of particles orbiting, compared the single MOON orbiting the third planet EARTH. Saturn has additionally in excess of 30 moons orbiting. The debris is held in orbit by gravitational pull. The galactic dust appears to form several confined rings of material grouping together. The rings of Saturn perform a WAVE MOTION similar to a tidal action which is one of the mechanisms that keeps the rings from coalescing. Note that most planets, moons, and comets form elliptic ORBITS for the reduction of stored angular momentum and rotational kinetic ENERGY to balance against the potential energy of the gravitational attraction in addition to minimal moment-of-inertia. Saturn revolves around the Sun in 29.42 earth-years, whereas its own revolution is 10.2 earth-hours. Due to the enormous angular velocity the planet is compressed the most out of all in the solar system with ellipsoidal ratio, oblateness: $R_{oblate} = (r_e - r_p)/r_e = 0.098$, where r_e is the equatorial radius and r_p the polar radius with equatorial diameter 120,540 km, whereas for Earth $R_{oblate} = 0.003353$. The mass of Saturn is $m_{Saturn} = 5.69 \times 10^{26}$ kg with a low density of $\rho_{Saturn} = 0.70 \, kg/m^3$ (see Figure S.12).

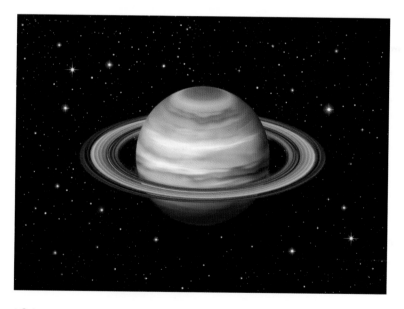

Figure S.12 Planet Saturn.

Saunders, Frederick Albert (1875–1963)

[computational, nuclear] Optical scientist and physicist from Canada, focused on SPECTROSCOPY. The work of Fredrick Saunders and HENRY NORRIS RUSSELL (1877–1957) describes the spectroscopic results from a specific atomic configuration that has more than one VALENCE electrons in the outer most shell (as described by the BOHR ATOMIC MODEL) that produce the spectral lines resulting from absorption and emission. The phenomenon is called RUSSELL-SAUNDERS COUPLING spectroscopy. Due to the plural electron configuration there are two momenta involved, the orbital (identified by the parameter L) and angular rotational SPIN (identified by the parameter S), hence also called $L-S$ COUPLING.

Sauveur, Joseph (1653–1716)

[acoustics, computational, general, mechanics] computational physicist and mathematician from France. Even though he was deaf, his interest in the VIBRATION aspect of SOUND waves lead him to recognize that the RESONANCE FREQUENCY (ν) of a vibrating object primarily depended on the mass per unit length (m_l) next to the spring constant (k_{mech}) or ELASTICITY in deformation: $\nu = 1/2\pi \int_0^l \sqrt{(k/m_l)}\,dl$. His pioneering efforts in ACOUSTICS are known for the introduction of the concepts of FUNDAMENTAL FREQUENCY, harmonics, and node (see Figure S.13).

Figure S.13 Joseph Sauveur (1653–1716).

Savart, Félix (1791–1841)

[acoustics, electromagnetism, energy, general, mechanics] Physicist, medical doctor and engineer from France. He contributed to the understanding of ACOUSTICS as well as the behavior of magnetic fields and their interaction with paramagnetic materials. Together with JEAN BAPTISTE BIOT (1774–1862) they described the behavior of magnetic objects in a changing magnetic field, more precisely the MAGNETIC FIELD (B) distribution in space ($\vec{r}$) generated by a steady-state current ($\vec{I}$) flowing through a CONDUCTOR is known as the BIOT-SAVART LAW: $B = \mu_0/4\pi \int_l (\vec{I} \times \vec{r}/|\vec{r}|^3)\,dl$ for an integral over the length (l) of a conductor, where μ_0 is the DIELECTRIC permeability of VACUUM. Beyond the validity of the boundary conditions of the Biot–Savart approximation the JEFIMENKO'S EQUATIONS are the tools of the trade (see Figure S.14).

Figure S.14 Félix Savart (1791–1841).

Savery, Thomas (1650–1715)

[general, mechanics] "Captain Savery." Inventor of a steam driven water pump ENGINE in 1698, the principle was based on the concept of the PRESSURE COOKER presented by DENIS PAPIN (1647–1712) from 1679, also called a Digester. The PUMP was designed to use VACUUM technique to pump water out of coal mines, however unsuccessful due to the limitations in height that could be overcome by the steam-vapor driven suction. Condensation of the water VAPOR at the raised outlet created a low level vacuum that pulled liquids upwards for discharge. Savery later teamed up with THOMAS NEWCOMEN (1664–1729), in collaboration with JOHN CALLEY (1644–1725), to develop the atmospheric reciprocating steam engine in approximately 1710. Other inventions by Savery include a mechanism to measure DISTANCE traveled for ships, also called an odometer for ships (see Figure S.15).

Figure S.15 Thomas Savery (1650–1715).

SAW

[acoustics] *See* SURFACE ACOUSTIC WAVE.

Scaffold

[biomedical, mechanics] In regenerative MEDICINE scaffolds are used to "grow" organs on, as internal permanent or biodegradable matrices. By carefully selecting the chemical structure of the materials that make up the fabric of the scaffold, CELL will adhere to the scaffold, forming a three-dimensional biological structure that conforms to the geometry of the scaffold as well as the genetic predisposition that can be implanted as a messenger to result in a the formation of a single biological feature that can be used for transplant surgery. The natural scaffolds in biology are collagen and epithelial cells. Since the building blocks (i.e., cellular fundamentals from stem-cell sources) are from the person for whom the novel biological feature grown on the scaffold is intended for there will be minimal risks for rejection as a foreign body. Another particular application of biological scaffolds is in vascular grafts and prosthetics. The scaffold can be designed to disintegrate or remain intact, depending on the intended function and mechanical requirements. In mechanical ENGINEERING a scaffold is also a mechanical construction that in this case allows for access to a structural formation, such as a building or an artwork that reaches above the reach of the people working on it (see Figure S.16).

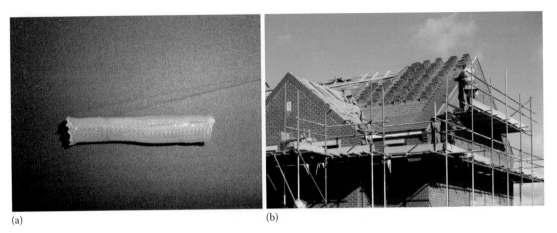

(a)   (b)

Figure S.16 Scaffold: (a) organ scaffold used in regenerative medicine to grow an arrangement of various tissues in a specified configuration and (b) metal building scaffold.

Scalar

[computational, general] Magnitude without direction, quantity. The alternate use would be a vector, which has both MAGNITUDE and direction.

Scanning acoustic microscope (SAM)

[acoustics, biomedical, mechanics] Imaging device based on the probing by focused MECHANICAL WAVE patterns. The propagation of SOUND through solids is a function of the local elastic properties, specifically the acoustic impedance which is a function of the wavelength of the density wave and the temperature next to the medium itself. The pressure wave or stress-wave propagation is indicated by the AMPLITUDE of the pressure at a point in the path of the WAVE. The migration of the stress wave is confined by the mechanical attributes of the media, that is, localized COMPLIANCE ($C = \partial V / \partial P$) or Young's modulus ($E_{mech}$) as a function of location. The time factor describing the propagation is called stress confinement or stress relaxation time, $\tau_s = \delta / V_a$, where V_a is the speed of sound in tissue. The acoustic transmission through the tissue layers is governed by the acoustic impedance, Z, a quantity defined as a product of density, ρ (tissue, temperature) and sound velocity, $v(\nu) = \sqrt{E_{mech}/\rho}$, yielding $Z = \rho v$ for the acoustic impedance. The acoustic impedance has a dispersive relation in inhomogeneous tissue as well as composite materials, providing one of the elementary tools for diagnostic sensing. The RESOLVING POWER is directly proportional to the half wavelength of the probing sound wave. The sound is reflected from boundaries and dispersed and scattered to be analyzed by means of path reconstruction by means of time of flight measurements from array type sensor configurations. The incident acoustic wave used in mechanical acoustic microscopy can be generated by piezoelectric devices and requires focusing techniques to enhance the RESOLUTION, since the resolution will be restricted by the width of the acoustic beam. The mechanically produced acoustic wave will need to be coupled into the imaging medium by means of a medium that provides acoustic impedance matching. The use of water is routine, however liquid helium can significantly enhance the LATERAL RESOLUTION by an order of MAGNITUDE. The acoustic SIGNAL retrieval is primarily performed by piezoelectric sensing arrays. The use of large APERTURE acoustic lenses for signal retrieval can provide radial resolution enhancement through INTERFERENCE inside the "LENS." The reconstruction process is based on inverse SCATTERING theory and time-resolved detection used for phase analysis. A Scanning Laser Acoustic Microscope (SLAM) uses a pulsed laser to generate the acoustic pulses (photoacoustic effect) resulting from localized EXPANSION due to the absorption of LIGHT, and the laser is scanned across the medium under interrogation for a three-dimensional reconstruction of the mechanical properties. As in ULTRASONIC IMAGING the operating FREQUENCY SPECTRUM is in the MHz to GHz range. Based on the scanning laser acoustic microscope another modality was added with special emphasis on the PHASE detection of the acoustic wave resulting in the Scanning tomographic acoustic microscope (STAM); also found as Scanning Acoustic Tomography (SAT). Due to the random phase of the acousto-optical pulse the constraints for the tomographic imaging are in the theoretical analysis and the use of multiple arrays of sensors to perform scattered wave reconstruction, based on both time-of-flight and phase-sensitive detection. Acoustic microscopy can be used for nondestructive testing, revealing the REFLECTION from MICROSCOPIC cracks and stress and strain anomalies (*also see* PHOTOACOUSTIC IMAGING) (see Figure S.17).

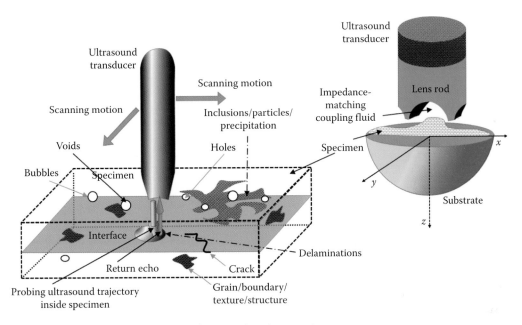

Figure S.17 Scanning acoustic microscope design and implementation.

Scatchard, George (1892–1973)

[biomedical, chemical] Scientist and chemist from the United States. Scatchard made significant contributions in physical chemistry of solutions. He focused on the theoretical explanation of steady-state solutions in equilibrium and nonsteady-state solutions, ranging from simplest mixtures of nonpolar molecules to systems containing polar molecules of various degree as well as ions, and he also included MACROMOLECULES, specifically the unexplored area of proteins (see Figure S.18).

Figure S.18 George Scatchard (1892–1973). (Courtesy of Chemical Heritage Foundation, Philadelphia, PA.)

Scatchard equation

[biomedical, chemical] Formulation of the LIGAND affinity to the distribution of various proteins. $r_{\_b}/c_l = nK_a - rK_a$, where $r_{\_b}$ is the ratio of the concentration of bound ligand to the number of available binding sites, c_l the free ligand concentration, $K_a = [A_b - A_g]/([A_b][A_g])$, where $1/K_a$ is the slope and is the affinity constant, with $[A_b]$ the concentration of antibody binding-sites, $[A_g]$ the antigen concentration (monovalent), $[A_b - A_g]$ the concentration of antigen bound to anti-body, and n is the number of binding sites per protein MOLECULE. Introduced by GEORGE SCATCHARD (1892–1973). This expression is equivalent to the one of the three linear transformations of the MICHAELIS-MENTEN EQUATION.

Scatchard plot

[biomedical, chemical] Plot of specific binding bound ligands versus the ratio of specific binding (bound ligands) with respect to the concentration of free ligands; that is, "bound in correlation to free." Introduced by GEORGE SCATCHARD (1892–1973) (*also see* MICHAELIS–MENTEN KINETICS [MICHAELIS–MENTEN EQUATION]) (see Figure S.19).

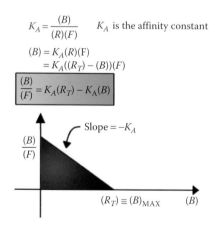

Figure S.19 Scatchard plot. (Courtesy of Stanford Medicine. http://mips.stanford.edu/courses/pharmacokinetics/Nonlin_comp/Rec_Lig_plex/2.html.)

Scatchard–Rosenthal plot

[biomedical] *See* SCATCHARD PLOT.

Scattering

[acoustics, astrophysics/astronomy, general, nuclear, optics] Redirection of the trajectory of ENERGY either lossless or lossy. The scattering mechanism is primarily based on diffuse discontinuities and nonuniformities in a medium of transport, which can be subatomic in size. The MAGNITUDE of interaction can be very locally diverse, rendering the observation an average over the selected size of the volume of interaction. The energy can be the representation of a PARTICLE moving with velocity *v*, or electromagnetic or acoustic energy. COMPTON SCATTERING describes the particle scattering during interaction with the NUCLEUS, where optical scattering involves the remittance of photons after resonant coupling with atomic and molecular constituents of a medium, such as tissue. The "EQUATION OF RADIATIVE TRANSFER" or "Radiative Transfer Equation" describes the PROBABILITY of redirection within a SOLID ANGLE for either galactic dust or biological media. Scattered ACOUSTIC WAVES are usually plagued by DISPERSION resulting from stress and strain in the medium, partially due to the acoustic density distortions themselves. The scattering phenomenon has a probability distribution which ties directly to a mean-free path-length. The mean-free path-length is an indication of the DISTANCE over which there are no anticipated interactions of both scattering or absorption. Optical scattering has been classified under two main formats: RAYLEIGH SCATTERING and Mie scattering, where the Rayleigh scattering pertains to small particle interaction and Mie scattering is more MACROSCOPIC (see Figure S.20).

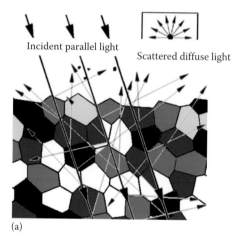

Incident parallel light

Scattered diffuse light

(a)

(b)

Figure S.20 (a) The scattering concept exemplified and (b) pinball machine analogy how a photon is scattered by atoms in a turbid medium. (*Note:* A hole in the surface would represent absorption.)

Scattering cross section, Rayleigh

[general, optics] In case electromagnetic waves interact with particles that are smaller than the wavelength, the LIGHT is not necessarily absorbed, it will most likely be scattered. The ELASTIC SCATTERING of electromagnetic RADIATION on particles smaller than the wavelength is described by the work of the English mathematician JOHN WILLIAM STRUTT LORD RAYLEIGH (1842–1919). Lord Rayleigh made an effort to explain the appearance of the blue sky and red sunset in his work published in 1871. His approximations were based on the assumption that electromagnetic waves interacted with items smaller than the wavelength, the atomic dimensions of the gasses in the upper ATMOSPHERE.

These conditions can be expressed as

1. $r \gg (\lambda/n)$
2. $r \ll (\lambda/n)$

With r the radius of the atomic dimension, λ wavelength, and n index of refraction.

The average SCATTERING CROSS SECTION: σ_R per particle as a function of wavelength is given by

$$\sigma_R(\lambda) = \frac{\left(128\pi^5\alpha^2\right)}{3\lambda^4} \times \frac{(6+3\sigma)}{(6-7\delta)}$$

$$\alpha = \frac{(n-1)}{2\pi N_0} \quad \text{for } \tilde{n} \to 1 \frac{\left(n^2-1\right)}{4\pi N_0}$$

where n index of refraction, N_0 the density of molecules per unit volume at standard pressure, temperature, and δ the DEPOLARIZATION factor.

For n approximately unity, the RAYLEIGH SCATTERING CROSS SECTION can be written as

$$\sigma_R(\lambda) = \frac{8\pi^3\left(n^2-1\right)^2}{3\lambda^4 N^2}$$

This shows the $1/\lambda^4$ dependency of the SCATTERING cross section, which can be recognized in many tissue spectra.

Under these assumptions Rayleigh scattering can describe the interaction of ULTRAVIOLET and visible light with the molecules of AIR in the atmosphere, for example, O_2, N_2, He, and CO_2. Also it can explain the interaction of INFRARED radiation with small aerosols, and MICROWAVE radiation with water droplets in clouds and RAIN. Some of the practical applications of Rayleigh theory are in weather radar and lidar for the remote detection of pollution in the air.

In matrix format, the Rayleigh scattering operator takes the form:

$$P(\theta) = \begin{bmatrix} \frac{1}{2}\left(1+\cos^2\theta\right) & -\frac{1}{2}\left(1-\cos^2\theta\right) & 0 & 0 \\ -\frac{1}{2}\left(1-\cos^2\theta\right) & \frac{1}{2}\left(1+\cos^2\theta\right) & 0 & 0 \\ 0 & 0 & \cos\theta & 0 \\ 0 & 0 & 0 & \cos\theta \end{bmatrix}.$$

Also see RUTHERFORD SCATTERING (see Figure S.21).

Note that this expression is for alpha particles with $Z_p = 2$. For projectiles with another charge Z_p, then you would multiply this expression by $Z_p^{2/4}$

$$\sigma = \pi Z^2 \left(\frac{ke^2}{KE}\right)^2 \left(\frac{1+\cos\theta}{1-\cos\theta}\right)$$

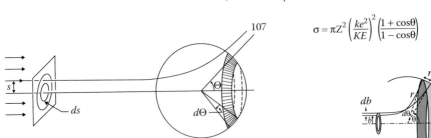

Figure S.21 Scattering cross section.

Scattering length, singlet

[nuclear] In the NUCLEON scattering process the interaction of the ENERGY stream with the discontinuity or perturbation can be viewed for ELEMENTARY PARTICLES such as proton—proton two-body interaction is defined by the strength of the interaction, or the likelihood of the event to take place and at what energy transfer, defined by the scattering length. During the interaction of particles with simple SPIN configuration the SCATTERING process is strictly defined in a uniform energy approach. For atoms colliding with relative momentum $p = k\hbar$, the scattering length (a_{scat}) is related to the s-WAVE PHASE shift δ_0 defined as $a_{scat} = -\lim_{k\to 0}\left(\tan(\delta_0/k)\right)$, where $k = 2\pi/\lambda$ is the wavenumber, λ the wavelength (deBroglie wavelength), and $\hbar = h/2\pi$; $h = 6.62606957 \times 10^{-34}$ m^{2}kg/s PLANCK's CONSTANT.

Scattering length, triplet

[nuclear] In the NUCLEON scattering process the interaction of the ENERGY stream with the discontinuity or perturbation can be viewed as nucleon—nucleon interaction that may take place with certain PROBABILITY, defined by the scattering length. During the interaction of nucleons with complex spin configuration the SCATTERING process needs to be defined with respect to the spins involved and the SPIN conversion probabilities. A nucleon with a spin TRIPLET STATE will have the probability for exchanging angular momentum in various formats and the energy configuration can be arranged in spin triplet channels. Each channel will be bound by a critical momentum for interaction. For resonant interaction this interaction length can be several hundred Bohr radii, yielding a high probability with significant exchange of energy, as a direct function of the interaction potential.

Scattering phase function

[astrophysics/astronomy, computational, optics] $p(\vec{s}, \vec{s'})$, is defined by the ANGLE (θ) between the direction of the rays incident on a sphere of medium ($\vec{s}$) with small but finite dimensions and the exiting, redirected rays with vector designation $\vec{s'}$: $\theta = \vec{s} \cdot \vec{s'}$. The PHASE function $p(\upsilon, \upsilon')$, is a function of the SCATTERING angle θ only, and can be expanded in a series of Legendre functions to the order n (which in fact represents the order of scattering events), where the following substitution has been made: $\upsilon = \cos\theta$; $p(\upsilon, \upsilon') = 4\pi\sum_0^\infty [1/(2n+1)]w_n p_n(\upsilon) p_n(\upsilon')$, where w_n is the scattering albedo, $w_0 = \mu_s/(\mu_a + \mu_s)$ the albedo of single scattering, with μ_s the scattering coefficient of the medium and μ_a the absorption coefficient (see Figure S.22).

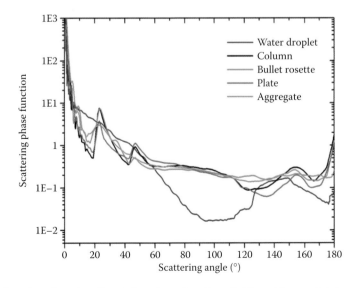

Figure S.22 Scattering phase function. Scattering phase function of different ice crystals in comparison to water droplets at wavelength of 700 nm and a particle dimension of 95 μm. (Courtesy of André Ehrlich, University of Leipzig, Leipzig, Germany.)

Scattering phase function, Henyey-Greenstein

[astrophysics/astronomy, biomedical, computational, optics] The Henyey–Greenstein scattering phase function has been shown to be a good approximation of the true PHASE function of biological tissue and is given by $P_{HG} = (1/4\pi)[(1-g^2)/(1-2g\mu^* + g^2)^{3/2}]$, where g is the mean cosine of the scattering ANGLE (anisotropy factor: $\langle\cos\theta\rangle$) and $\mu^* = \vec{s} \cdot \vec{s'} = \cos\theta$. A plot of the scattering phase function P_{HG} on a polar diagram represents the angular distribution of the scattering angle for an infinite medium and an infinite number of photons.

Schawlow, Arthur Leonard (1921–1999)

[optics, solid-state] Physicist from the United States. Arthur Schawlow was instrumental in the development of the predecessor to the LASER, the MASER (Microwave Amplification by Stimulated Emission of Radiation) introduced in 1954 in collaboration with CHARLES HARD TOWNES (1915–), for which they both received the Nobel Prize in Physics in 1964 (see Figure S.23).

(a)   (b)

Figure S.23 (a,b) Arthur Leonard Schawlow (1921–1999), photograph by Kenneth Sherwin and Frans Alkemade. (Courtesy of Stanford University, Stanford, CA.)

Scheele, Carl Wilhelm (1742–1786)

[chemical, optics] Researcher from Sweden, chemist and pharmacologist. The work by Scheele published in 1777, describes the discoloration of paper coated with silver chloride when exposed to sun-light. Forefather of PHOTOGRAPHY. Scheele was also credited for the discovery of oxygen (joint discovery) and documented barium, manganese, molybdenum and tungsten next to several other chemical compounds. His discovery of chlorine, derived from pyrolusite, lead to a systematic disinfection of water. The use of chlorine, next to bleaching (discovered also by Scheele) offered a SOLUTION to the eradication of the spread of several disease through drinking water (see Figure S.24).

Figure S.24 Carl Wilhelm Scheele (1742–1786).

Scherrer, Paul (1890–1969)

[atomic, nuclear] Swiss physicist working in diffraction in the beginning of the twentieth century. Scherrer's work included the mathematical description of the correlation between the PARTICLE configuration (i.e., shape), captured by the shape factor (K_{shape}), spacing of the scattering matrix ($\tau_{crystaline}$) and the angular distribution of the scatter of X-RAY radiation (θ) or Bragg ANGLE. The correlation is captured by Scherrer as a function of wavelength: $\tau_{crystaline} = K\lambda/\beta\cos\theta$, where β is the line-broadening of the probing ray at full-width half-maximum (FWHM). Particularly in X-ray diffraction used in crystallography the SHAPE FACTOR plays a crucial role and is usually smaller than 0.9. The boundary conditions for the Scherrer equation are nanometer range (<100 nm). The experimental verification was defined in the DEBYE-SCHERRER METHOD, which has led to naming the diffraction distribution the DEBYE–SCHERRER EQUATION on occasion (see Figure S.25).

(a)   (b)

Figure S.25 (a,b) Paul Scherrer (1890–1969). (a—Courtesy of ETH-Bibliothek Zurich, Switzerland; Bildarchiv: Com_XS129–02; b—Courtesy of Paul Sherrer Institute, Villigen, Switzerland.)

Schiff, Leonard Isaac (1915–1971)

[nuclear] Researcher from Germany involved with the photo-nuclear aspects of X-RAY imaging and specifically BREMSSTRAHLUNG. More specifically Schiff described the spectrum of X-ray diffraction PHOTON scattering (see Figure S.26).

Figure S.26 Leonard Isaac Schiff (1915–1971).

Schlieren imaging

[fluid dynamics, imaging] Described by AUGUST TOEPLER (1836–1912) in 1894. Method based on the DISPERSION of LIGHT resulting from density gradient and discontinuities. On transillumination of a medium optical density differences can be revealed based on BIREFRINGENCE that are indicative of temperature effects or composition by means of special filtering. The feature recognition aspects are based on the Cauchy theorem. The IMAGE formation is based on the angular deflection of a light ray when passing through a region characterized by boundaries between regions of different refractive index, as defined by Schell's law. The localized strain in the medium resulting from temperature effects or from deformation resulting from an applied torque can in this manner by revealed by Schlieren imaging and can be used for quality control and testing for integrity (see Figure S.27).

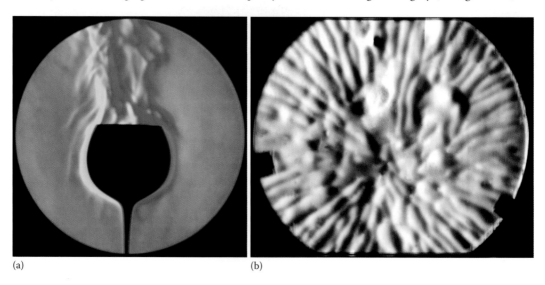

(a)   (b)

Figure S.27 (a) Schlieren imaging represented by the diffraction of light in the thermal convective flow above a heated object. (Courtesy of Andrew Davidhazy.) (b) Reflection "intensity" Schlieren for paraffin solution agitated by vibration.

Schlieren imaging for concentration

[biomedical, imaging, optics] Screening method for determination of molecular separation while applying the ULTRACENTRIFUGE principle. The general concept of LIGHT distortion resulting from density and associated index-of-refraction differences creates a diffraction pattern that illustrates the gradient in concentration of SOLUTE as a function of DISTANCE to the axis of rotation. The most obvious example of this is seen when adding sugar to water in a transparent beaker, showing the diffraction patterns (i.e., DISPERSION) in the SOLUTION as the solute migrates (see Figure S.28).

Figure S.28 Schlieren imaging for concentration, illustrating the dispersion in an inhomogeneous sugar solution.

Schmidt, Ernst Heinrich Wilhelm (1892–1975)

[fluid dynamics, general, thermodynamics] Engineer and physicist from Germany. Ernst Schmidt is best known for his contributions to the THERMODYNAMICS of flow as well as flow velocity profiling (see Figure S.29).

Figure S.29 Ernst Heinrich Wilhelm Schmidt (1892–1975). (Courtesy of Johanneum Lüneburg Informations system, Lüneburg, Germany.)

S

Schmidt number, (Sc = η/ρD_{AB})

[fluid dynamics] Dimensionless number defining the ratio of the momentum DIFFUSION to the molecular diffusion, where η is the viscosity, ρ the density and D_{AB} the diffusion coefficient for the constituents A and B. The number is named after the person who introduced the concept ERNST HEINRICH WILHELM SCHMIDT (1892–1975). The Schmidt number plays a role in identifying the EQUILIBRIUM STATE for OSMOTIC PRESSURE based on the transport of chemical species from the flow of BLOOD to the vascular (i.e., arterial/venous) WALL. For blood the Schmidt number is in the order Sc ~ 10^5.

Schottky, Walter Hermann (1886–1976)

[electronics, solid-state] German scientist who made several pivotal discoveries in solid-state ELECTRONICS and crystal structure. Schottky is also known for the invention of the screen-grid VACUUM tube. The screen-grid vacuum tube as introduced in 1915, is used to suppress the CATHODE ray emission flow of secondary electrons that are ejected from the ANODE on impact of the primary electrons and are hence a source of noise. Screen-grid vacuum tubes have a superior high frequency performance, with high gain. Walter Schottky is best known for the description of the solid-state ENERGY configuration that provided the tools for the development of the DIODE semiconductor. Of other theoretical description of the energy of a point-charge (with charge q) with respect to a flat metal surface: $E_{charge} = -q^2/16\pi\varepsilon_{EM0}r$, where r represents the DISTANCE from the surface, and the permittivity of free space: $\varepsilon_{EM0} = \varepsilon_0 = 8.85419 \times 10^{-12}\,\text{C}^2/\text{Nm}^2$ (see Figure S.30).

Figure S.30 Walter Hermann Schottky (1886–1976) in 1953. (Courtesy of Archiv der Max-Planck-Gesellschaft, Berlin-Dahlem, Germany.)

Schottky barrier

[electronics, solid-state] Metal-semiconductor ENERGY BARRIER for electron transport in a PN-JUNCTION configuration, often metal-silicon. The concept was introduced by WALTER HERMANN SCHOTTKY (1886–1976). The Schottky barrier may provide rectifying properties, converting alternating current in direct current, lending itself for the development of diodes. The Schottky barrier is defined based on the free-space SURFACE ENERGY when solving for a one-dimensional SCHRÖDINGER EQUATION for a single charged PARTICLE. The Schottky barrier representing the energy threshold that a charge needs to overcome to "conduct" through the barrier is defined as $E_{Schottky}(r) = b_{Barrier} - eEr - (q^2/4\pi\varepsilon_r\varepsilon_0 r)$, where $e = 1.60217657 \times 10^{-19}$ C is the electron charge (positive value), $E = V/d = F/q$ the applied electric field resulting from the externally applied POTENTIAL (V) spanning a DISTANCE d, b_{Barrier} the electric barrier height for the junction, often taken to be the work-function of the material (ϕ_{work}), the absolute permittivity of free space: $\varepsilon_0 = 8.85419 \times 10^{-12}$ C^2/Nm^2 and the RELATIVE PERMITTIVITY with respect to the material ε_r. The Schottky barrier fits in the Schrödinger equation as an operator as $(d^2/dr^2)\psi(r) = (2m/\hbar)E_{\text{Schottky}}(r)\psi(r)$, with m the particle mass, $\hbar = b/2\pi = 6.62606957 \times 10^{-34}$ m^{2}kg/s PLANCK'S CONSTANT, and $\psi(r)$ the wave-function. The forward voltage for the Schottky barrier is in the range of $0.15 - 0.45$ V (in comparison to the normal p-n silicon DIODE of $0.6 - 1.7$ V). Schottky barriers have a very fast response time. The metals used in the junction are for instance tungsten, chromium, molybdenum and platinum.

Schottky diode

[electronics, solid-state] DIODE based on the junction between a METAL and a semiconductor, thus creating an asymmetric ENERGY configuration. In comparison, the first PN-JUNCTION was created in 1939 as a forerunner to semiconductor ELECTRONICS.

Schottky effect

[electronics, solid-state] The application of an external electric field to a METAL in VACUUM will increase the current density of the electrons being released from the metallic surface when administering heat. Raising the temperature of metals can result in the emission of electrons, THERMIONIC EMISSION. Even though the vacuum forms an INSULATOR, the ENERGY BARRIER for electron release can still be approximated by the SCHOTTKY BARRIER.

Schriefer, Howard Lawrence (1948–)

[computational, general] Scientist from the United States with a special philosophy on force and ENERGY, called the GRAND UNIFIED THEORY, building on the work of Howard Mason Georgi III (1947–) and SHELDON LEE GLASHOW (1932–) published in 1974 (see Figure S.31).

Figure S.31 Howard Lawrence Schriefer (1948–).

S

Schriefer Unified Theory

[computational, general] Also referred to as a Grand Unified Theories. Unification of all theories, introduced by HOWARD LAWRENCE SCHRIEFER (1948–). In principle, the unified theories provides the basis for the formation of planets, satellites, next to continents on earths. The UNIFIED THEORY describes the operation of pulsars and how they are formed. It also provides a common GROUND for WAVE and PARTICLE theory. Furthermore, the GRAND UNIFIED THEORY postulates that time and temperature are inappropriate characteristics to be used in scientific descriptions due to their convoluted properties, as are their antecedents. It also provides a unique description for gravitational interaction. The Grand Unified Theories are for all means and purposes consistent with the Lorentz Law, AMPÈRE's Law and electromagnetic gauge invariance. The concept of unified theory is based on the unification of several electromagnetic theories by JAMES CLERK MAXWELL (1831–1879). The concept is based on the fact that the strong, weak and ELECTROMAGNETIC THEORY of nuclear forces do not share the inverse square law that applies to GRAVITATION and the strict formulation of conservation of charges. The "unified" process makes an attempt to bridge the differences between electromagnetic theory and gravitational theory. The unified theories incorporate a broader range of symmetries, extending beyond the coordinate invariance principles of ALBERT EINSTEIN (1879–1955), incorporating the electromagnetic gauge invariance. In the unified theory the concept of "symmetry" loses significance after developing the gauge- and gravitational forces in a series beyond the second iteration, symmetry is lost/broken. The unified theory introduced by Schriefer (*see* **GRAND UNIFIED THEORIES**).

Schrödinger, Erwin Rudolf Josef Alexander (1887–1961)

[atomic, computational, energy, general, mechanics, nuclear, quantum] Physicist from Austria who, inspired by the principle of the DE BROGLIE WAVE, introduced the relativistic concept (determined by PROBABILITY rather than cause-and-effect) of wave-mechanics; the SCHRÖDINGER EQUATION OF MOTION, or SCHRÖDINGER WAVE EQUATION (see Figure S.32).

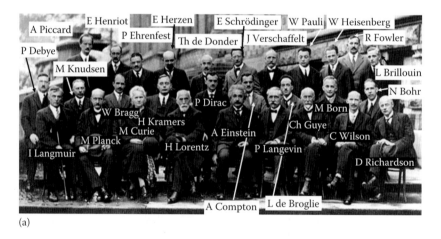

(a)

Figure S.32 Erwin Rudolf Josef Alexander Schrödinger (1887–1961) at the various Solvay conferences: (a) 1927.

(*Continued*)

(b)   (c)

Figure S.32 (Continued) Erwin Rudolf Josef Alexander Schrödinger (1887–1961) at the various Solvay conferences: (b) 1933 and (c) Erwin Schrödinger in 1933.

Schrödinger equation

[thermodynamics] *See* SCHRÖDINGER EQUATION OF MOTION.

Schrödinger equation of motion

[computational, nuclear, thermodynamics] Experiments performed in the early twentieth century gave rise to the notion that all particles in MOTION exhibit wavelike characteristics. The most formidable evidence came from the electron orbit model described by PRINCE LOUIS DE BROGLIE (1892–1987), requiring a standing WAVE to satisfy the filling of the various ORBITS. A PARTICLE moving in one dimension: $x-$direction, with mass: m, and with inherent kinetic ENERGY E and under a resident potential energy V, the SCHRÖDINGER WAVE EQUATION is defined as $(\partial^2\psi/\partial^2 x) + (8\pi^2 m/h^2)(E-V)\psi = 0$, where $h = 6.62606957 \times 10^{-34}$ m^{2}kg/s PLANCK'S CONSTANT, and Ψ is the wave-function for the particle in motion describing the PROBABILITY distribution for have a specific configuration at a specific location. The SCHRÖDINGER EQUATION defines the kinetic energy combined with the potential (also known as the Hamiltonian: H operator) of the wave function Ψ, which encompasses all the dynamic statistics about a system. The function Ψ is a SCALAR function with complex values: $(E-V)\psi = H\psi = -(ih/2\pi)(\partial\psi/\partial t) = (-h^2/8m)\nabla^2\psi + V(0,x)\psi$, where the Laplace operator represents the location derivative in second order: $\nabla^2 = (\partial^2/\partial x^2) + (\partial^2/\partial y^2) + (\partial^2/\partial z^2) = (\partial^2/\partial\theta^2) + (\partial^2/\partial r^2) + (\partial^2/\partial\phi^2)$. For the time-independent Schrödinger case, energy is derived using the operator $-ih\partial/2\pi\partial t$, with the kinetic energy defined by the square of the momentum operator: $ih\nabla^2/8m$. Using the boundary condition for the potential at $t = 0$: $V(0,x)$ and applying all the suitable boundary conditions, solving the Schrödinger differential equation generates a wave function Ψ which comprises all the characteristics and properties of the system. Alternatively, the Schrödinger equation can be expressed using the momentum of the particle, defined by $\breve{P}\psi(r,t) = -(ih/2\pi)\nabla^2\psi(r,t)$, where the energy is linked to the momentum as $E = \breve{P}^2/2m$; where $\breve{P}$ defines the Momentum operator; $\breve{P} = m\vec{v}$, for a mass traveling with velocity $\vec{v}$. There is a remarkable similarity with the energetic format of the Hamiltonian equation, describing the total energy ($KE + U = E$, the sum of kinetic [$KE = (1/2)mv^2 = p^2/2m$] and potential [U] energy) as $(1/2m)p^2 + U = E$ described by WILLIAM HAMILTON (1805–1865). This concept was adapted by ERWIN

SCHRÖDINGER (1887–1961) into a differential equation; the wave equation. The EQUATIONS OF MOTION in Hamiltonian space are $\dot{p}_j = -(\partial H/\partial q_j)$ and $\dot{q}_j = +(\partial H/\partial p_j)$, with $H(p,q) = \sqrt{(m^2 + p^2)}$ the Hamiltonian function of energy for a particle. Also known as the Schrödinger Equation (see Figure S.33).

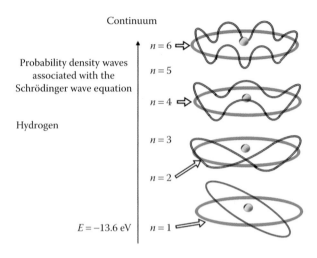

Continuum

Probability density waves
associated with the
Schrödinger wave equation

Hydrogen

$n = 6$

$n = 5$

$n = 4$

$n = 3$

$n = 2$

$E = -13.6$ eV $n = 1$

Figure S.33 Schrödinger motion.

Schrödinger Wave Equation

[computational, general, nuclear, thermodynamics] Mathematical description of the PROBABILITY of a phenomenon being at a certain place in a certain timeframe, expressed as $(1/2m)(i\hbar)^2 \{(d^2\Psi/dx^2) + (d^2\Psi/dy^2) + (d^2\Psi/dz^2)\} + U\Psi = -E\Psi$, with E is the total ENERGY of the phenomenon, (x, y, z) three-dimensional CARTESIAN COORDINATES, Ψ the WAVE function of the phenomenon, U is the potential energy, m the mass of the object, $\hbar = h/2\pi$, where $h = 4.13567 \times 10^{-15}$ eVs the Planck constant, or referred to by MAX KARL ERNST LUDWIG PLANCK (1858–1947) as "the QUANTUM of action."

Schrödinger's cat

[atomic, computational, energy, general, mechanics, nuclear, quantum] Paradox describing the fact that in quantum PHYSICS and WAVE MECHANICS all events are described in PROBABILITY of state. An event is not certain unless it is observed. The PARABOLA with the cat was introduced by ERWIN SCHRÖDINGER (1887–1961) in 1935. The interpretation of the Copenhagen description of QUANTUM MECHANICS left many questions in the interpretation of how reality and probability are not compatible in quantum physics. The cat anecdote describes how one event may control the outcome of another event without a definite cause and effect. The cat is supposedly locked in a box that contains a mechanism controlled by a nuclear disintegration. The mechanism is initiated by the DECAY of a RADIOACTIVE ISOTOPE such as uranium that will result in the registration by a GEIGER COUNTER which in turn engages a hammer that shatters a GLASS jar containing the poisonous hydrocyanic ACID. In case the uranium decays the cat will be dead after inspection of the cage when 1 h has lapsed, in case the ISOTOPE did not decay the cat will be alive. In QUANTUM mechanical terms the cat is bot alive and dead at the same time, whereas is classical terms the cat will be either alive or dead based on a more predictable cause–effect relationship, such as being confined with a mouse for 1 h (see Figure S.34).

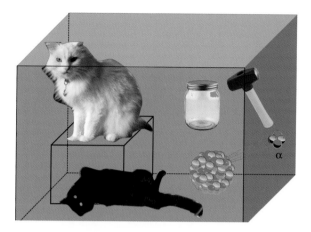

Figure S.34 Concept of probability explained by Schrödinger's cat; which decay event will make the hammer strike the glass jar which will release the poisonous gas, there will be a probability associated with this occurrence.

Schuster, Arthur, Sir (1851–1934)

[astrophysics/astronomy, computational, optics] German physicist who provided critical steps in the development of a computational mechanism to describe the diffuse propagation of LIGHT through turbid media. Schuster worked on X-RAY imaging and OPTICS as well as SPECTROSCOPY. The works of KARL SCHWARZSCHILD (1873–1916) and SUBRAHMANYAN CHANDRASEKHAR (1910–1995) where inspired by his efforts on the mathematical description of the propagation of light through an attenuating and scattering medium. The culmination of Dr. Schuster's work on optics is found in the EQUATION OF RADIATIVE TRANSFER, pertaining to both astronomy and BIOMEDICAL OPTICS. Schuster also provided elementary contributions to the discovery of the electron. In this work he provided a mechanism to derive the ratio of charge to mass for CATHODE RAYS, discriminating protons from electrons, later formalized by ERNEST RUTHERFORD (1871–1937) (see Figure S.35).

Figure S.35 Sir Arthur Schuster (1851–1934) in 1912, by William Orpen.

Schwarzschild, Karl (1873–1916)

[astronomy, biomedical, computational, general, optics] Astrophysicist and mathematician from the Prussian Empire (Germany). Karl Schwarzschild worked parallel with SIR FRANZ ARTHUR FRIEDRICH SCHUSTER (1851–1934) on the theoretical description of RADIATIVE TRANSFER with respect to the RADIATION emitted from stars traversing a UNIVERSE filled with dust, gasses and planets, published in 1905 and 1906, respectively. Karl Schwarzschild used photographic recordings for QUANTIFICATION of the brightness of stars and deriving the optical path for reaching EARTH. The HEAT TRANSFER and emission of radiation from stars and the interaction with cosmic material forms the basis of BIOMEDICAL OPTICS in the EQUATION OF RADIATIVE TRANSFER, also found as Radiative Transfer Equation (*also see* **BIOMEDICAL OPTICS**) (see Figure S.36).

Figure S.36 Karl Schwarzschild (1873–1916).

Scuba gear

[biomedical, fluid dynamics] Apparatus used for deep-sea diving that will provide an oxygen supply under controlled circumstances. The equipment concept was described by the French author Jules Verne (1828–1905) in "Vingt Mille Lieues sous les mers," 1870 (*Twenty Thousand Leagues Under the Sea*). The Jules Verne concept was based on the explorations by earlier engineers and inventors such as the British engineer, John Smeaton, who invented the AIR pump in 1771. Another self-sustaining breathing device was constructed in 1825 by the English inventor William James using a copper helmet attached to a vessel (belt) filled with compressed air. Another Englishman, Henry Fleuss, conceived a recirculation device infusing pure Oxygen into the respiratory system in 1876, which made him fall victim to the fact that pure Oxygen deregulates the human breathing mechanism. The inhalation of the pure oxygen killed him as a result of the biofeedback deregulation. The human RESPIRATION is regulated by chemical sensors that respond to dissolved Carbon Dioxide; the reaction of WATER (H_2O) with CO_2 forms H_2CO_3 (carbonic ACID), which has an inherent acidity. The lack of CO_2 makes the autonomic nervous system shut down the desire to inhale fresh air. In 1873 an entirely new approach resulted from the work of Benoît Rouquayrol and Auguste Denayrouze resulting in a rigid diving suit with a regular air supply. The concept was made of METAL and weighed approximately 100 kg. Further improvements resulted from the efforts by engineer and sensationalist Harry Houdini in the year 1921 (born Ehrich Weiss 1874–1926 in Budapest, Hungary). The first metallic caissons used for underwater exploration were cumbersome and did not allow free movement. These constructions used an air-hose that lead to the surface of the water requiring manual labor to PUMP fresh air to the diver. In 1943 the French naval officer Jacques-Yves Cousteau (1910–1997) and his fellow inventor and engineer Émile Gagnan (1900–1979) made a breakthrough contribution to the work of several predecessors and contemporaries in the introduction of the compressed air breathing devices for extended underwater exploration: the "Aqualung." Jacques Cousteau is mostly known for his oceanographic explorations, documentaries and nature conservation efforts pertaining to the marine flora and fauna (see Figure S.37).

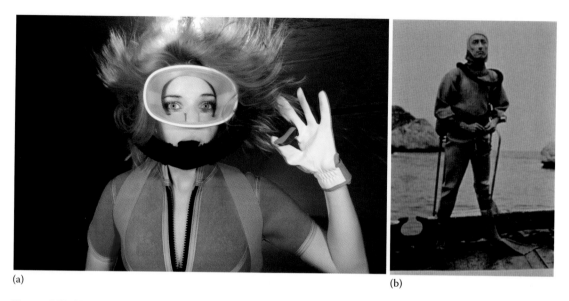

(a)   (b)

Figure S.37 (a) Diver in scuba gear and (b) Jacques-Yves Cousteau (1910–1997). (Courtesy of the Cousteau Society, Paris, France.)

Second

[general] Measurement of time; Definition: SI: based on the earth's revolution in 24 h, originally introduced as the fraction of the average length of a day as $1/60 * 1/60 * 1/24 *$ mean duration of a day averaged over a year. The current definition of the second is the duration of 9,192,631,770 oscillations of the Cesium-133 ATOM between the lowest two ENERGY states, accurate to 1 in 10^{13}. This standard is referred to as the "ATOMIC CLOCK," introduced in 1967 (see Figure S.38).

Figure S.38 The second on an analog time keeping piece.

Second law

[thermodynamics] *See* SECOND LAW OF THERMODYNAMICS.

Second law, Kelvin–Planck's statement

[thermodynamics] "It is unachievable to build a fully functional ENGINE that is solely based on the extraction of heat from a reservoir at a single temperature while converting all the acquired heat perfectly into MECHANICAL ENERGY." Introduced by LORD KELVIN (1824–1907).

S

Second law of Faraday

[Atomic, general, nuclear, quantum, thermodynamics] "The total mass of SOLUTE liberated from a SOLUTION is proportional to the total quantity of charge traversing through a circuit that has the solution as the integral part of the sole current loop" (*see* FARADAY, SECOND LAW OF).

Second law of thermodynamics

[general] "It is unachievable to build a fully functional ENGINE that is solely based on the extraction of heat from a reservoir at a single temperature while converting all the acquired heat perfectly into MECHANICAL ENERGY." The change in ENTROPY (S) of all systems involved in a process will always be positive: $\Delta S \geq 0$, noting that for an ideal (theoretical case) reversible process the entropy will remain unchanged (*see* THERMODYNAMICS, SECOND LAW OF).

Second law of thermodynamics, Carathéodory's statement of the

[computational, thermodynamics] Axiomatic expression by the Greek mathematician CONSTANTINE CARATHÉODORY (1873–1950) with respect to the subsystems with equal or less parameters and equal or less data-points/coordinates expressed in 1910 pertaining to the SECOND LAW OF THERMODYNAMICS, centered around PFAFFIAN differential equations eliminating the need for imaginary engines to compensate for deviations resulting from the improbability of the "perpetuum mobile," based on geometric formulation. The basis of the Carathéodory's theorem is the fact that "In the proximity of any EQUILIBRIUM STATE of a system (composed of any number of thermodynamic coordinates, and valid in any geometric configurations), there will be states that cannot be achieved through reversible adiabatic processes."

Second law of thermodynamics, Clausius formulation

[general, thermodynamics] Expression of the lack of 100% efficiency in ENERGY conversion, similar to the SECOND LAW, KELVIN–PLANCK'S STATEMENT. RUDOLF JULIUS EMANUEL CLAUSIUS (1822–1888) formulated that a refrigeration system cannot transfer heat from the cold to the hot reservoir without the use of an external source and hence requires external energy.

Second order differential equations

[computational] Differential equations that include derivatives up to the second order, generally either time or location specific.

Second order phase transition

[computational, thermodynamics] At the critical point, where the critical temperature and critical pressure are reached, the PHASE TRANSITION between LIQUID and VAPOR anomalous behavior is observed in the thermodynamic parameters such as SPECIFIC HEAT and compressibility due to the fact that the density of the liquid and vapor phase at the raised temperature and pressure has reached equilibrium, they are identical. At the critical point the correlation length associated with the physical phenomena has exceeded the standard length (e.g., intermolecular DISTANCE) for the normal phase transition (see Figure S.39).

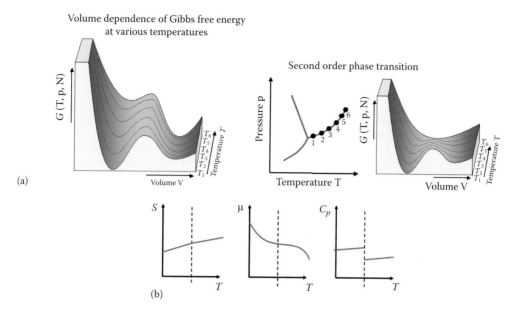

Figure S.39 (a,b) Diagram outlining the configuration of a second-order phase transition.

Second-generation of matter

[atom, high-energy, nuclear, solid-state] ELEMENTARY PARTICLES discovered in a certain order, as outlined under Quarks. Quarks (CHARM, strangeness); Leptons (MUON, μ-neutrino).

Sediment equilibrium

[biomedical, chemical, mechanics] Mechanism of action used to determine molecular weight of the SOLUTE under ULTRACENTRIFUGE treatment. At the point of equilibrium between DIFFUSION and sedimentation the concentration $[C]$ will depend on the DISTANCE (r) to the axis of rotation: $[C_{r_i}]$ as a function of ANGULAR VELOCITY ω. The MOLECULAR WEIGHT (M) distribution under ABSOLUTE TEMPERATURE (T) and rotational angular velocity: ω, with the assigned partial specific volume of the solute $\bar{V}$ expressed as $M(r) = RT \ln([C_{r_2}]/[C_{r_1}])/[(1-\rho\bar{V})\omega^2(r_2^2 - r_1^2)]$, where R is the UNIVERSAL GAS CONSTANT, and ρ is the SOLVENT density based on the dissolved constituent. Under conditions of very large molecular weight (i.e., MACROMOLECULES) the sedimentation time duration will reach equilibrium after an extensive period of slow rotational centrifuge revolution, and can take in access of 24 h in certain cases.

Sediment equilibrium in a density gradient

[biomedical, chemical, mechanics] Mechanism of action used to determine molecular weight of a binary solutions under ULTRACENTRIFUGE treatment. Solutions where the SOLUTE with low MOLECULAR WEIGHT (M) has a close to equivalent weight to the SOLVENT it will tend to segregate as a function of DISTANCE to the rotational axis (r), which can be quantified when equilibrium is established. Due to the equivalence the solute will be buoyant and segregation will depend on the density gradient in the medium: $d\rho/dr$, where ρ is the solvent density based on the dissolved constituent, with a band-width per concentration that is identified by the one-dimensional standard deviation σ. The molecular weight (M) distribution under ABSOLUTE TEMPERATURE (T) and rotational ANGULAR VELOCITY: ω, with the assigned partial specific volume of the solute $\bar{V}$ expressed as $M = RT/[\bar{V}\omega^2(d\rho/dr)\sigma^2 r]$, where R is the UNIVERSAL GAS CONSTANT.

Sedimentation velocity

[biomedical, chemical, mechanics] Used in the process describing the rate of change expressed by the sedimentation coefficient: $\zeta = (dr/dt)/\omega^2 r$, with ρ the SOLVENT density based on the dissolved constituent, the DISTANCE to the axis of rotation r and rotational ANGULAR VELOCITY ω, and dr/dt the SOLUTE sedimentation velocity. This mechanism of action is used to determine molecular weight of the solute under ULTRACENTRIFUGE treatment. The MOLECULAR WEIGHT M of the solute follows from $M = RT\zeta/(1-\bar{V}\rho)$, where R is the UNIVERSAL GAS CONSTANT, ρ is the solvent density and D is the DIFFUSION coefficient.

Seebeck, Thomas Johann (1770–1831)

[energy, thermodynamics] Scientist from the Prussian Empire/Estonia (Russia ?). Thomas Seebeck discovered in 1821 that a compass needle would be deflected by a closed loop formed by two different metals joined in two places, with a temperature difference between the junctions. Additional work by Thomas Seebeck is in the precursor to the discovery of PHOTOGRAPHY. Seebeck described the change in appearance of silver-chloride under the influence of LIGHT in 1810 (*see* LOUIS-JACQUES-MANDÉ DAGUERRE [1771–1851]) (see Figure S.40).

Figure S.40 Thomas Johann Seebeck (1770–1831). (Courtesy of Hans Wahl, Anton Kippenberg: Goethe und seine Welt, Insel-Verlag, Leipzig 1932 S.204.)

Seebeck effect

[electromagnetism, thermodynamics] The conversion of temperature differences directly into ELECTRICITY. The voltage (electromotive force: EMF: V_{EMF}) produced between two junctions is proportional to the temperature difference between those two point: $V_{EMF} = S_{Seebeck}\left(T_{high} - T_{low}\right)$, where the coefficient $S_{Seebeck}$ represents the influence between the two media in contact on the voltage difference, which relates to the PELTIER COEFFICIENT (Π_j) as $TS_{Seebeck} = \Pi_j$. The EMF produces a current which can be registered by a GALVANOMETER. This effect was described in 1826 by THOMAS SEEBECK (1770–1831) (*also see* PELTIER EFFECT).

Segrè, Emilio Gino (1905–1989)

[nuclear] Physicist from Italy. Segrè received the Nobel Prize in Physics in 1959 for his contributions and discoveries in PARTICLE physics, including the discovery of the ELEMENTS technetium and astatine, as well as his work on the antiproton (subatomic antiparticle) with Owen Chamberlain (1920–2006) and Clyde Wiegand (1915–1996) in 1955 (see Figure S.41).

Figure S.41 Emilio Gino Segrè (1905–1989).

Seismic

[acoustics, general, geophysics, mechanics] Physical phenomena associated with shallow earthquakes causing surface faulting (i.e., instability or mode of VIBRATION) or the damped oscillatory GROUND movements with destructive effects resulting from a major EARTHQUAKE. Seismic models rely on finite ELEMENT reconstructive structural and stratigraphic representation. Here stratigraphy pertains to the study of the composition, relative ages with associated historical value, as well as the distribution of layers of sedimentary rock (i.e., strata), combined with the interpretation of strata to uncover the Earth's geological history (see Figure S.42).

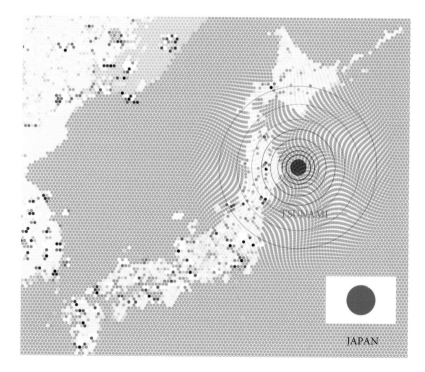

Figure S.42 Graphical representation of the seismic concept.

Seismic acoustic imaging

[acoustics] Large-scale imaging of predominantly geological and aquatic features by means of artificially induced seismic ACTIVITY, for example, explosions or impact collisions (either using a heavy weight or compressed AIR). The induced pressure wave resulting from the impulse source, acts as an imaging source. Using the obtained FREQUENCY SPECTRUM assumptions can be made about the elastic modulus distribution of the volume under interrogation, which can be used to define the WAVE-EQUATION responses and hence use time-of-flight of echoes for imaging purposes, including compensations for SCATTERING resulting from inhomogeneities and discontinuities. This type of imaging is used in the localization of water sources or OIL pockets (e.g., SEISMIC prospecting) (see Figure S.43).

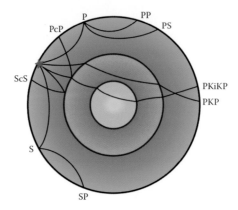

Figure S.43 Seismic imaging diagram, based on S-wave and P-wave; Cross section of Earth with different seismic paths with reflection and refraction on the layers. Mechanism using two or more locations where seismic activity is recorded to triangulate the source of the seismic activity, which could be man-made such as underground nuclear explosions.

Seismic wave

[acoustics, general, geophysics, mechanics] Deformation WAVE resulting from natural forces such as volcanic eruptions, METEOR impacts, tsunamis, earthquakes, next to man-made impulse forces such as explosions. Underground nuclear tests are easily identified at great DISTANCE based on seismic wave propagation, specifically using triangulation from several detection bases (see Figure S.44).

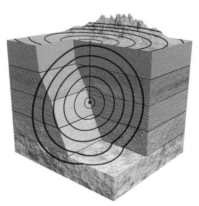

Figure S.44 Diagram of Seismic wave propagation.

Seismic wave, dissipative effects

[acoustics, geophysics, mechanics] The propagation of seismic waves resulting from earthquakes and other natural (e.g., volcanic eruptions) and man-made phenomena (e.g., explosions, fracking) is a perturbation that is subject to a broad frequency spectrum, and additionally the attenuation parameters with respect to the damped waves are a function of the frequency and local geological material configuration (e.g., visco-elastic behavior). The attenuation is generally described by an elastic—ENERGY dissipation factor defined by the concept "q," where $q = \Delta E / 2\pi E_{max}$, where E_{max} represents the maximum energy contained in the SEISMIC event and ΔE is the loss of INTERNAL ENERGY during one cycle of the mechanical/acoustic perturbation. The full range of frequencies associated with mechanical oscillations of the EARTH'S CRUST can be described by extending from 0.0005 Hz (period greater than 2000 s, ~35 min) to approximately 100 Hz (period 0.01 s). The other identifier related to the seismic dissipative effects is the QUALITY FACTOR: $Q \equiv 1/q$. The attenuation as a function of FREQUENCY ($\nu = \omega/2\pi$; ω the ANGULAR FREQUENCY) can generally approximated by a POWER LAW, providing the equivalence: $q \propto \omega^{-\alpha_{acc}}$, where generally $\alpha_{acc} < 0.5$ is the model factor for the phenomenon. This indicates that higher mechanical displacement frequencies will DECAY faster than low frequency patterns. The anelastic and elastic properties of the earth's crust are a function of the local geological formations and configurations. Geological pattern may be rock formations, clay and water; all of which may be function of depth. These differences in related and associated Young's Moduli will result in dispersive effects. The frequency dependency is further complicated by the fact that the seismic waves can be composed of spheroidal modes (large scale) expressed in propagating SURFACE WAVES, or normal mode standing waves. When these modes reach discontinuities at an ANGLE the WAVE will refract, similar to optical electromagnetic waves. The FREQUENCY SPECTRUM of the attenuation can be represented in "frequency modes," or "angular (frequency) modes" (angular modes is the preferred term). The attenuation as a function of angular mode can be written with local radial shear and bulk moduli: $\mu_{shear,0}$, respectively $K_{bulk,0}$; next to the radial attenuation for shear, respectively bulk: $q_{\mu,shear,0}$, respectively $q_{\kappa,bulk,0}$: $q = \int_0^R (\kappa_0 q_{\kappa,bulk,0} K_\kappa + \mu_{shear,0} q_{\mu,shear,0} K_{\mu shear}) dr$, where R is the earth's radius and K_κ respectively $K_{\mu shear}$ are the bulk and shear kernels, the mathematical vector ELEMENTS that provide an indication of discontinuity or deviation from a "smooth" pattern. For long period seismic waves, greater than 300 s, the model factor decreases and eventually becomes negative. The DISPERSION between waves with different frequencies can be captured by the wave propagation velocity (v_{ω_i}) in the form: $v_{\omega_2}/v_{\omega_1} = 1 + (q/\pi)\ln(\omega_2/\omega_1)$ in case the model factor is zero ($\alpha_{acc} = 0$), which describes phenomena occurring in the lower mantle. For the upper mantle the model factor is generally nonzero and the dispersion becomes: $v_{\omega_2}/v_{\omega_1} = 1 + [q(\omega_1)/2]\cot(\alpha_{acc}\pi/2)[1 - (\omega_2/\omega_1)^{\alpha_{acc}}]$.

Seismology

[energy, fluid dynamics, general, geophysics, mechanics] Field of PHYSICS dealing with physical phenomena in the solid part of the PLANET considered to be behaving as a LIQUID. The process of earthquakes and WAVE propagation (e.g., SEISMIC WAVES) falls under seismology. Additionally the sonic probing of the planets crust is also part of seismology, in this case small explosions generate a sonic (i.e., acoustic) wave that can be used to IMAGE the structural composition of the solid surface layer of the planet in a manner similar to ULTRASONIC IMAGING in biology and MEDICINE. The formation and propagation of TSUNAMI waves in water beds also falls under seismology.

Seismometer

[acoustics, general, geophysics, mechanics] Device used to register oscillations in the EARTH'S CRUST. Specific applications are in earthquakes, using the Richter scale as an indicator of MAGNITUDE on a logarithmic basis (see Figure S.45).

(a)   (b)

Figure S.45 (a,b) Seismometer.

Selectin

[biomedical, chemical] Molecular chains that provide the ADHESION of the surface of the membrane of leukocytes (their host environment) and endothelial cells that have been activated for construction in vascular assembly and healing. The main binding attraction of the selectin (glycol-) protein is to carbohydrates. Selectins form a specific class in biology providing cell-to-cell interaction. This interaction can be divided in four types of receptors: CADHERINS, selectins, INTEGRINS and IMMUNOGLOBULIN SUPERFAMILY (*see* CADHERINS).

Selection rule and

[atomic, computational, nuclear, quantum] (*see also* angular momentum conservation, parity conservation) Quantum-mechanical rules setting the stage for ENERGY balance pertaining to CONSERVATION OF ANGULAR MOMENTUM and conservation of PARITY in electron orbital configuration. The selection rules form the guide-book to electron transitions, as well as the PROBABILITY of each potential transition. The notation and rules are slightly different between atomic transitions and those for molecular excitation and DECAY. Two phenomena stand out in the electron transition: the PASCHEN BACK EFFECT and the ZEEMAN EFFECT. The Zeeman effect is generally determined by the selection rules, with specific selection rules applied to the NORMAL ZEEMAN EFFECT and the ANOMALOUS ZEEMAN EFFECT. Most orbital transitions are forbidden by selection rules. The standing order of selection rules are as follows. The value of the magnetic moment QUANTUM NUMBER ℓ changes in unity: $\Delta\ell = \pm 1$ and the MAGNETIC moment remains unchanged or changes by unity: $\Delta m = 0, \pm 1$. For the normal Zeeman effect: $\Delta L = 0, \pm 1$, however there is no ALLOWED TRANSITION that involves $L = 0$ to $L = 0$; $\Delta M_L = 0, \pm 1$; $\Delta S = 0$; and $\Delta M_S = 0$, where L represents the angular momentum of the ORBITAL ANGULAR MOMENTUM of the electron, S represents the ELECTRON SPIN (which cannot change, since that would mean a reversal of rotation direction), J represents the TOTAL ANGULAR MOMENTUM quantum number (a transition that involves $J = 0$ to $J = 0$ is also not allowed), respectively M_L the magnetic moment and M_S the SPIN moment, and in reference n is the primary quantum number. Some of the rules find their origin in the RUSSELL–SAUNDERS APPROXIMATION OF ELECTRON COUPLING.

Selectively permeable

[biomedical] The restrictive transport of molecules and particles through the membrane of CELL based on charge polarity and/or shape and size (more specifically pertaining to MOLECULAR WEIGHT or macroscopically to the chemical "nanoparticle").

Self-avoiding walk

[computational] In computational methods the SOLUTION is derived for a process involving each point in the process only once, meaning that the path in n-dimensional space never intersects in the steps in the mathematical algorithm. This process resembles a very tightly organized maze or LATTICE. The process is used in simulation techniques, more prevalent in for-instance Monte-Carlo simulations and Java programming. Expressed in matrix format this would entail a one-sided matrix, specifically if the matrix would be symmetric. For an $n \times m$ matrix the computational process can migrate from one diagonal to the other diagonal. When numerically moving in the positive direction there will be a total of $\left(n + m/n, m\right)$ different potential paths available (see Figure S.46).

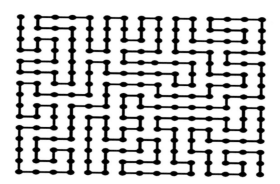

Figure S.46 Diagram illustrating the concept of Self-avoiding walk.

Self-consistent field

[atomic, computational] Method used to calculate the three-dimensional potential distribution for an electron cloud also referred to as the Hartree–Fock method.

Self-energy, coulomb

[nuclear] In the computation of the Coulomb ENERGY ($E_{Coulomb}$) with respect to the electron potentials ($V(\vec{r})$) of an electron (e) distribution with charge density ($\rho(\vec{r})$) over space ($\vec{r}$) the total Coulomb energy representing the total energy between the protons of the NUCLEUS is given by $E_{Coulomb} = (1/2)e\int_0^\infty \rho(\vec{r})V(\vec{r})4\pi r^2 dr = 1/8\pi\int_0^\infty \left(\varepsilon(\vec{r})\right)^2 4\pi r^2 dr$, where $\varepsilon(\vec{r})$ is the local electric field. The SOLUTION is proportional to r^4 inside the nucleus and r^{-2} outside. The self-energy is the Coulomb energy of a single isolated PROTON with its WAVE-function spread-out over the entire volume of the nucleus.

Self-excited vibration

[computational, dynamics, fluid dynamics, general, mechanics] In contrast to forced vibrations the driving mechanism comes from within the system, maintaining the MOTION with INTERNAL ENERGY. The OSCILLATION frequency is thus not linked to a driving oscillation frequency. The phenomenon is described by the EQUATION OF MOTION $(m(d^2x/dt^2) + c(dx/dt) + kx = 0)$, where m is the mass of the oscillating object, x the displacement, k the spring constant, $d^2x/dt^2 = a$ the acceleration, and $c = $ const representing the

predictable pattern of temporal changes in boundary conditions, including density, for instance COMPLI-
ANCE) as a homogeneous SOLUTION that however is unstable. Examples of self-excited vibration are the
hysteretic whirl, and pulsatile longitudinal loading. Another example is found in the FLUID motion of an
enclosed rotor or rotor-axis.

Self-induced electromotive force

[general] The response in induced electro-motive-force voltage resulting from a change in a CURRENT (I) in a
circuit that has a coil as a component as defined by LENZ'S LAW. The induced rate of change in the MAGNETIC
FIELD resulting from the change in current inflicts its own emf. The self-induced EMF will be opposite the
naturally occurring EMF resulting from external sources: $\varepsilon_{EMF} = -L_{ind}(dI/dt)$, where L_{ind} is the coefficient
of self-inductance, a proportionality factor.

Self-inductance (L_{ind})

[electromagnetism, general] Proportionality that indicates the readiness of the MAGNETIC FLUX (Φ_m) to follow the change in current (I): $N_{coil}\Phi_m = L_{ind}I$, where N_{coil} represents the loops of the coil.

Semiconductors

[atomic, general, nuclear] Material made of ELEMENTS with specific ELECTRON configuration, for instance
crystalline structures consisting of, but not limited to Galena, Silicon, Galium or Germanium. An ATOM
has the electrons arranged according to the BOHR ATOMIC MODEL with electrons in specific allowed ENERGY
LEVELS or ORBIT SHELLS. In comparison with either INSULATOR or CONDUCTOR the electron configuration
falls between these two. In an insulator the CONDUCTION BAND containing FREE ELECTRONS is unpopulated
and separated by a forbidden gap from the VALENCE BAND, whereas in conductor configuration the valence
band is overlapping the conduction band, hence populating the conduction mechanism of action with free
electrons. In electron device fabrication the concept of DOPING refers to the introduction of foreign atoms
into the LATTICE structure or random atomic structure of the semiconductor decreasing the gap between
the conduction band and the valence band, hence lowering the ENERGY requirements to initiate conduction.
Two kinds of doping can be used: N-TYPE referring to the introduction of an atom with an excess odd
number of valence electrons (for instance, arsenic with five valence electrons) which can be transferred to
the conduction band of the semiconductor atoms. The other doping is P-TYPE, referring to a deficiency in
electrons (i.e., hole) in the valence band, such as three valence electrons in GALLIUM, which will retrieve
loosely bound electrons for instance from the semiconductor Silicon. Both n-type and p-type doped semiconductors create an adjustable conductor, which can be turned into a conductor by an externally applied
electric field. In electronic device design p-type and n-type materials are matched in various combinations:
pn-JUNCTION, and sandwich structures: pnp, and npn and the like. In the energetic configuration the p and
n structure are separated by a DEPLETION LAYER that forms a transition between the energy levels in the
respective media. These combinations can create a DIODE or TRANSISTOR respectively and more complex
INTEGRATED CIRCUITS.

S

Semipermeable membrane

[biomedical, chemical, thermodynamics] Membrane that will permit selective transportation of ions and molecules based on charge and size respectively or combined (see Figure S.47).

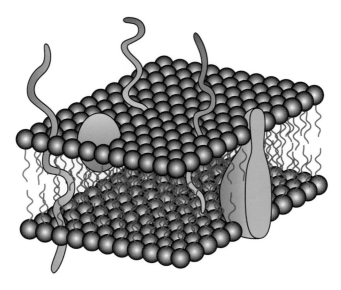

Figure S.47 Semipermeable membrane.

Separation boundary layer

[fluid dynamics] In fluid flow the LAMINAR FLOW may be disturbed by surface features with respect to the flow lumen that cause TURBULENCE that can be confined to a layer that is attached to the surface starting at the "point of separation" at the WALL. The flow outside the separation layer will maintain the original laminar profile and can be initiated at an abrupt change in radius or localized attachments, such as rust or plaque (biological vascular atherosclerosis).

Separation of variables

[computational, nuclear] Mathematical method for solving convoluted expressions, that use more than one dependent variable by separating the dependent variables out as independent variables. In spherical coordinates this yields: $\Psi(r,\theta,\phi) = R(r)\Theta(\theta)\Phi(\phi)$, giving three functions that can be solved independently, in this case with respect to radius (r), azimuth ANGLE (θ) and ZENITH ANGLE (ϕ).

Sextant

[computational, general, geophysics] Instrument used by sailors in the late seventeenth and most of the eighteenth century for navigation at sea. The sextant can determine the ANGLE between two points in a distant field, such as celestial objects and when the location of one of the objects is known as a function of time, the other object can provide the mechanism for determining the orientation as well as latitude and longitude of the location from which the MEASUREMENT is made. The device uses two mirrors that can be used to merge (superposition) the images of two objects by adjusting the angle of the second MIRROR, yielding the angle of the second object (e.g., the SUN) with respect to the first (i.e., the horizon).

The accuracy of the sextant is 10 s, where a degree is subdivided in 60 minutes and a minute in angle is subdivided in 60 s (see Figure S.48).

Figure S.48 Sextant.

Shadowgraph method

[acoustics, fluid dynamics, optics] Imaging method that uses the optical BIREFRINGENCE in a medium to indicate temporal and spatial gradients and discontinuities. The imaging mechanism relies primarily on transmission of LIGHT, and is used to highlight TURBULENCE and Mach-lines in fluid-flow with respect to steady-state or moving objects. Acoustic WAVE propagation can this way by illustrated due to the density gradient for the through and crest regions (*also see* SCHLIEREN IMAGING) (see Figure S.49).

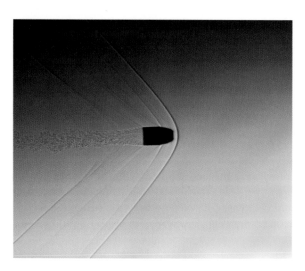

Figure S.49 Shadowgraph from a flying bullet, using the birefringence of the Mach-line edge of the wave-front.

Shaft horsepower

[fluid dynamics] The power produced by the shaft of a PUMP, or PROPELLER after the transferal by a gear system from the ENGINE classified by engine horsepower (the power output of the engine itself). Even though horsepower is not a standard unit it is still used in general descriptive specification, such as for a car, boat or compressor. The conversion from HORSEPOWER (hp) to the SI unit Watt is: 1 hp = 0.745699872 kW. Also referenced as break-horsepower.

Shallow-water tides

[fluid dynamics] Tidal movement in shallow seas and estuaries. The movement of water in shallow seas is hardly affected by the gravitational influences from the SUN and MOON as in the deep water TIDAL MOTION described by PIERRE-SIMON DE LAPLACE (1749–1827) in 1775 when he developed the dynamic theory of tides, in follow-up on the work by DANIEL BERNOULLI (1700–1782) in 1740. In shallow seas and estuaries the tides are a fluid-dynamic response to the deep-water tides based on restrictive flow due to a gradient in water level at the inflow and outflow point(s) with respect to deep sea tidal motion. Tides are WAVE that conform to special formulations of the WAVE-EQUATION, where the solar influence is strictly periodic (semidiurnal; twice daily), however the Moon will provide a modulation effect. Water is considered shallow when the depth is less than one twenty-fifth of the perceived tidal wavelength. Normal SURFACE WAVES can be represented by a PARTICLE at the surface moving in a circular pattern, however for shallow alter this motion becomes elliptical (see Figure S.50).

Figure S.50 Shallow water tides in Cornwall England, Polperro harbour.

Shannon, Claude Elwood (1916–2001)

[computational, electronics, imaging, theoretical] Mathematician and electronic engineer from the United States. Claude Shannon is best known for his SAMPLING theorem, also known as the Shannon–Nyquist theorem, or plain Nyquist theorem. Claude Shannon may be considered as one of the initial explorers into the concept of information theory. Shannon was also a cryptographer (*also see* **Harry Nyquist** [1889–1976]) (see Figure S.51).

Figure S.51 Claude Elwood Shannon (1916–2001). (Courtesy of Bell Labs, Murray Hill, NJ, USA.)

Shannon entropy (H_S)

[imaging, theoretical] Measure of randomness and uncertainty in a parameter (χ) observed in a state-space coordinate system (Ω), expressed as $H_S(\chi) = -\int_\Omega p(\chi)\log p(\chi)d\chi$, where $p(\chi)$ defines the PROBABILITY density function of the variable χ. The Shannon entropy is used in IMAGE processing, specifically with respect to image registration. Also referred to as DIFFERENTIAL ENTROPY.

Shannon sampling law

[computational, thermodynamics] *See* **Nyquist–Shannon sampling theorem.**

Shannon sampling theorem

[computational, thermodynamics] *See* **Nyquist–Shannon sampling theorem.**

Shape factor

[atomic, imaging, nuclear] Descriptive form without specific defining magnitudes that relate to a specific functional purpose. Frequently represented by DIMENSIONLESS NUMBERS. In SIGNAL processing the shape-factor of a band-pass filter provides a spectral format, while in X-RAY crystallography the shape factor describes the correlation between the X-ray diffraction pattern and the crystallite structures; in fluid-dynamics this defines the BOUNDARY LAYER geography. In IMAGE analysis the shape factor determines the "compactness" of a shape. One example is the ratio of the area of a random shape to the comparative area of a circle which has the same perimeter, since the circle is the most compact shape, known as the isoperimetric quotient.

Shape memory alloys (SMAs)

[biomedical, mechanics] Memory material that will return to a preset shape ("memory") when exposed to a predetermined temperature. The most used alloys is Nickel–titanium, known as NITINOL (known for the origin in 1961 Nickel Titanium Naval Ordinance Laboratory), additional alloys with shape retention are copper–aluminum–nickel, copper–zinc–aluminum, and a variety of iron–manganese–silicon alloys. The memory effect can be explained by a crystal structure on an atomic level with an associated low equilibrium ENERGY which is accessed through a set of PHASE changes, known respectively as martensite and austenite, where the austenite phase is the "memory shape phase" of the configured alloy (see Figure S.52).

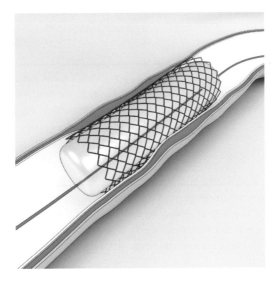

Figure S.52 Diagram of placement of Nitinol stent in blood-vessel.

Shark

[biomedical, general] Group of aquatic animals (i.e., fish) characterized by a cartilaginous skeleton, that in general has a highly evolved sensory system that relies on electrosense functionality; defined as electroreception, the ability to sense electric and MAGNETIC fields. Sharks also possess a pectoral fin that is not fused to the head, which increases its maneuverability. The electrosense is also found in birds to provide navigation. The shark uses the electrosense to detect pray based on cellular DEPOLARIZATION and muscular contraction. The sensing organ is modified epithelial tissue that forms specific sensory ELEMENTS call the Ampullae of Lorenzini. Certain well-known sharks are great white shark, tiger shark, mako shark, nurse shark, whale shark, and the hammerhead shark (see Figure S.53).

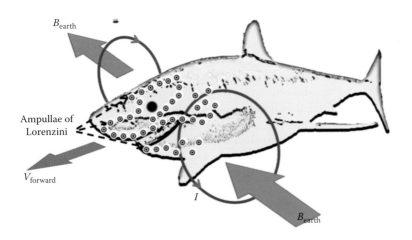

Figure S.53 Diagram of sensing organs of certain sharks used for detection of electromagnetic waves, both earth's magnetic field (static) and muscular contraction (dynamic; believed to reach up to 2 km distance in detection range).

Sharp series

[atomic, nuclear] Fine structure of spectral lines within the DOUBLET ATOMIC EMISSION lines of alkali metals representing transitions between the n^*s and the $2p$ electron configurations. This is place in reference against the principal lines resulting from the n^*p to $2s$ electron configurations transitions, the diffuse lines of the transitions: $n^*d \rightarrow 2p$, and the fundamental lines of the $n^*f \rightarrow 3d$ transitions.

Shear flow

[fluid dynamics] For non-Newtonian liquids the stress appears as if it has a memory of prior conditions and the shear-stress is not a linear function of the flow gradient, however, depending on the LIQUID, become a function of the gradient as well as their derivatives; expressed in viscosity as $\eta(\dot{\mu}_s) = \eta(\dot{\mu})/\mu_s$, where $\mu_s = dx/dy$ is the shear strain and the rate of shear is $\dot{\mu}_s = [d(dx/dy)]/dt = D_{xy}$, also recognized as the velocity gradient.

Shear force

[biomedical, mechanics] Tangential component of a contact force, or the lateral force inside a deforming medium. Force that change the shape of an object without changing its volume. Shear stress is the ration of the shear force to the area involved, whereas shear strain is the ratio of deformation as the displacement of one level layer with respect to the DISTANCE to the fixed surface (see Figure S.54).

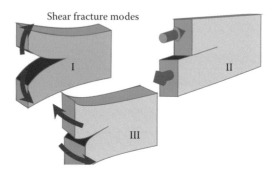

Figure S.54 Shear force: diagram of shear forces.

Shear Modulus (G_∞)

[acoustics, biomedical, computational, general, mechanics] Modulus of rigidity or stiffness. One of three parameters that are used to describe the stiffness and COMPLIANCE of a medium. The other two parameters are the YOUNG'S MODULUS and the BULK MODULUS. The shear modulus is defined as $G_\infty = \sigma_{xy}/\gamma_{xy} = (F/A)/(\Delta x/\ell)$, where $\sigma_{xy} = F/A$ is the shear stress, F the acting force parallel to the face of the object that is being deformed with surface area A, and the linear deformation of the position of the face with respect to the reference frame is Δx, which is applied over the height of the deformed object ℓ yields the shear strain: $\mu_{xy} = \Delta x/\ell = \tan\theta$, where θ represents the deformation ANGLE of the edge of the face plate with respect to the base (origin) of the object at rest. The Bulk modulus represents the response of a medium to an applied uniform pressure, whereas the Young's modulus defines the compliance in response to linear STRAIN (e.g., extension).

Shear Péclet number

[fluid dynamics, mechanics] *See* **Péclet number, mass transfer.**

Shear strain (μ_s)

[biomedical, fluid dynamics, general, mechanics] The ratio of lateral displacement (x) to the height with respect to the fixed surface (h): $\mu_s = x/h$ (see Figure S.55).

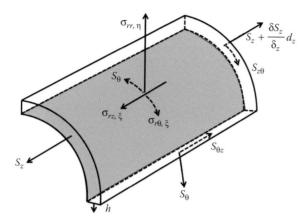

Figure S.55 Shear strain.

Shear stress (σ_s)

[acoustics, biomedical, fluid dynamics, general, mechanics] Ratio of shear force (F) to the surface area (A) that the force is applied to: $\sigma_s = F/A$. In acoustics the shear stress signifies the relative magnitude of the mean acoustic impedance across each respective layer or shear-surface (see Figure S.56).

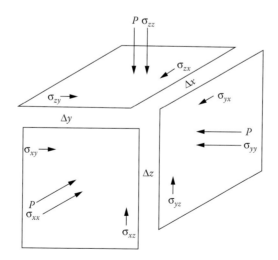

Figure S.56 Shear stress.

Shear-thickening fluid

[biomedical, fluid dynamics] Non-Newtonian fluid for which the VISCOSITY (η) increases with the flow velocity gradient $D = \dot{\gamma} = [d(dx/dy)]/dt \equiv (dv_x/dx) + (dv_y/dy)$, in turn the viscosity (η) is defined to behave according to: $\eta = K_{mat}\dot{\gamma}^{n-1}$, K_{mat} a material constant (*see* DILATANT FLUID *and* NON-NEWTONIAN FLUID) (see Figure S.57).

Figure S.57 Shear-thickening fluid. Silly-Putty® dripping through a hole in a Plexiglas® plate. Other applications are found in novel body-armor designs.

Shear-thinning fluid

[biomedical, fluid dynamics] Non-Newtonian fluid for which the VISCOSITY (η) decreases with the flow velocity gradient D (*also see* SHEAR-THICKENING FLUID; *see* PSEUDOPLASTIC FLUID *and* PSEUDOPLAST) (see Figure S.58).

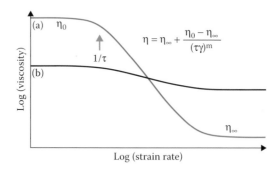

Figure S.58 Shear-thinning fluid.

Shedding frequency (ν_V)

[computational, fluid dynamics, mechanics, thermodynamics] Frequency of detachment of flow from a bluff or rounded surface such as under KÁRMÁN EDDY CURRENT VORTEX STREET development and maintenance. (*see* VORTEX SHEDDING FREQUENCY).

Shell model

[atomic, nuclear, solid-state, thermodynamics] The BOHR ATOMIC MODEL is constructed in shells, which are named in outgoing order as follows: K, L, M, N, O, P, and Q, corresponding with the PRINCIPAL QUANTUM NUMBER n, which is a positive integer and starts at $n = 1$ associated with the K-shell. The principal quantum number was the only QUANTUM NUMBER defined by NIELS HENRIK DAVID BOHR (1885–1962) in 1913 in his original atomic model. The electrons in the inner shell, the K-shell are tightly bound to the NUCLEUS and the most difficult to be excited, let alone extracted. The K-shell has only one SUBSHELL: 1s and can hold two electron only, with respective opposite SPIN. The orbital or azimuthal quantum number (second quantum number) of the K-shell is $\ell = 0$. The L shell consists of two subshells: 2s and 2p, providing for a total of two electrons in the 2s and six electrons in the 2p. The quantum number of the L-shell is $\ell = 1$. The M-shell has three subshells: 3s, 3p, and 3d, with the potential for harboring a total of 18 electrons (*see* **BOHR ATOMIC MODEL**) (see Figure S.59).

Figure S.59 Shell model.

Shepp-Logan phantom

[acoustics, biomedical, computational, general, imaging] Model of the human head introduced by Lawrence (Larry) Alan Shepp (1936–2013) and Benjamin Franklin Logan (1927–) in 1974 based on the geometric and Fourier decomposition of the general anatomical outline of the volumetric configuration of the generalized human head. The model has specific applications in validation of tomographic IMAGE reconstruction algorithms, specifically acting as attest-image for algorithm calibration in image reconstruction with respect to TOMOGRAPHY (*see* POSITRON EMISSION TOMOGRAPHY [**PET**], COMPUTED TOMOGRAPHY [**X-RAY CTR**], *and* MAGNETIC RESONANCE IMAGING [**MRI**]) (see Figure S.60).

Figure S.60 Shepp-Logan phantom, three-dimensional rendering of the Shepp-Logan phantom used for image reconstruction algorithm testing shown in the image domain.

Sherwood number (Sh = $h_m L / D_{AB}$)

[biomedical, fluid dynamics] Dimensionless number identifying the concentration gradient at a surface, where h_m is the DIFFUSION rate, L the characteristic dimension, and D_{AB} the diffusion coefficient for the constituents A and B. The Sherwood number is the ratio of the mass DIFFUSIVITY with respect to the molecular diffusivity. In BLOOD flow the Sherwood number describes the PROBABILITY of SOLVENT desorption through the vascular WALL, where h_m now describes the wall permeability. The Sherwood number has various specialized definitions pertaining to specific geometries.

Shock absorber

[general, mechanics] Device that converts MECHANICAL ENERGY in other forms of energy, using fluid-flow or FRICTION mechanisms. The most well-known application of shock absorbers is on the axles of automobiles and motorcycles, compensating for unevenness in the road-surface and increasing the traction stability by maintaining proper surface contact between the road surface and the tire surface (see Figure S.61).

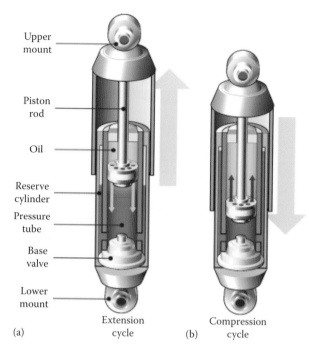

Upper
mount

Piston
rod

Oil

Reserve
cylinder

Pressure
tube

Base
valve

Lower
mount

(a)

Extension
cycle

Compression
cycle

(b)

Figure S.61 Shock absorber: (a,b) diagram of operation and examples of use.

Shock wave

[fluid dynamics, general] Abrupt change in pressure, generating a pulse propagation through a FLUID or a solid medium. One specific example is in EARTHQUAKE shock propagation. Other examples include the breaking of the sound BARRIER when flying and exceeding the Mach velocity, or bursting of a balloon. The shock-WAVE has an impulse due to the incremental change (see Figure S.62).

Figure S.62 Shock-wave.

S

Shunt

[biomedical, electromagnetism, fluid dynamics, general] By-pass mechanism that has the ability to mitigate risks and constraints that are present in the main line of a flow pattern. The flow can consist of fluids, charges, magma or gasses. On specific example of a biomedical fluid-dynamic shut is the bridging between a VEIN and an artery in the arm of a person with kidney problems to accommodate the high flow requirements for the KIDNEY dialysis equipment that is connected externally to the body (see Figure S.63).

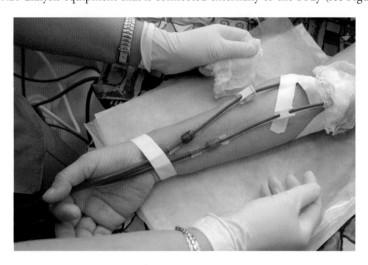

Figure S.63 Kidney dialysis shunt in arm of patient.

SI units

[general] *See* SYSTÈME INTERNATIONAL (D'UNITÉS).

Sievert (Sv)

[biomedical, electronics, nuclear] Unit used in RADIATION exposure to indicate the biological effect, not specifically the MAGNITUDE of radiation. The SI unit for the combined quantity and mechanism of delivery (alpha, beta or gamma rays) of ionizing radiation that will produce the same biological effect in comparison to one rad of X-RAY radiation exposure. The scale compares to the unit gray used in X-ray exposure.

Sievert, Rolf Maximilian (1896–1966)

[biomedical, electronics, nuclear] Radiologist from Sweden. Sievert's work focused on the biological effects of RADIATION, introducing the biological equivalence, later assigned the unit Sievert. Sievert also introduced a standard for measuring ABSORBED DOSE of radiation, described by the "Kerma rate"; the kinetic ENERGY absorbed per unit mass. The Air Kerma rate ($\dot{K}_{air,P}$) is associated with nonionizing radiation (IONIZATION is secondary effect) in air, associated with photons, neutrons, and fast neutrons, expressed as $\dot{K}_{air,P} = A_{cc}'\Gamma_{AKR}\int_{\theta_1}^{\theta_2}(e^{-\mu_{en}d/\cos\theta}/P^*)d\theta$, where A_{cc} the "activity" of the source (rate of emission), Γ_{AKR} the Air-Karma rate constant (this is linked to the exposure rate constant of the radiation), μ_{en} is the radiation attenuation coefficient, d is the source material thickness, $P^* = Lh'$, with L the length of the source, h' the DISTANCE from source to target, θ the angular field-of-view. A similar approach applies for water. This is important in brachytherapy, a form of RADIATION THERAPY where the radiation source is implanted in close proximity to the volume that requires treatment; radiation seed implants as used for instance in prostate therapy (see Figure S.64).

(a)   (b)

Figure S.64 Rolf Maximilian Sievert (1896–1966), (a) in 1958. (Courtesy of Kungl. biblioteket, National Library of Sweden, Picture collection, KoB, Fc) and (b) photograph by Hans Weinberger.

Sigma particle

[atomic, nuclear] BARYON particle. Particle in the family of HADRON subatomic elementary constituents. Unstable hyperon with ELECTRIC CHARGE +2, +1, −1, or zero and strangeness −1.

Signal

[acoustics, biomedical, electronics, general, mechanics, optics, quantum] Stream (temporal) or distribution (spatial) of data. Signals can be described in one or more dimensions. A one-dimensional SIGNAL is an orderly sequence of numbers that describes the modulations and trends of a parameter. The successive acquisition of a physical quantity over time is the typical signal found in science and ENGINEERING. The temporal order of the numbers in a signal is a direct function of the order of events (i.e., measurements) in "time." The characterization of a signal is defined by the order in which the data points are collected as well as the MAGNITUDE (amplitude) of the recorded numbers. Signal processing provides the tools to analyze the signal in order to extract important knowledge that may not be directly visible to the HUMAN EYE. One-dimensional signals are not necessarily ordered in time alone, the data-points may be location specific derived from a sensor array. The aspect of "time" forms the primary basis to describe the axis that identifies order. The temperature of a METAL rod as a function of location along the length is not directly a function of time, however the location-specific temperature may still be time dependent. In biomedical data acquisition the recording of the electrical activities of the DEPOLARIZATION of the HEART muscle is referred to as the ELECTROCARDIOGRAM (ECG), which is the main diagnostic signal in assessment of the cardiovascular system and general health, hence it is part of the "vital signs." Multidimensional signals are the extensions or convolution of the one-dimensional signals. An IMAGE is a two-dimensional array of data. In a grey-scale image, the signal magnitude for a specified set of coordinates (x, y) identifies the level of brightness of the image at those coordinates, expressed by the response function $g(x, y)$. Signals identify the mechanism to obtain critical information about the origins of a phenomenon, based on the method of acquisition and the applied computational processing algorithm(s). Three types of signal can be recognized: analog, discrete, and digital. Analog signals are continuous both in time and amplitude, discrete signals are intermittent burst of continuous amplitude, the digital signal relies on encoding for the information, and both time and amplitude are discrete. Neural impulses are a specific example of digital signals, whereas in most other scientific applications an analog-to-digital (AD) conversion is required (see Figure S.65).

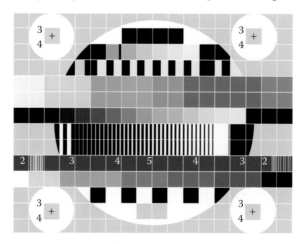

Figure S.65 Signal.

Signal-to-noise ratio (S/N or SNR)

[acoustics, biomedical, electronics, general, mechanics, optics, quantum] Quality measure for the reliability and accuracy of a SIGNAL with respect to other measured data-points that are not directly related to the MAGNITUDE of a phenomenon (i.e., NOISE; also referred to as background, or background-noise). The signal-to-noise ratio is generally defined as the power (generally defined proportional to the AMPLITUDE squared) of the signal (P_{signal}) divided by the power of the noise (P_{noise}): $SNR = P_{signal}/P_{noise}$, for an alternating signal with mean amplitude zero the signal-to-noise ratio can be expressed as a function of the variance for the respective "signals": $SNR = \sigma_{signal}^2/\sigma_{noise}^2$. In IMAGE processing a threshold for accuracy based on signal-to-noise is defined by the Rose criterion, stating $SNR \geq 5$ for well-defined feature analysis at 50% or better to distinguish the object from "background," introduced in 1973 by the American physicist Albert Rose (1910–1990). The ratio is usually expressed in DECIBEL (dB): $SNR_{dB} = 10\log_{10}\left(P_{signal}/P_{noise}\right)$. Noise can be thermal (e.g., electronic influence produced by charge agitation) or result from the ambient conditions, such as equipment switching or in ACOUSTICS the voices of bystanders. Noise is a random feature that can provide a large magnitude data point produced by the equipment used to collect the features representing specific physical consequences (see Figure S.66).

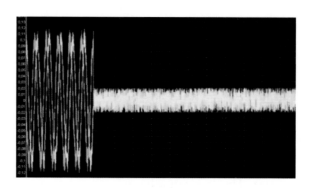

Figure S.66 Signal–to-noise ratio: example of sinusoidal signal with imbedded noise, and noise alone.

Silastic™

[biomedical, chemical, mechanics] Highly configurable, inert silicone rubber, specifically used in prosthetic devices. Introduced by Dow Corning®.

Silicon (Si)

[chemical, solid-state] ELEMENT $^{28}_{14}$Si, metalloid, discovered in 1823. Electron configuration: $1s^2 2s^2 2p^6 3s^2 3p^2$; with electrons in the consecutive shells: 2, 8, 4. Silicon is the world's second most prevalent element, by mass (after oxygen), however virtually never found in pure form. The most common form is in silicate minerals, some forming the basis for what is known as sand. Silicon forms a major constituent in the popular chemical composite Silicone, as well it wide use in semiconductor design (*see* SILICONE RUBBER, SEMICONDUCTOR, *and* ***pn***-JUNCTION) (see Figure S.67).

Figure S.67 Silicon wafer of semiconductor fabrication.

Silicon nitride

[biomedical, chemical] White chemically inert compound consisting of the ELEMENTS silicon and nitrogen (Si_3N_4), and may be classified as a ceramic. Silicon-nitride is a solid with a high-melting-point of ~1900°C. Silicon-nitride has excellent shock RESISTANCE and high durability and is used in many applications that have impact or VIBRATION risks, such as the automotive industry (e.g., cylinder lining, bearings) and medical devices as an alternative to TITANIUM and PEEK (polyether ether ketone), and is used for instance in orthopedic applications such as spinal FUSION devices.

Silicone rubber

[biomedical, chemical, mechanics] Mixed inorganic–organic ELASTOMER composed of a silicon-POLYMER, consisting of the ELEMENTS silicon (Si), CARBON (C), hydrogen (H), and oxygen (O), based on a silicon-oxygen backbone. Silicone has the following generic chemical formula $\left[R_2SiO\right]_n$, where R represents an organic group, for instance: ethyl, methyl, or phenyl. Silicone has found many applications, ranging from house-hold sealers to medical applications, specifically breast augmentation inserts. The high temperature range makes the material very attractive, operational from −100°C to +300°C. Silicone has very durable properties, including resilient chemical, mechanical and THERMODYNAMICS properties under a wide range of conditions and exposure to external influences. Silicone was first produced by Dow Corning® in 1943, and was invented around the turn of the century, beginning of the twentieth century by the British chemist Frederick Kipping (1863–1949) who also coined the term silicone. The concept was rapidly picked up by General Electric (GE), now under the company name "Momentive Performance Materials," as well as "Wacker Chemie" and "Shin-Etsu Chemical" in the late 1940s and early 1950s. Only a select group of manufacturers produces Silicone. As a lubricant the most well-known form is polydimethylsiloxane

S

(PDMS), in OIL consistency. Recent advance introduced silicon in a self-healing elastomer format (see Figure S.68).

Figure S.68 Silicone rubber and example of use: gel.

Simple harmonic motion

[general] A MOTION is harmonic when the FORCE (F) on the object in motion is directly negatively proportional to the body's displacement (s), for instance under the influence of a spring-force or under GRAVITATION force (i.e., simple PENDULUM). The SPRING FORCE for a MASS-SPRING SYSTEM is defined by $F = -ks = ma$, where k is the spring constant and a the acceleration of the mass m. The displacement of the object around the point of equilibrium ($s = 0$) needs to be small enough to satisfy $F(s) = \left[dF(s)/ds\right]_{s=0} s$. The motion needs to satisfy the following equation: $(d^2s/dt^2) + (k/m)s = 0$. The motion by the body varies sinusoidally with time and can generally be described by sine and cosine functions or in complex notation including the range of motion called AMPLITUDE (A), the FREQUENCY ($\nu = \omega/2\pi$) (or angular frequency: $\omega_0 = \sqrt{k/m}$, also called the NATURAL ANGULAR FREQUENCY), period ($T = 2\pi/\omega$) and PHASE ($\omega t + \phi$; with phase constant: $\phi = \tan^{-1}\left(\omega s(t)/v(t)\right)$, with) of the location, all as a function of time; that is, $s(t) = A\sin(\omega t + \phi)$. For the simple pendulum with length: ℓ, the harmonic deviation is in the ANGLE: θ the harmonic oscillation satisfies: $(d^2\theta/dt^2) + (g/\ell)\sin\theta = 0$, which for small deviations reduces to: $(d^2\theta/dt^2) + (g/\ell)\theta = 0$. Harmonic oscillators appear in many locations, on an atomic level it accounts for the temperature effects, while RESONANCE plays a major role in musical instruments, whereas most phenomena are damped oscillations. An OSCILLATION under constant reinforcement (i.e., applied mechanism of force) will result in resonance (*also see* MASS-SPRING SYSTEM) (see Figure S.69).

Figure S.69 Illustrations of simple harmonic motion with wave pattern.

Simpson's rule

[computational] Method used in NUMERICAL integration, providing exact solutions up to polynomials of the third power. Simpson's rule is most elegantly implemented by integration of a third-order Lagrange interpolating polynomial fit ($f(x)$) to the base function of the integral, taken at three points, performing the equivalent linear interpolation at three equally spaced points, separated by a DISTANCE ℓ:

$$\int_{x_0}^{x_1} f(x)dx = \int_{x_0}^{x_0+2\ell} f(x)dx = \frac{1}{3}\ell\left(f_0 + 4f_1 + f_2\right) + \frac{1}{6}\int_{x_0}^{x_1}\left(x_0 - x'\right)^2\left(x_1 - x'\right)f^{(3)}\left(x'\right)dx'$$

$$+ \frac{1}{6}\int_{x_0}^{x_1}\left(x_2 - x'\right)^2\left(x_1 - x'\right)f^{(3)}\left(x'\right)dx' = \frac{1}{3}\ell\left(f_0 + 4f_1 + f_2\right) - R_{\text{rest}}$$

where f_n represents the function at the respective interpolation points: $f_n = f\left(x_n\right)$, and $R_{\text{rest}} = \left(n\ell^5/90\right)f^{(4)}\left(x^*\right)$ the error term using the forth order derivative.

Simulated annealing

[computational] Mathematical approach in PROBABILITY used for solving problematic SOLUTION techniques involving combinatory methods. It may be improbable to find an optimal solution, however a reasonably good solution may be derived under simulated annealing probability optimization. One particular example is the process of mimicking misplaced atoms in a METAL undergoing heating followed by a slow cooling process, often termed the "traveling salesman" problem. The salesman must optimize (minimize) the mileage traveled for work based on the itinerary spread over randomly located locations in multiple cities, this is done by pairwise trading the order of visits, finding a local minimum, without ever reaching a global minimum. Certain trades in the order in which places are "visited" may have no impact on the direct outcome, but may lead to reductions further down the path.

Simultaneity

[nuclear, relativistic] Under relativistic concepts two events that happen at the same time (e.g., two simultaneous observations) may not be perceived as simultaneous for two different observers due to two different concepts of time for the respective observers.

Single photon emission computed tomography (SPECT)

[biomedical, imaging] Imaging modality that acquires information with respect to the concentration of radionuclides that have been previously introduced into the patient's body. SPECT has its origin in the early 1960s, when the idea of emission traverse section TOMOGRAPHY was introduced by the physician DAVID EDMUND KUHL (1929–) and the engineer ROY Q. EDWARDS (mid twentieth century–) prior to the introduction of the imaging mechanisms of positron emission tomography (PET), X-RAY computed tomography, or magnetic resonance imaging (MRI). SPECT imaging is inferior to PET because of attainable RESOLUTION and sensitivity. Different radionuclides are used for SPECT imaging that emit a single PHOTON (usually with ENERGY of about 140 keV), rather than positron emission (resulting in two high energy 511 keV photons) as in PET. Because only a single photon is emitted from the radionuclides used for SPECT, a special LENS known as a collimator is used to acquire the IMAGE data from multiple views around the body. The use of a collimator results in a tremendous decrease in detection efficiency as compared to PET. For positron emission tomography, location and collimation is inherently achieved by the fact that the pair of detected photons (gamma rays) can be traced back to their origin since they travel along the same line, in opposite direction, after being produced. In PET, in access of 500 detectors are used to detect a PET ISOTOPE at any one time where as in SPECT, there the imaging relies on only one or three collimators. Although the SPECT imaging resolution is not nearly as high as that of PET, the availability of specific SPECT radiopharmaceuticals, and the economic aspects of SPECT as well as the practical implications of the instrumentation make this mode of emission tomography particularly attractive for clinical studies of the brain. The cost of SPECT imaging is about one third that of PET.

Single photon photoelectric effect

[general] The photoelectric effect is the result of photons liberating electrons from the VALENCE BAND of a METAL. The MINIMUM ENERGY requirement for the generation of a PHOTOELECTRON is called the work-function and is a function of the material: $E_{\text{work}} = h\nu_0 = \phi_w$, where $h = 6.62606957 \times 10^{-34}$ m^{2}kg/s is PLANCK'S CONSTANT, ν_0 the threshold frequency of electromagnetic RADIATION. A single photon can generally liberate only one electron (conversion into kinetic energy), where sometime multiple photons of low energy can combined release an electron. Since the photoeffect can be considered to be a single photon effect the total number of photons is generally immaterial to the energy of the ejected electron.

Single-slit diffraction

[general, optics] Experimental design first executed by JOSEPH VON FRAUNHOFER (1787–1826) around 1814. The far-field INTERFERENCE pattern resulting at a distant screen can be interpreted as having an infinite number of individual sources spread out over the width of the opening of the slit, creating individual Huygens wavelets (*see* HUYGENS PRINCIPLE). The locations of the minima (dark space) resulting from cancelation interference are spaced from the central maximum directly under the center of the slit described as $b\sin\theta = m\lambda$, where b is the width of the slit, θ the ANGLE with the central axis, m an integer, and λ the respective wavelength within the source LIGHT. The intensity measured electronically is defined as $I = I_0\left(\sin\beta_{\text{Fr}}/\beta_{\text{Fr}}\right)^2$, where $\beta_{\text{Fr}} = \pi b\sin\theta/\lambda$; note that the intensity of electromagnetic RADIATION does not exist, since there are two components to the WAVE; the MAGNITUDE of EM radiation is provided as radiance or fluence, depending on the geometry of impact. Compare to FRESNEL DIFFRACTION in the near-field (see Figure S.70).

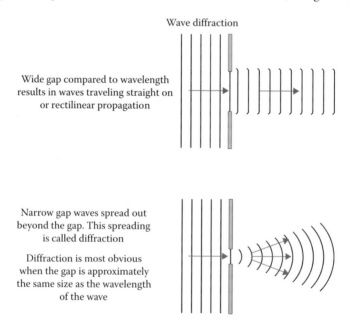

Wave diffraction

Wide gap compared to wavelength results in waves traveling straight on or rectilinear propagation

Narrow gap waves spread out beyond the gap. This spreading is called diffraction

Diffraction is most obvious when the gap is approximately the same size as the wavelength of the wave

Figure S.70 Graphical representation of the formation of the Single-slit diffraction pattern.

Singlet scattering length

[nuclear] During the RADIATIVE CAPTURE of an incident NEUTRON by a PROTON a characteristic length can be identified as the s-wave elastic triplet scattering probability (singlet): $a_{t(s)} = -f_{t(s)}(0)$, where $f_{t(s)}$ is the singlet scattering AMPLITUDE; $\hat{f}(k) = f_t(k)\hat{Q}_t + f_s(k)\hat{Q}_s$, with $\hat{Q}_t = (3\hat{I} + \hat{\sigma}^{(n)}\hat{\sigma}^{(p)})/4$, $\hat{Q}_s = (3\hat{I} - \hat{\sigma}^{(n)}\hat{\sigma}^{(p)})/4$, $\hat{\sigma}^{(n)}$, and $\hat{\sigma}^{(p)}$ the Pauli SPIN operators for the neutron and proton respectively, $\hat{I}$ the fourth row unit matrix; and k the wavenumber with $p = \hbar k$ the neutron momentum defined in the center-of-mass for the neutron-proton system, $\hbar = h/2\pi$, $h = 6.62606957 \times 10^{-34}$ m^{2}kg/s is PLANCK'S CONSTANT.

Singlet state

[atomic, nuclear] Any pair of particles with spin-1/2 can form total spin 1 in three different states, which is called a triplet, alternatively they combine to form a state of spin 0, the singlet state. The singlet state represents a TOTAL ANGULAR MOMENTUM of zero for a group of particles or represents a vanishing PARTICLE. The component can switch between triplet and singlet state multiple times during an extensive period and may prefer the singlet state. Oxygen however is preferably in TRIPLET STATE, however a singlet state can be configured, which is poisonous to many biological systems, specifically used in cancer therapy. Singlets occur both in atomic and nuclear configurations. In hydrogen two electrons are antiparallel in the ground-state forming a singlet, however the protons are in triplet state, creating an ENERGY configuration that is degenerate (see Figure S.71).

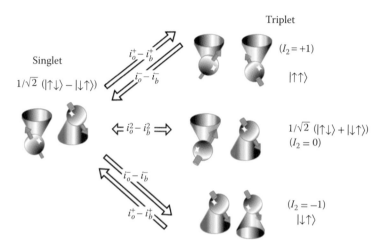

Figure S.71 Diagram of singlet atomic state of excitation and energy transfer states. The singlet state is highly reactive and in photodynamic therapy, singlet oxygen is the reactive oxygen that initiates the break-down of the cellular nucleus by oxidation and decay, resulting in cell-death.

Singularity

[computational] Location in space where a mathematical function (and hence the described phenomenon) cannot exist. In calculations these points will need to be avoided. For instance the expression $1/r$ will let the function go to infinity at the origin (see Figure S.72).

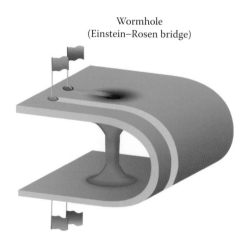

Figure S.72 Example of singularity: worm-hole diagram, galactic space discontinuity.

Sink and source

[fluid dynamics] Modeling concept in fluid-dynamics describing the flow pattern definition with respect to a theoretical source. In case the source is negative this becomes a sink. The velocity profile expressed in spherical coordinates is $v_r = \Lambda/2\pi r$ and $v_\theta = 0$, where r is the radius to the center of the phenomenon, and Λ the source strength, specifies the rate of volume flow going outward with respect to the source; when negative the flow in inward. The corresponding flow potential is $\phi(r,\theta,\phi) = (\Lambda/2\pi)\ln r$, and the STREAM FUNCTION is defined as $\psi(r,\theta,\phi) = (\Lambda/2\pi)\theta = (\Lambda/2\pi)\arctan(y/x)$.

Skeggs, Leonard T. Jr. (1918–)

[biomedical, chemical] Chemist from the United States. Skeggs received recognition for his discovery of two angiotensin peptides in relation to hypertension (high blood-pressure, predominantly with respect to a SYSTOLIC PRESSURE over 140 mm Hg, but a DIASTOLIC PRESSURE exceeding 90 is gaining more importance) through the angiotensin converting enzyme. Additional work of Skeggs resulted in significant improvements in KIDNEY dialysis procedures (see Figure S.73).

Figure S.73 Leonard T. Skeggs, Jr. (1918–).

Skeletal muscle

[biomedical, mechanics] In tissues there are three prominent types of muscles, skeletal muscle, cardiac MUSCLE and smooth muscle. Skeletal muscle is attached to the bone structure of vertebrate animals and provides a mechanism to apply force and torque and yield movement and displacement (*see* MUSCLE).

Skin

[biomedical, chemical, general] Part of ANATOMY, organ for many classes of animals, primarily applies to vertebrates. Most known for the human skin. The skin is a multilayered structure with several attributes, such as imbedded sensors for touch, temperature, pressure as well as vascular integration to provide nourishment to sustain the biological functions. Parts of skin are semipermeable membranes that allow sweat to pass through but also provide a mechanism for chemical interaction (e.g., allergens) and specifically drug delivery. Skin can have a specific COLOR resulting from dye MOLECULE concentrations called carotene and melanin, in collaboration with hormonal influences, such as androgens. For humans the skin is the second largest organ next to the lung in surface area. Skin has three layers: the outermost layer epidermis; directly beneath the epidermis is the dermis, containing connective tissue, hair follicles, and sweat glands; the deeper hypodermis primarily consists of fat and connective tissue. The epidermis forms a waterproof BARRIER and form the skin-tone. The skin has certain electrical, physiological, and chemical properties that are used for diagnostic interventions as well as derived applications. Some of the nonspecific applications are in the lie-detector test, and more recently in bioelectric power supply for in situ monitoring devices (see Figure S.74).

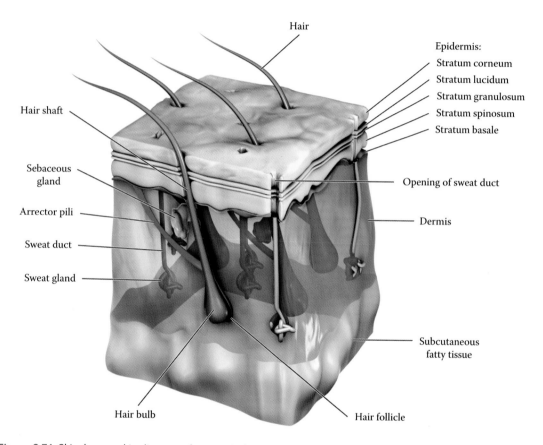

Figure S.74 Skin, human skin diagram of anatomical structure.

Slater determinant

[atomic, chemical, mechanics] An expression that describes the wavefunction (as SOLUTION to Schrödinger's equation) of an anti-symmetric system consisting of *more than two* fermionic configurations (e.g., electrons) that consequently satisfies the PAULI EXCLUSION PRINCIPLE. The anti-symmetry and Pauli exclusion are rolled together in the fact that the system changing sign when exchange of fermions takes place. The principle was introduced by John C. Slater (1900–1975) in the 1930s. The principle relies on approximation of the WAVE function for a many-particle system by SEPARATION OF VARIABLES, implementing the product of orthogonal wave functions of the individual particles that may be chosen appropriately based on the local conditions.

Specific applications are in atomic orbits and molecular electron orbits. The radial function is as follows: $R(r) = Nr^{n-1}e^{-\chi r}$, where n has the function of PRINCIPAL QUANTUM NUMBER, N a NORMALIZATION factor, r the radius, and χ provides the charge compensation for the NUCLEUS. The angular aspect of the Slater determinant is expressed in POLAR COORDINATES by the spherical harmonics: $Y_l^m(\vec{r})$. Also known as Slater orbital.

Slice

[imaging] Segment of computed TOMOGRAPHY data acquisition array that has one narrow dimension that is part of a stacked organization to form a three-dimensional reconstruction (*see*, for instance, **PET, MRI**, and **X-RAY COMPUTED TOMOGRAPHY**) (see Figure S.75).

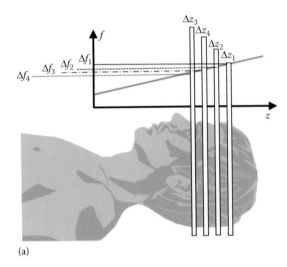

(a)

Figure S.75 (a) Representation of the "slice theorem" concept in imaging, where the object is sliced as if it were a piece of fruit. *(Continued)*

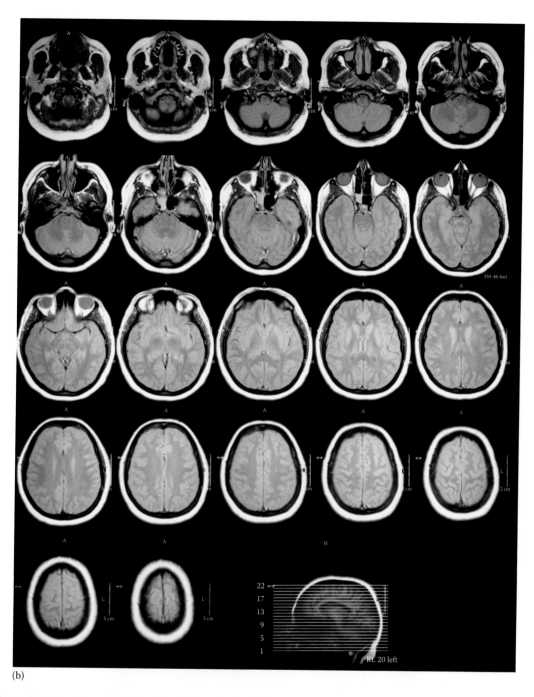

(b)

Figure S.75 (Continued) (b) The slice thickness (Δz) will determine the lateral resolution as exemplified for the magnetic resonance imaging diagram as a function of frequency modulation (Δf). Generally the slices are presented next to each other for evaluation.

Smoke method

[fluid dynamics] Visualization method for illustrating TURBULENCE effects. In gaseous FLUID flow the use of a smoke wire placed in the lumen of the flow can highlight the flow patterns. A specific example is the formation of a torus of smoke indicating fluid rolling around a circular axis; or less prominent, spinning around an imaginary axis line that forms a closed loop (see Figure S.76).

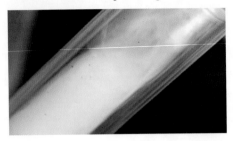

Figure S.76 Example of the Smoke method.

Smyth report

[atomic, nuclear] Report on the MANHATTAN PROJECT by the American physicist Henry DeWolf Smyth (1898–1986), focusing on the Allied Forces effort in World War II to develop the ATOMIC BOMB (*see* MANHATTAN PROJECT).

Snel ("Snell"), Willebrord Snel van Royen (Snellius) (1591–1626)

[optics] Scientist and mathematician from the Netherlands. Snell described the path of LIGHT at the interface of two media with a discontinuity in index of refraction in 1621. Willebrord Snell changed his name to the Latin equivalent: Snellius in celebration of his scientific achievement. The work of PTOLEMY (90–168) and IBN SAHL (940–1000) may be considered to predate that of Snell but these scientists lacked the proper instrumentation at the time to define the exact geometric relationship mathematically. Additionally, RENÉ DESCARTES (1596–1650) described similar concepts in 1637 (see Figure S.77).

Figure S.77 Willebrord Snel van Royen (1591–1626).

Snel's Law

[acoustics, general, optics] *See* **Snell's law.**

Snell's law

[acoustics, general, optics] Law of refraction discovered by Willebrord Snel (Snellius) van Royen (1591–1626) described as $\sin\theta_i / \sin\theta_r = n_2/n_1$, where θ_i is the angle of incidence with respect to the normal to the surface at the interface between two media, incidence media with index-of refraction n_1 and continuing medium with index-of refraction n_2, and θ_i is the angle of refraction into the second medium. The index of refraction will depend on the material properties of the medium as well as the wave phenomenon itself (e.g., mechanical, electromagnetic) (see Figure S.78).

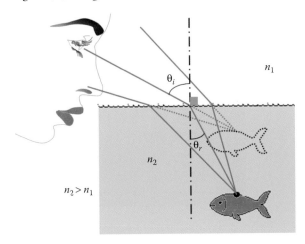

Figure S.78 Snell's Law.

Socrates (469–399 BC)

[general] Philosopher from Greece, born in Athens. Recognized as one of the architects of analytical thinking, sciences and western philosophy (see Figure S.79).

Figure S.79 Artist representation of Socrates (469–399 BC).

Soddy, Frederick (1877–1956)

[atomic, chemical, nuclear] Physicist and radiochemist from Great Britain. Soddy introduced the term ISOTOPE, explaining the RADIOACTIVE DECAY of certain ELEMENTS that have the same location in the periodic table, in collaboration with ERNEST RUTHERFORD (1871–1937). Fredrick Soddy received the Nobel Prize in Chemistry in 1921 for his contributions in the understanding of the RADIOACTIVITY in chemical substances and the pertaining chemical configuration (see Figure S.80).

Figure S.80 Frederick Soddy (1877–1956). (Courtesy of University of Glasgow, *College Courant*, the journal of the University of Glasgow Graduates' Association, no. 64, March 1980.)

Sodium ($^{22}_{11}$Na)

[biomedical, chemical, nuclear] Metallic element (Latin: Natrium). Silver white ALKALI METAL. The HUMAN BODY in particular uses sodium to mitigate BLOOD PRESSURE as well as blood volume. Sodium also serves as a catalyst in the operation of muscles and provide nerves with a chemical means to maintain a trans-membrane potential and form an ACTION POTENTIAL. Sodium was discovered in 1807 by HUMPHRY DAVY (1778–1829) as the result of the ELECTROLYSIS of sodium hydroxide (inorganic compound, commonly found as caustic soda; lye. Frequently used in detergents). Sodium is abundant on EARTH and ranks sixth as the most liberally available substance, most commonly found in "table-salt": sodium chloride. Sodium has a very prominent yellow spectral line (D line at λ = 589.3 nm), which is sometimes used in street LIGHT illumination (*see* SODIUM, ENERGY LEVELS) (see Figure S.81).

Figure S.81 Sodium crystal.

Sodium chloride (NaCl)

[biomedical, chemical] SALT, compound that easily dissociates into the ions Na^+ and Cl^- in water, certain alcohols and glycerol to name a few. Major component of biological system, specifically human BLOOD, and hence used as constituent in buffered Saline SOLUTION for infusion during hospitalization. As for most salts our tongue has specific sensors for metallic salts (including and highly sensitive for NaCl), as one of the five main "flavors."

S

Sodium cooled reactor

[nuclear] Nuclear reactor power plant that uses liquid Sodium as a coolant for the REACTOR process. Nuclear power plants use coolants to make the heat generated from the core available for power generation in steam turbines. Coolants also maintain a controllable pressure within the core of the reactor (*see* NUCLEAR REACTOR) (see Figure S.82).

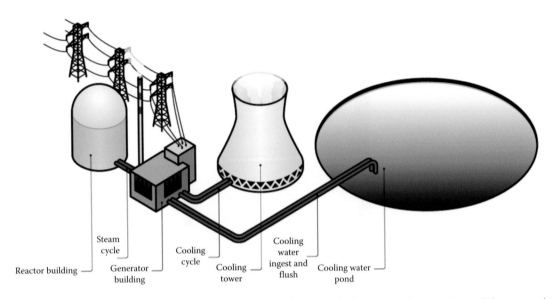

Figure S.82 Nuclear reactor diagram with a heat exchange between the internal sodium cooling and the external water cooling driving the steam reactors. One of the alternatives is a pressurized "heavy" water internal cooling.

Sodium iodide detector

[nuclear] Device used to measure radiation based on "scintillation" principles resulting from interaction of RADIOACTIVE DECAY with the ENERGY bands in the sodium iodine crystal, which generate photons that pass through a photomultiplier for gauging the MAGNITUDE of the incident radiation. Generally this type of detector ranks behind the gas-filled detector, which uses IONIZATION for detection, measured by an ANODE in a current meter set-up.

Sojourner

[astrophysics/astronomy, general] Robotic Mars rover delivered by the Pathfinder spaceship in 1997 used for extensive Mars exploration (see Figure S.83).

Figure S.83 Sojourner.

Solar power

[thermodynamics] The systematic use of the LIGHT from the SUN to produce ELECTRICITY resulting from the PHOTOELECTRIC EFFECT. The photoelectric effect was described by Alexandre-Edmond Becquerel (1820–1891), a physicist from France, observed the photoelectric effect in 1839. Solar panels are used in various sizes to power portable gear during camping trips or supply an entire city of all the electricity requirements for normal operation. To date the best ENERGY conversion for solar cells is in the order of 24%. Solar power relies on the photoelectric effect for the generation of electricity. The Romans built glasshouses in the thirteenth century. The first documented solar collector was built in 1767 by the scientist Horace-Bénédict de Saussure (1740–1799) from Switzerland. Horace de Saussure developed large cone shaped collectors that used ammonia which would boil to perform work acting as a locomotion or perform refrigeration. In 1861 Auguste Mouchout (1825–1911) developed a steam ENGINE powered by solar energy alone (see Figure S.84).

(a)

(b)

Figure S.84 Solar power: (a) solar farm and (b) solar-powered airplane, combining the solar energy to power flight in addition to the aerodynamics of the design of the plane and the mechanical integrity to withstand shear stress from wind turbulence. (Courtesy of Solar Impulse©, Lausanne, Switzerland.)

Solar system

[computational] Galactic arrangement of the planets orbiting our SUN, from the inside out, Mercury, VENUS, EARTH, MARS, JUPITER, SATURN, Uranus, Neptune, and Pluto. Earlier models were GEOCENTRIC, the most well described of this kind was by PTOLEMY (approximately 90–168 AD) published around 140 AD. The first attempt to account for the deviations in the Ptolemy model by placing the Sun in the center of the planetary revolutions was by the "Polish"/German (Prussia) scientist NICOLAUS COPERNICUS (1473–1543; Niclas Koppernigk) suggesting a HELIOCENTRIC model, published in 1543 ("De Revolutionibus Orbium Coelestium"), but presented the idea in the late 1400s to early 1500s. Based on the observations by the German astronomer and mathematician TYCHO BRAHE (1546–1601) in the late 1500s the foundation was made for a rigorous description of a solar centered planetary system, introduced by Johannes Kepler (1571–1630) in 1609, using the unpublished data from Tycho Brahe (see Figure S.85).

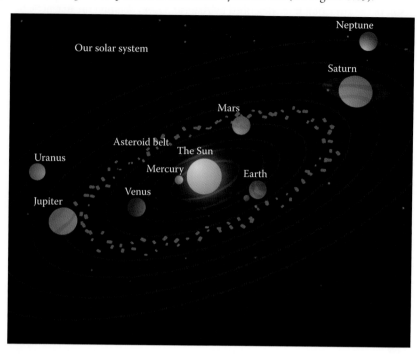

Figure S.85 Solar system.

Solar therapy

[biomedical, chemical, optics] Use of sun-light to treat SKIN disorders. Even though the beneficial effects of sunlight to the body for general health as well as for therapeutic applications to skin diseases (e.g., psoriasis, acne) and general benefits to mood were known for millennia by the Egyptians, healers in India and China the scientific description was provided by Niels Rydberg Finsen (1860–1904). The use of sunlight later progressed on to artificial light-sources in PHOTODYNAMIC THERAPY.

Solar wind

[astrophysics/astronomy, general] RADIATION pressure that exerts a force on ionic material, charged PARTICLE content, primarily resulting from the SUN due to the high radiance. The pressure inflicted by electromagnetic radiation can be defined based on absorption or REFLECTION, where the impulse of reflection is twice as large, respectively expressed as $P_{solar} = S/c$, where $\vec{S} = (1/\mu_0)\vec{E} \times \vec{B}$ is the Poynting vector (equivalent power flux), $\vec{E}$ the electric field, $\vec{B}$ the MAGNETIC FIELD, $\mu_0 = 4\pi \times 10^{-7}$ H/m the permeability of free space, and c the speed of LIGHT; alternatively $P_{solar}{}^{reflect} = 2(S/c)$. The solar wind will divert the direction of the ION tail (ionized gasses etc.) of comets, but will have only minor effect on the dust tail which will be in-line with the path of the COMET. Generally, the solar wind is much greater than the gravitational attraction force.

Solenoid

[general] Wound helical coil that can generate a magnetic field ($\vec{B}$) when a current is applied through the wiring that makes the windings. The MAGNETIC FIELD distribution of a solenoid is very uniform and is described as a function of location as $\vec{B} = [\mu_0(N/\ell)I]/2(\sin\theta_2 - \sin\theta_1)\vec{j}$, $\mu_0 = 4\pi \times 10^{-7}$ H/m the permeability of free space, I the MAGNITUDE of the current, $\vec{j}$ the unit vector for the current direction, θ_1 and θ_2 respectively the ANGLE with the normal to the coil with respect to a point in free space where the magnetic field magnitude is

desired to be known, from either edge of the coil respectively, and N/ℓ the number of windings/turns N per length ℓ of the solenoid. Solenoids are often used to open and close by moving a METAL object through the core of the coil as a result of the attraction force described by AMPÈRE's LAW, defining the magnetic field strength as a function of the applied current and the number of windings as a function of DISTANCE. The force resulting from a magnetic field on a charge is $F_{magn} = q\vec{v} \times \vec{B}$, with q the ELECTRIC CHARGE, $\vec{v}$ the velocity of the charge, which can be applied to EDDY CURRENT for ferromagnetic materials (see Figure S.86).

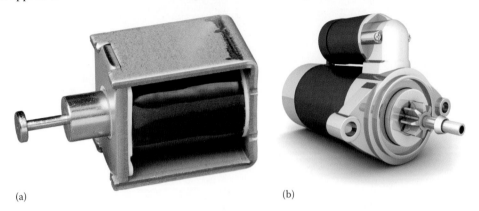

Figure S.86 Solenoid. (a) Simple solenoid as used on an automatic door-lock and (b) automobile starter with solenoid to "throw" the rotating starter gear into the teeth of the fly-wheel of the engine.

Solid angle

[computational, nuclear] The solid angle from a point O towards a surface area A with curvature C can be described by connecting the edges of the area A to the point of reference O. When a sphere is placed around the reference point O with radius r, this sphere will SLICE through the cone of lines connecting to the edge of area A. The MAGNITUDE of the surface area carved out by the cone has an area A'. In general the area of a sphere is $A = \pi r^2$. The area A' is also proportional to r^2 this way, since it is a fraction of the total surface area of the sphere. The solid angle Ω that is enclosed by the cone originating in O is defined as $\Omega = A'/r^2$. The units of the solid angle: Ω are steradians. The solid angle is independent of the shape of the surface, since it only demarcates the outline in space and relief has no impact on that, and it does not depend on the radius to the reference point (see Figure S.87).

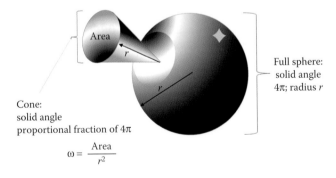

Cone:
solid angle
proportional fraction of 4π

$$\omega = \frac{\text{Area}}{r^2}$$

Full sphere:
solid angle
4π; radius r

Figure S.87 Solid angle.

Solid form of aggregation

[thermodynamics] The solid phase, one of the four states of a composite material or ELEMENT: gas, LIQUID, solid, and PLASMA.

Solidification

[thermodynamics] The process of converting a medium into solid state. Generally achieved by lowering the temperature below the FREEZING point.

Solid-state

[atomic, nuclear, thermodynamics] Sometimes also referred to as condensed MATTER, depending on the thermodynamic ENERGY balance.

Solid-state physics

[atomic, nuclear, thermodynamic] Branch of condensed MATTER physics dealing with the investigation of the properties of solids by means of for instance crystallography, QUANTUM MECHANICS. Additional mechanisms involve electromagnetism and more generally material science; which deals with mechanical properties such as hardness, elastic modulus, thermal conduction, electrical conductivity, and more under different thermodynamic and chemical conditions.

Soliton

[acoustics, computational, fluid dynamics, mechanics, quantum] A WAVE that acts as a PARTICLE. A solitary wave, which by definition are nonlinear in nature. Particular reference as a SOLUTION to the KORTEWEG—DE VRIES EQUATION (see Figure S.88).

(a) (b) (c)

Figure S.88 (a–c) Soliton, water wave progression (excerpts). (Courtesy of Onno Bokhove, Wout Zweers, with Anthony Thornton; University of Technology Twente, Enschede, the Netherlands.)

Solstice

[astrophysics/astronomy, general, geophysics] The astronomical events where the axis of the EARTH cantilevers to position the SUN directly over either the Tropic of Capricorn in the southern hemisphere marking the onset of winter or the Tropic of Cancer in the northern hemisphere, indicating the beginning of summer for the northern hemisphere. This indicates respectively the winter and summer solstice (see Figure S.89).

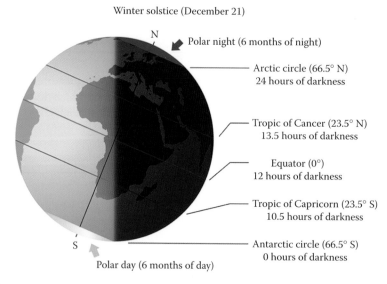

Figure S.89 Solstice.

Solute

[thermodynamics] Medium mixed-in with a SOLVENT to form a SOLUTION. The solute is dissolved in the solvent. The solute can be in the same phase (FLUID or GAS) as the solvent but has a smaller quantity either in mass or in volume.

Solution

[chemical, thermodynamics] Mixture of at least two substances, one usually a LIQUID, the other can be liquid, or solid, if the liquid is in gaseous form the SOLUTE (mixed-in substance, in this case identified by a smaller quantity) can also be a GAS. The mix of substances will be homogeneous. The solute can remain intact or dissolve into the ionic component that make the component, the most well-known example is the solute NaCl (SALT) in water. Solutions in water are referred to as aqueous solutions. The concentration of the solution is the quantity of the solute with respect to the solute, expressed in gram per liter or MOLE per liter. A saturated solution has reached the limit by which the solute's ions or molecules can be covalently bound to the solution and the solute will precipitate and condensate or solidify on the WALL of the container, primarily the bottom for solid solutes. The SATURATION or the amount of solute that can be dissolved in the SOLVENT is dependent on the temperature of the solvent. Cooling a solution can (and will, depending on the temperature range; some solutions have a very broad range of stable BINDING ENERGY balance) result in condensation of the solute. An IDEAL SOLUTION will adhere to RAOULT'S LAW; the partial (e.g., vapor-) pressure of a solution of a nonvolatile mixture is equal to the partial/VAPOR PRESSURE of the pure constituent/solvent at that temperature multiplied by its mole fraction. Raoult's law was introduced in 1882 by FRANÇOIS-MARIE RAOULT (1830–1901), a chemist from France.

Solvent

[thermodynamics] Liquid medium that allows MIXING with other medium LIQUID or solid or GAS to form a SOLUTION.

Somesthesis

[biomedical, mechanics] The ability to detect stimuli internal and external to the body. The stimuli can be thermal, mechanical, or even painful. This mechanism is part of the senses and is primarily serving the need for protection of the biological entity for instance is the stimulus sufficiently strong to damage tissues. An additional purpose of somesthesis is general experience of one's surroundings and the associated enjoyment or disgust based on the mental processing and predetermination.

Sommerfeld, Arnold Johannes Wilhelm (1868–1951)

[atomic, computational, fluid dynamics, general, nuclear] Physicist and mathematician from Germany. Arnold Sommerfeld provided significant contributions to the theoretical field of quantum PHYSICS and the description of atoms. He introduced the azimuthal QUANTUM NUMBER with respect to atomic wavemechanics, the second quantum number (ℓ), as well as the SPIN quantum number, the fourth quantum number (s). Arnold Sommerfeld was a contemporary of, and collaborator with Léon Brillouin (1889–1969). He also introduced the FINE-STRUCTURE CONSTANT, and pioneered X-RAY wave theory (see Figure S.90).

Figure S.90 Arnold Johannes Wilhelm Sommerfeld (1868–1951).

Sonic boom

[general] Acoustic WAVE generated as the result of the oscillating source overpassing the pressure WAVEFRONT when traveling at velocity exceeding the speed of SOUND with respect to the FLUID. The pressure wave can be described by the Rankine-Hugoniot relation as $P_2/P_1 = ([(\gamma_c + 1)/(\gamma_c - 1)](\rho_2/\rho_1) - 1)/([(\gamma_c + 1)/(\gamma_c - 1)] - (\rho_2/\rho_1))$, where $\gamma_c = c_v/c_p$ the ratio of SPECIFIC HEAT under constant volume to the specific heat under constant pressure, P the pressure, and ρ the density in the respective locations (i). For ideal gasses (e.g., atmospheric AIR) this transforms under velocities (v) in the Mach range (exceeding the speed of sound) to: $(P_2 - P_1)/P_1 = 2[\gamma_c / (\gamma_c + 1)](Ma^2 - 1)$. *See* **MACH NUMBER** ($Ma = v/v_{\text{sonic}} = \sqrt{\text{Re} \times \text{Wi}} = v\sqrt{\rho/E}$; Young's modulus ($E$), also called Elastic modulus. In the definition

the following are also used: Re the REYNOLDS NUMBER and Wi the Weisenberg number) (*see* SHOCK-WAVE *and* MACH-CONE) (see Figure S.91).

Figure S.91 Sonic boom of airplane flight past, with condensation illustrating the rarefaction of the Mach cone.

Sonogram

[acoustics, biomedical, general, mechanics] Image obtained by ULTRASOUND imaging, primarily in medical diagnostics, also referred to as ULTRASONOGRAM. The IMAGE is formed by reflected PRESSURE WAVES that result from piezoelectric transducers placed in contact with the object under investigation. The trajectory of the pressure waves obeys SNELL'S LAW of REFLECTION and REFRACTION and can be collected at the same location where the pressure waves are generated. The ultrasound TRANSDUCER will intermittently emit pressure WAVE, and in the un-powered state there will be a quiet period in which the same transducer is used to detect the returning pressure wave. The time delay (Δt) between emission and detection will provide the DISTANCE (d) traveled from the source to the point of reflection based on the SPEED OF SOUND (v) defined by $d = v \times \Delta t$. Using the signals collected from various external positions correlated over time can be used to reconstruct the two-dimensional pattern of boundaries of mismatched INDEX-OF-REFRACTION, more specifically mismatched ACOUSTIC-IMPEDANCE resulting from layers of media. This process is accomplished by a sweeping or PHASED-ARRAY transducer. A linear transducer will generate a two-dimensional SLICE, which can be expanded using IMAGE REGISTRATION techniques to provide a lateral EXPANSION to the scan resulting from redirection of the pressure wave source orientation. Alternatively, a two-dimensional ultrasound array can provide a three-dimensional image virtually instantaneously. Ultrasound attenuates rapidly in a gaseous environment, which requires that the contact between the object and the transducer is directly mechanical. ACOUSTICAL IMPEDANCE matched, direct mechanical contact is often accomplished by the use of an IMPEDANCE MATCHING gel placed between the ultrasound source and the test object. One of the primary sonographic applications is in tracking the growth rate of a fetus in the womb of a WOMAN. The pressure waves supposedly form minimal risk to the unborn child, whereas X-RAY of other IONIZING RADIATION or high power forms of ELECTROMAGNETIC RADIATION (i.e., MRI) can interfere with the development of the fetus (see Figure S.92).

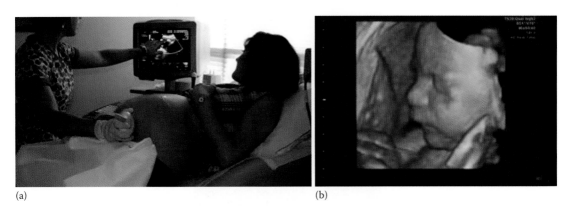

(a)   (b)

Figure S.92 Sonogram. (a) Scanning motion over belly of pregnant woman and (b) three-dimensional reconstructed ultrasound image of baby in womb.

Sonography

[acoustics, general, imaging] *See* ULTRASOUND IMAGING.

Sonohysterography

[acoustics, general, imaging] Minimally invasive ULTRASOUND technique applying saline infusion. The saline forms a "impedance matching" condition, since AIR or GAS in human cavities creates significant ULTRASONIC IMAGING distortions due to scatter and attenuation. Specifically used to IMAGE the inside of a woman's uterus. Saline is injected into the uterine cavity, by which means it is distended or enlarged. The saline impedance matching provides clear visualization of the outline of the endometrium (i.e., the lining of the cavity of the uterus), revealing polyps.

Sonoluminescence

[acoustics, energy] Specifically BUBBLE Sonoluminescence, the process of CAVITATION after bubble collapse where the acoustic ENERGY is converted in high-temperature atomic thermal agitation or even PLASMA formation and inherent emission of electromagnetic RADIATION.

S

Sørensen, Søren Peder Lauritz (1868–1939)

[chemical] Chemist form Denmark responsible for the initial concept of acidity and alkaline behavior of LIQUID, expressed as pH:: $pH = -\log_{10} H^+$, based on the hydrogen ION concentration ($[H^+]$). This was later revised to use the hydrogen ion activity (see Figure S.93).

Figure S.93 Søren Peder Lauritz Sørensen (1868–1939) in 1918; photograph by Julie Laurberg (1856–1915) and Franziska Gad (1873–1921)—Royal Library, Copenhagen, Denmark.

Sound

[acoustics, fluid dynamics, general] Mechanical longitudinal waves generally considered operating in the frequency range 20–20,000 Hz. Sound is primarily acquired by the EAR (in both mammals and non-mammalian species), however the entire biological body is sensitive to mechanical vibrations and can sense sound COMPRESSION WAVES. Sources are vibrating solid objects, such as the vocal cords, GUITAR string and gaseous expansions such as electric spark discharges (e.g., LIGHTNING) and contractions such as during endothermic and exothermic chemical reactions. Sound can be recorded by electronic devices as well as mechanical means (e.g., needle attached to resonant fork carving pattern in for instance vinyl and wax) (*also see* HEARING). Sound is identified by the SPECTRAL CONTENT. Since sound devices will generate a FUNDAMENTAL FREQUENCY with associated higher HARMONICS which creates a SPECTRAL PROFILE. For instance in a string the fundamental frequency is directly correlated to the tension in the string, the cross-sectional dimension, the material(s) (certain strings are coaxially composed of various materials with specific structural characteristics, such as weave, braid, solid, etc.) and the length of the string. Sound has specific applications in music which has its own detailed phenomenological descriptions. Musical sound is denoted by splitting the spectral range in frequency interval such as octaves (from the Greek), which describes doubling the frequency in each step (i.e., fundamental to first harmonic = 1:2); in case the frequencies of two respective waves relate as 2:3 the ratio is called a perfect fifth *or* "quint" (e.g., a musical instrument can be tuned in "quint" setting), equivalently the ratios are segmented as: 3:4 = fourth *or* quart; 4:5 = major third *or* great terts; 5:6 = minor third *or* small terts, 3:5 = major sixth *or* sext; 8:9 = major second; 9:16 = minor seventh; 8:15 = major seventh and the 12th "note" 15:16 = minor second. All these tuning modes are segmented in six consecutive triads, building a 12 note chromatic scale as developed in the eighteenth century. This scale is also referred to as the Helmholtz pitch notation, developed by the German physicist HERMANN VON HELMHOLTZ (1821–1894). The 12 note mechanism was devised to build up a musical sequence using just one ratio, exemplified by the Thomas Young's tuning formula (also known as Thomas Young's 1799 well temperament). This supposedly has the advantage of making modulating between keys possible, however this aspect ratio segmentation does not hold exact. Two other segments were later added, called tritons: 5:7 and 7:10. The current theoretical execution of the OCTAVE is thoroughly described in the works of Praetorius in 1619 (see Figure S.94).

Figure S.94 Examples of the principle of sound.

South geographic pole

[general] *See* **GEOGRAPHIC SOUTH POLE**.

South magnetic pole

[general] *See* **MAGNETIC SOUTH POLE**.

Speaker

[acoustics, electronics, fluid dynamics, mechanics] *See* **LOUDSPEAKER**.

Special theory of relativity

[general, nuclear, quantum] *See* **THEORY OF RELATIVITY**.

Specific heat

[nuclear] ENERGY stored in lattice vibrations calculated from the Debye model is providing one specific aspect of the specific heat $(C_v) = (12\pi^4/5)\, N_A\, K_B\, (T^3/T_D^3)$, where $T_D = h\nu_D/k$ is the Debye temperature; ν_D is the Debye frequency; $K_B = K = 1.38064852(79) \times 10^{-23}$ J/K is the Boltzmann constant; $N_A = 6.022140857(74) \times 10^{23}$ mol^{-1} is the Avogadro constant; $C = \varepsilon T^{3/2}$, the low temperature "spin-wave" (MAGNETIC) specific heat, with T is the temperature, and ε is the ferromagnetic Debye coefficient; $C_e = \gamma T_e$ is the electronic heat capacity, with γ the reciprocal of the "RELAXATION TIME," and T_e the "electron temperature" for the LATTICE vibrations. The total specific heat expression is as follows: $C = \gamma T + \varepsilon T^{3/2} + \beta T^3 + $ correction, the correction will account for environmental variables and boundary conditions.

Specific heat (c_{sp})

[biomedical, general, mechanics, quantum, thermodynamics] The amount of heat that needs to be added to 1 g of material in order to raise the temperature of the material by 1 K, or sometimes also regarded as 1°C, to maintain accuracy in units: $c_{sp} = Q/m\Delta T$, describing the HEAT (Q) required to change the TEMPERATURE (T) of a MASS (m) by 1 K. The majority of this ENERGY is applied to increase the INTERNAL ENERGY with a rudimentary amount pertaining to work. The work effort is greater for heating under constant pressure than under constant volume, which applies primarily to gasses. Under very high temperature conditions the specific heat times the ATOMIC WEIGHT of all the respective chemical constituents is nearly constant, which is referred to as the LAW OF DULONG AND PETIT. This constant specific heat ("atomic heat") results from the fact that at high temperatures the internal energy of atoms becomes approximately constant. This temperature phenomenon can be explained with QUANTUM THEORY.

Specific heat capacity (c_{sp})

[general] *See* **SPECIFIC HEAT**.

Specific resistance

[biomedical, electronics] The electrical RESISTANCE of a material with a length of 1 m and a cross-sectional area of 1 cm², this value is a characteristic value for the material. The specific resistance for copper at 18°C is 0.0000017 Ω.

Specific viscosity

[fluid-dynamics, mechanics] *See* VISCOSITY, SPECIFIC.

Specific weight

[general] The relative weight of a material/substance with respect to the weight of an equal volume of water at 4°C.

Spectroscopic ellipsometry

[imaging, material sciences, optics, solid-state] Diagnostic method for thin-film thickness determination as well as analyzing the location-specific chemical composition and film homogeneity. The spectroscopic analysis relies on polarization sensitive measurements of reflected electromagnetic RADIATION from interfaced between various layers of media, hence yielding the complex index-of-refraction of the respective media the LIGHT has traversed. Spectroscopic ellipsometry can be single-wavelength, which employs a MONOCHROMATIC LIGHT source, or multiwavelength. Ellipsometry determines the change in polarization of the light that is reflects from the layers of a stacked medium or from the transmitted light through a layer material structure. The POLARIZATION is generally defined by the relationship $\rho_{pol} = \tan(\Phi)e^{i\Delta}$. The polarization change is represented by means of the determination of the an AMPLITUDE ratio, Φ, as well as the PHASE difference, Δ, based on the complex index-of-refraction. The "ellipsometry" is defined by $\langle \tilde{\epsilon} \rangle (\lambda) = \sin^2(\vartheta)\left[1 + \tan^2(\vartheta)\{(1-\rho_{pol})/(1+\rho_{pol})\}^2\right]$, which technically is a function of wavelength (λ) hence the spectral aspect. Furthermore, the process uses the fact that the index-of-refraction can be described under the Cauchy or Sellmeier relationship as $n(\lambda) = A + (B/\lambda^2) + (C/\lambda^4)$. The index of refraction is directly linked to the DIELECTRIC permittivity and follows the Kramers–Kronig description relating the dielectric permittivity to the molecular ENERGY configuration, in addition to being confined through SNELL'S LAW. The measured quantities are a function of the optical properties and thicknesses of individual material layers. Ellipsometry is primarily used to determine film thickness with the added benefit of identification of optical constants, thus providing details about the composition of each layer in particular DOPING concentration. Ellipsometry provides the sensitivity necessary to measure nanometer-scale layers, in particular used in quality control for wafer production in microelectronics. Next to this it is also applied to characterize crystallinity, and ROUGHNESS. Application of ellipsometry are found in analysis of flat panel display, biosensor, next to the optical coating industries such as solar polar construction.

Spectroscopy

[atomic, general, optics] In general spectroscopy stands for the spectral analysis of emitted light, and is equivalent in many ways to the PARTICLE phenomenon of COMPTON SCATTERING, both energetically and in spatial distribution. When intense MONOCHROMATIC LIGHT of frequency ν, illuminates a sample, it has been shown that light scattered from the sample not only contains RADIATION of frequency ν, but also weaker radiation of frequency $\nu \pm \nu'$. The weaker radiation components of the scattered light are known as the RAMAN SPECTRA. RAMAN SPECTROSCOPY is a measure of the frequency shift from the incident frequency. Assuming that incident photons carry sufficient ENERGY (directly linked to the wavelength; the shorter the wavelength—the higher the energy), a MOLECULE has the potential to absorb the energy from an incident PHOTON. The absorption results in an excited state for the molecule. The molecule prefers to revert to the lowest possible energy configuration, such as everything else in nature. However, instead of decaying with loss of all excitation energy by means of a full transition back down to the GROUND STATE, the molecule may prefer, based on energy conditions from neighboring molecules, make a transition down to another excited vibrational state. The reemitted photon in this process depends on CONSERVATION OF ENERGY, and hence the (what is considered) scattered photon will be composed with slightly less energy with respect to the incident photon. The energy difference between the incident photon and the scattered photon matches the amount of energy required to bring the molecule in the higher energy excited vibrational state. The vibrational energy structure of the molecule can be gauged by determination of the frequency shift v' with respect to the incident electromagnetic frequency v. This vibrational energy structure (spectrum) for each molecule defines a fingerprint representing the molecular bonding within the specific sample. Several diagnostic techniques have been developed that are based on this specific and characteristic spectral profile by means of the spectral analysis of scattered light. Examples of certain diagnostic applications of Raman-Spectroscopy are for instance the in vivo analysis and characterization of chemical blood-gasses, next to BLOOD glucose sensing. Raman spectroscopy is frequently used in forensic sciences for the detection of toxic substances next to the comparison of sample with "culprit" in determination of cause and effect and quantification of probability of validity of correlations between various sources for the chemical constituents and mixtures. The latter technique can be called Raman spectroscopy assisted histology (see Figure S.95).

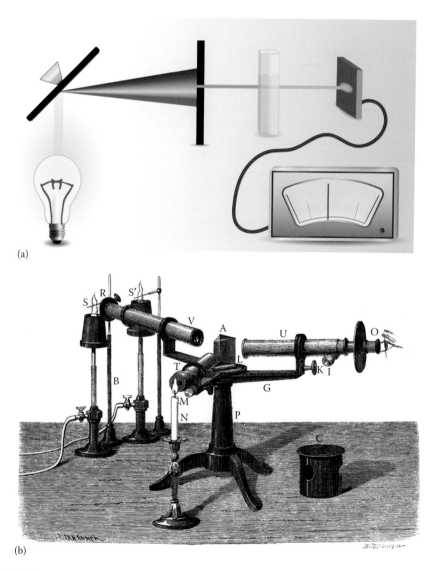

(a)

(b)

Figure S.95 (a,b) Spectroscopy.

Speed (*v*)

[general] Magnitude of the change in location as a function of time: $v = |dx(t)/dt|$, MAGNITUDE of the velocity vector. The time rate of displacement; DISTANCE moved per unit time. CGS unit: cm/s. The ANGULAR SPEED (ω) is the rate of change in the angular position (θ) of an object: ANGULAR VELOCITY: $\omega = |d\theta(t)/dt|$.

Speed of wave propagation in a confined liquid

[fluid dynamics] v_s, (FLUID DYNAMICS), speed of WAVE propagation in a confined liquid. $v_s = \sqrt{(K/\rho)/(1+(D/b)(K/E)\text{Const})}$, with the LIQUID flow density ρ, K the bulk modulus of the liquid with regard to compressibility, D the inside diameter of tube with wall-thickness b, E the Young's modulus of the flexible PIPE and Const a correction factor for dimensional and material factor affecting the speed of SOUND.

Spherical wave

[general, optics] $U(\vec{r}) = (A/r)e^{ik\vec{r}}$, where A a constant (i.e., AMPLITUDE), $k = 2\pi/\lambda$ the wavenumber, and $\vec{r}$ the vectorial DISTANCE to the source.

Sphygmomanometer

[biomedical, fluid dynamics] BLOOD PRESSURE sensing device based on application of external pressure in order to close off the blood-flow in the artery (specifically in the elbow of the arm) and subsequently reducing the external pressure. The principle relies on the pressure balance from the cuff applied to the tissue, where the pressure equilibrium ensures the sealing of the artery when the external pressure exceeds the internal pressure. The pressure inside the brachial artery is directly proportional to the applied pressure from the contractile MOTION of the HEART, the brachial artery is directly connected to the AORTA. As the pressure in the inflated cuff that is wrapped around the arm is reduced the pressure will reach a point where at the time of ventricular contraction the brachial pressure equates the applied pressure, which will be a function of the vascular health of the person as well as the heart function of the person under examination. At the high pressure equilibrium the SYSTOLIC PRESSURE will allow blood to flow under intermitted episodes, coinciding with the heartbeat. As the pressure in the cuff of the Sphygmomanometer is reduced even further at the low pressure an equilibrium with the DIASTOLIC PRESSURE will be reached, from which point onward (decreasing external pressure even further) the flow will be continuous. The sphygmomanometer was introduced in 1881 by Samuel Siegfried Karl Ritter von Basch (1837–1905) from Schechoslovakia/Austria (Prussian Empire) and refined by SCIPIONE RIVA-ROCCI (1863–1937) from Italy with further refinements to the detection mechanism by the surgeon NIKOLAI KOROTKOV (1874–1920) from Russia in 1905. Also referred to as a Sphygmomanometer (*also see* **KOROTKOFF SOUND**) (see Figure S.96).

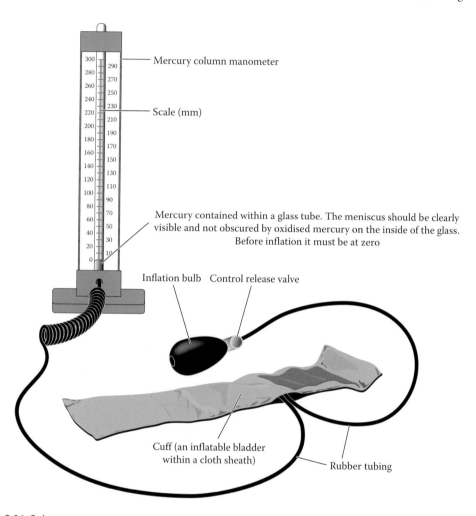

Mercury column manometer

Scale (mm)

Mercury contained within a glass tube. The meniscus should be clearly visible and not obscured by oxidised mercury on the inside of the glass. Before inflation it must be at zero

Inflation bulb   Control release valve

Cuff (an inflatable bladder within a cloth sheath)

Rubber tubing

Figure S.96 Sphygmomanometer.

Spin

[atomic, general, mechanics, quantum, thermodynamics] Rotation of a solid object around its central axis. Examples of object with spin are a top, or a system of particles grouped together: electron constructed of ELEMENTARY PARTICLES, PROTON and NUCLEUS; next to the EARTH consisting of atoms and molecules. The rotation creates an angular momentum: $\vec{L} = I\vec{\omega}$, I the MOMENT OF INERTIA of the object with respect to the axis of rotation and $\vec{\omega}$ the angular velocity. The spinning MOTION presents a mechanism that counteracts a change in the ANGLE of the axis of rotation. This phenomenon is observed when the front wheel of a bicycle is lifted from the GROUND and made to rotate, while rotating there is the sensation of a torque in the opposite direction to the applied torque applied to turn the direction in which the wheel points. The angular momentum pointing perpendicular to the area of the wheel, pointing in the direction defined by the crock-screw rule; following the rotation of the wheel with a crock-screw will either move forward or backward from within the stopper in the wine-bottle. The angular momentum vector points in the direction of the advancement of the crock-screw. The reactionary force resulting from the SPIN in response to the applied torque is defined through the right-hand rule, resulting in a torque in the opposite direction with respect to the applied torque, making it difficult to turn the rotating wheel. Steering to the left generates a TORQUE (τ_F) to the right as a result of the change in orientation of the wheel as a function of time: $\tau_F = dL/dt$. This inherent property of the rotating (spinning) device for the basis for the uncanny and relentless stability of the GYROSCOPE. The first gyroscope was introduced in 1852 by JEAN BERNARD LÉON FOUCAULT (1819–1868) to illustrate the rotation by the Earth. Also, the inherent, intrinsic angular momentum of an atomic PARTICLE is identified by a QUANTUM NUMBER in modern atomic theory. The concept of "spin-up" refers to rotation from west to east, such as the earth's rotation; in contrast "spin-down" refers rotation in the opposite angular direction. In atomic notation the concepts of spin-up and spin-down separates the energetic stages of two electrons in the same orbit, with identical BINDING ENERGY (based on the primary quantum number: n). For atomic notation the spin angular quantum number is s, with potential values of $s = +(1/2); -(1/2)$. An object with spin exposed to external forces (torque) is generally subject to PRECESSION of the axis of rotation as well as NUTATION. The rocking and swaying motion under nutation is more broadly defined than precession, including for instance a wavy pattern embedded in the precession. The angular momentum for the spin of, for instance an electron in orbit with the HYDROGEN ATOM produces a MAGNETIC FIELD with magnetic angular momentum: $L_z = m_\ell \hbar$, m_ℓ the MAGNETIC QUANTUM NUMBER and, $\hbar = h/2\pi$, with $h = 6.62606957 \times 10^{-34}$ m^{2}kg/s the PLANCK'S CONSTANT. The total orbital angular momentum in the Bohr model is defined by the ORBITAL ANGULAR MOMENTUM quantum number ℓ as $L = \sqrt{\ell(\ell+1)}\hbar$, $\ell = 0,1,2,...(n-1)$ (see Figure S.97).

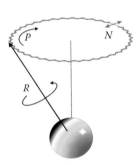

Figure S.97 Spin.

Spring force

[general, mechanics] Force (F) resulting from mechanical deformation of a solid object, primarily compression/extension but also TORSION (e.g., McPherson strut) as well as compression or EXPANSION of a GAS in a sealed container with a plunger (gas-spring or gas SHOCK-ABSORBER), but also electrostatic spring. For the solid object the force is directly proportional to the mechanical displacement (x) defined linearly by HOOKE'S LAW as $F = -kx$, where k is the spring constant. For the electrostatic spring the spring constant is defined as $k = -(CV_b^2/d)$, where C is the capacitance, d the CAPACITOR gap and V_b the bias voltage. For a gas-spring (with a moveable plunger) the spring constant can be described as $k = \rho_m(\partial P/\partial \rho)(A^2/V_m)$, with ρ the gas density, V_m the mean volume (https://mospace.umsystem.edu/xmlui/bitstream/handle/10355/4560/research.pdf?sequence=3) for high pressure as $k = PA/d$, with P the pressure, A the plunger-cross sectional area and d the displacement, however theoretically the frequency dependence will need to be incorporated for certain applications. For the volume of FLUID in a sound-pipe the spring constant is defined by

$k = \rho v_s^2 (A^2/V)$, where v_s is the speed of SOUND, A the cross-sectional area of the "organ pipe," and V the volume of the device (see Figure S.98).

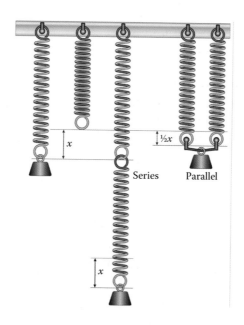

Figure S.98 Spring-force.

STANI

[acoustics] *See* SCANNING TOMOGRAPHIC ACOUSTIC MICROSCOPE.

Stanton number ($St = h/\rho v c_p = Nu_L/Re_L Pr$)

[energy, fluid-dynamics] Dimensionless number used for identification of the scale of HEAT TRANSFER to the thermal capacity of a FLUID, where h is the heat transfer coefficient, ρ the density, v the characteristic velocity, c_p the heat capacity, and Nu_L the Nusselt number, Re_L the REYNOLDS NUMBER and Pr the Prandtl number.

Stanton number, mass transfer ($St_m = h_m/v = Sh_L/Re_L Sc$)

[energy, fluid dynamics] Dimensionless number relating concentration differences to flow velocity, where h_m is the mass transfer coefficient related to the DIFFUSION rate, v the velocity, and Sh_L the Sherwood number, Re_L the REYNOLDS NUMBER, and Sc the Schmidt number.

Star

[astrophysics, atomic, energy, fluid dynamics, general, geophysics, nuclear] Galactic body that emits LIGHT and other electromagnetic RADIATION. The SUN is one of our most well-known stars and with the closest proximity for detailed investigation. The Sun radiates light resulting from proton-proton collision, forming a DEUTERON along with the emission of a NEUTRINO and a positive electron (positron). Stars can be quantified by size and ENERGY/surface temperature. The radiant emission: luminosity and surface temperature are generally directly proportional to the mass of the STAR. Examples of nomenclature in star classification are: giant, super giant, QUASAR, and WHITE DWARF (dim, dense star near its end), and exploding star formations as novae and supernovae. Generally the life and death of stars can be described by a nuclear and a mechanical phenomenon. The nuclear aspect is the fact that the star gains its massive amount of energy and associated emission from NUCLEAR FUSION and NUCLEAR FISSION processes. The mechanical component is driven partially by the thermal gradient resulting in both convective mass and heat DIFFUSION. The nuclear processes eventually deplete the elementary constituents of the molten and gaseous amalgam resulting in an oscillatory behavior that changes character with the composition of the star. Pulsating stars are a clear and obvious example of this OSCILLATION phenomenon, whereas the process also takes place on smaller scales. Radial modes of oscillation are the most obvious and easily recognizable, however nonradial modes such as standing waves on the surface are also observed as well as running waves. The Sun has a standing WAVE on the surface with a period of 5 min, and other stars have radial waves with periods of days. Longer periods are also identified, and these are classified by the CEPHEID VARIABLES (see Figure S.99).

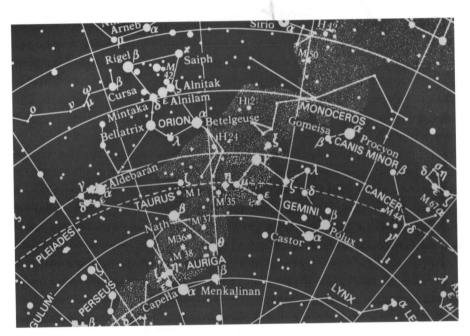

Figure S.99 Star. Galactic grouping of stars that was defined as the constellation Orion and our Sun.

S

Stark, Johannes (1874–1957)

[chemical, electromagnetism, general, solid-state] German physicist. Stark empirically verified the COMPTON EFFECT in 1909. Stark contributed to the explanation of the ENERGY splitting concept described by the Zeeman–Stark Effect, also described as the Star-effect. The work of Stark contributed to the basic understanding of electron orbital structure and energy, chemical bindings and ATOMIC ENERGY structures (see Figure S.100).

Figure S.100 Johannes Stark (1874–1957). (Courtesy of University of Wurzburg, Wurzburg, Germany.)

Stark effect

[computational, electromagnetism, energy, general, solid-state] *See* ZEEMAN AND STARK EFFECT.

Starling, Ernest Henry (1866–1927)

[chemical, fluid dynamics] Chemist from Great Britain. Ernest Starling introduced the OSMOTIC PRESSURE effects in a system separated by a semipermeable WALL. The principles are similar to those described by JACOBUS HENRICUS VAN'T HOFF (1852–1911) and are outlined under the STARLING'S LAW (see Figure S.101).

Figure S.101 Ernest Henry Starling (1866–1927). (Courtesy of National Library of Medicine, Bethesda, MD.)

Starling's law

[chemical, fluid dynamics] Hydrodynamic flow of colloid solutions separated by a membrane as defined by ERNEST STARLING (1866–1927) in 1915. Also called the Starling equation and the Frank–Starling law, based on the contributions by Otto Frank (1865–1944). Fluid MOTION between two compartments separated by a SEMIPERMEABLE MEMBRANE is the result of the combined hydrostatic and osmotic pressure. The OSMOTIC PRESSURE is described by the JACOBUS HENRICUS VAN'T HOFF (1852–1911) VAN'T HOFF EQUATION and in modified format by the MORSE EQUATION. The hydrostatic pressure in the flow and pressure process with respect to the CELL MEMBRANE is derived by means of the principles of the Bernoulli equation. The porosity of the membrane (L_p), also referred to as membrane permeability, directly influence the passage of the solutes, mainly placing restrictions on the size of the particles and molecules that can be exchanged to influence the osmotic pressure. The OSMOTIC PRESSURE (Π) is the result of the following components in the SOLUTE exchange, TONICITY (quantity of dissolved salts, proteins and other chemicals), hydrostatic pressure of hemoglobin, BLOOD colloids, interstitial fluid hydrostatic pressure (resulting from muscular compression and volume extension next to gradient in elevation with respect to the point of exchange), interstitial FLUID colloidal solution. The filtration pressure (P_{filter}) resulting from the combined osmotic pressure ($\Pi = iMRT$, where i is the dimensionless VAN'T HOFF FACTOR, M the molarity of the solutes, $R = 8.3144621(75)$ J/Kmol is the UNIVERSAL GAS CONSTANT, and T the temperature of the reaction and SOLVENT) and hydrostatic pressure (P^{hydro}) over a surface area (A) is describes as (see Figure S.102)

$$P_{filter} = \left\{ \left(L_p * A \right) * \left(P^{hydro}_{capillary} - P^{hydro}_{interstitial} \right) \right\} - \left\{ \left(A \right) * \left(\Pi_{capillary} - \Pi_{interstitial} \right) \right\}.$$

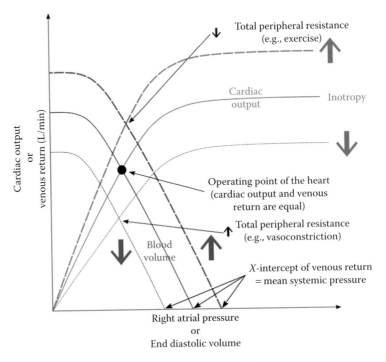

Figure S.102 Diagram illustrating the Frank–Starling law for the pump function of the heart, expressed as the cardiac function. The cardiac output, respectively the stroke volume, or stroke work are outlined by the vertical axis (y-axis). The horizontal axis (x-axis) generally denotes the end-diastolic volume. Alternatively, the x-axis can express the right atrial pressure, and sometimes is used to note down the pulmonary capillary wedge pressure as a parameter. The three curves indicate the change in preload, alternatively: afterload or contractility.

Static head

[fluid dynamics] For a PUMP, the maximum height the FLUID can reach under standard pump conditions. For a windmill used in drainage of low-lying areas (e.g., the Netherlands) the static head is approximately 1.5 m, which required placing these pumps in series with a moat separating two or more pump stages to overcome the technically feasible elevation of the LIQUID by the pump. Respectively, pumps used at drinking water wells can pump approximately against a static head of 20 m. Also known as hydraulic head. The static head is a pressure in liquid (most often water) column. This limitation can be overcome by using electric pumps in comparison to the use of windmills in the Netherlands to drain the low-lying areas north of Amsterdam as done by the hydraulic engineer from the Netherlands Jan Adriaanszoon Leeghwater (1575–1650) in 1607. A large water drain windmill in the Netherlands can pump approximately 38 m³/min against a static head of 1.3 m, such as used in the polders near Rotterdam, dating as far back as 1414. Note that windmill history can be traced back at least to seventh century Persia (see Figure S.103).

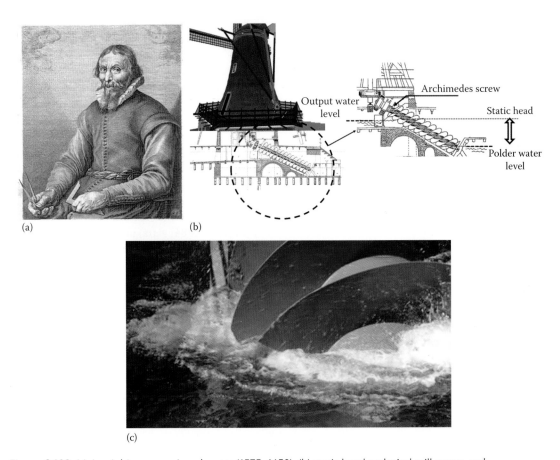

(a)   (b)

(c)

Figure S.103 (a) Jan Adriaanszoon Leeghwater (1575–1650), (b) static head and wind-mill pump, and (c) worm-wheel pump.

Stefan, Joseph (1835–1893)

[general] Physicist and mathematician from Austria (Slovenia). Joseph Stefan is known for his experimental contributions to radiation PHYSICS, in particular the Stefan–Boltzmann equation, with theoretical support from LUDWIG EDUARD BOLTZMANN (1844–1906) (see Figure S.104).

Figure S.104 Joseph Stefan (1835–1893).

Stefan–Boltzmann law

[atomic, nuclear] ENERGY or PHOTON spectral emission power profile. The energy power profile is derived from integration of the Planck radiation law. Josef Stefan derived in 1879 that the radiance emitted from a blackbody is proportional to the fourth power of the ABSOLUTE TEMPERATURE of the blackbody as $\Phi^b(T) = \sigma_{\text{Stefan}} T^4$, $\sigma_{\text{Stefan}} = 5.67 \times 10^{-8}$ W/m^{2}K^4 Stefan-Boltzmann coefficient/constant; with theoretical proof provided by LUDWIG EDUARD BOLTZMANN (1844–1906) in 1884; FLUX, units Watt per meter squared. The fully developed empirical and theoretical formula of the energy emission from a blackbody comes to $\Phi^b(T) = (2\pi^5 k_b^4 / 15 h^3 c^2) T^4$, where $k_b = 1.3806488 \times 10^{-23}$ m^{2}kg/s^{2}K the Boltzmann coefficient, $h = 6.62606957 \times 10^{-34}$ m^{2}kg/s the PLANCK'S CONSTANT, and $c = 2.99792458 \times 10^8$ m/s the speed of LIGHT. Alternatively the photon emission can be written as $\Phi^b_p(T) = \sigma'_{\text{Stefan}} T^3$, where σ'_{Stefan} represents the empirical Stefan-Boltzmann coefficient/constant for photon emission. The Radiance (L) of a body incident on an area A, under ANGLE of incidence θ, within solid angle Ω is linked to the Stefan-Boltzmann emission flux $\Phi^b(T)$ through: $L = \partial^2 \Phi^b(T) / \partial\Omega \partial \cos\theta$.

Stereo

[acoustics, general, optics] Primarily the three-dimensionally specified PERCEPTION of sound. Sometimes also used to describe depth perception by the combinatory effects from two eyes. The stereophonic HEARING is the result of the phase discrimination from the two ears with respect to the angular placement of the SOUND sources. As the EAR performs a spatially motivated FOURIER transform of the acoustic WAVE based on the local sensitivity of the cochlea, the phase-discrimination will be a function of frequency. Human hearing as a frequency sensation has the ability to distinguish sounds that are less than 5 ms apart in time with respect to defining the individual acoustic events, whereas the wave RESOLUTION is better than 150 μs. Although in general the DEPOLARIZATION rate for the ORGAN OF CORTI in the BASILAR MEMBRANE of the cochlea of the ear is directly proportional to the stimulus frequency, the audio nerve cannot provide depolarization rates of 20 kH, the upper limit of hearing. Three types of nerves can be identified for the SIGNAL transmission to the brain, one with frequency range around 700 Hz, one with frequency range around 1.3 kHz and one with frequency range around 10 kHz, with respective decreasing bandwidth for the higher transmission rates. The high response rate is tied into the frequency section for the high frequency detection close to the entry point at the oval window. This fact will be one of the limiting factors for phase discrimination apart from the mechanical elastic dampening of the basilar membrane. The frequency hearing is in fact spatially defined by location on the basilar membrane. The locations on the basilar membrane are sensitive to one frequency only, with high frequency sensitivity at the cochlear base (oval window; modulated by the stapes from the INNER EAR) and low frequency sensation at the cochlear apex. Low frequencies (base) is not very useful in stereophonic detection due to the long wavelengths involved that are several times the dimensions of the human head. An acoustic wave in AIR of 20 Hz has a wavelength of 17 m, while 2000 Hz corresponds to 0.1717 m, based on the elastic <u>modulus</u> of air of $Y_{elast} = 1.41 \times 10^5 \, \text{N/m}^2$ and density $\rho = 1.29 \, \text{kg/m}^3$, or respectively a speed of sound $v_s = \sqrt{(Y_{elast}/\rho)} = 331 \, \text{m/s}$ as experimentally verified. The use of two ears for humans can distinguish the PHASE of a single frequency of better than 90°, which will provide millimeter wave discrimination at the higher frequencies (note that the upper limit is approximately 10 kHz, at which the approximately wavelength is 3 cm with quarter wavelength resolution: 7.5 mm in the spatial domain; <150 μs in the time domain) with associated spatial resolution of better than 5° in free space; whereas bats have a resolution of better than 1.5°. The auditory signal processing on a central nervous system and cranial level also applies a form of phase-locking for ultimate frequency discrimination and ensuing spatial resolution. All these auditory features provide the means for the human ear to mentally determine the location of the violinist, cellist, the trumpet player and the GUITAR player on the podium, as well as several other instruments. The location of the base drum is generally not specifically known from frequency information, however there is also AMPLITUDE information encoded that will assist in the spatial location determination using the phase locking mechanism-of-action of hearing. Humans can distinguish sound levels as small as 2 dB, specifically at low amplitude (note that 3 dB signifies half the amplitude). Even though stereo is primarily applied to hearing, however in theory stereoscopic VISION refers to the fact that with both eyes humans and other animals (e.g., mammals, birds, amphibians, and reptiles) can perceive depth, while insects with compound eyes have a very different signal processing concepts.

Stern, Otto (1888–1969)

[atomic, nuclear, quantum] German physicist who experimentally verified the QUANTUM THEORY, specifically for ELECTRON SPIN, in 1920, 2 years prior to the release of the official definition of electron spin, in collaboration with WALTHER GERLACH (1889–1979) (see Figure S.105).

Figure S.105 Otto Stern (1888–1969) in 1928, photographer P. Toschek.

S

Stern-Gerlach experiment

[atomic, nuclear, quantum] Experimental observation of a split in a bea on neutrally charged particles passing through a MAGNETIC FIELD. This experiment illustrated the inherent magnetic properties of the ATOM, and subsequently for electrons. The atomic MAGNETIC DIPOLE could be the only explanation for the split, based on the quantization of the angular momentum of the magnetic SPIN of the electrons, since the silver atom as used is balanced in electron configuration (BOHR ATOMIC MODEL). Since the beam of silver-atoms was split is two and this could only be attributed to the any single electron, hence the ELECTRON SPIN was baptized as 1/2. The experiment was executed by OTTO STERN (1888–1969) and WALTHER GERLACH (1889–1979).

Stevin, Simon (1548–1620)

[engineering, general] Scientist and mathematician from the Netherlands. Simon Stevin was active in astronomy, GEOGRAPHY, mathematics, and logics. Stevin also introduced the Dutch word for mathematics: "wiskunde." Simon Stevin published an all-encompassing review of mathematical approaches for ENGINEERING and PHYSICS in 1608 that were known up to that time from the early Greek philosophers, Arabic mathematicians, to more recent contributions, at least with supporting work from LEONARDO DA VINCI (1452–1519). The work predates the contributions from the range of well-known mathematicians that introduced their work in the mid and late 1600s and from there on: RENÉ DESCARTES (1596–1650), BLAISE PASCAL (1623–1662), GIOVANNI DOMENICO CASSINI (1625–1712), JEAN-BAPTISTE LE ROND D'ALEMBERT (1717–1783), JOHANN HEINRICH LAMBERT (1728–1777), JOSEPH LOUIS LAGRANGE (1737–1813) [comte de Lagrange], PIERRE-SIMON DE LAPLACE (1749–1827), and ADRIEN-MARIE LEGENDRE (1752–1833), in addition to a broad range of experimentalists that also supported their work with pure and applied mathematics. Also predating SIR ISAAC NEWTON (1642–1727) (see Figure S.106).

Figure S.106 Simon Stevin (1548–1620).

Stimulated emission

[atomic, optics] The encouragement (i.e., enhanced PROBABILITY) provided by a PHOTON that passes an excited electron state to release its ENERGY in the form of a photon. The stimulation process is based on the fact that the incident photon has an energy content ($E = h\nu$, $h = 6.62606957 \times 10^{-34}$ m^{2}kg/s the PLANCK'S CONSTANT, ν the electromagnetic frequency) that is equal to or greater than the difference in energy between the excited state and the GROUND STATE of the electron in the unstable raised energy condition. When the medium of excited atoms/molecules only has one mechanism for EXCITED STATES than the released photon will by definition be identical to the stimulating passing photon. This latter condition provides the foundation for the LASER operational mechanism-of-action (*see* LASER).

Stirling, Robert (1790–1878)

[mechanics, thermodynamics] Clergyman and scientist from Scotland, Great Britain. Robert Stirling is known for the introduction of the closed-cycle ENGINE, also referred to as a external combustion engine. The closed Striling process relies on a heat-exchanger for supplying the ENERGY to maintain the MOTION in the PHASE DIAGRAM (P-V diagram; pressure vs. volume), respectively temperature versus entropy diagram (T-S diagram) (see Figure S.107).

Figure S.107 Robert Stirling (1790–1878).

Stirling cycle

[thermodynamics] Gas compression cycle consisting of two isochoric (i.e., constant volume) step and two isothermal (i.e., constant temperature) segments. The process and ENGINE was patented by ROBERT STIRLING (1790–1878) in 1816. Compare to OTTO CYCLE and CARNOT CYCLE (see Figure S.108).

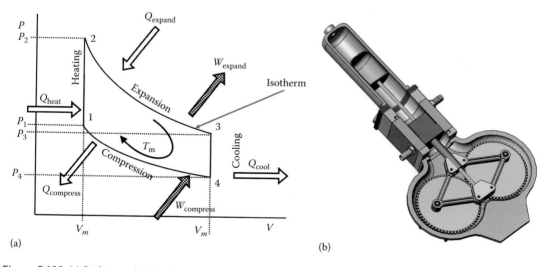

(a)

(b)

Figure S.108 (a) Stirling cycle. (b) Rhombic drive Beta type Stirling engine design. (Courtesy of Tobias.)

Stochastic process

[biomedical, computational, quantum] Events that are nondeterministic and are defined through a statistical PROBABILITY distribution. One specific example is BROWNIAN MOTION. Another being "RANDOM WALK" in optical simulation as illustrated by the use of a "Monte Carlo" simulation.

Stoichiometric coefficient, ($v_i^{(j)}$)

[chemical, thermodynamics] In chemistry the Stoichiometric Coefficients are the constants in the reaction in relative proportions to form a product: $2H_2 + O_2 \rightarrow 2H_2O$. In THERMODYNAMICS the Stoichiometric Coefficients ($v_i^{(j)}$) indicate the respective number of participating constituents (reactants) and products [A_j], where the products have a negative value and the ingredients have a positive value so that the sum of the reaction balances at zero: $\sum_{i=1}^{r} v_i^{(j)} A_j(p) = 0$; where "$p$" indicates the PHASE of the component: GAS, liquid, or solid. Also known as Stoichiometric number.

Stoichiometry

[chemical, thermodynamics] Accounting of quantities of reactants and products in relative proportions with respect to chemical reactions. Stoichiometry is based on the law of CONSERVATION OF MASS. The total mass of the sum of all the reactants is equal to the total mass of all the products. This prescribes the relations among quantities of reactants and products in the form of a ratio of positive integers: $2H_2 + O_2 \rightarrow 2H_2O$.

Stokes, George Gabriel, Sir (1819–1903)

[atomic, computational, fluid dynamics, general, optics] Irish mathematician and physicist. Pioneer in the mathematical description of FLUID flow, CREEP and optical phenomena such as diffraction. Additional work of Sir Stokes refers to the ENERGY loss in FLUORESCENCE with the associated longer emission wavelength than excitation wavelength. In the field of fluorescence he is best known for the STOKES LINES (see Figure S.109).

(a)   (b)

Figure S.109 (a) Sir George Gabriel Stokes (1819–1903). (b) Painting by Lowes Cato Dickinson. (Courtesy of Collection: Pembroke College, Cambridge, UK.)

Stokes drift

[fluid dynamics] In shallow water there is deviation from linear behavior in flow conditions. Liquid packages will be considered to circulate in closed loops during WAVE MOTION, however the particles moving with the wave motion and with the flow in the exterior of the WAVE have a higher velocity than LIQUID packages in the submerged part of the FLUID, which is moving in the opposite direction as the surface package flow and against the fluid-flow direction breaking the presumed circular package pattern. A net fluid-package motion can be defined that accounts for this nonlinearity in a second order phenomena. This phenomena also contributes to the description of the occurrence of undertow. The second-order liquid flow average velocity (v_{Stokes}) is described by the Stokes-drift as $v_{Stokes} = C_{Stokes} \left(a_w k \right)^2 e^{-2k h_a}$, where the average depth of the liquid level is h_a, the wavenumber is $k = 2\pi/\lambda$, C_{Stokes} is a constant and a_w is AMPLITUDE of the wave. When the wave amplitude is in the range of the depth of the water a phenomenon called wave-shoaling occurs. During wave shoaling the water waves are subject to refraction, generating so called longshore currents. This nearshore CIRCULATION can cause hazardous swimming conditions with longshore current velocities reaching 2.5 m/s, and rip current velocities on the order of 1.5 m/s. This DISPERSION is associated with the phase and group velocities and is linked to the high waves followed by low waves, generating a periodic fluctuation in water level, referred to as "surf beat," a pulsation effect. These rip currents can have a history tracing outward into sea for over 1.5 km (see Figure S.110).

(a)   (b)

Figure S.110 (a,b) Ocean shoreline Stokes drift.

Stokes' Law

[atomic, computational, fluid dynamics, general] Description of the characteristic sedimentation speed (v) for a particle in suspension in LIQUID or GAS. Introduced by SIR G. STOKES (1819–1903). The process also applies to two liquids that do not mix (e.g., water and OIL), or the dissociation of gas/vapor-bubbles from a liquid. This applies for instance to centrifugation and can be formulated as $v = (2(\rho_p - \rho_\ell)gr^2)/9\eta$, where ρ_p

S

is the particulate (solved constituent) density, ρ_ℓ the density of the liquid, η is the VISCOSITY, r the PARTICLE radius, and g the GRAVITATIONAL ACCELERATION. For the removal of BUBBLES the approach needs to take into consideration the BUOYANCY acting against DRAG force.

Strain (ϵ_s)

[general] Deformation (ΔL) per unit length (L), used as linear strain: $\epsilon_{s,\ell} = \epsilon_{\text{strain},\ell} = \Delta L/L_0$, shear strain; the angular deformation $\epsilon_{\text{strain},\alpha} = \Delta\alpha/\alpha_0$, and volumetric strain; the change in volume per unit volume: $\epsilon_{\text{strain},V} = \Delta V/V_0$. Elastic strain will allow the medium to return to its original shape and size. Inelastic strain usually requires exceeding a threshold strain, at which point the deformation becomes permanent, or at least no full recovery is achieved upon unloading the applied stress. Under certain conditions the atomic configuration can be modified to become more resistant to elastic deformation, strain hardening. Strain hardening can be achieved by material treatment process, most well-known is a temperature treatment. Hardening can be induced by deformation at a temperature below the recrystallization temperature (cold-forming) followed by low-temperature heating, or by rapid cooling of low-carbon steel, both used for instance in the treatment of sward-blades by a blacksmith. The high temperature heating followed by rapid cooling is referred to as quenching and creates a hard but brittle structure (martensite). The cold-forming treatment creates a durable METAL (*also see* HOOKE'S LAW) (see Figure S.111).

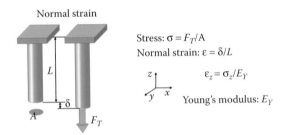

Figure S.111 The strain principle.

Strain gauges

[general] Sensor strip that sends off an electrical SIGNAL on deformation. Strain gauges are made from piezoelectric ceramics materials as well as polyelectrolytes, metallic [microelectromechanical systems (MEMS)] and carbon-nanotube—POLYMER composites (e.g., PVA: polyvinyl alcohol; conductive PDMS: polydimethylsiloxane, with carbon backing), and gold nanoparticle composites and a range of electrically conductive materials. Other RESISTANCE straingauges use a conductive material embedded in a flexible strip or band, for instance in biomedical applications the "mercury-in-rubber" gauge is popular due to its versatile applications for fitting around biological appendages (toes, fingers, ankle). Most of these applications rely on resistive changes for determination of degree of starin. A different variety of strain gauge uses capacitive coupling for two layers of thin material. Other mechanisms-of-action include fiberoptic LIGHT guides. The FIBER-OPTIC changes the local reflectivity on the core-cladding transition, changing the interferometric standing wave conditions. This type of fiber is extremely narrow and can be imbedded with little or no influence on the structural integrity. The fiber-optic strain gauge is used in monitoring the structural integrity of METAL or concrete bridges and buildings, as in polymer/fiberglass structures, such as race boats and racecars for safety information. The primary difference for the fiber-optic straingauge is the location-specific information that can be imbedded in the optical signal structure for a single fiberoptic strand. The location-specific information is derived from multiplexing. Multiplexing is a technique that is also used in fiber-optic communications, carrying multiple signals simultaneously on a single fiber leading to

numerous individual terminal stations on a station-specific basis. The strain gauge was invented by Arthur Claude Ruge (1905–2000) and Edward E. Simmons Jr. (1911–2004) in 1938. Strain gauges have a very high duty cycle and can measure strain fluctuation in the order of several hundred kHz, also dependent on the size and thickness of the sensor material. There is usually a trade-off between the range of applied force that can be tolerated and the frequency response. A flexible strain gauge can be wrapped around a flexible tube to measure relative local pressure changes based on the radial EXPANSION. In order to enhance accuracy and avoid environmental influences two strain gauges can be matched in a WHEATSTONE BRIDGE type configuration, adjusting for optimal RESOLUTION on one strain gauge while the other is not subjected to change, other than environmental conditions, specifically temperature effects (see Figure S.112).

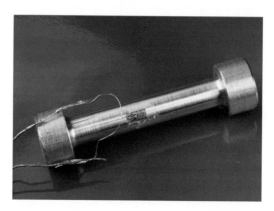

Figure S.112 Strain gauge. (Courtesy of www.doitpoms.ac.uk/; University of Cambridge, Cambridge, UK.)

Stratosphere

[energy, general, geophysics, thermodynamics] Atmospheric shell around the EARTH, the second layer of ATMOSPHERE on top of the TROPOSPHERE and below the MESOSPHERE. The stratosphere spans from an altitude at approximately 10–50 km, while the stratosphere above the poles starts at an altitude of 8 km and above the equator as high as 18 km. The stratosphere forms a protective layer from ULTRAVIOLET RADIATION due to the absorption of UVB and UVC in the formation of atomic (O) and diatomic oxygen (O_2) from ozone (O_3) in the outer edge of the stratosphere (stratopause), which are recombining in the mid-stratosphere to form ozone again. The recombination process releases ENERGY, which makes the middle stratosphere warmer than the lower stratosphere, which contributes to its stability. The outer edge of the stratosphere has a temperature just at $270\,\mathrm{K} \cong -3°C$, just below the FREEZING point of water. Commercial AIR traffic takes place in the lower stratosphere, 9–12 km altitude. Due to the lower density than the troposphere the air-drag for the planes is reduced, resulting in more fuel-efficient flight. In comparison, the Concorde would fly at 18 km altitude with velocity of Mach 2 (twice the speed of SOUND), and the Lockheed SR-71 blackbird spy plane would cruise at 26 km altitude at Mach 3. The stratosphere has various flow mechanisms. Horizontal MIXING is more prevalent than vertical mixing. One specific flow mechanism resulting from thermal and chemical gradients under the influence of GRAVITATIONAL WAVES is quasi-biennial OSCILLATION. Quasi-biennial oscillation is characteristic for the stratosphere and was discovered in the 1950s by meteorologists from Great Britain and has shown great influence on large weather patterns, such as the monsoon. In the quasi-biennial oscillation the quasiperiodic oscillation period in 28–29 months, yielding fluctuations in wind passage in the equatorial zonal alternating between eastward and westward. The alternating wind regimes originate in the upper level of the lower stratosphere and migrate downwards at about 1 km per month, where the propagation is subject to a damped oscillation, dissipating at the tropical tropopause. The downward propagation on the westward flow is usually more irregular than that of the westward flow. Hence the

AMPLITUDE of the easterly migration is about twice as large as that with respect to the westerly PHASE. The quasi-biennial oscillation has been confirmed by weather balloon observations (see Figure S.113).

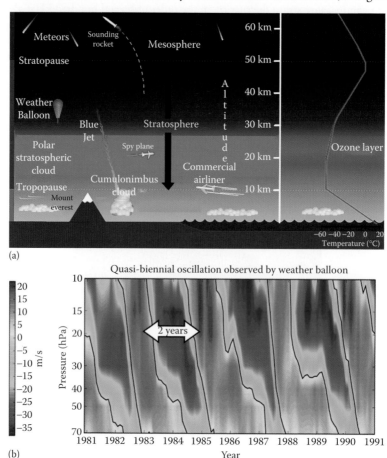

(a)

(b)

Figure S.113 (a) Stratosphere. (Courtesy of Randy Russell, University Corporation for Atmospheric Research [UCAR], Copyright 2009, http://scied.ucar.edu/imagecontent/stratosphere-diagram.) and (b) Quasi-biennial oscillations in the pressure outline of the stratosphere. (Courtesy of The Freie Universität Berlin [Germany; Markus Kunze] supplies a QBO data set that comprises raw "insonde" observations from Canton Island, Gan, and Singapore based on the work of Naujokat, B. and Naujokat, B., 1986. An update of the observed quasi-biennial oscillation of the stratospheric winds over the tropics. *J. Atmos. Sci.*, 43, 1873–1877.)

Stream function

[fluid dynamics] A two-dimensional flow will originate in any arbitrary (but fixed) point (point A) and flow to a second point in the two-dimensional plane that is variable (point B) in its location. The FLUX between these two point can be represented by any line connecting point A and B, without leaving the boundary conditions (remaining with a confined area), without losing or gaining mass, represented by a stream function Ψ. The flow will adhere to the Navier-Stokes equation. For any point in the coordinate system (x, y) {"x" the abscissa for the coordinate of point A} there are velocities associated $u = -(1/\rho)(\partial\Psi/\partial s)$ and $v = +(1/\rho)(\partial\Psi/\partial s)$ (fluid density: ρ) that provide stream-lines that form an ANGLE (θ) with the normal to the curve (s) connecting A and B at any location δs, represented as $\theta' = \cos\theta$; $\theta'' = \sin\theta$. The flux is represented by the steam function as $\Psi = \int_A^B (\theta' u + \theta'' v) ds$. For IRROTATIONAL FLOW the following condition applies: $(\partial^2\Psi/\partial x^2) + (\partial^2\Psi/\partial y^2) = 0$. This is the Lagrange stream-function. In three-dimensional flow (coordinate system $[r, \varphi, z]$) the flow function for incompressible, rotation free flow (axial symmetry) will adhere to $u_r = -(1/\rho)(\partial\Psi/\partial z)$, $v_z = +(1/\rho)(\partial\Psi/\partial r)$. From the stream function the streamlines can be derived through: $\nabla \Psi \cdot \vec{u} = 0$. The streamlines provide a graphical interpretation of the flow by means of the density of the lines, and the cross-sectional area traversed. In practicality, the streamline represents the track followed by an individual PARTICLE, on average for a large number of particles (i.e., molecules).

Stress (σ_s)

[fluid dynamics, general, mechanics] Force (F) parallel to a cross-sectional area A resulting in the potential for deformation: $\sigma_s = F/A$. TENSILE STRESS describes the linear deformation, stretching or compressing, with forces acting along the line of action. Bulk stress is equivalent to pressure, imposing a change in volume. Shear stress represents two equal but opposing forces acting in parallel planes, providing angular deformation (*also see* SHEAR-STRESS) (see Figure S.114).

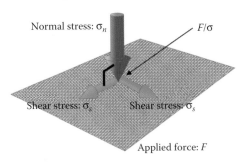

Figure S.114 The concept of Stress illustrated by vector diagram.

Stress birefringence

[general, optics] Stress applied to an optically transparent object will result is stress related changes in index-of-refraction, generating a focusing and DISPERSION, resulting in a COLOR pattern in response to the transmission of WHITE LIGHT. STRESS BIREFRINGENCE can be used for noninvasive quality control purposes. The stress may result from the structure of the device or as a result of an externally applied force (see Figure S.115).

Figure S.115 Stress birefringence. (Courtesy of Andrew Davidhazy.)

Strong nuclear force

[computational, energy, general, nuclear, quantum, relativistic, solid-state, thermodynamics] Short range strong force maintained by the elementary PARTICLE gluon. The range is approximately 1×10^{-15} m. The strong nuclear force is the strongest of the FOUR BASIC FORCES. The strong nuclear force acts on a property defined as "COLOR," which has three states: r, g, b (also referenced as: red, green and blue). This in comparison with the electromagnetic forces that act on charges (positive and negative) and the gravitational force which acts on mass (see Figure S.116).

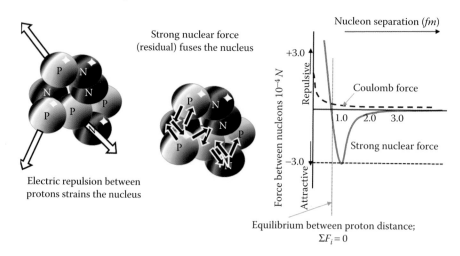

Figure S.116 Strong nuclear force interaction. The two opposing forces in a nucleus are (1) the electrical Coulomb repulsion between the positively charged protons and, respectively, (2) the residual strong nuclear force. The strong nuclear force provides the attraction between the protons and neutrons, specifically if the numbers of neutrons and respectively protons are not too much different in quantities, and hence overpowers the repulsive electrical forces.

Strouhal number (Sr = vL/ v$_v$)

[biomedical, fluid dynamics] Dimensionless number in momentum transfer relating the inverse of the VORTEX SPACING, specifically for Von Kármán vortices and in UNSTEADY FLOW. The Strouhal number provides a classification of the ratio of forces resulting from acceleration under unsteady flow to the inertial forces from changing velocity (both magnitude and direction) in the turbulent flow pattern as a function of location. In the definition the following parameters are used: v_v: frequency of VORTEX SHEDDING (VORTEX SHEDDING FREQUENCY), L characteristic length and v the velocity of flow. The Strouhal number classifies and describes the characteristic phenomena of oscillating flow, such as pulsatile BLOOD flow. For most fluids both the flow frequency and velocity profile depend on the viscosity, more specifically the FLUID characteristics (e.g., pseudoplast, Newtonian, or dilatant fluid). A small Strouhal number (Sr $\ll$ 1) correlates with a QUASI-STEADY STATE flow pattern, while high Strouhal numbers reference vortex shedding, the separation of a vortex flow pattern (at approximately Sr $= 0.2$).

Student's t-test

[biomedical, computational, solid-state] Statistical PROBABILITY distribution. The name "Student" was the pseudonym for W.S. Gosset, a quality control engineer with the Guinness beer brewery in Dublin, Ireland to hide his identity from the employers that were afraid of information about the processes leaking out. The publication in 1908 set the stage for all modern statistical analysis based on the distribution of the deviation from the mean value ($\bar{X}$) of a series of observations (n) described as $P_{\text{population}} = (\bar{X} - \mu_{\text{stat}})/(s_{\text{variance}}/\sqrt{n})$, where $\mu_{\text{stat}} = \sum_{i=1}^{k} x_i P_{\text{stat}}(x_i)$ provides the weighed mean based on individual value (x_i) with respective probability of occurring ($P_{\text{stat}}(x_i)$) and s_{variance} ($s_{\text{variance}}^2 = [1/(n-1)]\sum_i^n (x_i - \bar{x})^2$) is the standard deviation (also referred to as σ_s) of the variable x, with mean value $\bar{x}$. The t-test depends on whether the population distribution is a "NORMAL DISTRIBUTION." The distribution of the population of values ($P_{\text{population}}$) is evenly distributed around zero, or the mean value (depending on notation), with a "Gaussian shaped" slope that is a function of the number of DEGREES OF FREEDOM defining the variable x, described in the t-distribution as t_m, with m the number of degrees of freedom. The larger the number of degrees of freedom the closer the t-distribution approaches a Z-distribution.

Sturgeon, William (1783–1850)

[general] Scientist and inventor from Great Britain who developed the electromotor in 1832, based on the work of the early (static ELECTRICITY) work by the Scottish monk Andrew Gordon (1712–1751) in the 1740s. additional contributions came from the theoretical work by ANDRÉ-MARIE AMPÈRE (1775–1836) in 1820 and MICHAEL FARADAY (1791–1867) in 1821 (see Figure S.117).

Figure S.117 William Sturgeon (1783–1850).

Sturm, Jacques Charles François (1803–1855)

[computational] Mathematician from France. Jacques Sturm dedicated his work to solving complex integral equations and polynomials, specifically defining the roots of higher order polynomials (see Figure S.118).

Figure S.118 Jacques Charles François Sturm (1803–1855).

Sturm–Liouville technique

[computational] Standard procedure to solve certain types of differential equations by developing into eigenfunctions, with solutions containing eigenvalues. The Sturm–Liouville technique is a collaborative effort between JACQUES CHARLES FRANÇOIS STURM (1803–1855) and JOSEPH LIOUVILLE (1809–1882). The differential equation is expressed as a interaction between a set of functions (continuous functions: $f(x)$; $g(x)$; $h(x)$) with EIGENFUNCTION "SOLUTION" $y(x)$ outlined as $-(d/dx)\left[f(x)[\partial y(x)/\partial x]\right] + g(x)\,y(x) = c_i h(x)\,y(x)$, with the boundary conditions specified through the constant c_i, the eigenvalues ($c_1 < c_2 < c_3 < \cdots < \infty$). The constraints on the eigenfunction is that it is continuously differentiable in the domain of the function. The function $h(x)$ defines the weight or NORMALIZATION.

Subatomic particles

[general] Particles that constitute the atomic model described by Bohr as well as the ELEMENTARY PARTICLES that form the atomic particles. Whereas atoms for the building blocks for MACROSCOPIC entities, ranging from LATTICE structures to molecules to objects. The objects form the components and dressing for planets and the atoms and molecules for the foundation of the nuclear reactions maintaining stars. In the opposite direction the ATOM is constructed from constituents that can be dissected in smaller and smaller entities. Atomic particles are electrons in the shells; respectively neutrons and protons in the NUCLEUS (nuclides). The atomic components are constructed form elementary PARTICLE we categorize as fermions and bosons. Fermions is a subgroup of what is known as elementary particles with odd spin (1/2, 3/2, 5/2, …), whereas BOSON have integer spin (0, 1, 2, …). These groups are further split in quarks and leptons. These subgroups are further subdivided in generations. The first generation of elementary particles are the ELECTRON ($\bar{e}$), UP-QUARK (u), down quark (d) and electron-type NEUTRINO (v_e). The second generation consists of MUON (μ), strange quark (s), CHARM quark (c) and muon-type neutrino (v_μ). The third generation has top quark (t; also known as truth) and bottom quark (b) next to the tau particle (τ) and tau-type neutrino (v_τ). In addition all these first through third generation particles also have anti-particles, generally designated by a bar across the base symbol for the first order particle ($\bar{u}$, $\bar{d}$, $\bar{v}_e$, etc.), except for the positron; the anti-particle of the electron: e^+. Hadrons are a family of particles that are constructed from quarks and antiquarks in a range of combinatory assemblies, presumably the PROTON the only stable HADRON in existence; accounting for their possible neutron DECAY (however in general the NEUTRON is also stable as NUCLIDE. Hadrons consist of subfamilies: baryons and mesons. For every hadron species there is an antiparticle. Baryons are MATTER particles, and mesons are designated as force particles. All baryons consist of three quarks, most well-known are the neutron and the proton in this class. Additional baryons are "Lambda-Zero" (Λ^0); "Omega Minus" (Ω^-); as well as permutations of Δ; Ξ; and Σ. Mesons are constructed of quark—anti-quark pairs only. So far no further delineation has been found for even smaller units that form the fermions and bosons, but this is currently mainly due to the equipment limitations required for verification. Some of the "elementary" particles were only theoretical assumptions dating back half a century and have only recently been provided with experimental support. (*Note*: The HIGGS BOSON [*see* QUARK, ELECTRON, *and* PROTON]) (see Figure S.119).

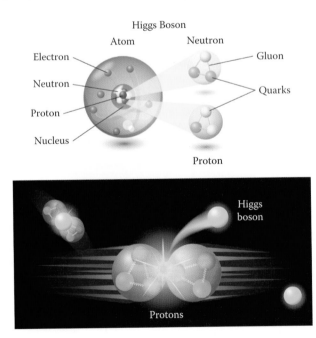

Figure S.119 Subatomic particle outline.

Sublimation

[general, thermodynamics] Phase transition from solid to gas. The terminology vapor is frequently used to identify a gas in equilibrium with its solid or liquid phase. The atomic or molecular energy exceeds the binding energy constraining them to their solid phase. Sublimation reduces the fraction of high-energy components in the solid, hence bringing the average kinetic energy down, thus reducing the overall temperature of the system, that is, cooling (see Figure S.120).

Figure S.120 Sublimation.

Subshell

[atomic, solid-state, thermodynamics] The Bohr atomic model is constructed in primary and secondary shells. The primary shells are named in outgoing order as follows: K, L, M, N, O, P, and Q, corresponding with the principal quantum number n, which is a positive integer and starts at $n = 1$ associated with the K-shell. The subshells are named: s, p, d, f, and g. The spins of the respective electrons is defined by Hunds' rule (sometimes also called Hund's law). The s-subshell can hold two electrons, with respective opposite spin. The s-subshell has orbital quantum number (second quantum number, the first or principal quantum number n represents the) $\ell = 0$ and is present in every shell, with incremental numerator number: 1s for K-shell, 2s for L-shell, and so on. In the L-shell there are two subshells 2s and 2p, where the p-subshell is present in every shell outward from the second ordinal. The p-subshell has orbital or azimuthal quantum number. $\ell = 1$ and has the potential for containing six electrons (respectively two each for the third quantum number (i.e., magnetic quantum number) which defines the angular momentum, which ranges from $m_\ell = [-\ell, -\ell + 1, \ldots, 0, \ldots, \ell - 1, \ell]$, or $2\ell + 1$ possible states, yielding: $m_\ell = -1$, $m_\ell = 0$, $m_\ell = 1$). In the Bohr atomic model the f—subshell may contain a total of 7 pairs of electrons, 14 total and the f—subshell appears in the N-shell for the first time. One can illustrate the configuration of the shell/subshell arrangement with the appropriate energy nomenclatures in tabular format.

Sun

[astrophysics, atomic, general, geophysics, nuclear, optics, quantum] Star central to our own solar system. Hydrogen nuclear fusion reactor producing a broad spectrum of particulate and electromagnetic radiation, and emitting on average 63×10^6 W/m^2. Of which only approximately 1.2×10^3 W/m^2 reaches Earth on perpendicular incidence. Note that the global radiance fluctuations are a function of the location on Earth (angle of incidence), time of day and the seasonal distance to the Sun (r^{-2} dependance). The average distance from the Sun to Earth is 1.496×10^{11} m. The average surface temperature of the Sun is 5778 K. The mass of the Sun is in approximation $M_\odot = 1.989 \times 10^{30}$ kg, containing greater than 99.8% of the total mass for our solar system of Sun and planets (Jupiter containing a significant total mass as second largest object), with solar radius $R_\odot = 6.958 \times 10^8$ m. The Sun and associated solar system including Earth are close to the outer edge of the Milky Way galaxy and we all orbit the center of the Milky Way galaxy.

Sunlight takes on average 8.3 min to reach Earth, traveling at the speed of LIGHT. The FUSION process in the PLASMA of the Sun proceeds as follows. The first to steps are the fusion of hydrogen; proton fusion ($_1^1H$) with the release of a positron (e^+) and electron NEUTRINO (ν_e): $_1^1H + _1^1H \rightarrow _1^2H + e^+ + \nu_e$, followed by step two $_1^1H + _1^2H \rightarrow _2^3He + \gamma$, emitting high ENERGY gamma radiation (γ) and deuterium ($_1^2H$). There are a number of possibilities for the third stage fusion process, the dominate process: $_2^3He + _2^3He \rightarrow _2^4He + _1^1H + _1^1H$, forming helium. All three process produce approximately $27\,MeV = 4.326 \times 10^{-12}$ J. The outlines of this process was first described by the German nuclear physicist HANS ALBRECHT BETHE (1906–2005) in 1939, for which he was awarded the Nobel Prize in Physics in 1967. The work of Hans Bethe was based on the initial conceptual description by the British physicist Sir ARTHUR STANLEY EDDINGTON (1882–1944) in 1920. The Sun holds the planets in the solar system, with respective mass m, in orbit by means of gravitational attraction as a function of distance (r) as defined by SIR ISAAC NEWTON's (1642–1727) LAW OF UNIVERSAL GRAVITATION: $F = G(mM_\odot/r^2)$, with $G = 6.67 \times 10^{-11}\,Nm^2/kg^2$ the gravitational constant. The Sun frequently ejects plasma jets known as solar flares, which are accompanied by intense RADIO frequency emissions that influence the wireless communications on Earth (see Figure S.121).

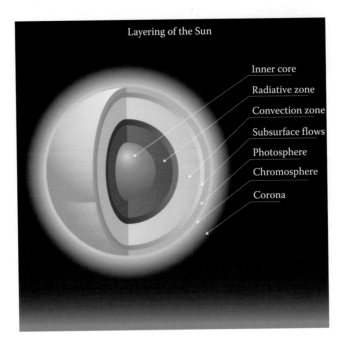

Figure S.121 Sun.

Sun spot

[geophysics, optics] Disturbances in the Sun's convection currents. Sun spots have an apparent 11 year cycle, first observed by GALILEO GALILEI (1564–1642) in 1610. Sun spots are associated with a MAGNETIC FIELD in the order of 1kG (compared to BAR MAGNET $B = 100$ G) (see Figure S.122).

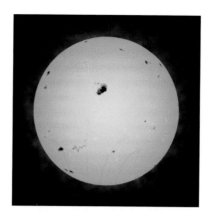

Figure S.122 Sun spots.

Sundog

[geophysics, optics] Atmospheric phenomena that form "mirror" images of the SUN on either side of the Sun in the sky, also referred to as parhelion, frequently coinciding with a halo. The mock suns are the result of atmospheric diffraction due to pressure layers and thermal gradients. The primary aspect of sundogs is in the refraction from ice crystals. In case the Sundogs are formed in pairs they will be at approximately 22° angle from the Sun from the point of the observer (*also see* RAINBOW) (see Figure S.123).

Figure S.123 Sundog.

Superconducting quantum interference device (SQUID)

[general] Superconductive MAGNETIC FIELD sensing device. SQUIDS are used to measure minute magnetic fields, such as produced by the brain, with RESOLUTION and sensitivity down to 10^{-18} T. In comparison, the magnetic field at the surface of an atomic NUCLEUS: 10^{12} T; hair dryer in close proximity 10^{-3} T; small BAR MAGNET near the poles 10^{-2} T; and the geomagnetic filed at the earth's surface 10^{-12} T. Squids are miniature superconductive current loop devices developed by the team at the Ford Research Laboratories (part of the Ford Motor Company; Dearborn, MI, USA) consisting of Robert C. Jaklevic (mid-twentieth century–), John J. Lambe (mid-twentieth century–), James Mercereau (mid-twentieth century–), and Arnold Silver (mid-twentieth century–) in 1964. The squid mechanism-of-action is based on the Josephson Effect defined

by the theoretical physicist from the United Kingdom (Wales), BRIAN DAVID JOSEPHSON (1940–) in 1962. The sensitivity is based on the measured current which is a function of the magnetic FLUX passing through the SQUID loop with diameter d and under applied magnetic field strength B, under constraints: $I_c^2 = \left(I_{c1} - I_{c2}\right)^2 + 4I_{c1}I_{c1}\cos^2\left(\pi d^2 B/(h/2e)\right)$, where the current is split in the half circumferential proportions I_{c1}, respectively I_{c2}, where $h = 6.62606957 \times 10^{-34}$ m^{2}kg/s the PLANCK'S CONSTANT (see Figure S.124).

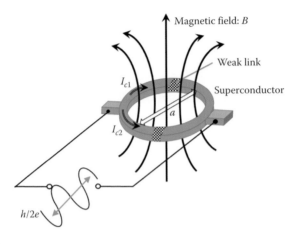

Figure S.124 SQUID design.

Superconductivity

[atomic, energy, solid-state] The fact that materials lose all electrical BARRIERS and have impedance of zero at cryogenic temperatures. The work of KAMERLINGH ONNES (1853–1926) revealed the first signs of superconductivity in 1911.

Supercritical fluid state

[thermodynamics] Specific phenomenological state/phase of a liquid or GAS that is only available above the CRITICAL POINT, explained best in the P–T DIAGRAM (pressure vs. temperature). For water the critical point is defined by $P = 218.3$ atm, $T = 374.15°C$, at this point the FLUID is a supercritical fluid with density $\rho = 0.315$ g/mL. In comparison the respective characteristics of gas, liquid and supercritical state are exemplified in the table in order of MAGNITUDE respectively.

STATE	DENSITY (kg/m³)	DIFFUSIVITY (cm²/s)	VISCOSITY (kg/ms)
Supercritical	200–900	10^{-4}	10^{-3}
Gas	1	10^{-1}	10^{-3}
Liquid	1000	10^{-4}	10^{-1}

The supercritical state is identified by conditions of compressibility, which for a LIQUID would under normal circumstances be not allowed, meanwhile the supercritical fluid has the density of a liquid under standard pressure and temperature. The supercritical fluid does neither behave as a liquid nor as a gas, but has characteristics of both and is a new PHASE or state-of-matter.

Supercritical mass

[general] A threshold mass of ISOTOPE material beyond which the material spontaneously fusses, the fissionable material spontaneously initiates a CHAIN REACTION. The most well-known critical mass is the FUSION of URANIUM (enriched) (^{235}U) to produce an extraordinary amount of ENERGY when two segments of approximately half the critical mass ate forcefully joined (by means of an explosion) to result in an increase in volume that its surface area, producing a perceived surplus of emitted neutrons causing the DECAY reaction to escalate, resulting in a thermo-nuclear explosion at 52 kg. Other critical mass data for specific ELEMENTS are ^{233}U → 15 kg; ^{236}Pl → 9.04–10.07 kg (range); ^{236}Np → 7 kg; and ^{252}Ca → 2.73 kg.

Superfluid

[atomic, nuclear] Extraordinary PHASE of a medium, not GAS, not LIQUID, not solid, which behaves with viscosity $\eta_{Kin} = 0$. The superfluid has entropy $S = 0$, and all atoms are in the same QUANTUM STATE, with identical momentum. The best known example of a superfluid state is Helium, which becomes a superfluid with decreasing temperature at 2.18 K. Superfluid Helium is the most remarkable heat CONDUCTOR (virtually perfect conduction), while remaining electrically neutral, that is, an INSULATOR.

Superheated steam

[general, thermodynamics] Water VAPOR at temperature above 100°C at 1 atmosphere pressure.

Superheated vapor state

[thermodynamics] Evaporated state of a LIQUID at temperature above the vaporization temperature.

Supernova

[astronomy/astrophysics, energy, general] The classification of the end-stage of a STAR, culminating in an explosion and associated massive emission of NEUTRON, photons, neutrinos and variety of charged particles and electromagnetic RADIATION in massive quantities. On EARTH the NEUTRINO and PHOTON emission from an exploding supernova (SN 1987A) in the Tarantula Nebula (also known as the "star-forming region" 30 Doradus or NGC 2070) in the Southern hemispherical orientation for the general direction of the GALAXY: Large Magellanic Cloud (LMC) in the Dorado constellation; at 168,000 light-years DISTANCE from Earth reached the underground detection stations in Cleveland, Ohio, and Tokyo, Japan, in 1987. The emissions from Supernova 1987A, called for the first observation, are still being observed (see Figure S.125).

Figure S.125 Supernova.

Supersonic flow

[fluid dynamics] Flow conditions with propagation velocity greater than the speed of SOUND. Supersonic flow results in a dramatic cooling effect, for instance accelerating from rest at room temperature ($25°C = 298\,K$) to Mach 3 will reduce the temperature of the FLUID to $-166°C = 107\,K$. Alternatively an object traveling at Mach 3 will increase its surface temperature due to FRICTION to $530°C \approx 800\,K$ $530°C \approx 800\,K$. Supersonic flow can be achieved through SHOCK-WAVE formation (see Figure S.126).

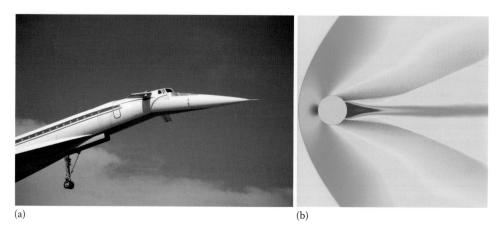

(a)   (b)

Figure S.126 Supersonic flow. (a) Supersonic aircraft carrier: Concorde (discontinued air transport plane) and (b) computer flow simulation, false-color indication of stream flow velocity.

Surface charge density (σ_{elec})

[general] Charge density on the surface of a CONDUCTOR, evenly spread, defined by the total charge Q on the object, divided by the surface area A: $\sigma_{elec} = Q/A$. For a nonconductive medium the local charge density will be location specific since there is no free migration of charge. The charge surface density on a curved surface for a conductor will be a function of the radius of curvature, with greater charge density with smaller radius of curvature: $\sigma_{elec}, r/\sigma_{elec}, R = R/r$, where R denotes the large radius of curvature (such as defining the outline for the body of a rounded cone) and r the radius of curvature of the pointy tip (see Figure S.127).

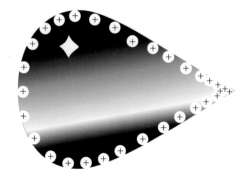

Figure S.127 Surface charge density.

Surface energy

[chemical, fluid dynamics, mechanics, thermodynamics] ENERGY aspect of SURFACE TENSION. The work performed by the force that creates the new surface area. Materials have specific surface energy, for instance the surface energy for the following solids is as follows: KCl has a surface energy of $E_s' = 0.11\,J/m^2$, glass

(BK7) $E_s' = 4.4\,\mathrm{J/m^2}$, mica in VACUUM $E_s' = 5.0\,\mathrm{J/m^2}$, whereas mica in AIR has $E_s' = 0.38\,\mathrm{J/m^2}$, granite has $E_s' = 200\,\mathrm{J/m^2}$. Contamination of the substance will reduce the surface energy. Surface energy is an important factor in crack formation for a solid, but also defines the BUBBLE formation for a VAPOR bubble from a LIQUID or solid.

Surface gravitational wave

[acoustics, fluid dynamics, geophysics, mechanics] WAVE on the surface of a fluid (LIQUID or GAS) that are influenced by gravitational restoring forces. Surface GRAVITATIONAL WAVES are described as Lamb waves on the surface of an AIR mass, or the "surf" on the water of oceans and lakes, in particular breaking on the shore of a landmass (*see* WAVE *or* SURFACE WAVE). On a QUANTUM mechanical level the other concept of gravitational wave relates to transverse wave of massless quantum PARTICLE. The concept of quantum-mechanical gravitational waves is directly linked to the ALBERT EINSTEIN's (1879–1955) principle of general relativity (see Figure S.128).

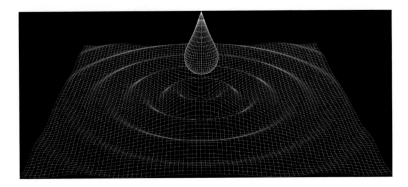

Figure S.128 Surface gravitational wave.

Surface phenomena of Liquids

[chemical, fluid dynamics, mechanics, thermodynamics] A LIQUID is a continuous medium with minimally one surface (spherical symmetry), the surface is exposed to forces and ENERGY constraints. Within a medium similar phenomena can occur in the form of BUBBLE, also only one continuous surface. In a container the walls of the container define the number of surfaces and one surface may be exposed to GAS (i.e., AIR or liquid vapor). At any surface the LIQUID will have stress and strain expressed by one of the phenomena: SURFACE TENSION.

Surface Potential Energy

[biomedical, chemical, computational, fluid dynamics, mechanics, thermodynamics] Theoretical model of the ENERGY configuration of a system, specifically atoms with respect to their arrangement. The concept is used primarily in computational chemistry. The surface potential energy, also known as potential energy surface, defines the relationship between the energy configuration of a MOLECULE and the geometry of the molecule, either in graphical format or mathematically. The graphical representation for instance represents the potential energy for a molecule as a function of the bond-length and the ANGLE of the atomic bond. In molecular MECHANICS the potential surface energy described the molecular energy with respect to bending, TORSION, stretching, and so on. Under QUANTUM mechanical approach the energy function outlines the work effort with respect to the SCHRÖDINGER WAVE EQUATION. The two-dimensional energy surface can illustrate the atomic configuration (bond length and bond angle) that is more susceptible to chemical interaction: transition state. This model does not account for the inherent incessant vibrations of the molecule, neither for deviations from equilibrium. Under equilibrium conditions the SCHRÖDINGER EQUATION for the molecule can be solved by assuming a simple HARMONIC OSCILLATION (with spring constant k) around equilibrium (interatomic equilibrium DISTANCE $\vec{q}_e$) in the direction of the connecting line of the interatomic bond links ($\vec{q}$); using $E = (1/2)k(\vec{q} - \vec{q}_e)^2$. This potential energy is however not valid when the atomic separation is far from equilibrium length. The potential energy levels off, drops off, with increasing separation on the bond-length. In QUANTUM MECHANICS the molecular Hamiltonian is defined by the ATOMIC NUMBER (Z) and respective distances between nuclei (R_{12} [fixed]; r_{1i}; r_{ij}, electron orbits: i, j) within the molecular structure and respective molecular constituents ($_1$; $_2$; mass m_1) as $\hat{H} = -(1/2)\sum_i \nabla_i^2 - \sum_i(1/2m_1)\nabla_1^2 - \sum_{1,i}(Z_1/r_{1i}) + \sum_{1>2}(Z_1 Z_2/R_{12}) + \sum_{i>j}(1/r_{ij})$, where the term $V_{eN}(\vec{r}, \vec{R}) = -\sum_{1,i} Z_1/r_{1i}$ represents the electron (e) nuclear potential energy (N DEGREES OF FREEDOM). The SURFACE ENERGY potential prevents the Hamiltonian from being separated. Without surface potential energy the Hamiltonian is separable with energy eigenvalues: $E = E_A + E_B$, and eigenfunctions: $\Psi(q_1, q_2) = \Psi_A(q_1)\Psi_B(q_2)$; $\hat{H}_A(q_1)\Psi_A(q_1) = E_A\Psi_A(q_1)$, and $\hat{H}_B(q_2)\Psi_B(q_2) = E_B\Psi_B(q_2)$. The electron–nuclear potential inherently ties the electronic degrees of freedom to the nuclear degrees of freedom. The potential energy surface applies to the molecular dimension (R) as $\hat{H}_e(\vec{r}; \vec{R})\Psi(\vec{r}; \vec{R}) = E_e(\vec{R})\Psi(\vec{r}; \vec{R})$ (*also see* BORN–OPPENHEIMER APPROXIMATION) (see Figure S.129).

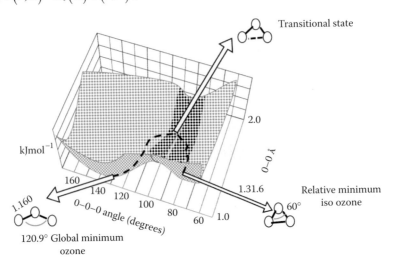

Figure S.129 Graphical representation of Surface potential Energy.

Surface roughness

[acoustics, fluid dynamics, mechanics] Unevenness in the profile of a system, either object, channel (river) or PIPE. The ROUGHNESS defines the absolute or relative deviations from ideally smooth for a segment or with respect to the attainable effects resulting from a surface treatment or construction technique, next to the choice of material (e.g., ceramics vs. wood vs. metal). Commonly used surface parameters are: roughness area $R_a = 1/n\sum_{i=1}^{n}|z_i|$ (z_i the localized deviation from perfect flat, measured in n locations); root-mean-squared roughness $R_q = \sqrt{(1/n\sum_{i=1}^{n} z_i^2)}$; or with respect to the maximum allowable height of the imperfections. More detailed, in three dimensions: $R_a = 1/mn\sum_{k=0}^{m-1}\sum_{\ell=0}^{n-1}|z(x_k, y_\ell) - \mu_{ave}|$, $\mu_{ave} = 1/mn\sum_{k=0}^{m-1}\sum_{\ell=0}^{n-1}z(x_k, y_\ell)$ representing the preferred level (e.g., radius) or average. Additional parameters used in defining the surface profile, as for instance used in design drawings (CAD drawings) is the slope of the unevenness by means of deviation from level under ANGLE α: $R_{dq} = \sqrt{(1/n\sum_{i=1}^{n}\alpha_i^2)}$ or $R_{da} = 1/n\sum_{i=1}^{n}|\alpha_i|$. The angular deviations are determined from surface elevation iterations. One standard compares unevenness as a function of linear location x as $\alpha_i = 1/60dx(z_{i+3} - 9z_{i+2} + 45z_{i+1} - 45z_{i-1} + 9z_{i-2} - z_{i-3})$, around flat z_i. The latter would apply to machining instructions such as turning a rod on a lathe. These parameters are set under industry standards implemented by professional organizations such as American Society of Mechanical Engineers (ASME) or ISO STANDARDS (International Organization for Standardization). Surface finish contributes to the FRICTION between two surfaces as well as the influence on the formation of BOUNDARY LAYER effects during flow. The three-dimensional configuration of a surface can be examined by atomic force microscopy, Optical interference profilometry scanning (e.g., OPTICAL COHERENCE TOMOGRAPHY) or Scanning Electron

Microscope on MICROSCOPIC level, or by surveying tools on MACROSCOPIC scale. Controlling the roughness can result in expensive processes, increasing the final price/cost for the device. In general during design the surface roughness is specified with acceptable tolerance for the specific goal of the use of the material, device or structure. Optical devices are specified in surface treatment with respect to the wavelength (λ), not more deviation than a fraction of the average or standard wavelength. Also referred to as roughness. May also be described as surface texture (see Figure S.130).

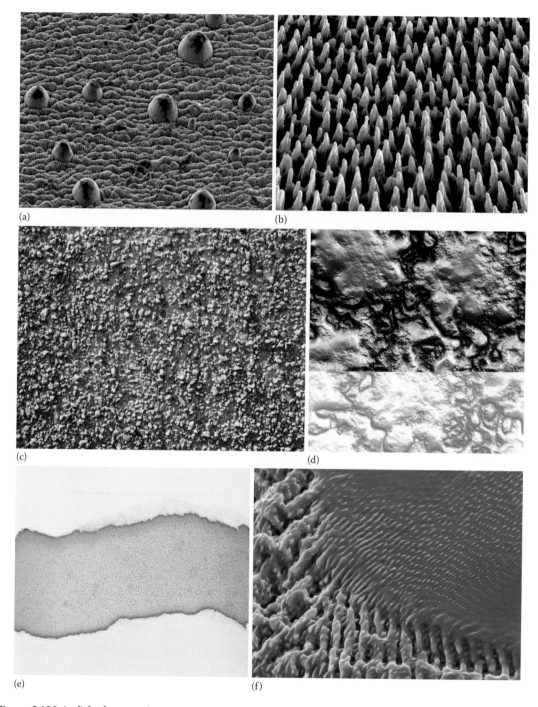

(a)

(b)

(c)

(d)

(e)

(f)

Figure S.130 (a–f) Surface roughness.

Surface tension

[biomedical, chemical, fluid mechanics, mechanics, thermodynamics] Stress in the SURFACE of a LIQUID, equivalent to the WORK (i.e., force [F] multiplied by displacement $d\ell$ given as $W = Fd\ell$) per unit area to change the size of the area (dA) (increase, work performed by decrease; most liquids at most TEMPERATURE ranges): $\sigma_{surface} = Fd\ell/dA$. For a cord or rod confining a soap film the area can for instance be expressed as $dA = 2Ld\ell$, since the demarcation between the film and outside has a length on both sides of the BARRIER. Physical equivalence in a SKIN stretched over a hoop, for instance for a musical drum. A surface layer may be on a continuous medium or film (e.g., soap BUBBLE). Surface tension is generally independent of the layer thickness, reducing the effect to a molecular phenomenon (i.e., VAN DER WAALS FORCE). Surface tension on a droplet will confine a medium by force, hence the pressure (VAPOR PRESSURE) inside the droplet will always be greater that the outside pressure. The surface tension on a single surface medium is defined by the LAPLACE LAW. One specific exception to the single surface is in the ALVEOLI of the LUNG. Another surface tension phenomenon is in the boundary between a vessel and the surface of a liquid. Liquids may adhere to the vessel surface ("wet the surface of the container") or be repelled by the container WALL ("liquid does not wet the surface"). When the liquid ADHESION (i.e., COHESION) is strong the liquid will form a negative meniscus, in case the adhesion to the vessel is stronger than the cohesion of the liquid the liquid will form a positive meniscus. One specific example is water in a glass beaker. Since glass is polar it will tend to attract the polar water molecules applying grease to the wall of the beaker will separate the polar attraction by the GLASS from the cohesive Vander Waals force and the MENISCUS will flip negative. A positive meniscus is often an indication that there is potential for the liquid to actively CREEP up the wall. The creep is especially noticeable in a narrow tube, creating CAPILLARY ACTION, making the liquid climb the wall of the tube for a considerable DISTANCE, depending on the tube diameter and the density of the liquid. Contact ANGLES for some interfaces vary as a function of temperature. Wetting liquids on a clean surface (i.e., water on glass) will continue to spread until the water has reach molecular thickness (i.e., MONOLAYER). Surface tension can be broken by means of chemical binding (dissolve the chemical based on the match in polar nature, whereas OIL is very nonpolar) with a SURFACTANT, such as ordinary soap (see Figure S.131).

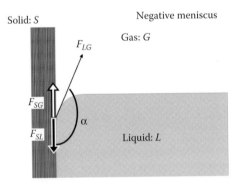

Figure S.131 Surface tension: tension between liquid and solid surface of container.

Most organic liquids—glass	0°–10°
Mercury—copper	0°
Pure water—glass	0°
Water—glass	20°
Kerosene—glass	26°
Water—silver	90°
Water—parafin	106°
Mercury—glass	148°

Surface waves

[fluid dynamics] Waves on the surface of a medium (primarily liquid, alternative approach for solids) generated from equilibrium (*also see* WAVE EQUATION, for general theoretical description of periodic motion). Surface waves can result from wind blowing over the waver surface, or as a result of EARTHQUAKE (i.e., TSUNAMI). This phenomenon is governed by the CONSERVATION LAWS in the form of the Euler equations for a medium with constant density: $\rho = \rho_0$. The VELOCITY POTENTIAL (ϕ) for a two-dimensional plane-wave with displacement in the y-direction, propagating in the x-direction will be irrotational and satisfies the condition: $(\partial\phi^2/\partial x^2) + (\partial\phi^2/\partial y^2) = 0$, with the condition $\partial\phi/\partial n = 0$. This is described by the Cauchy-Poisson wave equation. The vertical displacement (i.e., MOTION around equilibrium level) as a function of linear direction of propagation is given as $h(x,t) = 1/\pi x \left\{ (gt^2/2x) - (1/3\times5)(gt^2/2x)^3 + (1/3\times5\times7)(gt^2/2x)^5 - \ldots\ldots \right\}; (gt^2/2x) \ll 1$, with a constant acceleration of the PHASE of the WAVE given as $a_{ph} = (g\pi A_w/\lambda)[\cosh(2\pi^{b_a+h(x,t)/\lambda})]/[\cosh(2\pi^{b_a/\lambda})]\sin((2\pi x/\lambda) - (2\pi t/T))$, where g the GRAVITATIONAL ACCELERATION, A_w is the wave AMPLITUDE, b_a is the average depth of the water or the average DISTANCE from the solid bottom to the surface of the FLUID in motion, T the wave period and λ the wavelength. Generally, for a small displacement the surface motion can be described by a FOURIER SERIES as a sine and cosine sum (*see* WAVE EQUATION). The surface wave propagation in fact stretches the wave pattern out as it propagates with wavelength: $\lambda = 8\pi s^2/gt^2$ with t the elapsed time. The surface-wave itself propagates with the group velocity: $v_g = 0.5c\left(1 + (2kb_a/\sinh 2kb_a)\right)$, where $c = \sqrt{(g/k)}\tanh kb_a \cong$ Constant, at constant depth (b_a, the average surface height from the seafloor), and $k = 2\pi/\lambda$ is the wavenumber. Note that for example, the wave breaking on the surface is the result of a nonlinearity in the acceleration, the DISPERSION in this case is the direct result of a difference in linear acceleration on the surface as a function of both wavelength and depth defined by $a = dv_g/dt$. Alternatively: $h(s,t) \cong \sqrt{g}\,t^2/\rho\,2^{5/2}\pi^{1/2}s^{5/2}\left\{\cos(gt^2/4s) - \sin(gt^2/4s)\right\}; (gt^2/2s) \geq 1$, where s is the path of propagation. The PHASE VELOCITY of surface waves is gives as $v_{ph} = \sqrt{((g\lambda/2\pi) + (2\pi T_s/\rho\lambda))\tanh(2\pi b_a/\lambda)}$, where T_s is the LIQUID surface tension, ρ the liquid density. (p36 Fundamentele Natuurkunde, deel 3 Golven; Alonso & Finn//Fundamental University Physics #3.) Since the phase velocity is apparently a function of the wavelength a phenomenon known as WAVE DISPERSION will occur. Under dispersion the complex wave constructed of the superposition of multiple waves with a range of frequencies will deform in the process of propagation in the dispersive medium. The deformation results from the different velocities of the respective spectral components of the complex wave. The phase velocity of surface waves can be derived under condition that the wave amplitude is sufficiently small using linear theory providing for deep water: $v_{ph} = \sqrt{(g/k)}; h(s,t) > 0.4\lambda$, and for shallow water: $v_{ph} = \sqrt{((g\lambda/2\pi)(2\pi h/\lambda))} = \sqrt{gh}; h(s,t) < 0.04\lambda$ (see Figure S.132).

Figure S.132 Surface wave resulting from earthquake causing destruction due to vibration.

Surfaces of discontinuity

[fluid dynamics] *See* DISCONTINUOUS MOTIONS.

Surfactant

[biomedical, chemical, fluid mechanics, mechanics, thermodynamics] Chemical medium that has as property to lower the SURFACE TENSION of a FLUID when mixed or applied to the surface. Soap/detergents is a surfactant, designed to modify the tension between two media, for example, lowering the ADHESION of loose material from a solid (e.g., food on plate; dirt on clothing). Wettings agents and detergents generally have a molecular structure that is hydrophobic on one side and hydrophilic on the opposite side (amphiphilic). A surfactant may also be designed to have a nonlinear relation to the surface area (specifically applied to spherical configuration), defying the LAPLACE LAW. In the lungs the surfactant on the inside of the alveoli is specifically that way, made of six lipids and four proteins, adjusting to the size of the alveoli for optimal oxygen transfer between the AIR in the lung and the CELL layer. Lung surfactant is produced between week 24 and 28 of gestation. Premature babies (prior to week 35) often require surfactant replacement therapy to ensure proper VENTILATION of oxygen and carbon-dioxide. Lung surfactant can be produced artificially under synthetic circumstances (see Figure S.133).

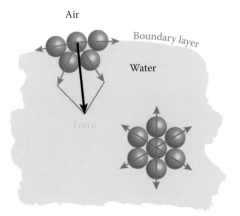

Figure S.133 Surface forces diagram.

Synapse

[biomedical, chemical] Chemical transponder between nerve CELL (at the terminal end of an axon or dendrite) that releases chemicals upon excitation by an action potential. The release of the specific chemicals are correlated to the function and location of the nerve-cell and are a chemical mediator to induce a chemical imbalance at the synapse across from the junction that will lead to a trans-membrane potential resulting in the initiation of an action-potential in the next link of SIGNAL transport to reach the final destination, either MUSCLE, brain or specific chemical organ (e.g., digestive or regulatory in the form of BLOOD acidity) (*See* NERVE) (see Figure S.134).

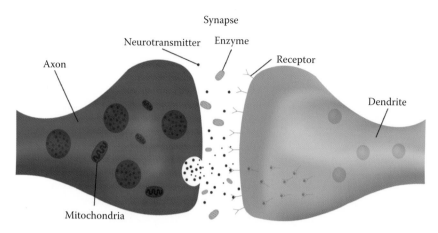

Figure S.134 Synapse.

Synaptic signaling

[biomedical, chemical, energy] Secretion of signaling molecules (i.e., NEUROTRANSMITTERS) between neurons. The chemical exchange initiates an ACTION POTENTIAL in all the neurons connecting at the "router-station." Signals can be amplified in this manner by exciting multiple neurons and hence increasing the communication channels to one or multiple terminal locations in the sympathetic and PARASYMPATHETIC NERVE SYSTEM as well as the brain and brain-stem (see Figure S.135).

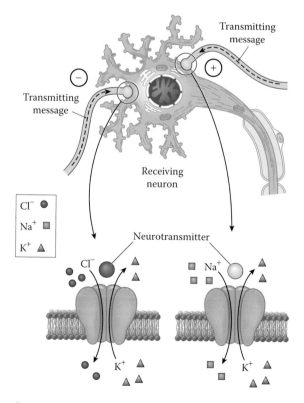

Figure S.135 Synaptic signaling.

Synchrotron

[astronomy/astrophysics, atomic, energy, nuclear] Linear PARTICLE ACCELERATOR. The largest linear accelerator is at the European Organization for Nuclear Research; CERN facility ("Conseil Européen pour la Recherche Nucléaire" French) at the border between Switzerland and France. The CERN SYNCHROTRON can reach kinetic energies for protons in excess of 10^3 GeV, simultaneously for in the order of 10^{13} protons (see Figure S.136).

Figure S.136 Synchrotron. (Courtesy of Fermi National Accelerator Laboratory [Fermilab], Batavia, IL.)

Synchrotron radiation

[astronomy/astrophysics, atomic, energy, nuclear] RADIATION emitted by a charged PARTICLE when accelerated around a curved path, change in direction. In comparison, every charged particle under linear acceleration will emit electromagnetic radiation.

Systolic pressure

[biomedical] Pressure achieved by the full contraction of the HEART. The maximum pressure applied to BLOOD ejection into the compliant vascular system of the biological body. High level pressure is measured by the SPHYGMOMANOMETER. The auscultation technique involves wrapping an inflatable cuff around the elbow of the arm and inflating the external pressure above any reasonably known high systolic pressure, and subsequently systematically reducing the applied pressure to balance with the pressure in the tissue applied to the brachial artery in order to listen for the KOROTKOFF SOUNDS. In combination with the DIASTOLIC PRESSURE these are some of the vital signs acquired during a routine visit to the doctor's office, next to heart-rate and body temperature. The aortic pressure fluctuates between the systolic and the diastolic pressure with each heartbeat. In case any of these show deviations from the norm additional diagnostic techniques may involve obtaining an ELECTROCARDIOGRAM (ECG), next to further analysis of the respiratory system with breathing exercises. A variety of physical and psychological reasons can result primarily in a change in systolic, and secondary in diastolic, pressure. One of the most common causes for BLOOD PRESSURE variability is general heart disease, followed in second place by reduction in vascular COMPLIANCE or respectively an increase in RESISTANCE for the down-stream fluid-dynamics system (the CIRCULATION) (see Figure S.137).

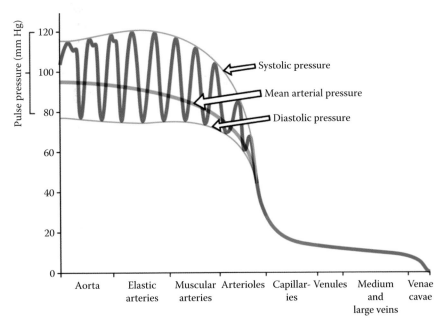

Figure S.137 Systolic pressure of the human heart obtained during contraction, facilitating pumping action.

't Hooft, Gerard {Geradus} (1946–)

[atomic, general, solid-state] Scientist from the Netherlands. 't Hooft made his first contribution as a graduate student in 1969 on the Yang–Mills gauge fields, showing how they could be renormalizable; thus formulating the concept of renormalization (see Figure T.1).

Figure T.1 Gerard 't Hooft (1946–).

Tachyon

[general, quantum, relativistic] Hypothetical massless PARTICLE that moves at velocities greater than the speed of LIGHT. In current theoretical context, a velocity faster than the speed of light under special relativistic doctrines will violate the causality principles. The tachyon concept was introduced by Olexa-Myron Bilaniuk (1926–2009), VIJAY DESHPANDE (mid-twentieth century–), and George Sudarshan (1931–) in 1962. In this assumption, the ENERGY is thought of as imaginary, avoiding the relativistic rest-mass constraints: $E^2 = p^2 c^2 + m^2 c^2$, where $p = mv$ the momentum, v the velocity, m the mass, and $c = \sqrt{\mu_0 \varepsilon_0}^{-1} = (\mu_0 \varepsilon_0)^{-1/2} = 2.99792458 \times 10^8 \, \text{m/s}$ the speed of light.

Tacoma Narrows Bridge

[general] Infamous bridge in the Washington state of the United States that had a design of suspension cables. The bridge spanned across the Tacoma Narrows strait of Puget SOUND. The suspension cables were subject to wind blowing in from the Pacific Ocean. Under specific conditions, the wind was able to bring the cables into

VIBRATION. At one time, the vibrations of the cables matched the RESONANCE vibration frequency of the main bridge, causing the entire bridge to oscillate, eventually leading to mechanical failure in 1940. The failure occurred only months after the completion of the bridge's construction (*also see* RESONANCE) (see Figure T.2).

Figure T.2 Tacoma Narrows Bridge under oscillation resulting from the Aeolian sounds generated by the wind stroking the suspension cables.

Tait, Peter Guthrie (1831–1901)

[general] Scientist from Scotland, Great Britain, contemporary and colleague of LORD KELVIN (1824–1907), WILLIAM HAMILTON (1805–1865), and JAMES CLERK MAXWELL (1831–1879). The work of Guthrie Tait focused on general PHYSICS, and he introduced several mathematical treatments and definitions for general physics concepts, specifically MECHANICS (see Figure T.3).

Figure T.3 Peter Guthrie Tait (1831–1901).

Tangential acceleration (a_T)

[general, mechanics] Acceleration associated with the revolution of an object and the associated change of angular velocity (direction and MAGNITUDE): $\alpha_c = a_T/r$, with a_T the tangential acceleration, r the radius from the center of the revolution, and the centripetal acceleration, changing the tangential ANGULAR VELOCITY (ω) as a function of time (t): $\alpha_c = d\omega/dt = d^2\theta/dt^2$, θ the ANGLE of rotation. The tangential acceleration forms a counterforce to maintain circular MOTION (see Figure T.4).

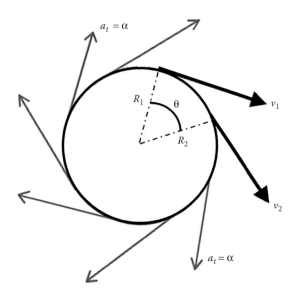

Figure T.4 Tangential acceleration, changing the direction of the constant velocity of revolution.

Tangential stress

[fluid dynamics, mechanics] Angular or circumferential STRESS (stress holding the shear for the potentially expanding "shell of the medium." In contrast to shear stress that is parallel to the plane of the material CROSS SECTION. Alternatively, normal stress is applied perpendicular to the material cross section. In tubes there are generally three stresses to be considered: longitudinal stress, radial stress, and hoop or tangential stress. Hoop stress is a tangential stress, in the circumferential direction. The hoop stress, specifically for a thick-walled tube, at any location r within the WALL of the tube with an inner radius r_i, outer radius r_o, wall thickness $d = r_o - r_i$ is $\sigma_{c,\text{thick}} = [(P_i r_i^2 - P_o r_o^2)/(r_o^2 - r_i^2)] - [r_i^2 r_o^2 (P_o - P_i)/r^2(r_o^2 - r_i^2)]$. Alternatively for a thin-walled tube (e.g., balloon; "holding the balloon together") the tangential stress is $\sigma_{c,\text{thin}} = P_t r_i / d$, also known as SHEAR STRESS (see Figure T.5).

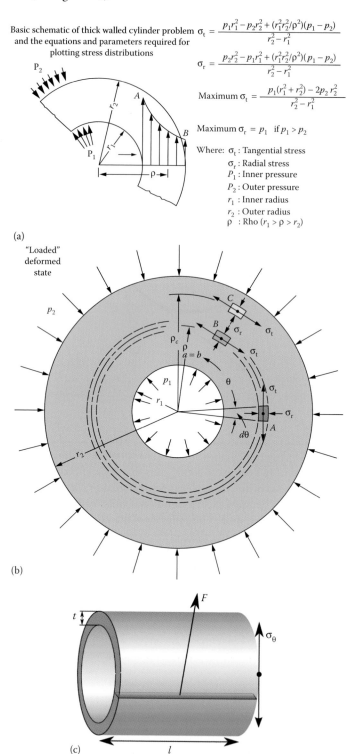

Basic schematic of thick walled cylinder problem and the equations and parameters required for plotting stress distributions

$$\sigma_t = \frac{p_1 r_1^2 - p_2 r_2^2 + (r_1^2 r_2^2 / \rho^2)(p_1 - p_2)}{r_2^2 - r_1^2}$$

$$\sigma_r = \frac{p_2 r_2^2 - p_1 r_1^2 + (r_1^2 r_2^2 / \rho^2)(p_1 - p_2)}{r_2^2 - r_1^2}$$

$$\text{Maximum } \sigma_t = \frac{p_1 (r_1^2 + r_2^2) - 2 p_2 r_2^2}{r_2^2 - r_1^2}$$

$$\text{Maximum } \sigma_r = p_1 \quad \text{if } p_1 > p_2$$

Where: σ_t : Tangential stress
σ_r : Radial stress
P_1 : Inner pressure
P_2 : Outer pressure
r_1 : Inner radius
r_2 : Outer radius
ρ : Rho ($r_1 > \rho > r_2$)

(a)

"Loaded" deformed state

(b)

(c)

Figure T.5 (a–c) Tangential stress, for instance on blood vessel. (a,b: Courtesy of Dr. Romesh Batra; Virginia Polytechnic Institute, Blacksburg, Virginia.) (c: Courtesy of Häggström, Mikael. "Medical gallery of Mikael Häggström 2014.")

Tate, John Torrence, Jr. (1925–)

[chemical, general, mechanics] Scientist and mathematician from the United States. Tate provided a wealth of information with regard to tension, specifically SURFACE TENSION, and THERMODYNAMICS (see Figure T.6).

Figure T.6 John Torrence Tate, Jr. (1925–), photograph by George M. Bergman.

Tate, John Torrence, Sr. (1889–1950)

[general, mechanics] Physicist from the United States, father of JOHN TORRENCE TATE, JR. (1925–) (see Figure T.7).

Figure T.7 John Torrence Tate, Sr. (1889–1950).

Tate's law

[general, mechanics] Boundary condition in droplet formation, for a LIQUID with mass m_{liq}, subject to a SURFACE TENSION (as may be described by the Marangoni surface tension T_s) the droplet will detach from the stream when the surface curvature reached $\chi = 90°$, or that the droplet confinement needs to satisfy: $m_{liq}g \leq 2\pi r_{stream} T_s \sin\chi$, which yields $m_{liq}g = 2\pi r_{stream} T_s$, where r_{stream} is the radius of the FLUID stream, or the radius of a CAPILLARY tube, and g the GRAVITATIONAL ACCELERATION. As defined in 1864 by JOHN TORRENCE TATE, SR. (1889–1950) and applied in the stalagmometer device to measure surface tension, T. Tate introduced this equation to define the MAGNITUDE (diameter and weight) of a drop of liquid.

Tau lepton

[general] Long-lived elementary PARTICLE; lifetime: $4.6 \pm 1.9 \times 10^{-13}$s. One of the six (6) recognized and identified leptons: electron, NEUTRINO (e): ν_e, MUON: μ^-, NEUTRINO (μ): ν_μ, tau: τ, and neutrino (τ): ν_τ. The tau lepton has the shortest lifetime of all leptons, with the muon second (2.197×10^{-6}s) and the rest stable. Also known as the tau (see Figure T.8).

Figure T.8 Collision experimental design with Large Hadron Collider in Switzerland in search of the tau lepton.

Taylor, Brook (1685–1731)

[computational] Mathematician from Great Britain. Brook Taylor is best known for the Taylor Series, published in 1715 (see Figure T.9).

Figure T.9 Brook Taylor (1685–1731), painting by Louis Goupy.

Taylor, Geoffrey Ingram, Sir (1886–1975)

[computational, fluid dynamics, nuclear] Scientist and mathematician from Great Britain. Sir Geoffrey Taylor provided computational evidence of the Young double slit experiment based on the WAVE theory. Sir Taylor also contributed significantly to the development of PROPELLER blades, based on the fluid-dynamic aspects. Additional work was on the electric discharges under thunderstorms (see Figure T.10).

Figure T.10 Sir Geoffrey Ingram Taylor (1886–1975).

Taylor dispersion

[biomedical, fluid dynamics] Radial DISPERSION of a SOLUTE during an axial LAMINAR FLOW through a straight tube (the radius of curvature: infinity) with a circular CROSS SECTION. However, the principle also applies to curved conduits, more specifically in a bifurcated arterial and venous flow in the biological CIRCULATORY SYSTEM. Analogous applications can be derived for a turbulent flow as well. Based on the work by SIR GEOFFREY INGRAM TAYLOR (1886–1975). The FLUID flow for a PIPE with radius R, in the z-direction with the flow velocity in the z-direction w, distributed over a radius r has a velocity profile defined by $\vec{u} = w_0 \left[1 - \left(r^2 / R^2 \right) \right] e_z$, where e_z is the unit vector in the z-direction. For a solute, the DIFFUSION associated with this flow is defined by $\left(\partial [C] / \partial t \right) + \vec{u} \cdot \nabla [C] = D_{diff} \nabla^2 [C]$, with $[C]$ the chemical concentration and

D_{diff} the DIFFUSIVITY. The diffusivity is linked to the Péclet number (Pe_d) through the effective diffusivity: $D_{\text{diff,eff}} = D_{\text{diff}}\left[1 + (1/192)Pe_d^2\right]$, which indicates that the TAYLOR DISPERSION (the shear effect on the disbursement of the chemical concentration in the direction of flow) is more pronounced for a higher Péclet number (e.g., formation of "Taylor vortices").

Taylor expansion

[computational] Discrete representation of a function as an infinite sum of derivatives of the function itself in a single point and was introduced by the British mathematician BROOK TAYLOR (1685–1731) in 1715, based on the work on curves and geometry by the Scottish astronomer and mathematician JAMES GREGORY (1638–1675) in 1668. Also known as TAYLOR SERIES.

Tectonic plates

[geophysics, mechanics] Concept introduced and validated in the 1960s considering the continents to be located on individual lithospheric plates of approximately 150 km thickness that apparently float on the magma of the ASTHENOSPHERE (see Figure T.11).

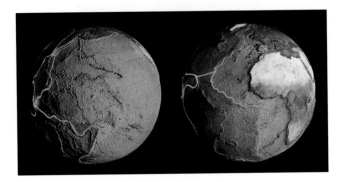

Figure T.11 Tectonic plates and fault-line between tectonic plates.

Tectonics

[acoustics, astrophysics/astronomy, chemical, electromagnetism, fluid dynamics, geophysics, mechanics, solid-state, thermodynamics] The study of the physical phenomena and processes of a planet's crust (*also see* EARTHQUAKE *and* SEISMIC) (see Figure T.12).

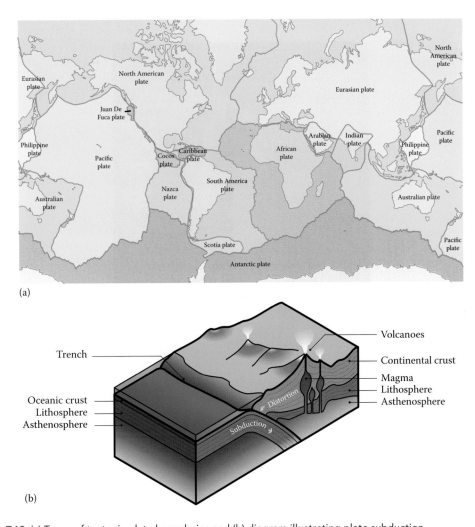

Figure T.12 (a) Types of tectonic plate boundaries and (b) diagram illustrating plate subduction.

Teflon®

[biomedical, chemical, mechanics] Brand name for polytetrafluoroethylene (PTFE), a synthetic fluoropolymer of tetrafluoroethylene; registered trademark from the DuPont corporation, discovered in

1938 by the chemist from the United States Roy Plunkett (1910–1994). The high MOLECULAR WEIGHT material has a very low coefficient of FRICTION; this will result in an extremely low degree of static and KINETIC FRICTION with respect to virtually any material. Teflon has a high stability temperature and is hence used as a nonstick coating for a broad range of industrial and commercial applications (e.g., pots and frying pans). The additional mechanical and chemically inert properties have provided ample applications as tape and gasket material (see Figure T.13).

Figure T.13 Burj Al Arab hotel in Dubai with a Teflon-coated screen that encloses the three sides of the Burj al Arab atrium. The screen covers a surface area of several hundred square meter and is made of glass fiber fabric with a thickness of approximately 1 mm; the Teflon® is intended to stop dirt from sticking to it.

Telegraph

[computational, electric, general] Device used for the decoding of information in a binary fashion and transmission by electrical means. The device was initially designed in 1792 by Claude Chappe (1763–1805), an engineer from France who also introduced the term "telegraph." Claude Chappe started out with the semaphore concept, which uses an optical SIGNAL for conveying messages over great distances, either by the position of mechanical arms (also used in the Netherlands with the position of the blades/sails of the windmills, dating back to the seventeenth century), or towers with pivoting shutters. Subsequently SAMUEL FINLEY BREESE MORSE (1791–1872), a painter and inventor from the United States introduced the MORSE CODE for communication of succinct messages. The efforts of Samuel Morse led to the commercial proliferation of a consumer device. The later mathematical design is based on the mathematical and electronic efforts of the engineer Oliver Heaviside (1850–1925) from Great Britain. Note that semaphores are still used for signaling in train traffic as well as directing traffic by police officers, and traffic LIGHT is also a clear example of semaphores (see Figure T.14).

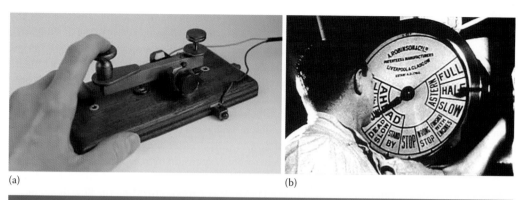

(a)   (b)

(c)

Figure T.14 (a) Telegraph machine and operator and (b) old design ship communication telegraph. The device would "ping" a bell to indicate the desired operating instructions; for example, "full steam ahead." (c) Example of modern trail traffic controlling semaphore device.

Telegraph equation

[biomedical, computational, energy, fluid dynamics] Mathematical differential equation describing the propagation of a periodic phenomenon (e.g., WAVE), developed by the scientist and engineer from Great Britain Oliver Heaviside (1850–1925). In electrical ENGINEERING, the telegraph equation describes the propagation of a harmonic wave over a conducting cable for analog data transmission.

The electrical potential (U_{pot}), which varies with time, is a function of the propagation path length (dz) and a function of TIME (t) as can be found by solving a one-dimensional differential equation: $(1/LC)(d^2U_{pot}/dz^2) = (d^2U_{pot}/dt^2) + [(R/L) + (\mathbb{R}/C)](dU_{pot}/dt) + (\mathbb{R}R/LC)U_{pot}$, where $\mathbb{R}$ represents the conductivity over a length of schematic. Alternatively for a conducting medium with properties inductance (L), capacitance (C), and RESISTANCE (R): $(d^2V_m/dt^2) - (c_1 + c_2)(dV_m/dt) = c_3^2(d^2V_m/dz^2) + c_1c_2V_m$, where $c_1 = (1/C_m)(1/R_m dz)$, $c_2 = R_p/L_p$, and $c_3^2 = 1/L_pC_m$, with z the direction of propagation along the length of the CELL (axon), and $\square_p$ and $\square_m$ with respect to the direction of propagation and the boundary ("shell" of the CONDUCTOR), respectively. The potential migration reduces to $d^2V_m/dt^2 = c_3^2(d^2V_m/dz^2)$ in the absence of resistance and electron/ionic leak current (e.g., POLARIZATION of either the insulating layer surrounding the cable or external FLUID or LIQUID), which is a plain HARMONIC OSCILLATION. Next to electronic transmission, the propagation of a wave pulse in liquid in FLUID DYNAMICS can be analyzed by implementing a perturbation on a steady-state axial flow $u(r,t)$ to derive the DISPERSION and frequency-dependent flow from developing the expression in a harmonic expansion by means of a Poisson series as $u(r,t) = u'(r)e^{i\omega_n t}$, ω_n represents the harmonics in the frequency pattern of the PULSATILE FLOW. This time-dependent expression can be substituted in the Poiseuille equation, providing the flow dynamic equivalent of the telegraph equation for the flow velocity as a function of radius and time as well as axial location: $u(\vec{r},t) = Re\{-(ia_n/\omega_n)e^{i\omega_n t}[1 - J_0(\sqrt{-i}\alpha(r/R))/J_0(\sqrt{-i}\alpha)]\}$, using a_n as defining the coefficients of the FOURIER SERIES for the polynomial series expansion in frequency, furthermore $\alpha^2 = Re * S_r$, and R is the radius of the vessel. In this expression, the following definitions are used: Re the REYNOLDS NUMBER, S_r the Strouhal number, and J_0 the first-order Bessel function. The frequency parameters for a non-Newtonian fluid, such as the pulsatile BLOOD flow in the arteries, are determined from the Strouhal number. The Strouhal number defines the ratio of the fluidic forces due to TURBULENCE phenomena with respect to the localized internal forces specifically as a result of localized flow accelerations. The Strouhal number provides a tool to estimate the time scale for VORTEX formation. The Strouhal number is defined as $S_r = \omega D/V$, with V the average (axial) flow velocity, D is the vessel diameter, and ω the ANGULAR VELOCITY of the (dispersive/turbulent) periodic phenomenon of flow. The flow characteristics are inherently tied to the flow rate, the tube diameter, and the pulsatile frequency of the flow mechanism.

Telemetry

[biomedical, general, mechanics, meteorology] The use of WAVES for gauging DISTANCE, direction, and MAGNITUDE (i.e., velocity) as well as wind direction, primarily based on ELECTROMAGNETIC (radio)-waves, but also by mechanical means (e.g., wind direction and velocity). Also used by BATS in ACOUSTIC format. An alternative interpretation is remote sensing, next to noninvasive sensing. The determination of BLOOD flow by acoustic and LASER Doppler flow METROLOGY can be considered telemetry as well (see Figure T.15).

Figure T.15 The use of telemetry by means of assisted device in tracking the migration pattern of birds.

Telescope

[astrophysics/astronomy, general, nuclear, optics] Device used to increase the RESOLUTION with respect to a distant phenomenon or object. Telescopes use a broad range of the ELECTROMAGNETIC SPECTRUM, from ULTRAVIOLET to the MICROWAVE. Telescopes operating in the visible spectrum provide a means to visually enlarge an object at a great DISTANCE. Telescopes operating in other parts of the electromagnetic spectrum require SIGNAL and image-processing techniques to reveal specific characteristics of the phenomenon under observation, such as a STAR or GALAXY. Radio telescopes are used in astronomy in order to observe in the radio-frequency and microwave bands by means of an array of dish antennas. RADIO telescopes often need to rely on INTERFERENCE properties to provide location-specific information. The first use of an optical telescope was described by the scientists and spectacle makers from Germany/the Netherlands, HANS LIPPERSHEY (1570–1619; also known as Johannes Lipperhey) and ZACHARIAS JANSSEN (1580–1640) in 1608, with contributions from Jacobus Metius (1571–1624; also known as Jacobus Adriaanszoon). GALILEO GALILEI (1564–1642) built his own telescope in 1609 based on the Dutch inspiration. A brief list of notable researchers in astronomy are NICOLAUS COPERNICUS (1473–1543), Tycho Brahe (1546–1601; Tyge Ottesen Brahe, scientist from Denmark), and EDWIN POWELL HUBBLE (1889–1953). Telescopes can rely on reflective imaging or refraction imaging. Optical telescopes use both REFLECTION and refraction, often in combination, where the reflection aspect provides a larger opening ANGLE and provides smaller constraints on the material properties. Long wavelength telescopes primarily rely on reflection-based focusing (*also see* **HUBBLE TELESCOPE** *and* **RADIO-TELESCOPE**) (see Figure T.16).

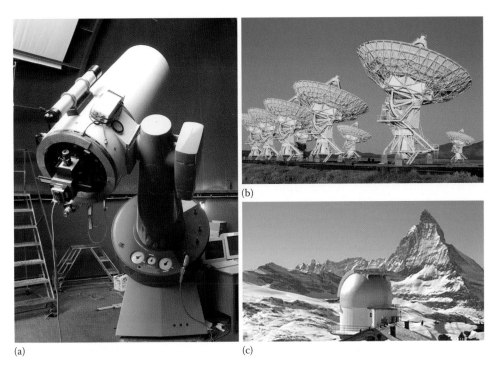

(a)

(b)

(c)

Figure T.16 (a) Picture of the telescope at North Carolina State University observatory in Durham, North Carolina; (b) image of the very large radio telescope array, consisting of 27 radioantennas, located in New Mexico; and (c) optical telescope at the base of the Matterhorn mountain in the Pennine Alps, located on the border between Italy and Switzerland.

TEM

[biomedical, imaging, nuclear, solid-state] *See* TRANSMISSION ELECTRON MICROSCOPE.

Temperature (*T*)

[general, solid-state, thermodynamics] Analogous to the definition of ABSOLUTE TEMPERATURE, temperature as a general definition may be interpreted as the aptitude for ENERGY to flow (i.e., heat) between two systems in contact, specifically from a high to low temperature (i.e., ZEROTH-LAW OF THERMODYNAMICS). Additionally temperature is the average kinetic energy of the atomic and MOLECULAR MOTION and is dependent on the atomic structure. In general, the solid-state and gaseous state can all be represented as an atomic GAS with the following characteristics: a one-atomic gas has $(3 + 0)$ degrees of freedom, a two-atomic gas has $(3 + 2)$ DEGREES OF FREEDOM, whereas the remaining multiatomic gases have $(3 + 3)$ of freedom, of which the first three are translational in a three-dimensional space (i.e., translational, vibrational, scissor action, and rotational) and the kinetic energy correlates with temperature as $(3/2)kT = KE = (1/2)mv^2 = (3/2)mv_0^2$, where k is the Boltzmann constant, m is the mass of the particles in MOTION (atoms/molecules), and v is the velocity of the motion. Temperature is expressed in either degree Celsius, degree Fahrenheit, or kelvin. The Fahrenheit scale [unit: °F] was introduced in 1717 by GABRIEL D. FAHRENHEIT (1686–1736), the CELSIUS SCALE [unit: °C, also known as the *centigrade scale*] was introduced by ANDERS CELSIUS (1701–1744) in 1742, and LORD (WILLIAM THOMPSON) KELVIN (1824–1907) introduced his temperature rendition [unit: K] in 1854. The Fahrenheit scale has 0°F defined as the MELTING POINT of water with ammonium chloride SALT (calibration point: ice and water with), a middle (third) point at the FREEZING point of distilled water at 32°F (based on the fractional distribution, i.e., powers of 2), and the upper reference the average adult HUMAN BODY temperature set at 96°F (measured with equipment and choice of MEASUREMENT, under the tongue, of the time) devisable by 12, as customary in the English unit system, with 1°F increments. Celsius uses the melting point of distilled water as the lower reference 0°C and the boiling point of distilled water as the upper calibration point at 100°C, subdivided in 100 segments. An alternative scale is the RANKINE temperature scale introduced by WILLIAM JOHN MACQUORN RANKIN (1820–1872) that follows Fahrenheit's example, but uses the ABSOLUTE ZERO defined similar to the kelvin ($T_R = (9/5)T_F$; in °R), all under standard pressure at sea level of $P = 101.325 \times 10^3 \text{N/m}^2$. There is an easy conversion from Fahrenheit to Celsius: $T_C = (5/9)(T_F - 32)$. The Kelvin scale is similar to the Celsius scale with the elementary difference that the minimum temperature is the lowest temperature attainable (i.e., absolute zero: −273.16 K), also referred to as the *absolute temperature*. The conversion from degrees Celsius to kelvin is as follows: $T_C = T_K + 273.15$. Temperature is easily (and routinely) measured by EXPANSION, either by a change in pressure under constant volume, or by a change in volume under constant pressure (i.e., volumetric) (e.g., gas THERMOMETER; Galileo, 1592), or linear (LIQUID: e.g., water, ALCOHOL, mercury, as well as solid metals) by means of the expansion coefficient: $\Delta \ell / \ell = \alpha \Delta T$, with ℓ the length (~column), $\Delta \ell$ the linear expansion, and α the linear expansion coefficient for the material in question. Otherwise temperature is derived from electric phenomena (bimetallic junctions changing electromotive force, V_{emf}, or conductivity as a result of the local temperature-dependent electron motion) and electronic properties (*pn-* junctions depending on the kinetic electron action), and finally colorimetric (i.e., change in COLOR due to temperature, alternatively used in quantifying colors). All mechanisms are assumed to operate within the linear response temperature range of the device, which imposes limitations. Since temperature is a measure of energy content, when two objects of unequal temperature are joined together the exchange of heat between the two bodies will strive for an equilibrium that has a direct correlation to the heat exchange, which in turn depends on the energy, mass, and temperature. The heat exchange will strive for equilibrium, eliminating the temperature gradient at the interface between two bodies at unequal temperatures while in contact. This defines the concept of thermal equilibrium. Combining the temperature data with material properties such as volume characteristics yields state equations, such as the van der Waals state equation (see Figure T.17).

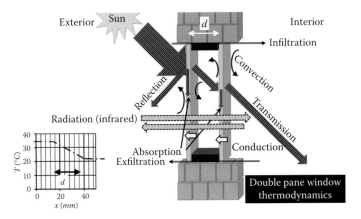

Figure T.17 Temperature gradient with respect to double glaze window, and presumed associated heat transfer.

Temporal period (T)

[acoustics, general, optics] The time frame for a harmonic event, which is directly linked to the FREQUENCY (v) of the OSCILLATION as $T = 1/v$, expressed in seconds. In the electrocardiogram, for instance, the temporal period is the average time between the Q-peak for a range of QRS segments (see Figure T.18).

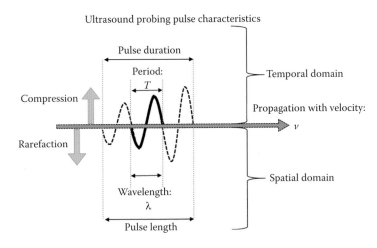

Figure T.18 Temporal period, in this diagram representing the acoustic wave in a medium.

Temporal width

[imaging, optics, quantum, ultrafast phenomena] {use: spectroscopy, hyperspectral imaging} Pulse duration of picoseconds (10^{-12} s) and shorter duration. The temporal width provides the means to measure phenomena that occur on a very short time scale, by essentially "FREEZING" the "MOTION," as well as chemical processes of ATOMS and MOLECULES. The short temporal width allows for a detailed analysis of chemical constituents and the stages involved in the development of a chemical reaction. Ultrashort pulses inherently have a broad spectral band and are often characterized by a high ENERGY (i.e., irradiance) at the peak emission. Also used in coherent X-RAY imaging for short biological event such as intercellular PROTON motion. On a biomedical diagnostic level, the analysis of wound healing requires terahertz SPECTROSCOPY for an accurate classification of burn wounds, and the apropos identification of the particular physiological processes involved. Two important spectroscopic phenomena in biological functionality in the ultrashort timeframe are found in PHOTOSYNTHESIS and VISION. The LIGHT interaction in the RODS and CONES of the EYE (receptor protein: rhodopsin, CHROMOPHORE derived from vitamin A) as well as in both the SKIN and in plants with respect to the conversion of light into CHEMICAL ENERGY and oxygen production takes place on a femtosecond scale. Rhodopsin is present in both rods and cones for vision. In vision, the QUANTUM states of the excited molecules yield information on the energy transfer. The chemical processes of 11-cis retinal in rhodopsin isomerization to all-trans bathorhodopsin in a photochemical process on PHOTON absorption (energy: $h\nu$) that takes place in a 3.0 ± 0.7 ps transfer between two molecular species, approximately 1 ps into the photochemical process. One significant detectable interaction is the 11-cis to 12-cis isomerization [$C_{11} = C_{12} - $ isomerization], which reveals itself through vibrational modes in the polyene backbone (torsions); specifically the low $C_{12} - H$ VIBRATION frequency in bathorhodopsin that shows anomalous behavior. The first chemical process is associated with a transition defined by the Frank–Codon state, which has an approximate lifetime of 200 fs.

Tensile force ($\vec{F}_T$)

[general, mechanics] Force with the potential for stretching a material (*also see* TENSION).

Tensile strain

[mechanics] A rod under tension will express a normal strain, increasing in length until the ULTIMATE TENSILE STRENGTH is reached and the device will shear-off (separate) (see Figure T.19).

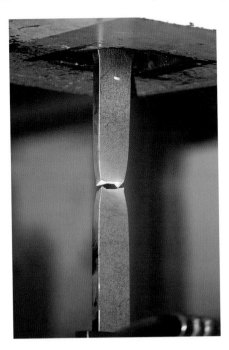

Figure T.19 Tensile strain.

Tensile (ultimate) strength

[engineering, general] Indication of the permissible mechanical shear stress and strain. It is of particular interest for the prediction of mechanical failure of a structure or device. The ULTIMATE TENSILE STRENGTH follows from the graphical interpretation of a plot of stress versus strain, where the stress will have an optimum, which corresponds to the ultimate TENSILE STRESS. The shear strain limit will be defined as a function of the shear strain ANGLE of distortion: $\gamma_s = \sin^{-1}\left(\Delta x / \ell_0\right) \approx \Delta x / \ell_0$, with Δx the lateral displacement at the far end of the construction/device and ℓ_0 the characteristic length (i.e., the orthogonal DISTANCE to the origin with respect to the angle of rotation of the material strain motion). Certain biological materials can stretch at greater than 800% of the EXPANSION of most natural rubber, but not reaching the stretch for latex or nylons. The rubber balloon was introduced, almost accidentally, as the result of GAS-LAW experimentations by MICHAEL FARADAY (1791–1867) in 1824 (see Figure T.20).

Figure T.20 Tensile strength tow truck pulling car out from snowbank.

Tensile stress

[mechanics] The normal force in response to the tensile force on a cross-sectional area in a solid (e.g., rope, rod) (see Figure T.21).

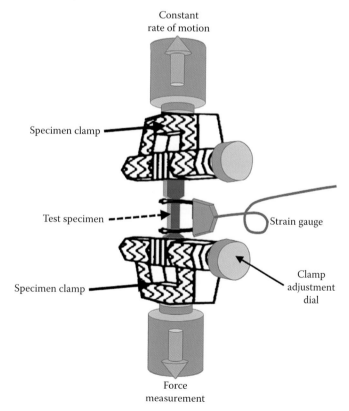

Figure T.21 Tensile stress.

Tension (F_T or τ)

[general, mechanics] SCALAR quantity of the tensile force between neighboring ELEMENTS, either in the linear direction or parallel plane. The tension in a rope will be equal in every point between the two attachment locations where an external force is applied. For a special case of surface elements (*see* SURFACE TENSION). In liquids, there is no friction and hence only normal tension will apply. In cases of lateral forces, TANGENTIAL TENSION (i.e., stress) needs to be taken in consideration (see Figure T.22).

Figure T.22 Tension.

Tension, surface

[hydrodynamic] *See* SURFACE TENSION. *Also see* CAPILLARITY *and* SURFACE ENERGY.

Tension, tangential

[mechanics] *See* STRESS.

Tensor

[atomic, fluid dynamics, solid-state] In order to place phenomena in symmetry, group theory treats the average effects, specifically applied to crystals, and respectively lattices, but also applicable to, for instance (but not limited to), FLUID DYNAMICS, general relativity, and ELASTICITY. The tensor concept introduces mathematic and geometric framework that are a generalization of vectors, matrices, and scalars. A tensor has multiple dimensions, indicated by the indices that represent the DEGREES OF FREEDOM in the applicable space. The format of the tensor as an "indexed" parameters resembles the notation of the matrix ELEMENTS, apart from the fact that the number of indices and placement of indices are arbitrary and not limited to a matrix pattern

$$A = \begin{bmatrix} a_{11} & \cdots & a_{1m} \\ \vdots & a_{ij} & \vdots \\ a_{n1} & \cdots & a_{nm} \end{bmatrix}$$

(matrix ELEMENT a_{ij}); instead tensors are found as a_{ijk}; $a_i{}^{jk}$; a^{ijkl}; etc. A tensor of rank 1 is a SCALAR ($3^0 = 1$ component, e.g., temperature), tensor of rank 2 is a vector ($3^1 = 3$ components, e.g., velocity), tensor of rank 3 is a dyad ($3^2 = 9$ components, e.g., permeability, stress, flow [vortices]), tensor of rank 4 is triad ($3^3 = 27$ components, e.g., VELOCITY POTENTIAL), and so on.

Terminal velocity

[general, mechanics] The velocity of an object when all forces are balanced, resulting in a net force of zero. Under freefall, this means that GRAVITATIONAL ACCELERATION and DRAG are canceling out when a certain velocity is reached, where the ultimate velocity is a function of the elapsed time and the sum of the accelerations is a function of time. The object is in equilibrium at this point: $\sum \vec{F}_i = 0$. The terminal velocity (v_T) of a sphere with density ρ_s traveling in a FLUID with density ρ_f can be approximated based on the Stokes STREAM FUNCTION as $v_T = (2/9)\left[\left(\rho_s - \rho_f\right)/\eta\right]gR^3$, where η is the VISCOSITY, g the acceleration, and R the radius of the spherical object. Analogously, for a cylinder in flow, the VORTICITY ($\vec{\omega} = \partial\chi/\partial\varphi$; φ the ANGLE of the velocity with the VORTEX axis) surrounding the cylinder will provide a significant influence, assuming the cylinder traveling long ways in the flow, in response to the balancing torque on the "rod." The terminal velocity can be derived from: $v_T = \left[(1/2) - \gamma^* - \log\left((1/2)k^*R\right)\right]C$, where γ^* represents the first term in the EXPANSION: $\int_0^\infty e^{-k^* r \cosh\vec{\omega}} d\vec{\omega} = -\left[\gamma^* + \log\left((1/2)k^* r\right)\right]Y_0\left(k^* r\right) + s_1\left(k^{*2}r^2/2^2\right) + s_2\left(k^{*4}r^4/2^2\,4^2\right) + s_3\left(k^{*6}r^6/2^2\,4^2 6^2\right) + \cdots$, where $Y_0\left(k^* r\right)$ is a zero-order Bessel function of the second kind, $k^* = |u|/2\eta$ an indicator of the MAGNITUDE of the viscous forces (tied to the viscous forces: $\eta\nabla^2 u$; $\eta\nabla^2 v$; and $\eta\nabla^2 w$), and C is the coefficient in the series for the vortex field solution developed in the WAKE $\chi = Ce^{k^* x}\int_0^\infty e^{-k^* r \cosh\vec{\omega}} d\vec{\omega}$, with $\vec{\omega} = \partial\chi/\partial\varphi = (3/2)uR\left(1 + k^* r\right)\left(\varphi/r^3\right)e^{-k^*(r-x)}$ the vorticity, and r the radius; as a SOLUTION to $u = -\left(\partial\phi/\partial x\right) + \left(1/2k^*\right)\left(\partial\chi/\partial x\right) - \chi$, where ϕ is the VELOCITY POTENTIAL and u the velocity in the direction of net flow (see Figure T.23).

Figure T.23 Terminal velocity without parachute.

Tesla, Nikola (1856–1943)

[general] Scientist from Croatia. Nikola Tesla dedicated his research to the electrical ACTIVITY of charges and the MAGNETIC FIELD effects. One of Tesla's major contributions to modern ENGINEERING is the alternating current electrical system, leading to the electromotor and the GENERATOR. The ac-induction MOTOR is very actively in use with modern hybrid and electric automobiles. The "Tesla coil" invented in 1891 has found many applications, such as the one in RADIO technology. The Tesla coil constitutes a high-voltage low-current high frequency electrical resonator that can go beyond the frequency range of an electrical TRANSFORMER. The Tesla coil is also used for display purposes with PLASMA arcs propagating through AIR.

T

Nikola Tesla designed the hydroelectric power plant in operation at Niagara Falls, New York, the United States in 1895 (see Figure T.24).

Figure T.24 Nikola Tesla (1856–1943).

Tesla (T)

[general] Unit for the MAGNITUDE of a MAGNETIC FIELD, adopted in the SI UNITS in 1960. The unit is named after a pioneer in the magnetic field theory NIKOLA TESLA (1856–1943). The unit has the following equivalents: $T = (Vs/m^2) = (N/Am) = (Wb/m^2) = (kg/Cs)$. The range of magnetic field strength is broad. Examples of the magnetic field strength under various conditions are as follows: for the atomic NUCLEUS: $10^{12} T$; at the surface of a NEUTRON STAR: $10^8 T$; artificially produced under laboratory conditions: $\sim 10^3 T$; a small MAGNET: $10^{-2} T$; kitchen blender: $\sim 10^{-3} T$; the earth's magnetic field $\sim 10^{-4} T$; high voltage electric transmission lines (within close proximity): $10^{-4} T$; the HUMAN BODY: $\sim 10^{-10} T$; the smallest value in shielded environment: $10^{-14} T$.

Thales (c. 624–546 BC)

[general] Greek scientist and philosopher. Founder of the first principles of scientific method, separating divine intervention from phenomena (i.e., natural events) that have a cause that can be explained scientifically and theoretically. Some later Greek philosophers credited Thales with the first introduction of celestial navigation referring to Ursa Minor (i.e., "Little Bear") as the point of reference. Records also mention that he proposed water as the primary ELEMENT, the source of all media (see Figure T.25).

Figure T.25 Impression of how Thales (ca. 624–546 BC) may have looked like.

Theodolite

[general, geophysics] Instrument designed to provide the ANGLE with respect to a horizontal plane using a telescopic viewer that can pivot in vertical and horizontal directions, introduced by and used in areal construction and land surveying. The theodolite measures the azimuth angle. The concept was introduced in the 1500s and is in everyday use today (see Figure T.26).

Figure T.26 Theodolite.

Thermal conductivity

[thermodynamics] Coefficient of HEAT TRANSFER (heat transfer rate: $\dot{Q} = dQ/dt$) for a medium with CROSS SECTION A over a length ℓ and with an applied thermal gradient $(T_b - T_l)$ to provide $\dot{Q} = \lambda_T \left[A(T_b - T_l)/\ell \right]$.

Thermal diffusivity ($\propto_{\text{dif}} = \kappa/\rho c_p$)

[thermodynamics] Where κ the thermal conductivity, ρ the density, and c_p the heat capacity. Thermal DIFFUSIVITY describes the ability of an object to adjust to the ambient changes in temperature and the rate of change to reach equilibrium. A high thermal diffusivity means that an object adjusts rapidly, whereas a low thermal diffusivity might entail a larger ENERGY requirement.

Thermal energy

[general, nuclear, thermodynamics] Atomic and molecular kinetic ENERGY, contained as the temperature of an object. Thermal energy is part of the CONSERVATION OF ENERGY principle. Thermal energy may develop due to FRICTION or result from combustion.

Thermal equilibrium

[engineering, general, thermodynamics] Conditions for which there is no transfer of heat, all bodies with a system are at the same temperature. (*also see* ZEROTH LAW OF THERMODYNAMICS).

Thermal expansion

[engineering, general, nuclear, thermodynamics] Increase in VOLUME (V) for a system due to a change in the TEMPERATURE (T) of the system, generally considered under constant PRESSURE (P). The volume expansion is defined by the volume expansion coefficient as $\gamma_{\text{th}} = (1/V)(dV/dT)_p$. Generally the thermal expansion coefficient is a function of temperature itself, expressed as $\gamma_{th} = a + bT + cT^2$, where a, b, and c are material constants. The EXPANSION for metallic objects is subject to both LATTICE expansion and conduction electrons, expressed by the SPECIFIC HEAT under constant pressure: $c_p = a_{el}T + a_{lat}T^3$, where a_{el} and a_{lat} are coefficients with respect to the contributions due to the electrons and the lattice. The electron and lattice expansion translates into the GRÜNEISEN EQUATION for thermal expansion: $\gamma_{th} = (1/VB_s)(\gamma_{el}a_{el}T + \gamma_{lat}a_{lat}T^3)$, where B_s is the adiabatic bulk modulus. This reduces to $\gamma_{th} = \gamma_{GR}(c_p/VB_s)$, with γ_{GR} the Grüneisen coefficient, indicating the temperature dependence for the expansion. Water is one of the few media that decreased in volume between the FREEZING point and a few degrees above freezing, with the highest density at 4°C. A large segment of metals has an almost uniform expansion coefficient around the MELTING POINT for the LIQUID phase as $\gamma_{th} \sim 10^{-4}$ K^{-1}. Under certain conditions, linear thermal expansion is required, where $\gamma_{th} = 3\alpha_{th}$; $\alpha_{th} = (1/L)(dL/dT)_p$, L the characteristic length, and α_{th} the linear expansion coefficient (see Figure T.27).

Figure T.27 Thermal expansion for a hot-air balloon, using a flame to heat up the air that will force the balloon filled with expanding air to increase in volume that will provide it buoyancy. The volume of hot air inside the balloon has a lower density and is hence lighter than the colder surrounding air providing an upward force.

Thermal neutrons

[atomic, nuclear] Slow moving NEUTRON, with velocities in the distribution of room temperature AIR molecules. Thermal neutrons were found very inquisitive for the examination of materials, from LIGHT to heavy metals (including uranium) during the research into the structure and ISOTOPE formation performed by ENRICO FERMI (1901–1954).

Thermal wave

[acoustic, quantum, solid-state, thermodynamics] The ability to produce CAPILLARY WAVES (at an interface) on a molecular scale by means of thermal MOTION. The thermal wave is confined by the SURFACE TENSION ($\sigma_{surface}$) and can be described as the ENERGY content ($E_{SurfaceTension}$) in the lateral displacement (height: h) along the surface (in the x- and y-directions) as $E_{SurfaceTension} = \sigma_{surface}$

$\int\{\sqrt{1+[(dh/dx)^2+(dh/dy)^2]}-1\}\,dx\,dy \cong (\sigma_{surface}/2)\int[(dh/dx)^2+(dh/dy)^2]\,dx\,dy$, where the displacements are of a small AMPLITUDE (*also see* SURFACE ACOUSTIC WAVE *and* CAPILLARY WAVE).

Thermionic emission

[atomic, nuclear] Release of electrons from a METAL surface under heating, generally heated through an electrical current. The process was recognized by Thomas Alva Edison (1847–1931) in 1883. The thermionic emission is used for the generation of X-RAY from the impact on a metal target (e.g., bismuth or tungsten).

Thermistor

[electronics, general] Material that has a RESISTANCE (R) that varies with applied temperature. The TEMPERATURE (T) can be derived from the CURRENT (I) under an applied VOLTAGE (V) through OHM's LAW: $V = IR$, assuming a linear response with respect to temperature change: $\Delta R = \epsilon_{const}\Delta T$. The mechanism of action is different from a THERMOCOUPLE.

Thermoacoustic imaging

[optics, thermodynamics] *See* PHOTO-ACOUSTIC IMAGING *and* SCANNING ACOUSTIC MICROSCOPE.

Thermocouple

[electromagnetism, general, thermodynamics] Temperature sensor, generally made by joining two metals together that will provide a voltage that is a function of the temperature based on the SEEBECK EFFECT, as recognized by the German scientist Thomas Seebeck (1770–1831). One commonly used thermocouple uses two alloys: chromel (consisting of 90% nickel and 10% chromium) and alumel (consisting of 95% nickel, 2% manganese, 2% aluminum, and 1% silicon). The potential difference (V_i, measured at the distal end of the wire; the junction of the two metals generates a balancing current to cancel out the external potential difference) as a result of temperature (T) is defined as $V_b - V_c = \int_{T_c}^{T_b}[S_A(T) - S_B(T)]\,dT$, with $S_A(T)$ and $S_B(T)$ the Seebeck coefficients for materials A and B, and the subscripts $_b$ and $_c$ represent the temperature at the two junctions. The inverse process with respect to the thermocouple principles is the Peltier effect (see Figure T.28).

Figure T.28 Thermocouple used for temperature measurement.

Thermodynamics

[biomedical, chemical, engineering, mechanics, quantum, thermodynamics] Branch of engineering and physics that deals with the aspects of work, heat, temperature, and equilibrium conditions. Thermodynamics is based on the following four laws: ZEROTH LAW OF THERMODYNAMICS (any two systems in contact at the same temperature are in thermal equilibrium); FIRST LAW OF THERMODYNAMICS (conservation of ENERGY, INTERNAL ENERGY, and work and heat need to balance); SECOND LAW OF THERMODYNAMICS (heat will not flow from a cooler to warmer location without external assistance); and the THIRD LAW OF THERMODYNAMICS (it is impossible to reach ABSOLUTE ZERO temperature [in kelvin] by any process of finite number of steps). The concept of PERPETUAL MOTION is rejected based on at least the last two laws. Other aspects of thermodynamics include statistical MECHANICS and thermometry.

Thermodynamics, first law of

[energy, fluid dynamics, general, thermodynamics] The change in the INTERNAL ENERGY (U) of a system is the confluence of the HEAT (Q) introduced in the system and the work (W) done by the system on the surroundings, formulated as $\Delta U = \Delta Q - \Delta W$. The work performed can be mechanical: $W_m = P\Delta V + V\Delta P$, with P the internal pressure and V the volume of the system; or when the work is electrical: $W_e = -nF_a\Delta V_e$, with n is the number of charges transferred in the process, $F_a = 96,485$ C/mol the FARADAY CONSTANT, and ΔV_e is the maximum difference in electrical potential resulting from the transferred charges. This law is another version of the CONSERVATION OF ENERGY.

Thermodynamics, second law

[biomedical, energy, fluid dynamics, general, thermodynamics] If a system is isolated (no ENERGY is added to it) its entropy is destined to increase with time. Consider a flower that has been cut and is left in a closed container without water. The flower and stem will eventually DECAY, meaning that the entropy of the system has increased. Life is one of the most obvious examples where the requirement of energy input to sustain order is evident. Such processes are called energonic, in which the energy of the final state is higher than the energy of the initial state.

Thermodynamics, third law

[biomedical, energy, fluid dynamics, general, thermodynamics] For any mixture of constituents, known as a system, there exists one stable equilibrium that will be at zero temperature (0 K; zero degrees kelvin). The third law also states that the ABSOLUTE ZERO kelvin cannot be reached by any finite number of discrete steps. An equivalent statement relates to the fact that the CARNOT ENGINE can never have the perfect efficiency. (*also known as* NERNST PRINCIPLE).

Thermodynamics, zeroth law of

[general, thermodynamics] Concept introduced by JOSEPH BLACK (1728–1799) around 1760. The zeroth law describes the fact that every system will be endowed with the property of temperature. Placing two systems in contact will establish thermal equilibrium where both systems possess the identical temperature and no net heat will be transferred. When systems A and B are in thermal equilibrium, possessing the same physical quantity of temperature, as are systems B and C, then systems A and C are (also) in equilibrium.

Thermography

[fluid dynamics, imaging, thermodynamics] Imaging method using the INFRARED "signature" to identify the temperature distribution. The thermography concept is based on PLANCK'S LAW (accurate) or alternatively Wein's displacement law (approximation). WIEN'S DISPLACEMENT LAW provides the peak emission wavelength (λ) as $\lambda = \left(2.898 \times 10^{-6}/T\right)$nm, with temperature ($T$) in kelvin. The PLANCK'S RADIATION LAW gives the radiant power as a function of wavelength as $W = 2\pi hc^2/\lambda^5 \left(e^{hc/\lambda k_b T} - 1\right)$ W/m^{2}μm. Thermography uses the spectral profile in near infrared (wavelength range $\lambda = 0.66$–$2\,\mu$m); mid-infrared (wavelength range: $\lambda = 3 - 5\,\mu$m); to long infrared (wavelength range: $\lambda = 7$–$14\,\mu$m) spectrum, depending on the specific application. The two primary thermal imaging wavelength bands are $\lambda = 3 - 5\,\mu$m and $\lambda = 8 - 12\,\mu$m. Thermographic imaging owes its limitations to these two specific bands based on the spectral response limitations of the available photodetectors next to the transmission passband windows of the ATMOSPHERE; specifically within a bandwidth portion.

The monochromatic emissive power of a black-body radiation at the typical room temperatures (296 K) has an emission peak at 9.6 μm. For analysis, the EMISSIVITY of the surface is assumed to be ~96% ($\varepsilon_T = 0.96$; note that polished aluminum or platinum has an emissivity of only 4%, whereas water and human tissue is ~96%, and soot 99%), but in cases otherwise known corrections can manually be entered for the surface with respect to the imaging device software processing and user interface. The modern day photodetectors use various mechanisms, ranging from photovoltaic to photodiode to photoresistive. Photovoltaic operation relies on the electron release based on the work function of the medium, generating a current that is proportional to the overall collected PHOTON radiance within a bandwidth. A photodiode renders a reverse bias current resulting from photoenergy exposure. The photoresistive ELEMENT changes its charge-carrier density under the influence of photon ENERGY; this type of device is semiconductor based. Typical photoresistive ELEMENTS designed for the $\lambda = 8 - 12$ μm band are MCT ($Hg_{0,8}Cd_{0,2}Te$) detectors, one of the few molecular structures that has a small enough bandgap with the VALENCE BAND. The detectors can be actively balanced in a Wheatstone configuration to minimize the conductive heating aspects, which will influence the sensitivity and accuracy. Generally a CCD imaging device uses MOSFET photodiodes that operate based on charge depletion under exposure. Each PIXEL is its own MOSFET element. Thermographic cameras are constructed with an array of infrared sensitive elements (pixels) that is processed for MAGNITUDE with a certain spectral band to provide the spatial distribution of surface temperatures. Virtually all thermographic-sensing devices require cooling, primarily designed to reduce the thermal noise as well as to increase the dynamic range. The cooling processes can be either by means of LIQUID nitrogen (temperature 77.4 K, −196°C) or through Peltier elements (thermopile), next to Joule–Thompson cooling devices (relying on isentropic EXPANSION of a pressurized GAS, similar to household refrigeration). Because of the fact that infrared RADIATION is readily attenuated by any material except for AIR and VACUUM, only the external surface of an object is analyzed for temperature. Any coating, plastic BARRIER, or wax/OIL covering will change the spectral profile of the LIGHT emitted from the BLACK BODY, hence altering the perceived temperature. Thermal imaging is subject to a variety of NOISE sources, ranging from thermal noise to shot noise (intrinsic semiconductor defect) and the random generation of charge carriers/holes (G–R noise; generation–recombination noise), which is not thermally activated, and has a spectral profile. Night-vision instrumentation also provides a form of thermographic imaging since it applies to near infrared, only slightly above the RED vision cut-off. Infrared imaging dates back to 1929, starting with night VISION, designed by the Hungarian scientist Kálmán Tihanyi (1897–1947). The next developmental PHASE was a spectral line scanner, which reconstructed images from obtaining emissions from points on parallel lines traced out on the surface of the object as designed by Texas Instruments in 1947, requiring up to an hour exposure. The last major breakthrough prior to the current state-of-the-art instrumentation was through pyroelectric scanning integrated with a full surface view developed by Michael Francis Tompsett (1939–) in 1969, later on perfected with solid-state sensor technology (CCD). (*see* BLACK-BODY RADIATION) (see Figure T.29).

Figure T.29 False-color image captured by thermography camera displaying temperature distribution of an object based on the Planck radiation profile, by means of collection of infrared radiation. Most thermographic cameras operate in the wavelength band of 3–5 μm, other detection bands are available, including but not limited to, 1–2 μm and 8–12 μm.

Thermokinetic oscillator

[chemical, energy, thermodynamics] *See* OSCILLATORY REACTION.

Thermometer

[energy, fluid dynamics, general, geophysics, thermodynamics] Device designed to quantify local temperature. The mechanism of action for the determination of the temperature can be THERMOCOUPLE based, thermo-electric (semiconductor), or linear EXPANSION of a FLUID in a confined tube under vacuum. The most well-known thermometers are the mercury and ALCOHOL liquid thermometers and the thermocouple-based probe, next to the thermographic (INFRARED sensitive) semiconductor sensor used for in-ear thermometry (see Figure T.30).

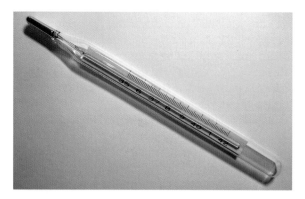

Figure T.30 Illustration of the use of a thermometer to measure body temperature and establish whether the person has a fever.

Thermonuclear energy

[atomic, general] ENERGY released from NUCLEAR FUSION or NUCLEAR FISSION processes (*see* THERMONUCLEAR FISSION *and* THERMONUCLEAR FUSION).

Thermonuclear fission

[atomic, general] Most nuclear power plants operate on induced fission of uranium-235, under prodding from colliding neutron (η). In this process, the NEUTRON briefly merges with the uranium to subsequently disintegrate in barium-138, krypton-95, and three new neutrons. This process results in the release of ENERGY that is based on the energy transfer for the nuclear binding forces in the molecular balance: $_0^1 n + {}_{92}^{235} U \rightarrow {}_{92}^{236} U^* \rightarrow {}_{56}^{141} Ba + {}_{36}^{92} Kr + 3{}_0^1 n + 220 \text{ MeV}$, where some energy is applied to the recombination (~20 MeV). The neutrons released in the FISSION process can continue to fuel the fission process. The effective 200 MeV fission energy almost all goes into THERMAL ENERGY (at least a verified 165 MeV as kinetic energy, whereas an additional 10 MeV out of all 200 MeV is released as kinetic energy, not as the anticipated neutrinos; 7 MeV as kinetic BETA PARTICLES [totaling 182 MeV in kinetic energy, producing thermal effects: $KE = (3/2) k_b T$]; next to 5 MeV as kinetic neutrons [used for fission] and the remaining theoretical distribution is $7\,\text{MeV} + 6\,\text{MeV}$ to gamma RADIATION; primary and secondary) (*see* NUCLEAR FISSION *and* FISSION) (see Figure T.31).

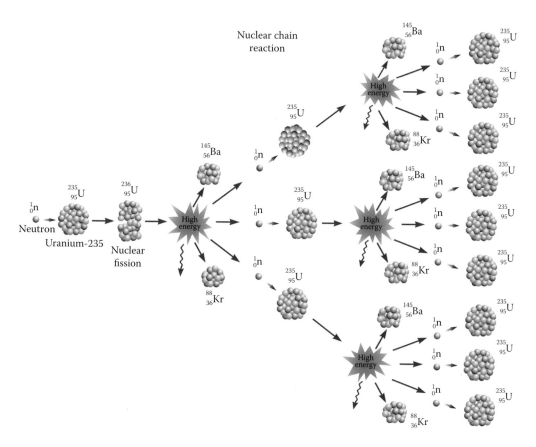

Figure T.31 Nuclear chain reaction for uranium fission.

Thermonuclear fusion

[atomic, general] Most galactic stars operate on the process of NUCLEAR FUSION, joining two light nuclei (e.g., hydrogen (H)/proton ($_0^1$n)) into larger/heavier nuclei: $_0^1\text{n} + _0^1\text{n} \rightarrow _0^2\text{H} + e^+ + v + 0.42\,\text{MeV}$, e^+ a positron that will annihilate a free electron and release an additional $1.02\,\text{MeV}$ of ENERGY and v a NEUTRINO. The gain in energy is provided based on the fact that the BINDING ENERGY is different for a set number of nuclides based on the ATOM number. Protons can be brought in close contact to the point where they will overcome their Coulomb repulsion. The KINETIC ENERGY (KE) to achieve proximity will need to exceed the center-to-center potential energy PE (Coulomb energy) of approximately $0.14\,\text{MeV}$, for separation of $r = 10^{-14}\,\text{m}$ for the respective protons. This energy level equates to an approximate temperature of $T = 1 \times 10^9\,\text{K}$ ($KE = (3/2)k_b T$, $k_b = 1.3806488 \times 10^{-23}\,\text{m}^2\text{kg/s}^2\text{K}$ Boltzmann constant). In practicality, the effective fusion temperature is 50 times lower (only at 2% of the thermal equilibrium) due to the fact that there will be an energy distribution around the calculated maximum energy, next to TUNNELING events. Fusion can be used to generate power on an artificial basis; however, most nuclear power plants are fission plants. The FUSION plants in experimental use operate on tokamak (MAGNETIC) principles or laser INERTIA confined plasmas (*see* NUCLEAR FUSION *and* FUSION) (see Figure T.32).

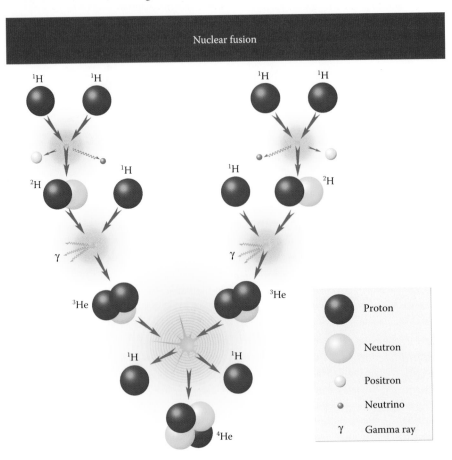

Nuclear fusion

●	Proton
○	Neutron
◦	Positron
·	Neutrino
γ	Gamma ray

Figure T.32 Diagram of nuclear fusion and energy balance.

Thermophysical properties

[thermodynamics] Theoretical and experimental parameters associated with a single constituent system in one-phase, two-phase, or three-phase states. The system consists of n molecules in a volume V, specific volume: $v_V = V/n$ with internal ENERGY (U), specific internal energy: $u_U = U/n$, entropy (S), and respectively specific entropy: $s_S = S/n$ and has a TEMPERATURE (T), PRESSURE (P) and DENSITY ($\rho = m/V$, for a PHASE with mass m of a chemical with MOLECULAR WEIGHT M). The amounts of constituents can be expressed in MOLE or mol (i.e., GRAM MOLE). With respect to phase transitions, the following specific thermophysical properties apply. The critical pressure (P_c), at which the LIQUID and VAPOR phase are treated as identical. The CRITICAL TEMPERATURE (T_c), at which the vaporization process reduces to an infinitesimal event. And an additional critical specific volume is also identified: v_{V_c}. Combining the three conditions of critical pressure, critical temperature, and critical specific volume yields the critical state or critical point. Particular to the form of AGGREGATION at the phase changes, there are specific LATENT HEAT values that define the energy requirements to accommodate the PHASE TRANSITION from one phase to the other. For a two-phase mixture, the chemical potential μ_i defines the phase MIXING under the CLAUSIUS–CLAPEYRON RELATION. Next to the specific latent heat at the phase transitions, there is also the specific heat under constant pressure (c_p) and SPECIFIC HEAT under constant volume (c_v) that both define the heat requirements per degree of temperature rise per unit mass. The equation of sate provides a means to interconnect a range of thermophysical properties and predict the course of events. Furthermore during EXPANSION and compression, the thermophysical properties of isothermal compressibility (K_T) and isobaric expansion (α_P) are important for the description of a process, plus they tie into the equations of state. The final thermophysical property on the list is the speed of SOUND for the medium under particular values of the aforementioned thermophysical properties. The speed of sound (v_s), as all the other thermophysical properties, can be measured and is correlated to some of the other properties through

$$v_s^2 = \left(\partial P/\partial \rho\right)_{ss} = -\left(v_V/M\right)\left(\partial P/\partial v_V\right)_{ss} = -\left(v_V/M\right)\left\{\left(c_p/c_v\right)\left(1/K_T v_V\right)\right\} = \left(c_p/c_v\right)\left(1/\rho K_T\right) = \gamma_r\left(1/\rho K_T\right),$$

where γ_r is the ratio of the specific heats.

Thermoscope

[general, thermodynamics] THERMOMETER equivalent designed by GALILEO GALILEI (1564–1642), however, without a scale, introduced in 1617. A bowl partially filled with LIQUID has a tube leading upward where the rising liquid can spill into a bulb. The GAS pressure in the partially filled bowl will exert pressure on the fluid surface, pushing the liquid up through the tube, where the fill fraction of the bulb will be an indirect function of the temperature. The first practical temperature scale was introduced by OLAUS ROEMER (RØMER) (1644–1710) in 1701; followed shortly by GABRIEL DANIEL FAHRENHEIT (1686–1736) in 1717. Without much consequence at the time, a physician from France, Jean Rey (1583–1645) turned the Galilei thermoscope upside down and filled the bulb with water and started using it for measuring body temperature as a relative value in 1631, a definite preamble to the modern thermometer (see Figure T.33).

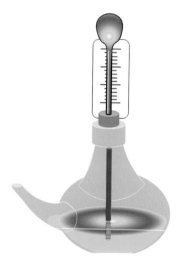

Figure T.33 Thermoscope.

Thermosphere

[energy, geophysics, thermodynamics] Shell of the Earth's ATMOSPHERE, the layer with the greatest thickness; spanning from 85 to 500 km. The thermosphere is located above the MESOSPHERE and has the EXOSPHERE on the outside. Within this layer, gaseous molecules and atoms are ionized under the exposure of the sun's short ULTRAVIOLET RADIATION. This ionization is what is observed as the auroras: AURORA BOREALIS and AURORA AUSTRALIS. The IONIZATION layer also provides a "reflective" layer for RADIO communications. Especially long-wave electromagnetic radiation can reflect of the ionized layers in the atmosphere and back from the earth's surface and allow long-wave radio waves to travel half-way around the EARTH (e.g., ham radio transmissions from Australia can be received in the United States, depending on atmospheric conditions). The temperature in the thermosphere increases with altitude as a result of the solar interaction. The thermosphere has a dynamic character, including atmospheric tides, a THERMAL WAVE pattern driven by DIURNAL heating. The atmospheric tides form a global OSCILLATION in the atmosphere. Atmospheric tides are also common in the TROPOSPHERE and the STRATOSPHERE, based on the solar absorption in the high concentration of water VAPOR and ionization of oxygen to ozone. Based on the solar interactions, the tides have a period on the order of 12 and 24 h intervals; however, the periods become longer with greater altitudes. The flow direction of the tides is also subject to the orientation of the earth's axis with respect to the orbit around the SUN (seasonal fluctuations). The atmospheric tides are affected by gravitational influences next to the solar heating, and hence are also dependent on the lunar orbit. Atmospheric tides are considered as linear perturbations and are eigenvalues of the Hough functions. The Hough functions are special cases of the Laplace tidal equations. The Laplace tidal equation describes the fluctuations resulting from the flow around a rotating sphere. The LAPLACE EQUATION for the tidal WAVE of the atmospheric flow uses the Hough EIGENFUNCTION ($\Theta_n(\varphi_e)$) and Hough eigenvalues ($\zeta_n = (2\omega_e R_e)^2/g(r,\varphi)r_n$, where $g(r,\varphi)$ is the GRAVITATIONAL ACCELERATION as a function of global atmospheric location) and is written as $L\Theta_n(\varphi_e) + \zeta_n\Theta_n(\varphi_e) = 0$, with the Laplace tidal operator $L = (\partial/\partial\Phi^*)\{[(1-\Phi^{*2})/(Z^2-\Phi^{*2})](\partial/\partial\Phi^*)\} - [1/(Z^2-\Phi^{*2})]\{(k_z/Z)[(Z^2+\Phi^{*2})/(Z^2-\Phi^{*2})]$ $[k_z^2/(1-\Phi^{*2})]\}$, introducing $\Phi^* = \sin\varphi_e$ and $Z = v_e/2\omega_e$. The solutions are placed in the reference frame longitudinal (θ_e) and latitude location (φ_e), with the angular velocity of Earth (ω_e), the atmospheric density ($\rho \propto e^{-r/H}$, r the altitude, H_a the "thickness" of the atmosphere), and $k_z = 2\pi/\lambda_z$ the zonal wavenumber, λ_z is the zonal wavelength, v_e zonal frequency, r the altitude, and R_e is the radius of Earth. The general solutions to the Laplace equation are the Lamb waves in the Bessel function of a decaying order (lower impact for higher order BESSEL FUNCTIONS) as well as other propagating damped wavefunctions (*also see* **HOUGH EQUATION, LAMB WAVES,** *and* **BRUNT-VÄISÄLÄ BUOYANCY FREQUENCY OF THE ATMOSPHERE**) (see Figure T.34).

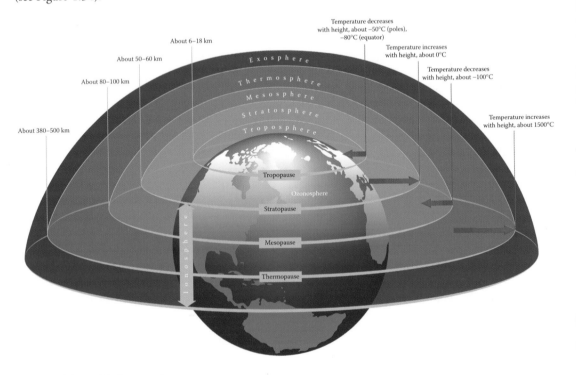

Figure T.34 Earth's thermosphere.

Thermostatics

[thermodynamics] Classical THERMODYNAMICS defining equilibrium states. Also known as "highest-entropy" PHYSICS.

Thévenin, Léon Charles (1857–1926)

[electronics] Electrical engineer from France. The circuit theory EQUIVALENCE PRINCIPLE as derived by Léon Thévenin in 1883 was apparently independently derived by HERMANN VON HELMHOLTZ (1821–1894) in 1853. The Thévenin theorem is cited more frequently than the Helmholtz theorem (see Figure T.35).

Figure T.35 Léon Charles Thévenin (1857–1926).

Thévenin's theorem

[electronics] The combination of several supplies with independent EMF (electromotive force; electrical potential) and any combination of circuit ELEMENTS all between two terminal poles is equivalent to a single EMF in series with a single equivalent impedance between the same two poles. The Thévenin's theorem was described by LÉON CHARLES THÉVENIN (1857–1926). The value of the equivalent EMF source is the potential difference measured between the two terminals when the current is zero and the equivalent impedance is the same as the impedance measured when the equivalent EMF is zero (*also see* KIRCHHOFF'S LAW) (see Figure T.36).

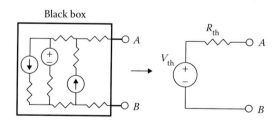

Figure T.36 Thévenin's theorem.

T

Thick lens

[optics] Lens with a separation between the two surfaces on the optical axis that can result in the formation of an IMAGE within the LENS material. The ray shaping is described by the LENS MAKER'S EQUATION (see Figure T.37).

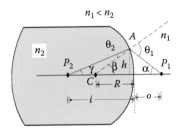

Figure T.37 Thick lens configuration and derivation of lens equation.

Thin lenses, combinations of

[general, optics] In practice, this describes an optical device that does not form on IMAGE inside the transparent object. The thin-lens equation describes the formation of an image at DISTANCE "i" from the LENS with respect to the object at distance "o" with respect to the radius of curvature of the incident surface (R_1) and the emerging surface (R_2), both taken with respect to the center of the lens with index of refraction n_2 as $(1/i)+(1/o)=[(n_2-n_1)/n_1][(1/R_1)-(1/R_2)]=(1/f)=P$, where f represents the focal length of the lens, n_1 the index of refraction for the medium outside the lens, and P the power of the lens in diopters. A concave lens surface will result in a negative radius of curvature for that surface (*also see* LENS EQUATION *and* THICK LENS). Combinations of thin lenses will have a focal length that is the reciprocal sum of the individual focal lengths: $(1/f_{tot})=+(1/f_1)+(1/f_2)+\cdots$ (see Figure T.38).

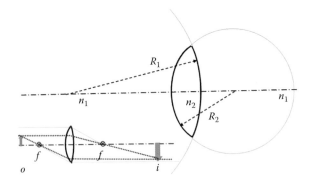

Figure T.38 Thin lens configuration and image formation.

Third law of thermodynamics

[thermodynamics] *See* THERMODYNAMICS, THIRD LAW.

Thixotropic liquid

[fluid dynamics] Fluid with a decreasing APPARENT VISCOSITY as a function of time while under a constant shear rate.

Thomas precession

[atomic, relativistic] Correction factor to the ENERGY shift in the spectral FINE STRUCTURE (primarily for the HYDROGEN ATOM) related to the ORBITAL ANGULAR MOMENTUM, with magnitude ½ (named after Llewellyn Hilleth Thomas [1903–1992] based on his 1926 publication) with respect to the influence of a MAGNETIC FIELD ($\vec{B}$) on the MAGNETIC MOMENT ($\overrightarrow{\mu_{mag}}$) expressed by $\Delta E = -\overrightarrow{\mu_{mag}} \cdot \vec{B} = \left(Ze^2\hbar^2/8\pi\varepsilon_0 c^2 m_e^2\right)r^{-3}$, where r^{-3} is the expectation for the location r, which can be considered the BOHR RADIUS ($n^2 a_0$) under nonrelativistic conditions, $e = 1.60217657 \times 10^{-19}$ C the electron charge, Z the PROTON number (atomic number), $\hbar = h/2\pi$, with $h = 6.62606957 \times 10^{-34}$ m^{2}kg/s the PLANCK'S CONSTANT, c the speed of LIGHT, m_e the electron mass, and $\varepsilon_0 = 8.85419 \times 10^{-12}$ C^2/Nm^2 the permittivity of free space. The correction is based on the fact that a horizontal spin axis (e.g., top with "circumference" equivalence for atom) will be thrown off balance when a mass is added on one side of the ring. The process can take place during the L-S COUPLING (orbital angular momentum coupled to SPIN momentum; referred to as the relativistic spin–orbit effect), providing a torque on an electron that has its spin "flipped." The applied torque will provide a PRECESSION analog to the LARMOR PRECESSION.

Thompson, Benjamin, Sir (1753–1814)

[general, thermodynamics] COUNT RUMFORD. Physicist from the United States. Ben Thompson had a passion for explosives and gunpowder, which led him to work on thermodynamic concepts, experimentally deriving the SPECIFIC HEAT for several substances. His efforts also applied to the THERMAL CONDUCTIVITY of gasses, or better, indicating the lack thereof (see Figure T.39).

Figure T.39 Sir Benjamin Thompson (1753–1814). Painting by Thomas Gainsborough 1783.

T

Thomson, George Paget, Sir (1892–1975)

[atomic, general, nuclear] Physicist and Nobel Laureate from Great Britain. George Thomson and CLINTON JOSEPH DAVISSON (1881–1958) shared Nobel Prize for their verification of the DE BROGLIE WAVELENGTH during electron–electron diffraction (see Figure T.40).

Figure T.40 Sir George Paget Thomson (1892–1975). (Courtesy of Nobel Foundation, Stockholm, Sweden.)

Thomson, Joseph John (1856–1940)

[atomic, energy, general, nuclear, quantum] Physicist from Great Britain. J.J. Thomson constructed a VACUUM tube to investigate the nature of CATHODE RAYS, and this resulted in the discovery of the electron in 1897, also based on the findings by his colleague, the French scientist, JEAN BAPTISTE PERRIN (1870–1942). The electron was the first verified subatomic PARTICLE. Thomson also invented the MASS SPECTROMETER. Thomson experimentally showed the defection of a charged particle with charge e, smaller than an ATOM, moving with velocity v with mass m_e under the influence of an external electric field ($\vec{E}$) applied by two charged plates with length L, along with a MAGNETIC FIELD ($\vec{B}$) applied parallel to the orientation of the plates. The deviation in DISTANCE from the central axis and the axis of incidence is expressed as $e/m_e = 2\,y\vec{E}/L^2\vec{B}^2$, due to the large deflection the mass of the charged particle had to be less than the known mass of the hydrogen ion (H^+), by a factor 1836, and hence the mass had to be equally smaller and was thus recognized as the first subatomic particle, later identified as the electron. In 1899, Thomson further detailed his discovery with the PHOTOELECTRIC EFFECT. The work by Thomson inspired the charge qualification set up by ROBERT ANDREWS MILLIKAN (1868–1953) with the "oil-drop" experiment. Robert Millikan also further refined the photoelectric effect and defined it mathematically in 1914–1915. J.J. Thompon dedicated a great deal of his time on the essential characteristics of the cathode ray and discovered that the ray was not equivalent to electromagnetic RADIATION with a much slower propagation velocity in 1894 (see Figure T.41).

Figure T.41 Joseph John Thomson (1856–1940).

Thomson, William (1824–1907)

[general, thermodynamics] Scientist from Scotland, Great Britain. Generally referred to as Lord Kelvin (*see* KELVIN [LORD KELVIN; 1ST BARON KELVIN]).

Thomson atom

[atomic, general] Even though JOSEPH JOHN THOMSON (1856–1940) revealed the existence of the electron, there was ample prior work indicating a charge distribution in the ATOM. The electronic force description by CHARLES-AUGUSTIN DE COULOMB (1736–1806) was inconclusive, and the follow-up remarks by the mathematician from Great Britain, SAMUEL EARNSHAW (1805–1888) in 1831 [EARNSHAW'S THEOREM], stating that an inverse square law does not create an equilibrium condition unless the charges are in MOTION, led to the atomic model produced by J.J. Thomson in 1903. Additional contributions by JEAN BAPTISTE PERRIN (1870–1942) in 1901 and LORD KELVIN (1824–1907; WILLIAM THOMSON) in 1902 provided the building blocks of the "RAISIN-PUDDING ATOM" published in 1903. The incorporation of the full impact of Earnshaw's statement by ERNEST RUTHERFORD (1871–1937), eighty years later, did not happen until

T

1911 when the atomic model with a NUCLEUS surrounded by electrons in ORBITS like planets around the SUN was adopted. The Rutherford "planetary" model still provides the best description for all relativistic and nonrelativistic atomic phenomena (see Figure T.42).

Figure T.42 Thomson atom model.

Thomson scattering

[atomic, nuclear] SCATTERING of the CATHODE ray "particles" that interacted with the "AETHER," dissociating the cathode ray from electromagnetic RADIATION as investigated by JOSEPH JOHN THOMSON (1856–1940) in the period 1895–1897 (see Figure T.43).

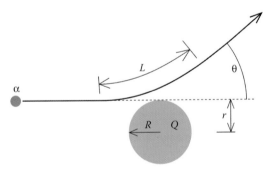

Figure T.43 Thomson scattering.

Thorium radioactive series

[atomic, nuclear] Thorium DECAY is used to identify one of three kinds of decay, next to radium or uranium decay, and the ACTINIUM decay families. The family indication represents the fact that the end product of these three series of decay is a different stable ISOTOPE of lead. Thorium-232 is abundantly available in nature, and itself produces radon, a radioactive GAS found in the basement of many houses (*see* DECAY CHAIN) (see Figure T.44).

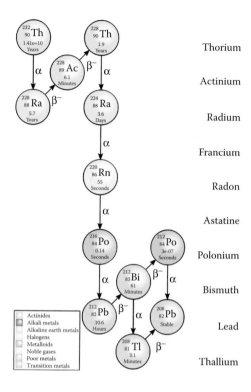

Figure T.44 Thorium.

Thorndike, Edward M. (1906?–)

[general] Physicist from the United States, who in 1932 in collaboration with Roy J. Kennedy, experimentally refuted the AETHER–wind contraction theorem postulated by ALBERT EINSTEIN (1879–1955). Their means of experimentation involved a modified Michelson–Morley INTERFEROMETER and confirm the special relativity aspects of the phenomenon.

Three Laws of planetary motion

[astro, general] Laws introduced by JOHANNES KEPLER (1571–1630) based on the experimentally derived data from TYCHO BRAHE (1546–1601). The first law states that planets move in elliptical ORBITS around the SUN, not in circular orbits as generally assumed (in practice the ellipse is not far from a circle, but the mechanical impact is crucial). The SECOND LAW states that the orbit around the Sun for each PLANET within incremental equal time frames demarcates equal areas, though with different chord lengths or arcs.

The third law correlates the orbital period (T) for different planets in our SOLAR SYSTEM to the average radius ($r_\odot$) to the Sun as a constant ($C_\odot$) ratio: $r_\odot^3/T^2 = C_\odot$ (see Figure T.45).

Kepler's first law

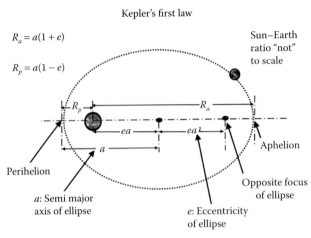

(a)   All planets move in elliptical orbits, with the Sun at one focus

Kepler's second law

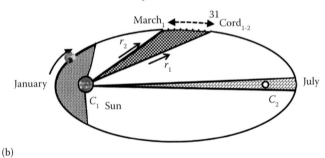

(b)

Kepler's third law

Square of orbital period: $T^2 = \dfrac{4\pi^2}{GM}a^3$; a the planetary orbital radius (average)

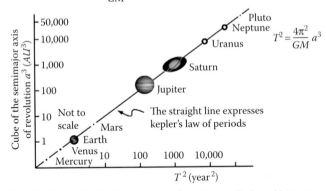

The third law is derived from the law of gravitation. Sir Isaac Newton
(c)   Kepler's third law to base his law of gravitation on.

Figure T.45 Kepler's laws of planetary motion (a) first law, (b) second law, and (c) third law.

Throttle

[fluid dynamics, thermodynamics] PIPE segment with initial sharp decrease in CROSS SECTION in the direction of flow leading up to an ORIFICE, followed by a discontinuous increase to the original cross-sectional area. The function of the throttle is to introduce TURBULENCE at the discontinuity and facilitate a pressure drop. The general purpose of the throttle is to control the pressure drop between the inlet and output of a pipe segment. In certain cases, the orifice is adjustable in cross section, in which case it is called a throttle VALVE. The throttle valve has for instance been used in carburetor-controlled engines to regulate the flow of gasoline and hence control the revolutions of an INTERNAL COMBUSTION ENGINE and thus influence the velocity of movement for the automobile (*also see* **VENTURI**) (see Figure T.46).

Figure T.46 Throttle.

Thrust

[fluid dynamics] Push force. The push force can result from a jet ENGINE or a PROPELLER. The thrust force from a propeller can be defined as $F_T = (\pi/4)D^2\rho\Delta U\left[U + (\Delta U/2)\right]$, with D the propeller diameter, U the incoming flow velocity, and ΔU the increase in flow velocity due to the propeller action, assuming constant and equal pressure before and after the propeller. This principle applies in approximation both to airplane and boat PROPULSION. Alternatively, the thrust from a jet engine is defined by the impulse resulting from the combustion, measured by the ejected quantity of molecules resulting from the JET explosion, in which the bulk mass of molecules (m) is expelled at a high time averaged velocity over the diameter of the jet engine while the plane is in MOTION ($\vec{v}$), providing a momentum $\vec{p} = m\vec{v}$. The impulse force is now $\sum F = dp/dt = m\left(\partial\vec{v}/\partial t\right) + \vec{u}\left(\partial m/\partial t\right)$, note that mass is expelled and the mass rate of ejection is linked to the DENSITY (ρ) as $dm/dt = \rho Av$, where A is the CROSS SECTION of the output flow; $\vec{u}$ is the flow velocity with respect to the reference frame of the plane. Hence the thrust is provided by the expelled exhaust

T

$\overrightarrow{F_T} = \vec{u}\left(\partial m/\partial t\right)$. Note that the same principle applies to opening a fire extinguisher while sitting on a chair (see Figure T.47).

Figure T.47 Thrust.

Thyratron

[atomic, electronics, nuclear] ELECTRON TUBE design that applies a grid structure to the gas DIODE rectifier. The introduction of the GAS (e.g., argon, mercury vapor, or xenon) reduces the voltage BARRIER, hence increasing the efficacy as a RECTIFIER. Applying a variable potential (ranging from negative to positive) as positioned between the CATHODE and the ANODE regulates the electron and ION flow across the tube. The grid may also provide a means of deionization for the gas, with time frames ranging from 10 to 1000 μs, the shortest time with hydrogen as the facilitating gas. In the 1960s, the thyratron has been replaced by the THYRISTOR. The thyratron cannot provide amplification.

Thyristor

[electronics] SOLID-STATE (semiconductor) switch. Some thyristors have photosensitive characteristics.

Tidal breathing

[biomedical, fluid dynamics] The periodic and repetitive inhalation and exhalation of GAS in and out of the lungs respectively under stable boundary conditions, no exercise and under normal pressure and oxygen SATURATION. Some of the parameters associated with tidal breathing and derived parameters are expiratory reserve volume, functional residual capacity, INSPIRATORY CAPACITY, INSPIRATORY RESERVE VOLUME,

RESIDUAL VOLUME, TIDAL VOLUME, total lung capacity, and vital capacity. All the breathing parameters can be determined by spirometry (*see* RESPIRATION) (see Figure T.48).

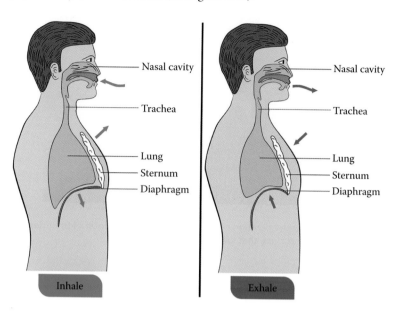

Figure T.48 Tidal breathing as an integral aspect of the respiration.

Tidal forces

[general, geophysics, mechanics] Forces that influence the DYNAMICS of the earth's surface water. Atmospheric flow, as well as EARTH'S CRUST, is primarily the result of gravitational attraction from the MOON and the SUN. The gravitational force is a function of the DISTANCE (r) between two or more bodies of mass (m_i), which can be LIQUID segments, expressed as $\vec{F_g} = G\left(m_1 m_2 / r^2\right)\vec{e_r}$, where $\vec{e_r}$ represents a unit vector in the direction of the connecting line between the two mass segments, and $= 6.67259 \times 10^{-11} \mathrm{Nm}^2/\mathrm{kg}^2$ the gravitational constant. Taking one of the masses as a solid distant object (M) influencing the attraction on a volume of liquid on EARTH will create an incremental drop in GRAVITATIONAL ACCELERATION ($\vec{a_g}$) with increasing distance (Δr) on the curvature of the face of the PLANET, expressed by the Maclaurin series as $\vec{a_g} = -G\left(M/r^2\right)\vec{e_r} \pm 2G\left(M/r^2\right)\left(\Delta r/r\right)\vec{e_r} \mp 3G\left(M/r^2\right)\left(\Delta r/r\right)^2 \vec{e_r} \pm \cdots \mp \cdots$. The gravitational force exerted by the moon's angular momentum on the earth's crust is gradually slowing down the earth's rotation, at a rate of 2.5×10^{-9} s/day. The tidal force is providing a nonuniform force on a large body, specifically when the body is free to move with respect to its "host." Since GRAVITY obeys the inverse square law, the attraction will be greatest at the closest proximity on a curved surface facing another object. The gravitational tides on the earth's crust add to the centripetal forces of rotation to provide an elongation of the sphere, converting it into an ellipsoid. Based on the relative size and distance between the influences from the Sun and the

Moon, the sun's effect on the tides is approximately 45% that for the Moon, depending on the location of the Earth in its elliptical orbit and proximity to the Sun (see Figure T.49).

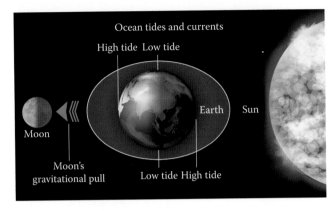

Figure T.49 Tidal forces. Influence of the position of both the Sun and the Moon of the tides by means of gravitational attraction on the liquid surface that can move freely.

Tidal motion

[general] Primarily observed for the earth's surface water. The oceans will be attracted to the MOON due to the gravitational interaction between the LIQUID mass and the mass of the Moon. The water surface closet to the Moon will be attracted with the greatest force, causing the highest elevation with respect to the average sea level (in the absence of CIRCULATION and external gravitational attraction). Water on the opposite side of the EARTH will experience attraction that will lower the water level with respect to "sea level" (see Figure T.50).

Figure T.50 (a,b) Tidal motion.

Tidal volume

[biomedical, fluid dynamics] (TV) During normal TIDAL BREATHING, the volume of inspired and expired AIR from the lungs. Tidal volume and other tidal breathing parameters can be measured with a spirometer (see Figure T.51).

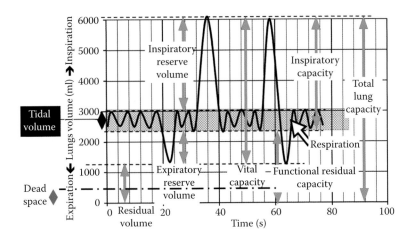

Figure T.51 Tidal volume.

Tidal waves

[fluid dynamics, geophysics] The small AMPLITUDE oscillation in a LIQUID with a free surface induced by GRAVITY. Tidal waves have an elegant solution to the WAVE EQUATION. Tidal waves can also been referenced as CANAL WAVES. In zero-order approximation, the wave equation for the surface wave can be treated as a wave traveling with no deformation in the surface contour. The Lagrange approach for solving the displacement uses the kinetic ENERGY (E_k) derived from the surface matrix of n coordinates (q_n) that vanish at equilibrium ($q_1 = q_2 = q_3 = q_4 = \cdots = q_n = 0$), with respective velocities $v_i = \dot{q}_1 = \partial q_i / \partial t$ described as $E_k = (1/2)\{c_{11}\dot{q}_1^2 + c_{22}\dot{q}_2^2 + \cdots + c_{nn}\dot{q}_n^2 + \cdots + 2c_{12}\dot{q}_1\dot{q}_2 + 2c_{23}\dot{q}_2\dot{q}_3 + \cdots + 2c_{n,n-1}\dot{q}_n\dot{q}_{n-1}\}$. The potential energy stored in the raised water level is similarly defined as $U_p = (1/2)\{c_{11}'q_1^2 + c_{22}'q_2^2 + \cdots + c_{nn}'q_n^2 + \cdots + 2c_{12}'q_1q_2 + 2c_{23}'q_2q_3 + \cdots + 2c_{n,n-1}'q_nq_{n-1}\}$. The Lagrange equation for the movement of the respective coordinates now becomes $(d/dt)(\partial E_k/\partial \dot{q}_1) - (\partial E_k/\partial q_i) = -(\partial E_k/\partial q_i) + D_i$, where D_i are the coefficients of displacement in the direction normal to the undisturbed surface, $i = 1, 2, 3 \ldots n$, describing the matrix of surface displacement as $D_1\Delta q_1 + D_2\Delta q_2 + \cdots + D_n\Delta q_n$. This yields $D_i = c_i\ddot{q}_i + c_i'q_i$, where $\ddot{q}_1 = \partial^2 q_i/\partial t^2$. The "forced" OSCILLATION solution now becomes $q_i = C_i/(c_i' - \tau_\pi^2 c_i)\cos(\tau_\pi t + \epsilon_\pi)$, where the wave has a period

$2\pi/\tau_\pi$, with $\tau_\pi^i = \sqrt{c_i'/c_i}$, with C_i the coefficients for the simple harmonic solutions ($Q_i = C_i \cos(\tau_\pi t + \epsilon_\pi)$). Also referred to as Tidal Bore (see Figure T.52).

Figure T.52 Tidal bore, captured in Sumatra. (Courtesy of photographer Muhtar Sanusi and Antony Colas; www.bonosurf.com.)

Tide-generating forces

[fluid dynamics, geophysics] The gravitational attraction of the MOON in an orbit around the EARTH exerts a force on both the Earth and the free-flowing liquid on the surface, creating TIDAL WAVES. In large bodies of water (ocean and sea), this creates tidal waves. On the ebb and flood aspect of the main bodies of water, the rivers will drain or fill, creating canal tidal waves. The mass (m_{moon}) of the Moon at a variable DISTANCE (d_{moon}) from the Earth exerts a force that is dependent on the location on the earth's surface (with radius: r_{earth}) as well as the moon's zenith (the ANGLE with respect to a fixed meridian at longitude ϕ_{long} yields the ZENITH as a function of TIME (t) $\vartheta_{moon} = m_\omega t + \phi_{long} + f$, where ϕ represents the PHASE of the MOTION wavefunction and $m_\omega = r_{earth}\omega$, with ω the ANGULAR VELOCITY of the earth's revolution at a given location (P). The gravitational pull provides an ENERGY potential (U_Ω) that is linked by the gravitational constant (γ_{grav}) as $U_\Omega = (3/2)(\gamma_{grav} m_{moon} r_{earth}^2/d_{moon}^3)[(1/3) - \cos^2(\vartheta_{moon})]$. The potential provides the horizontal acceleration vertically beneath the Moon in the tangential direction as $a_{//} = \partial U_\Omega/r_{earth}\partial\vartheta_{moon} = (3/2)(\gamma_{grav} m_{moon} r_{earth}/d_{moon}^3)\sin(2\vartheta_{moon})$; note that the Earth's gravitation (g) is linked to the mass of Earth (m_{earth}) to yield: $g = \gamma_{grav} m_{earth}/r_{earth}^2$. Similarly the SUN (mass: m_{sun}; distance: d_{sun}) exerts a force that influences the tides in a similar fashion (i.e., presenting a cumulative effect). Now the equation of motion for the displacement (ξ) of the surface of the LIQUID with respect to "sea level," that is, the earth's surface): $\partial^2\xi/\partial t^2 = v^2(\partial^2\xi/r_{earth}^2\partial\phi_{long}^2) - (3/2)(\gamma_{grav} m_{moon} r_{earth}/d_{moon}^3)\sin(2[m_\omega t + \phi_{long} + \phi])$, where v is the speed of WAVE propagation. The AMPLITUDE A_{tidal} (i.e., the maximum range of low to high water during the semidiurnal period ($T_{diurnal}$) of the wave: $T_{diurnal} = 2\pi r_{earth}/nv$, with $n:1-\infty$) is represented for a uniform river basin floor bed as $A_{tidal} = r_{earth}[(3/2)(\gamma_{grav} m_{moon} r_{earth}/d_{moon}^3)/g] = r_{earth}(f/g)$. The "free" OSCILLATION solution to the wave equation under the influence of the Moon can be expressed under the FOURIER THEOREM as $\xi = -(1/4)[f r_{earth}^2/(v^2 - m^2 r_{earth}^2)]\sin(2[m_\omega t + \phi_{long} + \phi])$, yielding for the physical perpendicular surface displacement: $\chi = -(1/2)[A_{tidal} v^2/(v^2 - m^2 r_{earth}^2)]\cos(2[m_\omega t + \phi_{long} + \phi])$. Keeping in mind that the depth of the river will place a limiting factor on the wave phenomenon, not to have the amplitude exceed the depth. At great depths (as what may be found in the far off-shore ocean), the tidal wave will be antiparallel, or in counterphase (*see* TIDAL WAVE *and* TIDAL FORCE).

Timbre

[acoustics, general] The FREQUENCY SPECTRUM associated with the SOUND produced by an instrument. Often referred to as the "COLOR" of the sound. The introduction of higher harmonics by the instrument design and the way the primary tones are generated (the way the instrument is played) influence the spectral power profile as well as the range/expanse of the spectrum. For instance, for a wooden instrument, the local HUMIDITY will affect the elastic modulus of the casing for the REVERBERATION produced by an oscillating string. The elastic modulus will affect the VIBRATION AMPLITUDE as a function of wavelength. The choice of material can be instrumental in defining the sound quality as is the functional geometric design (shape and material thickness, etc.). For instance, the construction and finish (e.g., varnish) will be crucial; a Stradivarius violin still catches the attention of the audience after more than 300 years of AGE. The Stradivarius name was known as a family instrument makers business during the seventeenth and eighteenth century, particularly famous was Antonio Stradivari (1644–1737) for his skills in design, material selection, and material preparation as well as assembly (see Figure T.53).

Figure T.53 Metal straight flute.

Time (*t*)

[general] Sequence of events placed in relative respect to each other. Early concepts of time were attributed to the solar night–day rhythm (circadian rhythm), which as divided into two 12 segments by the Egyptians approximately 3000 years ago, defining the 24 h day. Persian mathematics (i.e., Babilonia) had the number 60 as the base (*Note*: the French arithmetic has the number 24 as base), which influenced the later subdivision of the hour into 60 min introduced in the fourteenth century when keeping track of time became more feasible with mechanical devices. As more intricate and accurate time keeping devices were developed, the minute was divided in 60 s. In 1967 a formal definition of the second as the standard of time was defined by the Si as the duration of 9192631770 oscillations of the RADIATION from cesium ^{133}Ce, the introduction of the ATOMIC CLOCK. The atomic clock in Boulder, Colorado, the United States is approximately 15.5 nanoseconds faster than the atomic clocks in Washington, DC, or Paris, France, which was indicated by ALBERT EINSTEIN (1879–1955) that time MEASUREMENT in this manner depends on GRAVITY. Early Babylonian and Egyptian time-keeping records used water flow and syphons as far

back as the sixteenth century BC. Additional early mechanisms of measuring used the Sun in the form of sundials (see Figure T.54).

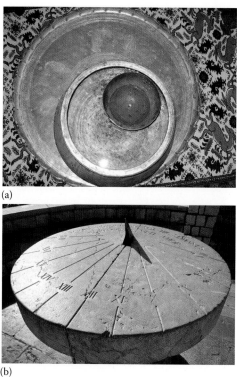

(a)

(b)

Figure T.54 (a) Ancient water clock and (b) historic sun dial.

Time dilation

[atomic, general, relativistic] *See* DILATION.

Time perturbation, colliding black holes

[astrophysics, general] In 1916 ALBERT EINSTEIN (1879–1955) predicted that under the concept of general relativity, the space-time CONTINUUM could be disrupted, making the UNIVERSE "ring." At this point of time, no confirmed observations are documented for collisions of BLACK HOLES, nor has the time RIPPLE been measured. Based on theoretical considerations and the composition of the universe as we currently understand it, there may be small probabilities that black holes will collide in the next several million years, two black holes in the QUASAR PG 1302-102 can indeed merge. The two black holes are at approximately 3.5 billion light-years DISTANCE from our SOLAR SYSTEM. Another supposed double black-hole galaxy is NGC 6240, which is located at 140 million light-years from our solar system. This provides a better opportunity for two black holes, within the same GALAXY, to merge. So far the predictions indicate that this merger of two black holes in the NGC 6240 galaxy will at least not happen for another 100 million years. The MILKY WAY itself is supposedly meeting up with the ANDROMEDA GALAXY in several billion years from now, as we approach at 120 km per SECOND. In general, when galaxies merge, the central black holes of the respective galaxies will be placed in orbit with each other. Several known galaxies have been shown to have a BLACK HOLE at its center. The Milky Way has a confirmed central black hole at a distance from our solar system of approximately 28,000 light-years (*Note*: estimate diameter of the Milky Way is 100,000 light-years). The anticipated perturbations in the spacetime continuum (e.g., ripples in time) resulting from black-hole collisions are represented by "GRAVITATIONAL WAVES." The Einstein Equations elegantly allow the unification of space and time into a format known as "SPACETIME." When trying to solve for impact on either space (GRAVITY) or time the Einstein equations will need to be decomposed so that mathematical approach reverts to the "Cauchy problem" (mathematician from France: BARON AUGUSTIN-LOUIS CAUCHY (1789–1857)). During a collision of two black holes in approximation roughly 0.1% of the mass of the merged system is "radiated away" as gravitational waves. The impact on "pure time" can be imagined in the SPACETIME representation by means of expression of points with coordinates of both space and time. Slices in the SPACETIME of constant time will intersect with spatial coordinates. The lapse in "proper time" (as we live it) can be derived using the decomposition of the EINSTEIN EQUATIONS in the Cauchy problem version specific to solving partial differential equations on a hypersurface in a multidimensional domain. The Cauchy problem consists of finding the SOLUTION u of the differential equation for the functions f_k on the surface S of order m that satisfies $\partial^k u(x)/\partial n^k = f_k(x)$ $\{k = 1, 2, 3, m-1\}$, where n is the normal vector to the surfaces, which is known as the Cauchy data, under the boundary condition $u(x) = f_0(x)$. Under SPECIAL RELATIVITY, the spacetime continuum is considered to be "flat," meaning no change in time associated with changes in gravitational MOTION. In this case, the interval (ds) between two points in space and time is defined as $x^a = \left(t, x^1, x^2, x^3\right) = t\left(x^i\right)$, with concurrent changes $x^a + dx^a = (t + dt, x^i + dx^i)$, which can be rewritten using the PYTHAGOREAN THEOREM as $(ds)^2 = -dt^2 + (dx^1)^2 + (dx^2)^2 + (dx^3)^2 = \sum_{a,b} \eta_{ab} dx^a dx^b$. The matrix is normalized by means of the Minkowski metric TENSOR (Russian mathematician HERMANN MINKOWSKI (1864–1909)): η_{ab} with diagonal $\eta_{ab} = \text{diag}(-1, 1, 1, 1)$. In this interval, the time (τ) is defined by means of proper time under the condition $d\tau^2 = -ds^2$, that is, less than zero. Under general relativity, specifically when "SPACETIME" is curved, the Minkowski metric tensor changes to provide the tools for (3 + 1) decomposition (representing the Cauchy problem) as g_{ab}; $ds^2 = \sum_{ab} g_{ab} dx^a dx^b$. The (3 + 1) decomposition constraints the gravity fields (in the EINSTEIN EQUATIONS) for every instance of time, and allows for an additional time perturbation of the gravitational fields, thus splitting the SPACETIME into space and time. In the (3 + 1) decomposition SPACETIME can be considered to be foliated into slices defined by constant time coordinates. In the (3 + 1) decomposition, spacetime "points" are connected by vector t^a, using a time vector that stands normal to the SPECIAL RELATIVISTIC space, defined as n^a. The SPACETIME slices will be separated by dt, defined by a lapse function α_{lapse}. The "lapse function" relates to "proper time" (as we live it) in SPACETIME in the displacement (dx^a) between two points $[A^{x^i, t}$ and $B^{x^i + dx^i, t + dt}]$ written using the Pythagorean theorem as $ds^2 = -\alpha_{\text{lapse}}^2 + \sum_{i,j} \gamma_{ij} \left(dx^i + \beta^i dt\right)\left(dx^j + \beta^j dt\right)$, where γ_{ij} is a quantity defining the spatial separation between the two SPACETIME slices. Under these conditions, the curvature in SPACETIME is defined by the time derivative of the spatial metric γ_{ij} to yield the extrinsic curvature K_{ij} (see Figure T.55).

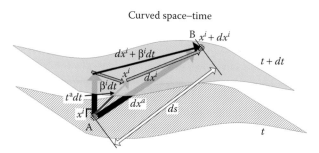

Figure T.55 Geometric representation of space–time described under the conditions of curved space. The transition between two points in the spacetime matrix is described by general relativity methods.

Timocharis

[astrophysics, general] Fourth century BC, Greek scientist and astrophysicist. Together with ARISTYLLUS, they documented the first list of visible fixed stars.

Tip angle

[energy] ANGLE of airplane WING with a horizontal reference plane, with the vertical plane in which the PROPELLER rotates (ship, wind TURBINE). The tip angle changes during the take-off for an airplane, and can be adjusted for a wind turbine or old-fashioned windmill to adjust for influences generated by the wind direction, wind velocity, as well as desired performance. The tip angle for a plane obtaining a cruising altitude, steady-state flight, is also referred to as the tip-settling angle. For a propeller (airplane engine, ship/motor-boat, and wind turbine), there is an angle associated with the performance (efficacy and efficiency). Also referred to as the turbine blade angle (see Figure T.56).

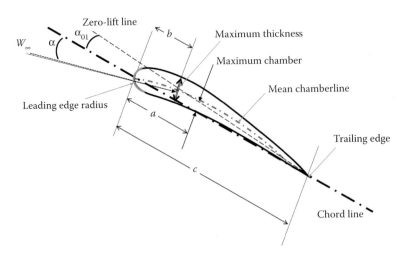

Figure T.56 Tip angle of an airplane wing.

Tissue characterization

[acoustics, biomedical, imaging] Mechanism-of-action applied in acoustic (ULTRASOUND), optical, magnetic (MRI), X-RAY, or positron emission (PET) imaging to identify the characteristic properties that allow for discrimination between tissue functionality, tissue composition, and tissue density. The parameters used for characterization can be any of the following with their respective potential for identification: FREQUENCY SPECTRUM (tissue type or stage of development: collagen/fat/bone; METABOLIC ACTIVITY; general subjective health: "you don't look so good"); attenuation (elastic modulus, density, phase [liquid/solid]); and refraction/reflection (boundary detection). Under certain circumstances, a "tag" is required to assist in the characterization process; for PET, this tag is fluorine-18-fluorodeoxyglucose, which acts as GLUCOSE but has a specific positron EMISSION SPECTRUM that can be acquired as a function of location hence revealing the local metabolic activity. These imaging methods can be applied in vivo. The other imaging technique performed ex vivo is optical microscopy. Optical imaging generally requires staining with dyes and chemicals for visible or fluorescent recognition of CELL types in order to screen for deviations from the norm. One optical technique that can provide in-vivo imaging is OPTICAL COHERENCE TOMOGRAPHY, which can apply all the optical features (PHASE, wavelength, MAGNITUDE, and combinations of factors to reveal physiological features next to anatomical features). Another relatively new imaging technique is photoacoustic imaging, combining the acoustic and optical modalities to reach deeper than standard optical imaging and provide acoustic RESOLUTION (see Figure T.57).

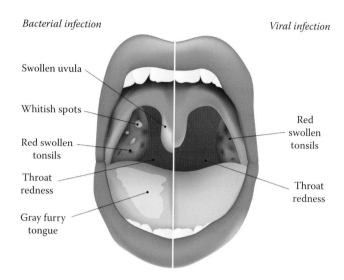

Bacterial infection   *Viral infection*

Swollen uvula

Whitish spots

Red swollen tonsils

Throat redness

Gray furry tongue

Red swollen tonsils

Throat redness

Figure T.57 Visual rudimentary characteristics of the appearance of tissue under (left) bacteria compared to tonsillitis of the throat and (right) viral versus bacterial infection diagnosis.

Titanium

[biomedical, mechanics, solid-state] Chemical ELEMENT, metal: $^{48}_{22}$Ti. Titanium was discovered in 1791 by William Gregor (1761–1817); it is a very strong and light-weight METAL with a silver COLOR with a relatively high MELTING POINT (1941 K, compare to 1811 K for IRON; 1357 K for copper). Titanium has excellent biocompatibility, no toxic effects, and is resistant to the acidic nature for decades of functional use. Titanium is used in durable devices such as JET engines, missiles, automotive/motorcycle, orthopedic implants, and implantable defibrillators/pacemakers. Titanium can form alloys with several other metals: iron, aluminum, vanadium, and many more. Titanium is an excellent CONDUCTOR of electrical current. Titanium alone does not function well as a biological ELECTRODE due to POLARIZATION effects. The use of Titanium for electrode material will result in a gradual loss of signal AMPLITUDE as a result of the localized charge accumulation.

Toepler, August Joseph Ignaz (1836–1912)

[biomedical, energy, general, optics] Physicist from Germany (Prussian Empire) who made several discoveries related to electrostatic behavior next to investigations in fluids. In his analysis of FLUID flow and associated shock waves, he applied Foucault's knife-edge test for TELESCOPE mirrors (1864) as a mechanism for imaging. He is credited with describing the heat-induced BIREFRINGENCE in materials in 1894. The imaging mechanism under the birefringence discovered by August Toepler was characterized as SCHLIEREN IMAGING. Schlieren imaging has only had limited applications so far, but is gaining interest (see Figure T.58).

Figure T.58 August Joseph Ignaz Toepler (1836–1912). (Courtesy of Österreichische Zentralbibliothek für Physik 1908.)

Tokamak Fusion Reactor

[general] REACTOR accelerator designed for NUCLEAR FUSION based on a close to ideal toroidal MAGNETIC FIELD. The name is a Russian acronym that loosely translates into "toroidal chamber with magnetic coils." The toroidal confinement provides the boundary conditions for theoretical stability of a PLASMA in equilibrium. The specific plasma confinement is provided by an additional poloidal magnetic FLUX in the toroid, which provides conservation of the canonical angular momentum. The toroidal canonical angular momentum conservation results in a characteristic closed orbit. The plasma is initially created as the result of ohmic current interactions with an ionizing gas. The plasma is confined by "scraping off" the outer layer using a diverter separatrix, preserving the D-shaped tokamak plasma. The tokamak principle and prototype were constructed by the physicists from Russia (USSR: Union of Soviet Socialist Republics; in short Soviet Union) Igor Tamm (1895–1971) and Andrei Sakharov (1921–1989), in the 1950s (see Figure T.59).

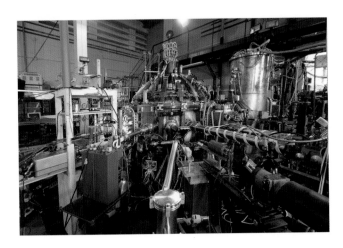

Figure T.59 Image of the Tokamak Fusion Reactor design.

Tomographic slices

[biomedical, imaging] In order to view the content of any three-dimensional construction, one will require a SLICE to observe the pertinent information within the structure. There are several ways of slicing a tomographic reconstruction, primarily axial (a slice of the body on the axis of the body); coronal (a view of a plane that is parallel to the plane marked out by the extremities; arms and legs); and a sagittal view that carves the body from anterior to posterior, dividing left and right side of the body at various distances from the center (see Figure T.60).

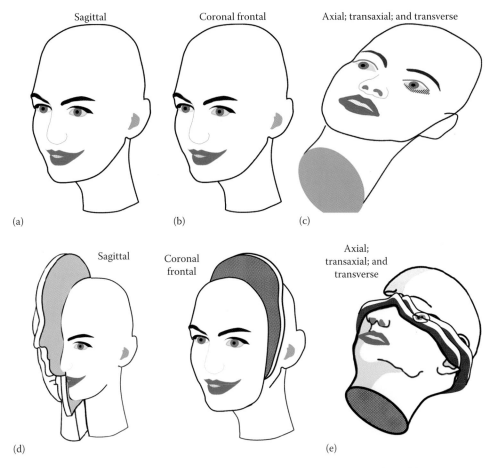

Figure T.60 (a–e) Designation with respect to tomographic slice configuration. (e: Adapted from Prince, J.L. and Links, J., *Medical Imaging Signals and Systems*, Pearson Education, Upper Saddle River, NJ, 2006.)

Tomography

[acoustics, biomedical, electromagnetism, imaging] Two- or three-dimensional reconstruction of an IMAGE formed by probing line-of-flight radiation. Generally the source to detector correlation is on opposing sides of a circular band; the sensors are simultaneously collecting at multiple locations from within the same toroidal configuration. The RADIATION can be X-RAY, RADIONUCLIDE positron emission from artificially induced radioactive isotopes that generates the release of two perfectly opposite gamma ray photons (PET) and line-of-sight capture of radiofrequency RESONANCE signals induced by magnetic fields (MRI). An additional form of tomography uses geometric reconstruction based on the BACKSCATTER of LIGHT under optical coherence tomography (OCT), where the scanning pattern defines the extend of the two-dimensional outline, with the depth providing the third dimension. The depth of OCT probing is confined by the SIGNAL strength collected form depths of several micrometers from OPAQUE media (see Figure T.61).

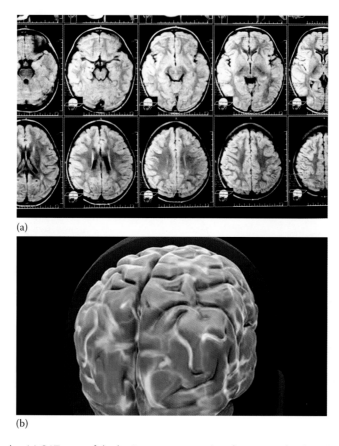

(a)

(b)

Figure T.61 Tomography: (a) CAT scan of the brain; computer assisted tomography; imaging with X-ray and (b) three-dimensional rendering of the brain from acquired images slices.

Tomonaga, Sin-Itiro (朝永 振一郎) (1906–1979)

[general] Physicist from Japan. Sin-Itiro Tomonaga received the Nobel Prize in Physics in 1965 for his contributions to quantum PHYSICS theory, specifically quantum ELECTRODYNAMICS. He shared the Nobel Prize with RICHARD FEYNMAN (1918–1988) and Julian Schwinger (1918–1994). Sin-Itiro Tomonaga performed experimental verification of the pair creation of the PHOTON–electron pair in 1939, and worked closely with WERNER HEISENBERG (1901–1976) in Germany. On his return to Japan, he developed the theoretical definition of the MESON cloud around the NUCLEON. In 1942, he proposed the covariant field theory, in which the QUANTUM STATE was also relativistically covariant (see Figure T.62).

Figure T.62 Sin-Itiro Tomonaga (朝永 振一郎) (1906–1979). (Courtesy of University of Chicago Press, Chicago, IL.)

Tonicity

[biomedical, chemical] Expression of the OSMOTIC PRESSURE gradient across a SEMIPERMEABLE MEMBRANE (such as a CELL MEMBRANE) of two ionic/molecular solutions. Due to the fact that the cell membrane of most mammals is permeable to only a select few ions and molecules and highly diffusive to water, the changes in concentration of certain cellular constituents can result in the release or gain of water. The release of water as a result of OSMOSIS will result in cell shrinkage. Alternatively when the extracellular FLUID is diluted, the cell will gain water and will swell. A swollen cell will activate its sodium, potassium, and chlorine channels, resulting in an efflux primarily of K^+ and Cl^- due to the difference in mobility. This chemical exchange will not affect the MEMBRANE POTENTIAL, due to the opposite charge signs

T

involved. Both cell swelling and shrinking will dramatically impair the function of the cell, potentially resulting in cell death (see Figure T.63).

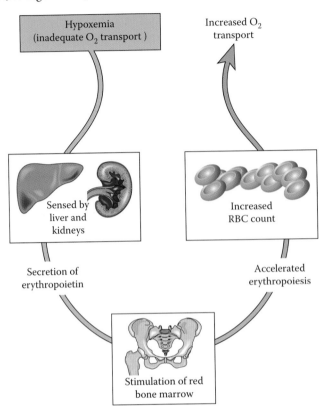

Figure T.63 Hypoxemia.

Tornado

[fluid dynamics, geophysics, mechanics, meteorology] Air-flow vortex of large proportions. Note that tornadoes are different from hurricanes, although hurricanes can SPIN off tornadoes. The rotation of a column of AIR can touch the surface while stretching out into cumulonimbus clouds, and on rare occasions may reach upward to the cumulus cloud portion of the ATMOSPHERE. Tornadoes form as a result of converging air masses from different directions, specifically the convergence of a cold and a warm airstream. The tornado is generally preceded by a rotation in the upper atmosphere that is observed in geological radar stations that observe the formation and precipitation of RAIN and snow clouds, at the level of cumulonimbus clouds. Tornadoes are also referred to as twisters or as cyclones and are found all over the world. The majority of tornadoes occur in what is known as Tornado Alley in the central part of the United States. Tornado Alley stretches from south to north starting in Texas, going through Oklahoma, Kansas, Nebraska, and North and South Dakota. The Tornado Alley gains its reputation from warm Gulf of Mexico air colliding with cold air from Canada and the Arctic. Tornadoes can have a diameter of over 75 m to close to 2 km. Small tornadoes travel slowly, at about 40 km per hour, whereas speeds up to 300 km per hour have been clocked for large tornadoes. A strong and destructive tornado is referenced as an F-5, whereas lower numbers are less potent. Tornadoes last from several minutes to, rarely, one hour. Due to Coriolis forces, tornadoes on the northern hemisphere turn counterclockwise and clockwise on the southern hemisphere. The F-scale is derived from Tetsuya Fujita (1920–1998) who designed the scale based on anticipated or experienced destruction. The VORTEX phenomenon can LIFT entire houses of their foundation, and the accompanying pressure gradient will shatter most windows within its path and direct vicinity (see Figure T.64).

(a)

(b)

Figure T.64 Tornado: (a) Doppler radar image of air stream flow velocity and direction during a tornado and (b) diagram of the outline of a tornado.

Torque (τ)

[general] The sum of the tangential components of the net LEVER force multiplied by the DISTANCE from the point of rotation to the point where the forces are applied, that is, the MOMENT ARM. Torque is mathematically defined as $\vec{\tau} = \sum \vec{F} \times \vec{r}$. Torque resulting in clockwise rotation is positive, whereas counterclockwise rotation has a negative torque (see Figure T.65).

Figure T.65 Torque wrench with dial for indication of applied torque.

Torr

[general] Unit of pressure, equivalent to 1 Torr = 1 mmHg = 133.3 Pa on the MERCURY BAROMETER scale (*see* **EVANGELISTA TORRICELLI** [1608–1647]).

Torrey, Henry Cutler (1911–1998)

[atomic, imaging, nuclear] Physicist from the United States who contributed to the theoretical understanding of nuclear MAGNETIC RESONANCE. The work of Henry Torrey provided significant advancement of magnetic resonance imaging (MRI), in collaboration with EDWARD MILLS PURCELL (1912–1997) and ROBERT VIVIAN POUND (1919–2010), based on the earlier work of ISIDOR RABI (1898–1988) and FELIX BLOCH (1905–1983).

Torricelli, Evangelista (1608–1647)

[fluid dynamics, general, geophysics, meteorology]: mathematician and physicist from Italy, protégée of GALILEO GALILEI (1564–1642). Following in the footsteps of Galileo and his work with experimental observations on the "weight" of AIR (glass bulb), Torricelli realized the cause and effect in 1643. His work in COMMUNICATING VESSELS led to the construction of a device to measure the fluctuating pressure in the ATMOSPHERE with changing weather conditions, or better in anticipation of changing weather conditions. The TORRICELLI BAROMETER was confirmed and details were added by BLAISE PASCAL (1623–1662) in 1648. Torricelli lent his name to the TORR or mmHg (millimeter mercury) as a unit for pressure, mostly used for low pressure, whereas the PASCAL (Pa) is the recognized standard unit for pressure (see Figure T.66).

Figure T.66 Evangelista Torricelli (1608–1647).

Torricelli's barometer

[fluid dynamics] Barometer as introduced by EVANGELISTA TORRICELLI (1608–1647) around 1643 that consists of a GLASS tube inserted in a bowl of mercury. The tube is closed on the top, and the ATMOSPHERE provides a column of AIR resting on the surface of the mercury in the bowl, raising the mercury level. GALILEO GALILEI (1564–1642) had already determined that air has mass (weight), which led Torricelli to the correlation and derived the pressure resulting from a tall volume of air surrounding the globe as a function of weather conditions and altitude. The location-dependent pressure variability was derived in collaboration with BLAISE PASCAL (1623–1662) in 1648. The same principle was applied to measure BLOOD pressure in 1726. The first recorded attempts to measure BLOOD PRESSURE are the work of the clergyman, astronomer, chemist, and botanist from Great Britain, Stephen Hales (1677–1761). The reverend Stephen Hales used a brass PIPE (one-sixth of an inch in diameter) connected to a narrow glass tube and attached it to the carotid artery of a horse to investigate what was ailing the dying animal. The tube was 12′ 9″ tall (388 cm) and the blood reached approximately 8 feet in height (2.44 m). Repeating his experiments for other locations and with other animals, he was able to provide a diagram of blood pressure distribution based on the ANATOMY and DISTANCE to the HEART for several animals and developed a system to apply this to humans as well. This fluid-dynamics system has considerable DAMPING and provides an average pressure value. For humans, Hales concluded a pressure of 7′ 6″ (apparently based on hypothesis), corresponding to a SYSTOLIC PRESSURE of 176 mmHg on "modern" standards. This type of MEASUREMENT was performed on humans by a French surgeon in 1820 providing the equivalent of 120 mmHg on the femoral artery when his patients had to have a LEG amputated. In 1876, the first SPHYGMOMANOMETER was developed that measures the corresponding blood pressure on the wrist by means of a balloon pressed against the radial artery (as connected to the brachial artery that is currently used to measure the blood pressure in the elbow). The wrist sphygmomanometer was developed by Karl Samuel Ritter Von Basch (1837–1905) from Czechoslovakia (now Czech Republic). In 1896, the Riva Rocci Sphygmomanometer was developed, which measures the blood pressure at the elbow and is the predecessor to the current state-of-the-art device. It was not until 1904 that the Russian army surgeon NIKOLAI KOROTKOFF (1874–1920) realized that closing off the brachial artery allowed for measuring the systolic versus DIASTOLIC PRESSURE using the fluttering sounds of blood rushing through a pinched blood vessel (KOROTKOFF SOUNDS) (*see* MERCURY BAROMETER, BLOOD PRESSURE, *and* NIKOLAI KOROTKOFF) (see Figure T.67).

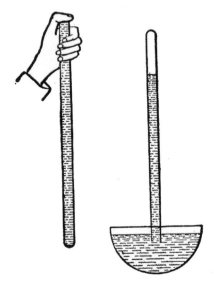

Figure T.67 Torricelli barometer.

Torsion

[computational, general, mechanics] In mechanical ENGINEERING, this refers to the mechanical twisting of an object under the influence of an applied torque. The mechanical torsion is represented by the torque τ_T, defined by the shear stress in the twisted material on the outer surface (σ_s^*), the material properties imbedded in the torsion constant (J_τ), as a function of the DISTANCE of the farthest point out from the rotational axis of symmetry to the outer surface (r) expressed as $\tau_T = \left(J_\tau / r \right) \sigma_s^* = \left(J_\tau / \ell \right) G_\sigma \theta$, where G_σ is the shear modulus for the material and geometry (also referred to as the MODULUS OF RIGIDITY), θ the ANGLE or rotation/twist in the material with respect to relaxed state, and ℓ is the length over which the torque is applied. In ALGEBRA, the torsion characterizes the twisting of a moving reference frame around a curve. The torsion TENSOR ($T(X,Y)$) defining the manner in which a moving frame is screwed around a state curve is described with respect to the vector fields X and Y as $T(X,Y) = \nabla_X Y - \nabla_Y X - [X,Y]$. In this notation, $[X,Y]$ represents the Lie bracket of vector fields, the Lie derivative $\mathcal{L}_X Y = \lim_{t \to 0} [((d\Phi_{-t}^X) Y_{\Phi_t^X(x)} - Y_x)/t]$, where Φ_t^X represents the flow associated with the vector field, and $d\Phi_t^X = \partial \hat{\Phi}^X / \partial u^t$ is the tangent map derivative operator applied to the flow field, providing the linear map of the differential of Φ_t^X, $\hat{\Phi}$ the smoothed vector field Φ_t^X, and u the transform of x in the vector flowchart (see Figure T.68).

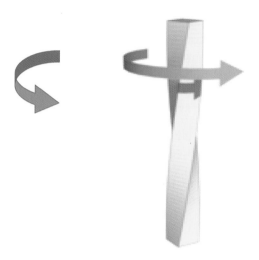

Figure T.68 Torsion.

Torsion wave

[fluid dynamics, general, mechanics] Under rotational agitation of a FLUID or solid, the harmonic perturbation will travel forming a torsion wave. For instance, the axle of a car is under continuous torsional forces that vary with time, hence creating a torsional wave, specifically the use of the torsion bar suspension. Another example is in the vertical agitating top-loader washing MACHINES (driven torsional OSCILLATION). The torsion wave (*also see* DAMPED HARMONIC MOTION *and* FORCED VORTEX) (see Figure T.69).

Figure T.69 Torsion wave. (Courtesy of Kay Wyatt.)

Torsional oscillations

[fluid dynamics, general, mechanics] Two prime examples or TORSION WAVE are for a hollow sphere filled with viscous LIQUID oscillating around its vertical axis and a sphere oscillating around its vertical axis surrounded by viscous liquid. The vertical agitating laundry washing machine found in the United States and Great Britain and other locations (different from the front-load washing machine) would be the cylindrically symmetric version for the spherical oscillation surrounded by a viscous liquid. The situation for the hollow sphere with radius R, oscillating at an ANGULAR FREQUENCY ω, that is filled with viscous liquid will have PARTICLE movement as a function of radius described by $\omega' = \left[\psi_1(hr)/\psi_1(hR)\right]\omega$, where $h^2 = -(\sigma_\omega/\nu_{kin})$ represents the "functional" DISTANCE from the center on the rotating axis, $\nu_{kin} = \eta_{kin}/\rho$ the coefficient of KINEMATIC VISCOSITY (η_{kin} the kinematic viscosity, ρ the density), $\sigma_\omega = v_r k$ the angular velocity of rotational motion (v_r the wave propagation velocity), and ψ_1 is the first-order spherical harmonic component. The general SOLUTION to the WAVE EQUATION, $(\nabla^2 + k^2)\phi(r,\theta,\varphi) = 0$, provides $\phi = \sum\{A\psi_n(kr) + B\Psi_n(kr)\}r^n S_n$, where A and B are constants, k is the wavenumber, and S_n represents the surface harmonic of order n. The functions are linked to BESSEL FUNCTIONS ($J_k(\xi)$), of the order $\pm(1/2)(2m+1)$, as $\xi^n \psi_n(\xi) = \sqrt{[(\pi/2\xi)J_{n+(1/2)}(\xi)]}$; $\xi^n \Psi_n(\xi) = (-1)^n \sqrt{[(\pi/2\xi)J_{-n-(1/2)}(\xi)]}$, respectively $\psi_n(\xi) = 1/1.3....(2n+1)\{1 - [\xi^2/2(2n+3)] + [\xi^4/2.4(2n+3)(2n+5)] -\}$ and $\Psi_n(\xi) = 1.3....(2n+1)/\xi^{2n+1}\{1 - [\xi^2/2(1-2n)] + [\xi^4/2.4(1-2n)(3-2n)] -\}$. Due to the fact that the MOTION at the central axis (origin) is finite (no motion on the vertical axis) only the term $= A\psi_n(kr)r^n S_n$ is retained. The sphere will be suspended by the external axis. The angular velocity on the axis for the liquid within the sphere will need to be zero under consideration of ENERGY constraints. For the viscous liquid inside the rotationally oscillating sphere there are two situations: low- or high-viscosity medium. The high-viscosity case yields (the Stokes theorem): $\omega' = \left[\psi_1(hr)/\psi_1(hR)\right]\omega = \omega\cos(\sigma_\omega t + \epsilon)$, where ϵ is the phase shift. Under these high-viscosity OSCILLATION conditions, the net torque (sometime also described as "couple") is given as $\tau_F = (8/3)\pi\eta_{kin}R^3\left[h^2R^2\psi_2(hr)/\psi_1(hr)\right]\omega$. In contrast, the low-viscosity case changes the boundary conditions to include more elaborate details: $2i\psi_n(hR) = [-(d/\xi d\xi)]^n(e^{i\xi}/\xi)$. The low-viscosity oscillation yields for the torque as a function of time $\tau_F = -(4/3)(\pi\rho R^5/\beta'\sigma_\omega)(d\omega/dt) - (8/3)\pi\eta_{kin}R^3(\beta'\sigma_\omega)\omega$, where the first term is an indication of the INERTIA of the sphere, the second term introduces DAMPING from FRICTION, and $\beta' = \sqrt{(\sigma_\omega/2\nu_{kin})}$ represents the reciprocal viscous influence, a scaling factor. Next the torsional oscillating sphere around its vertical axis surrounded by viscous liquid is discussed. Under these conditions, the outside medium is assumed to have an infinite radius. Due to the infinity condition, the solution reduces to functions of the first class ($n=1$) only. The torque on the oscillating sphere due to the outside viscous medium is now, in complex notation (accounting for damping), $\tau_F = -(8/3)\pi\eta_{kin}R^3[(3 + 3ihR - h^2R^2)/(1 + ihR)]\omega$. This torque reduces for long period to $\tau_F = -8\pi\eta_{kin}R^3\omega$, the negative sign indicates the counteracting influences of the viscous friction. A special case for this would be the harmonic rotation of a sphere within a sphere (*also see* FORCED VORTEX) (see Figure T.70).

Figure T.70 Torsional oscillation for a top-load washing machine.

Total angular momentum

[atomic, nuclear] The general mechanics definition of angular momentum is $\vec{L} = \vec{r} \times \vec{p} = \vec{I} \times \vec{\omega}$, $\vec{p} = m\vec{v}$, where I is the MOMENT OF INERTIA for the device and its orientation, r the radius, and v is the velocity of the object with mass m moving at a DISTANCE r. On a quantum-mechanical scale, the orbital angular momentum can be coupled to the SPIN angular momentum for the same electron, providing the respective total angular momentum. Similarly, the angular momentum of the NUCLEUS also provides its own influences. The total angular momentum on the quantum-mechanical level is defined by the orbital quantum number (ℓ) and spin quantum number ($s = \pm \frac{1}{2}$) with QUANTUM NUMBER $j = \ell \pm (1/2)$, yielding $J = \sqrt{[j(j+1)]}\hbar$, where $\hbar = h/2\pi$, $h = 6.62606957 \times 10^{-34}$ m^{2}kg/s is the PLANCK'S CONSTANT; with $(2j+1)$ z-projections $J_z = m_j \hbar$.

Total internal reflection

[general, optics] Under SNELL'S LAW of refraction $n_1 \sin \theta_1 = n_2 \sin \theta_2$ (the subscript $\square_i$ identifying the specific medium, n the index of refraction, and θ is the ANGLE with the normal to the surface at the interface), the ratio of index of refraction for the two media at a boundary can become smaller than 1 when the originating medium is more dense than the bordering medium. At a certain angle of incidence, the refraction angle becomes $90° = \pi/2$, at which point the LIGHT will continue parallel to the interface after incidence. At greater angles of incidence, the electromagnetic RADIATION will be reflected, obeying the LAW OF REFLECTION: $\theta_r = \theta_i$. This phenomenon can render items "invisible" under water due to the viewing position of the observer with respect to the object at a great linear DISTANCE.

Total loss

[fluid dynamics] For a flow in a pipeline, the factors contributing to losses in ENERGY are the following: entrance loss; frictional loss due to shear at the WALL, frictional losses in elbows, valve orifices, friction losses in discharge branch off line (bi-, trifurcations, etc.), exit loss due to EXPANSION, next to the elevation of the flow (z). The respective head-loss factors add up as $h_{L,T} = K_i \left(v_s^2/2g\right) + \left[f_s(L/D)\left(v_s^2/2g\right) + f_d(L/D)\left(v_d^2/2g\right)\right] + \left\{K_b \left(v_s^2/2g\right) + \left[f_{dT}\left(L_e/D\right)_{\text{elbow}} \left(v_d^2/2g\right)\right]_{90°}\right\} + f_{dT}\left(L_e/D\right)_{\text{valve}} \left(v_d^2/2g\right) + \text{branch-off} + K_e\left(v_d^2/2g\right) + (z_2 - z_1)$, where the average velocity can be derived from the flow rate ($\dot{Q}$) as $v_s = \dot{Q}/A_s$ (A_s the total suction line exit cross-sectional area), $v_d = \dot{Q}/A_d$ (A_d the total discharge line exit cross-sectional area), f_s and f_d the FRICTION factor for suction and discharge respectively, D the tube diameter (assuming a constant diameter for the main section, the FLUID under consideration will provide the COEFFICIENT OF FRICTION (v_{kin}) and overall friction (η_{kin}). The REYNOLDS NUMBER for the flow yields information about the flow structure (turbulent or laminar), $Re = v_s D\rho/\eta_{\text{kin}}$, for both the main line and the respective discharge line(s). One important consideration is the RELATIVE ROUGHNESS of the wall $\chi_r = D/\epsilon_s$, where ϵ_s is the average "height" of the raised and carved general unevenness in the surface. The relative SURFACE ROUGHNESS (listed in reference tables, material property) in combination with the Reynolds number will provide the respective friction factors from Moody's diagram. The entrance coefficient K_i is a function of the shape, $K_i = 0.5$ for square edges; $K_i = 1$ for round outflow, similarly for the branches K_b and exit flow K_e. The values $\left(L_e/D\right)_{\text{valve}}$ for a valve, $\left(L_e/D\right)_{\text{elbow}}$ for an elbow can be found in design tables. The power supplied to enforce the flow in this case is $P_f = h_{L,T} \rho_f \dot{Q}$, where ρ_f is the fluid density. Incorporating

T

the pump efficiency γ_f will provide the operational requirements for the PUMP (in kwatt or horse power), where the electric pump quickly reach 75% efficiency (see Figure T.71).

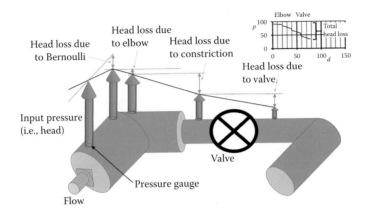

Figure T.71 Total loss for a pipe flow system.

Total lung capacity (TLC)

[biomedical, fluid dynamics] The total volume of GAS filling the lungs at completion of a maximum inspiration. Total lung capacity and other TIDAL BREATHING parameters can be measured with a spirometer. (*see* **RESPIRATION**) (see Figure T.72).

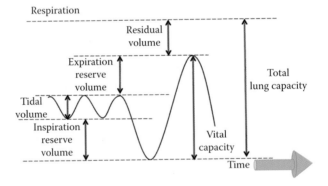

Figure T.72 Diagram illustrating total lung capacity.

Total potential

[thermodynamics] The total potential of a system $\mu = \mu_0 + RT \ln\left(\rho RT / M p_0\right) - (1/2)\varepsilon^2 \left[\alpha + \left(d^2/3kT\right)\right]$, where ε is the MAGNITUDE of a uniform ELECTROSTATIC FIELD (for instance in a CAPACITOR $\varepsilon = \epsilon Q/A$ [ϵ is the DIELECTRIC permittivity, Q the total charge on the capacitor plates, and A is the area of the capacitor]), k is the Boltzmann constant, d the ELECTRIC DIPOLE MOMENT of the respective molecules in the volume, ρ the density, M the MOLECULAR WEIGHT, α the molecular POLARIZATION, and p_0, μ_0 are constants, with $R = 8.314462175$ J/Kmol the universal gas constant. Similarly the total potential for the individual contributions by the electrons (sub$_e$), ions (sub$_i$), and atoms (sub$_a$) are given by the following respective expressions: $\mu_e = kT \ln\left[b^3 \rho_e(x) / g_e \left(2\pi m_e kT\right)^{3/2}\right] + \epsilon_{0e} - q_e \psi(x)$; $\mu_i = kT \ln\left[b^3 \rho_i(x) / g_i \left(2\pi m_i kT\right)^{3/2}\right] + \epsilon_{0i} - q_e \psi(x)$; and $\mu_e = kT \ln\left[b^3 \rho_a(x) / g_a \left(2\pi m_a kT\right)^{3/2}\right] + \epsilon_{0a}$, where $\psi(x)$ is the electrostatic potential at position x.

Townes, Charles Hard (1915–)

[optics, solid-state] Physicist from the United States. Charles Townes worked on quantum ELECTRONICS principles and microwave ENERGY configuration, with a particular focus on radar applications. In 1964, Charles Townes received the Nobel Prize in Physics for his work on the MASER (microwave amplification by stimulated emission of radiation) with respect to the work published in 1954, the prelude to his participation in the development of the LASER. He shared the Nobel Prize with Nicolay G. Basov (1922–2001) and Aleksandr M. Prokhorov (1916–2002) (see Figure T.73).

Figure T.73 Charles Hard Townes (1915–).

Townsend, John Sealy Edward, Sir (1868–1957)

[atomic, nuclear] Mathematical physicist from Ireland. Townsend was a contemporary of ERNEST RUTHERFORD (1871–1937) at Cambridge University. In 1897, John Townsend conceived a method to measure the electrical charge, specifically the charge quota contained on an OIL drop in various amounts, hence deriving the QUANTUM effect and determining the single electron charge. This mechanism was later perfected by ROBERT ANDREWS MILLIKAN (1868–1953). Additional work was in the WAVE theory for electrons and the general QUANTUM THEORY (see Figure T.74).

Figure T.74 Sir John Sealy Edward Townsend (1868–1957). (Courtesy of Biographical Memoirs of Fellows of the Royal Society 1957; JSTOR.)

Trace

[computational] In matrix theory, the sum of the ELEMENTS on the diagonal of an $n \times n$ matrix:

$$\begin{bmatrix} m_{11} & \cdots & m_{1n} \\ \vdots & m_{ii} & \vdots \\ m_{n1} & \cdots & m_{nn} \end{bmatrix}.$$

Tracers

[atomic, biomedical, fluid dynamics, geophysics, meteorology, nuclear] Chemically reactive agents and radioactive isotopes used for identification of metabolic and physiologic processes in specific anatomical locations. Additionally, tracers are used in FLUID DYNAMICS for flow pattern recognition; dyes. The iodine ISOTOPE is used in diagnostic modalities of the thyroid gland, based on gamma RADIATION emission from the iodine, by means of a gamma CAMERA. In the diagnosis of metabolic processes, the use of ^{18}fluorine in POSITRON EMISSION TOMOGRAPHY (PET) provides insights into the GLUCOSE uptake and cellular consumption as integrated in 2-deoxy-2-(18F)fluoro-D-glucose. Other tracers used in PET imaging are ^{11}carbon, ^{13}nitrogen, and ^{15}oxygen. Histochemical tracers are used for analysis of chemical communications in the synapsis of neural connections. This type of tracer often consists of enzymes and is brought out by staining a biopsy sample. TRACER is an acronym for transition radiation array for cosmic energetic radiation, which is used in atmospheric analysis to gauge cosmic ray MAGNITUDE by means of sensor arrays attached to balloons.

Transcytosis

[biomedical, mechanics] Process under the active process of cellular ingestion of ENDOCYTOSIS, in this case the assimilation of large molecules such as ALBUMIN by means of the invagination process of the CELL MEMBRANE. The forming enclosure produces a vesicle that transports the package to the intercellular content where the vesicle detaches from the cell-membrane lining and subsequently the vesicle disintegrates to release the content for cellular integration.

Transducer

[acoustics, electronics, general, mechanics] Device with a specific transfer function, converting the MAGNITUDE of one phenomenon into another. The transfer function consists of a predetermined mathematical relationship that will prescribe a PROBABILITY distribution of the output. The translation of the magnitude of one physical quantity into another generally has a predictable response in order to preserve the integrity of the imbedded information. Transducers can function linearly or obey a square law response, or logarithmic/exponential behavior, generally smooth without discontinuities in the range of operations of interest. Transducers are used to convey information on electrical signal strength, temperature, acoustics, optics, as well as MAGNETIC and electric field strength next to a range of particles for RADIOACTIVE DECAY and elementary PARTICLE detection. The majority of devices have an electrical SIGNAL as output or for instance for acoustic probes as both input and output (piezoelectric). The most widely used is the SOUND transducer as a MICROPHONE and a "SPEAKER." Inductive transducers are used as pick-up ELEMENTS for electric guitars. Photocells measure LIGHT radiance as well as respond to the remote control actuator.

Transformer

[electromagnetism, electronics, general] Electric device operating on the basis of the Faraday induction law. The transformer consists of two parts. An electrical potential applied to the primary winding produces a current that results in a MAGNETIC FIELD that is proportional to the number of windings. The magnetic field is captured in a METAL core that conveys it to a secondary coil. In the secondary coil, the magnetic field induces a current with associated electrical potential, where the electrical potential MAGNITUDE (V) is proportional to the number of windings (N). The conversion of the input to the output voltage ratio is directly proportional to the ratio of windings in the primary versus the secondary coil $(V_1/V_2) = (N_1/N_2)$ (see Figure T.75).

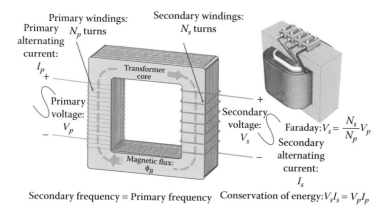

Figure T.75 Diagram outlining the mechanism of action for the transformer.

Transient equilibrium

[nuclear] Equilibrium that is reached through a mediator stage. In nuclear science, the transient state is accomplished through a parent daughter transition where the half-life of DECAY for the daughter is shorter than the parent but not intrinsically negligible. The transient equilibrium in RADIOACTIVE DECAY is represented by the Bateman equation, linking the parent decay half-life time (τ_p) to the daughter decay half-life time (τ_d) by the definition of the ACTIVITY of parent ($A_p = \lambda_p N_p$; $dN_p/dt = -\lambda_p N_p$, λ_p the decay constant of the parent) and offspring ($A_d = \lambda_d N_d$; $dN_d/dt = -\lambda_d N_d$) respectively, captured as $A_d/A_p = \tau_p/(\tau_p - \tau_d)$BR, where BR is the branching ratio (ratio of decaying particles under a specific process of decay to the total number of decaying particles). The Bateman equation defines the activity

of the daughter as $A_d = BR\left\{A_p(0)\left[\lambda_d/(\lambda_d - \lambda_p)\right]\left[e^{-\lambda_p t} - e^{-\lambda_d t}\right]\right\} + A_d(0)e^{-\lambda_d t}$. The time of maximum activity (t_{max}) for the daughter activity in transient equilibrium has an inherent maximum defined as $t_{max} = 1.44\left[\tau_d \tau_p/(\tau_p - \tau_d)\right]\ln(\tau_p/\tau_d)$, which may exceed the parent activity under certain conditions, in which case there will be *no* EQUILIBRIUM STATE.

Transistor

[atomic, electronics, general, nuclear] Electronic device made from semiconductor materials, or a VACUUM tube that can provide a special electronic function. By means of connecting resistors, capacitors, or inductors to the poles of a transistor, the function can be designed to provide SIGNAL amplification, integration, or differentiation. The specific integration of the transistor in circuits can provide an operational amplifier (also known as INTEGRATED CIRCUITS: IC). The general transistor design consists of two. The semiconductor construction can be npn or pnp. The "n" represents a semiconductor with a donor impurity, doped with electrons, providing a rise in the FERMI LEVEL for the ENERGY structure. A P-TYPE SEMICONDUCTOR has an ACCEPTOR IMPURITY that creates a "shortage" of electron, rather represents "holes" with an inherent lowering of the Fermi level. Joining the *p*- and *n*-type media provides a preferred electron migration as is seems for the DIODE. In the transistor, there are three regions of impurities, two of similar nature separated by the complementary energy structure. The material that is sandwiched between the two identical media can have its energy structure manipulated under the influence of an external electrical potential, referred to as the base. The other constituents are the emitter and the collector. The applied electrical potential on the base of the transistor can raise or lower the Fermi level that will accommodate the transport of electrons between the emitter and the collector. Note that the collector "accepts" current, which relates to the emission of electrons; current running from the external power supply's positive to negative terminal through any electronic device. The construction of the semiconductor layers generally allows for only very thin segment reserved for the "base," which provides a limited constraint for the electron migration between the emitter and collector only. The base thickness is directly affected by the DRIFT VELOCITY for the electrons; hence, a small thickness yields minimal RESISTANCE. The moment the electrons penetrate the collector volume they have passed the junction that holds a POTENTIAL BARRIER; thus, back DIFFUSION is deemed impossible. Transistors form an essential component in electronic design, using the RESISTOR, CAPACITOR, and INDUCTOR as a means to perform a specific task. Recently a new class of transistors has been introduced: organic luminescent transistors (*see* PNP-TRANSISTOR, NPN-TRANSISTOR, OPERATIONAL AMPLIFIER, *PN*-JUNCTION, *and* DIODE) (see Figure T.76).

Figure T.76 Classic transistor design, before surface mount miniaturization.

Transmission electron microscope

[biomedical, imaging, nuclear, solid-state] ELECTRON MICROSCOPE that measures the transmitted intensity of electrons as a function of location to form an IMAGE. The electron microscope was a major implication of the discovery of the electron by JOSEPH JOHN THOMSON (1856–1940) in 1897. HEINRICH HERTZ (1857–1894) was one of the first who realized that CATHODE RAYS were a form of WAVE MOTION. Electrons are still generated as a result of a thermoelectric event: thermionic electron gun. In 1899, both the French physicist Alfred-Marie Liénard (1869–1958) and the German scientist Emil Johann Wiechert (1861–1928) independently performed the first mechanism of action to concentrate the cathode rays by means of an axial MAGNETIC FIELD produced by a long SOLENOID. Hans Busch (1884–1973) provided the theoretical evidence of electron focusing in 1926 (German pioneer in electron optics). In 1931, two German engineers Ernst Ruska (1906–1988) and Maximillion Knoll (1897–1969) performed the first magnification of an electron image. In 1933, Ernst Ruska built the first prototype electron microscope, which was perfected in 1938 by Eli Franklin Burton (1879–1948) in collaboration with his graduate students Cecil Edwin Hall (1912–1991), James Hillier (1915–2007), and Albert Prebus (1931–2000). The transmission microscope, as the word indicates, uses an electron beam, operating at the DE BROGLIE WAVELENGTH (LOUIS VICTOR PIERRE RAYMOND DUC DE BROGLIE (1892–1987), French physicist postulated the WAVE theory of matter in 1924), with the collection of electrons as a function of location on the opposite side of a sample. An electron beam is steered through the manipulation of magnetic fields (STEM: scanning transmission electron microscopy). Since the interrogation is performed by means of ballistic electrons, the in-path attenuation must be kept to a minimum; hence, the imaging needs to be performed under mid to high VACUUM conditions ($< 10^{-3}$ torr $= 0.133$ pa). The probing beam is on average $0.5 - 1$ µm in diameter. The resolution (D_r) for the wavelength (λ) associated with the electron trajectory can be defined including an aberration correction with respect to spherical distortions due to the objective's magnetic field (C_s) as $D_r = AC_s^{1/4}\lambda^{3/4}$, where $0.43 < A < 0.7$ is a device and sample material preparation constant. The RESOLUTION ranges from 0.5 nm for an acceleration potential of 20 kV to 0.12 nm for an acceleration potential of 1000 kV ($\lambda = 0.004$ nm) (*see* ELECTRON MICROSCOPE) (see Figure T.77).

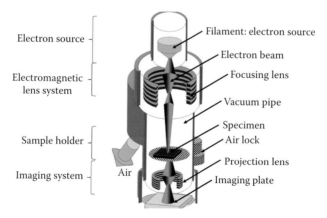

Electron source

Electromagnetic lens system

Sample holder

Imaging system

Air

Filament: electron source

Electron beam

Focusing lens

Vacuum pipe

Specimen

Air lock

Projection lens

Imaging plate

Figure T.77 Transmission electron microscope and operational design and transmission electron imaging representation of neutrophil cells.

Transport equation

[astrophysics/astronomy, fluid dynamics, general, mechanics, optics] Theoretical approach to describe the ordered MOTION of particles and photons. The forced migration of particles covers a broad range of phenomena, including but not limited to, the LIGHT propagation in tissue under laser irradiation, the NEUTRON transport in a NUCLEAR REACTOR, the "DIFFUSION" of gas and solutes, and the electromagnetic and particle emission for galactic entities (primarily stars). In all cases, the migration process is hindered by the interaction with substances in the trajectory such as, molecules, ions, dust, uranium-238, and control RODS (boron or hafnium or cadmium). The transport equation is a mix of integration and differential operators, accounting for diversion, attenuation, and gain next to source conditions, all as a function of location. Each PARTICLE for a system consisting of a fixed or known number of components (N) has an associated $6N$ first-order differential equations describing the interaction, not accounting for the internal DEGREES OF FREEDOM of the ELEMENTS. The approximation is made that there is consistency for all particles, assuming a PROBABILITY distribution for the spread in parameters associated with the system as a whole. In this case, the transport equation is defined for a single particle. The Transport equation can be considered either as a steady-state problem or as a time-dependent process. The steady-state condition will reduce the complexity on various levels. The introduction of the equation of transfer/transport equation was made by LUDWIG EDUARD BOLTZMANN (1844–1906) in 1872, although he received inspiration/assistance from JAMES CLERK MAXWELL (1831–1879). The formulation adheres to the migration process of a "dilute" GAS MIXTURE with the distribution function $P^{prob}{}_i\left(\vec{r},\vec{v_i},t\right)$ for constituent i at location r in the direction dr, each traveling with velocity v_i at a time t. The interaction probability is indicated by a CROSS SECTION σ_{ij}, with the redirection of the vector captured by $g_{ij}\left(\theta_i\right)$, with θ_{ij} the per incidence scattering ANGLE, which is the so-called scattering anisotropy factor or scattering function (also referred to as g-factor). All "particles" are considered to engage a finite volume in space where the items converge from with a solid angle $d\Omega'$ and those will leave the volume after interaction within a solid angle $d\Omega$. The "source" or origin of the particles (photons) is defined through the introduction of a source function $\vec{\xi}\left(\vec{r},\vec{v_i},t\right)$. The source can be designed a certain way or follows directly from material properties. A laser beam will be concise and has a Gaussian profile as a function of location (single wavelength; single propagation velocity), whereas a NEUTRON source will be covering full 4π solid angle (for simplicity, one can assume a fixed ENERGY and hence single velocity; and uniform emission angle). The time-dependent formulation is as follows:

$$\left(\partial P^{prob}{}_i/\partial t\right)+v_i\left(\partial P^{prob}{}_i/\partial \vec{r}\right)+\vec{\xi}\left(\vec{r},\vec{v_i},t\right)\left(\partial P^{prob}{}_i/\partial \vec{v_i}\right)=\sum_{j=1}^{n}\iiint\left\{P^{prob\prime}{}_i P^{prob\prime}{}_j - P^{prob}{}_i P^{prob}{}_j\right\}g_{ij}\left(\theta\right)\sigma_{ij}d\Omega dv',$$

integrated over all space under solid angle Ω. Generally this type of integro differential equation needs to be approximated under certain constrains, or the equation is solved numerically. One approximation is the reduction to a two- or three-flux model, or limit the SCATTERING interaction: only consider isotropic scattering; additionally confining the speed to a single velocity provides a more solvable problem. The transport equation can under limiting constraints be developed in a series that can be truncated under specific boundary conditions. One particular SOLUTION technique using computer simulation is referred to as the MONTE CARLO METHOD, referencing the chance interaction. The Monte Carlo method required defining an appropriate look-up table for the random processes captured by $P^{prob}{}_i$, while proposing a single value process for σ_{ij}, and $g_{ij}\left(\theta_i\right)$. A special case of the transport equation applies to the fluid-dynamics process of turbulent flow for particles mixtures. For the VELOCITY POTENTIAL of the SOLUTE particles the vorticity is defined as $\vec{\omega}=\nabla\times\vec{v}$. The vorticity transport equation is defined as $D\vec{\omega}/Dt=\left(\vec{\omega}\cdot\nabla\right)\vec{v}+\eta_{kin}\nabla^2\vec{\omega}$, where $D\vec{\omega}/Dt=\partial\vec{\omega}/\partial t+\left(\vec{v}\cdot\nabla\right)\vec{\omega}$, $\left(\vec{\omega}\cdot\nabla\right)\vec{v}$ is the "vortex stretching:" the change in particle rotation rate due to velocity gradients, $\vec{v}$ the velocity, $\eta_{kin}\nabla^2\vec{\omega}$ describes the diffusion under viscous flow, with η_{kin} the KINEMATIC VISCOSITY that is equal to the diffusion coefficient for diffusion of vorticity. Note that vorticity describes the degree of "rotation" experienced in flow VELOCITY ($\vec{v}$) as a function of location ($\vec{r}$) and TIME (t) expressed as $\vec{\omega}\left(\vec{r},t\right)=\nabla\times\vec{v}\left(\vec{r},t\right)$ (also see EQUATION OF RADIATIVE TRANSFER and TORSIONAL OSCILLATIONS).

Transuranic element

[atomic, nuclear] ELEMENT with atomic number greater than 92 ($Z>92$; heavy) as listed in the PERIODIC TABLE OF ELEMENTS. Note that $Z=92$ represents uranium. All elements at $Z>92$ are radioactive and short lived with lifetime smaller than the AGE of the UNIVERSE as we know it. All currently available transuranic elements have been formed artificially; however, an ISOTOPE of the element plutonium ($Z=94$) with a half-life of 80 million years has been identified in nature. The lighter transuranic elements ($89<Z<103$, full set of 15) is classified as actinides with similar chemical properties to the actinides $57<Z<71$. Elements with atomic numbers greater than 100 can only be formed by colliding heavy ions with the atomic number greater than that of helium, forming small quantities, at best several hundred atoms. Based on the formation of the very large nuclei, it has been indicated that $Z=109$ may be limit of "stable nuclei."

Although there is a hypothesis that predicts an "island" of nuclear stability in the region $114 < Z < 126$, this remains still to be verified.

Transverse electromagnetic (TEM) waves

[general] Electromagnetic waves in VACUUM are formed by an electric and a MAGNETIC FIELD that are perpendicular to each other as well as to the direction of propagation, which forms the standard definition of electromagnetic RADIATION. However, in CONDUCTOR and semiconductor materials, this may not always hold absolutely true.

Transverse waves

[general] WAVE with the displacement perpendicular to the direction of propagation, for instance a wave on a string or a WATER WAVE; in contrast to a LONGITUDINAL WAVE (compression wave, e.g., SOUND). For a transverse wave, the speed of propagation is a function of the inertial properties of the object in MOTION, the elastic properties of the medium providing the conduction but not the motion of the source. The velocity of propagation (v_w) for a transverse wave on a string is a function of the tension on the string (F_T), and the MASS (m) per unit length (L) with respect to the string itself: $v_w = \sqrt{\left[F_T/(m/L)\right]}$. By changing the tension, the resonant frequency (v_{res}) for the string is altered due to the wavelength (λ) dependency on the tension and the length of the string (ℓ) through $v_{res} = n\left(v_w/2\ell\right), n = 1, 2, 3, \ldots$ with the FUNDAMENTAL FREQUENCY for $n = 1$. This involves the tuning of any string instrument. The longest wavelength for a string fixed on both extremes will be one half the wavelength (*also see* COMPRESSION WAVE, ACOUSTICS, *and* SOUND) (see Figure T.78).

Figure T.78 Transverse wave concept illustrated string plucked generated displacement perpendicular to the direction of motion of propagation, which is along the length of the string.

Traveling salesman problem

[computational] Minimized RANDOM WALK outline. The traveling salesman is trying to configure a route that will allow him to visit each city on his sales list with the shortest time while visiting each city only once and returning to his home. The concept represents determining the optimized process and was introduced in the early 1930s.

Tremor

[acoustics, biomedical, geophysics, mechanics] Structural vibrations, as found in EARTH'S CRUST and buildings and smaller devices. Tremors also describe small EYE movement in the classification of fixation on a point. Other classifications are MICROSACCADE and DRIFT.

Triboelectric sequence

[general] "Tribo" is a Greek word that stands for "FRICTION," thus referring to the charge transfer between two surfaces as a result of physical contact under MOTION. The triboelectric process provides

the means to transfer charge and generate static ELECTRICITY potential ENERGY resulting from friction. Walking on a polyester carpet is the prime example, specifically under low HUMIDITY. One specific triboelectric phenomenon is the charge separation when clear plastic tape is quickly unwound, maybe using a mechanical rotary axle such as a drill. The charge separation will form arcs that are visible in blue and invisible ULTRAVIOLET. The speed of separation is critical based on the surface conduction leaching off the charge and discharge by means of conduction through the AIR by the lingering humidity. Similar effects may also be observed when spooling a recording tape on older tape-recorder MACHINES (see Figure T.79).

Figure T.79 Example of the conditions that may lead to triboelectric activity balloon has been rubbed and accumulates static charge.

Triple point

[general, thermodynamics] In a pressure versus temperature PHASE DIAGRAM of a substance there is a point where LIQUID, solid, and gas exist simultaneously. Raising or lowering the temperature or pressure will lead to phase transitions: EVAPORATION SUBLIMATION and liquification (as well as all the reverse processes). For instance, for water at this point will have the coexistence of liquid water, solid ice, and water vapour (see Figure T.80).

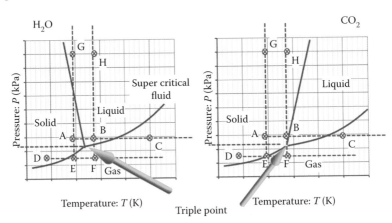

Figure T.80 Triple point, carbon dioxide compared to water.

Triplet, Wild's

[astrophysics/astronomy, geophysics, mechanics, optics] (syn.: galaxy) {use: energy, imaging, origin-of-life (Big Bang)} Wild's triplet GRAVITATION bridge between three galaxies, forming an optimal spatial ANGLE between the respective galaxies (*see* **WILD'S TRIPLET**).

Triplet state

[atomic, computational, condensed matter, energy, kinetics, nuclear, solid-state] Two coinciding SPIN states for two particles (electron and PROTON) within an atomic structure that result in a spectral HYPERFINE STRUCTURE splitting (spin $S = 1$, quantity $\hbar = h/2\pi$, with $h = 6.62606957 \times 10^{-34}$ m^{2}kg/s the PLANCK'S CONSTANT), for example, H$_2$ PROBLEM. This stands in contrast to a SINGLET STATE (spin $S = 0$). In case two electrons converge on a zero angular momentum than the three states are ENERGY degenerate in the values m_s. Singlet oxygen, $O_2(a^1\Delta_g)$, is the lowest excited electronic state that has been known for molecular oxygen, and has been recognized for at least 80 years. The characteristic chemistry of excited singlet oxygen sets it apart from the triplet GROUND STATE of molecular oxygen, $O_2(X^3\Sigma_g^-)$. The triplet state can potentially degenerate by PHOSPHORESCENCE. The DEGENERACY for the triplet state can however be removed when an external MAGNETIC FIELD is applied, as described by the ZEEMAN EFFECT (see Figure T.81).

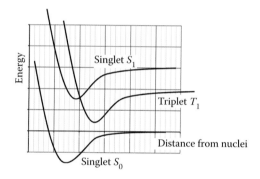

Figure T.81 Triplet state.

Triple-twin domain

[nanotechnology, quantum] {use: elementary particle} Gathering of misplaced ATOM clusters giving rise to local changes in the CRYSTAL STRUCTURE equivalent to the insertion of three nonrelaxed atomic cells. This phenomenon can be described by NUCLEAR FORCES (i.e., the sharing of elementary PARTICLE such as mesons) and van der Waals forces. The van der Waals interaction was discovered by the Dutch scientist JOHANNES DIDERIK VAN DER WAALS (1837–1923). They are the attractive or repulsive forces between molecules and ELEMENTARY PARTICLES that are not the larger scale covalent bonds or due to the ionic electrostatic interaction. The VAN DER WAALS FORCE (also: London–van der Waals) is described by an EQUATION OF STATE of a diluted IDEAL GAS (expressed by the GAS LAW: $P = (N/V)[1 - (aN/VkT)]kT$, where N is Avogadro's number, V and P are the volume and pressure respectively of the "GAS," k is the Boltzmann's constant, T the temperature of the "gas," and a the dilution factor) and is related to the Casimir effect for DIELECTRIC media. The phenomenological description assumes interactions between nonzero size particles (i.e., atoms) as a FLUID with and a pairwise attraction diminishing roughly according to $1/r^6$, r being the DISTANCE between the pair. Johannes Diderik van der Waals received the

Nobel Prize in Physics in 1910 for his work on the "Equation of state for gases and liquids" published in 1873. The modified IDEAL GAS LAW approximating fluids describing the van der Waals force is given as $F_{\text{vanderWaals}} = \left(d_1/r^s\right) - \left(d_2/r^t\right)$, where $s \approx 6$ and the second term represents a repulsion with $t \approx 2$ and d_1 and d_2 are size representing constants.

Trochoidal waves

[fluid dynamics] WAVE pattern defined as the curve traced out by a point on a circle as the circle is rolled along a line. The wavelength (λ) of the rolling circle with radius R now becomes $\lambda = 2\pi R$. The wave shape in longitudinal and transverse directions is respectively given as $x = \left(\lambda/2\pi\right)\theta - \left(\lambda/40\right)\sin\theta$ and $z = \left(\lambda/40\right)\left(1 - \cos\theta\right)$, where θ represents the ANGLE of rotation of the circle defining the MOTION of the "water molecules." One notable wave pattern approximation was introduced by William Newell Bascom (1916–2000). In this model, the peak of the wave becomes sharper with increasing AMPLITUDE of higher harmonics. In the Bascom model, the maximum wavelength to wave peak ratio is 7:1, while a peak is not considered a peak if the full angle of the high water level is less than 120° (see Figure T.82).

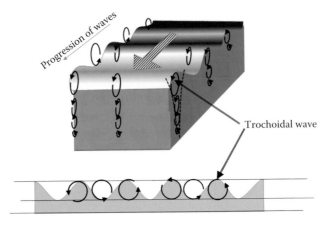

Figure T.82 Trochoidal wave patterns.

Troposphere

[energy, geophysics, thermodynamics] The portion of the Earth's ATMOSPHERE that we live in, reaching out to approximately 17 km altitude. The troposphere generally consists of the following elementary gasses: nitrogen (on average ~78.09%), oxygen (~20.95%), argon (~0.93%), and carbon dioxide (0.039%) and trace-elements, all as a function of location. Additionally, it holds better than 80% of the earth's water VAPOR, accounting for various forms of cloud formation, precipitation, and ABSOLUTE HUMIDITY. Pioneers in the study of the earth's atmosphere and troposphere are the French scientist and meteorologist Léon Teisserenc de Bort (1855–1933) and the German meteorologist Richard Aβmann (ASSMANN; 1845–1918) (see Figure T.83).

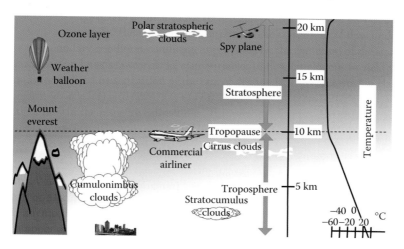

Figure T.83 Troposphere.

Trouton, Frederick Thomas (1863–1922)

[atomic, optics, thermodynamics] Physicist from Ireland. Frederick Trouton performed experimental verification of the earth's AETHER concept; the luminiferous aether (ETHER), the assumed medium required to propagate electromagnetic RADIATION. It was later discovered that the luminiferous aether does not exist; electromagnetic radiation is ENERGY transported through VACUUM as well as AIR and most solids. Trouton's work on THERMODYNAMICS revealed the correlation between the MOLECULAR WEIGHT of substances and the heat of vaporization, known as Trouton's law. Additional work in OPTICS by Frederick Trouton indicated the POLARIZATION interaction on a molecular level, associating the molecular VIBRATION of a substance with the direction of polarization for transmitted LIGHT, also used by EDWIN HERBERT LAND (1909–1991) in 1928, for the polaroid film design (see Figure T.84).

Figure T.84 Frederick Thomas Trouton (1863–1922). (Courtesy of Proceedings of the Royal Society (London), A110, 4, 1926.)

Trouton's rule

[atomic] The entropy of vaporization (ΔS_{vap}) at the boiling point is virtually identical for most LIQUID substances: $\Delta S_{vap} = 10.5R$, where $R = 8.3144621(75)$ J/Kmol is the GAS constant. This rule was expressed in 1884 by FREDERICK TROUTON (1863–1922). With modifications including TEMPERATURE (T) dependence, the validity was extended and is defined as $\Delta S_{vap} = 4.5R + R \ln T$.

Tsunami

[fluid dynamics, general, geophysics, mechanics] Significant water mass displacement in a WAVE pattern resulting from a sudden perturbation, such as an underwater EARTHQUAKE, volcanic eruption, or landslide, next to for instance a METEOR impact. Tsunamis may be created artificially by explosions as well. In deep water, the tsunami may be composed of a wave pattern over a large surface area with AMPLITUDE of only several CENTIMETERS, but may be as high as several meters. When the wave pattern approached the shallow waters on the shoreline, the wave amplitude may increase dramatically with significant destructive effects due to the sheer MAGNITUDE of the volume of water and the associated force. Due to the deep water at the origin and the large quantity involved, the velocity of the tsunami WATER WAVE can reach excessively high numbers, the wave will slow down as the water depth decreases, potentially in deep water in excess of 200 m/s (see Figure T.85).

Figure T.85 Tsunami (exagerated).

Tsvet, Mikhail Semyonovich {Михайл Семёнович Цвет} (1872–1919)

[biomedical, optics] Russian scientist and botanist. Inventor of the concept of CHROMATOGRAPHY, using spectral analysis for identification of biological entities based on molecular optical attenuation information (see Figure T.86).

Figure T.86 Mikhail Semyonovich Tsvet (1872–1919).

Tuft flow

[fluid dynamics] The use of "streamers" to visualize flow patterns. Streamers or tufts are finite length strips attached to a surface of specific contour, placed at regular intervals. Flow can be represented in several different ways in a two-dimensional manner: arrow plots (sometimes referred to as hedgehogs), ribbons, streamlines, line-integral convolution, or streaklines. Arrow plots are an instantaneous representation of the vectors of flow velocity as a function of location. In experimental setting, the use of streamers is used to TRACE the flow. The streamers can be solid material strips or can also be smoke emerging from small orifices spread out over the surface of interest, as well as ink jets. The use of mechanical tufts can indicate streamlines, outlining where the flow field is tangent. Used in the automobile industry for aerodynamic assessment. Also seemingly random WAVE pattern in the grassy leaves on the soil. The grass bends in directions that are compatible with the pressure patterns associated with a turbulent and inhomogeneous wind pattern. The leaning ANGLE and direction of the grass leaves are visual indications of flow stream and to a degree of vorticity. The tuft used for artificial experimental indication of direction and MAGNITUDE resembles the grass leaf, tapering out to the point of attachment. Due to the mechanical structure of the tuft, the full extension of lean provides an indication of magnitude, since the thicker portions at a lower height require a greater force to bend. The physical representation of the bending tuft considers the tuft as a damped bending/flexing strip of variable thickness that obeys Hook's law: $F_{\text{spring}} = k_s \left(\ell_{\text{distended}} - \ell_{\text{rest}} \right)$, with k_s the spring constant and ℓ_i the length. The DAMPING force of the bending spring is proportional to the velocity of movement (proportional to the flow velocity) (v) and the dampening constant (k_d) expressed as $F_{\text{damping}} = k_s v(t)$. The flow will apply an external force (F_{flow}) that provides the sum of forces: $F_{\text{total}} = F_{\text{flow}} + F_{\text{spring}} + F_{\text{damping}}$. Due to the variable "thickness" of the streamer, the streamer (e.g., grass leaf) can for convenience be subdivided in segments with different material properties, with a lower limit of 3 to minimize the complexity of the problem without losing critical information about the flow. Additional segments will add to the computational intricacy. The tip displacement is a direct indication of the flow velocity (direction and magnitude) and the applied flow force, within certain limits (there will be a maximum force that will LAY the streamer flat on the surface). The SOLUTION process can use either the Euler method or RUNGE–KUTTA METHOD for the integration over the different segments (see Figure T.87).

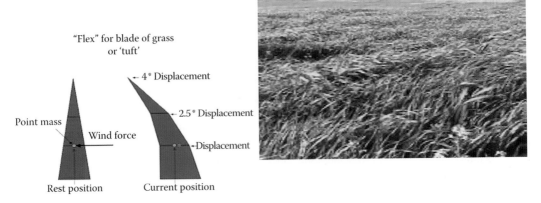

Figure T.87 Tuft flow, plants blown over in various directions due to strong localized wind gusts in random directions for a rice field.

Tungsten filament

[general] "black-body" metal ELEMENT composed form the element tungsten, specifically used in the light-bulb design based on Thomas Alva Edison's (1847–1931) invention in 1879 that emits LIGHT under the conduction of current (I), while resistive heating of the tungsten wire yields a temperature that provides a COLOR in the yellow/while visible light. The electrical RESISTANCE (R) results in a power conversion (electric to kinetic) of $P = I^2 R$. Resistance generally increases with TEMPERATURE (T) and is generally expressed by the resistivity (ρ_{res}; $R = \rho_{res}(L/A)$ for a wire of length (L) and cross-sectional area (A) as $\rho_{res} = \rho_{res,0}(1 + \alpha_0 \Delta T)$, with α_0 the temperature coefficient of resistivity; a material property (see Figure T.88).

Figure T.88 Tungsten filament.

Tunneling

[nuclear] Also known as TUNNELLING (*see* QUANTUM TUNNELLING *and* BARRIER PENETRATION).

Turbine

[energy, fluid dynamics, thermodynamics] Device that under the influence of mechanical MOTION (momentum, force), generally in the format of flow, generates work or specifically ELECTRICITY. The CONSERVATION OF ENERGY law applies and provides the conversion of potential ENERGY to kinetic energy, next to conversion of kinetic energy to work or electric energy (with a loss term as heat, resulting from FRICTION). The mechanism of action for the generation of electrical power relies on rotation combined with a MAGNETIC FIELD, which provides a changing magnetic FLUX captured by a wire loop. The wire-loop magnetic field combination provides an induction, based on the principles of the Faraday induction law. Either a PERMANENT MAGNET is rotating within a wire loop or a wire loop is rotating within a fixed magnetic field. The FLUID flow may be water as in a hydroelectric plant, steam (nuclear power plant, fossil fuel burning power plant), wind as applied to wind-mill generators, piston ENGINE driven axle, and free-running cart with rotating axle as the core of the GENERATOR (turbine). Additional mechanisms are available, such as WAVE MECHANICS where a hinge attached to two plates is changing the ANGLE of attachment under the influence of ocean SURFACE WAVES. The hinge will thus provide an alternating change in captured magnetic flux from the interaction between the "knuckles" of the casing and the axle. An alternative configuration may be by means of a worm-wheel gear system, providing continuous rotation in response to a back-and-forth motion. Wind mills provide several work functions dating back to millennia. The use of wind power to PUMP water out of the GROUND may be the oldest. Wind mills have also been used to pump water from low areas to higher areas to dry out the land for habitation as was done in the north-western part of the Netherlands (north of Amsterdam) in 1533, further institutionalized by the engineer and architect Jan Adriaanszoon Leeghwater (1575–1650) in 1607 (by the way, the last name "Leeghwater" translates as "empty water," where the original last name was most likely "Adriaanszoon," but he is known as *Leeghwater*) (see Figure T.89).

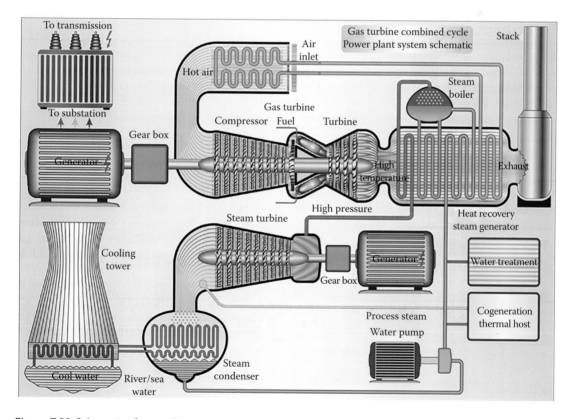

Figure T.89 Schematic of gas turbine.

Turbo machine

[fluid dynamics, mechanics] An assembly of blades, or scoops that require ENERGY to operate (e.g., PUMP) or generate energy (e.g., TURBINE) by means of facilitating flow of a LIQUID through a system of channels, or passages that are configured around an axis of rotation to form a rotor. The turbo mechanism of action either adds energy to the system resulting from an external source of power to operate the system or extracts energy from flow and generates another form of energy, potentially ELECTRICITY (see Figure T.90).

Figure T.90 Turbo charger.

Turboprop engine

[fluid dynamics, mechanics] Combustion TURBINE engine that engages a PROPELLER through a reduction gear. The exhaust gases of the turbine transmit the power from the turbine by means of a shaft to a reduction gear. The use of a down shift in gear is required due to the fact that optimum propeller performance performs at much slower speeds than the revolutions per minute of the turbine. Turboprop engines are a compromise between turbojet engines and mechanical propeller engines (see Figure T.91).

Figure T.91 Turboprop engine.

Turbulence

[computational, fluid dynamics, geophysics] Fluid flow with a diverse vector spread of flow velocity as a function of location in a three-dimensional space. Turbulent flow will contain vortices, specifically near boundaries that are changing direction with respect to the flow; or obstructions. The potential for developing turbulence is indicated by the REYNOLDS NUMBER, which defines the boundary conditions for an incompressible, inviscid viscous flow as a function of flow velocity and interaction range. Under a low Reynolds number, a flow is laminar ($Re < 2000$), while turbulence will be in effect for $Re > 3000$. Turbulence can result from colliding/passing airstreams, as experienced during airplane flight. An associated phenomenon is turbulent MIXING, taking place in the SURFACE BOUNDARY LAYER with respect to airflow in close proximity to the earth's surface in response to the amalgamated relief patterns as well as colliding airstreams (see Figure T.92).

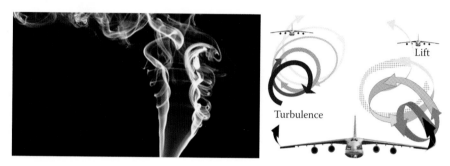

Figure T.92 Turbulent flow.

Twin "paradox"

[general] A popular concept in special relativity is traveling at velocities close to the speed of LIGHT. In this case, when two people (twins) are separated based on their profession to perform certain tasks, where one of the twins will have to travel to a distant planetary system at 6 light-years away, while the other twin remains on EARTH performing the data communications with the other twin. The spaceship travels at $v = 0.9c$, $c = 2.99792458 \times 10^8$ m/s the speed of light. Upon the return the time lapse is $t = (2 \times 6 \text{ light-years})/0.9c = 13.3$ years. The person remaining on the Earth will have aged 13.3 years, while the person in the spaceship has only aged $\Delta t = 13.3 \text{ years} \sqrt{[1 - (0.9)^2]} = 5.8$ years. The paradoxical part of this process is that both persons are going to AGE at the same rate. The traveling person may return sooner than anticipated (note that at this point the GENERAL THEORY OF RELATIVITY has not been considered). The two people may consider themselves at the origin of their own reference frame, traveling with respect to each other. The INERTIAL REFERENCE FRAME of the astronaut changes from the same as the twin to the inertial reference frame of the outbound voyage, followed by the inbound voyage (not stopping at the remote location) and returning to the fourth and final inertial reference frame that is the same as the inertial reference frame of the person remaining behind on the Earth. The fact that accelerations are involved for the traveling astronaut, leaving Earth, changing direction on location, and slowing down to land will affect the personal process of time. During the two trips themselves, there is no relativistic interaction. Due to the aspect of acceleration, the general theory of relativity needs to be invoked as well. Integration of all aspects of relativistic MOTION results in

a physical changes/differences in AGE, making the traveler arrive back younger (*also see* TIME DILATION, SPECIAL THEORY OF RELATIVITY, *and* GENERAL THEORY OF RELATIVITY (see Figure T.93).

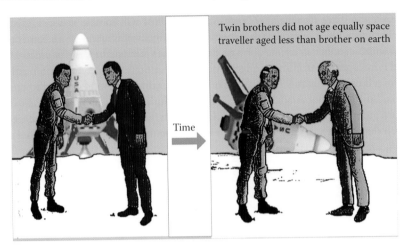

Twin brothers did not age equally space traveller aged less than brother on earth

Time

Figure T.93 Twin paradox.

Two-photon absorption

[general, imaging, optics, quantum] Absorption process where two photons are converging on the identical absorbing atomic structure at the exact same time, and, based on the superposition principle, the ENERGY content will have doubled upon interaction, hence providing the exact same effect as the interaction of a single photon with half the wavelength. In this manner, the deeper penetration of long WAVE photons can provide the advantage of deeper penetration and hence avoiding surface effects. The only manner in which the conditions of two-photon absorption can be created is by increasing the PROBABILITY through the release of a massive amount of photons. This large PHOTON quantity corresponds to a high fluence, which can only be achieved under extremely short-pulse duration. Two-photon absorption provides an essential and useful spectroscopic tool.

Two-slit diffraction

[optics] *See* DOUBLE SLIT.

Tyndall, John (1820–1893)

[general, geophysics] Physicist from Ireland. John Tyndall worked on THERMODYNAMICS aspect related to the optical properties of gasses and constructed the first known relative spectrophotometer, measuring the absorption as a function of wavelength in relation to neighboring wavelengths (qualitatively). Based on his observation, Tyndall concluded that the water VAPOR in the Earth's ATMOSPHERE acted as a "blanket" preventing radiative heat loss, thus keeping the surface warm. Tyndall also worked on MAGNETISM and diamagnetic polarity. John Tyndall concluded in 1865 that the emission from a platinum wire heated to 1473 K was approximately 11.7 times more powerful than at 798 K. These experiments were repeated in 1879 by the Austrian scientist JOSEF STEFAN (1835–1893) who derived a generalized statement of emission proportionality with respect to TEMPERATURE (T) to the order T^4. This was later supported by

Ludwig Eduard Boltzmann (1844–1906) in 1884 to provide the Stefan–Boltzmann law for black-body emission as a power function $P = \sigma_{SB}AT^4$, where $\sigma_{SB} = 5.67 \times 10^{-8}\,\text{W/m}^2\text{K}^4$ the Stefan–Boltzmann coefficient, and A the emissive area (see Figure T.94).

Figure T.94 John Tyndall (1820–1893). (Courtesy of Chandler B. Beach, The New Student's Reference Work for Teachers Students and Families, Chicago, IL: F. E. Compton and Company, 1909 the private collection of Roy Winkelman.)

T

U-234 ($^{234}_{92}$U)

[atomic, general, nuclear] Uranium isotope, the least prevalent ISOTOPE of uranium (TRACE).

U-235 ($^{235}_{92}$U)

[atomic, general, nuclear] Uranium, the second most abundant ISOTOPE of uranium (~0.72%). When a uranium $^{235}_{92}$U ATOM is bombarded by a NEUTRON ($^1_0$n), the FISSION results are as follows: three neutrons, a barium atom ($^{138}_{56}$Ba), and a krypton atom ($^{95}_{36}$Kr) (see Figure U.1).

Figure U.1 Decay process for an unstable uranium isotope.

U

U-238 ($^{238}_{92}$U)

[atomic, general, nuclear] Uranium, the most abundant ISOTOPE of uranium (~99.27%) (*see* URANIUM) (see Figure U.2).

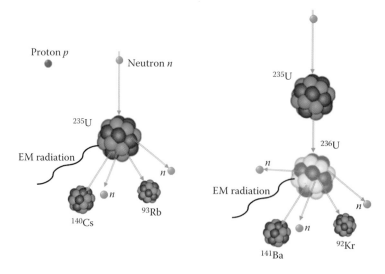

Figure U.2 Illustration of the element uranium.

Uhlenbeck, George Eugene (1900–1988)

[atomic, nuclear] Physicist and chemist from the Netherlands who, in 1925, introduced the concept of ELECTRON SPIN simultaneously but independently from SAMUEL GOUDSMIT (1902–1978) while working under PAUL EHRENFEST (1880–1933), based on the description of the four QUANTUM numbers associated with the electron introduced by WOLFGANG PAULI (1900–1958) (see Figure U.3).

Figure U.3 George Eugene Uhlenbeck (1900–1988).

Ultimate stress

[biomedical, general, mechanics, solid-state] Parameter defining the strength of a material, at this applied stress the material will fail.

Ultimate tensile strength

[general, mechanics, solid-state] Generally strength of a material indicates the ability to resist applied force without failure. The point in the stress–strain curve where the stress starts to decline with increasing strain is the ultimate strength. At the point of the ultimate strength, the material will start to "neck-down" as seen under the stress applied by a device such as an instron, a standard for quality control (see Figure U.4).

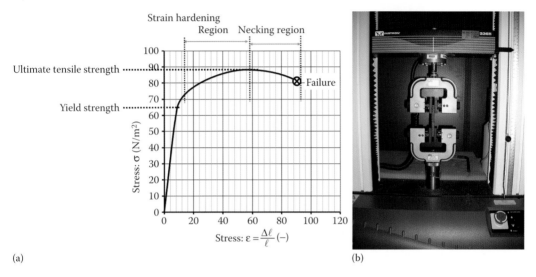

(a)   (b)

Figure U.4 Ultimate tensile strength, fracture under externally applied tension. (a) Graphical representation of the stress curve for a medium until failure and (b) device used to test for yield stress and ultimate tensile strength. (Courtesy of Kerina Yin.)

Ultracentrifuge

[biomedical, mechanics] Rotating device used for molecular analysis. The centrifuge spins vials, ampoules, or test tubes containing SOLVENT with SOLUTES to separate the SOLUTE primarily by weight or size. The functional purposes of the ultracentrifuge can be categorized as follows: (1) determine the VISCOSITY of the solutes and hereby derive the shape and size of the MACROMOLECULES in the SOLUTION, (2) classify constituents on DENSITY, BUOYANCE and density gradient, and (3) characterize the respective MOLECULAR WEIGHTS of dissolved molecules. The specimen containers can be spinned at ANGULAR VELOCITIES greater than 120,000 π rad/s, which amounts to the radial ACCELERATION equivalent of $260,000g$. Molecular weight can be determined by four different means: SEDIMENT VELOCITY, SEDIMENT EQUILIBRIUM, SEDIMENT EQUILIBRIUM IN A DENSITY GRADIENT, and ARCHIBALD APPROACH TO EQUILIBRIUM METHOD. The segregation and molecular distribution in the container are determined primarily by optical means. The three optical mechanisms that are used are the SCHLIEREN IMAGING for CONCENTRATION, RAYLEIGH SCREENING,

U

and straight forward OPTICAL ATTENUATION SCREENING. An additional mechanism uses RADIOACTIVE LABELING and counts the RADIOACTIVITY in the sediment with spatial RESOLUTION (see Figure U.5).

Figure U.5 Ultracentrifuge.

Ultrafast biological events

[biomedical, chemical, mechanics, optics] Certain biological phenomena are faster than they might appear. In VISION, it has been shown that in contrast to the slow overall phenomenological mechanism of vision there are events in ROD and CONE sensibility that take place in the femtosecond and even picosecond range. The vision experience itself is however in the 20–100 Hz range with a response time in the order of a few hundredths of a second for the various species. The physiochemical process of the PHOTOCHEMICAL EFFECT in the RETINA is in the same time-scale range as the PHOTOELECTRIC EFFECT for metals. *Also see* **PHOTOVOLTAICS/ PHOTOELECTRIC EFFECT** *and* **SOLAR PANELS**, where the use of biochemical processes generates substantial amounts of electrical potential. Other photobiological processes are at the cellular MEMBRANE level. In the purple bacteria (*Halobacterium halobium*), for instance, light can energize the TRANSMEMBRANE PROTON PUMPING on a femtosecond time scale. In biological cells, there are vibrational mode transitions, specifically in amino-acids, that take place on a femtosecond or shorter scale. Two important spectroscopic phenomena in biological functionality in the ultrashort timeframe are found in PHOTOSYNTHESIS and VISION. The LIGHT interaction in the RODS and CONES of the EYE (receptor protein: rhodopsin, CHROMOPHORE derived from vitamin A) takes place on a femtosecond scale. Rhodopsin is present in both rods and cones for vision. In vision, the QUANTUM states of the excited molecules yield information on the ENERGY transfer. One significant detectable interaction is $C_{11} = C_{12}$ isomerization, which reveals itself through torsional vibrations; specifically the low $C_{12} - H$ VIBRATION frequency in bathorhodopsin that shows anomalous behavior. The first chemical process is associated with a transition defined by the Frank–Codon state, which has an approximate lifetime of 200 fs (see Figure U.6).

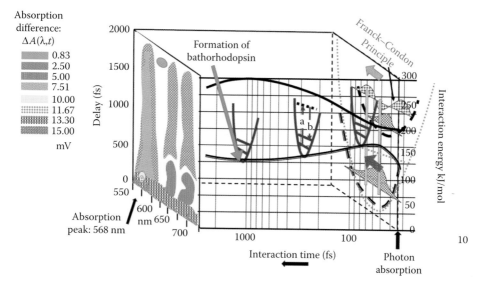

Figure U.6 Ultrafast biological effect. Graphical representation of the chemical response for rhodopsin, transforming into bathorhodopsin. The photon interaction with the associated energy deposition takes place in the first 50 fs of the chemical energy process, depicted on the far right of the graph; indicated by a Franck–Condon event. The spectral information imbedded is shown by the detected Raman emission "a" as well as the detected broadband restructuring fs event with a time-dependent energy profile in the transition "b." The chemical transformation into bathorhodopsin takes place approximately 1–2 ps into the process. The molecular interaction exemplified by a vibrational process is most pronounced at $\lambda = 568\,nm$.

Ultrafast phenomena

[general, solid-state] Ultrashort light pulses can be produced by LASER and more recently light-emitting diodes have accomplished a femtosecond pulse duration. Lasers can operate in MODE-LOCKED MODE, Q-SWITCHED, or COLLIDING PULSE MODE to create femto- and picosecond pulses. Most ultrafast phenomena apply to spectroscopic events, the formation and breakdown of chemical links, either by external excitation (ENERGY source), or in the transition from one state to another (*see* ULTRAFAST BIOLOGICAL EVENTS *and* FRANCK–CONDON EFFECT). The phenomenon itself is so fast that the process cannot be observed and can only be derived from related physical conditions and measurements.

Ultrahigh pressure

[atomic, general, geophysics, thermodynamics] The pressure range from 50 to 250 GPa. Under ultrahigh pressure conditions, the PHASE transitions take place on a atomic/molecular LATTICE structure level, for general rocks as well as the formation of diamond. One topic of specific interest is the formation of diamonds from carbon under high temperature and high pressure. Graphite will form into a "diamond" lattice under temperatures ranging from 400°C – 1800°C under respective pressures ranging from 2.5 to 65 Gpa, which can be under normal geological conditions at depths of 150 km and more.

U

Ultrasonic ablation

[biomedical, mechanics] SOUND waves have ENERGY associated with the time-dependent pressure ($P(t)$) fluctuations (and the associated harmonic changes in the density as a function of time (t): $\rho(t)$) as a function of location based on the INTERNAL ENERGY ($U(t) = (1/\rho)[P(t)/(\gamma-1)]$, with $\gamma = (1-[u_0/v_s]^2)^{-(1/2)}$, the Lorentz factor, with u_0 the eddy speed for acoustic propagation and v_s the speed of sound) and the kinetic energy in the direction of interest (which is generally the direction of propagation, which can be in three dimensions) ($KE(t) = \iint (1/2)\rho(\tau)\vec{v}(\tau)\cdot\vec{v}(\tau)\,d\tau dV'$, for an infinitesimally small volume ELEMENT V', small enough to be adiabatic and relatively constant). Where the pressure gradient between the crests and troughs provides a mechanism of flow (flow velocity: $\vec{v}(t)$), a potentially rotational flow since the phenomenon can be in a three-dimensional medium (SURFACE WAVES may also have TURBULENCE associated with the WAVE propagation in the three-dimensional medium, but the effects can generally be negligible). Note that the pressure applies a FORCE (F) on the virtual surface, with area A, in the medium of the wave propagation. The total energy provided from the transverse WAVE MOTION in the direction of propagation can be expressed as $\bar{E} \sim A * \overline{P' * \vec{v}'}|_{\text{direction}}$, for an ISENTROPIC medium ($k_b(\partial T/\partial x_i) = 0$, where T is the temperature and $k_b = 1.3806488 \times 10^{-23}\,\text{m}^2\text{kg/s}^2\text{K}$ the Boltzmann coefficient; and $P = \text{Const} * \rho^\gamma$) that is also considered to act as an ideal system (i.e., $\sigma_{ij} = -P\delta_{ij}$, where σ is the local Cauchy stress TENSOR at the plane with "coordinate" i in direction j; and δ_{ij} the Kronecker delta). This acoustic energy can be applied by focused directional application in the ablation of, for instance, KIDNEY stones, known as lithotripsy. The vibrational energy will intentionally exceed the ULTIMATE TENSILE STRENGTH and the associated shear stress threshold: yield stress of the crystalline aggregate formed from minerals extracted from the digested food products (see Figure U.7).

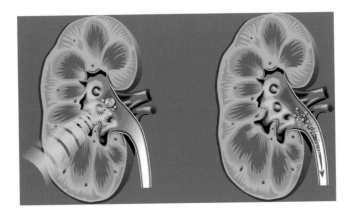

Figure U.7 Ultrasonic ablation; lithotripsy.

Ultrasonic computerized tomography

[acoustics] Imaging process that resembles the mechanism of action for X-RAY computerized TOMOGRAPHY, using pressure WAVE transmission IMAGE formation, and SIGNAL processing based on a line integral of the attenuation on a propagation path. The main difference from ULTRASOUND with X-ray is that the pressure wave PHASE and transmission velocity can be used as a mechanism to localize the mechanical properties of interest at any point along the length of the propagation path of the SOUND wave. The advantage of transmission tomography is the ability to image bulk tissues, not just interfaces, as is generally the case for REFLECTION ultrasound imaging. Hard materials however can significantly block the acoustic transmission, if not at least cause refraction distortions. Some of the density and related Young's modulus information of the transmission media is also imbedded in the spectral profile of the received signal, which is deconvolved by FOURIER ANALYSIS. Specific material structures, such as fiber structure, can additionally result in DISPERSION that provides material details but also provides distortions if not recognized as such. Ultrasonic computerized tomography is starting to form an alternative to mammography. Note that reflection pulse-echo ULTRASOUND imaging (as used to image for instance a baby in the womb) with an imaging array is also providing a tomographic image reconstruction (see Figure U.8).

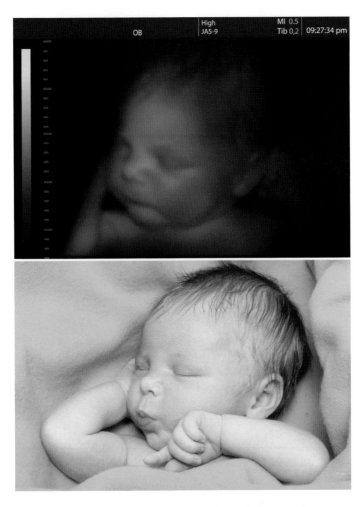

Figure U.8 Three-dimensional reconstruction form of multiple slices of ultrasound scanning arrays. Most well known in the rendering for baby embryo or fetus in the womb. Specifically clear in the comparison between the ultrasound tomography of the baby just prior to birth and a real image captured a few days after birth. Often these images are real time and can display the motions made by the fetus in the womb. In comparison to traditional B-mode ultrasound.

U

Ultrasonic flow meter

[fluid dynamics] Flow meter based on DOPPLER shift. Designs are available in various shapes and sizes, ranging from a tubular probe that wraps around an artery to a hand-help probe for external flow assessment of a subcutaneous vessels flow (*see* **DOPPLER**) (see Figure U.9).

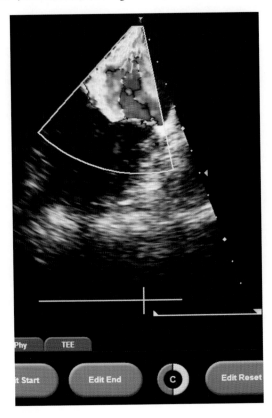

Figure U.9 Ultrasonic flow meter.

Ultrasonic imaging

[biomedical, mechanics] *See* ULTRASOUND.

Ultrasonic levitation

[general] Lifting an object by means of the force exerted by a JET of FLUID; related to aerodynamic levitation, since SOUND is a pressure wave. The acoustic ENERGY produces a flow of a medium with density ρ, and flow velocity v, that has its roots in the Bernoulli equation and the resulting FORCE (F) is equivalent to the time-averaged gradient in the flow direction (z) for the kinetic energy density: $F = \partial/\partial z \left(-\rho(v^2/2)\right)$.

The force produced by a standing WAVE is obviously more powerful than a free-flowing stream. Generally, frequencies in the kHz range are sufficient to produce LEVITATION (see Figure U.10).

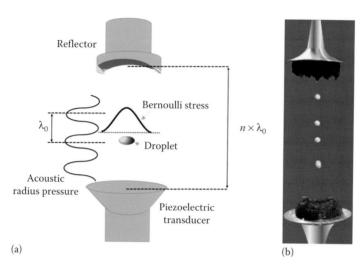

Figure U.10 (a,b) Acoustic levitation. (Courtesy of Mike Szczys.)

Ultrasonics

[acoustics, electronics, mechanics] Using ULTRASOUND; composed of a combination of compressional waves, fast shear waves, and slow shear waves; part of acoustic imaging (see ULTRASOUND). Ultrasonics can be used to determine the SHEAR STIFFNESS and SHEAR VISCOSITY of LIQUIDS. Machines using TORSIONAL and SHEAR-WAVE distortions measure the ACOUSTIC RESISTANCE also referred to as ACOUSTIC IMPEDANCE. The acoustic impedance implies that the medium has both elastic and viscous properties. Ultrasonics can be considered a component of nondestructive acoustic testing for flaws in materials. Ultrasonics also refers to the high-frequency probing of animals with reference to their orientation within a volume filled with obstructions as well as recognizing potential targets based on the FREQUENCY SPECTRUM acquired from a back-scattered SOUND, such as the one used by, for instance, bats and dolphins (see Figure U.11).

Figure U.11 Example of ultrasonic nondestructive testing.

Ultrasonograms

[acoustics, biomedical, imaging] Image obtained by ULTRASOUND imaging, primarily in medical diagnostics, also referred to as SONOGRAM.

Ultrasound

[acoustics, biomedical, general, mechanics] Rhythmic pressure disturbances that are beyond the audible range of human detection (range approximately 20–20,000 Hz, depending on the AGE of subject and other factors) for the higher frequencies (v). Generally ultrasound is considered operating at frequencies of $v \geq 20,000$ Hz. The existence of acoustic (pressure-wave) frequencies above 20 kHz was discovered around 1780, but is was not until 1942 that KARL THEODORE DUSSIK (1908–1968), engineer and physician from Austria, used high-frequency pressure WAVE for medical imaging applications. Prior to this, ultrasound was used for detection of flaws in metallic structures in nondestructive quality control. Earlier applications of ultrasound were in echo location, specifically for underwater guidance. REGINALD FESSENDEN (1866–1932) patented the echo-location mechanism of action in 1912. Diagnostic ultrasound relies on the wavelength (λ) for RESOLUTION: $\lambda = v/v$, with v being the speed of SOUND in the medium. The smallest items that can be resolved are in the order of half the wavelength in the longitudinal direction when used for imaging. The LATERAL RESOLUTION primarily depends on the acoustic array density (*also see* **RAYLEIGH CRITERION** *and* **PHASED ARRAY**). In diagnostic imaging using ultrasound, the frequency range is generally from 2.0 to 60 MHz. Higher frequencies will have a shallower penetration due to the increased attenuation ($\alpha(v)$) according to the relationship $\alpha(v) = \beta v^n$, where β is a material constant and $1 \leq n \leq 2$ is also a function of the medium in which the compression wave travels. The material constants β and n can be derived from a least square curve fit to the measured attenuation as a function of frequency. Ultrasound is used in biological imaging (e.g., SONOGRAM of fetus), nondestructive testing, and echo location (e.g., submarine navigation, radar as well as navigation used by BATS). In diagnostic use, both MACROSCOPIC and MICROSCOPIC, there are various sources available that can generate longitudinal ultrasonic waves. In medical imaging, the use of anisotropic ferro-electric ceramic crystals has the upper hand, namely piezoelectric transducers (e.g., quartz [one of the initial sources], barium titanate [$BaTiO_3$], lead zirconate [$PbZrO_3$], LEAD ZIRCONATE TITANATE [PZT] and lead titanate [$PbTiO_3$]). Other LONGITUDINAL WAVE sources are lithium niobate ($LiNbO_3$), lead metaniobate ($PbNb_2O_6$), zinc oxide (ZnO), polyvinylidene fluoride (PVDF), and Poly(vinyl alcohol) film, PVA. Zink-oxide can generate frequencies up to 96 GHz. In piezoelectric materials, there is an inherent anisotropy combined with the DIELECTRIC properties of the crystalline structure that will change the crystalline structure under the influence of an external electric field, allowing it to unidirectionally compress under an applied electric potential. The crystalline displacement can be translated to an external medium, causing this medium to compress and expand at the same rate as the crystal subjected to an alternating voltage. The longitudinal pressure wave forms the basis of acoustic imaging or, on a more basic level, DISTANCE gauging. Any vibrating mechanism can produce ultrasonic waves; bats use specialized vocal chords. The acoustic wave traversing the medium will encounter objects that will diffract, scatter, and reflect the wave, in addition to discontinuities in density in general that create acoustic discontinuities in the speed of propagation of sound also known as the acoustic index-of-refraction. Changes in speed of propagation will also obey SNELL'S LAW for ACOUSTICS. High-energy ultrasound can also be used in a destructive mode. Kidney stones are routinely pulverized with the use of intense focused ultrasound, whereas industrial applications include carving and etching of metallics and ceramics and other solids. As a nondestructive testing tool, ultrasonic surface ACOUSTIC WAVES (SAWs) are used to identify anisotropic behavior indicating weaknesses, operating in the GHz range. A similar principle is used for seismologic characterization; in this case the devices are large mechanical tools or even operating under explosive charges.

U

Other ultrasonic applications are in destructive high-power use from a sonicator, typically operating at 600 W at frequencies around 20 kHz (see Figure U.12).

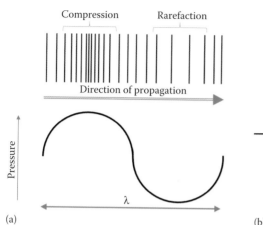

(a)

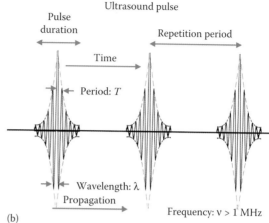

(b)

Huygens' principle applies; medium constituents provide the mechanism for secondary source and propagation

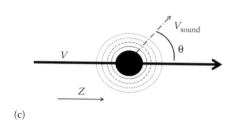

(c)

Snell's Law of refraction applies; at microscopic and macroscopic interfaces between component media providing the imaging mechanism-of-action

θ_i θ_r

Medium 1
with impedance: $Z_1 = \rho v$
Density: ρ_i; Local speed of propagation: v_i

Z_2

θ_t

(d)

Diagnostic ultrasound imaging

- Operation under several modes, A-, B-, and M-mode; C-mode scans in plane normal to B-mode and Doppler scanning provide motion, for example, flow information

Amplitude (V)   Boundaries

A-mode

Depth of penetration (µm)

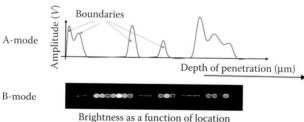

B-mode

Brightness as a function of location

M-mode   Probe is moved or uses a phased-array to sweep; image is reconstructed by "connect the dots"

(e)

Figure U.12 (a–e) Ultrasound, the clinical term of using acoustic waves to perform noninvasive imaging.

(Continued)

Acoustic wave-Propagation

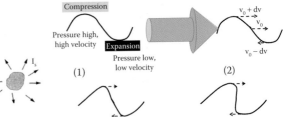

Ultrasound propagation: scatter

- The scattering cross section: σ_s, which is the power scattered by the object per unit incident internsity, can be solved for a simple sphere with a much smaller dimension than the wavelength as rayleigh scattering

$$\sigma_s = \frac{4\pi}{9} k^4 a^6 \left\{ \left| \frac{G_s = G}{G} \right|^2 + \frac{1}{3} \left| \frac{3\rho_s - 3\rho}{2\rho_0 + \rho} \right|^2 \right\}$$

(f)

(g) The pressure gradient resulting from the acoustic wave results in local differences in propagation velocity, in turn causing dispersion

- Harmonic imaging concept

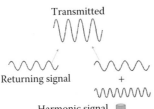

Transmitted   Reflected   Second harmonic

(h) Harmonic wave generation can be facilitated by means of contrast agents

- Harmonic imaging concept

- Harmonic imaging concept

Harmonic wave generation can be facilitated by means of contrast agents

- Harmonic imaging concept

- The returning signal includes not only the fundamental frequency, but also signals of other frequencies.

- The harmonic frequency is twice the fundamental frequency.

(i)

- Harmonic imaging concept

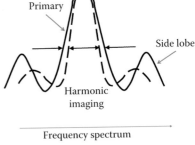

(j)

Figure U.12 (Continued) (f–j) Ultrasound, the clinical term of using acoustic waves to perform noninvasive imaging.

Ultraviolet

[optics] Part of the ELECTROMAGNETIC SPECTRUM recognized in 1801–1804 by the Prussian scientist (now Poland) JOHANN WILHELM RITTER (1776–1810) with wavelengths shorter than the visible blue; wavelength range: ~12 to 360 nm. The ultraviolet spectrum is subdivided in three regions, where the extreme ultraviolet (EUV) covers the range: ~12 to 130 nm, and boarders X-RAY RADIATION; far ultraviolet covers 130–200 nm; mid UV: 200–300 nm, and near ultraviolet is the spectrum: 300–400 nm. Note that these are approximations and that definitions vary based on the specific field of use or research. Another classification is in the general ranges of ultraviolet, which is more regulated, defining UVC as 100–280 nm; UVB 280–315 nm and UVA in the span 315–400 nm. Ultraviolet in the UVA provides the ENERGY for the CELL to generate vitamin K and changes the chromophores to create a SUN tan. Human VISION ranges roughly from

330 to 660 nm; however, these are not sharp cut-off thresholds. Note that the PERCEPTION has a curve with trailing edges for the CONES on the blue and the RED side, as well as for the "green" cone. Certain animals can see well into the ultraviolet. Most bacteria can be killed by ultraviolet radiation in the range 260–300 nm; wavelengths shorter than 260 nm are even more effective (see Figure U.13).

Figure U.13 Ultraviolet, as used in tannin bed. Used in forensics for highlighting chemical components without the direct need for chemical analysis, such as revealing finger print by means of the resident oils.

Ultraviolet catastrophe

[atomic, energy, general, nuclear] The original attempts to model the ENERGY of electromagnetic RADIATION to wavelengths were based on a WAVE theory only, whereas the introduction of QUANTUM MECHANICS applying the energy conversion $E = h\nu = h(c/\lambda)$, with $h = 6.6256 \times 10^{-34}$ Js PLANCK's CONSTANT, ν the frequency of radiation, $c = 2.997925 \times 10^{8}$ m/s the speed of LIGHT, and λ the wavelength showed the energy drop in black-body radiation at short wavelengths in contrast to the original EMISSION THEORY as described in the radiation theory introduced by MAX PLANCK (1858–1947). The original radiation theory would allow for an ever increasing energy with a decreasing wavelength emitted under excitation, for instance heat; the ultraviolet catastrophe. Since the original Rayleigh–Jean theory describes unlimited energy to be generated under limited resources ($E = ck_BT/\lambda^4$, where $k_B = 1.38066 \times 10^{-23}$ J/K is the Boltzmann constant, T the temperature), the "catastrophe" was introduced as the energetic conundrum. Experimental observations showed a peak in emission wavelength as a function of temperature, but at shorter wavelengths the emission would drop. QUANTUM THEORY introduced a Boltzmann energy distribution that compensated for the ever increasing WAVE ENERGY with decreasing wavelength (see Figure U.14).

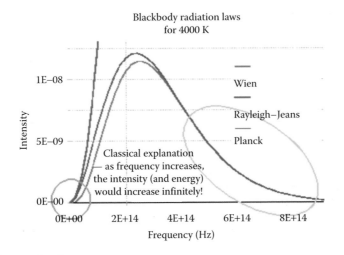

Figure U.14 Ultraviolet catastrophe.

Umbilical cord

[biomedical, chemical, fluid dynamics] Hemodynamic link between the placenta in the mammalian mother and the unborn offspring, containing a variety of step-cell lines and a BLOOD BARRIER that will not allow different blood types of host and fetus to interact. The umbilical cord provides a means of separation by semipermeable membranes among other mechanisms. There are four different blood group phenotypes: O, A, B, and AB, with rhesus factor either positive or negative (Rh factor). Specifically, since certain blood types cannot mix and will result in instant death for the fetus if no preventative action is taken. Specifically, when the mother is Rh negative and the baby is Rh positive, complications may arise during childbirth if no preventative action is taken. Latin: umbilicus (navel). In aerospace and aviation terms, the umbilical cord refers to the combination fuel-line and control cabling that attaches to a rocket to the main station and is detached on takeoff (see Figure U.15).

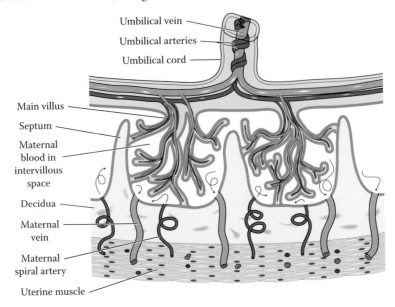

Figure U.15 Umbilical cord, and the chemical exchange through the placenta in the female womb.

Unbestimmtheitsprinzip

[atomic, computational, general, nuclear, solid-state] *See* UNCERTAINTY PRINCIPLE.

Uncertainty principle

[atomic, computational, general, nuclear, solid-state] QUANTUM mechanical principle formulated by WERNER KARL HEISENBERG (1901–1976). In Heisenberg's words: "UNBESTIMMTHEITSPRINZIP" (German). The uncertainty principle entails that the observation of a phenomenon will influence the phenomenon, more specifically either the location (x) or the momentum (p) can be known, but not both with total accuracy, expressed in one-dimensional analysis as $\Delta p_x \Delta x \geq (1/2)\hbar$, where Δ identifies the uncertainty in the parameter, $\hbar = h/2\pi$, with $h = 4.13567 \times 10^{-15}$ eVs $= 7 \times 10^{-34}$ Js the Planck constant, or referred to by Max Karl Ernst Ludwig Planck (1858–1947) as "the quantum of action." The use of a PHOTON to identify a phenomenon or an object will be linked to the photon momentum $p = h/\lambda$. During the probing action, the photon may transfer all of its momentum to the object; however, the resulting momentum of the object will be uncertain by an amount $\Delta p = h/\lambda$, whereas the location of the object can only be defined as accurate as approximately half a wavelength: $\Delta x \cong \lambda$. The uncertainty principle ties in with QUANTUM MECHANICS due to the fact that the product of the uncertainty in location and momentum (c.q. ENERGY [E]: conceptually $\Delta E \Delta x \geq (1/2)\hbar$) is finite and not zero. Under classical mechanics conditions, the speed of LIGHT would yield $c = \infty$ and the constant, at this point undefined, would be $\hbar = 0$. Uncertainty with respect to nuclear electrons; based on the general terms of the uncertainty principle that no electrons can exist inside the NUCLEUS based on the fact that the nucleus has a diameter in the order of $\Delta x = d = 1.0 \times 10^{-14}$ m, providing a kinetic energy $KE = 9.3\,\mathrm{MeV}$ greater than any electron ACTIVITY related phenomena, meaning that the nucleus has too much energy content for an electron. In three-dimensional analysis of a WAVEFUNCTION (ψ), the uncertainty principle can be expressed as $\psi, \left(\boldsymbol{p} - \overline{\boldsymbol{p}}\right)^2 \psi\psi$, and $\left(\boldsymbol{x} - \overline{\boldsymbol{x}}\right)^2 \psi \geq 9\hbar^2/4$, where $\boldsymbol{p} = -i\hbar\nabla$ is the momentum operator, with $\nabla = \sum_{i=1}^{n} d/d\xi_i$ the Laplace operator, ξ_i denoting the DEGREES OF FREEDOM, $\boldsymbol{x}$ the position operator in the ξ space, $\overline{\boldsymbol{p}} = \psi$, $\boldsymbol{p}\psi$ is the average momentum, and $\overline{\boldsymbol{x}} = \psi$, $\boldsymbol{x}\psi$ is the average position. Note the DE BROGLIE WAVE for moving objects still applies. Generally under these conditions, the expected value for an observable parameter (X) (i.e., operator) is expressed as $\psi, X\psi = \int \psi\left(\boldsymbol{x}\right)^* X\psi\left(\boldsymbol{x}\right) d^3\xi$ (see Figure U.16).

Figure U.16 Graphical illustration of the uncertainty principle: the observation of the location for a phenomenon is obscured by the momentum and associated velocity of the phenomenon. One cannot identify the location of a moving object due to the combined velocity and mass of the phenomena associated with the object.

Uncorrelated states

[thermodynamics] Generally ENERGY has an additive quality, where a system containing two or more subsystems will contain the sum of the energy of both subsystems. This also means that the encompassing system will contain all the states of the subsystems to form a composite system. Keeping this in mind, the states will be interrelated. In certain cases, the environment of the system will have states of its own, when the external states do not influence the internal states, and as such are isolated (and hence autonomous), they are considered uncorrelated. The uncorrelated states are hence impervious to the values of the properties of external systems, which is most often the general assumption in describing a physical phenomenon unless there is a direct exchange with the environment, which would imply that the environment is part of the system and is not a separate system. One rudimentary example is a thermos flask that is being uncorked, which connects the outside system.

Underdamped system

[general] OSCILLATION with a slow decreasing AMPLITUDE after the driving FORCE has been removed. The driving force generates a FORCED OSCILLATION. Even though a true underdamped system would be energetically unsupported, the closest examples are the free oscillation of a gong or a tuning fork. In theory,

U

the only underdamped system is the PHOTON, where perfect MONOCHROMATIC LIGHT has an infinite wavelength. Compare to CRITICALLY DAMPED, UNDERDAMPED, DAMPED SYSTEM, and OVERDAMPED system (*also see* DAMPED OSCILLATION) (see Figure U.17).

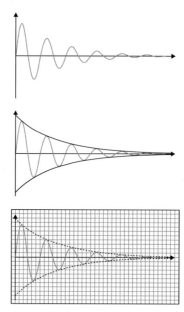

Figure U.17 Underdamped system of the photon, underdamped system of the gong or tuning fork.

Unequal-arm balance

[general] Weighing system that uses a torque as a means of equating the (gravitational) force multiplied by the arm length from an unknown mass against that of a known and calibrated mass and the respective arm length on the balance.

Unified atomic mass units (*u*)

[atomic, general, solid-state] One kilo MOLE of an ELEMENT of choice has a mass in kilogram that is by definition equal to the molecular mass of that element expressed in units u.

Unified Fourier reconstruction

[acoustics] Graphic reconstruction from ULTRASOUND data using unevenly spaced data SAMPLING values to shape the outlines of an object/perimeter of a boundary relying on interpolation. The spatial domain FOURIER TRANSFORM is adjusted for discontinuities as such revealing the discontinuities by adaptively spatially limiting the range over which the Fourier transform is composed.

Unified theories of the weak and electromagnetic interactions

[computational, electrodynamics, electromagnetic, general, quantum] Even though weak interactions (very large vector field $W'' = C_1 \vec{p_e} \cdot \langle \vec{J} \rangle + C_2$, with $\vec{p_e}$ the momentum vector of the electron distribution and $\vec{J}$ the charge POLARIZATION for the NUCLEUS, C_i constants, which apropos, are nonconservative with respect to PARITY) and electromagnetic interactions (PHOTON) there is a computational analogy between the two mechanisms in vectorial form.

Unified theory

[computational, dynamics, electromagnetism, general, quantum] In the theoretical description of weak and electromagnetic interactions, there are commonalities that transgress the interactions of massless photons versus extensive values for the mass-equivalent weak interactions found in leptons and hadrons. The scale at which this phenomenon gains importance is of the order of 1/1000th the size of a NUCLEUS. The WEAK INTERACTION is described as a weak-interaction density distribution ($\mathcal{L}_W$) with the Lagrangian formulated in vectorial quantities as $\mathcal{L}_W = -(G/\sqrt{2})J_\alpha^\dagger(x)J^\alpha(x)$, where $J^\alpha(x)$ represents the charge current, $Ja^\dagger(x)$ the current equivalence for raising a charge in a transition such as from n state to p state, and G is the gravitational constant (see Figure U.18).

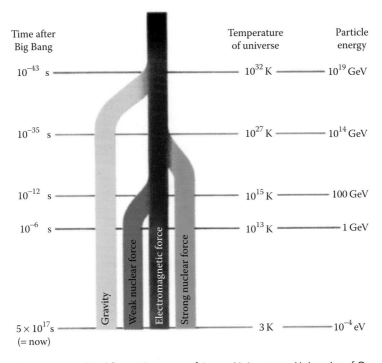

Figure U.18 Unified theory in graphical form. (Courtesy of James N. Imamura, University of Oregon, Eugene, OR.)

Universal gravitation, law of

[astrophysics/astronomy, general] *See* LAW OF UNIVERSAL GRAVITATION.

Universal gravitational constant (G)

[astrophysics/astronomy, general] Based on SIR ISAAC NEWTON's (1642–1727) deduction that gravitational attraction is directly proportional to the product of the masses (m_i) of the respective objects involved, and inversely proportional to the square of the separating DISTANCE (r), as described in his LAW OF UNIVERSAL GRAVITATION; he introduced a constant that holds true for all planetary gravitational interactions: $F = G(m_1m_2/r^2)$, with the universal gravitational constant $G = 6.6720 \times 10^{-11}\,\mathrm{Nm^2/kg^2}$.

Universe

[astrophysics, general, geophysics] Collection of all galaxies, containing solar systems and meteors and galactic dust resulting in what is currently believed to be the result of an explosion that occurred approximately 1.5×10^9 years ago. Currently, the Universe is consistently expanding supporting this theory, making certain galaxies move away from us, whereas other galaxies that we more to the center of the "explosion" seem to gain on us. The knowledge supporting the EXPANDING UNIVERSE is based on data acquires by Hubble, and the Hubble TELESCOPE in outer space. These relative galactic movements can be verified by the red- and BLUE-SHIFT phenomena (regular and relativistic DOPPLER EFFECT). One major dilemma with respect to the "BIG BANG" THEORY is that this seemly requires the generation of ENERGY out of "nothing" (*also see* **BIG BANG THEORY**) (see Figure U.19).

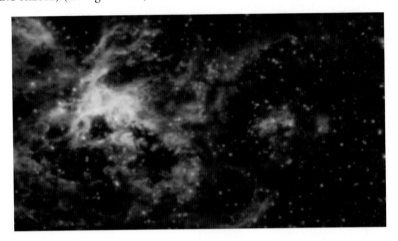

Figure U.19 The universe, artist impression and images acquired by the Hubble Space Telescope.

Unstable equilibrium state

[atomic, geophysics, solid-state, thermodynamics] State of medium that can spontaneously transition into another state, or series of cascading states with associated short-lived interactions. An example of a specific unstable equilibrium would be a supercritical NUCLEAR REACTOR, without NEUTRON. Introducing a single neutron will cause a sequence of events that can generate a substantial amount of ENERGY. Alternatively, an object that is supported above the CENTER OF GRAVITY (center of mass) will be in stable equilibrium, whereas when the object is supported below the center of gravity this will provide an unstable equilibrium (see Figure U.20).

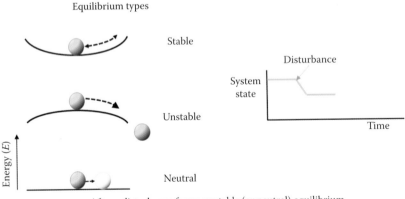

Figure U.20 Energy diagram for an unstable equilibrium state.

Unsteady flow

[fluid dynamics] Flow process that involves discharge at the initial or final segment of the flow process. There are multiple inlet and outlet access routes that add or subtract from the flow process. Unsteady flow is a complex mechanism and requires computational fluid-dynamic analysis (see Figure U.21).

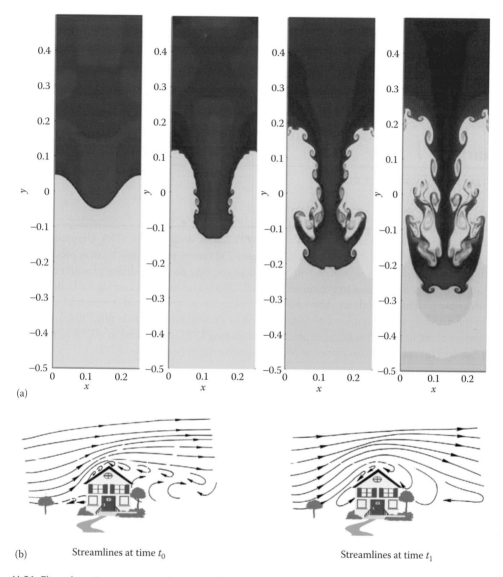

(a)

(b)　Streamlines at time t_0　　　　Streamlines at time t_1

Figure U.21 Flow changing over time, due to the flow developing process based on the boundary conditions as well as the initial conditions or changing flow conditions due to perturbations. (a) Hydrodynamics simulation of the Rayleigh–Taylor instability. (Courtesy Shengtai Li, Hui Li; the U.S. Department of Energy.) (b) Streamlines for flow development with respect to onset of flow (e.g., wind gust).

U

Unsteady state

[thermodynamics] The state of a medium that changes due to interactions with other systems. One specific example of an unsteady state is the electric charging of a BATTERY; this will proceed until the battery is fully charged.

Up antiquark

[atomic, general, nuclear] Antiquark that has flavor "up" (*also see* UP QUARK).

Up quark

[atomic, general, nuclear] Quark that has FLAVOR "up" (*also see* ELEMENTARY PARTICLE). Quark with the following characteristics: charge: $+(2/3)e$; SPIN: $(1/2)h$; BARYON NUMBER: $1/3$; strangeness: 0; CHARM: 0; bottomness: 0; and topness: 0 (*see* QUARK).

U-quark

[atomic, general, nuclear] *See* UP QUARK.

Uranium ($^{238}_{92}$U)

[atomic, nuclear] The most prevalent uranium ISOTOPE (99.275%), discovered in 1789. Uranium-238 is a stable isotope with a half-life of 4.5 billion years. Uranium-238 can be made into a FISSION product to generate ENERGY by bombardment with a NEUTRON, with subsequent two beta decays rendering plutonium-239, a nuclear component for fission used in explosive devices. U-238 is also used as a coating for bullets, providing them with armor-piercing capabilities. Also known as depleted uranium, reduced commercial value with respect to the naturally fissile uranium-235 (used in the first ATOMIC BOMB: "Little Boy," 1945). Uranium 238 is a by-product of the uranium enrichment process of extracting U-235, occurring at ~0.7% in natural state, where U^{235} is fuel for nuclear power plants; at 3%–4% concentration (see Figure U.22).

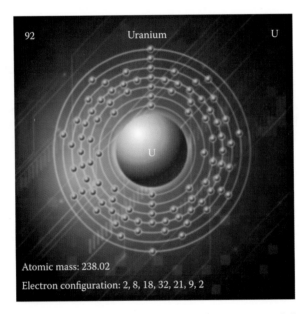

92   Uranium   U

Atomic mass: 238.02
Electron configuration: 2, 8, 18, 32, 21, 9, 2

Figure U.22 Uranium, ($^{238}_{92}$U), electron configuration; Mcarthur River Uranium Mine; drill core mineralized stable $^{238}_{92}$U uranium; uranium ore (uraninite) from Pribram, Czech Republic.

Urey, Harold Clayton (1893–1981)

[atomic, nuclear] Chemist and physicist from the United States who performed pioneering work in ISOTOPE analysis. Harold Urey is best known for his discovery of the deuterium isotope of hydrogen in 1931. Urey received the Nobel Prize in Chemistry for his work in nuclear PHYSICS in 1934, specifically the principal mechanisms of NUCLEAR FUSION. Additional work was in the isolation of various isotopes, including carbon, nitrogen, and sulphur (see Figure U.23).

Figure U.23 Harold Clayton Urey (1893–1981). (Courtesy of Columbia University, New York.)

U

V particles

[atomic, mechanics, nuclear, quantum] Generic name introduced in the 1940s describing unstable subatomic PARTICLE that, when undergoing its principle DECAY mechanism, will produce a pair of particles that are emitted in a v-form when observed in a BUBBLE CHAMBER. Since then these particles have been identified as MESON or BARYON particles (for instance, K-MESON and sigma-baryon) and the term v-particle has not been used anymore, but may still be found in reference material concerning the interaction of COSMIC RAYS with upper atmospheric conditions.

Vacuum

[general] Description of lower limit of pressure. Pressure by definition is the force per unit area for a volume that has an infinitesimal small surface area (A), expressed as $P = \lim_{A \to 0}(\rho g V / A)$, with the local density ρ, volume V, and GRAVITATIONAL ACCELERATION g. For vacuum $P \downarrow 0$, which means that for a finite volume the density shall approach zero, so that there are no intermolecular collisions possible that could yield a net force. Pressure in general was first measured in 1644 by one of GALILEO GALILEI's (1564–1642) assistants; the Italian scientist EVANGELISTA TORRICELLI (1608–1647) and this was expanded on by the French mathematician BLAISE PASCAL (1623–1662) in 1648, both man have their names associated with the units for the MAGNITUDE of pressure, specifically the "TORR" (1 torr = 1 mmHG; mercury) from Torricelli for low

pressure, and Pascal for ATMOSPHERIC PRESSURE and high pressure. Generally, the Pascal sets the standard for all pressure measures; 1 torr = 133.3 Pa (see Figure V.1).

Figure V.1 Vacuum; examples of conditions and applications of a pressure below atmospheric value. (a) outer space at deep (mm Hg) vacuum conditions, (sealed food with air removed to increase storage shelf-life) CRT scope tube with vacuum to increase electron flow conditions. (b) Suction pad used to attach to flat surfaces in order to facilitate lifting by means of the vacuum device.

Vacuum field equations

[astrophysics/astronomy, computational, optics] Description of gravitational interaction, including GRAVITATIONAL WAVES, and specifically the interaction with electromagnetic RADIATION known as Einstein's field equations under conditions at ABSOLUTE ZERO temperature, expressed as $\text{Ric} - (1/2)g_{\mu\rho}R + R_{\mu\rho}\Lambda = (8\pi/c^4)G\tau_{\mu\rho}$, where $\text{Ric} = R_{\mu\rho} = R^{\nu}_{\mu\nu\rho}$ the Ricci curvature TENSOR; a contracted Riemann tensor ($R^{\nu}_{\mu\nu\rho}$), which vanishes in VACUUM, $\tau_{\mu\rho}$ the stress ENERGY tensor, $g_{\mu\rho} = (\partial/\partial y^{\mu})(\partial/\partial y^{\rho})\left((1/2)F^2\right)$ the metric tensor derived from a matrix diagonal in Finsler structure (the metric tensor is directly linked to the Ricci factor, however with only half the number of independent components: 10) and F the Finsler structure; with property: $F(x,\lambda y) = \lambda F(x, y)$, operating in Finsler geometry, not Riemann geometry, subsequently: Λ the cosmological constant (the energy density of space vacuum, assuming a stationary universe), R the SCALAR curvature, G the gravitational constant, and c the speed of LIGHT. Einstein had to admit to an error in his assumption of the UNIVERSE, being an EXPANDING UNIVERSE, as revealed by EDWIN HUBBLE (1889–1953) in 1915; leading to a significant adjustment for the cosmological constant (Λ). Additionally, under the condition of absolute zero the energy density tensor ($\tau_{\mu\rho}$) drops to zero as well. Defined by ALBERT EINSTEIN (1879–1955), as part of his GENERAL THEORY OF RELATIVITY, in 1915.

Vacuum pump

[general] Mechanism used to achieve high VACUUM or ultra-high vacuum. High vacuum can be reached by a variety of methods with pressures down to 10^{-12} Torr $\sim 10^{-10}$ Pa. Vacuum can be achieved by rotary piston (roots pump), bellow pumps or reciprocating piston pumps; single (limit: 5×10^{-3} Torr) or

double stage (limit: 1×10^{-4} Torr). In order to reach a deeper vacuum additional techniques need to be incorporated, often applied in stages or in unison. High vacuum techniques include fluid jet, cryogenic means (GAS is frozen and hence removed), chemical reactions with solid residue, and IONIZATION with an applied electric field that forces the ions/polarized molecules out, with lower limit down to 1×10^{-8} Torr. For even lower pressure stages special techniques are required, such as a turbomolecular pump, reaching 1×10^{-10} Torr. Combinations of pumping techniques and potentially the introduction of cryogenic cooling and the assistance of helium or hydrogen can result in pressures as low as 1×10^{-12} Torr, operating at temperatures in the order of $10\,\mathrm{K}$. Generally, the process of vacuum application will involve removing the gasses trapped in the WALL of the container as well, a process called "outgassing." Outgassing may require heating the container. Proper material selection for the construction of the PUMP and container are crucial for ultra-low pressure consistency, seals in the junctions as well as in the pumps are all influencing the final outcome. Most vacuum chamber are constructed of high-grade stainless steel.

Valence

[atomic, general] The number representing the combining or displacing power of an ATOM; number of electrons lost, gained, or shared by an atom in a compound. The valence is the number of hydrogen atoms with which an atom will combine, or the number it will displace. Valence electron describes any electron which is gained, lost, or shared in a chemical reaction. Usually valence electrons are the outermost electrons in the BOHR ATOM model.

Valence band

[atomic, energy, general, quantum] Overlapping of ENERGY bands of individual atoms, creating a continuous energy band instead of discrete energy levels as described by the Bohr model. Electrons that move beyond the valence band into the CONDUCTION BAND are free to move. The valence band can provide a mechanism for sharing of the outermost electrons in this shared energy band, specifically in a CONDUCTOR; whereas in a semiconductor or INSULATOR the valence electrons are held close by the respective atoms. For an insulator the conduction band and valance band are separated by an energy gap greater than 10 eV, whereas for a semiconductor the separation is 1 eV or less. For a semiconductor the conduction process can be facilitated by DOPING, for instance introducing GALLIUM in silicon introduces a shared energy band that provides an escape mechanism for electrons bound to silicon, leaving holes in the silicon (i.e., POSITIVE CHARGE surplus) (see Figure V.2).

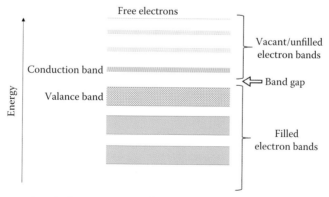

Figure V.2 Valence band concept illustrated by means of energy configuration for a hypothetical atom.

Valve

[fluid dynamics, thermodynamics] Closure mechanism applied to pipes and junctions in order to regulate the flow of fluids. Many types of valves exist, geared to achieve a specific goal or ease of use. Examples of valves in use are butterfly, ball, gate, globe (one of many type found in water faucets as well as other applications), GATE VALVE or check valve. The flow control mechanism can depend on a seal or gasket made, for instance, out of rubber or cork, or can be METAL-on-metal with a through-hole that can be made to misalign. Check valves were common in the airflow regulation in older model automobiles with GAS MIXTURE supplied by a carburetor system, controlling the ANGLE of the flap that determines the opening area by depressing the gas pedal that connects through a level system (see Figure V.3).

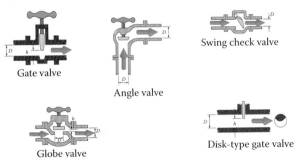

Gate valve

Angle valve

Swing check valve

Globe valve

Disk-type gate valve

Figure V.3 Various valve designs.

Valves closure, Allievi's equations

[fluid dynamics] Equation of MOTION for flow and EQUATION OF CONTINUITY defined in 1925 by the Italian mechanical engineer LORENZO ALLIEVI (1856–1941) with specific relevance to the "WATER HAMMER" effect. The equation of motion is defined by the flow (Q; [m^3/s]) and the change in height (h, also for instance associated with a diverging tube) as $Ag(dh/dx) + (\partial Q/\partial t) + kQ|Q| = 0$, where g is the GRAVITATIONAL ACCELERATION, A the cross-sectional area of the tube, and k is the equation of continuity reads $(\partial h/\partial t) + (v_{ch}^2/Ag)(\partial Q/\partial x) = 0$, where v_{ch} is the rate of change in flow (for instance, due to closure), or the velocity of propagation. Both are also found as $(\partial v/\partial t) + (1/\rho)(\partial P/\partial x)$, where the velocity v is the velocity parallel to the PIPE axis and averaged over the CROSS SECTION, P the pressure, and ρ the density of the FLUID. Alternatively, $E_Y(\partial P/\partial t) + (\partial v/\partial x)$, with E_Y the effective COMPLIANCE for the system.

Van Allen, James Alfred (1914–2006)

[astrophysics/astronomy, electromagnetism] Astrophysicist from the United States, specifically known for his discovery of the toroidal charged-particle bands encapsulating Earth: the VAN ALLEN BELTS (see Figure V.4).

Figure V.4 James Alfred Van Allen (1914–2006). (Courtesy of North American Space Agency [NASA], Washington, DC.)

Van Allen belts

[astrophysics/astronomy, electromagnetism] PLASMA belts around EARTH. The two torus shaped zones of energetic particles (primarily electrons and protons) emit RADIATION discovered and described by the astrophysicist from the United States, JAMES ALFRED VAN ALLEN (1914–2006). The belts represent particles that are "trapped" in the earth's MAGNETIC FIELD configuration. The existence of the belts was confirmed by the spaceship Explorer I in 1958. The Van Allen radiation belts form part of the mechanism leading to the AURORA BOREALIS. The Van Allen radiation belts form a protection from the sun's radiation and are formed resulting from the collision SHOCK WAVE of the sun's SOLAR WIND with the earth's magnetic field. Also known as the Van Allen radiation belts (see Figure V.5).

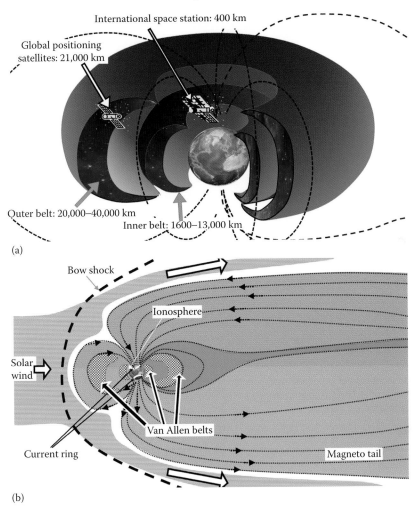

Figure V.5 (a,b) Van Allen belts.

Van de Graaff, Robert Jemison (1902–1967)

[general] Scientist, experimental PARTICLE physicist from the United States. Robert van de Graaff constructed the first belt-operated (electrostatic) charge GENERATOR in 1931 (see Figure V.6).

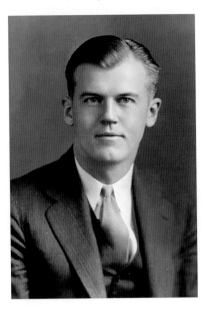

Figure V.6 Robert Jemison van de Graaff (1902–1967). (Courtesy of Massachusetts Institute of Technology, Cambridge, MA.)

Van de Graaff generator

[atomic, energy, nuclear] Static charge generator and collection station using a conveyor belt to transport charges that are generated by a high potential source, generating the equivalent to a CATHODE ray, positioned close to an insulating moving belt. The moving belt enters a hollow CONDUCTOR, while in contact with the sphere by means of a wire brush, transferring the charges on the belt to create a relatively high electric potential on a the hollow sphere over time, which is a function of the time and the radius of the sphere (generally several hundred thousand volts; *see* COULOMB'S LAW). The Van de Graaff generator was designed by ROBERT VAN DE GRAAFF (1902–1967) in 1931 to examine the conditions of high electrical potential and electric discharge. Static charge had been known for millennia prior to this invention, rubbing AMBER with fur to generate a static charge, dating back to 600 BC recorded by the Greek astronomer Thales (Thales of Miletus: ca. 624–546 BC) (*also see* **WIMSHURST MACHINE**) (see Figure V.7).

Figure V.7 Van de Graaff generator design, with Robert van de Graaff (1902–1967) operating the charge conveyor belt. (Courtesy of Massachusetts Institute of Technology, Cambridge, MA.)

Van der Meer, Simon (1925–2011)

[general] Scientist from the Netherlands, who together with the Italian scientist Carlo Rubbia (1934–), led a team of scientists to the discovery of the "intermediate vector bosons" (in particular the W and Z bosons) in 1983, for which they received the Nobel Prize in Physics in 1984 (see Figure V.8).

Figure V.8 Simon van der Meer (1925–2011). (Courtesy of Conseil Européen pour la Recherche Nucléaire [European Council for Nuclear Research]. Copyright CERN, Geneva, Switzerland.)

Van der Pol, Balthasar (1889–1959)

[electromagnetism, theoretical] Electrical engineer from the Netherlands who recognized the characteristic NOISE in VACUUM tubes while operating under an alternating current of specific driving frequencies (see Figure V.9).

Figure V.9 Balthasar van der Pol (1889–1959). (Courtesy of International Telecommunication Union (ITU), Geneva, Switzerland.)

Van der Pol equation

[biomedical, electromagnetism, geophysics, mechanics] Second-order differential equation describing the damped OSCILLATION in a dynamic system that is not subject to CONSERVATION OF ENERGY. $(d^2x/dt^2) - \epsilon(1-x^2)(dx/dt) + x = 0$, where x can be a location or other time-dependent variable, t is time, ϵ is a coefficient indicating COMPLIANCE (including system nonlinearities) and dampening, specifically $-\epsilon(1-x^2)(dx/dt)$ is the definition of RESISTANCE or FRICTION. In case $-\epsilon(1-x^2)(dx/dt)$ is negative positive the term applies to "negative resistance" and applies, for instance, to the gain (nonlinear) of a power amplifier. This equation is also used in biological application to describe the ACTION POTENTIAL of neurons in a planar field geometry, other relevant uses are in SEISMOLOGY to model the MOTION of TECTONIC PLATES at a FAULT LINE and to describe RESONANCE phenomena in compliant media, such as in NONDESTRUCTIVE TESTING using ACOUSTICS. The equation will need to solved numerically with for instance specialized segmented methods as described by the RUNGE–KUTTA METHOD.

Van der Pol oscillator

[biomedical, electromagnetism, geophysics, mechanics, theoretical] An OSCILLATION (primarily electric, but additional applications in MECHANICS and geophysics are supported) which is nonlinearly damped and as such inherently nonconservational (*also see* OSCILLATION). A forced Van der Pol oscillator is described by $(d^2x/dt^2) + \epsilon(x^2-1)(dx/dt) + x - A\sin(\omega t) = 0$, where x is a Cartesian coordinate, t is time, ϵ is a coefficient indicating COMPLIANCE (including system nonlinearities) and dampening, $A\sin(\omega t)$ is the driving alternating source with AMPLITUDE A, and frequency $2\pi\omega$.

Van der Waals, Johannes Diderik (1837–1923)

[atomic, solid-state, thermodynamics] Physicist and engineer from the Netherlands whose main contribution to SOLID-STATE PHYSICS was the description of medium-range attractive forces, the VAN DER WAALS FORCE (also described as VAN DER WAALS BONDING). Van der Waals made significant theoretical contributions to the description and understanding of the EQUATION OF STATE of gases and liquids, some substantial contributions were in his doctoral thesis. In 1910 Johannes van der Waals was awarded the Nobel Prize in Physics (see Figure V.10).

Figure V.10 Johannes Diderik van der Waals, (1837–1923). (Courtesy of Collection of the Van der Waals family.)

Van der Waals bonding

[biomedical, condensed matter, dynamics, general, nuclear, quantum, solid-state, thermodynamics] Also referred to as VAN DER WAALS FORCE. The force between molecules. This force distinguishes itself from the other known molecular forces defined as ELECTROSTATIC FORCE, covalent attraction, and hydrogen bonds. The Van der Waals force is a MACROSCOPIC force balance primarily applying to dipoles, both permanent and induced. Van der Waals forces act between molecules within the same structure, but also across an interface between different species of molecules such as at a surface, and work between atoms. The force is primarily derived from the fact that the atoms and molecules become charge polarized, the balance of negative and POSITIVE CHARGE shift to opposite sides respectively and forms an induced DIPOLE with limited lifetime or applies to permanent dipoles. The electrostatic interaction is also known as KEESOM FORCE. Groups of molecules can form charge distributions that lead to attractive force due to DISPERSION of the combined charges forming multipoles. Examples of clear Van der Waals bonds are for instance found for graphite and clay (see Figure V.11).

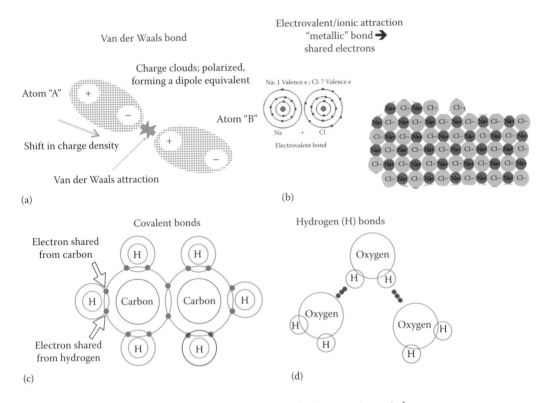

Figure V.11 (a–d) Van der Waals bonding in comparison to other (stronger) atomic forces.

Van der Waals equation of state

[atomic, nuclear, thermodynamics] Modification to the IDEAL GAS LAW: $\left(P + (a_f/V^2)\right)\left(V - b_f\right) = nRT$, where P is the PRESSURE, V is the volume, a is a positive constant: $a_f = (27/64)((RT_c)^2/P_c)$, b_f a small positive constant approximately corresponding to the specific volume of the FLUID when the molecules are packed close together (highest density): $b_f = RT_c/8P_c$, R the UNIVERSAL GAS CONSTANT, n the number of moles of substance, and T the TEMPERATURE. Where a_f and b_f are interaction constants question (*Note*: b_f represents the volume of the total number of individual molecules, the Avogadro number multiplied by the volume of one single MOLECULE), long-range and short-range attractive forces, respectively, and can be derived from the PT curves; V the volume occupied by n moles of atoms under pressure P, at temperature T, and $R = 8.3144621(75)$ J/Kmol be universal gas constant. The deviation from the IDEAL GAS conditions is represented by the COMPRESSIBILITY FACTOR: Z_{com}. The relationship between PRESSURE (P), TEMPERATURE (T), and VOLUME (V_m) describing the material state conditions from the lowest possible pressure and temperature to the highest. One of the ideal gas conditions considers no forces between the molecules of the GAS, which will cause deviations from ideal gas configuration the denser the gas is (i.e., pressure–volume relationship). Description of a liquid–GAS PHASE transition.

Van der Waals force

[atomic] *See* VAN DER WAALS BONDING.

Van Helmont, Johannes (Jan) Baptista (1579–1644)

[general] Alchemist from the Netherlands attributed with the formal introduction of the concept of GAS as a material PHASE, not as a unique phenomenon (see Figure V.12).

Figure V.12 Johannes (Jan) Baptista van Helmont (1579–1644) c. 1674, painted by Mary Beale.

Van Laar equations

[thermodynamics] Description of mixtures with molar fractions of the (*r*-) constituents (μ^{mol}_i; this forces $\sum_{i=1}^{r} \mu^{mol}_i = 1$). The van Laar equations are pertaining to binary mixtures specifically, yielding: $\ln \gamma'_1 = \ln \mu^{mol}_1 + (A/RT)/[1 + (A\mu^{mol}_1/B(1 - \mu^{mol}_1))]^2$ and $\ln \gamma'_2 = \ln(1 - \mu^{mol}_1) + (A/RT)/[1 + (B(1 - \mu^{mol}_1)/A\mu^{mol}_1]^2$, where $A = \Delta H_{1,mix}$ and $B = \Delta H_{2,mix}$, with $H_{i,mix}$ the enthalpy of the constituent, and $\gamma'_1 = \gamma'_1 \left(T, P, \mu^{mol}_1, \mu^{mol}_2, \ldots, \mu^{mol}_{r-1} \right)$ is the ACTIVITY of the ingredient (defining the excess in chemical potential relative to the state at reference pressure P_0 while at the same temperature) as a function of PRESSURE (P) and TEMPERATURE (T); however, not dependent on chemical composition.

Van Leeuwenhoek, Antonie Philips (1632–1723)

[biomedical, optics] Scientist, engineer, and merchant salesman from the Netherlands. Perfected the compound MICROSCOPE, reaching magnifications of 500×. Van Leeuwenhoek investigated biological materials such as bacteria, muscles, and spermatozoa. He also used his optical instrumentation to IMAGE

V

the PERFUSION of superficial vasculature and described capillaries. Considered the "father" of microbiology (see Figure V.13).

Figure V.13 Antonie Philips van Leeuwenhoek (1632–1723), painted by Jan Verkolje.

Van Musschenbroek, Petrus (1692–1761)

[energy, general] Physicist and mathematician from the Netherlands, instrumental in the development and experimental observations leading to the discovery of stored charge and the CAPACITOR (see Figure V.14).

Figure V.14 Petrus (Pieter) Van Musschenbroek (1692–1761), painted by Hieronymus van der Mij. (Courtesy of Leiden, Universiteits-Bibliotheek, Icones 147; Leiden, the Netherlands.)

Van Royen, Willibrord Snel (1591–1626)

[optics] *See* SNEL ("SNELL"), WILLEBRORD SNEL VAN ROYEN (SNELLIUS) **(1591–1626)**.

Van't Hoff, Jacobus Henricus (1852–1911)

[biomedical, chemical, thermodynamics] Scientist and chemist from the Netherlands. Johannes van't Hoff received the Nobel Prize in Chemistry in 1901. One of Van't Hoff most memorable contributions is the definition of partial pressure of a dissolved solution as the OSMOTIC PRESSURE: $\Pi_{\text{osmotic}} = P - P_{jj} = (RT/v_{jj})\sum_{k \neq j} \mathcal{Y}_k$, with $\mathcal{Y}_k = n_k/n = (x_k/M_k)/(\sum_{\ell=1}^{r}(x_\ell/M_\ell))$ the mole fraction of the dissolved constituent $_k$, with M_ξ the mean MOLECULAR WEIGHT OF SOLUTE $_\xi$, for the amount of constituent n_k summing to a total of solutes $n = \sum_{k=1}^{r} n_k \, x_\xi$ the fractional mass for constituent $_\xi$, P_{jj} the molar partial pressure of constituent $_j$ in SOLUTION, v_{jj} the volume of the INCOMPRESSIBLE FLUID per mole, PRESSURE P and TEMPERATURE T, and $R = 8.3145$ J/molK is the universal gas constant (see Figure V.15).

Figure V.15 Jacobus Henricus van't Hoff (1852–1911).

Van't Hoff equation

[biomedical, chemical, thermodynamics] Equation defining the pressure resulting from the gradient in concentration of solutes across a DISTANCE or a more physical BARRIER such as a SEMIPERMEABLE MEMBRANE. The Van't Hoff equation was defined by JACOBUS HENRICUS VAN'T HOFF (1852–1911), and is sometimes associated with the Starling equation. The OSMOTIC PRESSURE of a SOLUTION has the same value as if the particle solution would have as a GAS with the same volume and temperature as the solution. The OSMOTIC PRESSURE (Π_{osm}) can be expressed in the form used by the ideal gas law: $\Pi_{\text{osm}} = nRT/V = [C]RT$, where $R = 8.135$ J/molK is the gas constant, T the local temperature in Kelvin, n is the quantity of solutes in mol, and $[C]$ the concentration. The osmotic pressure is also referred to as the COLLOID OSMOTIC PRESSURE. Note that all solutions will add to the sum of the osmotic pressure of the LIQUID.

Van't Hoff factor

[fluid dynamics, geophysics, thermodynamics] Osmotic coefficient that applies to the partial pressure (Π_{osm}) of a SOLUTE described by the VAN'T HOFF EQUATION: $\Pi_{\text{osm}} = \Phi_{\text{osm}}RT\Delta[C]$, with $\Delta[C]$ the concentration gradient across a SEMIPERMEABLE MEMBRANE, where $R = 8.135$ J/molK is the GAS constant and T the local temperature in Kelvin. The expression $n_{\text{ion}} \times \Phi_{\text{osm}}$, where Φ_{osm} the osmotic coefficient or Van't Hoff factor, n_{ion} the number of ions respectively the solute concentration; yields the physically dissolved concentration contributing to the OSMOTIC PRESSURE. For NaCl (SALT) $\Phi_{\text{osm}} = 0.93$. Note that for electrolytes the Van't Hoff factor <1, however for nonelectrolytes the SOLUTION of particles becomes convoluted and complicated, rendering Van't Hoff factors <1, for instance, for hemoglobin the Van't Hoff factor = 2.57.

Van't Hoff law

[biomedical, chemical, thermodynamics] *See* **VAN'T HOFF EQUATION**.

Vapor

[thermodynamics] Material phase of a medium where the molecules or atoms are spaced relatively far apart, generally achieved when exceeding the boiling point for the material, a gaseous phase. Note that a solid may transform into GAS under SUBLIMATION ("steam" rising from ice). The heat of vaporization (b_v, or LATENT HEAT OF VAPORIZATION, based on the constant temperature of the process) defines the ENERGY required to convert 1 kg of liquid phase into vapor at constant temperature. Water vapor is referred to as steam. The phases of a material are represented by the PHASE DIAGRAM. At the TRIPLE POINT (three phase): solid, liquid, and gas/vapor exist at the same time under the same conditions in equilibrium. When a vapor cannot be described as an IDEAL GAS the Van der Waals equation needs to be used, specifically when the vapor is a dense mixture. The reverse PHASE TRANSITION process is condensation from vapor to LIQUID, or from vapor to solid desublimation, respectively (see Figure V.16).

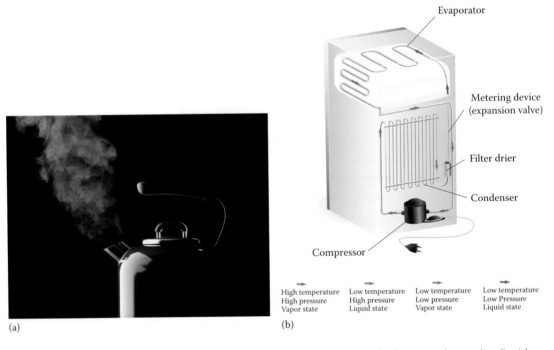

Figure V.16 (a) Vapor for boiling water and (b) vapor in the refrigeration cycle for freon or other cooling liquid.

Vapor pressure

[nuclear, thermodynamics] The pressure of a vapor in equilibrium with its condensed state (LIQUID or solid). The vapor pressure of a medium (P_v) is defined by the Clausius–Clapeyron equation: $\ln P_v = -(\Delta H_v/RT) + (\Delta S_v/R)$, where H_v is the enthalpy of vaporization, S_v the entropy of vaporization, T the local temperature, and $R = 8.3144621(75)$ J/Kmol the universal gas constant. The vapor pressure of mercury is of particular importance with respect to its use as an ENERGY transferral in certain types of nuclear power plants, primarily due to the toxicity of mercury. Other examples of METAL coolants are sodium, lead, and tin.

Vapor pressure equation

[atomic, fluid dynamics] *See* **CLAUSIUS–CLAPEYRON RELATION**.

Variable capacitor

[general] Plate capacitor with variable surface area, primarily used as a tuning mechanism for radios in the late 1900s. The change in surface area (A) directly influences the value of the CAPACITOR (C) as $C = \varepsilon A/d$, where ε represents the permittivity of the medium between the plates and d the plate separation (generally, the tuning plate capacitor has multiple plates). The capacitance determines the RESONANCE FREQUENCY of the RC circuit (resistor (R)–capacitor (C) circuit, with specific time constant: $\tau_C = RC$); hence providing a mechanism of influencing the PHASE-LOCKED LOOP that will collect only the RADIO signal that matches the resonance frequency of the tuner (see Figure V.17).

Figure V.17 Variable capacitor used for tuning an early model analog radio design.

Variable resistor

[general] Electrical device that can be adjusted for total resistance by means of rotation of a dial, which generally changes the length of a wire (ℓ) that the current passes through, hence changing the RESISTANCE since the SPECIFIC RESISTANCE ($\rho_{R,\text{spec}}$) of a METAL wire is a function of length: $R = \rho_{R,\text{spec}}\ell$. Also referred to as POTENTIOMETER (see Figure V.18).

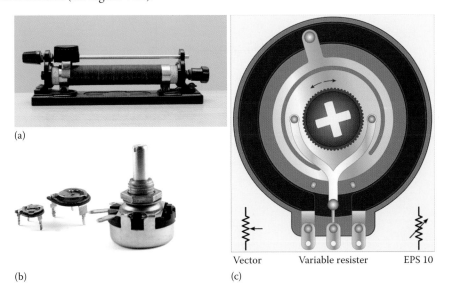

(a)

(b)

Vector   Variable resister   EPS 10

(c)

Figure V.18 (a) Variable resistor, (b) potentiometer, and (c) circuit diagram icons.

V

Variance (σ²)

[computational, quantum, signal, thermodynamics] The square of the standard deviation for a series (with sample size: N) of measurements (x_i), defined as $\sigma^2 = 1/(N-1)\sum_{i=1}^{N}(x_i - x)^2$, with the mean: $x = 1/N\sum_{i=1}^{N}x_i$. The variance provides an indication of the physical spread in data, how far are the data removed from the mean value, and hence is an indication of risk. A large variance is an indication of a broad spread of the measured values, not particularly correlated to the likelihood (probability distribution), more an indication of how far out can numbers enter into the analysis with respect to the mean value. A variance close to zero is an indication of a very close grouping of data. Additionally, variance is one of the moments of a distribution. The standard deviation for a sample distribution is the square root of the variance. In THERMODYNAMICS the concept of "variance" (F_{var}) relates the PHASE change of a chemical reaction to the number of coexisting phases of a system with r constituents defined as $F_{var} = r + 2 - q - \tau_{ch}$, where q is derived from the Gibbs PHASE RULE as the system operating in a q − phase state (heterogeneous stable equilibrium of coexisting phases; allowing each phase to be modeled as a simple system), and τ_{ch} represents the ordered number of potential chemical reactions, τ_{ch} is captured as a series (two constituents can have maximally one reaction, yielding $\tau_{ch} = 0,1$) (see Figure V.19).

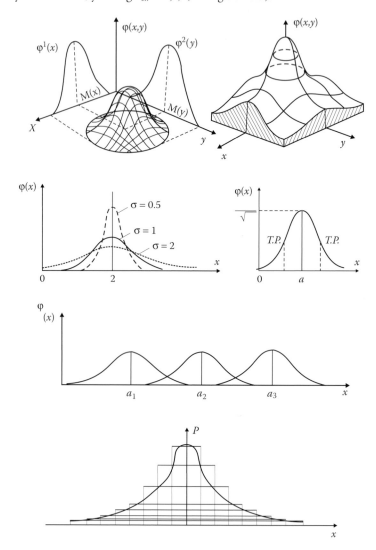

Figure V.19 Statistical variance.

Vector boson

[general] Bosons that are the exchange particles in a weak nuclear interaction, in particular the W and Z bosons. The WEAK INTERACTION delineates the interaction between electrons and neutrinos.

Vein

[biomedical] Anatomical feature, BLOOD vessel that is returning blood to the HEART. Blood in the veins is generally oxygen poor, except for the veins carrying blood from the lungs, which is oxygen rich. Veins have valves in intermittent locations to prevent blood from pooling and flowing back due to the lack of applied pressure. Veins are fairly similar to arteries, with the exception that the veins do not have a muscular WALL and rely on externally applied pressure from SKELETAL MUSCLE to provide the pumping action, mediated by the valves to force the flow in the direction of the heart (see Figure V.20).

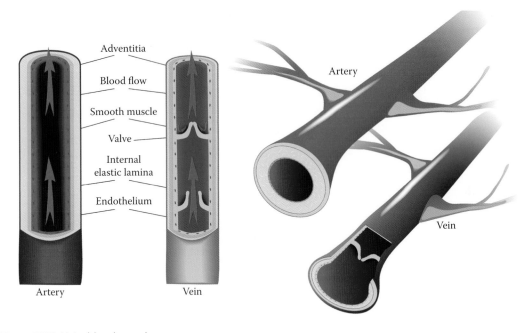

Figure V.20 Vein, blood vessel.

Velocity ($\vec{v}$)

[acoustics, biomedical, biophysics, dynamics, electromagnetism, engineering, general, geophysics, optics, ultra-fast phenomena] (syn.: speed) {use: energy, motion} Vector describing the MAGNITUDE and direction of the change in location (i.e., displacement) as a function of time: $\vec{v} = dL(x(t), y(t), z(t))/dt$, where $L\big(x(t), y(t), z(t)\big)$ is the position in the three-dimensional Cartesian coordinate system as a function of time t.

Velocity potential

[fluid dynamics, geophysics] A dynamic function that has many similarities with potential theories of attraction (e.g., potential ENERGY), ELECTRICITY and magnetics, and ELECTROSTATICS (e.g., electrical potential). The velocity potential defined by the energy involved in FLUID flow moving from a fixed point A^* to variable point P^* is for an irrotational MOTION defined as $\phi = -\int_{A^*}^{P^*} \big(udx + vdy + wdz\big)$, where in CARTESIAN COORDINATES $u = -(\partial\phi/\partial x)$ is the velocity in the x-direction, $v = -(\partial\phi/\partial y)$ is the velocity in the y-direction, and $w = -(\partial\phi/\partial z)$ is the velocity in the z-direction. For a VORTEX motion the velocity potential needs to include directional information defined by $\psi = \int_{A^*}^{P^*} \big(\chi_x \cos \vartheta_x u + \chi_y \cos \vartheta_y v + \chi_z \cos \vartheta_z w\big)ds$, where $\cos \vartheta_i$

described the respective ANGLE for all velocities with respect to the normal to the curved velocity profile and χ_i is a proportionality constant. The velocity gradients are now defined by $dw/dz = ((\partial\phi/\partial x) + (\partial\phi/\partial y)) + i((\partial\psi/\partial x) + (\partial\psi/\partial y))$, respectively, and so on. In turn the velocity profile for rotational flow is now defined by $\phi = (\kappa/4\pi)\iint(\chi_x \cos\vartheta_x(\partial/\partial x') + \chi_y \cos\vartheta_y(\partial/\partial y') + \chi_z \cos\vartheta_z(\partial/\partial z'))(1/r)ds'$, where $\kappa = \varpi'\sigma'$ is a measure of the strength of the vortex with ϖ' an indication of the vorticity and σ' a surface ELEMENT on the vortex filament, s' denotes the surface bounded by the vortex element, and $r = \sqrt{(x-x')^2 + (y-y')^2 + (z-z')^2}$ with (x', y', z') the location on the surface bounded by the vortex filament of importance and (x, y, z) the location in P^* where the velocities (u,v,w) will need to be derived. The work (W) done by rotational motion of an incompressible LIQUID can be related to the velocity profile (in accordance with general potential theories) as $W = (1/2)\rho\iiint\left[(\partial\phi/\partial x)^2 + (\partial\phi/\partial y)^2 + (\partial\phi/\partial z)^2\right]dxdydz$ (see Figure V.21).

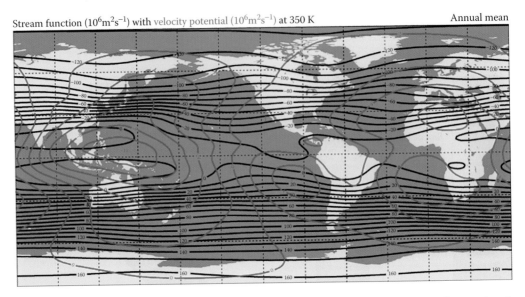

Stream function (10^6m^{2}s^{-1}) with velocity potential (10^6m^{2}s^{-1}) at 350 K   Annual mean

Figure V.21 Velocity potential for the geographic wind flow, averaged over 1 year. (Courtesy of University of Reading, Reading, UK; European Centre for Medium-Range Weather Forecasts [ECMWF].)

Ventilation

[biomedical, fluid dynamics, mechanics] Expansion and contraction of the chest cage coinciding with respective inspiration and expiration, known as breathing (*also see* RESPIRATION).

Ventilator

[biomedical, chemical, electronics, fluid dynamics, mechanics] Mechanical device providing an assist function to transport oxygen into the lungs by forcing AIR into the lungs by a PUMP mechanism. Ventilators are required during anesthesia since the normal muscular action that facilitate the volume EXPANSION of the lungs (inhaling) by means of either pulling down the diaphragm in the stomach by contraction (the diaphragm in relaxed state is curved upward), or elevating the ribs in the rib cage is rendered inoperable. Exhaling is an elastic process and relies on the ANATOMY to return to the position with the lowest ENERGY. In addition to mechanical ventilators that operate at the same frequency as with respect to unchallenged ACTIVITY for the person in question, other mechanisms are required as well. The VENTILATION process for premature babies is challenging to the extremely small size of the infants, size of a fist. In some cases the use of high-frequency modulation is used to induce a net flow, operating under kHz acoustic perturbation. The high-frequency approach provides a minimal net force/pressure to the lungs of the infant, thus preventing damage to the lungs resulting from excessive force (see Figure V.22).

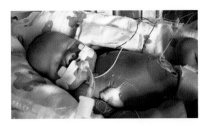

Figure V.22 Neonatal baby connected to special design ventilator specifically designed for the small tidal volume and respiratory rate boundary conditions.

Venturi, Giovanni Battista (1746–1822)

[fluid dynamics] Engineer and scientist form Italy who described the "suction" aspect of flow when passing through a narrowing tube with a hole in the WALL of the tube in 1791 (see Figure V.24).

Figure V.24 Giovanni Battista Venturi (1746–1822).

Venturi

[fluid dynamics] Mechanical configuration with respect to flow that results in an increase in flow velocity with a resulting drop in pressure, based on Bernoulli's law. Two boats that are traveling side by side will cause a localized increase in flow velocity due to the narrowing passage between the boats (specifically due to the curved outer hull of the ships), which will force the boats to move closer together due to the undisturbed pressure experienced on the hull of the boats on the perimeter. Another example is the flow of water over a container with chemical SOLUTION, drawing the chemical solution into the flow stream as a result of a venturi with an appropriately placed opening connecting to the reservoir. This mechanism is used to facilitate the diluted and controlled spread of fertilizer or weed killer. The physical process of creating "suction" by means of flow is referred to as the venturi effect. The process is named after the Italian scientist GIOVANNI BATTISTA VENTURI (1746–1822) who described this phenomenon in 1791. The venturi effect is also responsible for creating the mechanical MOTION of loose tissues in the nose and throat (airways in general) resulting in the snoring SOUND (see Figure V.23).

Figure V.23 Asthma inhaler with venturi for drug distribution: nebulizer.

Venus

[astrophysics/astronomy, general] Second PLANET from the SUN with an average diameter of 12,103.6 km, a mass of 4.86732×10^{24} kg, and an average surface temperature of 480°C. One SPIN revolution takes 243 Earth days, in the opposite direction with respect to earth's rotation, and the revolution around the Sun lasts 225 Earth days. The Magellan space mission has explored Venus with great detail, and a total of 40 spacecraft have been sent to Venus so far (see Figure V.25).

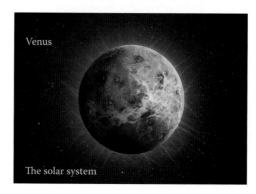

Venus

The solar system

Figure V.25 Venus.

Verlet method

[computational] Numerical integration technique, specifically designed to solve Newton's EQUATIONS OF MOTION, based on a TAYLOR EXPANSION with respect to the coordinates, introduced by the French physicist Loup Verlet (1931–) in 1967.

Versorium

[general] Elementary ELECTROSCOPE. One of the first devices used to measure static charge. The versorium was invented by the English astronomer and physician SIR WILLIAM GILBERT (1544–1633) around 1600 (see Figure V.26).

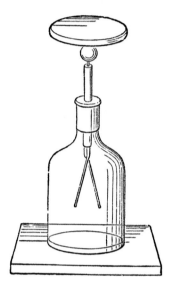

Figure V.26 Electroscope that uses the same principle as the versorium, a rod that can pivot freely. The original versorium had a close similarity to a compass needle, only for charge (i.e., electric field) and not for magnetic field. The illustrated gold-leaf electroscope was developed almost two centuries later, in 1787, by the clergyman and physicist Abraham Bennet (1749–1799) from Great Britain, following the introduction of the A pith-ball electroscope, which was a ball suspended from a thread, invented in 1754 by school teacher and physicist John Canton (1718–1772) from Great Britain, inspired by Benjamin Franklin (1706–1790) from the United States.

Vesalius, Andreas (1515–1564)

[biophysics, general] Scientist from Belgium describing the first documented dissection of the human ANATOMY: Humani Corporis Fabrica in 1543. This was a dissention from the Galenian school of biological investigation (*see* CLAUDIUS GALENUS [130–201] also named "Galen"), focusing on animal observation and bodily composition examination (see Figure V.27).

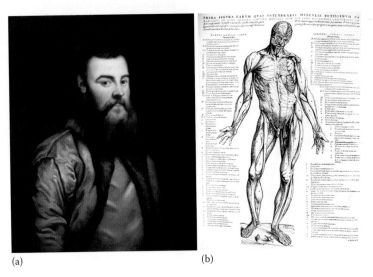

(a)　　　　　　　　　　　　　　(b)

Figure V.27　(a) Andreas Vesalius (1515–1564). (Courtesy of UCL Media Services; Collection: University College London Hospitals, London, Great Britain, example of the anatomic artwork by Andreas Vesalius.) (b) Epitome of Vesalius, Basel, 1543. (Courtesy of University of Glasgow Library, Special Collections; Glasgow, UK.)

Vibration

[acoustics, mechanics, solid-state, thermodynamics] Rhythmic motion with respect to a point of equilibrium, often with fixed frequency. Vibrations can be rotational (including "scissor action"), linear/translational, and "spherical" (general three-dimensional) EXPANSION, and are generally not confined to any single dimensional orientation; for instance, a drum SKIN, or GUITAR casing (acoustic guitar) can have a variety of oscillatory modes. The acoustic vibration, pressure wave, generates sound. Vibrations require an ENERGY source to support the MOTION, when the source is removed the OSCILLATION will dampen based on the elastic modulus of the medium. Vibrations supported by an external FORCE (F) obey the WAVE EQUATION with respect to the displacement $u(\vec{r},t)$ as function of location $\vec{r}$ and time t: $\nabla^2 u(\vec{r},t) = (1/v_s^2)(\partial^2/\partial t^2)u(\vec{r},t) - F$, where the displacement wave propagates through the medium with velocity v_s, the speed of SOUND for an acoustic wave (∇^2 is the Laplace operator, defining a second-order derivative with respect to location). Whistling generates a vibration with virtual single frequency, described by a sinusoidal function for the AMPLITUDE: $A(t) = A_0 \sin(\omega t - \varphi)$, where $\omega = 2\pi v$ the ANGULAR VELOCITY and v the frequency (the term "frequency" was introduced by GALILEO GALILEI [1564–1642]); as well as φ a PHASE difference depending on the boundary conditions. Vibrations are periodic motions with a periodicity or time constant that repeats the process for each cycle: $T = 1/v$, the total duration of a single oscillation (period). Vibration of an ELECTRIC CHARGE will provide a localized alternating current with associated alternating electric field and ensuing induced alternating MAGNETIC FIELD, providing an electromagnetic wave (PHOTON). Vibrations will have a base frequency and often higher harmonics superimposed. The harmonics will provide "COLOR" to a sound, or spectrum in the acoustic or optical analysis. Molecular vibrations are the main source for temperature, the mean kinetic energy; next to electronic vibrations as a result of temperature from a source of signal noise superimposed on the data, requiring filtering and smoothing to regain the clarity of the SIGNAL information. Undamped ("undampened") or underdamped oscillations with a continuous force source will result in

RESONANCE phenomena that can lead to excessively large amplitudes. It is also referred to as oscillation (see Figure V.28).

(a)   (b)

Figure V.28 Vibration: (a) soil compactor based on tempering by combustion engine and (b) weight-loss vibration belt.

Villard, Paul Ulrich (1860–1934)

[general] Chemist from France who discovered gamma RADIATION in 1903. The studies of Villard on radium involved a PHOTOGRAPHIC PLATE that was sealed by a sheath of lead (known to stop the already discovered alpha-particles), but still yielded exposure, which was shown to consist of two types of radiation, one being beta rays (electron radiation, also known at the time) and a new unknown type of radiation. ERNEST RUTHERFORD (1871–1937) proposed the name gamma rays since they were more penetrating than alpha- or beta rays (named by Rutherford in 1899). Villard made the introduction of quantifying radiation exposure, later quantified by the unit Röntgen, after the elementary work performed by WILHELM CONRAD RÖNTGEN (1845–1923). These exposure QUANTIFICATION efforts still determines the current field of dosimetry in both medical applications and nuclear power plants (see Figure V.29).

Figure V.29 Paul Ulrich Villard (1860–1934).

Viscoelastic

[biomedical, fluid dynamics, mechanics, solid-state] Non-Newtonian behavior that has both viscous and elastic characteristics under deformation. Viscoelastic media have time-dependent strain, whereas a viscous medium has a linear relationship for strain under flow and deformation conditions; that is, exposure to stress. A viscoelastic medium has a dependence to shear rate with respect to the equation of motion. Examples of viscoelastic behavior are pseudoplastic and dilatant media. The equation of motion for fluids is generally defined by the Navier–Stokes equation for the velocity of motion $\vec{v}$ in a liquid with density ρ under applied forces $\vec{F}$ and pressure P as a function of time (t), which will integrate compensation for elastic dampening: $\rho((\partial \vec{v}/\partial t)+(\vec{v}\cdot\nabla)\vec{v})=\rho\vec{F}-\nabla\cdot P+\eta_{\text{visc}}\nabla^2\vec{v}+(\eta_{\text{bulk}}+(\eta_{\text{visc}}/3))\nabla(\nabla\cdot\vec{v})$, where $\eta_{\text{visc}}=(5/16\sqrt{\pi})(\sqrt{(k_bT)}/\sigma_r^2\Omega_c^{2,2})$ defines the viscosity ($k_b=1.3806488\times10^{-23}$ m^{2}kg/s^{2}K the Boltzmann constant, temperature T, σ_r molecular diameter, $\Omega_c^{2,2}=n_in_i\int_{-\infty}^{\infty}\int_{4\pi}\{\phi_i(v^{*'})\phi_j(v^{**'})-\phi_i(v^*)\phi_j(v^{**})\}\chi\sigma_R d\Omega d^3v$ the Fokker–Planck collision integral, a special case of the Boltzmann collision integral ($\sigma_R=1/4(Z_iZ_j/4\pi\varepsilon_0 m)^2(1/\chi^2\sin^4(\varpi/2))$ the RUTHERFORD CROSS SECTION; $m=m_im_j/(m_i+m_j)$ the average mass for a two-component medium, Z_n the respective changes, $\varepsilon_0=8.85419\times10^{-12}$ C^2/Nm^2 the permittivity of free space, χ the SCALAR location within the vector potential, ϖ the ANGLE of impact, and $\phi_n(v^{n^*})$ the respective intermolecular potential for the interdependent constituents), η_{bulk} the bulk viscosity and the KINEMATIC VISCOSITY associated with the flow: $\eta_{\text{kin}}=\eta_{\text{visc}}/\rho$. The viscosity η_{kin} is linked to the material STRESS $(\sigma_s(t))$ and STRAIN $(\epsilon_s(t))$ as $\sigma_s(t)=\eta_{\text{kin}}(d\epsilon_s(t)/dt)$. The elastic compensations are introduced by the Volterra equations linking stress and strain as $\epsilon_s(t)=(\sigma_s/E_{Y,\text{creep}})+\int_0^t K(t-t')[\partial\sigma_s(t')/\partial t]dt'$, where $K(t)$ is a CREEP function; $\sigma_s(t)=E_{Y,\text{relax}}\epsilon_s(t)+\int_0^t R(t-t')[\partial\epsilon_s(t')/\partial t]dt'$, $R(t)$ a relaxation function, E_Y a elastic modulus for creep and relaxation (*also see* DAMPER). For a Maxwell damper the stress–strain relationship can be written as $d\epsilon_{\text{tot}}(t)/dt=\sigma_s(t)/\eta_{\text{kin}}+(1/E_Y)[d\sigma_s(t)/dt]$. Alternatively, for the Kelvin–Voigt model the stress–strain relationship can be written as $\sigma_s(t)=E_Y\epsilon_s(t)+\eta_{\text{kin}}[d\epsilon_s(t)/dt]$. More complex models are available, combining serial and parallel elastic arrangement of the first two models, for instance, the Maxwell–Wiechert (also known as the generalized Maxwell model, after JAMES MAXWELL [1831–1879], respectively with contributions by Emil Wiechert [1861–1928]) approach. An extreme example of viscoelastic behavior is for chewing gum. BLOOD behaves as a Newtonian liquid only for high shear rate (greater than 100 s^{-1}) and for large vessel diameters (see Figure V.30).

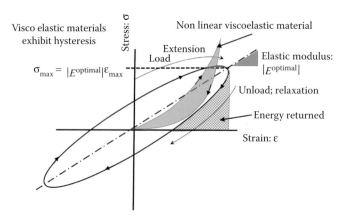

Figure V.30 Diagram representing the viscoelastic behavior for a medium.

Viscoplastic

[fluid dynamics, general, mechanics] Decomposition of the strain rate into an elastic and a plastic component; application of elastic stress–strain applied to the strain rate; the use of plastic flow potential and compliant with the plastic flow rule. The plastic flow rule defines the conditions of flow under multiaxial loads, with additional boundary condition confinement provided by the evolution of the state variables with respect to PLASTIC STRAIN and RESISTANCE of the state variables to flow (analogous to yield stress). The strain rate decomposition is formulated by separation of the rate of STRAIN $\left(\epsilon_s(t)\right)$ over time in elastic $(_e)$ and plastic $(_p)$ components: $(d/dt)\epsilon_s^{ij}(t)=(d/dt)\epsilon_{s,e}^{ij}(t)+(d/dt)\epsilon_{s,p}^{ij}(t)$, note $\epsilon_s^{ij}(t)=1/2\left((\partial v_i/\partial x_j)+(\partial v_j/\partial x_i)\right)$, with v_n the velocity of flow in the respective directions. This provides for the elastic strain rate:
$(d/dt)\epsilon_{s,e}^{ij}(t)=E_{Yijkl}^{*}(d/dt)\sigma_s^{kl}(t)=[(1+v_{Poisson})/E_Y](d/dt)\sigma_s^{ij}(t)-(v_{Poisson}/E_Y)(d/dt)\sigma_s^{kk}(t)\delta_{ij}+\alpha(d\Delta T/dt)\delta_{ij}$,
where E_{Yijkl}^{*} is referred to as the Elastic COMPLIANCE tensor (*Note*: inverse to the generalized elastic modulus), E_Y is the Young's modulus, $v_{Poisson}=-(\epsilon_x/\epsilon_z)=-(\epsilon_{transverse}/\epsilon_{logitudinal})$ the Poisson ratio where ϵ_i is the strain in direction i, δ_{ij} the Kronecker delta, α_m a material property, and T the temperature (*also see* CREEP) (see Figure V.31).

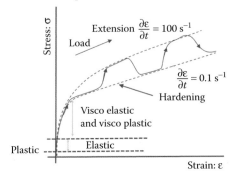

Figure V.31 Diagram representing the viscoplastic behavior for a medium.

Viscosity

[fluid dynamics, general, mechanics] The relation in torque between a rotating object and a stationary object separated by a LIQUID.

Viscosity (η)

[atomic, biomedical, computational, fluid dynamics, mechanics, nuclear, solid-state] Apparent RESISTANCE a fluid applies to a body in MOTION, and even itself (equating to flow resistance), measured as a standard by dropping a sphere in a FLUID and measuring the rate of decent, expressed as $\eta=[2(\rho_{sphere}-\rho_{liquid})gR^2]/9v$, where ρ the density of the sphere or LIQUID respectively, g the GRAVITATIONAL ACCELERATION, R radius of the sphere, and v velocity of the sphere dropping through the liquid (*see also* DYNAMIC VISCOSITY OR COEFFICIENT OF VISCOSITY). Proportionality constant connecting the SHEAR STRESS (τ_s) between two plates in linear parallel movement with respect to each other and the speed of respective motion $\tau_s=F/A=\eta(U/b)$, where A is the area of the contact surface between the two planes, h the separation DISTANCE between the planes, F the force applied to move one of the plates, and U the constant velocity of the MOTION. Another way of describing the viscosity of flow is in a tube where a column of flow experiences the resistance from the neighboring shell layer as a FRICTION force (F_f) expressed as a function of radius (r): $F_f(r) = \eta 2\pi r L(dv/dr)$, where L the characteristic length over which the pressure drop is measured, dv/dr the radial velocity gradient, for a laminar Newtonian flow the flow velocity will be a quadratic function with respect to radius, forming a parabolic velocity pattern with the maximum flow velocity in the center of the tube. Units centiPoise, dimensions: $ML^2 T^{-1}$ (*also see* NEWTONIAN FLUID, SHEAR THICKENING, *and* SHEAR THINNING) (see Figure V.32).

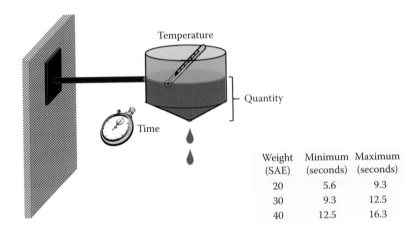

Weight (SAE)	Minimum (seconds)	Maximum (seconds)
20	5.6	9.3
30	9.3	12.5
40	12.5	16.3

Figure V.32 Impact of the particulate concentration on the viscosity.

Viscosity, apparent

[general] *See* APPARENT VISCOSITY.

Viscosity, dynamic (η_{dyn})

[atomic, biomedical, computational, fluid dynamics, mechanics, nuclear, solid-state] Viscosity pertaining to the "mechanical flow resistance" of a FLUID with the neighboring shell layer as a FRICTION force (F_f) is expressed as a function of DISTANCE to the WALL of the solid (y): $F_f(r) = \eta_{dyn} A(dv/dy)$, where A is the area of interaction with, for instance, a flat wall, where $A = Lw$, L the characteristic length of interaction over a width w, also: dv/dr. the shear velocity gradient. Units centiPoise and dimensions: $ML^2\,T^{-1}$. The wall can also be the surface of a sphere subject to flow, dropping through a LIQUID. The area of the sphere (only the area subject to flow) will replace the linear area mentioned earlier for the wall. The DYNAMIC VISCOSITY of gases can be determined by the absolute MANOMETER of Knudsen.

Viscosity, intrinsic

[fluid dynamics, general, nuclear] $[\eta] = \lim_{[c]\to 0}(\eta_{reduced})$, where $[c]$ is the SOLVENT concentration and $\eta_{reduced}$ the REDUCED VISCOSITY.

V

Viscosity, kinematic

[fluid dynamics] The standard viscosity multiplied by the GRAVITATIONAL ACCELERATION (g) and divided by the DENSITY (ρ) of the FLUID: $\eta_K = \eta(g/\rho)$, units St, dimensions: $L^2 T^{-1}$. One specific example of KINEMATIC VISCOSITY applies to MOTOR oil. To insure uniformity, the Society of Automotive Engineers (SAE) has designed specific tests to measure the flow rate of oil. The OIL grades are designated by a "weight" or viscosity grade, for instance, referred to as an SAE number. The SAE number is defined by a process that measures the time it takes for a predetermined quantity of oil to seep through an opening in a canister with a fixed diameter performed at a standard temperature. The temperature used for grading the viscosity of motor oil is generally 100°C. This temperature has been chosen to resemble the operating temperature for the average automobile engines. The higher the "weight" number in the SAE rating system, the thicker the oil, with respective slower flow; this refers to a single weight oil. In order to compensate for the changing temperature and LOAD conditions multiviscosity lubricants have been introduced. Multiweight lubricants are created by adding what is known as viscosity improver (VI) additives to oil, which makes the oils remain thicker at higher temperatures. Multiweight oils is designed to remain relatively constant in viscosity over a broad range of temperatures. The SAE classification for multigrade oils is described by two viscosity grades; for example, 10W-30, a common multigrade oil used in modern engines. Older engines were prescribed thicker oils such as 20W-50. The first number designates the viscosity at low temperature ("10W"), while the second number ("30") represents the viscosity at 100°C. The "W" refers to cold weather use, and is derived from Winter. The viscosity rating scale for lubricants has been standardized by the American Petroleum Institute (API). The oil specifications from the ENGINE manufacturer will best suit all of the LUBRICATION requirements, over the lifetime of the engine. The actual MEASUREMENT temperature used to evaluate the performance (e.g., "cold start") and define the grade of oil depends on the W-grade. For example, an oil with grade SAE 5W must be evaluated at −35°C, while an SAE 10W grade oil must meet the shear rate viscosities ranges defined by the SAE J300 standards at −30°C (see Figure V.33).

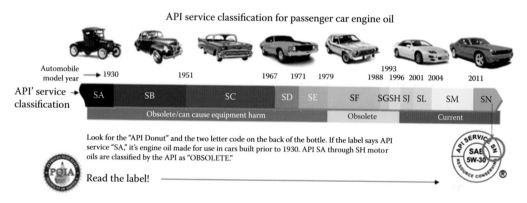

Figure V.33 Kinematic viscosity.

Viscosity, reduced

[fluid dynamics, general, nuclear] $\eta_{\text{reduced}} = \eta_{\text{specific}}/[c]$, where $[c]$ is the colloid concentration and η_{specific} the SPECIFIC VISCOSITY.

Viscosity, relative

[fluid dynamics, general, nuclear] $\eta_r = \eta_{\text{suspension}}/\eta_0$, where $\eta_{\text{suspension}}$ is the colloid viscosity and η_0 the viscosity of the SOLVENT.

Viscosity, specific

[fluid dynamics, general, nuclear] $\eta_{\text{specific}} = (\eta_{\text{suspension}} - \eta_0)/\eta_0$, where $\eta_{\text{suspension}}$ is the colloid viscosity and η_0 the viscosity of the SOLVENT.

Viscosity, static

[fluid dynamics, mechanics] Friction between two plates, one plate is moving with respect to the other plate, creating a force with respect to the stationary plate. Units centiPoise $\times$ gram $\times$ m$^{-3} = sv$, dimensions: $M^5 L^2 T^{-1}$.

Viscosity, structural

[fluid dynamics] $\eta = \eta_0 \kappa_{\text{visc}}^{\,n-1}$ where η_0 is a material constant or baseline viscosity (Newtonian), $\kappa_{\text{visc}} = v(r,t)/h$ is the shear velocity with $v(r,t)$ the flow velocity of a COUETTE FLOW and h the DISTANCE between the walls (e.g., thickness of the viscous layer), and n is an indicator for the type of viscous behavior, with $n = 1$ for Newtonian, $n < 1$ for pseudoplastic (SHEAR-THINNING FLUID) and $n > 1$ for dilatant (SHEAR-THICKENING FLUID), as introduced by Ostwald and De Waele (1924) (see Figure V.34).

Typical response of materials with various viscosity structures
to a step change in shear rate

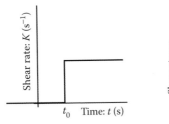 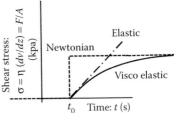

Figure V.34 Diagram illustrating the concept of structural viscosity.

Viscosity index

[fluid dynamics] *See* VISCOSITY.

Viscosity meter

[fluid dynamics, general] The viscosity of a flowing liquid can be determined from the flow: Q [m^3/s] as $Q = [\pi(P_2 - P_1)r^4]/8\eta L$, where η is the VISCOSITY, L the length of the flow segment separating point 1 and 2 with pressures: P_i at the respective cross sections, and r the radius of the tube used to measure the flow. The viscosity is primarily determined by determining the time is takes for a fixed volume to pass through a segment of uniform tube.

Viscosity model

[biomedical, fluid dynamics] In flow DYNAMICS, the following FLUID characteristics can be defined: Newtonian: $\tau_s = \eta\dot{\gamma}$. Alternatively, for NON-NEWTONIAN FLUIDS—expressing the viscosity as a power function: $\eta = C\dot{\gamma}^{n'-1}$. The non-Newtonian behavior can be described for many different models: Pseudoplastic: $\tau_s = K\dot{\gamma}^n$ power function: $(n < 1)$ $\{n' < 1\}$; Dilatant: $\tau = K\dot{\gamma}^n$ $(n > 1)$ $\{n' > 1\}$; Bingham: $\tau_s = \tau_\gamma + \eta\dot{\gamma}^n$; Casson: $\tau_s^{1/2} = \tau_0^{1/2} + \eta_c^{1/2}\dot{\gamma}^{1/2}$; Cross: the material stress σ_s is split for viscosity under low shear rate ($\dot{\gamma}$) η_0, or viscosity under high shear rate η_∞ as a power function (power n) as $\sigma_s = \dot{\gamma}\left(\eta_\infty + (\eta_0 - \eta_\infty)/(1 + m_{Cr}\dot{\gamma}^n)\right)$, m_{Cr} a model constant; Herschel–Bulkley: $\tau = \tau_\gamma + K\dot{\gamma}^n$; where τ_s is the shear stress, $\dot{\gamma}$ the shear rate, η the APPARENT VISCOSITY, K the consistency index for the medium, n is what may be best described as the "flow behavior index," the subscript: $_c$ indicates a critical value or threshold (see Figure V.35).

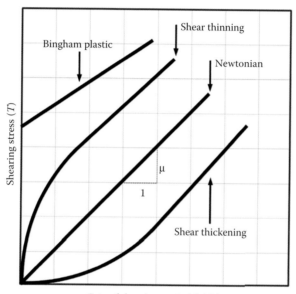

Figure V.35 Viscous models.

Viscosity of deformable spherical particles (η_{sph})

[fluid dynamics, general, nuclear] Spherical objects in SOLUTION that are forced into a spherical configuration by SURFACE TENSION will be compliant in contrast to rigid particles. The viscosity is defined by the FLUID viscosity of the droplets $\bar{\eta}$ and the material constant baseline Newtonian viscosity η_0 as $\eta_{sph} = \eta_0\left(1 + c_s\left[(1 + (5/2)(\bar{\eta}/\eta_0))/1 + (\bar{\eta}/\eta_0)\right]\right)$, which also shows that for rigid droplets the fluid viscosity of the droplet becomes infinite ($\bar{\eta} \to \infty$) and the INTRINSIC VISCOSITY becomes 5/2.

Viscous lubrication

V

[fluid dynamics] Flow BOUNDARY LAYER formed in close contact between a BUBBLE, red BLOOD CELL or solid object, and the WALL of the FLUID container.

Vision

[biomedical, chemical, optics] Conversion of electromagnetic RADIATION into electrical impulses by chemical conversion in the EYE. The eye is the anatomical component responsible for the electrochemical mechanism of vision. The electrical impulses are transmitted to the brain by neurons, which in turn generates a PERCEPTION with associated interpretation by the observer. In early Greek times the concept of EXTRAMISSION, postulated by EUCLID (c. 325–270 BC), PTOLEMY (90–168 AD), and PLATO (427–347 BC) in various versions, was used to describe vision. It was proposed that the eye supposedly emits radiation, which is returned by objects in its path back to the eye to be recognized as vision. Extramission, however, does not account for not being able to see when no external LIGHT is provided. Two kinds of vision are recognized based on the biological and anatomical features next to the chemical processes involved. The two types of vision are intensity (grayscale) and COLOR vision. Intensity vision is achieved by the anatomical feature of the RODS, whereas the color vision is achieved through the CONES. Human vision and vision of specific species can be very different due to the specific requirements in the daily routine. For instance, birds of prey have a segmented vision which relies on two components of the RETINA to act as low and high RESOLUTION vision as described under ABBE CONDITION. Vision in the mammalian and reptilian eye is primarily controlled by accommodation of the CRYSTALLINE LENS. In insects the vision has an entirely different compound structure, constructed of a multitude of fixed APERTURES arranged in a honeycomb structure, providing a similar structure as multiple CAMERA-OBSCURA projections (*also see* SCOTOPIC *and* PHOTOPIC VISION).

- Trichromat: sees using all three colors (red/green/blue)
- Color vision problems
- Anomalous trichromat: reception of one pigment is reduced or misaligned (anomalous)
- Dichromat: only two of the three visual pigments exist—red, green, or blue is missing
- Protanomaly: reduced red sensitivity in an anomalous trichromat
- Deuteranomaly: reduced green sensitivity in an anomalous trichromat
- Protanopia: unable to receive first visual pigment (RED)

- Deuteranopia: unable to receive second visual pigment (green)
- Tritanopia: unable to receive third visual pigment (blue) (see Figure V.36)

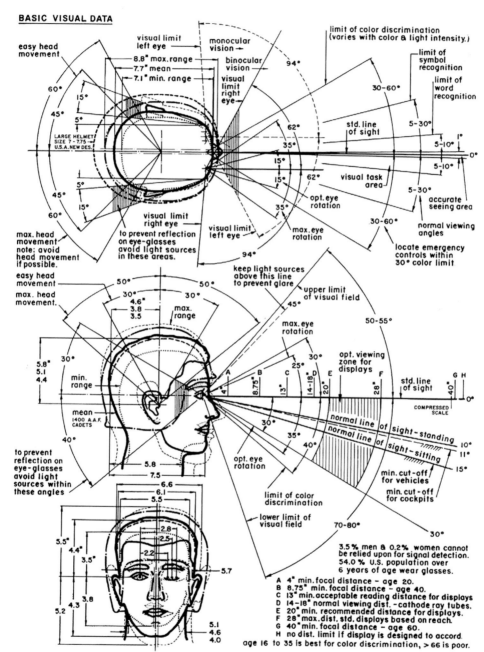

Figure V.36 Vision. (From Dreyfuss, H., *The Measure of Man; Human Factors in Design*, John Wiley & Sons, New York, 1959.)

Visual acuity

[biomedical, optics] The ability to see with high precision. One reference is with respect to the expression 20/20 vision for visual acuity. The statement 20/20 vision represents the ability to distinguish objects at a DISTANCE of 20 ft, set as the standard in the United States. Any deviations are expressed with different numbers; for instance, 20/100 vision reflect the fact that this person can see at 20 ft distance what a person with standard VISION can see at 100 ft distance. The statement 20/20 vision is no indication of perfect vision, just an indication of clarity; while vision clarity as high as 20/10 is possible for a normal person. An international standard for visual acuity is obtained with a reading chart, the Snellen chart (see Figure V.37).

Figure V.37 Vision acuity scale. As set as standards by the International Council on Ophthalmology in 1984.

Vital capacity (VC)

[biomedical, fluid dynamics] The maximum potentially exhaled volume of gas from the lungs after the lungs are filled to TOTAL LUNG CAPACITY (TLC) during inspiration. Vital capacity and other TIDAL BREATHING parameter can be measured with a spirometer (*see* RESPIRATION).

Vitreous humor

[biomedical, optics] Gel-like substance between the backside of the CRYSTALLINE LENS and the RETINA in the HUMAN EYE. The vitreous humor has an index of refraction of $n_{\text{vitreous humor}} = 1.337$, keeping in mind that water has $n_{\text{H}_2\text{O}} = 1.331$, and AIR $n_{\text{air}} = 1.0001$. The vitreous humor also has a designated canal within the gel that leads a confined path with a lower index of refraction directly to the FOVEA, the area of the retina with the highest density of RODS and CONES for high-resolution COLOR and brightness VISION (see Figure V.38).

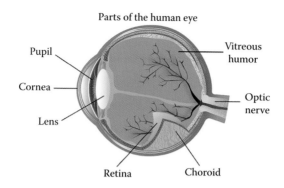

Figure V.38 Vitreous humor.

Voice

[biomedical, general] SOUND generated by the vocal cord of humans. Several factors determine the frequency content of the spoken sounds, specifically the difference between male and female voice spectrum is generally recognized, but is not defined absolute. A adult male bass voice can have an approximate frequency range from 65 to 400 Hz (starting at a "low-C" note), where an alto voice roughly ranges from 200 to 70 Hz, and a soprano spans in the range 261 to 1047 Hz ranging to a "high-C;" respectively for a female 261 to 1280 Hz. The adult female voice for general speech ranges generally from 165 to 255 Hz, while a female scream can reach 3000 Hz; whereas the male conversational voice is on average in the spectrum 85 to 155 Hz. Children may reach higher tones, up to 3500 Hz (see Figure V.39).

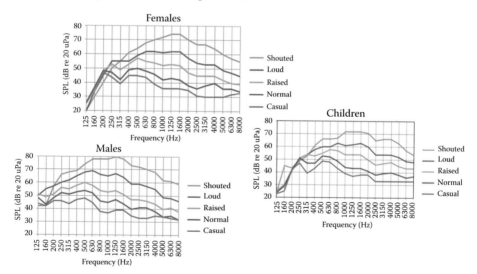

Figure V.39 Voice, as generated by the larynx, representative average spectral profile for man, woman, and child. (Courtesy of DPA Microphones, Alleroed, Denmark.)

Volcano

[acoustic, astrophysics, chemistry, electromagnetism, fluid dynamics, geophysics, mechanics, solid-state, thermodynamics] The study of the physical phenomena at the planet's surface due to eruption from the magma contained in the ASTHENOSPHERE when penetrating the lithospheric plates (see Figure V.40).

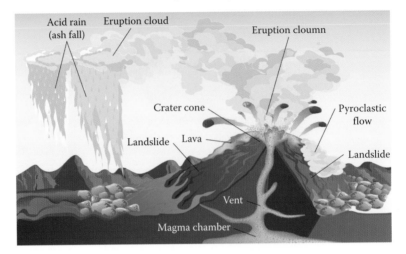

Figure V.40 Volcano; the erupting magma is hot enough to emit visible light under the Planck black-body radiation.

Volta, Alessandro Giuseppe Antonio Anastasio Gerolamo Umberto, Count (1745–1827)

[biomedical, electronics, energy, general] Italian scientist with a focus on PHYSICS, whose work was instrumental in the development of the BATTERY as well as the understanding of capacitance. Alessandro Volta was awarded the title Count by the Emperor Napoléon Bonaparte (1769–1821) in 1801 for his scientific contributions. Volta and his contemporary LUIGI GALVANI (1737–1789) had a close collaboration that formed the basis of several electrostatic and electrical current discoveries. Galvani was the inspiration to the formulation (1780) of the battery concept by Conte Alessandro Volta, as revealed in 1800 (see Figure V.41).

Figure V.41 Count Alessandro Giuseppe Antonio Anastasio Gerolamo Umberto Volta (1745–1827).

Voltage (V)

[electronics, general] Parameter used to define the electrical potential. Voltage is the electrical potential ENERGY per unit charge. Voltage difference between two POINT CHARGES is the electric field between the two locations multiplied by the separation of the two charges, expressed in units volt (V). The voltage between point A and point B is also equal to the work performed on an ELECTRIC CHARGE to move it from point A to point B, per unit charge (V_{AB}).

Voltaic pile

[general] Stack of alternating media designed by ALESSANDRA VOLTA (1745–1827) that provides a potential difference between the opposite ends of the stack. The pile was created out of disks made of zinc cardboard, silver and cardboard (i.e., cells), repeated (see Figure V.42).

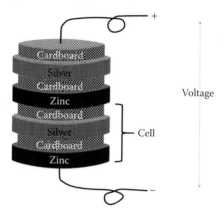

Figure V.42 Voltaic pile.

Voltaire

[general] Pseudonym of the writer and scientific activist from France: FRANÇOIS-MARIE D'AROUET (1694–1778). Voltaire used science to arouse the public awareness and to guard people against the unfounded tales of natural phenomena, specifically his fight against superstition. Although not a scientist himself, he used science to raise the standards of analytical thinking (see Figure V.43).

Figure V.43 Voltaire; François-Marie d'Arouet (1694–1778).

V

Voltmeter

[electromagnetism, general] Galvanometer in series with a resister with the primary purpose of measuring the electrical potential between two points. The RESISTANCE is chosen to provide the idealized conditions of zero current, in order to prevent influencing the charge storage on the device being measured for voltage difference. Generally, the voltmeter is integrated in a multifunctional device that can measure current, voltage, and resistance called a multimeter (see Figure V.44).

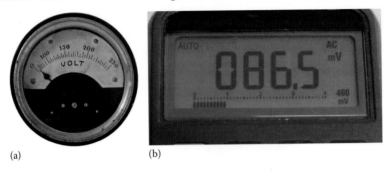

(a)   (b)

Figure V.44 Voltmeter: (a) analog and (b) digital.

Volume (V)

[general] Parameter with the primary meaning as the indication of three-dimensional containment. Reservoir with specific size, expressed in liter, m^3 in SI UNITS, or in gallon or FLUID ounces in the obsolete English (Imperial) unit system. Alternatively, the volume of SOUND is an indication of the AMPLITUDE of the acoustic WAVE, used for QUANTIFICATION of listing to audio (see Figure V.45).

Figure V.45 Volume measurement with calibrated flasks and beakers.

Volume charge density (ρ_e)

[general] The total charge ($Q = \sum q$) in a volume of medium divided by the respective volume (V): $\rho_e = Q/V$. In contrast, the charge can be spread over the surface of a medium, specifically a plate, but also for a CONDUCTOR all charge will be concentrated on the surface. The charge spread over a surface is expressed by surface density, respectively: σ_e. On a wire the charge density will be a line-charge density (one-dimensional), expressed as λ_e.

Von Fraunhofer, Joseph (1787–1826)

[optics] Scientist and physicist from the Prussian Empire (Germany) that was influential in optical discoveries. Joseph was born into a family of glassmakers, which led him to work on LENS development, making very accurate and proficient achromatic lenses. Based on his interests in OPTICS, Von Fraunhofer discovered the ATOMIC EMISSION SPECTRUM for the SUN in 1814, separating out more than 574 lines. Additional work by Fraunhofer was in the experimental and theoretical work on the diffraction from multiple thin slits, using closely spaced wires; DIFFRACTION GRATING. Josef von Fraunhofer is frequently referred to as "Fraunhofer." (see Figure V.46)

Figure V.46 Joseph von Fraunhofer (1787–1826).

Von Guericke, Otto (1602–1682)

[astronomy, general] Scientist, physicist, and engineer from Germany (Prussian Empire). The first static electricity charge generator was developed by Otto von Guericke in 1650. Additional work by Von Guericke was in. The VACUUM work by Von Guericke was performed on a system referred to as the Magdeburg hemispheres, two copper hemispheres with flanges attached on respective tips of the dome, and an outlet VALVE to provide the means to evacuate the dome. The flanges gave the hold to apply tensile force on both hemispheres. Von Guericke provided the foundation for modern METEOROLOGY, and worked on

ELECTROSTATICS as well. His electrostatic efforts provided one of the first documented devices to generate a substantial electrostatic charge (see Figure V.47).

Figure V.47 Otto Von Guericke (1602–1682), engraving after a portrait by Anselm van Hulle.

Von Helmholtz, Hermann Ludwig Ferdinand (1821–1894)

[biomedical, electrodynamics, energy, mathematics, thermodynamics] Physicist and mathematician from the Prussian Empire (Germany) (*see* **HELMHOLTZ, HERMANN LUDWIG FERDINAND VON**) (see Figure V.48).

Figure V.48 Hermann Ludwig Ferdinand von Helmholtz (1821–1894).

Von Kármán, Tódor (Theodore) (1881–1963)

[astrophysics, fluid dynamics] Physicist and mathematician from Hungary. Theodore von Kármán contributed to the theoretical description of vortices and TURBULENCE, next to his work in aerospace ENGINEERING. Von Kármán designed one of the first functioning helicopters in the early 1920s. Later in his career Von Kármán provided guidance to the design and development of rockets, guided missiles, and PROPULSION jets for fighter planes. Von Kármán's work in FLUID DYNAMICS has made significant contributions to the understanding of boundary layers and turbulence phenomena; specifically the "KÁRMÁN VORTEX STREET" description (see Figure V.49).

Figure V.49 Theodore von Kármán (1881–1963). (Courtesy of United States Army, United States Army Scientific Advisory Board, Washington, DC, USA.)

Von Kármán vortex street

[fluid dynamics, general] *See* **KÁRMÁN EDDY CURRENT VORTEX STREET.** It is also known as "Kármán vortex street." (see Figure V.50)

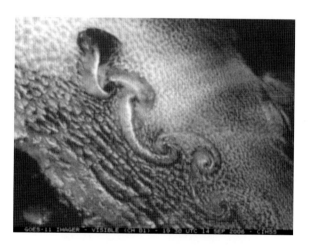

Figure V.50 Satellite image of von Kármán vortex street in the cloud cover, downwind from Guadalupe Island. (The Guadalupe island is located off the west coast of Baja, California). (Courtesy of University of Wisconsin, Madison, WI.)

Von Kleist, Ewald Jurgens (1700–1748)

[energy, general] Administrative clerk and engineer from Prussia (former greater German Empire) who discovered the mechanism of storing charge in a jar with LIQUID, the LEYDEN JAR. The charge storage was performed during his studies in Leiden (old Dutch vernacular: "Leyden"), hence the name (see Figure V.51).

Figure V.51 Ewald Jurgens von Kleist (1700–1748).

Von Laue, Max Theodor Felix (1879–1960)

[computational, electromagnetism, nuclear] Physicist from Germany. Max von Laue received the Nobel Prize in Physics for his X-RAY diffraction work (performed in 1912), and the ensuing understanding of crystal and LATTICE structure of atomic and molecular configurations. The lattice structure theory was supported by contributions from Sir WILLIAM LAWRENCE BRAGG (1890–1971) in 1913. Von Laue worked on crystallography, OPTICS, relativity, SUPERCONDUCTIVITY, and QUANTUM THEORY (see Figure V.52).

Figure V.52 Max Theodor Felix von Laue (1879–1960). (Courtesy of German Federal Archive [Deutsches Bundesarchiv], Koblenz, Germany.)

Von Laue's method

[computational, nuclear] Mathematical method based on the work of MAX THEODOR FELIX VON LAUE (1879–1960) describing electron and NEUTRON diffraction on atomic level, revealing the atomic and LATTICE structure of crystals and slid-state configurations. The Laue method provides a lattice description based on observations. The Laue method is based on the Miller index for lattice planes, using the lattice vector $(\vec{b})$, describing the plane spacing and orientation for the various lattice p-lanes, and the correlation with the respective LATTICE SPACING distance d_i, defined as $d_i = 1/|\vec{b}|$. The refraction of X-rays in a crystal is described by the Laue equation (based on the Bragg's law), in one dimension as $(AB - CD) = a\{\cos(\alpha_n - \cos\alpha_0)\} = n_x\lambda$, where λ is the wavelength of the probing RADIATION. The diffraction pattern of the crystal resulting from exposure to a collimated narrow the X-RAY beam produced a pattern of spots which were supposedly correlated to the internal symmetry of the crystal; which was experimentally and theoretically confirmed (see Figure V.53).

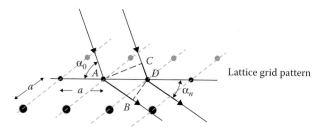

Figure V.53 Von Laue method diagram of action.

Von Leibniz, Gottfried Wilhelm

[general] *See* **LEIBNIZ, GOTTFRIED WILHELM VON.**

Von Lenard, Philipp Eduard Anton (Lénárd Fülöp Philipp Eduard Anton von Lenard) (1862–1947)

[atomic, nuclear] Scientist from Slovakia/Austria-Hungary, now Germany. Von Lenard's work revealed important details about the "cathode ray." Other work was with respect to the MECHANICS, that is, oscillations, of precipitated water droplets. His interests in PHOSPHORESCENCE and luminescence led him to artificially generate RADIATION. Lenard was able to generate LUMINESCENCE using a CATHODE ray in a VACUUM tube lined with aluminum, his discovery of the "Lenard window." (see Figure V.54)

Figure V.54 Philipp Eduard Anton von Lenard (1862–1947), approximately in 1900. (Courtesy of VendégVáró archív, http://lexikon.vendegvaro.utazom.com/lenard-fulop-philipp-e-a-von-lenard.)

Von Mayer, Julius Robert (1814–1878)

[general, thermodynamics] Physicist, physician, and engineer from Prussia (Germany), one of the founding fathers of THERMODYNAMICS. Von Mayer described the law of the CONSERVATION OF ENERGY (the FIRST LAW OF THERMODYNAMICS), and formulated the vital chemical process as the primary source of ENERGY for any living creature as OXIDATION, both in 1842. Von Mayer also proposed the rudimentary concept of PHOTOSYNTHESIS. His conservation of energy statement was largely overlooked and is mainly attributed to JAMES JOULE (1818–1889) who made his proclamation 1 year after Julius von Mayer (see Figure V.55).

Figure V.55 Julius Robert von Mayer (1814–1878).

Vortex

[computational, fluid dynamics, mechanics, thermodynamics] Conglomeration of particles involved in rotational motion, primarily relating to fluids. A detailed theoretical description of the velocity DISPERSION

in rotational MOTION of a LIQUID was first provided by HERMAN VON HELMHOLTZ (1821–1894). Due to the complex three-dimensional velocity profile Helmholtz-introduced velocity profiles with respect to the axis of rotation (i.e., vortex line) as the following directional gradient components of the vorticity:
$\xi_V = (\partial w/\partial y) - (\partial v/\partial z)$; $\eta_V = (\partial u/\partial z) - (\partial w/\partial x)$; $\zeta_V = (\partial v/\partial x) - (\partial u/\partial y)$, in CARTESIAN COORDINATES $u = -(\partial\phi/\partial x)$ is the velocity in the x-direction, $v = -(\partial\phi/\partial y)$ is the velocity in the y-direction, and $w = -(\partial\phi/\partial z)$ is the velocity in the z-direction, with ϕ is the VELOCITY POTENTIAL. The vortex line is defined as $(\partial x/\partial\xi_V) = (\partial y/\partial\eta_V) = (\partial x/\partial\zeta_V)$. In general, the rotation motion of a FLUID can be derived by solving: $(P/\rho) + (1/2)q_*^2 + E_V = (\partial\phi/\partial t) + F_V(t)$, where P is the local pressure on a streamline, ρ the fluid density, the resultant velocity in the vortex is defined by $q_* = \sqrt{u^2 + v^2 + w^2}$, $E_V = -\int P\,d(1/\rho)$ is the work performed by a unit of fluid mass in response to the external pressure, and $F_V(t)$ is a time function (t) describing the rotational characteristics. More accurately the vector potential with respect to two moving particles A and B along the streamline can be derived from: $\left[\int\left((P/\rho) + \Omega - (1/2)q_*^2\right)\right]_A^B = -(D/Dt)\int_A^B\left(udx + vdy + wdz\right)$, where Ω is the force potential resulting from all external forces involved in the movement of the particles in the vortex with potential ENERGY: $PE = \iiint\Omega\rho\,dx\,dy\,dz$. Since the velocity potential is tied to the kinetic energy the velocity potential can be linked to the force potential as $(P/\rho) = (\partial\phi/\partial t) - \Omega - (1/2)q_*^2 + F_V(t)$. The velocity field distribution: $\vec{v}(\vec{r_P})$ (i.e., vector potential) in the vortex can be derived based on the VORTICITY ($\vec{\varpi}$) as $\vec{v}(\vec{r_P}) = 1/4\pi\int_V(\vec{\varpi}(\vec{Q},t) \times \vec{r_{PQ}})/r_{PQ}^3\,dV_Q$, where $\vec{P}$ and $\vec{Q}$ are positions on the axis or rotation and at the revolution trajectory in the plane of interest and $\vec{r_{PQ}} = \vec{r_P} - \vec{r_Q}$, respectively. Using the vorticity $\left(\varpi(\vec{r},t)\right)$, the linear impulse ($I$) and angular impulse ($\mathbb{A}$) of a vortex within a VOLUME (V) at location $\vec{r}$ can be defined as follows: $I = (1/2)\rho\int_V\vec{r} \times \vec{\varpi}(\vec{r},t)dV$, and $\mathbb{A} = -(1/2)\rho\int_V\vec{r}^2\vec{\varpi}(\vec{r},t)dV$, where ρ is the local density of the INCOMPRESSIBLE FLUID with no viscosity (i.e., inviscid) (see Figure V.56).

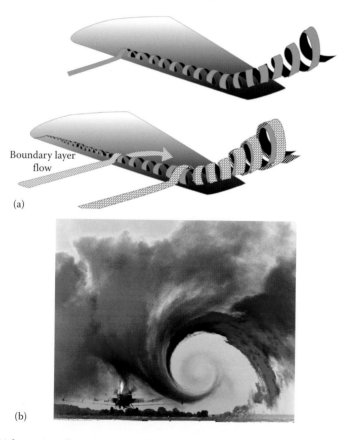

(a)

Boundary layer flow

(b)

Figure V.56 Vortex: (a) formation of vortex on wing tip and (b) vortex behind wing of plane landing. (Courtesy of NASA Langley Research Center, Hampton, VA.)

V

Vortex, Kármán

[fluid dynamics] *See* **KÁRMÁN EDDY CURRENT VORTEX STREET.**

Vortex shedding

[computational, fluid dynamics, mechanics, thermodynamics] During the flow around a bluff body a KÁRMÁN VORTEX street is formed which has a pattern of flow that detaches from different locations on the circumference of the body to form a VORTEX pattern in the WAKE of the body. This detachment (shedding) occurs at a characteristic frequency. The shedding frequency is characterized by flow conditions and geometry. For a cylindrical object with flow condition defined by a Keulegan–Carpenter number equal to or greater than 20 ($K_C \geq 20$; *Note*: in this range the REYNOLDS NUMBER is relatively constant), the vortex-shedding frequency can be defined. This range categorizes QUASI-STEADY-STATE shedding conditions. For $K_C < 20$ the flow has fractional vortex shedding which does not allow for a steady frequency pattern to develop. The vortex-shedding frequency for $K_C \geq 20$ can be defined as $v_V = Sr(U_o/D)$, where Sr is the STROUHAL NUMBER (accounting for the SURFACE ROUGHNESS of the cylindrical object, e.g., PIPE), U_o the instantaneous flow velocity, and D the diameter of the cylindrical object in the flow path. In the case of flow around a prolate spheroid the unsteady Navier–Stokes equation for incompressible flow at a function of TIME (t) will need to be solved: $\nabla \cdot u = 0$ and $(\partial u/\partial t) + u \cdot \nabla u = -\nabla P + (1/Re_\infty)\nabla^2 u$, where ∇ is the Laplace operator, u is the flow velocity, P the pressure, Re_∞ the Reynolds number based on the free-stream flow velocity u_∞, and d the diameter of the sphere. This spheroid vortex shedding frequency SOLUTION can only be obtained by NUMERICAL analysis.

Vorticity ($\vec{\omega}$)

[fluid dynamics] The degree of "rotation" experienced in flow VELOCITY ($\vec{v}$) as a function of location ($\vec{r}$) and TIME (t) expressed as $\vec{\omega}(\vec{r},t) = \nabla \times \vec{v}(\vec{r},t)$, which is the "curl" of the velocity at a given place (i.e., vector operator performing the rotation in infinitesimal steps of a three-dimensional vector field; curl: operator defining the rotation of the vector in infinitesimal steps, hence describing the projection of the vector upon all possible lines passing through the location in the three-dimensional space). The vorticity defines the CIRCULATION density derived from the flow velocity vector field. For an inviscid FLUID the rate of change in time for the VORTEX is described as $[d\vec{\omega}(\vec{r},t)/dt] = \vec{\omega}(\vec{r},t) \cdot \nabla \vec{v}(\vec{r},t) + \nabla \times \vec{F}$, where $\vec{F}$ is the externally applied force density.

Voxel

[computational, fluid dynamics, imaging] Three-dimensional configuration with unique and uniform parameters and characteristics. This is the three-dimensional equivalent of the two-dimensional PIXEL in IMAGE reconstruction. The voxel is an ELEMENT in finite element analysis, used in computer simulations (e.g., Monte Carlo, finite element), image reconstruction and geometric deconvolution of real-time events in well-defined compartments. The three-dimensional representation of PET, computed-tomography, ULTRASOUND and other imaging techniques uses voxels as the smallest unique geometric unit in the visualization rendering process (see Figure V.57).

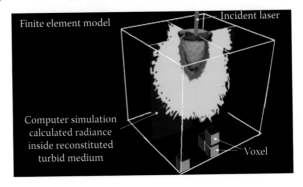

Figure V.57 Voxel.

V(z) inversion

[acoustics, imaging] SIGNAL processing technique used in acoustic microscope that allows for the extraction of material properties based on the power of the signal as a function of the location (position: "z;" the focal position) of the collection LENS. The spectral profile of the power profile of the acoustic imaging provides the means to derive the Young's modulus. The v-curve is a graphical deduction from the power losses per phase in a vector analysis of the Rayleigh wave velocities. The v-inversion extracts the material properties based on v-curves and applying PERTURBATION THEORY to the representation.

Wake

[fluid dynamics] Vortices where the BOUNDARY LAYER of a flow detaches from the fixed surface. This phenomenon is more pronounced when the flow separates around the back side of a symmetric body totally submerged, reducing it to a two-dimensional flow such as a symmetric round pillar or a stick sunken into a solid foundation. This process becomes increasingly noticeable with an ascending REYNOLDS NUMBER, separation at the 180° point starts in the approximate range $2 < Re < 30$, depending on the boundary conditions. When the Reynolds number comes in the range $10^2 < Re < 10^5$, separation occurs before the midway point of the bluff rounded object, mainly before the 80° angle on the curved surface of the rod, measured from the centerline with the rod. This detachment generates KÁRMÁN EDDY CURRENT vortices (see Figure W.1).

Figure W.1 Wake.

Walecka, John Dirk (1932–)

[nuclear, quantum] Nuclear physicist from the United States. Walecka is known for his work on QUANTUM THEORY, specifically for many particles. John Walecka led the electron accelerator research at CEBAF (Continuous Electron Beam Accelerator Facility in Newport News), Virginia (see Figure W.2).

Figure W.2 John Dirk Walecka (1932–). (Courtesy of Jefferson Lab, Newport News, VA; the U.S. Department of Energy's Thomas Jefferson National Accelerator Facility; U.S. Department of Energy; College of William and Mary, Williamsburg, VA.)

Wall

[biomedical, fluid dynamics, general, mechanics] Solid structure, mechanical separating structure, specifically with respect to objects or fluids in MOTION. The wall of a flow system determines the flow boundary conditions and flow-separation parameters. In biological context, a wall can have COMPLIANCE, such as the arterial wall, which stretches to accommodate the periodic in-flow with a high down-stream impedance (i.e., the vessel wall). The biological wall is different from many structural or industrial wall structures in the fact that it also provides a mechanism for osmotic DIFFUSION through the wall, well known as the diffusion of oxygen and carbon dioxide in the alveolar wall and the CAPILLARY wall of the lung organ structure. Generally walls are rigid and are designed mechanically to perform a specific function with thresholds for stability and durability. The wall of a confinement for a hydroelectric plant can burst when the security thresholds set as acceptable limits under design are exceeded. PIPE walls are generally made with metallic or POLYMER compounds, which can DECAY in strength over time and require frequent quality control inspections to identify hairline cracks, which may propagate and generate conditions where the pipe may break. The process of crack propagation is an elaborate and complex procedure (see Figure W.3).

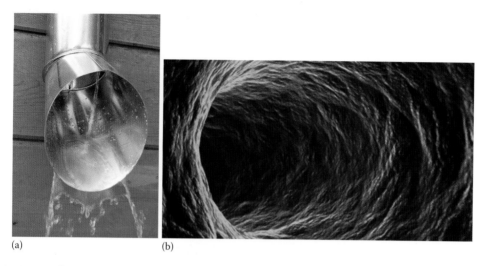

(a)   (b)

Figure W.3 (a) Wall, rigid drain pipe and compliant blood vessel (b) with an uneven surface structure.

Wall attachment phenomenon

[fluid dynamics] Fluid flow in close proximity to a WALL will form a BOUNDARY LAYER where the FLUID may attach to the wall and form a thin boundary layer in which there is no flow, that is, flow velocity is zero. The boundary layer can effectively generate the conditions to sustain the flow of the fluid with minimal friction (viscosity effects). Flow bordering a wall can result in detachment that results in turbulent pocket formation (the Coandă effect). Under Navier–Stokes dominated flow conditions, a boundary layer is formed with a thickness that is a function of the flow velocity (v) and the time constant (t') associated with the flow (respectively, periodic or continuous), defined as $\delta_b = \sqrt{vt'}$. At a low REYNOLDS NUMBER ($Re < 1$), the flow will not separate due to superior viscous behavior over inertial effects, maintaining a LAMINAR FLOW around an object. Certain sports ball designs use SURFACE ROUGHNESS to influence the boundary layer behavior and promote an early transition from a laminar to a turbulent flow. These ball games rely on operating in a Reynolds number range that is near the "minimum" of the "DRAG COEFFICIENT" ($C_d = F_d/(1/2)\rho v^2 A$, where F_d is the FRICTION of flow, the drag force, ρ density, and A the contact surface area) versus Reynolds number (Re) curve. Under these conditions, the drag will be lowest (*also see* BOUNDARY LAYER) (see Figure W.4).

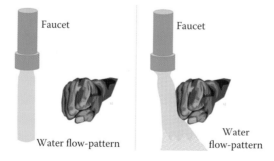

Faucet   Faucet

Water flow-pattern   Water flow-pattern

Figure W.4 Wall attachment phenomenon.

W

Wall factor 1 ($K_2 = 2(d_{PV}/D_C)$)

[fluid dynamics] Ratio of the sphere diameter to the column diameter for a ball falling down a LIQUID column, where d_{PV} is the sphere diameter equivalent to the PARTICLE volume, and D_C column diameter (see Figure W.5).

Figure W.5 Outline of the concept of Wall factor.

Wall factor 2 ($K_3 = (d_{PV}/D_C)(Z/D_C)$)

[fluid dynamics] Ratio of the sphere diameter to the column diameter for a ball falling down a LIQUID column multiplied by the relative SURFACE ROUGHNESS expressed as the size of the sediment (the bed height Z) over the flow diameter, where d_{PV} is the sphere diameter equivalent with the PARTICLE volume, and D_C is column diameter.

Wallis, John (1616–1703)

[general] Mathematician from Great Britain, involved in the scientific analysis of collisions. Wallis has one of the first documented applications of conservation of momentum, published in 1663. John Wallis formulated a method to solve for spatial indivisibles by means of interpolation (see Figure W.6).

W

Figure W.6 John Wallis (1616–1703) painted by Sir Godfrey Kneller. (Courtesy of The Wallis Project, University of Oxford, UK.)

Wall-tracing method

[fluid dynamics] Mechanism for visualization in close proximity to the WALL of flow, either by tufts or release of dye or BUBBLES. The wall-tracing method yields insights into attachment and detachment of flow at the BOUNDARY LAYER, flow velocity direction, and transition layers. One of several mechanism available to visualize flow patterns. Other techniques available are smoke lines, BIREFRINGENCE, wall tufts, bubble, dye, surface powder, schlieren, and PARTICLE suspension (equal density to the FLUID). These methods can elucidate four concepts: (1) streamlines, (2) timelines, (3) pathlines, and (4) streaklines. Streamlines are indicators of the flow-velocity vector, tangent to the flow direction. Timelines provide an instantaneous snapshot of the flow pattern of the mechanism used for visualization. Pathlines follow individual particles over a specific time interval. Streaklines yield information about a range of identifying units for a locus (single point) in the flow over a specific interval of time. The flow visualization techniques can be classified based on the mechanism of action as optical (Schlieren, shadow, birefringence, etc.), marker (SOLUTE, bubble, etc.), or mechanical (tufts, surface release, etc.) (see Figure W.7).

Figure W.7 Wall-tracing method for fluid flow.

Walton, Ernest Thomas Sinton (1903–1995)

[atomic, nuclear] Scientist from Ireland, primarily known for his work on PARTICLE ACCELERATOR technology to enhance the efficacy of nuclear interactions (the Cockcroft–Walton accelerator). The work of Ernest Walton was different from the earlier efforts by ERNEST RUTHERFORD (1871–1937) using helium ions (ALPHA PARTICLES) and were based on PROTON interaction under an applied force resulting from an external electric field in 1932. Ernest Walton and the British physicist John Cockcroft (1897–1967) received in 1951 the Nobel Prize in Physics for their combined effort on the particle accelerator (see Figure W.8).

Figure W.8 Ernest Thomas Sinton Walton (1903–1995).

Water (H₂O)

[biomedical, chemical, fluid dynamics, general] CHEMICAL COMPOUND consisting of hydrogen and oxygen in a two to one ratio, joined by covalent bonds. The water molecule is shaped in the form of a V, but spread out at an ANGLE between the O–H bonds of approximately 104.5°. The "lob-sided" configuration provides the platform for the polarity of the water MOLECULE. Water is one of the most abundant substances on the EARTH, covering more than 70% of the earth's surface area. Water is an essential medium to sustain biological life-forms, the HUMAN BODY for instance consists of approximately 59% of water. The constituents of water form one of the many options in the fuel-cell technology. Water forms the LIQUID phase of H_2O; alternatively ice is the solid phase and water VAPOR (steam) provides the GAS PHASE. Water forms the base for several scientific definitions of material properties. The SPECIFIC HEAT of water at standard pressure and temperature is $h_v = 1$ cal/g°C (old units, but illustrating the historical value). The density of water under standard conditions is $\rho = 1$ kg/L $= 1$ g/cm^3. Note that water has the highest density at 4°C. The "acidity" of water has a PH of 7, on a scale ranging from 0 to 14; considered neutral. A pH lower than 7 indicates ACID (acidic) and a higher pH is "alkali" or base. Water has formed the foundation for the temperature scale in Celsius and Fahrenheit. On the CELSIUS SCALE, the FREEZING point yielding 0 (0°C), and the boiling point providing the landmark 100 (100°C) on the scale, as introduced by the Swedish scientist ANDERS CELSIUS (1701–1744) in 1742. The Celsius scale is the most widely used temperature scale, in comparison to the Fahrenheit scale devised by the Polish (Prussian) scientist GABRIEL DANIEL FAHRENHEIT (1686–1736) in 1724 based on the MELTING POINT of a mixture of ice, water, and ammonium chloride SALT (brine) at 0°F, versus the human body temperature (his wife's oral temperature) as the second calibration point, providing 96°F at the time of the recordings (the Fahrenheit scale originally had a 12 base, hence 96 as the body temperature, later adjusted for accuracy and on a decimal scale; currently the average human body temperature is set at 98.6°F). The Fahrenheit scale is primarily used only in the United States, whereas the rest of the world uses the Celsius scale for household and medical use. The Kelvin scale is technically the standard for temperature, as devised by the Scottish (British) scientist Sir William Thomson, Lord Kelvin (1824–1907) in 1854, which is not based on water (see Figure W.9).

Figure W.9 Water.

Water clock

[fluid dynamics] Next to the sun dial, one of the oldest methods for measuring time. The water clock was first described based on historic finds dating back to the sixteenth century BC, whereas there are claims of Chinese water clocks as far back as 4000 BC. The Babylonian (city of Babylon; now part of Iraq [cultural and scientific center of Mesopotamia]), and later Greek, water clock was based on a set of bowls with fixed orifice regulating the outflow rate (see Figure W.10).

Figure W.10 Modern day equivalent of the ancient water clock concept.

W

Water hammer

[fluid dynamics] Hydraulic shock produced when the flow of a liquid (GAS or fluid) is suddenly inter-rupted. The phenomenon was first described by Lorenzo Allievi. In water VAPOR flow, the condensation of steam due to EXPANSION and the resulting cooling can remain in flow but the increased density will carry additional momentum that will be released in another form of ENERGY when impacting a WALL of the tube system (curve, flange or valve). This phenomenon can be solved in two different ways, as an INCOM-PRESSIBLE FLUID, or as a compressible fluid. When the kinetic event is gradual (e.g., slow valve closure), the FLUID may be considered as incompressible with the maximum pressure (P_{max}) in the fluid-filled tube using the rigid column theory: $F_{hammer} = AP_{max} = A\big((v_f L/t) + P_i\big)$, where P_i is the inlet pressure, v_f is the flow velocity, t is the VALVE closing time in seconds, and L is the PIPE length leading up to the event. Note that A is the area of the obstruction. Any sudden/instantaneous change in flow conditions or abrupt closure of the valve will incorporate the compressibility of the medium in flow primarily with respect to the role of the WAVE speed propagation. The force exerted by the fluid compartment in free flow is calculated by the JOUKOWSKY EQUATION, where the change in force yields: $\Delta F = (dP/dt)A_{surface} = \rho v_w (dv_f/dt)A_{surface}$, where v_w is the SPEED OF WAVE PROPAGATION in the fluid, ρ the density of the fluid, and v_f the velocity of flow on closure or impact on the surface area $A_{surface}$ that equals the maximum force exerted since the impact force is initially zero (open) (see Figure W.11).

Figure W.11 Water hammer as the mechanism of action in a pressure–washer system.

Water reactor

[nuclear, thermodynamics] Modern NUCLEAR REACTOR with ordinary water as the MODERATOR under pres-surized conditions. A separate CIRCULATION system with a LIQUID coolant transfers the ENERGY generated by the FISSION process to a third system that powers a steam TURBINE electrical GENERATOR (*see* NUCLEAR REACTOR).

Water wave

[electronics, general, mechanics] Water waves are generated because of the fact that the surface is disturbed by the shear stress force resulting from the wind with a component perpendicular to the normal to the water surface. There is a minimum wind speed of $v \geq 1.1$ m/s that needs to be exceeded to affect the surface. The flow of AIR over the water surface creates pressure gradients based on the Bernoulli principles that cause the surface to break out and allow the parallel component of the wind to apply a force directly on the protruding ripples. Under uniform and continuous exposure over a significant area of water surface, the height of the surface elevation departing from equilibrium (h_S) will develop a FREQUENCY (ν) spectrum profile that is primarily a function of the wind velocity, expressed as $h_S(\nu) = A_w (g^2/\nu^5)\exp\left(-1.25[\nu_m/\nu]^4\right)$, where $A_w = 5.2 \times 10^{-6}$ is a constant, $\nu_m = 0.13\, g/U_w$ is the frequency of the central peak of the spectrum, with U_w the wind velocity at 10 m above the water surface, and g the GRAVITATION acceleration. The length of the surface area minimally subjected to the surface wind shear stress is referred to as the fetch. Near the coast line with a wind blowing off-shore the fetch is limited, and both the constant (A_w) and central peak frequency (ν_m) become a function of the fetch. Due to the viscosity of the water, there is a nonlinearity in propagation (specifically nonlinear acceleration) where the short waves are damped more dramatically than long waves, resulting in long propagation distances for low-frequency waves, that is, swells (e.g., $\nu \sim 0.10$ Hz yields undisturbed waves over thousands of kilometers with little loss of ENERGY). Waves propagating in the opposite direction of a local water current will concurrently grow in height. Due to various conditions, the waves generated in one direction will not necessarily remain confined and generally will spread out angularly over the surface (θ, with respect to the original path of the wind or the primary WAVE direction) similar to a Lambertian angular distribution of LIGHT emitted from a surface approximated by the following mathematical formulation: $h_S(\nu,\theta) = h_S(\nu)(2/\pi)\cos^2\theta; \theta \le (\pi/2)$ and $h_S(\nu,\theta) = 0; \theta > (\pi/2)$ (*see* TROCHOIDAL WAVE; *also see* SURFACE WAVE, CAPILLARY WAVES, SURFACE WAVES, TIDAL WAVES, *and* WAVE) (see Figure W.12).

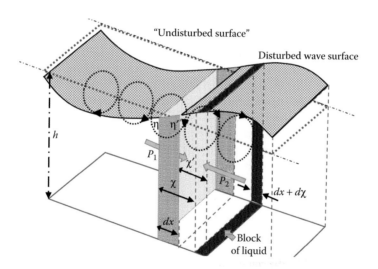

Figure W.12 Water wave.

Water wheel, power

[fluid dynamics] Consider a centrifugal blade-pump. The TORQUE (T) applied to the scoops is directly proportional to the force resulting from the FLUID between sections A_1 and A_2, expressed as $T = m\left(r_2 v_2 \cos\alpha_2 - r_1 v_1 \cos\alpha_1\right)$, where α_i is the ANGLE with the reference frame with regard to the absolute velocity vectors u_1 and u_2 respectively, r_i the respective radii at the inner (1) and outer (2) area of the scoop with mass flow rate m along the blade. In this way, the torque on the impeller shaft can be derived from the states of

W

the fluids, respectively the velocities on the inlet and the outlet relative to the impeller. Combining the ANGULAR VELOCITY (ω) of the impeller with the torque yields the POWER (P) to the shaft as $P = T\omega$ (see Figure W.13).

(a)   (b)

Figure W.13 (a) Water wheel; water wheel used to generate power, and water wheel as a mechanism of propulsion in the shape of a river boat paddle wheel (b).

Waterspout

[fluid dynamics, geophysics, meteorology] Updraft of water from a large water reservoir (lake, ocean), under an ATMOSPHERIC PRESSURE vortex. The pressure VORTEX is the result of the merging of two or more atmospheric pressure systems, generating a relatively small, confined rotational flow of AIR (air flowing from high- to low-pressure systems). The greatest ACTIVITY for water spout formation is over the Florida Keys in Florida. Larger waterspout contains more kinetic ENERGY and subsequently have a longer life-time. Waterspouts on the northern hemisphere generally rotate counter clockwise and on the southern hemisphere clockwise, due to the influence of the Coriolis forces. Occasionally the rotation will be clockwise on the northern hemisphere, as a result of the prevailing climatological conditions. Water VAPOR condensation provides an additional source of energy that fuels the TORNADO/waterspout mechanism of action (see Figure W.14).

Figure W.14 Waterspout.

W

Watson, James Dewey (1928–)

[general] Biologist (specialty: microbiology) and zoologist from the United States. James Watson and the scientist from Great Britain FRANCIS HARRY COMPTON CRICK (1916–2004) published the discovery of the double helix configuration of DNA in 1953, which makes up the human biological characteristics. Together with the third person, the physicist and biologist from New Zealand, MAURICE HUGH FREDERICK WILKINS (1916–2004), they received the Nobel Prize in Physiology/Medicine for their discovery in 1962 (see Figure W.15).

Figure W.15 James Dewey Watson [general], (1928–). (Courtesy of National Institutes of Health (NIH), Bethesda, MD.)

Watt, James (1736–1819)

[general] Scottish mechanical engineer and instrument maker by training, initially associated with the University of Glasgow. Watt never obtained the master title and was forced to seek employment outside the instrument maker guild's role of influence. He was a major contributor to developmental improvements to the recently introduced steam ENGINE developed by Thomas Newcomen in the early stages of the industrial revolution. At the AGE of 36, he partnered with Matthew Boulton to manufacture steam engines. His steam engine work inspired the development of the unit of power, the horse power (hp), later renamed after him as a credit to his contributions in the refinements to the steam engine (see Figure W.16).

Figure W.16 James Watt (1736–1819). (Courtesy of C. E. Wagstaff.)

Watt (W)

[general] The unit of power introduced by JAMES WATT in 1783, the horse power (hp), was derived from the fact that by general observation a horse walking at 2.5 miles per hour could consistently pull 150 lb of mass, but is currently officially replaced by the watt (W) as a unit for power; 1 hp = 550 ft(lb/s) = 746 W = 0.746 kW. The watt is also defined as ENERGY (i.e., joule) per SECOND: $(1\ \text{W} = 1\ \text{J/s})$.

Wave

[electronics, fluid dynamics, general, mechanics] Periodic phenomenon with specific, unique spatial or temporal profile, generally propagating with a velocity that is defined by both the WAVE mechanism and the local conditions for the medium of propagation. A wave is an ENERGY fluctuation with a fixed frequency, operating around a general EQUILIBRIUM STATE. Mechanical waves rely on the displacement of a medium, either as a transverse or LONGITUDINAL WAVE; TRANSVERSE WAVES appear in surfaces or structures (rope), whereas longitudinal waves are for instance pressure waves. A wave is part of an OSCILLATION. Mechanical waves are for instance water waves, SEISMIC shear waves (s-waves; part of EARTHQUAKE), waves in a rope, as well as sound waves. Another wave action is found in electromagnetic waves. Depending on the mechanism of action for the wave formation and propagation, the wave will conform to either then MECHANICAL WAVE equation, expressed in a one-dimensional format for a wave with displacement u traveling in the x-direction with velocity v as a function of time (t): $(1/v^2)(\partial^2 u/\partial t^2) = (\partial^2 u/\partial x^2)$; or the electromagnetic MAXWELL EQUATIONS. The general SOLUTION to the WAVE EQUATION travels in two opposite directions and has the format: $u(x,t) = u_0 \exp(\pm kx - \omega t + \varphi)$, where $k = 2\pi/\lambda$ is the wavenumber, with λ the wavelength, and $\omega = 2\pi\nu$ the ANGULAR FREQUENCY, with ν the FREQUENCY (the period $[T]$ of the wave is linked to the frequency as $T = 1/\nu$), and φ is a location-specific phase shift. Individual waves are subject to the superposition principle, adding the respective local displacement/magnitude or electric/magnetic energy magnitude from all waves converging in one location. Another wave phenomenon, directly related to superposition is INTERFERENCE, where identical waves will depend on the superposition principle to provide PHASE information about the merging waves, specifically the respective difference in phase. A group of waves with various wavelengths traveling together propagate with the group velocity $(v_g = \partial\omega/\partial k|_{\omega=\omega'}$, with ω' the "central" frequency of the spectrum), whereas the individual waves travel with the PHASE VELOCITY $(v_p = \omega/k)$. Group and phase velocities can be different, which results in DISPERSION. The MAGNITUDE of a wave phenomenon is generally expressed by means of the square of the maximum AMPLITUDE of the wave, the intensity; however, electromagnetic waves have two mechanisms that are at orthogonal directions and require a different means of quantifying the magnitude and use "fluence" or "radiance" as the parameter. A single waveform is identified by a sinusoidal expression, and in physical form will resemble a sinus function; under superposition, the addition of a broad range of frequencies can yield specific waveforms, for instance: sawtooth, square, or triangular. Electronically another phenomenon is introduced, the rectified wave, which has no negative deflection. A standing wave is the result of the superposition of two identical waves traveling under well-defined boundary conditions adding to a wave that does not migrate; the crests remain in single respective locations. For an open tube, the crest/through (maximum displacement in either direction) will be at the opening (for instance an acoustic wave in a tube or the free end of a string) by definition, similarly for a closed tube (SOUND) the zero-displacement "node" (equilibrium-point) will be at the closed end WALL, or the attached part of the string. For electromagnetic waves, the direction of the electric field defines the POLARIZATION direction of the RADIATION. The flow of water from a faucet consists of a superposition of a multitude of waves, creating interference. The three-dimensional interference in the water flow will make the stream appear as turning throughout its flow process, or it will make the stream expand and contract, next to a multitude of other visible wave and fluid-dynamic phenomena (*also see* BEAT FREQUENCY *and* AIR WAVES). *See* TIDAL WAVES, TIDAL BORE, TROCHOIDAL WAVE, WATER WAVES, HARMONIC OSCILLATION, *and* VIBRATION (see Figure W.17).

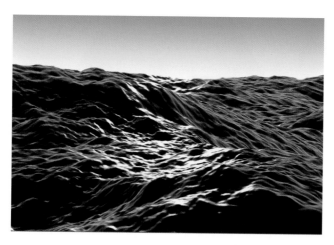

Figure W.17 Wave.

Wave dispersion

[acoustics, biomedical, biophysics, electromagnetism, engineering, fluid dynamics, general, geophysics, mechanics, optics, theoretical, ultrafast phenomenon] (syn.: crest, LIGHT, SOUND, surf, TIDAL WAVE, spatial domain fluctuations) {use: energy, imaging, spectroscopy} Wave propagation is controlled by various factors, such as liquid DENSITY (ρ) and discontinuities in the path. Wave dispersion is directly correlated to the definition of the GROUP VELOCITY OF WAVES: $v_g = d\omega/dk$. In GEOPHYSICS, the wave pattern produces a phenomenon called surf that is the result of the interrelation of the FREQUENCY (f) or WAVELENGTH (λ) (since: $f = v/\lambda$) and the average depth of the liquid level h_a, providing a dependency of the speed of propagation (v). The phase velocity of surface waves ($v_{p,s}$). The wave dispersion is caused by the phase velocity dependence on depth which in turn is also a function of wavelength. The phase velocity of SURFACE WAVES is gives as $v_{ph} = \sqrt{\left((g\lambda/2\pi) + (2\pi T_s/\rho\lambda)\right)\tanh\left(2\pi h_a/\lambda\right)}$, where g is the GRAVITATIONAL ACCELERATION, T_s is the liquid surface tension in the liquid surface under disturbed equilibrium conditions, and ρ the liquid density. The higher order Fourier components will have a higher speed of propagation as a result of a nonlinearity in acceleration (*also see* SURFACE WAVES) and will thus "run away" from the lower frequencies, creating a breaking wave approaching the shore. Generally the phase velocity equation can be reduced based on the boundary conditions; for instance, for long waves in deep water, the PHASE VELOCITY (v_{ph}) for GRAVITATIONAL WAVES reduces to $v_{p,s} = \sqrt{\left(g\lambda/2\pi\right)}$, where: $\omega = 2\pi/T$ = angular frequency = $2\pi v$ and the wavenumber $k = 2\pi/\lambda$. Material DISPERSION: wavelength dependence on the REFRACTIVE INDEX (n). Wave GROUP VELOCITY (v_g) will depend on the material properties, that is, the (localized) index of refraction. When the group velocity is smaller than the phase velocity ($v_g < v_p$), there is normal dispersion since ($dn/d\omega$) > 0. When the group velocity is greater than the phase velocity ($v_g > v_p$), the propagation suffers from anomal dispersion. The group velocity for longitudinal propagation related to material dispersion is described by filling in the parameter definitions in the equation for group velocity:

W

$v_g = d\omega/dk = c/[n + \omega(dn/d\omega)]$ revealing a dependence on the index of refraction of the medium, which may vary locally based on material properties and temperature effects (*also see* SURFACE WAVE, MASS–SPRING SYSTEM *and see* DISPERSION) (see Figure W.18).

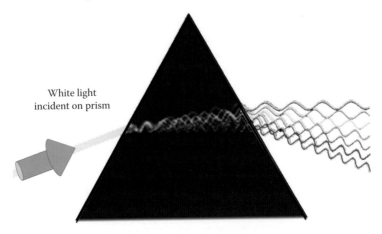

White light
incident on prism

Figure W.18 Wave dispersion.

Wave energy

[electromagnetism, fluid dynamics, mechanics] The ENERGY of a WATER WAVE is proportional to the square of the height of the WAVE with respect to "sea level," expressed as $U = (1/8)\rho g h^2$, where ρ is the LIQUID density and g is the local GRAVITATIONAL ACCELERATION. For electromagnetic waves, the energy is defined by the pointing vector as a function of the MAGNETIC FIELD strength and electric field strength: $\vec{S} = \sqrt{\varepsilon_0 \mu_0}/4\pi(\vec{E} \times \vec{B})$, units: W/m^2, $c = \sqrt{\varepsilon_0 \mu_0}$ the speed of LIGHT, ε_0 the DIELECTRIC permeability of VACUUM, and μ_0 the dielectric permittivity. Acoustic wave energy is expressed as $E = I/v_s = v^2\rho = P_{ac}/v_s A$, where I is the intensity of the SOUND, v_s the speed of sound, P_{ac} the acoustic pressure at the crest, A the area on which the acoustic wave is impinging, v the PARTICLE velocity of the medium in the wave, and ρ the density of the medium in which the wave travels.

Wave equation

[mechanics, nuclear, quantum] Correlation between displacement as a function of location and elapsed time $\nabla^2\Psi = -(1/v^2)(\partial^2\Psi/\partial t^2)$, where ∇^2 is the Laplace operator (i.e., second-order differential operator in the n-dimensional EUCLIDEAN SPACE), the derivative in all relevant spatial coordinates, Ψ the function describing the phenomenon (e.g., electric or MAGNETIC FIELD, position), t the time, and v the propagation velocity of the phenomenon. For linear WAVE problems (small AMPLITUDE approximation), one can consider FOURIER SERIES decomposition of any complicated surface elevation pattern, and this leads to the study of the simple Fourier components of $sin(lx - ctl)$ and $cos(lx - ctl)$ (*also see* SCHRÖDINGER EQUATION).

Wave motion

[general, mechanics] The progressive disturbance propagated in a medium by a periodic vibration of the particles of the medium. Transverse wave motion is that in which the VIBRATION of the particles is perpendicular to the direction of propagation. Longitudinal wave motion is that in which the vibration of the particles is parallel to the direction of propagation (*see* WAVE).

Wave number (*k*)

[atomic, nuclear, optics] Abbreviated from "angular wave number," defined as $k = 2\pi/\lambda$, with λ the wavelength of the electromagnetic RADIATION. The standard use of WAVE number identifies the spatial frequency of an OSCILLATION in the direction of travel (units, radians per meter). The historical significance of the wave number is the MAGNITUDE of the momentum of a wave in the direction of propagation $k = |\vec{k}| = |\vec{p}|$ (where $\vec{p} = (E/c)\vec{e}_t = h\nu/c$, with E representing the ENERGY, and $\vec{e}_t$ the direction of travel). In SPECTROSCOPY, the "ordinary wave number," defined as $1/\lambda = k/2\pi = \nu/c$ ($c = 2.99792458 \times 10^8$ m/s being the speed of LIGHT, and ν the frequency), is used to specify spectral lines in cm^{-1}. The ordinary wave number spells out the number of wavelengths per DISTANCE, and is an expression of energy content.

Wave particle duality

[electromagnetism, nuclear, optics] The concept of LIGHT as a particle was proposed by SIR ISAAC NEWTON (1642–1727), expressed in 1704 in his work "Opticks" (with a rudimentary introduction in his "Principia" in 1687). This followed on CHRISTIAAN HUYGENS's (1629–1695) proposition describing light as acting as a WAVE phenomenon in 1678. The particle concept was based on the ideas of ROBERT HOOKE (1635–1703). Newton's particle theory was however based on the AETHER concept, but still holds true for pure ENERGY. Newton's particle theory (the corpuscular theory of light) surpassed the wave theory and was generally accepted until THOMAS YOUNG (1773–1829) illustrated the concept of INTERFERENCE (e.g., DOUBLE-SLIT EXPERIMENT) in 1801, almost 100 years later. Meanwhile the experimental work by the scientists ARMAND HIPPOLYTE LOUIS FIZEAU (1819–1896) and JEAN BERNARD LÉON FOUCAULT (1819–1868), both from France, in 1850 revealed that the speed of light is different for different media, placing the PARTICLE definition in discredit, but it was still not abandoned. The theoretical work by the scientist from Scotland, Great Britain, JAMES CLERK MAXWELL (1831–1879), provided additional insights into the wave–particle duality, but did not fully convince the scientific community of the full extent of this concept. The particle model still held firm through the mid-1800, but the full duality was not fully understood until the 1920 experiments from the US physicist ARTHUR HOLLY COMPTON (1892–1962), who proved a particle phenomenon of photons: momentum. This provided the support to introduce the theory that matter and energy are interchangeable. In the same period, in 1923, the scientist and aristocrat PRINCE LOUIS VICTOR PIERRE RAMOND DE BROGLIE (1892–1987) from France, proposed that both MATTER and RADIATION have properties that equate to both a particle and a wave phenomenon (*also see* WAVELENGTH, DE BROGLIE).

Wave propagation speed

[biomedical, fluid dynamics, mechanics] The speed of propagation of waves can be described for various conditions; however, the basic definition is the rate of change in traversed DISTANCE: $v = dx/dt$, which is compounded by a host of material and WAVE characteristics. For mechanical waves, the following conditions can be distinguished: free medium (e.g., GAS), transverse wave in a stretched string, solids, and liquids. For a free medium, the speed of propagations is given as $v = \nu\lambda$, with ν the frequency and λ the wavelength; string under tension: $v = \sqrt{F_t/m_L}$, with F_t the tensile force on the string and m the mass per unit length of the string; longitudinal density wave in LIQUID: $v = \sqrt{B/\rho}$ (also accounts for EARTHQUAKE mantle-wave propagation) with ρ the density and B the BULK MODULUS ($B = \Delta P/(\Delta V/V_0)$; pressure P and volume V); longitudinal density wave in gas: $v = \sqrt{\gamma P/\rho}$ with P the local gas pressure and γ a thermodynamic constant defined by the ratio of the SPECIFIC HEAT at constant pressure and at constant volume of the gas respectively ($\gamma = c_P/c_V$), which reduces to $v = \sqrt{P/\rho}$ for ideal gasses, taking the temperature dependence in consideration this becomes $v = v_0\sqrt{1 + (T_c/T_0)}$, where v_0 is the speed at the reference temperature ($T_0 = 0\,°C$), and T_c the temperature of the IDEAL GAS (°C); longitudinal compression wave in elastic and rigid solids: $v = \sqrt{Y/\rho}$ with Y the Young's modulus. In terms of TRANSVERSE WAVES, the speed for electromagnetic radiation is

W

defined as $c = 1/\sqrt{\varepsilon_0\mu_0}$, with ε_0 the (DIELECTRIC) permittivity and μ_0 the (dielectric) permeability, both in VACUUM. Also $v = c = \nu\lambda$, in vacuum; $v = \nu(\lambda_0/n) = c/n$, in the medium with n the local index of refraction, λ the wavelength (sub zero in vacuum).

Wavefront

[general] The graphical and physical connections between points that are in the same PHASE and time stamp of a WAVE pattern. For instance, the (cylindrically symmetric) curve connecting all points of a radially expanding wave resulting from a centrally located perturbation. For LIGHT, the wavefront may be composed of a range of frequencies; considering a single wavelength, the wavefront for a oscillating source will form a spherically symmetric shell that travels outward, for a laser the wavefront will be within the beam only and travel in unison across the diameter of the beam as part of the coherence conditions associated with laser light.

Wavefunction

[nuclear] The SOLUTION to the SCHRÖDINGER WAVE EQUATION in the DE BROGLIE WAVE model for a PARTICLE: $\Psi = \Psi(x, y, z, t) = \psi(x, y, z)\tau(t) = C_1\psi(x, y, z)e^{-iE/\hbar^t} = C_1\psi(x, y, z)e^{-i\omega t}$. The wavefunction has the following properties: (1) it must be single valued, (2) it must be continuous everywhere, and (3) the first respective partial derivatives must be continuous. The first partial derivatives for all components are directly related to the particle FLUX, that is, the quantity of particles intercepting per unit cross-sectional area at a given point in time (removing the time dependence).

Wavelength (λ)

[general, mechanics, solid-state] The DISTANCE traveled by a WAVE over the duration of one period (T) defined as $\lambda = vT = v/\nu = c/\nu$, with v the speed of propagation (c for light) and ν the frequency of OSCILLATION. This temporal definition translates into the following spatial definition: the linear distance between any two similar points of two consecutive wave segments, for example, crest or trough, compression or expansion (i.e., rarefactions). The wavelength on a string is connected to the POTENTIAL ENERGY (PE_λ) and kinetic energy (KE_λ) in the string under the external force vibrating with AMPLITUDE A and ANGULAR FREQUENCY $(\omega = 2\pi\nu)$, defined by the total energy stored in one wavelength: $E_\lambda = PE_\lambda + KE_\lambda = (1/2)m_L\omega^2 A^2\lambda$, where m_L is the mass per unit length of the string. This converts for a gas into: $E_\lambda = PE_\lambda + KE_\lambda = (1/2)\rho A(s_{max}\omega)^2\lambda$, where ρ is the density of the gaseous medium and s the transverse displacement with amplitude: $s_{max} = \Delta P_{max}/\rho v\omega$, where ΔP_{max} is the maximum deviation in pressure from equilibrium in the wave pattern (i.e., full compression or maximum rarefaction). A standing wave in a string or a tube with length L with both ends fixed/closed satisfies $n(\lambda/2) = L$, whereas when one of the ends is lose or open, this becomes: $n(\lambda/4) = L$, with n an integer >0. In a disk, the process becomes more involved due to the various modes of standing waves in the area (e.g., drum, tambourine, xylophone, or cymbals). In case the membrane is symmetric with radius R, the standing waves need to satisfy the following conditions in cylindrical coordinates (due to symmetry; radial and angular, only two-dimensional): $\lambda^2 r^2 + [r^2/J_0(r(\alpha_{0n}/R))][d^2 J_0(r(\alpha_{0n}/R))/d^2 r] + [r/J_0(r(\alpha_{0n}/R))][dJ_0(r(\alpha_{0n}/R))/dr] = \text{Constant} \Rightarrow m^2$, as well as $-(1/\Omega(\omega))(d^2\Omega(\omega)/d\theta) = \text{Constant} \Rightarrow m^2$, where $J_0(r(\alpha_{0n}/R))$ is a Bessel function of order 0, r the radius of the membrane or plate, α_{0n} are roots of the Bessel function $(n = 1, 2, 3, \ldots)$, where $\lambda R \propto \alpha_{0n}$. With solutions to the angular equation $\Omega(\omega) = C_1\cos m\theta + C_1\sin m\theta$; C_i and m are constants. Light consisting of one single wavelength is considered monochromatic. The wavelength of the LIGHT emitted from an excited atomic state during the regrouping of electrons in the GROUND STATE is derived from the CONSERVATION OF ENERGY for the degenerating ATOM as $1/\lambda = (2\pi^2 k_0^2 e^4 m_e Z^2/h^3 c)[(1/n_f^2) - (1/n_i^2)]$, where the electron decays from the initial

(n_i) energy level indicated by $E_n = (2\pi^2 k_0^2 e^4 m_e / h^2)[Z^2/n_i^2]$, with k_0 the material constant for VACUUM ($k_0 = 1/4\pi\varepsilon_0 = 8.98755179 \times 10^9$, ε_0 the permittivity of vacuum), e the electron charge, m_e, the electron mass, h PLANCK'S CONSTANT, and Z is the atomic number, or the number of protons. This expression holds for the Lyman, Balmer, and PASCHEN SERIES (see Figure W.19).

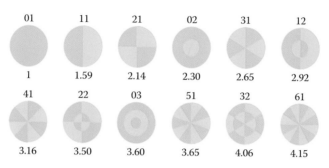

Elements of the medium moving out of the page at an instant of time

Elements of the medium moving into the page at an instant of time

Figure W.19 Waveforms, in particular, modes of vibration for a circular thin sheet (e.g., drum skin, metal surface of a drum, and plastic area of the bottom of a bucket.

Wavelength, de Broglie

[atomic, nuclear] Based on the principle that every moving object has an associated DE BROGLIE WAVELENGTH λ_d tied to the momentum of a particle (p) to the inherent wavelength as $\lambda_d = h/p$, where h is PLANCK'S CONSTANT. For PROTON and neutron with $v \ll c$, this translates into $\lambda_d = 28.6/\sqrt{\text{KE}}$ (in MeV), units fm.

Weak force

[general] *See* WEAK INTERACTION (*also see* VAN DER WAALS FORCE).

Weak interaction

[atomic, computational, electromagnetism, general, quantum, theoretical] The weak interaction is described as a weak-interaction density distribution ($\mathcal{L}_W$) with the Lagrangian formulated in vectorial quantities as $\mathcal{L}_W = -(G/\sqrt{2})J_\alpha{}^\dagger(x)J^\alpha(x)$, where $J^\alpha(x)$ represents the charge current, $J\alpha^\dagger(x)$ the current equivalence for raising a charge in a transition such as from n-state to p-state, and G is the gravitational constant. The current is described by polar and axial terms as illustrated by the charged weak current for leptons: $J_{\text{lept}}{}^\alpha(x) = \overline{e}\gamma^\alpha(1-\gamma_\Sigma)\nu_e + \overline{\mu}\gamma^\alpha(1-\gamma_\Sigma)\nu_\mu + \overline{\tau}\gamma^\alpha(1-\gamma_\Sigma)\nu_\tau$, where the leptons are $\overline{e}$ is the electron; ν_e the electron neutrino; $\overline{\mu}$ the MUON; ν_μ the muon neutrino and $\overline{\tau}$ the third charged LEPTON, tau (the heaviest); and ν_τ the "third-lepton/tau" NEUTRINO, with $\gamma_\Sigma = i\gamma^0\gamma^1\gamma^2\gamma^3\gamma^4$ the current matrix with partial SCALAR terms (*also see* FEYNMAN DIAGRAM) (see Figure W.20).

Diagram of one of several potential
weak interaction decay processes

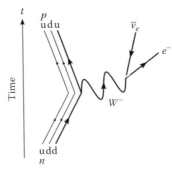

Figure W.20 Example of the concept of weak interaction.

Weber, Ernst Heinrich (1795–1878)

[biomedical, general] Physicist and scientist from Prussia (Germany). Apart from his work as a physician, Heinrich was interested in the scientific work of his brother WILHELM EDUARD WEBER (1804–1891), and together they described the culmination of two WAVE trains (sequence of wavefronts) to form a standing wave, which was made visible by mercury spread out over a sheet that was excited by acoustic (mechanical) waves from opposite sides. The mercury would under certain conditions pool in fixed locations, the nodes of the standing wave. Ernst Weber was interested in human locomotion and in particular the PHYSICS aspects of walking (see Figure W.21).

Figure W.21 Ernst Heinrich Weber (1795–1878). (Courtesy of Max Planck Institute for the History of Science, Berlin, Germany; lithographie von Rudolf Hoffmann, 1856; Österreichische Nationalbibliothek, Vienna; Austria.)

Weber, Wilhelm Eduard (1804–1891)

[general] Scientist and mathematician from Prussia (Germany). Wilhelm Weber was influenced by the work of his contemporary JOHANN FRIEDRICH PFAFF (1765–1825) as well as CARL FRIEDRICH GAUSS (Gauß; 1777–1855). Next to the acoustic work with his brother ERNST HEINRICH WEBER (1795–1878),

Wilhelm Weber worked on the MAGNETISM produced by an electric current and MAGNETIC radiation in general. Wilhelm Weber was responsible for designing a mechanism to quantify magnetic flux and the unit was named after his work performed in 1821, the weber. Additional work of Wilhelm Weber was in collaboration with Friedrich Gauss, which produced the first electromagnetic TELEGRAPH machine, used for long-distance communications. Wilhelm Weber also provided support for the observations by HIPPOLYTE FIZEAU (1819–1896) with his experimental conclusions in 1856, supporting the rudimentary formation of the WAVE–particle duality concept, as well as providing components for the theoretical efforts of JAMES CLERK MAXWELL (1831–1879). One of Wilhelm Weber's pupils was the German mathematician Georg Friedrich Bernhard Riemann (1826–1866) (see Figure W.22).

Figure W.22 Wilhelm Eduard Weber (1804–1891). (Courtesy of Max Planck Institute for the History of Science, Berlin, Germany.)

Weber (Wb)

[general, ectromagnetism] Unit of magnetic FLUX, $Wb = Tesla/m^2$, named after WILHELM EDUARD WEBER (1804–1891). The MAGNITUDE of magnetic flux is tied to the FARADAY LAW.

Weber number (We = Const($\rho v^2 L/\sigma$))

[fluid dynamics] Ratio of the inertial force to the SURFACE TENSION expressed as a dimensionless number, with the help of a dimensional constant, Const, where ρ is the density, v the velocity (for instance the velocity at impact on a surface where the droplet will experience the surface tension), L the characteristic length of the phenomenon (e.g., droplet diameter), and σ the surface tension. The Weber number is used to scale the phenomena in droplet formation, LIQUID jets, and momentum transfer in general. Under certain Weber number conditions, a water JET can be created, known as a WORTHINGTON JET.

Wedgwood, Josiah (1730–1795)

[general, solid-state] Material scientist (ceramist and potter) from Great Britain. The observations of Thomas Wedgwood as a manufacturer of fine china also made him interested in the physical aspects of the material treatment process. In 1792 Wedgewood described the thermal RADIATION associated with objects in a kiln, outlining the concepts of black-body radiation, well before the publication of the Kirchhoff radiation law in 1859. GUSTAV KIRCHHOFF (1824–1887) added his own theoretical contributions and provided physical proof in 1861 (see Figure W.23).

Figure W.23 Josiah Wedgwood (1730–1795). (Courtesy of the photographer Stephen Betteridge.)

Weight (F_w)

[general] The force on a body resulting from a gravitational pull. Note that mass is a material property, but weight is a function of GRAVITATIONAL ACCELERATION.

Weinberg, Steven (1932–)

[general] Physicist from the United States, best known for his theoretical work on electroweak interaction. Steven Weinberg received the Nobel Prize in physics for his work on unified weak and electromagnetic interaction between ELEMENTARY PARTICLES with SHELDON LEE GLASHOW (1932–) and Abdus Salam (1926–1996) in 1979 (see Figure W.24).

Figure W.24 Steven Weinberg (1932–).

Weir, John B. de V. (?–?, twentieth century)

[biomedical, chemical, energy] Physiologist from Great Britain. Weir is most known for his analysis of ENERGY production based on oxygen (O_2) consumption in metabolic reactions, producing carbon dioxide (CO_2). Weir described the energy production independently for carbohydrates, proteins, and fatty constituents in three equations based on measurable quantities of chemical reagents fueling the reaction and products from the reaction. The resting energy equation is known as the WEIR EQUATION.

Weir equation

[biomedical, chemical] Heuristic formulation of the ENERGY expenditure ($E_{metabolic}$) from a protein and/or CARBOHYDRATE oxidation chemical reaction based on volumetric oxygen intake (V_{O_2}), volumetric carbon dioxide production (V_{CO_2}), as well as nitrogen volume equivalent released in the urine (M''_N), calculated per liter of oxygen. The Weir equation used nowadays combines the three influences and is expressed in Kcal/L as $E_{metabolic} = 3.941 + 1.106(V_{CO_2}/V_{O_2}) - 2.17(M''_N/V_{O_2})$. Derived by JOHN B. DE V. WEIR in 1948.

Weissenberg, Karl (1893–1976)

[fluid dynamics, imaging] Physicist and mathematician from Austria. Karl Weissenberg was involved in the definition of the X-RAY diffraction crystallography for which he devised a goniometer in addition to his work in RHEOLOGY (see Figure W.25).

Figure W.25 Karl Weissenberg (1893–1976).

Weissenberg number, ($Wi = t_f |\vec{v}|/D$)

[fluid dynamics] Dimensionless number used in VISCOELASTIC (i.e., non-Newtonian) flow as an indication of anisotropy resulting from flow deformation under a constant stress. The Weissenberg number is used to scale the deformation rate describing the ratio of the RELAXATION TIME to the flow timescale: $Wi \sim (t_r/t_f)$, where $t_f = \sqrt{(tr(\dot{\varepsilon}))^2/2} = tr(\dot{\varepsilon})/\sqrt{2}$ describes the flow timescale, tr denotes TRACE, $\vec{v}$ the flow velocity, and D the PIPE diameter or characteristic size of the phenomenon. The flow timescale is dependent on the strain rate $\dot{\varepsilon}$, which is defined by the flow velocity with the CAUCHY STRAIN TENSOR as $\dot{\varepsilon} = \nabla \vec{v} + \left(\nabla \vec{v}\right)^{T}$ with ^{T} the transposed matrix. For a steady low REYNOLDS NUMBER shear flow, the flow time factor is a function of the shear rate (γ): $t_{f} = 1/\gamma$ describing simple shear, whereas the flow timescale for extensional flow is $t_{f} = 1/\varepsilon$, where ε is the extension rate or strain of the flow. The Weissenberg number becomes important when the flow timescale for the viscoelastic FLUID is less than the relaxation time (τ_{r}), and elastic effects become dominant. The Weissenberg number is closely related to the DEBORAH NUMBER ($De = t_{f}|\vec{v}|/L = \mathrm{Wi}(D/L)$), with L the length of the phenomenon or tube length), whereas the Deborah number refers to a nonconstant stretch.

Weisskopf, Victor Frederick (1908–2002)

[atomic, computational, general, nuclear] Physicist from Austria. Weisskopf was part of the MANHATTAN PROJECT team. Weisskopf contributed to the development of the QUANTUM THEORY and worked on the basic understanding of the ENERGY structure of the atomic NUCLEUS. Weisskopf also contributed to the calculation of the LAMB SHIFT (see Figure W.26).

Figure W.26 Victor Frederick Weisskopf (1908–2002). (Courtesy and copyright CERN©, Conseil Européen pour la Recherche Nucléaire [European Laboratory for Particle Physics], Geneva, Switzerland.)

Weisskopf half-life

[atomic] Theoretical estimation for the single ($_{\mathrm{SP}}$) gamma photon (γ) HALF-LIFE ($\tau_{1/2}$) for either nuclear electric transitions or MAGNETIC transitions. The PROBABILITY of transition within a certain time frame is expressed for either electric (EL) or magnetic (ML) DECAY phenomena as $\tau_{1/2}(\gamma)(EL)_{\mathrm{SP}} = [\ln(2)L\{(2L+1)!!\}^{2}\hbar]/[2(L+1)\mathrm{e}^{2}\mathrm{R}^{2L}][(3+L)/3]^{2}(\hbar c/E_{\gamma})^{2L+1}$ and $\tau_{1/2}(\gamma)(ML)_{\mathrm{SP}} = [\ln(2)L\{(2L+1)!!\}^{2}\hbar]/[80(L+1)\mu_{\mathrm{N}}^{2}\mathrm{R}^{2L-2}][(3+L)/3]^{2}(\hbar c/E_{\gamma})^{2L+1}$ respectively, where $\hbar = h/2\pi$ with PLANCK's CONSTANT $h = 6.62606957 \times 10^{-34}$ m^{2}kg/s, R $= 1.2 \times 10^{-13}$ $A^{1/3}$ cm a constant, which is linked to the Bohr shell model, $\mathrm{e}^{2} = 1.440 \times 10^{-10}$ keV cm, $\mu_{\mathrm{N}}^{2} = 1.5922 \times 10^{-38}$ keV cm^{3}, L the orbital angular QUANTUM NUMBER for the transition, and $c = 2.99792458 \times 10^{8}$ m/s the speed of LIGHT.

Weisskopf single particle transition probability

[atomic] The theoretical PROBABILITY for the emission of a PHOTON resulting from a single PARTICLE degeneration based on the WEISSKOPF HALF-LIFE expressed as $P_{\mathrm{prob}}(EL, ML)(W, u) = (\tau_{1/2}{}^{\gamma}(EL, ML)_{\mathrm{SP}})/(\tau_{1/2}{}^{\gamma}(EL, ML)_{\mathrm{exp}})$.

Wentzel, Gregor (1898–1978)

[computational, general, quantum] Physicist and mathematician from Germany best known for his theoretical work on the QUANTUM THEORY of fields and fueled the development of QUANTUM MECHANICS. Together with the Dutch scientist HENDRIK KRAMERS (1894–1952) and the French physicist Léon Brillouin (1889–1969), they formulated the WKB solution (Wentzel–Kramers–Brillouin) model for solving the one-dimensional time-independent SCHRÖDINGER EQUATION in 1962 (see Figure W.27).

Figure W.27 Gregor Wentzel (1898–1978). (Courtesy of University of Leipzig, Leipzig, Germany.)

Wentzel–Kramers–Brillouin (WKB) solution method

[acoustics, computational, fluid dynamics, mechanics, quantum] Mathematical method for obtaining an approximate solution to the one-dimensional time-independent SCHRÖDINGER equation proposed by the German scientist GREGOR WENTZEL (1898–1978), the Dutch scientist HENDRIK ANTHONY KRAMERS (1894–1952), and the French physicist Léon Nicolas Brillouin (1889–1969) in 1962. This SOLUTION method specifically has QUANTUM MECHANICS applications, using a classical mechanics approach. The roots for this solution method date back to the French mathematician JOSEPH LIOUVILLE (1809–1882) from his work published in 1837.

Westinghouse, George (1846–1914)

[general] Engineer and entrepreneur from the United States known for his innovation and commercialization of electrical products and electrical support industry. George Westinghouse was an inventor and businessperson creating one of the largest electrical corporations at the early stages of electrical integration. George Westinghouse created the hydroelectric plant at Niagara Falls in 1896. One of George's inventions was the TRANSFORMER, allowing ELECTRICITY to be distributed and transmitted over long distances.

W

The Westinghouse Electric Corporation was created in 1886 and was a major player in the electric distribution network for the entire United States until it went defunct in 1999 (see Figure W.28).

Figure W.28 George Westinghouse (1846–1914), photograph by Joseph G. Gessford. (Courtesy of U.S. Library of Congress Prints and Photographs Division)

Wet-bulb temperature

[thermodynamics] Temperature recording made with a THERMOMETER that has the "bulb" (liquid reservoir with mercury, ALCOHOL, or other expanding LIQUID) covered with a wick that is soaked in water, and the device is placed in a stream of MOIST AIR. The term comes from the field of PSYCHROMETRY (ENGINEERING dedicated to the thermodynamic properties of gas–vapor mixtures).

Wheatstone, Charles (1802–1875)

[energy, optics] Engineer and scientist from the Great Britain. Sir Charles Wheatstone is known for several inventions, one being the electric TELEGRAPH, and even though Wheatstone did not invent the MICROPHONE he did bring the term in CIRCULATION in 1827. In 1838, Sir Wheatstone designed a mechanism to view images in three dimensions by means of an optical structure, generating the 3D illusion. Additional work of

Charles Wheatstone was in the determination of unknown electronic components, introducing the WHEATSTONE BRIDGE (see Figure W.29).

Figure W.29 Charles Wheatstone (1802–1875).

Wheatstone bridge

[energy] Electric balancing circuit designed by CHARLES WHEATSTONE (1802–1875) in order to determine the value of an undetermined resistor by placing it in a PARALLEL CIRCUIT with power supply and adjust other known resistor values to form a circuit that has no current flowing. The RESISTOR value is derived from $R_1/R_2 = R_3/R_4$ (see Figure W.30).

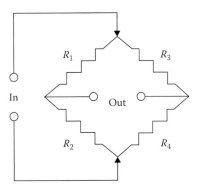

Figure W.30 Wheatstone bridge concept.

Wheeler, John Archibald (1911–2008)

[astrophysics/astronomy, atomic, computational, nuclear] Theoretical physicist from the United States. John Wheeler coined the term "BLACK HOLE" for phenomena in the UNIVERSE that seemed to have exceeding gravitational pull. Additional work by Wheeler was in the theoretical description of NUCLEAR FISSION in

W

collaboration with NIELS BOHR (1885–1962). One of Dr. Wheeler's students was RICHARD FEYNMAN (1918–1988) (see Figure W.31).

Figure W.31 John Archibald Wheeler (1911–2008). (Courtesy of Princeton University, Princeton, NJ.)

White

[general, optics] Range of ELECTROMAGNETIC SPECTRUM covering the range blue through RED, perceived by the HUMAN EYE as white (see Figure W.32).

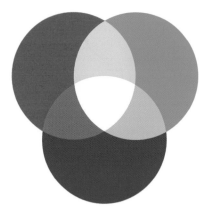

Figure W.32 White emission as the superposition of broad-band red, green, and blue light sources, in technicality covering the entire visible spectrum. Note that the combined paint of red, green, and blue dye will form a black appearance, whereas the lack of electromagnetic radiation absorbent dyes provides the reflected light of the superposition of all incident color wavelengths.

White dwarf

[astrophysics/astronomy, general] Medium size stars (with sizes less than eight times the size of our SUN) will degenerate into white dwarfs, processing through a stage of "RED GIANT" (for our Sun this object will have a diameter reaching the orbit of the planet EARTH) for approximately 1 billion years (in comparison to operating as a hydrogen FUSION STAR in the order of 10 billion years). Medium size stars are fusion engines producing helium from hydrogen in their cores. As the red giant collapses, the helium will fuse into carbon and other heavier ELEMENTS. The first observation pertaining to a white dwarf was made by FRIEDRICH WILHELM BASEL (1784–1846) in 1844, with respect to his observations of Sirius, which was recognized as an unexplained anomaly. In 1863, Alvan Graham Clark (1804–1887) recognized this anomaly as a white dwarf. Large stars will degrade into NEUTRON stars or "black hole." White dwarfs are extremely dense, approximately equivalent to the mass of our Sun compacted in the size of our Earth (see Figure W.33).

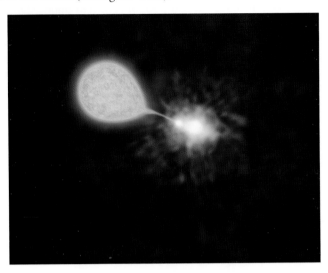

Figure W.33 Nova outburst with the White dwarf star in an orbit around a giant red star.

White light

[general] Temperature COLOR greater than 6000 K, broad range of emission wavelengths stretching from 340 nm or less through 650 nm or greater in the visible PERCEPTION. The SUN has an EMISSION SPECTRUM on the EARTH that equates to a black-body radiance of 5780 K, based on the Planckian radiator model (*also see* **WIEN'S DISPLACEMENT LAW** *and* **CIE COLOR CHART**).

White noise

[general] Indiscriminate and unsystematic arrangement of frequencies mixed in with the SIGNAL covering a broad wavelength range, with randomly fluctuating magnitudes as a function of frequency (see Figure W.34).

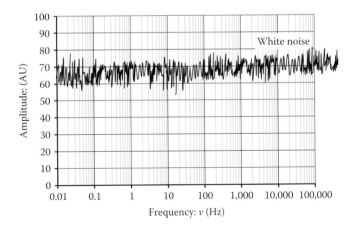

Figure W.34 Generalized frequency spectrum of White noise.

Wiedemann–Franz ratio

[atomic, nuclear, thermodynamics] *See* Lorentz number.

Wien, Wilhelm Carl Werner Otto Fritz Franz (1864–1928)

[atomic, general, nuclear, thermodynamics] Scientist from the Prussian empire (Lithuania), known for his contributions to radiation spectra, specifically "black-body" radiation. Additional work of Wien contributed to a rudimentary model of the atom, based on the cathode ray interaction with atomic compounds, creating positive particles that are deflected by both electric and magnetic fields. Since his work predates the quantum theory, the close resemblance to quantum physics in his atomic model was remarkable. The empirical Wien's displacement law devised by Wilhelm Wien was adjusted by his colleague Max Planck (1858–1947) to form the Wien–Planck law, with a theoretical basis (see Figure W.35).

Figure W.35 Wilhelm Carl Werner Otto Fritz Franz Wien (1864–1928), along with the Swedish ophthalmologist Allvar Gullstrand (1862–1930).

Wien–Planck law

[atomic, nuclear, thermodynamics] Radiation law theorized by Max Planck (1858–1947), based on the work of his colleague Wilhelm Wien (1864–1928) in 1900. The Wien–Planck law, also referred to as the Plank radiation law provides a spectral distribution, accounting for the emission in the longer (low-energy) wavelengths expressed as $I_{v,T} = 2h v^3 / c^2 \left\{ \exp\left(h v / k_b T \right) - 1 \right\}^{-1}$, which reduces to the Wien's displacement law when assuming $h v \gg k_b T$, where $I_{v,T}$ represents the energetic emission as a function of wavelength (with the associated frequency $v = c / \lambda$, with c the speed of light), at any specific wavelength, emitted per unit solid angle (Ω), as a function of

W

TEMPERATURE (T) per unit time (t) radiated over a normalized surface area (A), $h = 6.62606957 \times 10^{-34}$ m^{2}kg/s the PLANCK'S CONSTANT, and the Boltzmann coefficient $k_b = 1.3806488 \times 10^{-23}$ m^{2}kg/s^{2}K (see Figure W.36).

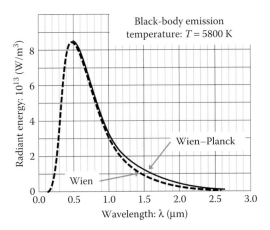

Figure W.36 Wien–Planck law.

Wien's displacement law

[atomic, nuclear, thermodynamics] RADIATION wavelength (emission peak in the distribution spectrum: λ_{peak}) versus temperature of the black-body (T) equivalence described by WILHELM WIEN (1864–1928) in 1893: $\lambda_{peak} T = \text{Const}$. In a greater detail, the energetic emission ($I_{v,T}$) spread out over a wavelength bandwidth, with a peak emission at λ_{peak} (with the associated frequency $v = c/\lambda$, with c the speed of light), per unit solid angle (Ω), as a function of temperature, per unit time (t) radiated over a normalized surface area (A) expressed as the spectral envelope function $I_{v,T} = (2hv^3/c^2)\exp\left(-(hv/k_b T)\right)$, with $h = 6.62606957 \times 10^{-34}$ m^{2}kg/s the PLANCK'S CONSTANT and $k_b = 1.3806488 \times 10^{-23}$ m^{2}kg/s^{2}K the Boltzmann coefficient (see Figure W.37).

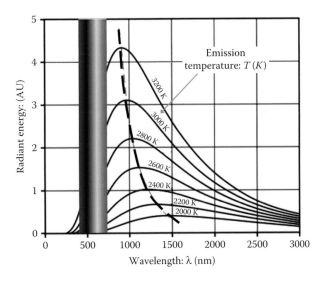

Figure W.37 Wien's displacement law.

Wigner, Eugene (Jenő Pál) (1902–1995)

[atomic, computational, nuclear, quantum] Physicist and mathematician from Hungary. Jenő Pál Wigner received the Nobel Prize in Physics for his work on ELEMENTARY PARTICLES and the theoretical description of the atomic NUCLEUS in 1963, shared with MARIA GOEPPERT-MAYER (GÖPPERT) (1906–1972) and JOHANNES HANS DANIEL JENSEN (1907–1973). Jenő Pál Wigner may be considered one of the founding fathers of QUANTUM chemistry (see Figure W.38).

Figure W.38 Eugene (Jenő Pál) Wigner (1902–1995). (Courtesy of Oak Ridge National Laboratory, U.S. Department of Energy, Oak Ridge, TN.)

Wigner distribution

[atomic, computational, nuclear] Momentum PROBABILITY distribution function expressed in 1932 by JENŐ PÁL (EUGENE) WIGNER (1902–1995), defining the WAVEFUNCTION ($\psi(q)$, as a function of location q; the wavefunction can contain electric and MAGNETIC FIELD) and the representative state of the medium in QUANTUM MECHANICS. The general Wigner distribution for the state of a system is defined as $W(q,p) = (1/\pi\hbar)\int_{-\infty}^{\infty} \psi^*(q+y)(\psi(q-y)e^{i2py/\hbar}dy$ $\overline{\text{semiclassical}}$ $(1/\pi\hbar)\int_{-\infty}^{\infty} q - y|\hat{\rho}|q + ye^{i2py/\hbar}dy$, where $\hbar = h/2\pi$, with $h = 6.62606957 \times 10^{-34}$ m^{2}kg/s the PLANCK'S CONSTANT, ψ^* is the complex conjugate, p the momentum, y the position in free space, and $\hat{\rho}$ a density matrix that can be applied for a classical mechanical approach. The Wigner distribution can be used to analyze audio signals and the representative audio PERCEPTION as well as electrocardiograms next to quantum mechanical applications. In classical mechanical terms, the Wigner distributions hold information about the FREQUENCY SPECTRUM the group delay and the response function.

Wilkins, Maurice Hugh Frederick (1916–2004)

[biomedical, general, imaging] Physicist and molecular biologist from New Zealand. In 1953, Maurice Wilkins provided the imagery to support the experimental and theoretical work by JAMES WATSON (1928–) and FRANCIS HARRY COMPTON CRICK (1916–2004) on their efforts in DNA analysis and the discovery of the nature of the genetic structure of living organisms. Wilkins shared the Nobel Prize in Physiology/Medicine with Watson and Crick in 1962 for their groundbreaking efforts supporting biological development and function and physiological formatting (see Figure W.39).

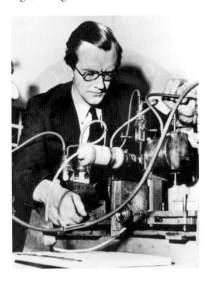

Figure W.39 Maurice Hugh Frederick Wilkins (1916–2004). (Courtesy of National Institutes of Health, Bethesda, MD.)

Wilson, Charles Thomson Rees (1869–1959)

[atomic, nuclear] Physicist from Scotland, Great Britain. Inventor of the cloud chamber used for tracking and identifying charged particles, for which he received the Nobel Prize in Physics in 1927, which he shared with ARTHUR HOLLY COMPTON (1892–1962) (see Figure W.40).

(a)   (b)

Figure W.40 (a) Charles Thomson Rees Wilson (1869–1959), in 1927. (Courtesy of Electric Scotland Muskegon, MI, USA.) (b) In 1936 painting by Herbert James Gunn. (Courtesy of Sidney Sussex College, University of Cambridge; Cambridge, UK.)

W

Wilson cloud chamber

[atomic, nuclear] Condensation chamber that produces a trail of droplets in suspension according to the trajectory of a charged PARTICLE or charge interaction. Generally an external electric and/or MAGNETIC FIELD is applied to influence the path of the respective particles and allow for QUANTIFICATION of charge and mass. The Wilson cloud chamber has been credited with the aid in the discovery of the positron, the verification of the COMPTON SCATTERING of electrons, experimentally illustrated PAIR FORMATION and pair annihilation, next to the transmutation of atomic nuclei. The Wilson cloud chamber was recognized by ERNEST RUTHERFORD (1871–1937) as one of the most influential discoveries of the day. Also known as cloud chamber (see Figure W.41).

Figure W.41 Wilson cloud chamber. (Courtesy of Electric Scotland, Muskegon, MI, USA.)

Wimshurst, James (1832–1903)

[electronics, general] Engineer and scientist from Great Britain. Inventor of the WIMSHURST MACHINE, creating sparks through electrostatic charge build-up from rotating disks that have opposite revolution rubbing against copper brushes to conduct the charges off to either Leyden Jars or electrodes. James Wimshurtst followed the example set out by the French scientist Ferdinand Philippe Edouard Carré (1824–1900), who also invented and designed refrigeration equipment, the German physicist Wilhelm Holtz (1836–1913), with his MACHINES exhibited in 1865 and 1867, as well as another German physicist, AUGUST JOSEPH IGNAZ TOEPLER (1836–1912) with his machine on display in 1865. Other inventors working on the same principle were by the German scientists ROGER VOSS (early eighteen hundreds) and J. ROBERT VOSS (early eighteen hundreds). James Wimshurst also invented a VACUUM machine. Other contributions by Wimshurst were in his field of nautical construction, devices to indicate the stability of large ships and designed the manner in which a lighthouse in open sea could be powered by ELECTRICITY (see Figure W.42).

Figure W.42 James Wimshurst (1832–1903).

Wimshurst machine

[electronics, general] Electrostatic device made with two insulting disks that rotate in opposite directions and form nonfriction based electrostatic charge build-up (no contact to generate charge build-up except for the current wires). The machine was designed and constructed by JAMES WIMSHURST (1832–1903) in 1878. The insulating disks have small sections of conducting material at fixed intervals that are brought in contact with copper brushes when rotating. The electrostatic charge generated from the two disks is transferred to either electrodes which produce an arc, or to Leyden Jars for "storage." The first primitive form of an electrostatic frictional machine was invented and fabricated by OTTO VON GUERICKE (1602–1682) in 1663. Various versions were created over the years, with a 1.6 m diameter set of GLASS disks in 1783 by the Dutch physicist and inventor Martin van Marum (1750–1837). The Van Marum disks had the capability to produce electrical charge of either polarity, using FRICTION (*also see* **VAN DE GRAAFF GENERATOR** *and* **TESLA COIL**) (see Figure W.43).

Figure W.43 Wimshurst machine. (Courtesy Lateral Science Co., UK.)

Wing

[astrophysics, fluid dynamics, mechanics] Structure that provides a LIFT during a flight. Bird wings have a special construction where the feathers create the optimal conditions to support a lift and elevation as well as sustain a flight while allowing for minimal INTERFERENCE on the upward force during the up–down movement of the wings during ascension. Mammals with wings, such as bats, squirrels, and monkeys have no feathers and rely on the turning of the solid wing (e.g., SKIN, membrane) while undergoing upward MOTION to still take advantage of the Bernoulli principle, and not push the animal down. Insect wings are generally also constructed from a membrane; however, some wings can be very intricate, such as the butterfly and moth wing. For a fixed-wing aeroplane (airplane), the Bernoulli principle is applied to provide a lift as a result of the forward velocity, creating a pressure gradient that provides a lift that supports the airplane and its LOAD (*also see* LIFT) (see Figure W.44).

Figure W.44 Wing design.

Wollaston prism

[general, optics] Polarizing prism, and beam splitter. The Wollaston prism separates the ordinary and the extraordinary rays, both polarized in respective orthogonal directions. The extraordinary ray is polarized parallel to the long-axis planes of all windows, specifically of the separation plane. The DIVERGENCE between the ordinary and the extraordinary ray is a function of the ANGLE of the PRISM windows. The Wollaston prism finds applications in CD and DVD players in combination with a quarter-WAVE plate (see Figure W.45).

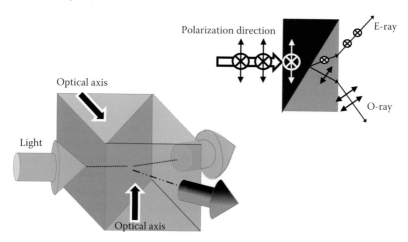

Figure W.45 Wollaston prism.

Womersley, John Ronald (1907–1958)

[biomedical, fluid dynamics] Physiologist and mathematician from Great Britain, known for his interpretation of viscous flow. Some of Womersley's major contributions have been to the fields of textiles and biomedical FLUID DYNAMICS. The work of Womersley expanded on the PULSATILE FLOW model developed by the German physiologist Otto Frank (1865–1944) based on the Windkessel phenomenon in 1899, integrating the Navier–Stokes equations (see Figure W.46).

Figure W.46 Computer conceived and produced by John Ronald Womersley (1907–1958).

Womersley number, $(\alpha_{Wo} = r\sqrt{\rho\omega/\eta})$

[biomedical, fluid dynamics] Dimensionless number used to scale the dominant features in a PULSATILE FLOW. The Womersley number is defined as the ratio of changing inertial forces resulting from the localized acceleration in each period of the pulsatile MOTION with respect to the viscous forces, where r is the radius of the conduit (BLOOD vessel, PIPE, etc.), ω is the ANGULAR VELOCITY due to changes in pressure gradient of the fluid in motion that is directly related to the FREQUENCY (ν) of the OSCILLATION ($\omega = 2\pi\nu$), ρ the fluid density, and η the VISCOSITY. In this approximation the elastic behavior of the WALL is considered to be negligible.

Wooster, William Alfred (Peter) (1903–1984)

[general] Scientist and mineralogist from the United States. The work of Wooster contributed to the material science aspects of crystallography.

Work (*W*)

[general, mechanics, nuclear] ENERGY resulting from a constant force F applied at an ANGLE θ with the MOTION performed over a DISTANCE s defined as $W = \vec{F} \cdot \vec{s} = Fd\cos\theta$, or in integral form: $W = \int \vec{F} \cdot d\vec{r} = \int F\cos\theta dr$. For rotation, this becomes: $W = \tau\Delta\theta$, where τ is the applied torque, and θ the angle of revolution. In case the force applied varies over time or over sections (s_i), the work can be summarized as calculated in stages in which the force can be considered as a constant: $W = \lim_{\Delta s_{i'} \to 0} \sum_i \vec{F}_i \cdot \vec{s}_{i'}$. (*Note*: work done by SPRING or by GRAVITY is a classic example of a nonlinear force.) With respect to energy, the following can also be said: work done on an object is equal to the change in KINETIC ENERGY (KE) of this object: $W = KE_2 - KE_1$. Work that is independent of the path followed between the beginning and the end point is defined as the result of a conservative force. The work done can be mechanical ($W_M = P\Delta V + v\Delta P$, where P is the pressure of a system, and V the partial volume occupied by the changing medium); or the work can be electrical ($W_e = -nF_{Far}\Delta V_{elec}$, where n is the number of transferred charges, $F_{Far} = 96{,}485$ C/mol the FARADAY CONSTANT, and ΔV_{elec} the maximum difference in electrical potential achieved through the motion of the charges) (see Figure W.47).

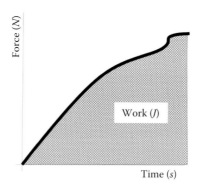

Figure W.47 Graph representing work as the area under the curve of force against the time the force is applied.

Work function (ϕ_{elec}, in electron volt: eV)

[atomic, biomedical, electronics, general, nuclear] ENERGY needed for an ELECTRON to free itself from a surface, such as in an ELECTRON TUBE, or a PHOTO CELL used in the detection of LIGHT or to generate ELECTRICITY (*also see* PHOTO-VOLTAIC *and* PHOTOELECTRIC EFFECT). The work function for sodium is $\phi_{elec}|_{Na} = 2.28$ eV, for copper: $\phi_{elec}|_{Cu} = 4.70$ eV, whereas the work function for platinum is $\phi_{elec}|_{Pt} = 6.35$ eV.

Work–energy theorem

[general, mechanics] The work (W) performed by a system equals the change in KINETIC ENERGY (KE) of that system: $W = \Delta KE$. This principle indicates the general interest in change, not so much to total energy content of a system, which technically includes all atomic and molecular energy.

Worthington jet

[fluid dynamics] Cavitation flow resulting from the impact of a solid sphere with a free (LIQUID) surface. The height of the JET (H_j) is a function of the object size (sphere diameter: D_b), velocity of impact, and the medium the object is impacting with, specifically there is a difference between Newtonian and non-Newtonian liquids. For an infinitely wide and infinitely deep pool of liquid, infinite being a relative term, at least three times the dimensions of the drop height may be a good approximation to avoid boundary effects. Note that the Worthington jet can also be generated by an object dropping in a pool of sand or other granular media. The viscosity of the liquid medium will dramatically impact the final outcome as well. With all factors considered, the height of the jet is defined by the following conditions: $H_j/D_b = f\left(\rho_r^*, Re.Fr\right)$, where $\rho_r^* = \rho_b/\rho_m$ the RELATIVE DENSITY from the ball ($_b$), to the medium ($_m$), $Re = \rho_m v D_b/\eta_e$ the REYNOLDS NUMBER, with η_e the effective viscosity of the medium, v the impact velocity, and subsequently $Fr = v/\sqrt{gD_b}$ the Froude number, with g the GRAVITATIONAL ACCELERATION. The mechanism of a liquid droplet falling on a solid surface also generates a Worthington jet; however, the conditions are different from breaking a liquid surface. The recoil force in the latter case is provided by the SURFACE TENSION of the liquid (F_τ), and is a function of the Weber number. The Weber number for a spherical fluid is $We = \rho v^2 D_b/F_\tau$. For a small Weber number, the surface tension will dominate and create a noticeable rebound and Worthington jet formation, whereas for a large Weber number, the kinetic ENERGY will dominate, resulting in a break-up and dispersal. No conclusive definition of the height of the rebound of the drop can be provided due to the wide range of boundary conditions, and only the influences can be described. The complete analysis of the Worthington jet falls under computational FLUID DYNAMICS (see Figure W.48).

(a) (b)

Figure W.48 (a,b) Worthington jet.

W

W-Particle

[nuclear] Product of the DECAY process for a NEUTRON, delivering a W-particle and a PROTON; the "W" represents "weak," for WEAK INTERACTION under the GAUGE THEORY. The W-particle is a VECTOR BOSON. All vector bosons are W+, W−, and Z0. The mass for the W-vector bosons is $81\,\text{GeV}/c^2$, with $c = 2.99792458 \times 10^8\,\text{m/s}$ the speed of LIGHT. W-particles are highly unstable (decay time $\tau_d = 10^{-24}\,\text{s}$) and decay into an electron–electron-antineutrino pair. The W-particle was introduced in 1956 by the theoretical physicist from the United States Julian Seymour Schwinger (1918–1994). Based on theoretical assumptions, the W-particle should be massless; however, due to the presence of the Higgs field, they acquire an ad-hoc spinless, SCALAR field, which provides the ENERGY to yield the REST MASS. In the theoretical description, the spin-0 Higgs bosons condense into a GROUND STATE that applies the classical field to the W-particles as well as the Z-particles, limiting their mobility to below light-speed interactions (see Figure W.49).

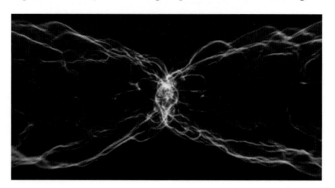

Figure W.49 W-boson (artist impression).

Wu, Chien-Shiung (Wú Jiànxióng; 吳健雄) (1912–1997)

[atomic, nuclear] Scientist from mainland China. Dr. Wu was a collaborator on the MANHATTAN PROJECT. On an experimental approach, Chien-Shiung Wu illustrated that conservation of PARITY does not apply under NUCLEAR FISSION and NUCLEAR FUSION. Other efforts by Wu were in RADIOACTIVITY and the beta DECAY of isotopes under gaseous DIFFUSION (see Figure W.50).

Figure W.50 Chien-Shiung Wu (Wú Jiànxióng; 吳健雄) (1912–1997), credit #2205. Wu, ChienShiungInLab. (Courtesy of University Archives, Columbia University in the City of New York, Photographer Manny Warman.)

X-ray

[biomedical, nuclear] Electromagnetic "Röntgen" RADIATION with wavelength between 0.01 and 10 nm. Quite frequently the term Röntgen radiation is found to describe this type of radiation to credit the German discoverer Wilhelm CONRAD RÖNTGEN (1845–1923), published in 1895. X-ray radiation is generated as a result of electron transitions (note that GAMMA RAY can be very similar, but its origin lies in the atomic NUCLEUS). X-ray radiation is a by-product of NUCLEAR FUSION or FISSION (ISOTOPE decay) and can be artificially generated by bombarding for instance a tungsten, rhenium, or molybdenum-alloy disk with fast electrons. The ANODE rotates to prevent localized overheating (cooling is a major require-ment for the filament). The X-ray exposure during a medical exam results from exposure of a rotating anode in a Coolidge type tube with electrons from a fixed location CATHODE. The exposure to X-ray radiation falls under dosimetry and has strict limits to ensure prevention of biological damage. X-ray radiation exposure is quantified by gray ([Gy]) or rad ([rad]) as units of cumulative exposure, or as equivalent dose with respect to the potential of generating IONIZATION, obtained by multiplication of the ABSORBED DOSE by a factor describing the type and ENERGY of the radiation in Sievert ([Sv], old unit [rem]). The gray is a unit for absorbed dose in joule per kilogram, named in honor of the British origina-tor of radiation control and his attempts to limit biological (i.e., genetic) and burn damage, Louis Harold Gray (1905–1965); proposed in 1940, defined in 1975. Exposure in excess of 100 Gy will result in an eventual, but unavoidable, death. Locally applied dosage in the order of 50 Gy is standard in RADIATION THERAPY, whereas a computed TOMOGRAPHY scan requires exposure in the order of 5 mGy and flying at 30,000 ft (~10 km) altitude is not significantly higher than the solar X-ray exposure obtained down on the EARTH during a picnic. The rad has primarily a historic value, defined in 1953 and 1 rad = 0.01 Gy; sometimes used as a equivalent to the sporadic and mainly colloquial röntgen unit. The radiation weight factor (W_R) is as follows to obtain the equivalent dose: X-ray, gamma, beta, and muons $W_R = 1$; protons $W_R = 2 - 5$; NEUTRON radiation $W_R = 5 - 20$ depending on the energy; and for ALPHA PARTICLES and heavy nuclei, PARTICULARLY those produced under NUCLEAR FISSION, $W_R = 20$. The discovery of X-ray fueled the research into RADIOACTIVITY and FLUORESCENCE. Additionally, X-ray is used for a three-dimensional inspection on a diffraction level for atomic structure and for attenuation based on the density applied to nondestructive testing, airport human body scanners, and medical inspection as well as treatment options. Computed tomography (CT- or CAT SCAN) uses X-ray radiation from a multitude of directions arranged in a circumferential array or by a moving source with fixed scintillation counters or photomultiplier tubes as the detection mechanism. The CT scan applies the line-of-flight principle to reconstruct a three-dimensional IMAGE form intersect points at the lines of attenuation in transmittance (see Figure X.1).

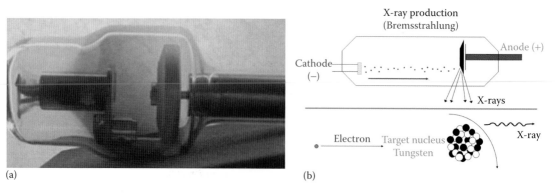

(a)   (b)

Figure X.1 (a) X-ray generation and (b) X-ray spectrum.

X-ray, characteristic

[atomic, nuclear] The RADIATION emitted resulting from ENERGY transitions in the inner bands of the BOHR ATOMIC MODEL, associated with a high-energy level electron BINDING ENERGY. Generally the narrow line-width characteristic radiation is superimposed on the broad-band BREMSSTRAHLUNG spectrum (BREMßTRAHLUNG). For the VALENCE electrons, the EMISSION SPECTRUM is defined by the ENERGY transitions in the outer bands. The electron orbits are defined in the Bohr atomic model, described by NIELS HENRIK DAVID BOHR (1885–1962). The change in ENERGY LEVEL in the outer bands of the atomic model generates photons with frequency v expressed by $hv = E_i - E_f$, where $h = 4.1356692 \times 10^{-15}$ J s is the Planck constant. In the inner electron bands, the energy levels are much greater and so are the energy QUANTA involved in the transitions. The wavelength (λ) of the emitted PHOTON is now proportional to the ATOMIC NUMBER (Z) of the material and the difference in the electron orbit from the inner orbit outward, with the inner orbit indicated by the condition $n = 1$, where n identifies the lower orbit with the highest energy and is defined as $1/\lambda = R_{Ry} (Z-1)^2 \left[(1/(n)^2) - (1/(n+1+m)^2) \right]$, with $n \geq 1$ and $m \geq 0$ and $R_{Ry} = 1.097373 \times 10^7$ m^{-1} the RYDBERG CONSTANT. The associated frequency is $v = c/\lambda$, with c the speed of LIGHT. Hence there are grouping of emission lines that result from electron transitions ending at the same orbital level but starting from one or more levels of separation. The emission lines were classified by CHARLES GLOVER BARKLA (1877–1944) in 1911 as K-lines, L-lines, M-lines, and N-lines, respectively: $K_\alpha, K_\beta, K_\gamma, K_\delta, L_\alpha, L_\beta, L_\gamma, L_\delta, M_\alpha, M_\beta, M_\gamma, M_\delta, N_\alpha, N_\beta, N_\gamma, N_\delta$, with each successive alphabetical indicator (capitalized Roman letter) indicating the lower level (K for $n = 1$), with alphabetical subscript (Greek) indicating an increment in the value m, or a larger QUANTUM JUMP. This holds due to the fact that the lower level (e.g., $n = 1$) has under normal equilibrium conditions two electrons, but will have one electron missing because of excitation. Concurrently the net NUCLEAR CHARGE will be reduced resulting in the equivalent COULOMB FORCE proportional to $+e(Z-1)$ (according to GAUSS's LAW), not $+e*(Z)$ (*see* CHARACTERISTIC X-RAY) (see Figure X.2).

X

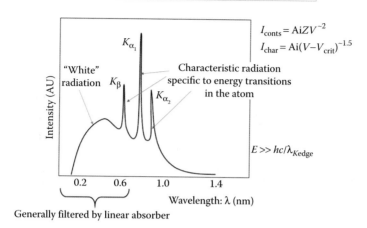

Figure X.2 Characteristic X-ray radiation.

X-rays diffraction in crystals

[atomic] The use of X-RAY radiation for crystal LATTICE analysis, crystallography (*see the* VON LAUE METHOD) (see Figure X.3).

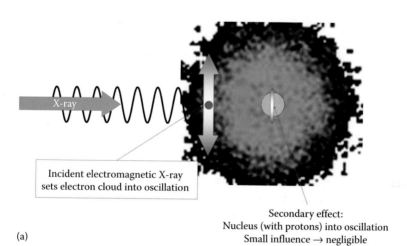

(a)

Figure X.3 (a–c) X-ray diffraction.

(Continued)

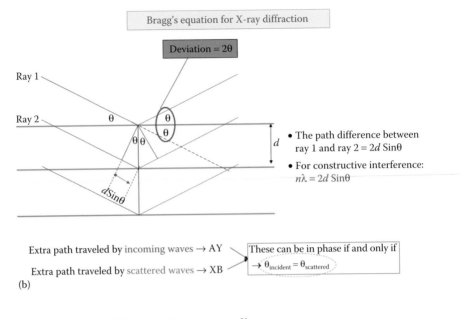

Bragg's equation for X-ray diffraction

Deviation = 2θ

Ray 1

Ray 2

θ

θ

θ

θ θ

d

*d*Sinθ

- The path difference between ray 1 and ray 2 = $2d\,\sin\theta$
- For constructive interference:
  $n\lambda = 2d\,\sin\theta$

Extra path traveled by incoming waves → AY

Extra path traveled by scattered waves → XB

These can be in phase if and only if
→ $\theta_{incident} = \theta_{scattered}$

(b)

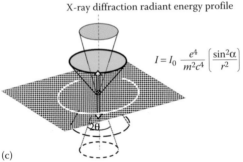

X-ray diffraction radiant energy profile

$$I = I_0\,\frac{e^4}{m^2c^4}\left[\frac{\sin^2\alpha}{r^2}\right]$$

2θ

(c)

Figure X.3 (Continued) (a–c) X-ray diffraction.

XY model

[computational, thermodynamics] Special case for the situation $n = 2$ with regard to the n-vector lattice model pertaining to classical MECHANICS in a multidimensional setting. The D-dimensional lattice model (Λ) is defined by sites (i), each occupied by a SPIN or rotator vector (spin configuration) $\vec{s} = (\vec{s}_i)_{i\in\Lambda}$, $\vec{s}_i = (\cos\theta_i, \sin\theta_i)$, which have orthogonal $O(2)$ symmetry (rotation around a fixed point) and $U(1)$ symmetry (GAUGE SYMMETRY, pertaining to the electromagnetic force). The XY model describes the PROBABILITY distribution for magnetization configuration of a medium that can be magnetized, for instance SUPERFLUID helium and certain LIQUID crystals, generally possessing a certain symmetry. The XY model contains the conditions for PHASE transitions within the system. In statistical mechanics, the probability $(P(\mathbb{S}))$ that a system possesses a certain state $(\mathbb{S})$ while at a certain TEMPERATURE (T) with ENERGY $E = \sum_{\langle i, j\rangle}\vec{s}_i\,\vec{s}_j$ is described as $P(\mathbb{S}) = e^{-[E(\mathbb{S})/k_bT]}/Z_\ell(1/k_bT)$, where $k_b = 1.3806488\times10^{-23}\ \mathrm{m^2kg/s^2K}$ the Boltzmann coefficient, and $Z_\ell(1/k_bT) = \sum_{\mathbb{S}} e^{-[E(\mathbb{S})/k_bT]}$ the linearized portion of the PARTITION FUNCTION that is tied to the free energy $G_\ell(1/k_bT) = (1/\ell^D)\ln Z_\ell(1/k_bT)$, with D the dimension of the system (i.e., the DEGREES OF FREEDOM). Also known as the classical rotor model or the classical rotator model.

Yang, Chen Ning (清华大学) (1922–)

[computational] Physicist from China. Chen Ning Yang received the Nobel Prize in Physics in 1957 for his work on the PARITY of ELEMENTARY PARTICLES, which he shared with Tsung-Dao Lee (李政道: 1926–) (see Figure Y.1).

Figure Y.1 Chen Ning Yang (清华大学) (1922–).

Yang–Mills field

[computational] The field that rules the Yang–Mills theoretical approximation. This QUANTUM field is based on PERTURBATION THEORY (developed in a series with units p), which can be solved only once the perturbation function ($\beta(\alpha_s)$; $\alpha_s = g_c^2/4\pi$ the coupling of the vector potential with g_c the gauge coupling constant that is indicative of the strength of the interaction) is known. The ENERGY field is a running coupling-based approach: $\mu_p^2(d\alpha_s/d\mu_p^2) = \beta(\alpha_s)$, μ_p the perturbation series components ($\mu_{p=0}$ providing the exact SOLUTION for the initial conditions). In this the perturbation at short wavelengths can be written as $\beta(\alpha_s) = -(11N/12\pi)\alpha_s^2 + (17N^2/24\pi^2)\alpha_s^3 + R(\alpha_s^4)$, where $R\left(\alpha_s^4\right)$ is a rest term (error term) and N represents the GAUGE SYMMETRY group rank, defining the number of gauge fields (e.g., photons, weak bosons, strong bosons, and gluons); however, the long wavelength limit is not well defined (INFRARED limit) (see Figure Y.2).

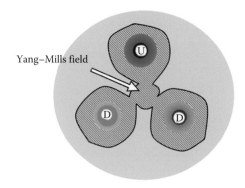

Yang–Mills field

Figure Y.2 Yang–Mills field. "U"—Up quark; "D"—Down quark.

Yang–Mills theory

[computational] Theoretical description of the elementary forces (the GAUGE THEORY) between protons and neutrons introduced by CHEN NING YANG (1922–) and Robert Laurence Mills (1927–1999), published in 1954. The Yang–Mills theory is a typical example of the gauge theory applied to the interaction of a weak current from a LEPTON interacting with a charged strong VECTOR BOSON.

Yield length

[general, mechanics] Stretch length applied before failure occurs (see Figure Y.3).

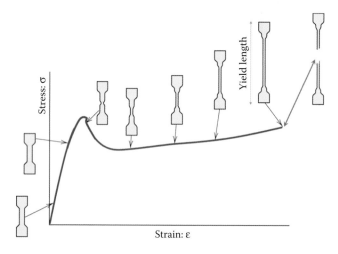

Figure Y.3 Yield length.

Yield stress (τ^*)

[fluid dynamics, mechanics] The applied stress threshold to transform a pseudoplastic or dilatant system into a homogeneous flow. $\tau^* = K_y(c - c_{min})^2$, where K_y is a constant that depends on the colloid solution PARTICLE size and shape (e.g., sphere, rod, ellipsoid, and the respective aspect ratio of the sizes), [c] the concentration of constituent "c," with threshold minimum concentration [c_{min}]. This applies to a tube flow, but also to stirrer interaction (see Figure Y.4).

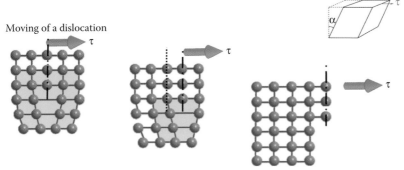

Moving of a dislocation

All the bonds do not have to be broken at the same time;
only one at a time to slide the plane

Figure Y.4 Yield stress.

Young, Thomas (1773–1829)

[mechanics, optics] English physician and physicist. Young provided experimental proof in 1801 that electromagnetic RADIATION has a WAVE characteristic next to the PARTICLE identity shown with Snell's experiments and theoretical description of REFLECTION and refraction. The wave characteristics were elucidated from the double slit INTERFERENCE pattern with a single source, resembling the node, crest, and through pattern produced by water waves (see Figure Y.5).

Figure Y.5 Thomas Young (1773–1829). (Courtesy of The Royal Institution, UK, originally painted by Thomas Lawrence; copied either by Hugh Goldwin Riviere or Mabel Beatrice Messer.)

Y

Young–Laplace equation

[biomedical, chemical, fluid dynamics, mechanics, thermodynamics] Nonlinear partial differential equation that is used to define the CAPILLARY pressure gradient across an equilibrium interface between two immiscible fluids, both stationary. The name is based on the experimental work of the English scientist THOMAS YOUNG (1773–1829) in 1805, describing SURFACE TENSION with the assistance of the French mathematician PIERRE-SIMON DE LAPLACE (1749–1827) in the mathematical formulation in 1806. The force balance between the pressure (P) and the surface tension (F_τ) at the surface S with circumference C is defined as $\int_S (P_1 - P_2) \vec{n}\, dS = -F_\tau \oint_C \vec{t} \times \vec{n}\, d\vec{r}$, where $\vec{t}$ is the tangent at the curve of the enclosure of the surface and $\vec{n}$ the normal to the surface, pointing in the direction from fluid 1 to fluid 2. Viscous forces are not applicable since the situation is stationary. This reduces to $(P_1 - P_2) = \Delta P = F_\tau \nabla \cdot \vec{n}$, where $\nabla = \sum_i \partial / \partial x_i$ is the Laplace operator, yielding $\nabla \cdot \vec{n} = 0$ for a flat interface.

Young's modulus (Y_n)

[general, mechanics] Plotting STRESS (σ_n) versus STRAIN (ϵ_n) provides a graph of the ELASTICITY of a solid; the linear section of the curve can be represented by a line function with a slope, where n indicates the DEGREES OF FREEDOM (primarily: x, y, z, respectively 1, 2, 3). Also called elastic modulus or bulk modulus under specific boundary conditions. The Young's modulus is hence defined as the stress in longitudinal direction per unit strain where the transverse modes are not confined (i.e., ϵ_2 and ϵ_3 are allowed to change). The slope of the linear part of the stress–strain curve is defined as the Young's modulus (Y_n) of that material under stress: $\sigma_n = Y_n \epsilon_n$, as defined by HOOKE'S LAW of linear elasticity. Technically the value of the Young's modulus can be different for a material under tension or under compression, in which case both values will be listed in reference books such as the *CRC Handbook of Chemistry and Physics*. The Young's modulus is the linear counterpart of the BULK MODULUS. Multidimensionally (specifically cubically), the Young's modulus can be expressed by the elasticity:

$$\sigma_m = C_{mn} \begin{bmatrix} \epsilon_{00} & \cdots & \\ \vdots & \ddots & \vdots \\ & \cdots & \epsilon_{nm} \end{bmatrix},$$

using $C_{mn} = \partial \sigma_m / \partial \epsilon_n$, as $Y_{cub} = [(C_{11} - C_{12})(C_{11} + 2C_{12})]/[(C_{11} + C_{12})]$. (see Figure Y.6)

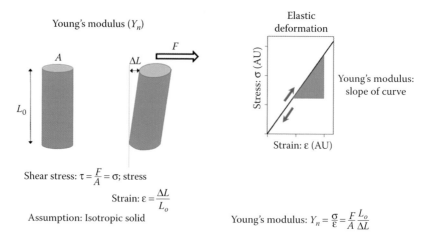

Figure Y.6 Young's modulus.

Young's slit experiment

[optics] In order to produce two apparently coherent sources (not truly coherent, but good enough for the day) THOMAS YOUNG (1773–1829) placed a LIGHT SOURCE behind a single slit, which in turn produced an expanding WAVEFRONT that illuminated two closely separated slits. The two slits in turn produced two relatively coherent sources that resulted in an INTERFERENCE pattern on a screen placed behind the two slits. This interference pattern produced in 1801 reaffirmed the original hypothesis that light is a WAVE. The Newtonian particle concept for light still prevailed until well into the twentieth century. The interference pattern resembles the pattern generated from waves in water with two "coherent" sources, generated in a similar fashion. The DISTANCE of the locations of maximum interference with respect to the central maximum is given in terms of wavelength, where a whole wavelength difference in path length produces a positive interference and half a wavelength extinguishes the light locally. The angular (θ) dependence for the maxima is given as $a \sin \theta_m = m\lambda$, where $m = 0, 1, 2, \ldots$ indicates the order of the maximum and a is the separation distance between the two slits. The original experiment used WHITE LIGHT, which resulted in a more pronounced separation of colors at greater distance from the center, with a white central interference line. Using a laser will produce a well-defined intensity (brightness) pattern (see Figure Y.7).

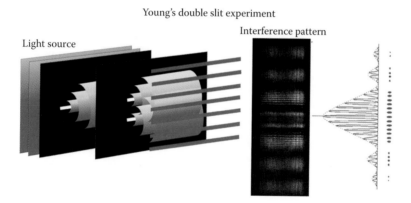

Figure Y.7 Young's slit experiment.

Yrast line

[nuclear] In the nuclear structure there is interaction between ENERGY levels, including the Coriolis coupling between energy bands (remember the Schrödinger WAVE equations [QUANTUM mechanical PROBABILITY] and the fact that every moving object has a wave associated; de Broglie). The yrast line connects the yrast states of the lowest energy in the nuclear structure for a given angular momentum (see Figure Y.8).

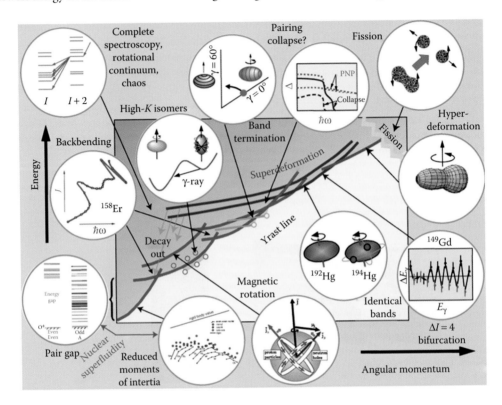

Figure Y.8 Yrast line. (Courtesy of Mark A. Riley, John D. Fox Accelerator lab, Florida State University, Tallahassee, FL and Witold Nazarewicz, Michigan State University, East Lansing, MI.)

Yrast region

[nuclear] In the nuclear structure, the ENERGY band just above the YRAST LINE is the yrast region. The yrast region consists of rotational energy levels that are correlated to the deformed GROUND STATE of the nulei. The deformation is the result of perturbations and influences, including Coriolis forces, "beta vibrations"

("breathing") and "gamma vibrations." In this model, the NUCLEUS has energy formats that are considered as fluids. For an IRROTATIONAL FLOW in a "spheroidal drop," the energy levels will be lowest (see Figure Y.9).

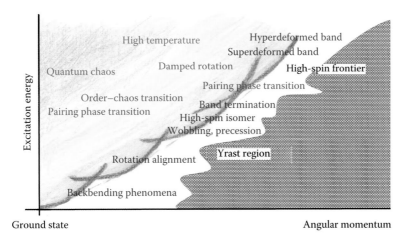

Figure Y.9 Yrast region; representative under extreme cold conditions.

Yrast state

[nuclear] In the nuclear structure, there are ENERGY levels associated with WAVE MOTION and momentum. The yrast state represents the lowest energy in the nuclear structure for a given angular momentum (see Figure Y.10).

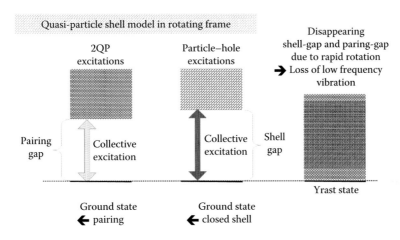

Figure Y.10 Yrast state.

Yukawa, Hideki (1907–1981)

[computational, energy, general, thermodynamics] Theoretical physicist from Japan. Hideki (also Hideky) Yukawa predicted the pi-meson (PION) in 1932 (also known as the Yukawa particle), which was experimentally verified in 1960 by the Brazilian scientist CÉSAR MANSUETO GIULIO LATTES (1924–2005). Hideki Yukawa's reasoning was that the strong interaction (hadron–hadron interaction) had to be mediated by the exchange of a virtual BOSON of relatively a large size (quantum-mechanically spoken, based on energy–mass equivalence), the virtual meson pi. The pi meson is a QUARK—antiquark composite PARTICLE. Hideki Yukawa received the Nobel Prize in Physics in the year 1949 (see Figure Y.11).

Figure Y.11 Hideki Yukawa (1907–1981). (Courtesy of Amon Carter Museum of American Art, Forth Worth, TX.)

Yukawa potential

[computational, energy, general, thermodynamics] For the atomic NUCLEUS the nuclear forces can be described as suspended in a POTENTIAL WELL, defined by HIDEKI YUKAWA (1907–1981) in 1932. The Yukawa potential describes the one-pion exchange potential, based on the transfer of one MESON from one NUCLEON to another, where the interaction potential energy $\left(U_P\right)$ between the nucleons separated at a DISTANCE r with the respective strength g_* is defined as $U_P = -g_*^2(e^{-\mu_m r}/r) \cong Q/4\pi r$, where $\mu_m = mc/\hbar$ (an operator in the

SCHRÖDINGER EQUATION), with m the REST MASS, $c = 2.99792458 \times 10^8$ m/s the speed of LIGHT, Q the collective charge, and $\hbar = h/2\pi$, with $h = 6.62606957 \times 10^{-34}$ m^{2}kg/s the PLANCK'S CONSTANT (see Figure Y.12).

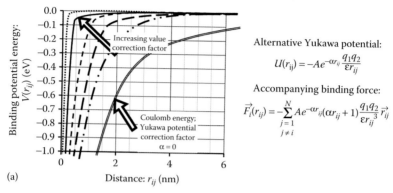

Alternative Yukawa potential:

$$U(r_{ij}) = -Ae^{-\alpha r_{ij}} \frac{q_1 q_2}{\varepsilon r_{ij}}$$

Accompanying binding force:

$$\vec{F_i}(r_{ij}) = -\sum_{\substack{j=1 \\ j \neq i}}^{N} Ae^{-\alpha r_{ij}}(\alpha r_{ij} + 1) \frac{q_1 q_2}{\varepsilon r_{ij}^3} \vec{r_{ij}}$$

(a)

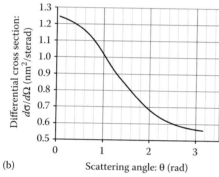

Differential elastic scattering cross section based on the Born approximation under the constraints of a Yukawa potential

(b)

Figure Y.12 (a) Yukawa potential and (b) scattering cross section under the Yukawa potential.

Z Boson

[general] Product of the DECAY process for a NEUTRON, delivering a Z-particle and a PROTON; subject to WEAK interaction under the GAUGE THEORY. The Z-particle is a neutral VECTOR BOSON. All vector bosons are W+, W−, and Z0. The mass for the Z-vector bosons is slightly more than the W-boson, 91 GeV/c², with $c = 2.99792458 \times 10^8$ m/s the speed of LIGHT. Z-particles are subject to the Yang–Mills GAUGE FIELD interaction and are highly unstable (decay time $\tau_d = 10^{-24}$ s) and decay into an electron–electron-antineutrino pair. The Z-particle was introduced in 1961 by SHELDON LEE GLASHOW (1932–), a pupil of the theoretical physicist from the United States Julian Schwinger (1918–1994) (Nobel Laureate [1965]), known for his discovery of the charged W-bosons a few years earlier. Glashow received a Nobel Prize for his work on his discovery of the fourth QUARK, the CHARM quark, and other elementary PARTICLE work, specifically the GRAND UNIFIED THEORY applied to the WEAK FORCE and electromagnetic interaction in 1979, along with STEVEN WEINBERG (1932–) and Abdus Salam (1926–1996) (*also see* **W-PARTICLE**) (see Figure Z.1).

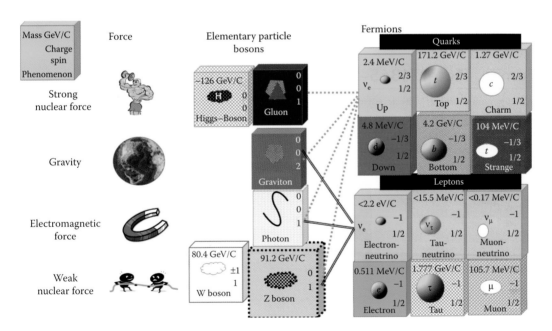

Figure Z.1 Representation of the concept of the Z-boson.

Zartman, Ira Forry (1899–1981)

[atomic, nuclear] Scientist from the United States who provided a detailed description of NEUTRON source FISSION processes. Ira Zartman also provided a theoretical description of the NUCLEAR FISSION process (see Figure Z.2).

Figure Z.2 Ira Forry Zartman (1899–1981).

Zeeman, Pieter (1865–1943)

[atomic, general, nuclear] Physicist from the Netherlands. The work of Pieter Zeeman illustrated the influence of an external MAGNETIC FIELD on the ATOMIC EMISSION lines of excited ELEMENTS, described under the ZEEMAN EFFECT. Zeeman had access to a power MAGNET and a fine DIFFRACTION GRATING, and experimented with the spectral emissions from a sodium flame (see Figure Z.3).

Figure Z.3 Pieter Zeeman (1865–1943).

Zeeman and Stark effect

[atomic, general, nuclear] ENERGY split in atomic electron transitions based on influences form magnetic fields modified by JOHANNES STARK (1874–1957) in 1913 based on the work of PIETER ZEEMAN (1865–1943) in 1896 (*see* ZEEMAN EFFECT *and* STARK EFFECT).

Zeeman effect

[atomic, computational, general, nuclear, quantum] ENERGY split in atomic electron transitions based on influences form magnetic fields. Introduced by PIETER ZEEMAN (1865–1943) in 1896. With several similarities to the STARK EFFECT (1913), this phenomenon is also known as the Zeeman–Stark effect, where the German scientist JOHANNES STARK (1874–1957) used an external electric field. When sending the emissions of the sodium LIGHT SOURCE through a DIFFRACTION GRATING under the exposure of an external steady-state MAGNETIC FIELD the D-line of the sodium emission was found to be split in constituent components. When an excited atomic state is exposed to an external magnetic field, the emission lines with respect to the unperturbed SOLUTION reveal a split that is associated with the ORBITAL ANGULAR MOMENTUM of the respective electron as well as the respective ELECTRON SPIN. This is different than the LAMB SHIFT. The phenomenon is dominated by the QUANTUM mechanical definition of ATOMIC ENERGY states. According to PETER DEBYE (1884–1966) and ARNOLD SOMMERFELD (1868–1951), the splitting of the spectral lines was associated with the orbital MAGNETIC QUANTUM NUMBER. The orbital "MAGNETIC" quantum number (m_ℓ) under the influence of an external magnetic field can assume values that are derived from the orbital ANGULAR MOMENTUM QUANTUM NUMBER (ℓ) ranging from $m_\ell = -\ell, (-\ell+1), \ldots, (\ell-1), \ell$, hence splitting the field-free emission line for ℓ into a range of closely spaced lines associated with the orbital quantum number m_ℓ, using the quantization of the magnetic field in the z-direction (the axis of precision) as $L_z = m_\ell \hbar = m_\ell(h/2\pi)$, with $h = 6.6261 \times 10^{-34}$ J s the PLANCK'S CONSTANT; note that the orbital angular momentum quantum number (ℓ) is limited by the PRINCIPAL QUANTUM NUMBER ($n; n: 1,2,3,\ldots$). The energy difference (ΔE) between the states with different ORBITAL MAGNETIC MOMENT under the influence of the small perturbation provided by the applied magnetic field yields the following split: $\Delta E = g_L \mu_B mB = \left(\langle \mu_{Lz} \rangle + \langle \mu_{Sz} \rangle \right) B$, with $g_L = 1 + [J(J+1) + S(S+1) - L(L+1)]/2J(J+1)$ the Lande's factor, J the TOTAL ANGULAR MOMENTUM, indicated by the QUANTUM NUMBER j, S the spin angular momentum (with quantum number m_S), and L the total orbital angular momentum, with the EIGENVALUE $L = \ell(\ell+1)\hbar^2$; $\mu_B = e\hbar/2m_e$ the Bohr magnetron, with m_e the electron mass; m the quantum number of the z-component of the magnetic moment and B the MAGNITUDE of the external magnetic field and $\langle \mu_{LZ} \rangle$, respectively $\langle \mu_{SZ} \rangle$, the z-components of the average respective magnetic moments. The magnetic moments are $\mu_{Lz} = (e/2m_e)\sqrt{L(L+1)}\hbar \cos\theta_L \cos\theta$ and $\mu_{Sz} = (e/2m_e)\sqrt{S(S+1)}\hbar \cos\theta_S \cos\theta$, with $\theta = m_J/\sqrt{J(J+1)}$ and θ_L the ANGLE of the total orbital angular momentum with the total angular momentum and θ_S the angle of the SPIN angular momentum with the total angular momentum. The energy splitting between states depends on the quantum numbers for the respective states. In a transition between two singlet states, the spin angular momentum will be zero for both and the three remaining conditions are $m_J = -1; 0; +1$, which is considered the NORMAL ZEEMAN EFFECT. Under the condition that $S \neq 0$, L can change in accordance with the selection rules (nuclear and atomic transition selection rules: $n > l$; $j = \ell \pm (1/2)$; $m_\ell: 0, \pm 1, \pm 2, \ldots, \pm \ell$; $m_J: -j, -j+1, \ldots 0, \ldots j-1, j$; $m_S = \pm(1/2)$), which contribute to changes in g_L providing a convoluted energy configuration and these transitions are referred to as the ANOMALOUS ZEEMAN EFFECT (*also see* PAULI EXCLUSION PRINCIPLE *and* FINE STRUCTURE) (see Figure Z.4).

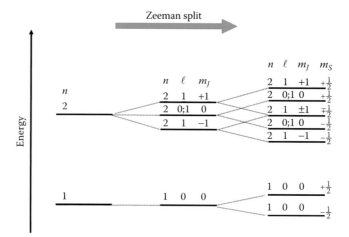

Figure Z.4 Zeeman effect.

Zehnder, Ludwig (1854–1949)

[optics] Optical physicist from Switzerland. Best known for the development of the Mach–Zehnder INTERFEROMETER in collaboration with ERNST MACH (1838–1916) (see Figure Z.5).

Figure Z.5 Ludwig Zehnder (1854–1949).

Zeiss, Carl (1816–1888)

[optics] Scientist and entrepreneur from Germany. In 1840, Carl Zeiss started a corporation building optical devices that had set the standard for most optical technology offered, initially starting out with the fabrication of high quality lenses. The corporation was located in the city of Jena, which has an excellent resource for components to produce quality glass. The market switched from large APERTURE microscope lenses to CAMERA lenses as the popularity of the camera increased. In 1872, ERNST ABBE (1840–1905) joined the group. Abbe used the WAVE properties of LIGHT to increase the accuracy of LENS design, specifically with respect to RESOLUTION (*also see* **ABBE CONDITION**). The GLASS quality was further improved through the contributions of the material expert Otto Schott (1851–1935) in 1885 (see Figure Z.6).

Figure Z.6 Carl Zeiss (1816–1888). (Courtesy of Carl Zeiss Archives, Carl Zeiss Microscopy GmbH, Jena, Germany.)

Z

Zenith

[astrophysics/astronomy, computational, geophysics] "Straight above." The highest point reached by a celestial object in its orbit with respect to the observer's frame of reference. Also used to define the moment in time when an observation or a phenomenon is most likely to occur (see Figure Z.7).

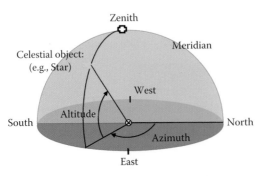

Zenith: Straight up; at normal angle to the surface

Meridian: N/S (North/South) line going through the zenith

Zenith angle: θ_z; 90° altitude

Altitude: The height above the horizon.

Azimuth: Where great circle connects stars and zenith touches the horizon; measured North through East.

Air mass: AM; a different measure of altitude, which measures path length through the atmosphere: $AM = \sec \theta_z$.

(a)

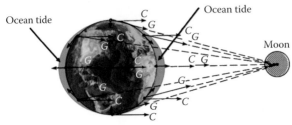

Graphical outline of the respective magnitude and directions of gravitational forces resulting from the Moon's attraction under the position of the Moon at Zenith with respect to water (oceans: G) as well as the solid mass of Earth (C).

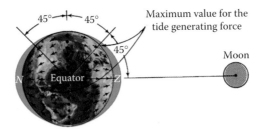

Vector representation of the net effective *translational* force on the surface waters of Earth. The tidal force is zero at 90° to the Earth-Moon zenith angle direction. The Forces at the zenith (Z) and nadir (N) directions are in theory zero.

(b)

Figure Z.7 Zenith. (a) Angular definition and (b) influence of zenith angle position of the Moon on the tidal force vector.

Zenith angle

[astrophysics/astronomy, computational, geophysics] Angle elapsing directly overhead, in spherical coordinates designated as φ, alternatively: ϕ. The angle with respect to the horizon measured in the vertical direction. In comparison, the azimuth angle is measured in the "horizontal" plane. The zenith angle is frequently used to describe the solar angle; specifically with respect to the seasons (see Figure Z.8).

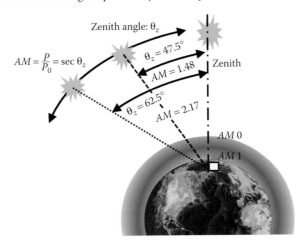

Figure Z.8 Zenith angle.

Zero-entropy state

[thermodynamics] In a diagram or graphical representation of the entropy states of a system as a function of boundary conditions, the state with the lowest entropy is referred to as the zero-entropy state. From a thermodynamic standpoint, there are no lower states, which makes the GROUND STATE zero plausible. Classical MECHANICS can often be considered a special case of THERMODYNAMICS: zero-entropy PHYSICS (see Figure Z.9).

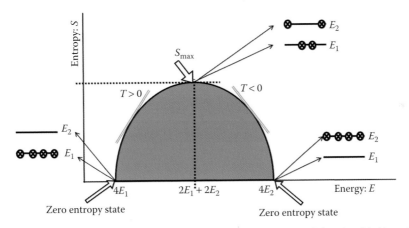

Figure Z.9 Graphical representation of the Zero-entropy state; keeping in mind that the third law of thermodynamics "predicts" that for a crystalline substance at $T = 0K$, the entry will as per the definition be equal to zero ($S = 0$). Diagram of the entropy for a system with four particles composed of two energy levels, described as a function of the total energy. The entropy is zero when all the particles are in either the lowest energy state or the highest state, whereas the entropy has a maximum value when the energies are split 50/50.

Z

Zero-equation model

[computational, fluid dynamics] In computational FLUID DYNAMICS, the special case of turbulent models that can be addressed by algebraic equations only are considered zero-equation TURBULENCE models. The conditions and circumstances can be derived directly from the supplied parameters. As such, these models may not be able to account for the history of a process nor account for DIFFUSION or convection phenomena. The primary zero-equation model is for steady-state boundary layers, the simple viscous model, which requires no integration or differentiation. Two well-known zero-equation models are the "Baldwin–Lomax" model and the "Cebeci–Smith" model. The Baldwin–Lomax model provides the eddy viscosity for a two-layer system as a function of the local BOUNDARY LAYER velocity profile. The process separates the layer in an inner and an outer layer, where the inner layer has a fixed viscosity defined by Prandtl, and the outer region has a different constant value primarily derived from force equilibrium states. In the Cebeci–Smith model the viscosity is also derived from the velocity profile; however, in this case, it uses the averaged kinetic profile for the inner layer (using the first-order derivative for location as velocity) with pressure gradient, whereas the outer region makes an approximation by introducing a "velocity thickness" as a virtual constant layer.

Zero-G

[general] Hypothetical effective weightlessness. Obtained in the apparent or true absence of gravitational attraction. An airplane in free fall will create a condition of zero GRAVITY on the internal frame of reference. In reality, there are always gravitational forces acting, no MATTER how small, from distant planets, stars, and galaxies, or just another HUMAN BODY or SATELLITE. Even galaxies provide gravitational attraction on each other, forming complex and contorted "pin wheel" constructions ranging over thousands of light-years; there are several sets of three or more galaxies that have been imaged as a "set" (see Figure Z.10).

Figure Z.10 Zero-G; weightlessness: ultimate zero-G in the outer space.

Zero-mass particles

[general, quantum] Particles with zero mass can theoretically only exist at the speed of LIGHT. Examples of zero-mass particles are photons and neutrinos as well as gravitons. The GRAVITON is the theoretical PARTICLE mediating the gravitational interaction in an orbit around the objects between which the gravitational attraction is experienced. In this hypothetical case, the (quantum mechanical) graviton forms an ENERGY field rather than just an existence of mass. The graviton model resembles the chemical attraction in a MOLECULE that shares one or MOLE electrons. The zero-mass follows from the "rest energy," which equals the momentum multiplied by the speed of light.

Zero-point energy

[atomic, nuclear] The lowest ENERGY of a system under QUANTUM mechanical conditions. Under the UNCERTAINTY PRINCIPLE, even a single particle out by itself in the outer space does not have zero kinetic energy; based on the definitions of the uncertainty principle, the PARTICLE will have zero-point energy. Alternatively, at the ABSOLUTE ZERO temperature, 0.0000000000000000 K, theoretically there will be no MOTION and hence no discernable energy content, although the particle does exist and hence it has (quantum-mechanical) probabilities associated with it, as well as motion of the nuclei and orbiting electrons. The latter makes the case purely theoretical, with no physical means of achieving the true absolute zero Kelvin. Under zero-point energy conditions, electromagnetic RADIATION is still allowed. This ELECTROMAGNETIC ENERGY density can reach excessive values, theoretically up to 10^{58} J/m^3 (see Figure Z.11).

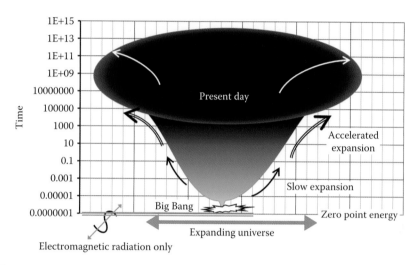

Figure Z.11 Zero-point energy.

Zero-temperature state

[thermodynamics] Ground ENERGY state for the constituents of the system, within a volume, which by definition has entropy zero and temperature zero. In physical terms, a temperature of ABSOLUTE ZERO Kelvin would mean that all MOTION has stopped and there is no energy in the system; all electron and nuclear motions would have come to a complete but hypothetical halt.

Zeroth law of thermodynamics

[general, thermodynamics] Concept introduced by JOSEPH BLACK (1728–1799) around 1760. The concept entails that when two materials of unequal temperature are brought in contact with each other they will both gradually reach a uniform equilibrium temperature (*see* THERMODYNAMICS, ZEROTH LAW).

Zhukovsky, Nikolay Yegorovich (also: Joukowsky; Николая Егорович Жуковский) (1847–1921)

[computational, fluid dynamics] Scientist and mathematician from Russia. Nikolay Zhukovsky contributed to the mathematical description of aerodynamic LIFT pertaining to flight. His work led to the implementation of the rounded frontal tip on a WING based on his theoretical analysis as well as the sharp tip on the rear to create a flow that exits without TURBULENCE. He also established the first aerodynamic institute near Moscow.

Z

His other work includes the WATER–HAMMER equation, which is also known as the JOUKOWSKY EQUATION (see Figure Z.12).

Figure Z.12 Nikolay Yegorovich Zhukovsky (also: Joukowsky; Николая Егорович Жуковский) (1847–1921) in 1915.

Zweig, George (1937–)

[energy, general, quantum, relativistic] Physicist from the Russian Federation (USSR; Union of Soviet Socialist Republics. Russian СССР Союз Советских Социалистических Республик, English translation: Soyuz Sovetskikh Sotsialisticheskikh Respublik). George Zweig along with MURRAY GELL-MANN (1929–), provided evidence that baryons (as well as the other HADRON group: mesons) are not primary ELEMENTARY PARTICLES. Dr. Zweig was a pupil of RICHARD FEYNMAN (1918–1988) (see Figure Z.13).

Figure Z.13 George Zweig (1937–). (Courtesy of CERN, Centre Européenne pour la Recherche Nucléaire, European Organization for Nuclear Research, Zurich, Switzerland.)

Appendix A

Common physical constants

Avogadro's number: $N_A = 6.022140857(74) \times 10^{23} \, \text{mol}^{-1}$

Boltzmann coefficient: $k_b = 1.38064852(79) \times 10^{-23} \, \text{m}^2\text{kg}/\text{s}^2\text{K}$

Coulomb's constant: $k_C = (1/4\pi\varepsilon_0)$, where: $\varepsilon_0 = 8.854187817.. \times 10^{-12} \, \text{C}^2/\text{Nm}^2$ the permittivity of free space

Electron charge: $ke = 8.987551787.. \times 10^9 \, \text{Nm}^2/\text{C}^2$

Electron Compton wavelength: $\lambda_C = 2.426312367(11) \times 10^{-12} \, \text{m}$

Electron mass: $m_e = 9.10938356(11) \times 10^{-31} \, \text{kg}$

Faraday constant: $F = 96485.3365 \, \text{sA}/\text{mol} = 9.648533289(59) \times 10^4 \, \text{C}/\text{mol}$

Gas constant: $R = 8.3144621(75) \, \text{J}/\text{Kmol}$

Gravitation constant: $G = 6.67408(31) \times 10^{-11} \, \text{Nm}^2/\text{kg}^2 = 6.67408(31) \times 10^{-11} \, \text{m}^3/\text{kg s}^2$

Permeability of free space: $\mu_{E0} = 1.2566370614.. \times 10^{-6} \, \text{H}/\text{m}$

Permittivity of free space: $\varepsilon_{EM0} = 8.854187817... \times 10^{-12} \, \text{C}^2/\text{Nm}^2$

Planck's constant: $h = 6.626070040(81) \times 10^{-34} \, \text{m}^2\text{kg}/\text{s}$, $\hbar = (h/2\pi)$

Proton mass: $m_P = 1.672621898(21) \times 10^{-27} \, \text{kg}$

Rydberg constant: $R_y = \dfrac{2\pi^2 k_b^2 e^4 m_e Z^2}{h^3 c} \underset{Z=1}{=} 10973731.568508(65) \, \text{m}^{-1}$

Speed of light: $c = \sqrt{\mu_0 \varepsilon_0}^{-1} = (\mu_0 \varepsilon_0)^{-1/2} = 2.99792458 \times 10^8 \, \text{m}/\text{s}$

Stefan–Boltzmann constant: $\sigma_{SB} = 5.670367(13) \times 10^{-8} \, \text{W}/\text{m}^2\text{K}^4$

Appendix B

Notable physicists

Ernst Karl Abbe (1840–1905)
George Biddell Airy (1801–1892)
Hannes Olof Gösta Alfvén (1908–1995)
Alhazen, Abū 'Alī al-Ḥasan ibn al-Ḥasan ibn al-Haytham (965–1040)
Lorenzo Allievi (1856–1941)
André Marie Ampère (1775–1836)
Anders Johan Ångström (1841–1874)
Knut Johan Ångström (1857–1910)
Aristotle (384–322 BC)
Aristocles (better known as Plato) (427–347 BC)
Archimedes (287–212 BC)
Svante August Arrhenius (1859–1927)
Pierre Victor Auger (1899–1993)
Lorenzo Romano Amedeo Carlo Avogadro (1776–1856)
Francis Bacon (1561–1626)
Antoine Henri Becquerel (1852–1908)
Alexander Graham Bell (1847–1922)
George Irvine Bell (1926–2000)
Daniel Bernoulli (1700–1782)
Jean-Baptiste Biot (1774–1862)
Niels Henrik David Bohr (1885–1962)
Ludwig Eduard Boltzmann (1844–1906)
Napoleon Bonaparte (1769–1821)
Max Born (1882–1970)
Matthew Boulton (1728–1809)
Robert Boyle (1627–1691)
William Henry Bragg (1862–1942)
William Lawrence Bragg (1890–1971)
Tycho Brahe (1546–1601)
Robert Bunsen (1811–1899)
Augustin Louis Cauchy (1789–1857)
John Calley (1644–1725)
Nicolas Léonard Sadi Carnot (1796–1832)
Giovanni Domenico Cassini (1625–1712)
Anders Celsius (1701–1744)
Sir James Chadwick (1891–1974)
Subrahmanyan Chandrasekhar (1910–1995)
Jacques Alexandre César Charles (1746–1823)
Rudolf Julius Emmanuel Clausius (1822–1888)
Henry Cavendish (1731–1810)
Arthur Holly Compton (1892–1962)

Nicolaus Copernicus (alias of Niclas Koppernigk) (1473–1543)
Charles Augustin de Coulomb (1736–1806)
Manya (Marie) Skłodovska Curie (1867–1934)
Pierre Curie (1859–1906)
Jean-Baptiste le Rond d'Alembert (1717–1783)
Leonardo da Vinci (1452–1519)
Louis Jacques-Mandé Daguerre (1787–1851)
John Dalton (1766–1844)
Charles Robert Darwin (1809–1882)
Clinton Joseph Davisson (1881–1958)
Prince Louis Victor Pierre Raymond duc de Broglie (1892–1987)
Lee de Forest (1873–1961)
Carl Gustaf Patrik de Laval (1845–1913)
Pierre de Maricourt (1220–1290)
Henri de Mondeville (1260–1320)
Petrus (Peter) Josephus Wilhelmus Debye (1884–1966)
René Descartes (1596–1650)
Henri-Alexandre Deslandres (1853–1948)
Paul Adrien Maurice Dirac (1902–1984)
Frederick Donnan (1870–1956)
Christian Johann Doppler (1803–1853)
Charles François de Cisternay du Fay (1698–1739)
Pierre Louis Dulong (1785–1838)
Karl Theodore Dussik (1908–1968)
Thomas Edison (1847–1931)
Albert Einstein (1879–1955)
Leonard Euler (1707–1783)
Daniel Gabriel Fahrenheit (1686–1736)
Michael Faraday (1791–1867)
Enrico Fermi (1901–1954)
Richard P. Feynman (1918–1988)
Armand Hippolyte Louis Fizeau (1819–1896)
Sir John Ambrose Fleming (1849–1945)
Jean Bernard Léon Foucault (1819–1868)
Benjamin Franklin (1706–1790)
Joseph von Fraunhofer (1787–1826)
Augustin-Jean Fresnel (1788–1827)
Otto Frisch (1904–1979)
Buckminster Fuller (1895–1983)
Claudius Galenus [Galen] (130–201)
Galileo Galilei (1564–1642)
Luigi Galvani (1737–1789)
Johann Carl Friedrich Gauss {Gauβ} (1777–1855)
Joseph Louis Gay-Lussac (1778–1850)
Johannes Geiger (1822–1945)
William Gilbert (1540–1603)
Josiah Willard Gibbs (1839–1903)
Lester Halbert Germer (1896–1971)
David E. Goldman (1910–1998)
Francesco Maria Grimaldi (1618–1663)
Gotthilf Heinrich Ludwig Hagen (1797–1884)
George Ellery Hale (1868–1938)

Stephen Hawking (1942–)
Werner Karl Heisenberg (1901–1976)
Hermann Ludwig Ferdinand von Helmholtz (1821–1894)
Joseph Henry (1797–1878)
Heinrich Rudolf Hertz (1857–1894)
Gustav Ludwig Hertz (1887–1975)
Sir Alan Lloyd Hodgkin (1914–1998)
Robert Hooke (1635–1703)
Edwin Hubble (1889–1953)
Sir Andrew Fielding Huxley (1917–2012)
Christiaan Huygens (1629–1695)
Constantijn Huygens (1596–1687)
Carl Gustav Jacob Jacobi (1804–1851)
Hans Jansen (early/mid-sixteenth century–early seventeenth century); *also* Hans Martens
Zacharias Jansen (1580–1638)
James Prescott Joule (1818–1889)
Heike Kamerlingh Onnes (1853–1926)
William Thomson, 1st Baron Kelvin (Lord Kelvin) (1824–1907)
Johannes Kepler (1571–1630)
Gustav Robert Kirchhoff (1824–1887)
Diederik Johannes Korteweg (1848–1941)
(Joseph Louis) Giuseppe Luigi comte de Lagrange (1737–1813)
Sir Horace Lamb (1849–1934)
Willis Eugene Lamb (1913–2008)
Johann Heinrich Lambert (1728–1777)
Adrien-Marie Legendre (1752–1833)
Pierre-Simon de Laplace (1749–1827)
Max Theodor Felix von Laue (1879–1960)
Antoine Laurent de Lavoisier (1743–1794)
Ernest Orlando Lawrence (1901–1958)
Sir John Edward Lennard-Jones (1894–1954)
Joseph Liouville (1809–1882)
Hans Lipperhey (1570–1619)
Aleksandr Mikhailovich Lyapunov (1857–1918)
Colin Maclaurin (1689–1746)
Hendrik Antoon Lorentz (1853–1928)
Ernst Mach (1838–1916)
Pierre Pelerin de Maricourt (AKA Peter Peregrine) (c. 1220–1270)
Ernest Marsden (1889–1970)
James Clerk Maxwell (1831–1879)
Maria Goeppert-Mayer (Göppert) (1906–1972)
Gustav Mie (1869–1957)
Dmitri Ivanovich Mendeleev (1834–1907)
Albert Abraham Michelson (1852–1931)
Robert Andrews Millikan (1868–1953)
Henry de Mondeville (1260–1320)
Earle Gordon Moore (1929–)
Edward Morley (1838–1923)
Henry Gwyn Jeffreys Moseley (1887–1915)
Henry Mosley (1887–1915)
Rudolf Ludwig Mössbauer (1929–2011)
Robert Sanderson Mulliken (1896–1986)

Edward Aloysius Murphy, Jr. (1918–1990)

Pieter van Musschenbroek (1692–1761)

Claude-Louis Navier (1785–1836)

Walther Hermann Nernst (1864–1941)

Thomas Newcomen (1664–1729)

Sir Isaac Newton (1642–1727)

Paul Gottlieb Nipkow (1833–1940)

Harry Theodor Nyquist ("Nyqvist") (1889–1976)

Hans Christian Oersted (1777–1851)

Georg Simon Ohm (1787–1854)

Heike Kamerlingh Onnes (1853–1926)

Robert J. Oppenheimer (1904–1967)

Denis Papin (1647–1712)

Blaise Pascal (1623–1662)

Alexis Petit (1791–1820)

Max Karl Ernst Ludwig Planck (1858–1947)

Plato (427–347 BC)

Jules Henry Poincaré (1854–1912)

Jean-Louis Léonard Marie Poiseuille (1799–1869)

Siméon Denis Poisson (1781–1840)

Ludwig Prandtl (1875–1953)

Claudius Ptolemaeus (also: Ptolemy) (approx. 90–168 AD)

Ptolemy (c. 90–168 AD)

Wolfgang Ernst Pauli (1900–1958)

Oscar Raab (1876–1986)

Isidor Isaac Rabi (1898–1988)

Sir Chandrasekhara Venkata Raman (1888–1970)

William John Macquorn Rankine (1820–1872)

Rembrandt van Rijn (1606–1669)

Olaus (Ole) Christensen Rømer (Roemer) (1644–1710)

Ernest Rutherford (1871–1937)

John William Strut, the 3rd Baron Rayleigh (1842–1919)

Osborn (Osborne?) Reynolds (1842–1912)

Wilhelm Conrad Röntgen (1845–1923)

Count Rumford (1753–1814), Benjamin Thompson

Ernest Rutherford (1871–1937), 1st Baron Rutherford of Nelson, Lord Rutherford of Nelson

Johannes Robert Rydberg (1854–1919)

Wallace Clement Sabine (1868–1919)

Joseph Sauveur (1653–1716)

Félix Savart (1791–1841)

Arthur Leonard Schawlow (1921–1999)

Paul Scherrer (1890–1969)

Sir Franz Arthur Friedrich Schuster (1851–1934)

Thomas Savery (1650–1715)

Erwin Schrödinger (1887–1961)

Sir Franz Arthur Friedrich Schuster (1851–1934)

Karl Schwarzschild (1873–1916)

Thomas Johann Seebeck (1770–1831)

Arnold Johannes Wilhelm Sommerfeld (1868–1951)

Johannes Stark (1874–1957)

Ernest Starling (1866–1927)

Joseph Stefan (1835–1893)

Sir George Gabriel Stokes, 1st Baronet (1819–1903)
Jacques Charles François Sturm (1803–1855)
Brook Taylor (1685–1731)
Edward Teller (1908–2003)
Nikola Tesla (1856–1943)
Thales of Miletus (c. 624–c. 546 BC; known as Thales: Θαλῆς)
Joseph John Thomson (1856–1940)
Charles Hard Townes (1915–)
Evangelista Torricelli (1608–1647)
Rudolf Snel van Royen (Snellius) (1546–1613)
Willebrord Snel van Royen (Snellius) (1591–1626)
Robert Jemison van de Graaff (1902–1967)
Johannes Diderik van der Waals (1837–1923)
Jacobus Henricus van 't Hoff (1852–1911)
Urban le Verrier (1811–1877)
Andreas Vesalius (1515–1564)
Leonardo da Vinci (1452–1519)
John Hasbrouck Van Vleck (1899–1980)
Count Alessandro Giuseppe Antonio Anastasio Volta (1745–1827)
James Watt (1736–1819)
Sir Charles Wheatstone (1802–1875)
John Archibald Wheeler (1911–2008)
Thomas Young (1773–1829)
Carl Zeiss (1816–1888)

Appendix C

Acoustics

CHRONOLOGY	NOTEWORTHY PEOPLE	EVENTS AND DISCOVERIES
27,000 BC	Lin-Lun	Huang-Zhong pipe, "calibrated musical tone," designed by Lin-Lun from bamboo under the reign of the Chinese Yellow Emperor Huangdi. The musical range of sound was further separated into 12 standard pitch pipes.
2,000 BC	Fohi	First documented attempt to correlate pitch and sounds produced by "the five elements: earth, water, fire, air, and wind."
~500 BC		Greek empire scientific division of sounds into three tone "genders:" chromatic, diatomic, and enharmonic, very similar to the present day musical classification. This musical note organization was derived from Arab influences who based their knowledge on Hindu influences dating back several centuries.
~500 BC	Pythagoras (570 BC–497 BC)	Definition of a single note generated as the result of the air motion with the same "frequency" as the reverberating body. Pythagoras paved the way for the musical definition in octaves (double-frequency segmentation) with mathematical formulation. Pythagoras also derived that the "sharpness" of the tone produced by a reverberating string is inversely proportional to its length, that is, frequency (pitch).
~350 BC	Aristotle (384 BC–322 BC)	Description of the movement of air under the influence of a vibrating body.
240 BC	Chrysippus (279 BC–206 BC)	Forming an analogy to water waves, the Greek philosopher Chrysippus derived that the waves on the string of the lute form a sound wave propagating in air with similar patterns of perturbation.
25 BC	Marcus Vitruvius Pollio (ca. 80 BC–15 BC)	Description of the use of vases in the amphitheaters that will attenuate low frequency sound, similar to current day acoustic baffles used in architecture. First documented use of architectural acoustic design.
1500	Leonardo da Vinci (1452–1519)	Description of the requirements of a medium to transmit sound. Da Vinci also made the same correlation between water waves and sound waves as the Greek philosopher Chrysippus (near 2,000 years prior). Leonard da Vinci also derived that sound has a distinct velocity of propagation.

(Continued)

CHRONOLOGY	NOTEWORTHY PEOPLE	EVENTS AND DISCOVERIES
1636	Marin Mersenne (1588–1648)	First scientific description of the audible tone, specifically 84 Hz. Marin Mersenne also introduced the formal concept of the octave and measured the velocity of sound
1638	Galileo Galilei (1564–1642)	Publication of *Mathematical Discourses Concerning the New Sciences* providing a definition of sound and frequency similar to that of his contemporary Marin Mersenne, but apparently independently derived.
1640	Pierre Gassendi (1582–1655)	Argument that sound was a steam of "particles" (atoms) emitted from a body. This concept was not accepted and is not in line with observations and deductions made over the past millenia.
1650	Francesco Maria Grimaldi (1613–1663)	Correlation between light wave refraction and similar aspect of visible and audible (mechanical) waves.
1660	Robert Boyle (1626–1691) and assistant Robert Hooke (1635–1703)	Experimental verification of the Leonardo da Vinci's argument for the requirement of a medium by means of an evacuated chamber with a ticking clock inside.
1678	Robert Hooke (1635– 1703)	Mathematical representation of force and deformation, providing the fundamentals for vibration and elastic theory.
1700	Joseph Sauveur (1653–1713)	Introduction of the word "acoustics" derived from the Greek word for sound. Joseph Sauveur actually was a deaf–mute and provided significant contributions to the present day understanding of acoustic concepts. Sauveur introduced the concepts of fundamental wave, harmonics, node, next to ventral segment.
1816	René-Théophile-Hyacinthe Laennec (1781–1826)	Inventor of the stethoscope, using a wooden horn to amplify the sound originating from a beating heart. Note that the use of animal horns for the collection of weak sounds (spoken word) has been recorded centuries prior to the beginning of the western calendar (before Christ; BC, even millennia BC).
1836	Ernst Florence Friedrich Chladni (1756–1827)	Discovered torsional vibrations. His work advanced acoustical engineering and acoustical architecture.
1842	Christian Andreas Doppler (1803–1853)	Introduction of the "Doppler effect," defining the change in perceived frequency of a wave (or other periodic event) for an observer and source moving relative to each other.
1845	Simon Ohm (1789–1854)	Introduction of the discrete concepts in hearing for the ear. Simon Ohm hypothesized that there are individual segments in the ear that respond to only a single sine wave frequency, the ear separates sound in its fundamental frequency and harmonics by mechanical means.
1847	James P. Joule (1818–1889)	Discovery of the magnetostrictive effect; paving the way for ultrasonic imaging.

(Continued)

CHRONOLOGY	NOTEWORTHY PEOPLE	EVENTS AND DISCOVERIES
1863	Hermann Ludwig Ferdinand von Helmholtz (1821–1894)	Foundations for spectral analysis of sound.
1877	Lord Rayleigh (1842–1919) [John William Strutt]	Theoretical publication on the physical aspects of acoustics; publication: *Theory of Sound*. Lord Rayleigh also introduced the mechanical (destructive) force associated with the cavitation aspect of sound. Cavitation would fall under fluid dynamics in the theoretical sense.
1880	Paul-Jacques Curie (1855–1941) and Pierre Curie (1859–1906)	Further evidence supporting the evolution of ultrasonic imaging with the discovery of electric charges emerging on the surfaces of certain crystals which are subjected to pressure or tension (shear or normal stress). This is referred to as the piezoelectric effect.
1900–1915	Wallace Clement Sabine (1868–1919)	Fundamental revisions to acoustical design. Established the Riverbank Acoustical Laboratories in Geneva, Illinois.
1910	Sir Horace Lamb (1849–1934)	Wave mechanics: Lamb wave. Theory of sound. Horace Lamb also contributed to hydrodynamic descriptions (1895).
1920–1930	Paul Earls Sabine (1879–1958) and son Hale Johnson Sabine (1909–1981)	Noise control and architectural acoustic design.
1937	Karl Theo (Theodore) Dussik (1908–1968)	Ultrasonic imaging.
1920–1940	Harvey Fletcher (1884–1990)	Introduction of quantifying the perception of sound and mechanical waves in the Bell Telephone Laboratories; referred to as "psychoacoustics." Introduction of the loudness concept and the decibel as a quantity for sound magnitude. Harvey Fletcher also introduced the first electronic hearing aid device.
~1940	Harry F. Olson (1902–1982)	Loudspeaker design and definition for the reproduction of sound from electronic sources.
~1954	Georg von Békésy (1899–1972)	Fundamental description of the mechanism of action in human hearing.
1964	Warren P. Mason (1900–1986)	Revolutionized the concept of ultrasound imaging. Refinements to soft-tissue imaging and work on three-dimensional reconstruction. The combination of different transducers enhances the resolution and can yield additional material-specific information.

Astronomy

CHRONOLOGY	NOTEWORTHY PEOPLE	EVENTS AND DISCOVERIES
13.8 billion years BC	Georges Henri Joseph Édouard Lemaître (1894–1966) and Edwin Powell Hubble (1889–1953)	"The Big Bang," in 1927 the expanding universe was recognized.
30,000 BC		Early human's impression of the heavens, drawings of eclipses, comets, specifically the drawing of a supernova, such as the Pueblo Petrograph.
4,500 BC	Carnac Stones	Arrangement of menhirs depicting the solar system in a rudimentary fashion, specifically the sun and the moon positions.
3,100 BC	Stonehenge	Neolithic (preceding the Bronze Era) astronomical abacus used for calculating the positions of planets and the occurrence of the changes in the Sun with respect to Earth: solstice. Alleged connection with the Druids of King Arthur's court.
ca. 2,800 BC		Mesopotamian astronomers use the moon as a guide for calendar development: lunar calendar. The Mesopotamian calendar has 354 days.
ca. 2,700 BC		Astronomers in Sumeria evolve the lunar calendar in a solar year.
1,600 BC	Babylonia	Recordings of planets, comets; the elliptical orbits time of transition, transcribed on clay tablets (this type of record keeping is referred to as cuneiform).
1,581 BC	King Ammizaduga of Nivevah (mid-eastern; Mesopotamia; stretching out into northern Africa, Europe, reaching out into Pakistan and Western Russia)	Description of scientific methodology used by the Babylonian astronomers. Detailed description of the orbital motion for the planet Venus.
~500 BC	Hellenistic culture	The ancient Greeks using astronomical records which they inherited from the Babylonians to generate a *cosmological framework*. Data was used for both practical goals, such as navigation, in addition to predicting future experiments. This may be interpreted as the introduction of the concept of the "natural philosopher." The Greek work "astronomy" refers to "law and order." The word expresses the attempts to seek order in the surroundings of the earth. The Greek combined the words: ἀστρονομία from ἄστρον astron, describing the concept of "star" and -νομία -nomia from νόμος nomos, meaning "law."

(*Continued*)

CHRONOLOGY	NOTEWORTHY PEOPLE	EVENTS AND DISCOVERIES
~580 BC	Thales (c. 624 BC–546 BC)	Greek astronomer who used the Babylonian data to predict the recurrence and orbital trajectories of solar eclipses.
~355 BC	Plato (424 BC–348 BC)	
~350 BC	Aristotle (384 BC–322 BC)	Geocentric model for the solar system.
330 BC	Heraclides (387 BC–312 BC)	First recorded scientific model of the "solar system" as a geocentric configuration. This initiated the debate of the geocentric versus heliocentric configuration. The orbits of all the planets were considered perfect spheres based on the assumption that the universe was "perfect" and with little data available to prove otherwise.
270 BC	Aristarchus [of Samos] (310 BC–230 BC)	Introduction of the heliocentric model for the earth's solar system.
220 BC	Eratosthenes (276 BC–194 BC)	The early Greeks derived that the Earth is a sphere based on the observed shadow of Earth on the Moon during lunar eclipses. Eratosthenes calculated the circumference of Earth (not using the mathematics outlined by Pythagoras (570 BC–495 BC)) using the length of the shadow in two location in Greece; at Syene the stick casts no shadow, while the shadow at the same time in Alexandria had a certain length. The value of the circumference derived by Eratosthenes of 40,320 km (252,000 stadia; 1 stadia = 0.16 km) while the current accepted circumference at the equator is 40,030 km.
150 BC	Hipparchus (190 BC–120 BC)	First recorded star catalog, including the names of constellations.
150 AD	Ptolemy (90–168)	Librarian of Alexandria who reintroduced the geocentric theory of Heraclides and formulated a complete description of the solar system that explained as well as predicted the apparent planetary motions using the combined data from centuries of observations on planetary motions. The mathematical model of Ptolemy was very complex and difficult to use to describe the elliptical orbits. The approximation used circles upon circles, requiring more than 28 circle combination to define the orbital patterns. The solution to retrograde motion explained the orbits of the planets by means of epicycles and deferents. The primary orbit is the deferent, the perturbation orbit is the epicycle.
ca. 1000	Mohammed ibn al-Hasan (Alhazen)`Abu Ali' ibn al-Haytham al-Basra (965-1039) [Iraq, Egypt]	Mathematical descriptions in optics and astronomy. The work of Al Hazen anticipated Newton's First Law of Motion {Sir Isaac Newton (1643–1727)}; the "principle of least action."
1054	China	Crab Nebula is the remnant of a star that was observed to explode by Chinese astronomers. The Crab Nebula is located at a distance of 6,523 light years from earth.
5th century– 15th century		Dark Ages; geocentric Ptolemy model.

(Continued)

CHRONOLOGY	NOTEWORTHY PEOPLE	EVENTS AND DISCOVERIES
4th century– 7th century		Renaissance.
1500	Nicolaus Copernicus (1473–1543)	Reintroduction of the heliocentric planetary model for earth. Challenging the doctrine of the Roman Catholic Church. Copernicus still used circular orbits.
1580	Tycho Brahe (1546–1601)	Construction of an observatory in Denmark. Tycho Brahe used a sextant and trigonometry to analyze the planetary orbits and derived their elliptical orbits. Telescopes were not available during his lifetime.
ca. 1600	Galileo Galilei (1564–1642)	Described laws of motion (falling bodies; gravitational acceleration) and inertia, before Sir Isaac Newton (1643–1727). Invented the pendulum clock and many more engineering feats. Additional contributions by Galileo Galilei are in astronomy, specifically the discovery of Jupiter's moons. Galileo also wrote about infinite equinumerosity, what is known as the "Hilbert's Hotel Paradox" (David Hilbert (1862–1943); "Hilbert Space"). Galileo once wrote "Mathematics is the language in which God has written the universe."
1600	Johannes Kepler (1571–1630)	Refinements to the models introduced by his mentor Tycho Brahe on the elliptical orbits. Formulation of the "laws of planetary motion," beginning of the conceptual introduction of the "clockwork universe."
1603	Johann Bayer (1572–1625)	Introducing named stars for their constellation by Greek letters, in "Uranometria" in the approximate order of (apparent) radiance "brightness," for example, Alpha Centauri.
1609		Introduction of the first telescope.
~1620	Galileo Galilei (1564–1642)	Introduction of laws of motion. Recorded observations of the universe with the first telescopes (refracting). Providing conclusive evidence for the heliocentric solar system, challenging the long-lasting geocentric solar system model. Galileo's observations led to the discovery that the sky filled with light is constructed of a multitude of stars, in our direct vicinity forming the Milky Way. He also discovered that the planet Jupiter has moons, the sun has "sun spots," and that the moon has a surface profile that is not flat (valley's and mountains).
1661	Johann Hevelius (1611–1687)	Published "Sternverzeichnis," the "meaning"/description of stars.
1666	Sir Isaac Newton (1643–1727)	Description of the spectral composition of the sunlight using a prism.
1679	Edmond Halley (1656–1742)	Publication of the first southern star catalog.

(Continued)

CHRONOLOGY	NOTEWORTHY PEOPLE	EVENTS AND DISCOVERIES
1680	Sir Isaac Newton (1643–1727)	Universal law of gravitation. Introduced the first reflecting telescope and formulated the theory of light.
1712	John Flamsteed (1646–1719)	*Historia Coelestis Britannica*, edited by Edmond Halley. This catalog introduces the Flamsteed Number, labeling stars (e.g., 21 Tauri).
1731	John Bevis (1693–1771)	Description of the Crab Nebula has been discovered near the star Z Tauri. John Bevis was at that time making his Stellar Atlas, which was published in the year 1786.
1750	Leonhard Euler (1707–1783)	Most prolific mathematician in the known history of mathematics. Euler developed the polyhedral theorem (with some suspicion that this may be traced back to René Descartes (1596–1650). Euler revolutionized the design of pumps based on his fluid dynamic theories, including turbine equations. Other theoretical interests of Leonhard Euler were optics, astronomy, acoustics, mechanics, and music. In his astrophysics work, he developed a formulation to determine the moon orbit in a three body motion problem; first ever. Additional theoretical efforts defined the rotational motion of rigid bodies of various configurations. Euler also introduced the definition for the square root of negative one as the letter "i", next to several other mathematical standard expressions for algebraic terms. Leonard Euler also introduced the exponential expression with the use of the complex number by means of sin and cosine: $e^{ix} = \cos x + i \sin x$. Euler popularized the use of the letter Sigma for a series summation.
1781	Charles Messier (1730–1817)	Recording of the Crab Nebula in the Messier catalogue as Number 1. The total catalogue contained 103 entries.
1782	William Herschel (1738–1822)	Published catalogue of 2500 celestial objects, including 269 double stars.
1799	Pierre Simon, Marquis de Laplace (1749–1827)	Laplace Law; Laplace transform to solve complex equations and his work on celestial mechanics (astrophysics).
1818	Joseph Fraunhofer (1787–1826)	Description of the solar spectrum, recognizing 576 dark lines. The more prominent lines were labeled with letters A to K. He also discovered that the light reflecting from the Moon and planets displayed spectral features that were also in that of the solar spectrum; furthermore that the spectra of planets differ from the solar spectrum. Joseph Fraunhofer designed and used the diffraction grating, one of which had the astounding (for the time) 3,625 lines per centimeter.
1832	David Brewster (1781–1868)	Spectra of cold gases produce dark absorption lines in continuous spectra.
1841	John W. Draper (1811–1882)	First picture made of the Moon. Picture made by J. W. Draper on Daguerre plates.

(Continued)

CHRONOLOGY	NOTEWORTHY PEOPLE	EVENTS AND DISCOVERIES
1845	William Parsons (1800–1876)	Lord William Parsons, 3rd Earl of Rosse (1800–1876) discovers the spiral pattern of M51, and subsequently for the M99 nebulae classification (Messier scale) and 13 other "nebulae" which were since known as "spiral nebulae."
1847	John W. Draper (1811–1882)	Discovery that hot solids emit light in continuous spectra, and in contrast, hot gases produce line spectra.
1857	Joseph von Fraunhofer (1787–1826) Carl August von Steinheil (1801–1870) William Lassell's (1799–1880)	Start of large size, high quality, reflector telescope construction and use. Telescope optics was notably improved by Joseph von Fraunhofer (1787–1826) with the development of the achromatic objective in 1824, this initiated the construction of larger refractor telescopes up to the Yerkes 102 cm. The reflector techniques followed significant improvement from the invention of glass mirrors by Carl August von Steinheil (1801–1870) in 1857 when constructing a 10 cm reflector, which was succeeded by the 33-cm reflector telescope developed by Michel Foucault (1926–1984), and the 60-cm glass mirrors of Lassell telescope named after William Lassell (1799–1880). Most big telescopes of the twentieth century are reflector telescopes made with glass mirrors. The first telescope exceeding Lord William Parsons, 3rd Earl of Rosse's (1800–1876) Leviathan of 1845, with 1.8 m opening, in aperture was the 2.54m diameter Mount Wilson telescope constructed 1917, followed by the Palomar telescope with diameter of 5.08 m in 1948, and the Zelenchukskaya telescope with diameter of 6.1 m in 1976, with only partial success unfortunately.
1852–1859	Friedrich Wilhelm Argelander (1799–1875)	Elaboration on the Messier catalog, containing the magnitude (radiance) and relative positions of 324,000 stars in the Bonner Durchmusterung. this is translated from German with liberal interpretation: the "Elaboration performed at Bonn"; the city Bonn in Germany (Die Rheinische Friedrich-Wilhelm-Universität Bonn) had instated a new observatory, designed by Friedrich Wilhelm Argelander.
1845–1890	Adalbert Krüger (1832–1896) and Eduard Schönfeld (1828–1891)	Collaborators. Introduction of the Star Catalogue: "Bonner Durchmusterung." Comprehensive outline of the stellar configuration.
1859	Gustav Robert Kirchhoff (1824–1887) and Robert Bunsen (1811–1899)	Discovery that characteristic spectrum of lines are resulting from individual chemical element (and compound), where the lines are at the same respective wavelengths in emission spectra and alternatively absorption spectra. Hence the chemical composition of any light source, including celestial bodies (both stars and planets from which light is reflecting), can be resolved from spectral analysis. Robert Kirchoff published the initial chemical constitution of the Sun in 1859.

(Continued)

CHRONOLOGY	NOTEWORTHY PEOPLE	EVENTS AND DISCOVERIES
1861	Karl Friedrich Zöllner (1834–1882)	Introduction of the to-date most accurate and quantifiable photometer used for classifying stellar object.
1863	Anders Jonas Ängstrom (1818–74)	Publication of the map of the Solar spectrum, identifying of lines corresponding chemical elements.
1864	John Herschel (1792–1871)	Published General Catalog of more than 5,000 nonstellar objects.
1864	William Huggins (1824–1910)	Discovery of gaseous nebulae spectra and found them to be emission line spectra. This observation provided as simple and unique criterion distinguishing the nebulae from star clusters. Star clusters, on the other hand, similar to the stars that composing, show a continuous spectrum (in which absorption and sometimes emission lines appear overlaid). Spiral "nebulae," however, show continuous spectra similar to stars.
1868	William Huggins (1824–1910)	Based on the work by Christian Doppler (1803–1853) describing the shifting spectral lines with respect to moving bodies, outlined how this should effect the galactic spectroscopy and that spectral lines of moving celestial objects should appear shifted. The first measurements affirming this effect were obtained in 1888 by Hermann Carl Vogel (1841–1907).
1872	Henry Draper (1837–1882)	First spectral photograph of the star Vega.
1876	Father Angelo Secchi (1818–1878)	Spectroscopic classification of first classification of 316 stars.
1880	John Louis Emil Dreyer (1852–1926)	J. L. E. Dreyer's New General Catalogue (NGC), building on the Messier Catalogue. The NGC lists over 13,0000 stellar and nonstellar objects.
1900	Cornelius Easton (1864–1929)	Description of the Milky Way as a spiral nebula, with the earth's solar system at a distance of approximately 8000 pc (parsec; 1 pc ≈ 3.26 light-years) from its center.
1906	Karl Schwarzschild (1873–1916)	Model development and publication for the solar atmosphere from theory of thermodynamical equilibrium. Description of the equation of radiative transfer.
1907		Potsdamer Durchmusterung; star catalog compiled in Potsdam, Germany.
1904–1908	Karl Schwarzschild (1873–1916)	Göttinger Aktinometrie; theoretical description of the radiance with respect to galactic location, stellar energy, and angular perception.
1914–1924	Harvard Observatory	Henry Draper Catalogue, describing the spectral profiles of 225,300 stars; referring to Henry Draper (1837–1882), pioneering astrophotography and associated spectral analyses.

(Continued)

CHRONOLOGY	NOTEWORTHY PEOPLE	EVENTS AND DISCOVERIES
1924	Edwin Powell Hubble (1889–1983)	Definition of the outer part of the Andromeda "Nebula (M31)" consisting of stars and found novae and Cepheid variables, in this manner it was established to be an external galaxy or star system.
1926	Bertil Lindblad (1895–1965) and Jan Oort (1900–1992)	definition of the theory of kinematics and dynamics of the Milky Way galaxy.
1929	Edwin Powell Hubble (1889–1983)	Derivation of distance–red shift relation for galaxies. Theoretical description of the expansion of the universe.
1951		Discovery of the 21-cm radio radiation emerging from galactic neutral hydrogen, which provided further supporting evidence for the spiral shape of the Milky Way.
1963	Maarten Schmidt (1929–)	Discovery of the first Quasar.
1957		Sputnik 1 (USSR) first artificial satellite.
1961		Venera 1 (USSR) first mission to another planet (Venus).
1969		Apollo 11 (USA) first men land on the Moon.
1972	Stephen Hawking (1942–), Jacob Bekenstein (1947–)	Thermodynamics of black holes.
1976		Viking 1 and 2 (USA) first successful unmanned landing on Mars.
1979		Voyager 1 and 2 (USA) fly by Jupiter.
1980–1981		Voyager 1 and 2 fly by Saturn.
1981		First space flight of the (NASA) Shuttle space orbiter.
1986		Voyager 2 fly by of Uranus.
1989		Voyager 2 fly by of Neptune.
1990		Hubble Space Telescope (USA/ESA) launched.
1998		Initiation of the construction of the International Space Station in outer space orbiting earth.
2011		Last space flight of the Space Shuttle space orbiter program.

Atomic

CHRONOLOGY	NOTEWORTHY PEOPLE	EVENTS AND DISCOVERIES
ca. 550 BC	Thales of Miletus (ca. 640 BC–546 BC)	Documented the magnetic attractive properties of rubbed amber and of lodestone.
ca. 450 BC	Leucippus (5th century BC)	Proposed an atomic concept of matter.
ca. 400 BC	Democritus of Abdera (ca. 460 BC–357 BC)	Student of Leucippus, one of the most famous of the atomists in ancient times. Democritus stated: "The only existing things are the atoms and empty space; all else is mere opinion."
ca. 335 BC	Aristotle (384 BC–322 BC)	Proposing that all matter was basically composed of the same "equal" continuous primordial material.
ca. 300 BC	Epicurus of Samos (ca. 342 BC–270 BC)	Philosophical system based on the atomism hypothesis expressed by Democritus.
ca. 300 BC	Zeno of Cition (ca. 336 BC–264 BC)	Foundation of the Stoic school of philosophy, based on the premise that matter, space, and natural phenomena were continuous.
ca. 60 BC	Titus Lucretius Carus (ca. 96 BC–55 BC)	Formulation explaining natural phenomena by implementation of the beliefs of Democritus and Epicurus. His poem: "De Rerum Natura," is the most comprehensive record of the Greek atomism stream of thought. The atomism of ancient times was primarily a metaphysics concept. The atomic view of matter in the modern interpretation was introduced only in its most elementary form by the beginning of the nineteenth century.
ca. 400	Saint Augustine (Aurelius Augustinus) (354–430)	Documentation of the impression that the forces exerted by rubbed amber (electric) and by lodestone (magnetic) are fundamentally different properties.
ca. 1600	William Gilbert (1540–1603)	First detailed study of magnetism and additionally for electrical phenomena showed that, in addition to amber, many other materials can be electrical charged (electrified).
1638	Galileo Galilei (1564–1642)	Description of two additional sciences with respect to "mechanics" and "local motions" in the publication: "Discors e Dimostrazioni Matematiche intorno a due nuove Scienze attenti alla Mecanica e Movementi locali" (*Discourses and Mathematical Demonstrations*). This establishes Galileo Galilei as the founder of dynamics, with fall-out to atomic and particle physics.
1650–1700	Robert Boyle (1627–1691), Robert Hooke (1635–1703), and Sir Isaac Newton (1642–1727)	Qualitative explanations of Boyle's gas law, assuming an indivisible unit forming the basis for the gas (the unknown atom), by assuming a kinetic theory of gases.

(Continued)

CHRONOLOGY	NOTEWORTHY PEOPLE	EVENTS AND DISCOVERIES
1675	Jean Picard (1620–1682)	Observation of a luminous glow (radiation) in the Torricellian vacuum of a mercury barometer resulting from the motion of the mercury when the instrument was transported.
1675	Sir Isaac Newton (1642–1727)	Introduction of the corpuscular theory of light.
1705	Francis Hauksbee (1666–1713)	Construction and operation of a powerful electrostatic generator and documented discovery of the conditions producing luminous electric discharges in gases.
1731	Stephen Gray (1666–1736)	Discovery of the electrical conduction principles.
1734	Charles Francois De Cisternay du Fay (1698–1739)	Showed that there are two kinds of electrification: resinous and vitreous, and then proposed a two-fluid theory of electric discharge. He also found that the air in the vicinity of a hot body is conducting.
1752	Benjamin Franklin (1707–1790)	Experimentally verification of the hypothesized electrical nature of lightning and introduced the one-fluid theory of flow for the concept of electricity—from surplus of positive to deficiency or negative (assuming flow of positive charges). The theory of Ben Franklin contained the first essential statement of the law of conservation of electric charge.
1753	John Canton (1718–1772)	Discovery of electrostatic induction.
1766	Henry Cavendish (1731–1810)	Discovery of hydrogen. Cavendish described the inverse square law of force action between electric charges and significant additional laws of electricity but unfortunately he largely withheld announcement of his experimental observations. The work by Henry Cavendish was not known until James Clerk Maxwell (1831–1879) published his papers in 1879.
1785	Charles Augustin Coulomb (1736–1806)	Definition of the law of force between electric charges.
1789	Antoine Laurent Lavoisier (1734–1794)	Publication of the particle aspect for chemical elements and the verification of the law of conservation of matter in chemical reactions.
1791	Bryan Higgins (1737–1820) and William Higgins (1769–1825)	Documentation of the first of a series of experiments resulting in the formulation of the laws of chemical combination.
1799	Joseph Louis Proust (1754–1826)	Introduction of the law of definite proportions for chemical compounds.
1803	John Dalton (1766–1844)	Publication of the first of a series of papers introducing the concept of atomic weights. Additional statements established the law of multiple proportions, and specifically introducing the atomic theory of matter.

(Continued)

CHRONOLOGY	NOTEWORTHY PEOPLE	EVENTS AND DISCOVERIES
1811	Lorenzo Romano Amedeo Avogadro (1776–1856)	Introduction of Avogadro's hypothesis and differentiation between atoms and molecules.
1813	Jons Jacob Berzelius (1779–1848)	Introduction of the presently known and used system of symbols for the chemical elements.
1815	William Prout (1875–1850)	Hypothesis that all elements are composed of an integral number of hydrogen atoms, described by Henry Cavendish (1731–1810) in 1766.
1815–1820	Joseph Fraunhofer (1787–1826)	Noted the spectral lines of several elements, obtained the first grating spectra, and observed the Fraunhofer (absorption) lines in solar spectra. Indication of the future recognition of the energy levels in the atomic structure (electron orbits) of elements.
1819	Pierre Louis Dulong (1785–1838) and Alexis Therese Petit (1791–1821)	Recognized the law of constancy of molar specific heat capacities of elements.
1820	Hans Christian Ørsted [Oersted] (1777–1851)	Discovery that an electric current produces a magnetic field. This revelation initiated the study of electromagnetism.
1821	Thomas Johann Seebeck (1770–1831)	Discovery of thermoelectricity.
1823	Andre Marie Ampere (1775–1836)	Published his mathematical theory of electromagnetism and the laws of magnetic field produced by currents. Some of these laws were also discovered independently by Jean-Baptiste Biot (1774–1862) and Félix Savart (1791–1841).
1826	Georg Simon Ohm (1787–1854)	Introduction of Ohm's law.
1827	Robert Brown (1773–1858)	Discovery of the concept of Brownian movement.
1833	Michael Faraday (1791–1867)	Discovery of electrolysis and introduced the terms "anode" and "cathode," with the associate flow of electrical charges.
1850–1900	August Karl Krönig (1822–1879), Rudolf Julius Emanuel Clausius (1822–1888), James Clerk Maxwell (1831–1879), Ludwig Boltzmann (1844–1906), and Josiah Willard Gibbs (1839–1903)	Kinetic theory of gases. Introduction of statistical mechanics. James Clerk Maxwell derived the velocity distribution law in 1860, Emanuel Clausius introduced the thermodynamic concept of entropy in 1865, and Ludwig Boltzmann related entropy to thermodynamic probability in 1877.

(Continued)

CHRONOLOGY	NOTEWORTHY PEOPLE	EVENTS AND DISCOVERIES
1858	Stanislao Cannizzaro (1826–1910)	Redefined the conflicting values of atomic weights by clarifying the terms "atomic," "molecular," and "equivalent" weights.
1859	Heinrich Geissler (1814–1879) and Julius Plucker (1801–1868)	Discovery of the "particle rays" (now known as cathode rays) from the negative electrode in gaseous discharge tubes, what we current know are electrons.
1860	Robert Wilhelm Eberhard Bunsen (1811–1899) and Gustav Robert Kirchhoff (1824–1887)	Recordings of the emission spectra of alkali metals in flames. Recognition of dark lines in the spectrum arising from absorption when illuminated by a bright light source through the flame. These dark lines are identical to the spectral lines observed in the solar spectrum observed by William Hyde Wollaston (1766–1828) and Joseph von Fraunhofer (1787–1826) in 1803: Fraunhofer lines, and it was argued that these lines in the sunlight are due to the absorption of light by gases in the solar atmosphere that are cooler than those "emitting the light" (not much was known about the mechanism of action of the sun), based on contemporary knowledge an oxidizing gas produces light.
1863	James Alexander Reina Newlands (1837–1898)	Stated the law of octaves for chemical structures, a limited and elementary form of the periodic table of the elements.
1865	Joseph Loschmidt (1821–1895)	Application of the equations of the kinetic theory of gases to allow for the first determination of Avogadro's number and of molecular diameters.
1869	Dmitri Ivanovich Mendeleev (1834–1907) and Julius Lothar Meyer (1830–1895)	Both independently introduced the periodic table of the elements, a concise summary of years of documented experimental and theoretical chemistry. The table is both heuristic and mnemonic.
1869	Johann Wilhelm Hittorf (1824–1914)	Observation of the deflection of cathode rays in a discharge tube, by means of a magnetic field.
1871	Cromwell Fleetwood Varley (1828–1883)	Recognition that the cathode rays are negatively charged.
1874	Jacobus Hendricus van't Hoff (1852–1911) and Joseph Achille Le Bel (1847–1930)	Description of the Carbon atom. Explanation of chirality (existence of two enantiomeric forms, virtually identical, but in actuality represent different molecules) based on the carbon atom asymmetry. Van't Hoff introduces the four (4) different types of chemical bonds, all available for carbon based structures. These four separate chemical bonds provide the mechanism of action for the tetrahedron configuration, providing different three-dimensional atomic arrangements for the same chemical formula. This applies in particular to organic chemistry

(Continued)

CHRONOLOGY	NOTEWORTHY PEOPLE	EVENTS AND DISCOVERIES
1876	Eugen Goldstein (1850–1930)	Introduction of the expression "cathode rays" and initiated experiments which eventually led to the discovery of the positive counterpart of the electron: Kanalstrahlen, meaning channel or canal rays. In 1886 Goldstein suggested that the aurora in the polar sky is due to cathode rays emerging from the sun, in fact these are a more complex range of ionizing particles.
1877	William Ramsay (1852–1916) next to Joseph Delsaulx (1828–1891), and Ignace J. J. Carbonelle (1829–1889)	Elaborated the first rather complete qualitative explanation of Brownian movement by attributing it to molecular impact. William Ramsay discovered several of the noble gases a few later, and he also made significant contributions to the study of radioactivity. He was awarded the Nobel Prize in Chemistry in 1904.
1879	William Crookes (1832–1919)	Initiated a series of experiments on the discharge of electricity through gases.
1881	Julius Elster (1854–1920), and Hans Friedrich Geitel (1855–1923)	Systematic investigation of the respective electrical effects produced by a broad range of incandescent solids.
1883	Thomas Alva Edison (1847–1931)	Recognition of the emission of negative electricity from incandescent filaments in a vacuum: Edison effect.
1884	Johann Jakob Balmer (1825–1898)	Derivation of an empirical relation for a spectral series of hydrogen as a function of wavelength. This was the first series equation found for any spectrum: Balmer series, linking atomic energy levels to spectral representations.
1887	Svante August Arrhenius (1859–1927)	Conclusively verified the ion dissociation theory of electrolytes which evolved from thermodynamic suggestions made by Rudolf Julius Emanuel Clausius (1822–1888) over the period 1850–1857. In 1903 Arrhenius was awarded the Nobel Prize in Chemistry.
1887	Heinrich Rudolph Hertz (1857–1894)	Description of the photoelectric effect while verifying the existence of the electromagnetic waves predicted by James Clerk Maxwell (1831–1879).
1888	Wilhelm Hallwachs (1859–1922)	Illustrated that only negative charges are emitted during the photoelectric effect.
1893	Philipp Eduard Anton Von Lenard (1862–1947)	Investigation of cathode rays by forcing them to pass through a Lenard window (thin window) tube into air. In 1905, Philipp Von Lenard was awarded the Nobel Prize in Physics for this and later work.
1895	Jean Baptiste Perrin (1870–1942)	Conclusively affirmation that cathode rays are negatively charged. In 1926 Jean Baptiste Perrin was awarded the Nobel Prize in Physics for this and later work.
1895	Wilhelm Conrad Roentgen (1845–1923)	Discovery of X-rays. Wilhelm Conrad Röntgen was awarded the Nobel Prize in Physics in 1901.

(Continued)

CHRONOLOGY	NOTEWORTHY PEOPLE	EVENTS AND DISCOVERIES
1896	Antoine Henri Becquerel (1852–1908)	Discovery of the radioactivity of the element uranium. He was awarded the Nobel Prize in Physics jointly with Marie Skłodowska Curie (1867–1934) and Pierre Curie (1859–1906) in 1903.
1896	Pieter Zeeman (1865–1943)	Observation of the splitting of spectral lines emitted by excited atoms while exposed to an intense external magnetic field. An earlier version of the theory of this effect was described by Hendrik Antoon Lorentz (1853–1928). They were jointly awarded the Nobel prize in Physics in 1902.
1897	Joseph John Thomson (1856–1940)	Determination of the electric charge value over the mass for cathode rays. In 1906 J. J. Thomson was awarded the Nobel Prize in Physics for this work.
1897	Ernest Rutherford (Lord Rutherford Of Nelson, 1st Baron) (1871–1937)	Experimental illustration that the radiation emitted by uranium was complex, consisting of "hard" (beta) rays as well as "soft" (alpha) rays. In 1908, Lord Rayleigh was awarded the Nobel Prize in Physics for this and for later work, he was awarded the Nobel Prize in Chemistry in 1908.
1898	Pierre Curie (1859–1906) and Marie Skłodowska Curie (1867–1934)	Isolation of the elements radium and polonium. They were awarded the Nobel Prize in Physics jointly with Antoine Henri Becquerel (1852–1908) in 1903. In 1911 Marie Curie was awarded the Nobel Prize in Physics for this work.
1899	Antoine Henri Becquerel (1852–1908), Stefan Meyer (1872–1949), Egon Von Schweidler (1873–1948), and Frederick Otto Giesel (1852–1927)	Independently observed the magnetic deflection of alpha and beta rays.
1899	Julius Elster (1854–1920) and Hans Geitel (1855–1923)	Experimental determination of the law of radioactive decay.
1899	Philipp Eduard Anton Von Lenard (1862–1947)	Experimental verification that photoelectric emission is due to electrons.
1899	Joseph John Thomson (1856–1940)	Explanation of the Edison effect is due to electrons.
1900	Antoine Henri Becquerel (1852–1908)	Experimental verification that beta rays are identical to the corpuscle character of cathode ray.
1900	Paul Villard (1860–1934)	Discovery of gamma rays.
1902	Philipp Eduard Anton Von Lenard (1862–1947)	Discovery of the photoelectric threshold frequency (i.e., minimum energy requirement) and additionally that the kinetic energy of photoelectrons is independent of the radiance of the incident light.

(Continued)

CHRONOLOGY	NOTEWORTHY PEOPLE	EVENTS AND DISCOVERIES
1903	Ernest Rutherford (Lord Rutherford of Nelson, 1st Baron) (1871–1937), and Frederic Soddy (1877–1956)	Illustrated that every radioactive process is a transmutation of elements. Frederic Soddy received the Nobel Prize in Chemistry in 1921.
1903	William Crookes (1832–1919), next to Julius Elster (1854–1920) and Hans Friedrich Geitel (1855–1923)	Uncovered that the luminescence produced when alpha particles strike zinc sulfide consists of discrete flashes of light of scintillations. This led to a method of counting individual alpha particles.
1904	William Ramsay (1852–1916) and Frederic Soddy (1877–1956)	Discovery of the remarkable recurrence of helium in all radium compounds.
1904	John Ambrose Fleming (1849–1945)	Application of the Edison effect to make the first thermionic valve ("radio" tube).
1904	Marian Von Smoluchowski (1872–1919)	Introduction of a statistical theory of Brownian movement.
1905	Albert Einstein (1879–1955)	Finalized the statistical theory of Brownian movement, based on the work of Marian Von Smoluchowski (1872–1919), introduction of the quantum explanation of the photoelectric effect, and published the special theory of relativity. Albert Einstein was awarded the Nobel Prize in Physics in 1921.
1905	Egon Von Schweidler (1873–1948)	Derivation of the law of radioactive decay based on probability theory, since it was not obtainable from causality.
1906	Owen Willans Richardson (1879–1959)	Series of important investigations regarding the emission of electricity from hot bodies: thermionic emission. Owen Willans Richardson was awarded the Nobel Prize in Physics in 1928.
1907–1912	Joseph John Thomson (1856–1940)	Devised methods of positive-ray analysis. These processes formed the beginning of mass spectroscopy.
1908	Charles Glover Barkla (1877–1944)	Discovery of the fact that the secondary X-rays of various elements are composed of groups of characteristic X-rays based on absorption experiments. Charles Barkle called these lines the K, L, and 117 radiations. He also demonstrated the polarization of X-rays. Charles Glover Barkla was awarded the Nobel Prize in Physics in 1917.
1908	Jean Baptiste Perrin (1870–1942)	Experimentally verification of several equations for Brownian movement. Perrin obtained more accurate values for Avogadro's number, and illustrated that equipartition of energy is verified for small particles suspended in a stationary liquid.

(Continued)

CHRONOLOGY	NOTEWORTHY PEOPLE	EVENTS AND DISCOVERIES
1908–1910	Alfred Heinrich Bucherer (1863–1927), Karl Erich Hupka (1884–1919), Charles Eugene Guye (1866–1942), and Simon Ratnowsky (1884–1945)	Independent precision measurements of the mass of an electron as a function of the velocity of the electron. The results confirmed the Lorentz–Einstein mass variation relation.
1909	Ernest Rutherford (Lord Rutherford ff Nelson, 1st Baron) (1871–1937) and Thomas Royds (1884–1955)	Experimentally illustrated that alpha particles are doubly ionized helium atoms, that is, helium nucleus.
1909–1910	Theodor Wulf (1868–1946) next to Albert Gockel (1860–1927)	Observation of charge leak rate from a highly insulated electroscope placed at the top of the Eiffel Tower, Paris, France, next to a study of the same effects in balloon ascents up to 4500 meters. The independent studies found the rate of leakage greater than at the surface of the earth. Their results were unexpected at the time because the effect at ground level had been attributed to local radioactivity of the soil.
1909–1911	Robert Andrews Millikan (1868–1953)	Introduction of the law of multiple proportions for electric charges and made the first precise assessment of the value for electronic charge: Millikan's oil-drop experiment. Robert Millikan was awarded the Nobel Prize in Physics in 1923.
1911	Peter Joseph Wilhelm Debye (1884–1966)	Application of the quantum theory to obtain a rather complete theory of specific heats, and subsequently applied the quantum concept to many problems and enigmas in physical chemistry. Peter Debye was awarded the Nobel Prize in Chemistry in 1936.
1911–1913	Ernest Rutherford (Lord Rutherford Of Nelson, 1st Baron) (1871–1937), Johannes Geiger (1882–1945), and Ernest Marsden (1889–1970)	Their experiments pertaining to alpha-particle scattering by thin metal foils illustrated that a nuclear model of the atom was required in order to explain the energy interaction
1911	Charles Thomson Bees Wilson (1869–1959)	Construction of the first expansion cloud chamber, used for particle research. This is one of the most important device in nuclear physics. Charles Wilson was awarded the Nobel Prize in Physics jointly with Arthur Holly Compton (1892–1962) in 1927.
1912	Max Theodor Felix von Laue (1879–1960), Walter Friedrich (1883–1969), and Paul C. M. Knipping (1883–1935)	Affirmation of the wave nature of X-rays by crystal diffraction. Max Theodor Felix von Laue received the Nobel Prize in Physics in 1914.

(Continued)

CHRONOLOGY	NOTEWORTHY PEOPLE	EVENTS AND DISCOVERIES
1912	Hans Geiger (1882–1945), and John Mitchell Nuttall (1890–1958)	Heuristic law relating the energy of an emitted alpha particle from a nucleus to the disintegration constant of the parent nucleus.
1913	Hans Geiger (1882–1945)	Detailed description of the radiation discharge counter tube which was developed from a simpler form first made in 1908: Geiger counter. This instrument was further improved in 1928.
1913	Frederic Soddy (1877–1956) and Kasimir Fajans (1887–1975)	Radioactive decay laws of displacement in the periodic table for elements. Frederick Soddy introduced the term "isotopes."
1913	George Charles De Hevesy (1885–1966) and Fritz Adolf Paneth (1887–1959)	Application of an isotope of lead: radium D, to study the solubility and the chemistry of lead compounds. This was the first documented use of an isotope as a tracer element. George De Hevesy received the Nobel Prize in Chemistry for his work in 1943.
1913	Neils Henrik David Bohr (1885–1962)	Atom model in which the electrons were presumed to occupy stable orbits demarcated by well-defined energy levels. This theory underwrites the quantum aspect of the absorption and emission of light by an atom resulting from the acceleration of an electron moving from one orbit to another orbit of different energy. This also provides an explanation of the absorption and emission at particular frequencies that are characteristic for that particular atomic energy configuration, depending on the element in question. Niels Bohr was awarded the Nobel Prize in Physics in 1922.
1913	Johannes Stark (1874–1957)	Observation of the splitting of spectral lines radiated by excited atoms in an applied intense external electric field: Stark effect. Johannes Stark received the Nobel Prize in Physics in 1919.
1913	James Franck (1882–1964) and Gustav Hertz (1887–1975)	Provided experimental evidence supporting the Bohr atomic theory pertaining to ionization and resonance potentials. Both James Franck and Gustav Hertz were awarded the Nobel Prize in Physics in 1925.
1913	William Henry Bragg (1862–1942) and William Lawrence Bragg (1890–1971)	Studied X-ray "reflection" (scatter) from crystals (Bragg law) and devised an X-ray spectrometer. They were awarded the Nobel Prize in Physics in 1915.
1913	Niels Henrik David Bohr (1885–1962)	Bohr atomic model.
1913	Frederick Soddy (1877–1956)	Formal introduction of the isotope concept.
1914	Niels Henrik David Bohr (1885–1962)	Description of the atomic energy layer model; hydrogen (Bohr atomic model).

(Continued)

CHRONOLOGY	NOTEWORTHY PEOPLE	EVENTS AND DISCOVERIES
1914	Henry Gwyn Jeffrey Moseley (1884–1915)	X-ray spectrograms of the elements which assisted in the establishment of the identity of the ordinal number of respective elements in the periodic table associated with its nuclear charge: atomic number.
1914	Karl Manne Georg Siegbahn (1886–1978)	Series of pioneering efforts in the theory and application of precision X-ray spectroscopy. Karl Siegbahn received the Nobel Prize in Physics in 1924.
1915	Sir Ernest Marsden (1889–1970)	Artificial transmutation, associated with the element radon enclosed by vacuum.
1915	Arnold Johannes Wilhelm Sommerfeld (1868–1951)	Improvements to the Bohr atomic model by introducing elliptical orbits and relativistic effects.
1915	William Duane (1872–1935) and Franklin Livingston Hunt (1883–1973)	Computational proof that the short-wavelength limit of emitted radiation is determined by the quantum theory.
1915	Albert Einstein (1879–1955)	Introduction of the general theory of relativity, describing the conditions that apply to the observations of phenomena on accelerated reference frames.
1916	Robert Andrews Millikan (1868–1953)	Experimental verification of Einstein's photoelectric equation.
1916	Peter Joseph Wilhelm Debye (1884–1966), Paul Scherrer (1890–1969), next to Albert Wallace Hull (1880–1966)	Obtained the first experimental x-ray powder diffraction patterns.
1916	Theodore Lyman (1874–1954)	Atomic absorption\emission series for hydrogen providing the Lyman series lines predicted by the Niels Henrik David Bohr (1885–1962) theory of the hydrogen atom. Theodore Lyman had documented observing at least one of these lines as early as 1906.
1918	Paul Scherrer (1890–1969)	X-ray diffraction, crystal structure. Nuclear energy development. Established the CERN institute in Switzerland as one of the founders. Directed the construction of the first cyclotron in 1940.
1919	Ernest Rutherford (1871–1937), 1st Baron Rutherford of Nelson, Lord Rutherford of Nelson	Artificial transmutation, hydrogen formation resulting from collisions of alpha particles with nitrogen, also generating oxygen and gamma rays.
1919	Ernest Rutherford (Lord Rutherford of Nelson, 1st Baron) (1871–1937)	Alpha particle bombardment of nitrogen producing hydrogen and oxygen, the first "man-made" transmutation of an element.

(Continued)

CHRONOLOGY	NOTEWORTHY PEOPLE	EVENTS AND DISCOVERIES
1919	Francis William Aston (1877–1945)	First high-precision determination series measurements of isotopic masses. Francis Aston received the Nobel prize in Chemistry in 1922.
1921	James Chadwick (1891–1974) and Étienne Samuel Biéler (1895–1929)	Strong nuclear force.
1921	Otto Stern (1888–1969) and Walter Gerlach (1889–1979)	Verification of the space quantization for silver atoms exposed to a magnetic field while measuring their magnetic moment. Otto Stern received the Nobel Prize in Physics in 1943.
1923	Arthur Holly Compton (1892–1962)	Discovery of the Compton effect, verifying that a photon has momentum. Arthur Holly Compton received the Nobel Prize in Physics jointly with Charles Thomson Rees Wilson (1869–1959) in 1927.
1923	Arthur Holly Compton (1892–1962)	Description of the deflection of photons by a charge unit, generally an electron, potentially the nucleus: Compton effect
1924	Edward Victor Appleton (1892–1965), Arthur Edwin Kennelly (1861–1939) next to Oliver Heaviside (1850–1925)	Initiation of a series of experiments that established the existence and properties of ionized layers in the upper atmosphere. The existence of this type of layers had been postulated by Arthur Edwin Kennelly (1861–1939) in 1902 and, independently, by Oliver Heaviside (1850–1925) to explain the observed implications for long-distance wireless telegraphy. Edward Appleton received the Nobel Prize in Physics in 1947.
1924	Satyendra Nath Bose (India, 1894–1974) next to Albert Einstein (1879–1955)	Independent introduction of the statistical formulation "obeyed" by bosons; a collective name for photons, nuclei of even mass number, and specific other particles.
1925	Johannes Geiger (1822–1945) and Walther Wilhelm Georg Bothe (1891–1957)	Conservation of energy for atomic and nuclear processes.
1925	Werner Karl Heisenberg (1901–1976)	Uncertainty principle.
~1925	Friedrich Hermann Hund (1896–1997)	Recognition of the "Coulomb barrier" in nuclear collision, providing a "tunneling" effect for the release of alpha particles. Also recognized as "quantum tunneling."
1924	Louis Victor Duc De Broglie (1892–1987)	Introduced the concept of de Broglie waves, the beginning of the wave theory of matter. Louis Victor, Duc De Broglie received the Nobel Prize in Physics in 1929.
1925	Walter M. Elsasser (1904–1991)	Predicted from de Broglie theory illustrating how electrons could be diffracted by crystals.

(Continued)

CHRONOLOGY	NOTEWORTHY PEOPLE	EVENTS AND DISCOVERIES
1925	Charles Drummond Ellis (1895–1980) and William A. Wooster (1903–1984)	Established that in a number of elements the emission of either an alpha or a beta particle precedes the radiation of gamma rays, and thus the latter should be associated with the daughter product, not with the parent.
1925	Pierre Victor Auger (1899–1993)	Discovery of a type of energy transition in which an electron in an atom transitions from a higher to a lower energy state by ejecting one of its own electrons, however, without the emission of electromagnetic radiation: Auger electron. This phenomenon was reported also by Lise Meitner (1878–1968) around the same time.
1925	George Eugene Uhlenbeck (1900–1988) and Samuel Abraham Goudsmit (1902–1978)	Introduction of spin and magnetic moment of the electron into atomic theory.
1925	Wolfgang Pauli (1900–1958)	Announced the exclusion principle. Wolfgang Pauli received the Nobel Prize in Physics in 1945.
1925	Patrick Maynard Stuart Blackett (1897–1974)	Obtained the first cloud chamber tracks of the induced transmutation of nitrogen and of other elements, and later made many cosmic ray studies. He was awarded the Nobel Prize in Physics in 1948.
1925	Max Born (1882–1970) and Werner Karl Heisenberg (1901–1976), and Pascual Jordan (1902–1980)	Development of quantum mechanics principles. Later, Born originated the statistical interpretation of wave mechanics. Max Born received the Nobel Prize in Physics jointly with Walther Wilhelm Georg Bothe (1891–1957) in 1954.
1926	Erwin Schrödinger (1887–1961)	Introduction of the wave mechanical theory for the hydrogen atom. Erwin Schrödinger was awarded the Nobel Prize in Physics and shared it with Paul Adrien Maurice Dirac (1902–1984) in 1933.
1926	Enrico Fermi (1901–1954) and Paul Adrien Maurice Dirac (1902–1984)	Independent introduction of the statistical formulation "obeyed" by fermions, a collective name for electrons, nuclei of odd mass number, some particles, and in particular the electron gas in a conductor. Both Enrico Fermi and Paul Adrien Maurice Dirac were awarded the Nobel Prize for work listed at a later time in this chronology.
1926	Eugene Paul Wigner (1902–1995)	Series publications on the application of group theory in quantum mechanics. Eugene Wigner shared the Nobel Prize in Physics jointly with Maria Goeppert-Mayer (Göppert) and Johannes Hans Daniel Jensen (1907–1973) in 1963.
1927	Werner Karl Heisenberg (1901–1976)	Announcement of the uncertainty principle; "Unbestimmtheit Prinzip." Karl Heisenberg received the Nobel Prize in Physics in 1932.

(Continued)

CHRONOLOGY	NOTEWORTHY PEOPLE	EVENTS AND DISCOVERIES
1927	Clinton Joseph Davisson (1881–1958), Lester Halbert Germer (1896–1971), and George Paget Thomson (1892–1975)	Electron diffraction from single crystals, and additionally George Paget Thomson obtained powder electron diffraction patterns. This work validated the existence of de Broglie waves. Clinton Davisson and George Thomson shared the Nobel Prize in Physics in 1937.
1927	Werner Karl Heisenberg (1901–1976)	Quantum uncertainty principle.
1927	Paul Adrien Maurice Dirac (1902–1984)	Description of antimatter.
1928	Edward Uhler Condon (1902–1974) and Ronald Wilfrid Gurney (1898–1953) next to George Gamow (1904–1968)	Solution to the nuclear problem of alpha particle emission using wave mechanics and they derived the Geiger–Nuttall law, in reference to the work of Johannes Geiger (1822–1945) and John Mitchell Nuttall (1890–1958).
1928	Paul Adrien Maurice Dirac (1902–1984)	Introduction of relativistic quantum mechanics and prediction of the existence of the positron. Paul Dirac shared the Nobel Prize in Physics with Erwin Schrödinger (1887–1961) in 1933.
1928	Chandrasekhara Venkata Raman (1888–1970)	Description of the Raman effect. This is the presence of frequencies differing from that of the incident light resulting from scattered by molecules. The shifts in frequency are characteristic of the scattering substance (molecular energy information) and independent of the incident frequency. Chandrasekhara Raman received the Nobel Prize in Physics in 1930.
1928	Dmitri Vladimirovich Skobeltsyn (1892)	Construction of the first cloud chamber, producing photographs of cosmic rays. These photographs revealed that cosmic rays either were, or produced, many charged, high-energy particles.
1928	Hans Geiger (1882–1945) and Walther Müller (1905–1979	Improved form of the 1913 Geiger counter, referred to as the Geiger–Müller counter.
1928	Walther Wilhelm Georg Franz Bothe (1891–1957) and Werner Heinrich Gustav Kolhörster (1887–1946)	Application of Geiger–Müller tubes to make coincidence counters and other innovative devices specifically designed for high sensitivity cosmic-radiation study. Walther Bothe shared the Nobel Prize in Physics with Max Born (1882–1970) in 1954.
1928	Johannes Geiger (1822–1945) and Walther Müller 1905–1979)	Introduction of an improved Geiger counter: the Geiger–Müller counter, using ionization of a confined gas.

(Continued)

CHRONOLOGY	NOTEWORTHY PEOPLE	EVENTS AND DISCOVERIES
1929	Leo Szilard (1898–1964) and Ernest Orlando Lawrence (1901–1958)	Particle accelerator: cyclotron. The cyclotron can accelerate protons to reach kinetic energy in excess of 700 MeV, with respective radius of 4.6 meter (1946). The first cyclotron was built in 1932, at the University of California Berkeley, California: Tevatron. Cyclotrons are specifically not exclusively, used to create isotopes for use in nuclear medicine, in particular for imaging (e.g., PET) and for cancer treatment.
1929	Otto Stern (1888)	Obtained crystal diffraction of a beam of helium atoms.
1930	Fredrik Carl Muelertz Stoermer (1874–1957), Georges Lemaitre (1894–1966), and Manuel Sandoval Vallarta (1899–1977)	Applied the theory of the motion of charged particles in the earth's magnetic field, originally developed to account for the aurora borealis, to integrate cosmic rays. This theory of the cause of geomagnetic effects was greatly expanded in 1933 by Georges Lemaitre Manuel Sandoval Vallarta. Additional theoretical work was implemented by William Francis Gray Swann (1884–1962) and others.
1930–1933	Ira Forry Zartman (1899–1981)	Experimental verification of the Maxwell distribution law of molecular velocities; Maxwell–Boltzmann distribution.
1931	Thomas Hope Johnson (1899–1998)	Experimental crystal diffraction of a beam of hydrogen atoms.
1931	Robert Jemison Van De Graaff (1901–1967)	First reliable, high-voltage, electrostatic generator for nuclear research.
1931	Wolfgang Ernest Pauli (1900–1958)	Expressed the hypothesis of beta decay processes postulating that a "new," small, neutral particle (the neutron) should be emitted concurrently with the electron. Energy when involved in beta decay up to 0.5 MeV. The experimental verification of the existence of the neutrino was not until 1956 by Frederick Reines (1918–1998) and Clyde Cowan Jr. (1919–1974).
1931	Carl David Anderson (1905–1991)	Discovery of the positron, anti-particle for the electron. The "positron" was predicted by Paul Adrien Maurice Dirac (1902–1984) in 1929. Carl Anderson received the 1936 Nobel Prize in Physics for this discovery in 1936, and he also discovered the muon in 1936.
1931	Harold Clayton Urey (1893–1981), Ferdinand Graft Brickwedde (1903–1989), and George Moseley Murphy (1905–1968)	Discovery of deuterium and composition of the first "heavy water." Harold Urey received the Nobel Prize for Chemistry in 1934.
1931	Carl David Anderson (1905–1991)	Discovery of the positron, anti-particle for the electron. The "positron" was predicted by Paul Adrien Maurice Dirac (1902–1984) in 1929.
1932	Sir James Chadwick (1891–1974)	Discovery of the neutron. Student of Ernest Rutherford (1871–1937).

(Continued)

CHRONOLOGY	NOTEWORTHY PEOPLE	EVENTS AND DISCOVERIES
1932	Ernest Orlando Lawrence (1901–1958) and Milton Stanley Livingston (1905–1986)	Construction of the first cyclotron. Ernest Lawrence was awarded the Nobel Prize in Physics in 1939.
1932	Sir John Douglas Cockcroft (1897–1967) and Ernest Thomas Sinton Walton (1903–1995)	Facilitated the transmutation of lithium by impaling by high-energy protons, and hence provided the first direct verification of the Einstein law for mass–energy equivalence. This experiment denotes the first time a high-voltage accelerator was successfully used to produce a nuclear reaction. Sir John Cockcroft and Ernest Walton shared Nobel Prize in Physics in 1951 for their work.
1932	James Chadwick (1891–1974)	Discovery of the neutron. This particle accounted for the penetrating "radiation" described by Walther Wilhelm Georg Bothe (1891–1957) and Herbert Becker (?). James Chadwick was awarded the Nobel Prize in Physics in 1935.
1932	Bruno Benedetto Rossi (1905–1993)	Realization that there is an initial increase in radiance under "transmittance" through an absorbing layer. Bruno Rossi associated this with cosmic ray showers. A transition to decreasing radiance was achieved when the layer thickness exceeded a certain value.
1932	Carl David Anderson (1905–1991)	Discovery of the positron during cosmic ray research. Carl David Anderson shared the Nobel Prize in Physics with Victor Francis Hess (1883–1964) in 1936.
1933	Patrick M. S. Blackett (1897–1974) and Giuseppe P. S. Occhialini (1907–1993)	Electron–positron pair production under cloud chamber observation; first cloud chamber photographs.
1933	Jean Valentin Thibaud (1901–1960) and Frederic Joliot (1900–1958)	Detection of radiation produced by electron-positron annihilation. Jean Thibaud and Frederic Joliot also showed the equivalence of the mass of the positron to that of the electron.
1933	Thomas Hope Johnson (1899–1998) and Jabez Curry Street (1906–1989)	Observation that the cosmic ray radiance from the west is greater than what is emerging from the east. This east–west asymmetry illustrates the excess of positively charged particles in the primary cosmic ray trajectory coming in from outer space, with a significant contribution from the Sun.
1934	Pavel Alekseyevich Cherenkov (1904–1990) [Russian: Па́вел Алексе́евич Черенко́в], Igor Yevgenyevich Tamm (1895–1971) [Russian: Игорь Евге́ньевич Тамм], and Ilya Mihajlovic Frank (1908–1990) [Russian: Илья Михайлович Франк]	Pavel Cherenkov observed a weak, bluish glow in transparent media when irradiated by high-energy beta particles. The theoretical explanation for this Cherenkov radiation was given by Ilya Mihajlovic Frank and Igor Yevgenyevich Tamm three years later. These three scientists shared the Nobel Prize in Physics in 1958.

(Continued)

CHRONOLOGY	NOTEWORTHY PEOPLE	EVENTS AND DISCOVERIES
1934	Stjepan Mohorovičić (1890–1980)	Prediction of a transitory non-nuclear "element"; later named positronium. This formation precedes electron–positron annihilation.
1934	Irene Joliot-Curie (1897–1956) and Frederic Joliot (1900–1958)	Discovery of artificial radioactivity. Irene Joliot-Curie and Frederic Joliot shared the Nobel prize in chemistry in 1935.
1934	Enrico Fermi (1901–1954), Edoardo Amaldi (1908–1989), Oscar D'Agostino (1901–1975), Franco Dino Rasetti (1901–2001), and Emilio Gino Segre (1905–1989)	Enrico Fermi developed Pauli's theory of beta decay and named the "new" particle the neutrino (little neutron). It is postulated in Fermi's theory that the neutron is radioactive, disintegrating into a proton with the formation of an electron and a neutrino just before beta emission. Fermi also began a series of experiments in collaboration to produce transuranic elements by irradiating uranium with neutrons. They were granted a patent on the graphite moderator in 1955. Fermi was awarded the Nobel Prize in Physics in 1938.
1934	Leo Szilard (1898–1964)	Recognition of nuclear decay chain reactions.
1934	Hideki Yukawa [湯川 秀樹], (1907–1981)	Introduction of mesons and the initial concept of anti-matter. In 1935 Hideki Yukawa postulation of his theory of nuclear binding resulting from a particle that has a mass that lies between that for an electron and a proton. Hideki Yukawa received the Nobel Prize in Physics for this work in 1949.
1934	Ida Noddack (1896–1978)	Formal introduction of the concept of "fission," however not recognized by her peers at the time. The fission phenomenon was only recognized when announced by Enrico Fermi (1901–1954) later that year.
1934	Enrico Fermi (1901–1954)	Interaction of slow neutron with nuclei and the resulting decay into different elements, including aluminum and uranium
1935	Arthur Dempster (1886–1950)	Discovery of the lighter uranium isotope: uranium-235
1935–1939	Isidor Isaac Rabi (1898–1988)	Precise determination of the nuclear magnetic moment within rays of atoms using an experimental set-up constructed with his radio frequency resonance method. Isidor Isaac Rabi received the Nobel Prize in Physics in 1944.
1936	Carl David Anderson (1905–1991) and Seth Henry Neddermeyer (1907–1988)	Discovery of a particle of the type postulated by Yukawa, observed during cosmic ray research The new particle was called "mesotron," later renamed as "meson."
1936	Marietta Blau (1894–1970)	First experimentalist to systematically make use of nuclear track plates.

(Continued)

CHRONOLOGY	NOTEWORTHY PEOPLE	EVENTS AND DISCOVERIES
1936	Otto Hahn (1879–1968) and Lise Meitner (1878–1968)	Neutron collision of uranium-induced decay examination.
1937	Carl David Anderson (1905–1991), Seth Henry Neddermeyer (1907–1988), Jabez Curry Street (1906–1989), and Edward C. Stevenson (20th century)	Confirmation of the existence of the meson and muon. Subatomic particles are governed by quantum physics principles, and will exhibit a wave–particle duality. The quantum state energy vectors are represented in Hilbert space.
1937	Niels Henrik David Bohr (1885–1962)	Introduction of the liquid drop model or the atomic nucleus.
1938	Irene Joliot-Curie (1897–1956) and Pavle Savic/Savitch (1903–1994)	Discovery of lanthanum in uranium after irradiation by neutrons.
1938	Otto Hahn (1879–1968) and Fritz Strassmann (1902–1980)	Bombarding uranium with neutrons produces alkali earth elements. Otto Hahn received the Nobel Prize in Chemistry in 1944.
1938	Niels Henrik David Bohr (1885–1962) and John Archibald Wheeler (1911–2008)	Formal description of the nuclear fission process.
1939	Jerome M. B. Kellogg (1905)	Discovery of a finite quadruple moment for the deuteron, requiring a non-central (tensor) nuclear force configuration.
1939	Lise Meitner (1878–1968) and Otto Robert Frisch (1904–1979)	Nuclear splitting in an attempt to explain the result from Otto Hahn (1879–1968) on the disintegration of uranium by neutron impact. They predicted the release of a substantial amount of energy resulting from fission.
1939	Niels Henrik David Bohr (1885–1962) and John Archibald Wheeler (1911–2008)	Introduction of theory of nuclear fission.
1939	Hans Albrecht Bethe (1906–2005) next to Carl Friedrich Von Weizsäcker (1912–2007)	Two groups that independently proposed two equivalent sets of nuclear reactions to account for stellar energies: the proton–proton chain and the carbon cycle.
1940	John Ray Dunning (1907–1975), Eugene Theodore Booth (1912–2004) and Aristid V. Grosse (1905–1980)	Experimental observation of the fission of U235, the less abundant isotope of uranium, by means of slow neutrons.

(Continued)

CHRONOLOGY	NOTEWORTHY PEOPLE	EVENTS AND DISCOVERIES
1940	Louis Leprince-Ringuet (1901–2000)	Obtained the first cloud chamber photograph of a collision between a meson and an electron, from which the mass of the meson could be derived.
1940	Donald William Kerst (1911–1993)	Construction of the first betatron, an induction type accelerator.
1940	Edwin Mattison McMillan (1907–1999), Philip Hague Abelson (1913–2004), Glenn Theodore Seaborg (1912–1999), Joseph William Kennedy (1916–1957), and Arthur Charles Wahl (1917–2006)	Production of the first transuranic element, neptunium. Additional work included the second transuranic element, plutonium. Edwin McMillan and and Glenn Seaborg shared the Nobel Prize in Chemistry in 1951.
1940	Otto Robert Frisch (1904–1979)	Development of the detonation mechanism for the first atomic bomb.
1940+	Julius Robert Oppenheimer (1904–1967)	Manhattan project: fission reaction. Prominent members: Arthur Compton (1892–1962), Enrico Fermi (1901–1954), Eugene Wigner (1902–1995), and dozens more.
1942	Enrico Fermi (1901–1954) and Leo Szilard (1898–1964)	Design and construction of the first successful self-sustaining fission reactor, located in Chicago, Illinois. The reactor was first placed in operation on December 2 and produced a power level of one-half watt.
1945	J. Robert Oppenheimer (1904–1967)	Director of the Los Alamos Scientific Laboratory, managing a large select group of scientists engaged in a program of basic nuclear research and development. The culmination of this work was the detonation of the first nuclear bomb at Alamogordo, New Mexico, on July 16, 1945.
1945	Edwin Mattison McMillan (1907–1999) next to Vladimir Iosifovich Veksler (1907–1966)	Independent introduction of the principle of the synchrotron. The synchrotron accelerator produces very high-energy particles, as in the Cosmotron, Brookhaven National Laboratory, Upton, New York, operating at 3.3 GeV and revealed mesons generally only generated under cosmic ray interaction; or Bevatron, Lawrence Berkeley National Laboratory, Berkeley, California, operating a proton beam at 10 BeV.
1946	Felix Bloch (1905–1983) and Edward Mills Purcell (1912–1997)	Designed the magnetic induction method. Independently, both groups developed the magnetic resonance absorption method for the determination of nuclear magnetic moments, using both liquids or solids. Their work led to the nuclear resonance spectrometer. Felix Bloch and Edward Purcell received the Nobel Prize in Physics in 1952.

(Continued)

CHRONOLOGY	NOTEWORTHY PEOPLE	EVENTS AND DISCOVERIES
1946		Introduction of the term "Lepton," defining weak nuclear interaction particles; electrons and muons are hence considered leptons.
1947	George Dixon Rochester (1908–2001) and Clifford Charles Butler (1922–1999)	Discovery of the subatomic particle: the "kaon," k-meson. Introduction of the "strangeness" concept for quarks, although the quark concept had not been introduced. In the elementary particle phenomenology the kaon is a bound state of an up- or down quark with a strange quark (anti-quark).
1947	Maria Goeppert-Mayer (Göppert) (1906–1972)	Theoretical concept development for the understanding of nuclear forces, based on a shell model, similar to the atomic electron model.
1947	William Webster Hansen (1909–1949)	Linear accelerator installation at Stanford University, California.
1947	Polykarp Kusch (1911–1993)	High precision assessment of the magnetic moment for the electron. Polykarp Kusch discovered a small but theoretically significant difference between the predicted value of the moment and the experimental results. Polykarp Kusch shared the Nobel Prize in Physics with Willis Eugene Lamb (1913–2008) in 1955.
1947	Willis Eugene Lamb, Jr., (1913–2008) and Robert E. Retherford (1882–1939)	Description of the Lamb shift, observed during the course of spectral measurements of the fine structure of hydrogen in the microwave region. This small displacement of an energy level from its theoretical position was predicted by Dirac's quantum theory of the electron (Paul Adrien Maurice Dirac [1902–1984]). Willis Lamb was awarded the Nobel Prize in Physics jointly with Polykarp Kusch (1911–1993) in 1955.
1947	Hans Albrecht Bethe (1906–) next to Julian Seymour Schwinger (1918–1994)	Explanation of the discrepancies published by Willis Eugene Lamb (1913–2008) and Polykarp Kusch (1911–1993) resulting from an interaction of electrons with an applied radiation field. Julia Schwinger shared the Nobel Prize in Physics with Richard Phillips Feynman (1918–1988) and Sin-Itiro Tomonaga [朝永 振一郎] (1906–1979) in 1965.
1947	Hartmut Paul Kallmann (1896–1978), next to John Wesley Coltman (1915–2010) next to Fitzhugh Ball Marshall (1912–1965)	Development of scintillation counters.
1947	Cecil Frank Powell (1903–1969), Guiseppe P. S. Occhialini (1907–1993), and Cesare Mansueto Giulio Lattes (1924–2005)	Discovery of the pi-meson. Cecil Powell received the Nobel Prize in Physics in 1950.

(Continued)

CHRONOLOGY	NOTEWORTHY PEOPLE	EVENTS AND DISCOVERIES
1947	George Dixon Rochester (1908–2001) and Clifford Charles Butler (1922–1999)	Discovery of V-particles and hyperons.
1948	Eugene Gardner (1913–1950) and Césare Mansueto Giulio Lattes (1924–2005)	First artificial production of mesons in the laboratory.
1948–1950	Willard Frank Libby (1908–1980) and James Richard Arnold (1923–2012)	Development of radiocarbon dating with his group at the University of Chicago, Institute for Nuclear Studies (now Enrico Fermi Institute for Nuclear Studies). Carbon dating has a time range limit of approximately 50,000 years. Frank Libby received the Nobel Prize in Chemistry in 1960.
1949	Maria Goeppert-Mayer (Göppert) (1906–1972) next to Otto Haxel (1909–1998), Johannes Hans Daniel Jensen (1907–1973) and Hans Edward Suess (1909–1993)	Introduction of the shell theory of the nucleus, which assumes a spherical organization of nucleons, similar to that for the electrons. Maria Goeppert-Mayer (Göppert) and Johannes Jensen shared the Nobel Prize in Physics with Eugene Paul Wigner (1902–1995) in 1963.
1950	Arthur Hawley Snell (1909–1989) and John Michael Robson (1920–2000)	While at the Oak Ridge National Laboratory, in collaboration with the Chalk River Laboratory provided the experimental verified that the free neutron is radioactive.
1950		Scientists began intensified research on light-element fusion reactions.
1950	Maria Goeppert-Mayer (Göppert) (1906–1972)	Introduction of the nuclear shell model for atomic nuclei.
1951	Martin Deutsch (1917–2002)	Experimental confirmation of the prediction of the existence of positronium.
ca. 1952	Ludwig von Helmholtz (1821–1894), Lyman Strong Spitzer, Jr (1914–1997) and Ronald Richter (1909–1991) and Edward Teller (1908–2003)	Nuclear fusion investigation and start of experimentation. The process was in principle described by Hermann Ludwig Ferdinand von Helmholtz (1821–1894), but is continuously in action at the Sun's surface.
1952		Brookhaven National Laboratory was the first accelerator to achieve the acceleration of proton particles to the giga-electron-volt energy range: 2.3-GeV.

(Continued)

CHRONOLOGY	NOTEWORTHY PEOPLE	EVENTS AND DISCOVERIES
1952	Aage Niels Bohr (1922–2009), Benjamin Roy Mottelson (1926–) and Leo James Rainwater (1917–1986)	Unified (collective) shell model of the nucleus. This shell model assumes a nonspherical nuclear core. The possibility of a distorted core had been suggested in 1950 by Ben Mottelson (1926–) and James Rainwater, for which they shared the Nobel Prize in Physics in 1975, along with Aage Bohr for their contributions to the description of the nonspherical geometry of atomic nuclei.
1952	Donald Arthur Glaser (1926–2013)	Construction of the first bubble chamber. Donald Glaser received the Nobel Prize in Physics in 1960. This first large-scale, terrestrial thermonuclear reaction was produced when a "hydrogen fusion device" was being tested on the Einewetok atoll, Marshall islands, on November 1.
1953	Murray Gell-Mann (1929–)	Introduction of the strangeness "numbers" for nucleons, mesons, and hyperons. Gell-Mann recognized that strangeness is conserved when part of strong interactions.
1953	Robert Hofstadter (1915–1990)	Experimental observation of the scattering of high-energy electrons by atomic nuclei and atoms. The results obtained led to the determination of the charge distribution and structure of nuclei and nucleons. Hofstadter was awarded the Nobel Prize in Physics jointly with Rudolph Ludwig Mössbauer (1929–2011) in 1961.
1954	James Power Gordon (1928–2013), Herbert J. Zeiger (1925–2011), and Charles Hard Townes (1915–2015)	Construction of the first maser (molecular [formerly, microwave] amplification by stimulated emission of radiation). In this device configuration, many molecules can simultaneously be placed into high energy states and are subsequently induced to emit their energy as radiation under stimulation from a weak incoming signal of the same frequency. Charles Hard Townes shared the Nobel Prize in Physics with Nikolay Gennadiyevich Basov [Russian: Николай Геннадиевич Басов] (1922–2001) and Alexander Mikhaylovich Prokhorov, [Russian: Александр Михайлович Прохоров] (1916–2002) in 1964.
1954	Chen-Ning Franklin Yang (1922–2004) and Robert Laurence Mills (1927–1999)	Introduction of "gauge theories." These gauge theories will eventually form the basis for the "standard model."
1955	Obninsk Nuclear Power Station, Russia	First nuclear power station for energy generation.

(Continued)

CHRONOLOGY	NOTEWORTHY PEOPLE	EVENTS AND DISCOVERIES
1955	Owen Chamberlain (1920–2006), Emilio Gino Segre (1905–1989), Clyde Edward Wiegand (1915–1996), and Thomas John Ypsilantis (1928–2000)	Creation of proton–antiproton pairs. Owen Chamberlain and Emilio Segre were awarded the Nobel Prize in Physics in 1959.
1956	Luis Walter Alvarez (1911–1988)	Cold fusion of deuterium using the negative mu-meson as a catalyst.
1956	John Bardeen (1908–1991), Walter Houser Brattain (1902–1987), and William Shockley (1910–1989)	These scientists shared the Nobel Prize in Physics in recognition of their work in the theoretical description of the solid state, in particular the semiconductor medium.
1956	Frederic Reines (1918–1998) and Clyde Lorrain Cowan, Jr. (1919–1974)	Experimental confirmation of the existence of the neutrino. Frederic Reines and Martin Lewis Perl (1927–2014) shared the Nobel Prize in Physics in 1995; since Clyde Lorrain Cowan, Jr. had passed away in 1974 he was not included since the Nobel Prize is awarded posthumously.
1956	Frederick Reines (1918–1998) and Clyde Cowan Jr. (1919–1974)	The experimental verification of the existence of the neutrino based on the 1931 work by Wolfgang Ernest Pauli (1900–1958).
1956		The world's first full-scale nuclear power plant was put into operation on October 17 at Calder Hall, England. The gas-cooled reactors develop 360 megawatts of thermal power to deliver 78 megawatts of electrical power.
1956	Tsung Dao Lee (1926–) and Chen Ning Yang (1922–)	Theoretical explanation that the law of conservation of parity, representing the invariance of spatial inversion, is invalid for weak interactions. They shared the Nobel Prize in Physics in 1957.
1956	Frederick Reines (1918–1998) and Clyde Lorrain Cowan Jr. (1919–1974)	Experimental confirmation of the neutrino introduced in 1931 by Wolfgang Pauli (1900–1958)
1956	Chien-Shiung Wu (1912–1997)	First experiment that exposed the violation of conservation of parity. Chien-Shiung Wu observed the beta emission from cobalt-60 (Co-60) at very low temperatures.
1957	Julian Schwinger (1918–1994), Sidney Bludman (1927–), Sheldon Lee Glashow (1933–), and Hideki Yukawa (1907–1981)	Bosons provide the weak attraction. Initially conceived by Hideki Yukawa (1907–1981) in 1937. These heavy bosons are referred to as W^- and W^+.

(Continued)

CHRONOLOGY	NOTEWORTHY PEOPLE	EVENTS AND DISCOVERIES
1957	John Bardeen (1908–1991), Leon N. Cooper (1930–) and John Robert Schrieffer (1931–)	First comprehensive theory of superconductivity. They all shared the Nobel Prize in Physics in 1972.
1958	Stanley Mandelstam (1928–)	Introduction of Mandelstam variables associated with the concept of "crossing symmetry," defining numerical quantities which encode the energy, momentum, and scattering angles of particles in a deflection process described in a Lorentz invariant fashion
1958	Lev Davidovich Landau [Russian: Лёв Давйдович Ландáу] (1908–1968), Arkady Beynusovich Migdal [Russian: Аркáдий Бéйнусович (Бенедйктович) Мигдáл] (1911–1991)	Theory of interacting electrons, specifically with respect to solids; condensed matter physics.
1958	Charles Hard Townes (1915–), John Perry Cedarholm (1927–), George Francis Bland (1927–2010), and Byron Luther Havens (1914–1989)	Experimental application of maser beams constructing the most precise ether-drift experiment yet. The results tentatively eluded to the fact that if the effect exists, it is less than one-thousandth of the earth's orbital speed or less than one ten-millionth of the speed of light. The precision in the frequency comparison of the masers was about one part in a 10^{12}.
1958	Rudolph Ludwig Mössbauer (1929–2011)	Predicted and experimentally verified an extremely small frequency spread in the low-energy gamma emission from nuclei bound in a crystal lattice. This effect results from transferring the gamma ray recoil momentum to the whole lattice instead of to an individual nucleus. The Mössbauer effect provides a very high precision frequency standard which lends itself for verification of several predictions made with regard to the special and general theories of relativity. Rudolph Mossbauer shared the Nobel Prize in Physics jointly with Robert Hofstadter (1915–1990) in 1961.
1959	James Alfred Van Allen (1914–2006)	Obtained data from instruments hosted on artificial satellites and derived that the earth is encircled by two zones, referred to as "Van Allen" (radiation) belts. The Van Allen belts consist of high-energy charged particles that are harnessed by the earth's magnetic field.
1960	Vernon Willard Hughes (1921–2003), Douglas W. McColm (1933?–), Klaus Otto Heinrich Ziock (1925–2010) and Richard Prepost (?–?)	Constructed and studied the atom muonium, a short-lived atom with a positive mu-meson as nucleus and a single orbiting electron.

(Continued)

CHRONOLOGY	NOTEWORTHY PEOPLE	EVENTS AND DISCOVERIES
1961	Murray Gell-Mann (1929–)	Description of elementary particles, eight-fold way of defining "strangeness" for the quark. Formal introduction of the elementary particle "quark" concept, the building blocks for protons and neutrons. The "quark" name is based on an expression in the book *Finnegans Wake* by James Joyce.
1962	Brian David Josephson (1940–)	Discovery and theoretically analyzation of a number of unexpected phenomena occurring at a "Josephson junction." The Josephson junction represents an arrangement consisting of two superconductors that are separated by a very narrow layer of insulating material.
1964	Charles Hard Townes (1915–2015), Nikolay Gennadiyevich Basov [Никола́й Генна́диевич Ба́сов] (1922–2001) and Aleksandr Mikhailovich Prokhorov [Алекса́ндр Миха́йлович Про́хоров] (1916–2002)	Quantum electronics.
1965	Oscar Wallace Greenberg (1932–), Moo-Young Han (1934–), and Yoichiro Nambu [南部陽一郎] (1921–)	Introduction of the concept of "color" change as designation and property for quarks.
1965	George Claude Pimentel (1922–1989) and Jerome V. V. Kasper (??)	Construction of first chemical laser, laser action relying on pumping energy supported by chemical reactions, in contrast to an external source of power, generally irradiation.
1970	Sheldon Lee Glashow (1932–), John Iliopoulos (1940–), and Luciano Maiani (1941–)	Introduction of the charm quark.
1973	Hugh David Politzer (1949–), David Jonathan Gross (1941–), and Frank Anthony Wilczek (1951–2015)	Discovery associating the quark color theory of the strong interaction to a special property, referred to as "asymptotic freedom." This "color" property is required to describe the data acquired over the prior period from 1968 to 1969 with respect to the substrate of the proton.
1974	Burton Richter (1931–) and Samuel Chao Chung Ting [Chinese: 丁肇中] (1936–)	Description of charm for the quark.

(Continued)

CHRONOLOGY	NOTEWORTHY PEOPLE	EVENTS AND DISCOVERIES
1975	Carlo Rubbia (1934–), Burton Richter (1931), Frederick Reines (1918–1998), Jack Steinberger (1921), Leon Lederman (1922–), Richard Taylor (1929–), Jerome Friedman (1930), and Martin Perl (1927–2014)	Standard model of particle interaction. Interactions between leptons and quarks, interacting by means of bosons. Listing the contributing scientist that led to the discovery of the various elementary particles, respectively: W and Z boson; charm quark; neutrino; muon–neutrino; muon–neutrino and b-quark; quarks (general); quarks (general); tau.
1975	Martin Lewis Perl (1927–2014)	Discovery of the tau lepton.
1977	Leon Max Ledderman (1922–)	Discovery of the "beauty" and "bottom" designation for quarks.
1978		Discovery of the "gluon" with the assistance of the PLUTO, the first electromagnetic superconductive solenoid located in Hamburg, Germany.
1983	Collider Detector at Fermilab	World's first and at the time highest-energy particle accelerator, colliding antiprotons, and protons propelled to center-of-mass energy reaching 2 TeV.
1995	Wolfgang Ketterle (1957–), Eric Allin Cornell (1961–), and Carl Edwin Wieman (1951–)	Experimental verification of Bose–Einstein condensation.
2012	François Baron Englert (1932–) and Peter Ware Higgs (1929–)	Higgs boson (126 GeV) discovery in the Large Hadron Collider at CERN, Geneva, Switzerland. The Large Hadron Collider construction started in 1998 and produces particle acceleration with respective energy levels for protons at up to 4 teraelectronvolts (0.64 microjoules), or lead nuclei: 2.76 TeV per nucleon or 574 TeV per nucleus. The proton energy level was increased to 6.5 TeV in 2015.

Biomedical

CHRONOLOGY	NOTEWORTHY PEOPLE	EVENTS AND DISCOVERIES
2900 BC		Construction of artificial eyes by Egyptian priest, without any optical function. These eyes were for "decoration" only, called Ectblepharons, worn generally outside the eye socket made from painted clay or enameled metal.
3000–2500 BC	Imhotep (c. 2650–2600 BC)	Papyrus scrolls describing several traumas and additional surgical procedures, in addition to the medical diagnosis and procedures related to pregnancy. The biomedical relevance primarily relates to the mechanical nature. Some aspects of the description of embalming for mummification and the removal of the brain through the nose are still relevant with respect to performing brain surgery, also through the nose if possible. But no reference to the functional aspects of the brain are made. Cancer was recognized and described.
1600 BC		Documented anatomical drawings found in Egypt displaying a rudimentary physiological and fluid dynamics as well as electrophysiological purpose of the following items hypothalamus, liver, kidneys, spleen, uterus, and bladder were documented. For the heart, with adjoining vessels, it was obvious that they were recognized to emanate from the heart. The papyrus scrolls also describe several identified ailments and diseases next to fractures and means to mend these afflictions.
ca. 400 BC	Plato, also known as Aristocle (427–347 BC)	Early misconceptions regarding vision. Object supposedly emit "light" which in turn is captured by the eye.
ca. 350 BC	Aristotle (384–322 BC)	Proposed the concept of light emitted by a source, such as a candle or the Sun, which is subsequently reflected by objects and hence captured by the eye; providing the fundamental principle of sight.
ca. 300 BC	Euclid of Alexandria (ca. 350 BC–280 BC)	Publication of the treatise on light: "optics" (Ὀπτικά), describing the principles of the image formation, next to general vision aspects related to the eye.
ca. 170	Claudius Galenus (130–201)	Detailed description of the anatomy of the eye: lens, retina, and optic nerve; however, still supporting the "extramission" concept introduced by Plato.
ca. 200	Claudius Galenus (130–201)	Initial measurements of the lung volume. Galen also introduced early concept of ventilation.
800s	Yaqub ibn Ishaq al-Kindi (801–873) and Abu Zayd Hunayn ibn Ishaq al-Ibadi (808–873)	Reiteration of the erroneous concept of extramission for sight

(Continued)

CHRONOLOGY	NOTEWORTHY PEOPLE	EVENTS AND DISCOVERIES
~900	Mohammad ibn Zakariya al-Razi (864–930)	Realization of the fact that the diameter of the pupil of the eye responds to the magnitude of light finally revised the vision concept to that initially introduced by Aristotle using the external light sources as a means to support vision.
ca. 1000	Avicenna (980–1037)	Description of the power of locomotion with respect to the torque applied on joints resulting from muscular contraction. He also provided a rudimentary description of the pump function for the heart.
~1300	Henri de Mondeville (1260–1320)	Treatment attempt for smallpox using light.
1480	Leonardo da Vinci (1452–1519)	Leonardo da Vinci initially supported the erroneous extramission concept for vision, but finally rejected this based on his experimentation with image formation using an ox eye from which he had scraped the retina, providing a lens with "screen" that forms an image. Leonardo da Vinci also contributed significantly to the pictorial record keeping of muscle structures, types, and contraction mechanisms.
~1500		In-socket artificial eye development, still without a true optical function.
1535	Andrés de Laguna (1499–1559)	Detailed anatomical description with terminology describing the heart, consisting of two ventricles (announcing the "right" and "left" ventricle, as we currently know and use it) and two "auricles" as he referred to the atria.
1503	Gregor Reisch (1467–1525)	Detailed human anatomical drawings in the publication: *Margarita Philosophica*. The total works of Gregor Reisch form a series of 12 books compiling an encyclopedia describing topics ranging from Latin grammar, to dialectics, rhetoric, arithmetic, music, geometry, astronomy, physics, natural history, physiology, psychology, and ethics
1543	Andreas Vesalius (1514–1564)	Detailed description and graphic representation of the anatomy of the human body, circulation system, and rudimentary description of the function of several organs and their respective engineering and physics applications. Founder of the principles of modern anatomy.
1621	Willebrord Snell (1591–1626) and René Descartes (1596–1650)	Fundamental theoretical description supporting the concept of image formation by the lens of the eye based on the law of refraction.
1628	William Harvey (1578–1657)	Detailed functional description of the cardiovascular circulation, left heart for whole body and right heart to lungs. Referring to the observations and descriptions by Andrés de Laguna (1499–1559) a century prior.

(Continued)

CHRONOLOGY	NOTEWORTHY PEOPLE	EVENTS AND DISCOVERIES
1629	Réne Descartes (1596–1650)	Description of muscles, tendons, and some reference to external stimulation, as what we now know are nerve impulses. Confirming/underwriting the pump function of the heart muscle (cardiac muscle).
1653	William Harvey (1578–1657)	Detailed description of the actin and myosin fibers defining muscle contraction.
1681	Giovanni Alfonso Borelli (1608–1679)	Measurement of vital capacity and other volumetric data regarding respiration.
1750	Robert Whytt (1714–1766)	Description of the electrical stimulation of the "optic nerve" resulting from light reaching the retina. Although the nerve as a functional unit was not understood yet. The observations were primarily derived from follow-up responses (e.g., muscle contraction) produced by the individual in the experimental set-up.
	Emanuel Swedenborg (1688–1772)	Realization that the brain is the central processing unit for nerve impulses and motor control. Published posthumously. Unfortunately, his efforts were not recognized until the year 1887.
1776	Luigi Galvani (1737–1789)	Biomedical connection to electricity and development of a mechanism to measure electrical energy
1781	Felice Gaspar Ferdinand Fontana (1730–1805)	Description of the functional aspects of the nerve fiber, but not including the phenomenological description. The description was based on the elaboration of the "electric fish" (eel) by John Walsh (1725–1795) and the work of electrical interactions with the human body by Luigi Galvani (1737–1798). The electricity of the eel was known for millennia, but not understood.
1812	Julien Jean César Legallois (1770–1814)	Recognition of the part of the brain regulation respiration (medulla). Also described the fact that gas exchanges between blood and the cells changes the partial pressure of elements in the blood with respect to the surrounding tissues, the supply of oxygen to support the metabolism and the secretion of waste carbon dioxide. His ideas also introduced the use of external supply of arterial blood to extend life, but this was not implemented until much later.
1841	Claude Bernard (1813–1878)	Recognition of the chemical equilibrium supporting life and functionality of the cell (homeostasis).
1824	Félix Savart (1791–1841)	Description of the motion of the Tympanic membrane inside the inner ear (cochlea) under the influence of applied sound.
1826	Johannes Peter Müller (1801–1858)	Description of nerve impulses, and that a nerve will produce only one particular sensation, irrespective of the stimulus. This ties to the fact that the brain interprets the stimulus, which was not known at that time in detail.

(Continued)

CHRONOLOGY	NOTEWORTHY PEOPLE	EVENTS AND DISCOVERIES
~1844	Ludwig Feuerbach (1804–1872)	Description of the five individual senses: sight/vision, hearing, touch, taste, and smell, in addition to more derived sensations such as thought, love, and experience.
1849	John Hutchinson (1811–1861)	Description of the mechanism of tidal breathing relating the pressure in the lung (alveoli) to the volume of the different stages of respiration. This work relates directly to the theoretical description by Pierre-Simon Laplace (1749–1827).
1849	Hermann Ludwig Ferdinand von Helmholtz (1821–1894)	Description of electrical stimulation resulting in muscle contraction. The decryption included a rudimentary reference to the concept of the action potential, which was at the time not known.
1855	Adolf Eugen Fick (1829–1901)	Fick's diffusion equation for gases and dissolved chemical constituents with respect to membranes.
1857	Hermann Ludwig Ferdinand von Helmholtz (1821–1894)	Theoretical description of hearing based on the (misplaced) assumptions of the basilar membrane within the cochlea acting as a resonating structure. In this resonance cavity model the low-frequency tones activating the membrane from the apical turn and high-frequency tones activating it from the basal turn. This was later corrected by the work of Georg von Békésy (1899–1972). There are also indications placing these statement at an earlier date (other contributing persons, for instance his teacher: Johannes Müller [1801–1858]).
~1860		Replacement lenses to facilitate artificial eyes reconstruction is making a functional introduction. Small ocular lenses were blown with relatively high-quality glass, initiated in Germany.
1864	Adam Politzer (1835–1920)	Description of the movement of the ossicles in the middle ear under the influence of sound. This was another step into the understanding of the auditory functioning.
1864	Wilhelm Kühne (1837–1900)	Defined the term "myosin" as a molecular component in the contractile mechanism of action for muscle. Not by long a full description of the functional aspect for the muscle since the remaining components were not discovered until 1942 and later.
1868	Julius Bernstein (1839–1917)	Introduction to the formal mechanism of action for the action potential.
1870	Adolf Eugen Fick (1829–1901)	First recorded measurement of cardiac output; using the Fick principle.
1875	Richard Caton (1842–1926) [Lord Mayor of Liverpool]	Recognized electrical activity of the brain; initial indication for the recording of the electro encephalogram (EEG). Richard Caton contributed to the general understanding of the electrophysiology concepts.

(Continued)

CHRONOLOGY	NOTEWORTHY PEOPLE	EVENTS AND DISCOVERIES
~1890	Niels Ryberg Finsen (1860–1904)	Successful treatment of smallpox with light, building on the early work of Henri de Mondeville (1260–1320).
1888–1889	Walter Nernst (1864–1941)	Definition of the electrochemical potential across a cellular membrane due to the gradient in chemical concentration for several elements. This process produces a "half-cell potential," similar to what is found in batteries. This can be placed in perspective to the first "battery" that is practical in use, designed by Alessandro Giuseppe Antonio Anastasio Volta (1745–1827) in 1800.
~1900	Oscar Raab (1876?–1986) and Giorgio Marcacci (18??–19??)	Discovery of the phototoxicity of light, specifically in the eradication of cancer.
1901	Willem Einthoven (1860–1927)	Invention of the first user friendly and reproducible electrocardiogram recorder (ECG, also found as EKG) pertaining to the electrical excitation for the contractility of the respective (cardiac-) muscle compartments of the hearts. Willem Einthoven used sting galvanometers of his own design. This provided an essential contribution to the understanding of cardiac arrhythmias and heart problems including the resulting fluid-dynamic results from the whole cardiovascular system.
1905	Nikolai Korotkoff (1874–1920)	Discovery of the sounds produced by arterial blood flowing through the brachial artery. When compressing the brachial artery the flow is interrupted, until the applied pressure is slowly dropped to the point where is matches the systolic pressure, producing an intermitted sound train, progressing in a steady rush when the applied pressure is dropped further to become equal to the diastolic pressure. Korotkoff sounds provide a noninvasive mechanism to determine blood pressure, used in every day medical applications with the aid of a stethoscope and an inflatable armband.
1911	Josiah Willard Gibbs (1839–1903); Frederick George Donnan (1870–1956)	Gibbs–Donnan equilibrium for transmembrane electrolytic solutions.
1914–1918		Mapping of brain function with respect to encephalographic location on soldiers while they are still alive with brain tissue exposed (resulting from explosives) in the trenches during World-War I.
1924	Hans Berger (1873–1941)	First official recording of brain activity by means of an electro-encephalogram (EEG). This recording provided a breakthrough in neurologic investigations and the integration of stimulus and response with respect to the respective central and peripheral nervous systems.

(Continued)

CHRONOLOGY	NOTEWORTHY PEOPLE	EVENTS AND DISCOVERIES
1926	Mark Cowley Lidwell (1878–1969) and Edgar Harold Booth (1893–1963)	Rudimentary, but effective, external cardiac pacemaker design.
1929	Otfrid Foerster (1873–1941)	Recognition of the stimulation of the occipital cortex for processing of images acquired by the eye.
1942	Brunó Ferenc Straub (1914–1996)	Description of the "actin" molecule as an integral part to the muscular mechanism of action. As a counterpart to myosin, discovered in 1864. Further refinements were introduced in 1957.
1950	John Alexander Hopps (1919–1998)	Introduction of the "portable" (45 kg) cardiac pacemaker, based on the earlier work by Mark Lidwell (1878–1969) and Edgar Harold Booth (1893–1963) in 1926. This led, with the development of microprocessors, to the first implantable pacemaker in 1958 by William Chardack (1919–2011) and Wilson Greatbatch (1919–2011) in 1958.
1953	Rosalind Elsie Franklin (1920–1958)	Discovery of the macromolecular structure (double helix) and configuration for deoxyribonucleic acid (DNA), as well as contributions to the chemical molecular description of RNA (ribonucleic acid), viruses, coal, and graphite. Rosalind Franklin used X-ray diffraction techniques for her analysis.
1956	Paul Winchell {Wilchinsky} (1922–2005)	Artificial heart (Jarvik 7).
1952		First mechanical blood pump used to assist in open-heart surgery.
1954	Andrew Fielding Huxley (1917–2012) and Alan Lloyd Hodgkin (1914–1998)	Mathematical description of nerve impulses with great accuracy, based on the (steady-state) membrane potential described by Walter Nernst (1864–1941).
~1954	Georg von Békésy (1899–1972)	Fundamental description of the mechanism of action in human hearing.
1954	David E. Goldman (1910–1998)	Goldman equation, describing the membrane potential accounting for the free migration of ions through the cell membrane, adding to the Hodgkin–Huxley equation (Andrew Fielding Huxley [1917–2012] and Alan Lloyd Hodgkin [1914–1998]).
~1955	Willem Johan Kolff (1911–2009)	First commercial artificial kidney; hemodialysis. The design was based on principles introduced by Thomas Graham (1805–1869) in 1854, next to the theoretical chemistry influences of Adolf Fick (1829–1901).

(*Continued*)

CHRONOLOGY	NOTEWORTHY PEOPLE	EVENTS AND DISCOVERIES
1957	Hugh Esmor Huxley (1924–2013)	Discovery of the integral motion activity of muscular contraction with the assistance of electron microscopy imaging.
1966	Michael E. DeBakey [Michel Dabaghi] (1908–2008)	First left-ventricular assist device implanted in a human.
1968	Viking Olov Björk (1918–2009) and Donald Pearce Shiley (1920–2010)	Introduction of the tilting disk replacement heart valve prostatic.
1968	Giles Skey Brindley (1926–) and Walpole Sinclair Lewin (1915–1980)	Initial implementation of experimental artificial vision using electronic imaging devices, preceding the retinal implant approved in 2013. This work was based on the pioneering efforts by Otfrid Foerster (1873–1941).
1981	Uri Dinnar (1939–2014)	Detailed theoretical description of the turbulent flow of cardiovascular fluid dynamics.
1982	Willem Johan Kolff (1911–2009) and Robert Koffler Jarvik (1946–)	First wearable artificial heart; "Jarvik heart."
1997	Nathan S. Lewis (1956?–)	development of an electronic "nose," resembling the human olfactory receptor system.
2001	Second Sight Inc.	First experimental artificial eye as a portable system, using a computer interface to the occipital lobe of the brain: ARGUS device.
2013		First FDA-approved retinal implant for regaining vision.

Chemical

CHRONOLOGY	NOTEWORTHY PEOPLE	EVENTS AND DISCOVERIES
"Ancient man"		Realization that the following chemical compounds were pure; what we currently consider as elements: gold (8000 BC), silver (<5000 BC), iron (<5000 BC), copper (9000 BC), mercury (<2000 BC), tin (~3500 BC), carbon (3750 BC), and sulfur (2000 BC). Element: a substance consisting of atoms with associated same number of protons (identical atomic number). Elements are the simplest chemical substances, which cannot be broken down further by means of chemical methods. Elements can be converted into other elements only using nuclear methods.
1700 BC	King Hammurabi's reign over Babylon	Known metals were documented and listed in relation to heavenly bodies.

(Continued)

CHRONOLOGY	NOTEWORTHY PEOPLE	EVENTS AND DISCOVERIES
ca. 600 BC	Thales of Miletus (ca 624 BC–ca 546 BC; known as Thales: Θαλῆς)	First person to question the basic principles that is documented as such (by Aristotle [384 BC–322 BC]), and specifically the originating substances of matter. Considered the founder of the school of natural philosophy.
450 BC	Leucippus (fifth century BC)	Argued that the universe consists as a structure of atoms and voids.
430 BC	Democritus (of Greece) (460 BC–370 BC)	Proclamation that the atom is the smallest and simplest unit of all matter. All matter is composed of atoms. The first rudimentary introduction of the elementary build block but with no scientific support. Greek word "atomos" (ἄτομος), meaning indivisible.
350 BC	Aristotle (384 BC–322 BC)	Declaration of only four (4) elements defining the existence on earth: fire, water, air, and earth. Matter only has the following properties: wet, dry, hot, or cold.
300	Alchemists	Based on the philosophy of Aristotle, the alchemists believed that "regular" metals could be converted into precious metal, specifically gold, a wishful thought. The item required to perform this conversion was referred to as the elusive "philosopher's stone."
"Dark Ages" 500–1300		
1615	Jean Beguin (1550–1620)	First diagram expression for a chemical reaction in a notation that we adhere to today.
1661	Robert Boyle (1627–1691)	End of the era of the Alchemists (perpetuated for 2000 years), partially based on the book by Robert Boyle, *The Skeptical Chymist*. First "modern chemist."
1669	Henning Brand (1630–1710)	Documented observation that phosphorus is an element.
~1650–1750	Jöns Jacob Berzelius (1779–1848), John Dalton (1766–1844), and Antoine Lavoisier (1743–1794)	Beginnings of "modern chemistry" indicated by the group of scientists considered the "fathers of modern chemistry."
ca. 1670	Sir Isaac Newton (1643–1727)	Sir Isaac Newton was one of the prominent proponents and advocates of the atom theory.
1757	William Cullen (1710–1790)	Introduction of the first formula for a chemical reaction.
1774	Antoine Lavoisier (1743–1794)	Discovery of oxygen; and the chemical process of oxidation.
1785	Charles Augustin de Coulomb (1736–1806)	Treatise on electricity: *Premier Mémoire sur l'Électricité et le Magnétisme*. The unit of electric charge is named after him posthumously. The free electric charge is the electron, which was not fully understood, nor described. The electron does form the basis for strong chemical connections, based on ion formation.

(Continued)

CHRONOLOGY	NOTEWORTHY PEOPLE	EVENTS AND DISCOVERIES
1789	William Higgins (1763–1825)	First use of the term molecule describing a chemical compound consisting of multiple atoms. The word molecule can be traced back to 1678. The expression and concept of the molecule has ties to Rene Descartes (1596–1650) and Robert Boyle (1627–1991).
ca. 1800	John Dalton (1766–1844)	Introduction of the "law of multiple proportions" describing the atomic concept based on chemical reactions taking place in ratios of small whole numbers.
1806	Sir Humphry Davy, 1st Baronet (1778–1829)	Discovery of several alkali next to alkaline earth metals, as well as contributions to the description and discovery of the elemental nature of the elements chlorine and iodine
1810	Joseph Louis Gay-Lussac (1778–1850)	Gas laws and the means to determine the alcohol content of a liquid, still used. Alcohol by volume is referenced as degrees Gay-Lussac in certain countries.
1811	Lorenzo Romano Amedeo Carlo Avogadro di Quaregna e di Cerreto, Count of Quaregna and Cerreto (1776–1856)	Molecular arrangements; molecular quantity in a mole of substance. Avogadro's law.
1820	Pierre Louis Dulong (1785–1838) and Alexis-Thérèse Petit (1791–1820)	Dulong and Petit law of specific heats.
1841	Claude Bernard (1813–1878)	Recognition of the chemical equilibrium supporting life and functionality of the cell (homeostasis).
1855	Adolf Eugen Fick (1829–1901)	Fick's diffusion equation for gases and dissolved chemical constituents with respect to membranes.
1857	Hermann Ludwig Ferdinand von Helmholtz (1821–1894)	Introduction of chemical thermodynamics concepts and definitions and electrodynamics. Hermann von Helmholtz also worked on sensory physiology, inspired by the work of Wilhelm Wundt (1832–1920). He also worked on the functional nerve physiology.
1864	Wilhelm Kühne (1837–1900)	Defined the term "myosin" as a molecular component in the contractile mechanism of action for muscle. Not by long a full description of the functional aspect for the muscle since the remaining components were not discovered until 1942 and later.
1868	Julius Bernstein (1839–1917)	Introduction to the formal mechanism of action for the action potential.
1860	Stanislao Cannizzaro (1826–1910)	Cannizzaro reaction.

(Continued)

CHRONOLOGY	NOTEWORTHY PEOPLE	EVENTS AND DISCOVERIES
1869	Dmitri Ivanovich Mendeleev (1834–1907) and Julius Lothar Meyer (1830–1895)	Both independently introduced the Periodic Table of the Elements, a concise summary of years of documented experimental and theoretical chemistry. The table is both heuristic and mnemonic.
1873	Josiah Willard Gibbs (1839–1903)	Chemical potential, a energy constituent within the Gibbs free energy. Thermodynamic concept describing the energy that can be released or absorbed during a chemical reaction.
1874	Jacobus Henricus van 't Hoff (1852–1911) and Joseph Achille Le Bel (1847–1930)	Two independent observations regarding the optical activity (rotation of polarization direction for transmitted light) for carbon compounds. They both derived that this can be explained by a four (4) way bound carbon atom (chemical saturation).
1879	William Crookes (1832–1919)	Cathode rays and realization that single charged particles must be involved.
1885	Eugene Goldstein (1850–1930)	Discovery of the proton.
1880	Paul-Jacques Curie (1855–1941) and Pierre Curie (1859–1906)	Discovery of electric charges emerging on the surfaces of crystals, which are subjected to shear or normal stress. This is referred to as the piezoelectric effect.
1880	Johannes Diderik van der Waals (1837–1923)	Description of the covalent bond. Van der Waals equation.
1897	Joseph John Thomson (1856–1940)	Discovery of the electron concept; using William Crookes's vacuum tube. The electron itself was at this point not identified.
1897	Marie Skłodowska Curie (1867–1934)	Discovery of radioactive isotopes.
~1890	Niels Ryberg Finsen (1860–1904)	Successful treatment of smallpox with light, building on the early work of Henri de Mondeville (1260–1320).
1888–1889	Walter Nernst (1864–1941)	Definition of the electrochemical potential across a cellular membrane due to the gradient in chemical concentration for several elements. This process produces a "half-cell potential," similar to what is found in batteries. This can be placed in perspective to the first "battery" that is practical in use, designed by Alessandro Giuseppe Antonio Anastasio Volta (1745–1827) in 1800.
~1900	Oscar Raab (1876?–1986) and Giorgio Marcacci (18??–19??)	Discovery of the phototoxicity of light, specifically in the eradication of cancer.
1906	Dmitri Ivanovich Mendeleev (1834–1907)	Periodic Table of Elements.

(Continued)

CHRONOLOGY	NOTEWORTHY PEOPLE	EVENTS AND DISCOVERIES
1911	Josiah Willard Gibbs (1839–1903) and Frederick George Donnan (1870–1956)	Gibbs–Donnan equilibrium for transmembrane electrolytic solutions.
1909	Robert Andrews Millikan (1868–1953)	Measurement of the mass of the electron.
1914	Henry Gwyn Jeffrey Moseley (1884–1915)	X-ray spectrograms of the elements which assisted in the establishment of the identity of the ordinal number of respective elements in the periodic table associated with its nuclear charge: atomic number.
1916	Niels Henrik David Bohr (1885–1962)	Atomic structure and quantum theory.
1916	Gilbert Newton Lewis (1875–1946)	Description of the shell filling for atomic electrons, and the related covalent bond and the concept of valence electrons.
1917	Ernest Rutherford, 1st Baron Rutherford of Nelson (1871–1937)	Discovery of the proton.
1926	1928: Paul Dirac (1902–1984); 1929: Dmitri Vladimirovich Skobeltsyn (1892–1990); and 1932: Carl David Anderson (1905–1991)	Discovery of positron. Generally, Carl Anderson is credited with the formal discovery (Nobel Prize).
1926	Jean Baptiste Perrin (1870–1942)	Physical proof providing the existence of molecules.
1927	Wolfgang Ernst Pauli (1900–1958), Ralph Kronig (1904–1995), George Eugene Uhlenbeck (1900–1988), Samuel Abraham Goudsmit (1902–1978), and Paul Adrien Maurice Dirac (1902–1984)	Introduction of the electron spin concept and a broad range of relativistic quantum mechanical principles. This formed the foundation for the development of the NMR imaging system: nuclear magnetic resonance (MRI).
1928	Sir Chandrasekhara Venkata Raman (1888–1970)	Raman spectroscopy; indicating the energy levels in atoms and molecules.
1931	Linus Carl Pauling (1901–1994)	Description of the general and detailed nature of various types of chemical bonds.
1932	James Chadwick (1891–1974)	Discovery of the neutron.

(Continued)

CHRONOLOGY	NOTEWORTHY PEOPLE	EVENTS AND DISCOVERIES
1940+	Julius Robert Oppenheimer (1904–1967)	Manhattan project: fission reaction. Prominent members: Arthur Compton (1892–1962), Enrico Fermi (1901–1954), Eugene Wigner (1902–1995), and dozens more.
1924	Niels Henrik David Bohr (1885–1962)	Introduction of the term: "element." This idea was formed based on Wolfgang Pauli's (1900–1958) exclusion principle. The element concept has been around for millennia.
1950	Maria Goeppert-Mayer (Göppert) (1906–1972)	Introduction of the nuclear shell model of atomic nuclei.
1953	Rosalind Elsie Franklin (1920–1958)	Discovery of the macromolecular structure (double helix) and configuration for deoxyribonucleic acid (DNA), as well as contributions to the chemical molecular description of RNA (ribonucleic acid), viruses, coal, and graphite.
~1955	Willem Johan Kolff (1911–2009)	First commercial artificial kidney; hemodialysis. The design was based on principles introduced by Thomas Graham (1805–1869) in 1854, next to the theoretical chemistry influences of Adolf Fick (1829–1901).
1992	Kenneth Kin Man Kwong (1948–)	Introduction of "functional MRI." In 2013 the sugar consumption was measured in cancer cells with respect to normal cells for diagnostic verification.

Computational

CHRONOLOGY	NOTEWORTHY PEOPLE	EVENTS AND DISCOVERIES
9000 BC–6500 BC	Ishango Bone	Bone with the first prime numbers carved in order.
3500 BC	Mesopotamian clay tablets	Clay carvings with geometrical shapes, fractions, and logarithm and a list of "squares." Most was published on a base of 60, not our current 10-base
1600 BC	Rhind papyrus	Papyrus scrolls with mathematical equations and fractions.
1750 BC–500 BC	Vedic period (India)	Advanced civilization with a great number of mathematical revelations. Algebra, trigonometry, and geometry expression by Lagadha, approx. 1300 BC; approx. 800 BC and Yajnavalkya also approx. 800 BC.
600 BC	Apastambha (ca. 630–560 BC)	Hindu (India) scholar that expressed the value of pi (π) well before the documented use in the Egyptian/Babylonian mathematics. This relates to the calculations of the circumference and area of circle and sphere. Apastambha may have described the angular concepts that are attributed to Pythagoras at least a century prior.

(Continued)

CHRONOLOGY	NOTEWORTHY PEOPLE	EVENTS AND DISCOVERIES
600 BC	Thales of Miletus (ca. 640 BC–546 BC)	First introduction to finite (differential) approximation. Father of philosophy. Alkso described the use of triangulation to measure dimensions of remote objects (i.e., height of pyramids). Greek philosopher who supposedly studied under the Egyptians (Mesopotamia).
530 BC	Pythagoras of Samos (ca. 578–505 BC)	Student of a student of Thales. Introduced the formal concepts in geometry.
450 BC	Zeno of Elea (ca. 495–435 BC)	Introduced the concept of infinitesimal steps (infinitesimally small; approach of a turtle that is moving away, paradox).
350 BC	Aristotle [of Stagira] (384–322 BC)	Teacher to Euclid. Documented axioms and proofs. Introduced the initial concepts of the wave theory for light, although not accepted for almost 2000 years.
300 BC	Euclid [of Megara and Alexandria] (ca. 322–275 BC)	"Father of modern mathematics." Introduced the Euclidean space for model formation representing real-life situations. He described spherical geometry and other complex geometrical forms such as the cone.
250 BC	Archimedes of Syracuse (287 BC–212 BC)	Student at the school of Euclid, most likely after Euclid's death. number theory, and square roots. Additional mathematics applied to specific physical phenomena such as buoyancy.
ca. 130	Claudius Ptolemaeus of Alexandria (ca. 90–168)	Introduction of various mathematical rules and theorems that allowed the introduction of more complex mathematics as seen in the following centuries. Ptolemy's theorem.
ca. 250	Liu Hui (ca. 220–280) [China]	Incorporation of negative numbers in mathematical expressions and arithmetic. Building on the work of Chang Tshang (ca. 200–142 BC) also from China. Liu Hiu is considered to be one of China's greatest mathematicians. He also formalized the decimal system. The number zero had a special meaning, introducing the initial concept of the "singularity." Hui also described the process for solving a series of linear equations (solving for multiple unknowns).
ca. 500	Aryabhata (476–550) [India]	Advanced mathematics, including series resembling the "Taylor series."
ca. 850	Ya'qub `Abu Yusuf' ibn Ishaq al-Kindi (803–873) [Iraq]; Al-Kindi referred to as Alkindus in the West	Popularized the implementation of the decimal system, developed spherical geometry, and many other science and engineering topics and pioneered the concept of cryptography (code breaking). (Al-Kindi, called the Arab Philosopher, however not one of the greatest of mathematicians, but was one of the most influential scientists between Aristotle (384 BC–322 BC) and Leonardo da Vinci (1452–1519).

(*Continued*)

CHRONOLOGY	NOTEWORTHY PEOPLE	EVENTS AND DISCOVERIES
ca. 1000	Mohammed ibn al-Hasn (Alhazen)`Abu Ali' ibn al-Haytham al-Basra (965–1039) [Iraq, Egypt]	Mathematical descriptions in optics and astronomy. The work of Al Hazen anticipated Newton's first law of motion (Sir Isaac Newton [1643–1727]); the "principle of least action."
ca. 1200	Leonardo `Bigollo' Pisano (Fibonacci) (ca. 1170–1245) [Italy]	Known today as "Fibonacci." Provided the persuasion for Europe to the decimal system, also using fractions. Defined congruous in addition to the theorems to provide the supporting proof. The work of Fibonacci has great relevance in biomedical applications, if not alone the Fibonacci code found for instance in the "veins" in a leaf of a tree.
1202	Leonardo Fibonacci (1170–1240) [Leonardo Bonacci/Leonardo of Pisa, Leonardo Pisano Bigollo]	First lecture text on algebra; introduction of the Fibonacci sequence, found in several natural phenomena.
ca. 1320	Levi ben Gerson `Gersonides' (1288–1344?)	Various basic scientific advancement resulted from his mathematical efforts. One specific example is the realization that in musical notes there are no consecutive harmonic numbers larger than (8, resp. 9).
1475	Luca Pacioli (1445–1572)	Collaborator with (mentor to) Leonardo da Vinci (1452–1519). Published work on geometry (in particular perspective), and accounting. One specific work on the Euclidean mathematics was a great step forward in conceptual mathematics.
1500	Leonardo da Vinci (1452–1519)	Renaissance man. Formal description of physical phenomena based on the state-of-the-art mathematical definitions, inventor, and prolific writer.
ca. 1500	Nicolaus Copernicus (1472–1543)	Astronomy and cartography. Telescope design and construction and associated calculations of the locations of observations on stars and planetary movements.
1575	Simon Stevin (1549–1620)	Civil engineering supported by stringent mathematical calculations. Windmill design, working as an engineering architect. Simon Stevin introduced the real number concept and the square root sign. Formally introduced the formal concept of decimal system in western Europe. Predated some observation and conclusion attributed to Augustin-Louis Cauchy (1789–1857).
ca. 1600	John Napier 8th of Merchistoun (1550–1617)	Formal introduction of the logarithm concept. Inventor of a rudimentary but pioneering calculator, next to the abacus.

(Continued)

CHRONOLOGY	NOTEWORTHY PEOPLE	EVENTS AND DISCOVERIES
ca. 1600	Galileo Galilei (1564–1642)	Described laws of motion (falling bodies; gravitational acceleration) and inertia, before Sir Isaac Newton (1643–1727). Invented the pendulum clock and many more engineering feats. Additional contributions by Galileo Galiei are in astronomy, specifically the discovery of Jupiter's moons. Galileo also wrote about infinite equinumerosity, what is known as the "Hilbert's Hotel Paradox" (David Hilbert [1862–1943]; 'Hilbert Space'). Galileo once wrote "Mathematics is the language in which God has written the universe."
ca. 1600		Acceptance of the decimal system in Europe. Early evidence of the decimal system dates as far back as 3000 BC China (used in the abacus). Furthermore, the Greek mathematicians also used the decimal system. (Northern) Europe prior to this used a system based on halves, still in use in the United States of America.
ca. 1600	Johannes Kepler (1571–1630)	As the understudy to Tycho Brahe (1546–1601) {Tyge Ottesen Brahe} Johannes Kepler used the astronomical data collected by Tycho Brahe to develop a detailed calculation for the planetary motion based on his derived elliptical orbits in contrast to the up to that time assumed circular orbits.
ca 1620	René Descartes (1596–1650)	Description of Euler's (Leonard Euler [1707–1783]) polyhedral theorem, pre-dating Euler. Description of a "vortex" theory for gravitation, next to various laws of motion.
ca. 1625	Francesco Bonaventura de Cavalieri (1598–1647)	Worked in optics and astronomy and proposed several limit series (theorems) for known algebraic problems, often based on his trigonometry interests. In specific he described the area for a spherical triangle.
1647	Bonaventura Francesco Cavalieri (1598–1647)	Derivation of the relationship between the radii of curvature for the respective two surfaces of a thin lens and the resulting focal length.
ca. 1650	Pierre de Fermat (1601–1665)	Developed infinitesimal (elementary) calculus. Instrumental in the development of the mathematical description of the optical refraction principle. Several of Fermat's efforts extended beyond the two-dimensional plane where most mathematicians were comfortable.
ca. 1650	Gilles Personne de Roberval (1602–1675)	Developed the initial principles for integration, basing his work on the publications from Archimedes (287 BC–212 BC), rather than on Francesco Bonaventura de Cavalieri (1598–1647). Roberval was instrumental in the development of cartography. Gilles de Roberval also worked alongside Blaise Pascal (1623–1662) on several experiments.

(Continued)

CHRONOLOGY	NOTEWORTHY PEOPLE	EVENTS AND DISCOVERIES
ca. 1650	Blaise Pascal (1623–1662)	Designed several calculator machines. Worked on pressure and introduced "the scientific method." Corresponded with Pierre de Fermat (1601–1665) on his ideas about probability and geometry. He also followed the work of Evangelista Torricelli (1608–1647) closely.
ca. 1650	Christiaan Huygens (1629–1695)	Developed the inverse square law of gravitation (before Sir Isaac Newton [1643–1727]) and various mechanical devices, including a reliable pendulum, leading to an accurate time-keeping mechanism. The Huygens' principle was a mathematical essay on the wave properties of light, still overpowered by the corpuscular interpretation by Sir Isaac Newton.
1665	James Gregory (1638–1675)	Inventor and designer of a reflecting telescope. Furthermore, Gregory developed several mathematical expressions, including a series expression for the inverted tangent. James Gregory anticipated the Cauchy convergence requirement in his analysis (Baron Augustin-Louis Cauchy [1789–1857]).
ca. 1670	Sir Isaac Newton (1643–1727)	Introduced revolutionary advances in optics, mechanics, thermodynamics, and acoustics and astronomy-based mechanics (astrophysics). Newton also developed a series to define the "'árcsin" function. Sir Isaac Newton is most known for his formal introduction of the gravity concept, but had earlier work to build on at his disposal. Isaac Newton was one of the prominent proponents and advocates of the atom theory. Newton also introduced one of the first colour–hue wheels. Sir Newton was a master at geometry, solving several problems that were so far unsolved. In 1687 Sir Isaac Newton published: *Philosophiae Naturalis Principia Mathematica*.
1675	Gottfried Wilhelm von Leibniz (1646–1716)	Formal introduction to the calculus concepts. Leibniz discovered and proved a very effective identity series for pi (π): $\pi/4 = 1 - 1/3 + 1/5 - 1/7 + 1/9 - \ldots$ Additionally, Leibniz introduced the mathematical notations that are still used to date.
1684	Jacob Bernoulli (1654–1705)	Developed integral and differential equations. Worked on fluid dynamics. Close friend of Gottfried Wilhelm von Leibniz (1646–1716). Older brother to Johann Bernoulli (1667–1748).
1700	Abraham De Moivre (1667–1754)	Contributed significantly to the development of probability theory, with close ties to Pierre Simon Laplace (1749–1827), following in his footsteps.

(Continued)

CHRONOLOGY	NOTEWORTHY PEOPLE	EVENTS AND DISCOVERIES
1700	Johann Bernoulli (1667–1748)	Johann learned from his older brother Jacob Bernoulli (1654–1705), and from Gottfried Wilhelm von Leibniz (1646–1716), and became a tutor to Leonhard Euler (1707–1783). Johann Bernoulli's son, Daniel Bernoulli (1700–1782) was just as much a polymath as his father and grandfather, next to his contributions to the description of gas dynamics: "Bernoulli's Law."
1715	Brook Taylor (1685–1731)	Rudimentary description and discovery of the Taylor Series described by the Scottish mathematician James Gregory (1638–1675) and later introduced formally by the English mathematician Brook Taylor (1685–1731).
1740	Daniel Bernoulli (1700–1782)	Son of Johann Bernoulli (1667–1748). He developed partial differential equation and used the "Fourier series" prior to the publication by Jean-Baptiste Joseph Fourier (1768–1830). The work of Daniel Bernoulli that he is most known for is in fluid dynamics and gas mechanics.
1750	Leonhard Euler (1707–1783)	Most prolific mathematician in the known history of mathematics. Euler developed the polyhedral theorem (with some suspicion that this may be traced back to René Descartes (1596–1650). Euler revolutionized the design of pumps based on his fluid dynamic theories, including turbine equations. Other theoretical interests of Leonhard Euler were optics, astronomy, acoustics, mechanics, and music. In his astrophysics work he developed a formulation to determine the moon orbit in a three body motion problem; first ever. Additional theoretical efforts defined the rotational motion of rigid bodies of various configurations. Euler also introduced the definition for the square root of negative one as the letter i, next to several other mathematical standard expressions for algebraic terms. Leonard Euler also introduced the exponential expression with the use of the complex number by means of sin and cosine: $e^{ix} = \cos x + i \sin x$. Euler popularized the use of the letter sigma for a series summation.
1760	Jean le Rond d' Alembert (1717–1783)	d'Alembert laid the foundation for modern meteorology with his mathematical descriptions of the formation of wind. Other work include collision dynamics, hydrodynamics, and vibration. Jean d' Alembert proved that every polynomial has a complex root (d' Alembert–Gauss theorem). Jean le Rond d' Alembert may have been the first person to express time as the fourth dimension, especially with respect to the complex physics phenomena evolving.

(Continued)

CHRONOLOGY	NOTEWORTHY PEOPLE	EVENTS AND DISCOVERIES
1760	Johann Heinrich Lambert (1727–1777)	Even after dropping out of school due to family circumstances at the age of 12, Johann Lambert became a renowned and influential mathematician. Johann Lambert made great contributions to astrophysics calculations, illustrating the existence of star clusters. Lambert also build the first operational photometer. In addition, on a geophysics level he contributed to the cartography and land movement dynamics.
1780	Joseph-Louis (Comte de) Lagrange (1736–1813) [Giuseppe Lodovico Lagrangia]	Introduced a range of polynomials, and introduced "group theory." The use of transforms for functions in order to facilitate solving them was introduced before (or in conjunction with) Pierre Simon, Marquis de Laplace (1749–1827). Lagrange introduced the use of comma notations for first and second order derivative.
1799	Pierre Simon, marquis de Laplace (1749–1827)	Laplace Law; Laplace transform to solve complex equations and his work on celestial mechanics (astrophysics). The Laplace transform converts a temporal function into a frequency domain function.
1800	Adrien Marie Legendre (1752–1833)	Introduced the Legendre polynomials concepts and Legendre transform to aid in solving complex equations by conversion of spatial parameters. Legendre worked on spherical geometry. Legendre made significant advances in the solution technique applied to elliptic integrals.
1800	Jean Baptiste Joseph Fourier (1768–1830)	The Fourier transform is one of the most widely used mathematical tools in all fields of physics and engineering; converting any periodic or instantaneous event into a series (superposition) of sin and cosine terms, mathematical solving technique using increasing orders of perturbation. The Fourier transform has many trades of the Laplace transform, referring to the time to frequency conversion. In thermodynamics, Fourier introduced his heat equation that provides significant practical applications.
1808	Étienne-Louis Malus (1775–1812)	Mathematical analysis of the concept of light. Verified the principles introduced by Christiaan Huygens (1629–1695). Observed the light reflecting from the windows, uncovering an effect that was later attributed to the polarization of light resulting from reflection. Member of the mathematics section of the Institut d'Égypte resulting from his travels with Napoléon Bonaparte (1769–1821). Introduction of Malus' law.
1810	Johann Carl Friedrich Gauss [Gauβ] (1777–1855)	Gauss constructed the theory of complex numbers in the form we use today. In astrophysics Gauss derived the orbit of an asteroid (Ceres), observed during his life-time, and predicted its return path around the Sun with great accuracy. Carl Friedrich Gauss is most known for his practical contributions to the field of electricity and magnetism: Gauss's law; magnetic flux theorem.

(Continued)

CHRONOLOGY	NOTEWORTHY PEOPLE	EVENTS AND DISCOVERIES
1810	Siméon Denis Poisson (1781–1840)	Poisson's analysis of the wave theory of light contributed to the evolution and understanding of interference principles and applications.
1820	William George Horner (1786–1837)	Introduction of the methodology for solving and calculating polynomials (roots): Horner's method. The methods were actually already described 600 years prior by the Chinese mathematician Qin Jiushao (秦九韶) (ca. 1202–1261).
ca. 1825	Baron Augustin-Louis Cauchy (1789–1857)	Pioneer in mathematical and structural analysis of data. Formally introduced several of the modern concepts of calculus. Cauchy also introduced the concept of convergent series, in order to obtain a finite solution.
1840	Carl Gustav Jacob Jacobi (1804–1851)	His work involved the development of what is known as cubic reciprocity, which was found very helpful by Carl Friedrich Gauss (1777–1855). Jacobi also worked closely with Sir William Rowan Hamilton (1805–1865), and he developed his own mathematical approach, the Jacobian matrix and determinants in vector calculus used to solve multiple co-dependent relations in multiple equations; specifically applied to partial derivatives. The Jacobian applies primarily to individual points in data space.
1840	Johann Peter Gustav Lejeune Dirichlet (1805–1859)	Dirichlet interpreted the work of Carl Friedrich Gauss (1777–1855), revealing various uncovered items. Gustav Dirichlet was a tutor, respectively mentor, to Sir William Rowan Hamilton (1805–1865), Bernhard Riemann (1826–1866) and Leopold Kronecker (1823–1891).
1842, 1851	Sir George Gabriel Stokes, 1st Baronet (1819–1903)	Fluid dynamics Stokes equation, aberration of light with respect to the wave properties of light. Additional work of Gabriel Stokes was in the initial full theoretical description of polarization of electromagnetic radiation.
1850	Sir William Rowan Hamilton (1805–1865)	Sir Hamilton is most known for his reformulation of Newtonian mechanics: Hamilton mechanics. Hamilton mechanics can be considered an essential building block to the development of quantum mechanics. Sir William Hamilton introduced the principles leading to the formulation of the Hamiltonian operator used in quantum mechanics, defining the total energy of a system.
1850	George Boole (1815–1864)	Known for the Boolean algebra and logic. The work of George Boole inspired Claude Shannon (1916–2001).
1860	Georg Friedrich Bernhard Riemann (1826–1866)	The work of Bernhard Riemann was instrumental in the development of the theory of general relativity and the supporting mathematical evaluation.
1865	James Clerk Maxwell (1831–1879)	Electromagnetic theory.

(Continued)

CHRONOLOGY	NOTEWORTHY PEOPLE	EVENTS AND DISCOVERIES
1874	Marie Alfred Cornu (1841–1902)	Described a graphical approach to the solution of diffraction problems: Cornu spiral.
1880	Leopold Kronecker (1823–1891)	Introduction of the "Kronecker Delta", isolating the one single location in function space where a function can be considered rational. His studies primarily focussed on the ergodic theoretical aspects, describing dynamic systems.
1899	Jules Henri Poincaré (1854–1912) and Jacques Salomon Hadamard (1865–1963)	Geodesic flow; mathematical and analytical description.
1890	Jules Henri Poincaré (1854–1912)	Introduction of methods and means for deriving accurate topographical data. Some of the work of Poincaré revolved around defining the geometry of the universe. Poincaré also contributed to fluid dynamic modeling in addition to the description of celestial motion.
1895	Diederik Johannes Korteweg (1848–1941) and Gustav de Vries (1866–1934)	Diederik Korteweg and his student Gustav de Vries derived a nonlinear partial differential equation defining the propagation of waves in shallow water. The Korteweg–de Vries (KdV) equation describes the solitary wave described by John Scott Russell (1808–1882). The KdV equation has had an important implications for the development of the mathematical description of solutions.
1900	Samuel Giuseppe Vito Volterra (1860–1946)	Description and formulation of cylindrical waves. Volterra became involved in the biological cause and effect, respectively predator–prey aspects pioneering the field of mathematical biology.
1900	David Hilbert (1862–1943)	Hilbert space: vector space designed to accommodate an infinite number of dimensions, with respect to the three-dimensional Euclidean space. The Hilbert spatial interpretation forms an indispensable tools in solving for partial differential equations, as well as pertaining to quantum mechanics, and Fourier analysis. In Fourier analysis this applies to applications in signal processing and heat transfer. Hilbert space is an ergodic theory, which provides the mathematical foundations of certain thermodynamics topics.
1905	Albert Einstein (1879–1955)	Energy–mass equivalence hypothesis introduced. Einstein also published his theoretical interpretation of the movements of object, specifically approaching the speed of light in his special theory of relativity and general theory of relativity. In 1917 he published his predictions on stimulated emission and hence the preliminary description of the operations of a LASER. Additional mathematical work eludes to quantum theoretical approach.

(Continued)

CHRONOLOGY	NOTEWORTHY PEOPLE	EVENTS AND DISCOVERIES
1908	Hermann Minkowski (1864–1909)	Developed a geometrical interpretation of the special theory of relativity in which time and the three space coordinates all had the same validity in a four-dimensional continuum.
1910	Amalie Emma Noether (1882–1935)	Master of abstract algebra. Amalie Noether also introduced the concept of conservation laws based on the symmetry in nature and physics and engineering.
1910	Hermann Klaus Hugo (Peter) Weyl (1885–1955)	Weyl studied under David Hilbert (1862–1943) and was also close to Amalie Emma Noether (1882–1935). Hermann Weyl uncovered a gauge invariance and with his interpretation of Riemann surfaces his teachings form the basis of many aspects supporting the theoretical explanation in modern physics concepts. Weyl also contributed to the efforts of Erwin Schrödinger (1887–1961).
1910	Edmund Georg Hermann Landau (1877–1938)	Known for his work on prime number theory.
1916	Niels Henrik David Bohr (1885–1962)	Atomic structure and quantum theory.
1921	Alfred Landé (1888–1976)	Mathematician who introduced the Landau factor for an electron with both self-rotation spin and orbital angular momentum.
1924	Sir John Edward Lennard-Jones (1894–1954)	Definition of the attraction between two neutral molecules or atoms: Lennard-Jones potential.
1924–1945	Harry Nyquist (1889–1976) [Harry Theodor Nyqvist]	Combining mathematical approach to telecommunications and electronic engineering. His work started out to find the most elegant manner to suppress thermal noise. The Nyquist theorem, also referred to as the Nyquist–Shannon theorem, defines the sampling rate for period signals to ensure capturing all information contained in the transient signals.
1922	Erwin Rudolf Josef Alexander Schrödinger (1887–1961) and Hermann Klaus Hugo Weyl (1885–1955)	Introduction of the quantum mechanical principles, supporting the understanding of high energy physics phenomena such as the atomic structure.
1923	John von Neumann (1903–1957) [original name: Neumann Janos Lajos]	Introduced finite element methodology (also known as Monte Carlo simulation), integration of random number generation. He was also instrumental in the design of thermonuclear bombs as well as significantly advanced the field of hydrodynamics.

(*Continued*)

CHRONOLOGY	NOTEWORTHY PEOPLE	EVENTS AND DISCOVERIES
1924	Satyendra Nath Bose (1894–1974) [সত্যেন্দ্র নাথবসু] and Albert Einstein (1879–1955)	Introduction of the Bose–Einstein statistics: one of two potential manners of energy occupation for a collection of noninteracting indistinguishable particles with respect to a set of available discrete energy states, this applies to thermodynamic equilibrium only. At extreme low temperatures these energy levels for bosons can result in a joining of states: condensation, the Bose–Einstein condensate.
1924	Louis-Victor-Pierre-Raymond, 7th duc de Broglie (1892–1987)	Introduction of the wave phenomenon with respect to all objects in motion. Matter wave, propagating with the de Broglie wavelength.
1925	Wolfgang Ernst Pauli (1900–1958)	Pauli exclusion principle for atomic energy levels.
1925	Werner Heisenberg (1901–1976)	Introduction of quantum mechanics, specifically in matrix formulation. Heisenberg also introduced the "uncertainty principle"; two parameters describing the same item or phenomenon cannot be known simultaneously with exact accuracy, such as momentum and position, but are inherently linked to each other with a product that yields the reduced Planck constant divided by two or greater.
1926	Eugene Paul Wigner (1902–1995)	Series publications on the application of group theory in quantum mechanics. Eugene Wigner shared the Nobel Prize in Physics jointly with Maria Goeppert-Mayer and Johannes Hans Daniel Jensen (1907–1973) in 1963.
1927	Wolfgang Ernst Pauli (1900–1958), Ralph Kronig (1904–1995), George Eugene Uhlenbeck (1900–1988), Samuel Abraham Goudsmit (1902–1978), and Paul Adrien Maurice Dirac (1902–1984)	Introduction of the electron spin concept and a broad range of relativistic quantum mechanical principles. This formed the foundation for the development of the NMR imaging system: nuclear magnetic resonance (MRI).
1935	Enrico Fermi (1901–1954)	Developed Fermi–Dirac statistics, although independent from Paul Dirac (1902–1984) but simultaneously. The Fermi–Dirac statistics applies to fermions; while the counterpart that it does not include are referred to as bosons. Fermi worked on X-ray crystallography, as well as energy levels in semiconductor structures. The Fermi level concept for electrons in atomic energy approximating absolute zero ties directly in with the Pauli exclusion principle. Fermi worked with and studied under Max Born (1882–1970), Werner Heisenberg (1901–1976), Pascual Jordan (1902–1980), Paul Ehrenfest (1880–1933), Hendrik Lorentz (1853–1928) Samuel Goudsmit (1902–1978), Jan Tinbergen (1903–1994), and Albert Einstein (1879–1955). Fermi concluded that beta decay from the nucleus formed another energetic particle and determined it to be real and named it a neutrino.

(Continued)

CHRONOLOGY	NOTEWORTHY PEOPLE	EVENTS AND DISCOVERIES
1935	Paul Adrien Maurice Dirac (1902–1984)	Developed Fermi–Dirac statistics, although independent from Enrico Fermi (1901–1954) but simultaneously.
1936	Inge Lehmann (1888–1993)	Description of the numerical assessment of data obtained during earthquakes (seismological data) and the image formation of the structure of the earth's structure, divided in shells with different material phase and composition. The image formation is based on what is referred to as S-waves and P-waves. Inge Lehmann discovered and described the shape, size, and composition (rudimentary) of the earth's inner core.
1945	Claude Elwood Shannon (1916–2001)	Sampling theory, minimum sampling rate for correct acquisition of periodic data. Sometimes introduced as the "father of information theory." The work of Shannon paralleled that of Harry Nyquist (1889–1976).
1950	Maria Goeppert-Mayer (Göppert) (1906–1972)	Introduction and mathematical description of the nuclear shell model for atomic nuclei.
1972	Stephen Hawking (1942–), Jacob Bekenstein (1947–2015)	Thermodynamics of black holes.
1973	Sheldon Glashow (1932–), Abdus Salam (1926–1996), Steven Weinberg (1933), Carlo Rubbia (1934–) and Simon van der Meer (1925–2011)	Reference to a presumed, but so far unconfirmed unified field theory; based on the work of James Clerk Maxwell (1831–1879), Hans Christian Ørsted (1777–1851), and Michael Faraday (1791–1867). However, a better understanding of electro-weak interaction and electro-strong forces has certainly evolved from this research and mathematical analysis and modeling.
1995	Andrew Wiles (1953–)	One of the theorems introduced by Pierre de Fermat (1601–1665) in his "Arithmetica" is proved. The original theorem states the following: "no three positive integers a, b, and c can satisfy the equation $a^n + b^n = c^n$ for any integer value of n greater than two."
1995	Edward Witten (1951–)	Introduction of "M-Theory"; also known as string theory, supported by Stephen Hawking (1942–). The M-theory attempts to reconcile quantum theory with gravity, but remains incomplete up to the t date of this publication.

Dynamics

CHRONOLOGY	NOTEWORTHY PEOPLE	EVENTS AND DISCOVERIES
ca. 6000 BC	Egypt	First recorded drawings of rudimentary water crafts.
ca. 4000 BC	Eastern Europe	First recorded drawing of craft with rudimentary wheels.
ca. 3300 BC	Egypt	Drawings of sailboat.

(Continued)

CHRONOLOGY	NOTEWORTHY PEOPLE	EVENTS AND DISCOVERIES
350 BC	Aristotle (384 BC–322 BC)	Founder of the Lyceum school of analytical thinking in Macedonia. Aristotle described the initial concepts of physics, motion, time as well as astronomy concepts. Aristotle supposed an external force (acting during flight) perpetuating the projectile motion of a ballistic object.
ca. 600 BC	Thales of Miletus (ca. 624 BC–ca. 546 BC; known as Thales: Θαλῆς)	Description of the "nature of objects." Thales believed that objects are alive; part of the stream of thought by the "Hylozoists."
ca. 250 BC	Archimedes (287 BC–212 BC)	Hand-operated cork-screw water pump. The philosophies of Archimedes shaped the development process of modern engineering.
40 BC	Marcus Vitruvius Pollio [Vitruvius] (ca. 80 BC–10 BC)	First recorded use and description of the mechanism of action of a steam-operated engine: Æolipile; described in *De Architectura*.
62	Hero of Alexandria [ρων ὁ Ἀλεξανδρεύς], (10–70)	Second recorded use of steam to provide power to a machine; Æolipile.
650		First recorded use of wind mills and wind energy in the Persian Empire.
1010	Eilmer of Malmesbury, 11th century Benedictine monk	First documented successful flight, performed with a wooden frame lined with parchment, traveling approximately 200 meter in free fall from a 18-meter elevation.
1206	Al-Jazari (1136–1206) [Turkey]; Badi'al-Zaman Abū al-'Izz ibn Ismā'īl ibn al-Razāz al-Jazarī (بْنُ أَلْعِزِ أَبُو الزمـان بــديع الجـزري الرّزاز بْنُ إسْماعِيلِ)	Publication of *Book of Knowledge of Ingenious Mechanical Devices*. Description of mechanical devices and mechanism of action.
1245	Thomas Aquinas (1225–1274)	Reformulation of the dynamic concepts of Aristotle (384 BC–322 BC).
1500	Leonardo da Vinci (1452–1519)	Formal description of physical phenomena based on the state-of-the-art mathematical definitions. Description of several machines, including "flying machines," and a rudimentary theoretical discourse on the respective mechanism of action for several dynamic systems. Description of early friction concepts.
ca. 1600	Galileo Galilei (1564–1642)	Description of laws of motion (falling bodies; gravitational acceleration), projectile motion (ballistics), and inertia, before Sir Isaac Newton (1643–1727). Invented the pendulum clock and many more engineering feats.

(Continued)

CHRONOLOGY	NOTEWORTHY PEOPLE	EVENTS AND DISCOVERIES
1673	Christiaan Huygens (1629–1695)	Construction of a "combustion engine" power by gunpowder.
ca. 1687	Sir Isaac Newton (1643–1727)	Sir Isaac Newton introduced several laws of motion. The publication of the *Philosophiæ Naturalis Principia Mathematica* provides detailed definitions regarding ballistic motion, circular motion (centripetal force), laws of action–reaction, gravitational acceleration, inertia, and force with respect to acceleration. Introduction of the three laws of motion.
1699	Guillaume Amontons (1663–1705)	Formal introduction of the concept of friction, based on the rudimentary introduction by Leonardo da Vinci (1452–1519).
1698	Thomas Savery (1650–1715)	Construction of the basic steam engine.
1712	Thomas Newcomen (1664–1729)	Construction of an "atmospheric" steam engine.
1743	Jean-Baptiste le Rond d'Alembert (1717–1783)	Publication on the concepts of forces and accelerating systems: *Traite de Dynamique*.
1750	Leonard Euler (1707–1783)	Introduction of the coefficients representing kinetic and static friction.
1757–1769	James Watt (1736–1819)	Modern steam engine design and operation with theoretical description of operation.
1769	Nicolas-Joseph Cugnot (1725–1804)	First operational steam-powered automobile, the predecessor to the internal combustion automobile.
1781	Charles-Augustin de Coulomb (1736–1806)	Verification of the friction principles that were introduced by Guillaume Amontons (1663–1705).
1827	Benoît Fourneyron (1802–1867)	First water turbine.
1833	Arthur Jules Morin (1795–1880)	Differentiation between sliding and rolling friction.
1840	Claude-Louis Navier (1785–1836) and George Gabriel Stokes (1819–1903)	Fluid dynamics, friction concepts.
1866	Osborne Reynolds (1842–1912)	Friction description with respect to fluid dynamics concepts.
1879	Karl Friedrich Benz (1844–1929)	Invention of the internal combustion engine-driven automobile. Close collaboration with Gottlieb Wilhelm Daimler (1834–1900).
1880	Paul-Jacques Curie (1855–1941) and Pierre Curie (1859–1906)	Discovery of electric charges emerging on the surfaces of crystals which are subjected to shear or normal stress. This is referred to as the piezoelectric effect.

(Continued)

CHRONOLOGY	NOTEWORTHY PEOPLE	EVENTS AND DISCOVERIES
1880	Johannes Diederik van der Waals (1837–1923)	Description of the covalent bond. Van der Waals equation.
1888	John Boyd Dunlop (1840–1921)	Invention of the pneumatic tire.
1897	Joseph John Thomson (1856–1940)	Discovery of the electron; using William Crookes's vacuum tube.
1899	Jules Henri Poincaré (1854–1912) and Jacques Salomon Hadamard (1865–1963)	Geodesic flow; mathematical description and physical analysis. With further analysis by George David Birkhoff (1884–1944) in 1927.
1900	Rudolf Christian Karl Diesel (1858–1913)	Proof of principke that an engine ("diesel engine") can operate on peanut oil. The mechanism was based on the efforts by Herbert Akroyd Stuart (1864–1927) in 1885.
1901	Ferdinand Porsche (1875–1951)	First hybrid automobile, internal combustion engine is used to rotate an electric generator, which in turn provides the power to operate a hub motor; an electric motor that is part of the axle of the automobile, attached to the wheel (ref. hubcap of the wheel).
1905	Orville Wright (1871–1948) and Wilbur Wright (1867–1912)	First sustained flight with a powered fixed-wing aircraft.
1909	Robert Andrews Millikan (1868–1953)	Measurement of the mass of the electron.
1915	Clinton Edgar Woods (1863–1930)	Hybrid automobile, powered by internal combustion engine as well as electric motor. Woods Motor Vehicle Company.
1916	Niels Henrik David Bohr (1885–1962)	Atomic structure and quantum theory.
1917	Ernest Rutherford, 1st Baron Rutherford of Nelson (1871–1937)	Discovery of the proton.
1924	Louis-Victor-Pierre-Raymond, 7th duc de Broglie (1892–1987)	Introduction of the wave phenomenon with respect to all object in motion. Matter wave, propagating with the de Broglie wavelength.
1927	Wolfgang Ernst Pauli (1900–1958) Paul Adrien Maurice Dirac (1902–1984)	Introduction of the electron spin concept, as a component of a broad range of quantum mechanical principles.
1924	Felix Heinrich Wankel (1902–1988)	Development and operation of the rotary engine ("Wankel motor").
1931	Georges Jean Marie Darrieus (1888–1979)	Introduction of the wind turbine.

(Continued)

CHRONOLOGY	NOTEWORTHY PEOPLE	EVENTS AND DISCOVERIES
1937	Sir Frank Whittle (1907–1996)	Introduction of the jet engine.
1947	Chuck Yeager (1923–)	Breaking of the sound barrier during level flight.

ElectroTechnology_Electronic

CHRONOLOGY	NOTEWORTHY PEOPLE	EVENTS AND DISCOVERIES
c. 600 BC	Thales of Miletus (c. 624 BC–c. 546 BC; known as Thales: Θαλῆς)	Description of static electricity. Static electricity could specifically be induced by rubbing amber with animal fur, hence the association of the electric charge with the Greek word "amber" (referred to in Greek as electrum [ἤλεκτρον, translated as ēlektron]) meaning electron. Amber is solidified and hardened tree sap, resin.
500 BC	Leucippus (5th century BC)	Potential Greek philosopher who mentioned the fact that all matter is made up of indivisible, imperishable constituents, and referred to them as atoms. These atoms were not specific to the nature of the element in question under this hypothesis, but assumed to be all alike.
450 BC	Democritus (460 BC–370 BC)	Proposed the concept of the atomic nature of matter, presumably based on his work under Leucippus (5th century BC), but not confirmed as the original source.
1500	Leonardo da Vinci (1452–1519)	The preverbal "Renaissance man," involved in all aspects of cultural evolution, science, engineering, politics, and art.
1503	Gregor Reisch (1467–1525)	Detailed outline of the state-of-the-art science and engineering knowledge to date, including human anatomical drawings in the publication *Margarita philosophica*. The total works of Gregor Reisch form a series of 12 books compiling an encyclopedia describing topics ranging from Latin grammar, to dialectics, rhetoric, arithmetic, music, geometry, astronomy, physics, natural history, physiology, psychology, and ethics
1512	Gregorius Reisch (1467–1525)	Introduction of the concept of the theodolite, used for topography and geographic location determination.
1543	Nicolaus Copernicus (1473–1543); Alias of Niclas Koppernigk	Introduction of the heliocentric model for the earth, sun, and planets close by. This follows the statement by the astronomer form Greece: Aristarchus of Samos (c. 310–c. 230 BC), made more than 1700 years prior. The scientific observations made by Copernicus were validated by Tycho Brahe (1546–1601) and Johannes Kepler (1571–1630).
1590	Francis Bacon, 1st Viscount of St. Alban (1561–1626)	Regulate the general scientific methodology.

(*Continued*)

CHRONOLOGY	NOTEWORTHY PEOPLE	EVENTS AND DISCOVERIES
ca. 1600	Sir William Schwenck Gilbert (1544–1603)	Experimentalist. Description of the generation of "electricity" [electricus] when rubbing amber with fur. The term electron is derived from the Latin word used to describe the material amber: electrum, or the Greek word ēlektron: ἤλεκτρον.
ca. 1600	Galileo Galilei (1564–1642)	Major contributor to the scientific revolution and the (re) introduction of analytical thinking in science, engineering, and general thought processes. Galileo Galilei was remanded under house arrest by the Roman Inquisition for his views and teachings where he died after 9 years. This was the trailing end of the Renaissance period.
1614	René Descartes (1596–1650)	Introduction to vortex motion. Introduction of the concept of general corpuscular motion, extending from small (maybe referring to the undefined atom), to planetary orbits. Descartes also made an illustration of the earth's magnetic field configuration in 1644, in his model the moon and celestial objects participated in the formation of the path of the magnetic field lines. Based on the limited experimental observations available in his time the premise was still not bad.
1632	Evangelista Torricelli (1608–1647)	Introduction of the barometer; essential in weather prediction; meteorology.
1650	Blaise Pascal (1623–1662)	Pascal's law, pressure in a container applies an equal force on all surface of the enclosure.
1657	Otto von Guericke (1602–1686)	Electrostatic repulsion.
1660	Robert Boyle (1627–1691)	Gas laws, definition of the behavior of gases. Boyle mentioned the compression of gas as a potential "shock-absorber," acting similar to a spring.
1673	Christiaan Huygens (1629–1695)	Construction of a "combustion engine" powered by gun powder. Huygens introduced several concept of mechanical engineering and described the mechanism of shock waves. Christiaan Huygens is most known for his lens manufacturing and optical design of telescopes. The mathematical efforts of Christiaan Huygens in probability theory were far advanced and he collaborated with the mathematician Pierre de Fermat (1601–1665) from France.
1679	Denis Papin (1647–c. 1712)	Pressure and thermodynamic and mechanical impacts.
1680	Robert Hooke (1635–1703)	Force applied by a compressed spring.

(*Continued*)

CHRONOLOGY	NOTEWORTHY PEOPLE	EVENTS AND DISCOVERIES
ca. 1687	Sir Isaac Newton (1643–1727)	Sir Isaac Newton introduced several laws of motion. The publication of the *Philosophiæ Naturalis Principia Mathematica* provides detailed definitions regarding ballistic motion, circular motion (centripetal force), laws of action–reaction, gravitational acceleration, inertia, and force with respect to acceleration. Introduction of the three laws of motion.
1698	Francis Hauksbee the Elder (1660–1713)	Repeated the experiment of electrostatic repulsion performed by Otto von Guericke (1602–1686). Francis Hauksbee illustrated the preliminary concept of the gas discharge lamp. Hauksbee used the design of the electric charge generated from Otto von Guericke and applied vacuum, while adding charge to the ball in the center of the vacuum bulb, which resulted in the generation of a glow of light, resembling Saint Elmo's Fire. Gas discharge tubes over the next centuries evolved in neon lamp, mercury vapor lamps, and the fluorescent light.
1733	Charles François de Cisternay du Fay (1698–1739)	Discovery of a different electric charge, opposite to that of the recognized electron, such as the result of rubbing glass with silk, producing a positive charge, however not recognized as such by Charles du Fay just yet. Charles du Fay described the two opposing charge types as "vitreous" and "resinous," respectively.
1745	Pieter van Musschenbroek (1692–1761) and Ewald Georg von Kleist (1700–1748)	Documented collection of electric charge (storage of static electricity) by means of the "Leyden Jar," performed at the university in the city Leiden of the Netherlands.
1752	Benjamin Franklin (1706–1790)	Kite experiment and the documentation of "electric current."
1781	Charles-Augustin de Coulomb (1736–1806)	Definition of the electric field related to electric charge. The electric charge itself was still an elusive concept in those days
1791	Luigi Aloisio Galvani (737–1798)	Discovery of bioelectricity, the preamble of the discovery of the actionpotential. Introduction of the galvanometer, the forerunner of the voltmeter.
1800	Count Alessandro Giuseppe Antonio Anastasio Volta (1745–1827)	Introduction of the battery; voltaic pile.
1821	Michael Faraday (1791–1867)	Discovery of electromagnetic rotation, leading to his law on electromagnetic induction in 1831. Meanwhile, in 1923 Michael Faraday experimentally verified the concept of refrigeration, introduced based on the work of John Dalton (1766–1844) in 1802 and William Cullen (1710–1790) in 1756.

(Continued)

CHRONOLOGY	NOTEWORTHY PEOPLE	EVENTS AND DISCOVERIES
1824	Nicolas Léonard Sadi Carnot (1796–1832)	Refrigerator for general public.
1825	William Sturgeon (1783–1878)	First documented design and application of the electromagnet. William Sturgeon also invented the first operational electric motor in 1832, operating on direct current (DC).
1827	George Simon Ohm (1789–1854)	Description of the linearly proportional relationship between voltage and current, introducing the resistance concept: Ohm's law.
1831	Michael Faraday (1791–1867) and Joseph Henry (1797–1878)	Law of electric induction, leading to the development of the electric generator, where a changing magnetic field induces an electromotive force (EMF), or known as electrical potential.
1833	Michael Faraday (1791–1867)	Recognition of the changes in resistance for materials when exposed to heat, providing the first introduction to the concept of semiconductor properties.
1839	Alexandre-Edmond Becquerel (1820–1891)	Description of the photovoltaic effect, which is different in principle from the photoelectric effect. When light is incident upon the surface of a material (metal or semiconductor), the electrons that reside in the valence band of certain elements of the semiconductor mixture or single metal absorb the electromagnetic energy and are raised to the conduction band (excited) and become free electrons, producing an electromotive force (EMF), yielding an electrical current. The photoelectric effect provided a step further in the recognition of the semiconductor concept, described in *Les Comptes Rendus de l'Academie des Sciences*. In contrast, the photoelectric effect describes the release of free electrons into free space, compared to conduction under photovoltaic effect. Alexandre-Edmond Becquerel was the father of Antoine Henri Becquerel (1852–1908), the prime discoverer of several fundamental radioactivity features. The photovoltaic effect led to the development of solar cells for the generation of electricity for personal consumption on a large scale.
1873	Josiah Willard Gibbs (1839–1903)	Chemical potential, a energy constituent within the Gibbs free energy. Thermodynamic concept describing the energy that can be released or absorbed during a chemical reaction.
1873	James Clerk Maxwell (1831–1879)	Theory of electromagnetic radiation: *A Treatise on Electricity and Magnetism*. James Maxwell made use of the prior work by Wilhelm Eduard Weber (1804–1891) and Johann Carl Friedrich Gauss {Gauß} (1777–1855)

(Continued)

CHRONOLOGY	NOTEWORTHY PEOPLE	EVENTS AND DISCOVERIES
1873	Willoughby Smith (1828–1891)	First formal introduction to semiconductor materials. This was followed by the work of Karl Ferdinand Braun (1850–1918) in 1874 and Sir Franz Arthur Friedrich Schuster (1851–1934), also in 1874.
1874	Karl Ferdinand Braun (1850–1918)	Discovery that joining two materials with different electrical properties (metal vs. semiconductor) acts as a rectifier under certain conditions. This paved the way for the development of diodes and transistors when semiconductor materials became more manageable, and more manufacturable.
1878	Edwin Herbert Hall (1855–1938)	Discovery of the Hall effect: the deflection of electric charge flowing under the influence of an applied magnetic field. The Hall effect was instrumental in the evolution of the diode and in particular the transistor, using semiconductor junctions.
1878	Thomas Alva Edison (1847–1931)	This development of the incandescent light bulb. In 1883, Edison published the discovery of the emission of "electrons" (not known in that sense at that time yet) by a hot wire in an electrical circuit; "Edison effect." The electron itself was recognized in 1897 by Joseph John Thomson (1856–1940).
1878	William Edward Sawyer (1850–1883)	Contributed to the development of the incandescent light bulb. There were several conflict on ownership to the right (patents) between William Sawyer and Thomas Edison (1847–1931).
1880	Johannes Diderik van der Waals (1837–1923)	Description of the covalent bond. Van der Waals equation.
1882	Thomas Alva Edison (1847–1931)	First commercial power plant serving Lower Manhattan, New York.
1883	Charles Fritts (1850–1903)	First solid-state photovoltaic cell created by coating the semiconductor material selenium with a thin layer of gold to form Schottky barrier junctions, based on the Fermi levels of the respective materials in contact, leading to the generation of electrical potential and electrical current under direct illumination by visible light. The concept device was only approximately 1% efficient, in comparison to current day better than 44%, and still increasing.
1885	George Westinghouse, Jr. (1846–1914)	Electric power distribution network development. George Westinghouse also invented what is known as air brakes (1869) drawing vacuum on a piston to reduce the revolutions of the crack axle, similar principles still apply to air brakes on large trucks.

(Continued)

CHRONOLOGY	NOTEWORTHY PEOPLE	EVENTS AND DISCOVERIES
1887	Heinrich Rudolf Hertz (1857–1894)	Radar development. Detection of electromagnetic radiation (radio waves). Heinrich Hertz also discovered that certain metal plates will release electrons (into free space) when exposed to light, specifically ultraviolet light: photoelectric effect. This concept was elaborated on by Albert Einstein (1879–1955) in 1905.
1893	Nikola Tesla (Serbian-Cyrillic: Никола Тесла; 1856–1943)	First alternating current (AC) electromotor. Nikola Tesla performed high voltage experiments, geared to induction, in Colorado and New York state. Nikola Tesla made significant contributions to the full complement of alternating current electrical device designs. Tesla also successfully experimented in remote control operations, as well as wireless communications. Nikola Tesla is most known for his extravagant experiments on wireless energy transmission, concerning significant voltage levels and current loads. The unit for magnetic flux was named after him in 1960 by General Conference on Weights and Measures, the Tesla. In 1888 Nikola Tesla demonstrated the functional polyphase brushless induction motor.
1893	Pieter Zeeman (1865–1943)	Description of the Zeeman effect: spectral line split under the influence of an applied static magnetic field (in contrast to the Stark effect, which was due to an applied electric field). Additional contributions were made by Hendrik Antoon Lorentz (1853–1928).
1897	Joseph John Thomson (1856–1940)	Discovery of the electron; using William Crookes's vacuum tube.
1897	Marchese Guglielmo Giovanni Maria Marconi, 1st Marquis of Marconi (1874–1937)	Introduction of wireless communications (radio telegraphy) and radio.
1898	Oliver Heaviside (1850–1925)	Description of the force on a point charge as the result of both an external magnetic and electric filed; commonly known as the Lorentz force. James Clerk Maxwell (1831–1879) described a similar principle in a paper in 1855. The work of Hendrik Antoon Lorentz (1853–1928) refined the concept, hence the association of his name.
1898	Antoine Henri Becquerel (1852–1908)	Introduction of units for radioactivity radiation. Collaborator with Manya (Marie) Skłodovska Curie (1867–1934). Henri Becquerel, Marie Curie, and Pierre Curie shared the Nobel Prize in Physics for their radioactivity discoveries in 1903.
1900	Max Karl Ernst Ludwig Planck (1858–1947)	Inception of quantum mechanics.

(*Continued*)

CHRONOLOGY	NOTEWORTHY PEOPLE	EVENTS AND DISCOVERIES
1904	Sir John Ambrose Fleming (1849–1945)	Introduction of the vacuum tube as an electronic mechanism, either performing as a diode, transistor, or even working in the function of an operational amplifier. Student of James Clerk Maxwell (1831–1879).
1905	Albert Einstein (1879–1955)	Theoretical description of the photoelectro effect: emission of electrons from a metal exposed to light. the Einstein theory was confirmed by Robert Andrews Millikan (1868–1953) in 1914. The discovery of the ramifications of the photoelectric effect further fueled the development of the concept of quantum physics. Additional theoretical concepts introduced by Albert Einstein around that time are the theory of special relativity: Relationship between space and time—(1) the laws of physics are invariant in any and all inertial systems, based on a nonaccelerating frame of reference configuration; (2) the speed of light in vacuum is identical to all observers, regardless of the motion of the frame of reference for the light source. The theory is "special" since it applies to the special case of inertial reference frames.
1907	Captain Henry Joseph Round (1881–1966)	Formal introduction of the electroluminescence concept. This would eventually led to the production of light emitting diodes, after the work by Oleg Vladimirovich Losev (1903–1942) in 1927, but not produced until 1962. Henry Round worked as an assistant to Guglielmo Marconi, 1st Marquis of Marconi (1874–1937)
1913	Johannes Stark (1874–1957)	Stark effect: spectral line split under the influence of an applied static electric field (in contrast to the Zeeman effect, which was due to an applied magnetic field).
1913	Niels Henrik David Bohr (1885–1962)	Bohr atomic model, supporting the fundamental understanding of the p-type and n-type semiconductor principles and the general mode of conduction for valence electrons.
1915	Walter Hermann Schottky (1886–1976)	Development of the basic principles of electron layers resulting from his work on vacuum tubes, which principles also applies to the semiconductor barriers between n-doped and p-doped semiconductor media. The concepts that were introduced included the Schottky barrier, and the Schottky diode.
1916	Gilbert Newton Lewis (1875–1946)	Description of the shell filling for atomic electrons, and the related concept of valence electrons, next to the covalent chemical bond.
1926	Erwin Schrödinger (1887–1961)	Quantum mechanical wave equivalence, wave theory for atomic and nuclear energy configurations.

(Continued)

CHRONOLOGY	NOTEWORTHY PEOPLE	EVENTS AND DISCOVERIES
1925	Julius Edgar Lilienfeld (1882–1963)	First publication of the field-effect transistor concept (applicable to semiconductor media), but not practical for production. The concept was refined in 1938 by Rudolf Hilsch (1903–1972) and Robert Wichard Pohl (1884–1976), providing the solid-state (semiconductor; in contrast to the vacuum tube design in place at the time) amplifier. In 1931 Julius Lilienfeld also introduced the electrolytic capacitor.
1927	Werner Karl Heisenberg (1901–1976)	Uncertainty principle; impossibility to know both the location and the momentum (energy) of a system with absolute accuracy simultaneously. This also removed the causality aspect from events, and substitutes probabilistic distributions.
1927	Oleg Vladimirovich Losev [Russian: Олёг Владимирович Лóсев] (1903–1942)	Development of the light emitting diode (LED). However, the LED was not manufactured until 1962.
1928	Felix Bloch (1905–1983)	Description of the migration process of electrons in an atomic lattice structure. The electron transport formed what Felix Bloch referred to as a wave process, now referenced as Bloch waves. The wave process (i.e., wavelength) directly corresponds to the periodic nature of the lattice structure, in particular for a crystal.
1931	Georges Jean Marie Darrieus (1888–1979)	Introduction of the wind turbine, generating electricity based on induction under wind-powered rotation.
1948	Julian Schwinger (1916–1994), Richard Phillips Feynman (1918–1988), and Sin-Itiro Tomonaga (1906–1979)	Quantum electrodynamics and quantum field theory. Supporting the development of next-generation central processing units (CPUs) for computational applications (computer).
1950	John Alexander Hopps (1919–1998)	Introduction of the "portable" (~44 kg) cardiac pacemaker, based on the earlier work by Mark Lidwell (1878–1969) and Edgar Harold Booth (1893–1963) in 1926. This led, with the development of microprocessors, to the first implantable pacemaker in 1958 by William Chardack (1919–2011) and Wilson Greatbatch (1919–2011).
1957	Jack St. Clair Kilby (1923–2005)	Introduction of the integrated circuit (IC)—chip.
1969	Gordon Earle Moore (1929–), Marcian Edward "Ted" Hoff (1937–) and Federico Faggin (1941–)	Introduction of the microchip/microprocessor/CPU (central processing unit). Gordon Moore is one of the founders of the Intel Corporation. Gordon Moore also introduced a principle known as Moore's law: the exponential increase of component density on a integrated circuit wafer with respect to years of development.

Energy

CHRONOLOGY	NOTEWORTHY PEOPLE	EVENTS AND DISCOVERIES
13.8 billion years BC	Georges Henri Joseph Édouard Lemaître (1894–1966) and Edwin Powell Hubble (1889–1953)	"The Big Bang"; in 1927 the expanding universe was recognized.
350 BC	Aristotle (384 BC–322 BC)	The word "energy" has the Greek origin "Enérgeia" [Greek: ἐνέργεια], which was documented by Aristotle, "Enérgeia" does not translate directly into English, the meaning resembles: "being at work."
40 BC	Marcus Vitruvius Pollio [Vitruvius] (ca 80 BC–10 BC)	Architectural designs that harness the solar energy.
550	Ireland	Introduction of tidal mills. Work performed by machine based on the flow of water resulting from the changing tides in ocean and seawater level as well as resulting from the flow of rivers based on elevation (waterwheel).
650	Persia	First recorded use of wind mills and wind energy in the Persian Empire.
800	Persia, the Netherlands; detailed scientific documentation by Simon Stevin (1548–1620)	Wind energy used to pump water, windmill water pump: windpump. Other use of the windmill was in manufacturing, for example, papermaking, cloth fabrication, wheat processing, and later for the generation of electricity.
1500	Leonardo da Vinci (1452–1519)	Energy conservation principle illustrated ("described") by several of the machines designed by Leonardo da Vinci.
ca. 1632	Galileo Galilei (1564–1642)	Account of friction in the energy exchange with respect to work. Additional work on energy conservation was described in the *Dialogue Concerning the Two Chief World Systems*, representing the Galilean invariance.
ca. 1687	Sir Isaac Newton (1643–1727)	Newton's statement on "conservation of energy": "Energy is not lost or destroyed, it is merely transferred from on party to the next."
1698	Thomas Savery (1650–1715)	Construction of the basic steam engine.
1712	Thomas Newcomen (1664–1729) and John Calley (1663–1717)	Construction of an "atmospheric" steam engine.
1757–1769	James Watt (1736–1819)	Modern steam engine design and operation with theoretical description of operation.
1769	Nicolas-Joseph Cugnot (1725–1804)	First operational steam-powered automobile, the predecessor to the internal combustion automobile.

(Continued)

CHRONOLOGY	NOTEWORTHY PEOPLE	EVENTS AND DISCOVERIES
1776	Luigi Galvani (1737–1789)	Biomedical connection to electricity and development of a mechanism to measure electrical energy, respectively, electrochemical potential.
1781	Charles-Augustin de Coulomb (1736–1806)	Definition of the electric field related to electric charge. The electric charge was still an elusive concept in those days.
1800	Count Alessandro Giuseppe Antonio Anastasio Volta (1745–1827)	Introduction of the battery.
1820	Pierre Louis Dulong (1785–1838) and Alexis-Thérèse Petit (1791–1820)	Dulong and Petit law of specific heats.
1821	Thomas Johann Seebeck (1770–1831) and in 1834 Jean Charles Athanase Peltier (1785–1845) [greater detail]	Thermoelectric effect.
1827	Benoît Fourneyron (1802–1867)	First water turbine.
1831	Michael Faraday (1791–1867) and Joseph Henry (1797–1878)	Law of induction, leading to the development of the electric generator.
1845	James Prescott Joule (1818– 1889)	Energy definition; mechanical equivalence of heat.
1839	Sir William Robert Grove (1811–1896)	Introduction of the first hydrogen–oxygen fuel cell.
1861	Augustin Mouchot (1825–1911	Presentation of the use of solar energy as a source for personal energy consumption.
1865	August Joseph Ignaz Toepler (1836–1912)	Electrostatic charge generation.
1873	Josiah Willard Gibbs (1839–1903)	Chemical potential, a energy constituent within the Gibbs free energy. Thermodynamic concept describing the energy that can be released or absorbed during a chemical reaction.
1876	Alexander Graham Bell (1847–1922)	Introduction of the telephone. Other efforts involved hydrofoils and aeronautics.
1877	Thomas Edison (1847–1931)	Introduction of the phonograph and telegraph machine and the electric light bulb.
1880	Johannes Diderik van der Waals (1837–1923)	Description of chemical bonding energy. Van der Waals equation.

(Continued)

CHRONOLOGY	NOTEWORTHY PEOPLE	EVENTS AND DISCOVERIES
1880	James Wimshurst (1832–1903)	Electrostatic charge generation.
1888	Inspired by Michael Faraday (1791–1867)	First electric power generator by means of induction based on revolutions provided by a bush postmill, wind energy.
1892	Sir John Ambrose Fleming (1849–1945)	Electrical transformer theory and communications. Introduction of the thermionic valve, electronic device.
1893	Nikola Tesla (1856–1943)	Design of modern alternating current technology. Worked for Thomas Edison (1847–1931) on telephony. On his own, he developed the induction motor design. Tesla also worked on X-ray imaging and radio transmission.
1897	Joseph John Thomson (1856–1940)	Discovery of the electron; using William Crookes's vacuum tube.
1900	Max Karl Ernst Ludwig Planck (1858–1947) and James Clerk Maxwell (1831–1879)	Formal description of the photon and the energy associated with the electromagnetic wave.
1904	Piero Ginori Conti, Prince of Trevignano, (1865–1939)	Geothermal electric generator.
1914	Niels Henrik David Bohr (1885–1962)	Description of the atomic energy layer model; hydrogen (Bohr atomic model).
1918	Paul Scherrer (1890–1969)	X-ray diffraction, crystal structure. nuclear energy development. Established the CERN institute in Switzerland as one of the founders. Directed the construction of the first cyclotron in 1940.
1923	Arthur Holly Compton (1892–1962)	Description of the deflection of photons by a nucleus: Compton effect.
1927	Werner Karl Heisenberg (1901–1976)	Quantum uncertainty principle.
1927	Paul Adrien Maurice Dirac (1902–1984)	Description of antimatter.
1929	Robert Jemison van de Graaff (1902–1967)	Electrostatic charge generation.
1931	Carl David Anderson (1905–1991	Discovery of the positron, anti-particle for the electron. The "positron" was predicted by Paul Adrien Maurice Dirac (1902–1984) in 1929.
1931	Georges Jean Marie Darrieus (1888–1979)	Introduction of the wind turbine.
1932	Sir James Chadwick (1891–1974)	Discovery of the neutron.
1934	Hideki Yukawa [湯川秀樹], (1907–1981)	Introduction of mesons and the concept of antimatter.

(Continued)

CHRONOLOGY	NOTEWORTHY PEOPLE	EVENTS AND DISCOVERIES
1937	Carl David Anderson (1905–1991), Seth Henry Neddermeyer (1907–1988), Jabez Curry Street (1906–1989) and Edward C. Stevenson (1937–)	Confirmation of the existence of the meson, and muon.
1940+	Julius Robert Oppenheimer (1904–1967)	Manhattan project: fission reaction. Prominent members: Arthur Compton (1892–1962); Enrico Fermi (1901–1954); Eugene Wigner (1902–1995), and dozens more.
1947	William Webster Hansen (1909–1949)	Linear accelerator installation at Stanford University, California.
1950	Maria Goeppert-Mayer (Göppert) (1906–1972)	Introduction of the nuclear shell model for atomic nuclei.
1955	Obninsk Nuclear Power Station, Russia	First nuclear power station for energy generation.
1958	Stanley Mandelstam (1928–2016)	Introduction of Mandelstam variables associated with the concept of "crossing symmetry," defining numerical quantities which encode the energy, momentum, and scattering angles of particles in a deflection process described in a Lorentz invariant fashion.
1958	Lev Davidovich Landau [Russian: Лёв Давидович Ландау] (1908–1968), Arkady Beynusovich Migdal [Russian: Аркадий Бейнусович (Бенедиктович) Мигдал] (1911–1991)	Theory of interacting electrons, specifically with respect to solids; condensed matter physics.
1960	George Irving Bell (1926–2000)	Fundamental contributor to the evolution of the nuclear energy program.
1961	Murray Gell-Mann (1929–)	Description of elementary particles, eight-fold way of defining "strangeness" for the quark.
1964	Charles Hard Townes (1915–2015), Nikolay Gennadiyevich Basov [Николай Геннадиевич Басов] (1922–2001) and Aleksandr Mikhailovich Prokhorov [Александр Михайлович Прохоров] (1916–2002)	Quantum electronics.

(Continued)

CHRONOLOGY	NOTEWORTHY PEOPLE	EVENTS AND DISCOVERIES
1972	Stephen Hawking (1942–), Jacob Bekenstein (1947–2015)	Thermodynamics of black holes.
1978		Discovery of the "gluon" with the assistance of the Pluto, the first electromagnetic superconductive solenoid located in Hamburg, Germany.
1983	Collider detector at Fermilab	World's first and at the time highest-energy particle accelerator, colliding antiprotons and protons propelled to center-of-mass energy reaching 2 TeV.
1995	Wolfgang Ketterle (1957–), Eric Allin Cornell (1961–), and Carl Edwin Wieman (1951–)	Experimental verification of Bose–Einstein condensation.
2012	François Baron Englert (1932–) and Peter Ware Higgs (1929–)	Higgs boson (126 GeV) discovery in the Large Hadron Collider at CERN, Geneva, Switzerland. The Large Hadron Collider construction started in 1998 and produces particle acceleration with respective energy levels for protons at up to 4 teraelectronvolts (0.64 microjoules), or lead nuclei: 2.76 TeV per nucleon or 574 TeV per nucleus. The proton energy level was increased to 6.5 TeV in 2015.

Engineering

CHRONOLOGY	NOTEWORTHY PEOPLE	EVENTS AND DISCOVERIES
1.8 million years BC		Use of stone tools, axe, scraper, and hammer.
200000 BC		*Homo sapiens.*
25000 BC		Ceramics; baked clay.
9000 BC		Bow and arrow.
6000 BC– 2000 BC	Stone Age	Mechanical labor and tool fabrication.
c. 6000 BC	Egypt	First recorded drawings of rudimentary water crafts.
c. 4000 BC	Eastern Europe, Arabic nations, Mesopotamia (specifically: Sumeria/Sumer)	First recorded drawing of craft with rudimentary wheels. Most prominent: use of pieces/slice of tree trunk as wheel, attached to an axle (Ljubljana, Slovenia).
4000 BC	Mesopotamia and Egypt	Documented recording of the construction of shelter, abandoning the nomadic structure.
4000 BC		First documented use of lime-based mortar. Prior to this most building assembly relied on clay or mud as the cohesive element to connect stone blocks together.

(Continued)

CHRONOLOGY	NOTEWORTHY PEOPLE	EVENTS AND DISCOVERIES
c. 3500 BC		First documented installation of sewer systems, primarily run-off.
c. 3300 BC	Egypt	Drawings of sail boats.
3300 BC–1000 BC	Bronze Age	Smelting and forging of soft metals using low heat: copper, tin, and gold. This age also introduces the written documentation.
2700 BC–2500 BC	Egypt	Construction of pyramids, requiring advanced mechanical engineering efforts and architectural design (civil engineering).
1600 BC	Babylonian empire	Use of water clocks for time keeping.
c. 1000 BC	Qanat aqueduct; Persia	Water supply over a length greater than 71 km, and potential relation with sewer as a secondary use for liquid transport as part of the civil engineering efforts.
1000 BC–700 AD	Iron Age	Higher heat requirements and more detailed tool manufacturing, introducing scientific and engineering challenges. Historical tracking of processes and developments and philosophies. Introduction of complicated mechanisms and requiring detailed analytical thinking.
c. 600 BC	Thales of Miletus (ca. 624 BC–ca. 546 BC; known as Thales: Θαλῆς)	Introduction of metrology, measurements of the height of pyramids with proposed standards. Introduced the concept of logic proof.
520 BC	Pythagoras (571 BC–495 BC)	Pythagorean theorem for a triangle.
430 BC	Socrates (469 BC–399 BC)	Scholar and educator, introducing analytical thinking.
c. 360 BC	Plato (427 BC–347 BC)	Student of Socrates (469 BC–399 BC). Founder of the principles for modern philosophy and science. The Plato school of teaching included, but not limited to astronomy, biology, mathematics, philosophy, and political theory.
300 BC	Roman empire	Waterwheel used for drainage next to perform work.
350 BC	Aristotle (384 BC–322 BC)	Introduction of modern physical science concepts (natural philosophy) and logic (including deductive reasoning). Aristotle's attention in teaching ranged from anatomy, to astronomy (promoting the wrong concept of a geocentric system for earth and the sun), embryology, geography, geology, meteorology, including physics as well as zoology.
c. 310 BC	Euclid (c. 350 BC– c. 275 BC)	Euclidean geometry; still valid for classical mechanics.

(Continued)

CHRONOLOGY	NOTEWORTHY PEOPLE	EVENTS AND DISCOVERIES
c. 300 BC	Zhou Bi Suan Jing (周髀算經) (Zhou Dynasty (1046 BC–256 BC)	Documented proof of the Pythagorean theorem, shortly after the "western" proof by Pythagoras (571 BC–495 BC)
c. 250 BC	Archimedes (287 BC–212 BC)	Revealed the properties that define buoyancy. Developed calculus and algebra and created a system for "abbreviating" large numbers by means of what we now consider exponential expressions. Archimedes also described the mechanics of a level, defining torque. Still primarily statics.
c. 280 BC–247 BC	Alexandria, Egypt	Lighthouse of Alexandria. The city of Alexandria was erected by Alexander the Great of Macedon [Greek: Ἀλέξανδρος ὁ Μέγας] (356 BC–323 BC) in 332 BC. The lighthouse was one of the tallest man-made architectural structures for many centuries and was partially destroyed as a result of a series of earthquakes over the period 956–1323.
c. 220 BC	China	Civil engineering effort of the architectural and mechanical design and construction of the Great Wall, Ming Dynasty. As mortar the engineers used sticky rice
142 BC	Rome, Italy	Oldest known arch bridge, made from stone.
40 BC	Marcus Vitruvius Pollio [Vitruvius] (ca 80 BC–10 BC)	Roman engineering architect and civil engineer. Vitruvius served under Gaius Julius Caesar (100 BC–44 BC). In the army position, he was also charged with the care of the infirmed, where he used early biomedical engineering approaches for novel diagnosis and treatment. Vitruvius provided a detailed description of the preparation and use of lime-based gypsum mortar for construction use. The Romans added volcanic ash to make the concrete mixture resistant to water, and used it in the construction of aqueducts; lime itself will not harden or will decay when continuously exposed to water. Description of the use of a waterwheel to measure the distance traveled by a ship (odometer).
10 BC	Strabo (64 BC–24 AD)	Description of the use of a waterwheel-powered mill; Turkey/Egypt/Mesopotamian empire.
62	Hero of Alexandria [ρωνό Ἀλεξανδρεύς], (10–70)	Mathematician, physicist, and mechanical engineer who also taught pneumatics. A set of two books: *The Pneumatica* describes mechanical devices worked by air, steam, or water pressure. Also known as Heron of Alexandria. He invented a steam-powered engine called the "Æolipile."
105	Apollodorus of Damascus (2nd century)	Architect and construction engineer for the longest known ancient technology arch bridge over the river Danube: Trajan Bridge. The bridge was created to facilitate the transport of troops across Europe.

(Continued)

CHRONOLOGY	NOTEWORTHY PEOPLE	EVENTS AND DISCOVERIES
120	Claudius Ptolemy {Ptolemaeus} [Πτολεμαῖος] (90–168)	Geographic recordings of a significant part of the Islamic and Western world (i.e., Roman and Persian Empire), living in Egypt, as a Roman with Greek education. His cartography extended all the way out, including parts of China (discovered in 15th century). He specifically developed arithmetical techniques for calculating astronomical phenomena, under the teachings of Babylonian astronomers. Also known as: بطليموس (Batlamyus; Arabic).
132	Zhang Heng (78–139)	First known construction and use of a seismograph, Han Dynasty.
400	Roman empire	Description of the use of a waterwheel for propulsion of a boat by means of an ox: paddle-wheel (publication *De Rebus Bellicis*).
644		Wind-powered devices developed by the Persians.
900–1200	Mexico, central America	Construction of temples which apparently have a close correlation to astronomical observations. Civil engineering.
1176	France	Mechanical clock tower: "horologe"; presumably powered by running water.
1430	Philip the Good, Duke of Burgundy (1396–1467)	Spring-driven clock.
1450	Machu Picchu, Peru	Construction of an Incan citadel in the Andes mountains. No mortar (no cement) was used in the assembly process.
1500	Leonardo da Vinci (1452–1519)	The preverbal "Renaissance man," involved in all aspects of cultural evolution, science, engineering, politics, and art. Da Vinci designed a water-powered gyroscopic compass.
1510	Peter Henlein (1485–1542)	Spring-driven time-keeping device: clock; "Nuremberg-egg" pocket watch.
1590	Francis Bacon, 1st Viscount of St. Alban (1561–1626)	Regulate the general scientific methodology.
c. 1600	Galileo Galilei (1564–1642)	Major contributor to the scientific revolution and the (re) introduction of analytical thinking in science, engineering, and general thought processes. Galileo Galilei recognized that motion would be uninterrupted if there were no constraints; that is, no friction.
1614	René Descartes (1596–1650)	Introduction to vortex motion. Introduction of the concept of general corpuscular motion, extending from small (maybe referring to the undefined atom), to planetary orbits.
1632	Evangelista Torricelli (1608–1647)	Introduction of the barometer; essential in weather prediction; meteorology.

(*Continued*)

CHRONOLOGY	NOTEWORTHY PEOPLE	EVENTS AND DISCOVERIES
1650	Blaise Pascal (1623–1662)	Pascal's law, pressure in a container applies an equal force on all surface of the enclosure.
1660	Robert Boyle (1627–1691)	Gas laws, definition of the behavior or gases. Boyle mentioned the compression of gas as a potential "shock-absorber," acting similar to a spring.
1673	Christiaan Huygens (1629–1695)	Construction of a "combustion engine" powered by gun powder. Huygens introduced several concept of mechanical engineering and described the mechanism of shock waves. Christiaan Huygens is most known for his lens manufacturing and optical design of telescopes. The mathematical efforts of Christiaan Huygens in probability theory were far advanced and he collaborated with the mathematician Pierre de Fermat (1601–1665) from France.
1679	Denis Papin (1647–c. 1712)	Pressure and thermodynamic and mechanical impacts.
1680	Robert Hooke (1635–1703)	Force applied by a compressed spring, linearly proportional to the compression length: spring constant.
c. 1687	Sir Isaac Newton (1643–1727)	Sir Isaac Newton introduced three laws of motion dynamics: (1) an object remains at rest, or move in steady-state velocity, unless an externally applied force persuades it to change the status quo; (2) the sum of the forces acting on a body will change the motion (i.e., acceleration) of that body in a linear proportion and in the direction of the resultant of these forces, (3) for every action there is an equal but opposite reaction. The publication of the *Philosophiæ Naturalis Principia Mathematica* provides detailed definitions regarding ballistic motion, circular motion (centripetal force), laws of action–reaction, gravitational acceleration, inertia, and force with respect to acceleration. Introduction of the three laws of motion.
1698	Thomas Savery (1650–1715)	Construction of the basic steam engine; using information obtained by Denis Papin (1647–c. 1712).
1705	Edmond Halley (1656–1742)	Discovery of, and mathematical description of the trajectory for "Halley's comet."
1712	Thomas Newcomen (1664–1729)	Construction of a "atmospheric" steam engine.
1714	Brook Taylor (1685–1731)	Fundamental frequency of vibration; string. Additional work on pure mathematics: Taylor series.
1727	Leonard Euler (1707–1783)	Introduction of the concept of the elastic modulus, experimentally verified by Giordano Riccati (1709–1790) in 1782 and mathematically introduced by Thomas Young (1773–1829) in 1807, now known as Young's modulus.

(Continued)

CHRONOLOGY	NOTEWORTHY PEOPLE	EVENTS AND DISCOVERIES
1732	Anders Celsius (1701–1744)	Thermometer scale calibration based on pure water phases.
1733	Daniel Bernoulli (1700–1782)	Acoustics, mechanical vibrations, and fluid-dynamic principles introduced. Definition of the fundamental frequency and higher harmonics, with supporting elaborate mathematical analysis (solutions to differential equations).
1735	Daniel Gabriel Fahrenheit (1686–1736)	Temperature scale in Fahrenheit based on body temperature and saltwater phases.
1743	Jean-Baptiste le Rond d'Alembert (1717–1783)	Publication on the concepts of forces and accelerating systems: *Traite de Dynamique*.
1752	Benjamin Franklin (1706–1790)	Kite experiment and the documentation of "electric current."
1756	John Smeaton (1724–1792)	Introduction of pozzolans (pozzolanic earth) mixed in with mortar to provide a water-resistant cement mortar.
1757–1769	James Watt (1736–1819)	Modern steam engine design and operation with theoretical description of operation.
1762	Joseph Black (1728–1799)	Realization of the concept of latent heat.
1760–1820		Industrial Revolution.
1769	Nicolas-Joseph Cugnot (1725–1804)	First operational steam-powered automobile, the predecessor to the internal combustion automobile.
1781	Charles-Augustin de Coulomb (1736–1806)	Definition of the electric field related to electric charge. The electric charge itself was still an elusive concept in those days. Introduction to the scientific aspects of electrical engineering.
1783	Antoine Laurent de Lavoisier (1743–1794)	Discovery of oxygen and the chemical impact, oxidation. Scientific approach to the chemical engineering aspects of phenomena, both natural and artificial.
1783	Joseph-Michel Montgolfier (1740–1810) and Jacques-Étienne Montgolfier (1745–1799)	Hot-air balloon; buoyancy.
1785	Jacques Alexandre César Charles (1746–1823)	Charles's law, expansion of gases.
1800	Count Alessandro Giuseppe Antonio Anastasio Volta (1745–1827)	Introduction of the battery. The introduction of the electrical engineering aspect of technology.
1802	Joseph Louis Gay-Lussac (1778–1850)	Ideal gas law; building on the work by Robert Boyle (1627–1691), more than a century earlier.

(Continued)

CHRONOLOGY	NOTEWORTHY PEOPLE	EVENTS AND DISCOVERIES
1807	Thomas Young (1773–1829)	Formal introduction of the Young's modulus for elastic deformation, tying strain to stress, based on the work by Leonard Euler (1707–1783).
1821	Michael Faraday (1791–1867)	Discovery of electromagnetic rotation, leading to his law on electromagnetic induction in 1831. Meanwhile, in 1923 Michael Faraday experimentally verified the concept of refrigeration, introduced based on the work of John Dalton (1766–1844) in 1802 and William Cullen (1710–1790) in 1756.
1824	Joseph Aspdin (1778–1855)	Introduction of portland cement; mixture of limestone, clay, and a blend or minerals in carefully controlled proportions. The constituents of the Portland cement were calcined (thermal treatment process used for decomposition or purification) and ground into a fine aggregate of particles. portland cement versus primarily produced and distributed from within Europe.
1824	Nicolas Léonard Sadi Carnot (1796–1832)	Refrigerator for general public.
1827	Benoît Fourneyron (1802–1867)	First water turbine.
1831	Michael Faraday (1791–1867) and Joseph Henry (1797–1878)	Law of induction, leading to the development of the electric generator.
1840	Jean Léonard Marie Poiseuille (1799–1869) and Gotthilf Heinrich Ludwig Hagen (1797–1884)	Pressure drop for incompressible fluids with respect to laminar flow.
1848	William Thomson, 1st Baron Kelvin (i.e., Lord Kelvin) (1824–1907)	Absolute temperature scale: Kelvin.
1851	Jean Bernard Léon Foucault (1819–1868)	Foucault pendulum, illustrating the impact of the earth's rotation on motion.
1852	James Prescott Joule (1818–1889) and William Thomson, 1st Baron Kelvin {Lord Kelvin} (1824–1907)	Joule-Thomson effect: rapidly expanding gas leads to a reduction in the temperature of the gas, even offering the potential for a phase change to solid, or liquid. Sometimes also found as the Joule-Kelvin effect.
1854	Robert Wilhelm Eberhard Bunsen (1811–1899)	Bunsen burner.
1859	James Clerk Maxwell (1831–1879)	Description of the distribution law of molecular velocities.
1861	Augustin Mouchot (1825–1911)	Presentation of the use of solar energy as a source for personal energy consumption.

(Continued)

CHRONOLOGY	NOTEWORTHY PEOPLE	EVENTS AND DISCOVERIES
1866	Ludwig Eduard Boltzmann (1844–1906) and Josiah Willard Gibbs (1839–1903)	Statistical mechanics, correlating energy, and heat, to the movement (velocity).
1873	Josiah Willard Gibbs (1839–1903)	Chemical potential: a energy constituent within the Gibbs free energy. Thermodynamic concept describing the energy that can be released or absorbed during a chemical reaction.
1873	James Clerk Maxwell (1831–1879)	Theory of electromagnetic radiation: *Treatise on Electricity and Magnetism*. James Maxwell made use of the prior work by Wilhelm Eduard Weber (1804–1891) and Johann Carl Friedrich Gauss {Gauß} (1777–1855).
1875	Siegfried Samuel Marcus (1831–1898)	Siegfried Marcus automobile, powered by an internal combustion engine; Vienna, Austria. Predecessor to the "modern" automobile. In 1883 Siegfried Marcus received a patent on a ignition magnet (ignition magneto), now know as a distributor, providing ignition electrical discharges to then respective cylinders in the correct order and on-time at the correct cylinder position, just a few degrees before the piston connecting-rod stretches to the top of the cylinder.
1880	Johannes Diderik van der Waals (1837–1923)	Description of the covalent bond. Van der Waals equation.
1883	John Joseph Montgomery (1858–1911)	Montgomery glider; first piloted flight with an aircraft "heavier than air" (vs. the hot-air balloon) transporting human passengers. Montgomery fell victim to his own ingenuity and died in a crash of one of his glider designs.
1887	Heinrich Rudolf Hertz (1857–1894)	Radar development. Detection of electromagnetic radiation (radio waves). Heinrich Hertz also discovered that certain metal plates will generate electricity when exposed to light: photoelectric effect.
1891		Manitou Springs, Colorado: Cog railway leading up to the top of Pikes Peak of the Rocky Mountains, mountain ridge.
1894	Max Karl Ernst Ludwig Planck, (1858–1947)	Black-body radiation.
1895	Folsom, California	First operational hydroelectric power plant.
1897	Guglielmo Marconi, 1st Marquis of Marconi (1874–1937)	Introduction of wireless communications and radio.
1900	Anne Rainsford French Bush (1878–1962)	First licensed female steam engineer in the United States of America.

(Continued)

CHRONOLOGY	NOTEWORTHY PEOPLE	EVENTS AND DISCOVERIES
1900	Ferdinand Adolf Heinrich August Graf von Zeppelin (1838–1917)	Successful dirigible, gas-filled air floatation device with propulsion.
1925	Karl von Terzaghi (1883–1963)	Foundation of geotechnical engineering, considered a subsection of civil engineering, linking structural design to the soil foundation mechanical conditions. Publication: *Erdbaumechanik*. One specific example of the influence of Karl von Terzaghi is the maximum slope (abutment; 90 degrees being vertical) for a dam that will hold under its own weight, such as found in ridges on which railways are raised above the topography of the terrain, or the design and construction of levees. For sand, the slope is roughly 45 degrees, whereas for bricks or clay the slope can be stable up to 60°.
1926	Mark Cowley Lidwell (1878–1969) and Edgar Harold Booth (1893–1963)	Rudimentary, but effective, external cardiac pacemaker design.
1930	Richard Buckminster Fuller (1895–1983)	Mechanical engineering and engineering architecture, as well as chemistry; Bucky-ball, multipoint connections in both chemical structures and mechanical structures.
1931	Georges Jean Marie Darrieus (1888–1979)	Introduction of the wind turbine.
1937–1959	Chester Floyd Carlson (1906–1968)	Photocopy machine, patented in 1942. The first photocopier was offered for sale by the Haloid company in 1959, later renamed Xerox.
1950	John Alexander Hopps, (1919–1998)	Introduction of the "portable" (45 kg) cardiac pacemaker, based on the earlier work by Mark Lidwell (1878–1969) and Edgar Harold Booth (1893–1963) in 1926. This led, with the development of microprocessors, to the first implantable pacemaker in by William Chardack (1919–2011) and Wilson Greatbatch (1919–2011).
1956	Paul Winchell {Wilchinsky} (1922–2005)	Artificial heart (Jarvik 7).
1969	NASA	First lunar landing; Apollo 11: Neil Armstrong (1930–2012), Michael Collins (1930–) [commander of lunar orbiter module], and Buzz Aldrin {Edwin Eugene Aldrin Jr} (1930–).
1979	K.V. Hall, R.L. Kaster, A. Wøien	Application of an in vivo artificial bileaflet replacement heart valve.

(Continued)

Fluid Dynamics

CHRONOLOGY	NOTEWORTHY PEOPLE	EVENTS AND DISCOVERIES
ca. 3300 BC	Egypt	Drawings of sailboat.
ca. 2000 BC	Egypt; India	Irrigation systems.
350 BC	Aristotle (384 BC–322 BC)	Founder of the Lyceum school of analytical thinking in Macedonia. Aristotle described the initial concepts of physics, motion, time as well as astronomy concepts. Aristotle supposed an external force (acting during flight) perpetuating the projectile motion of a ballistic object.
144 BC	Italy	Construction of aqueducts.
1010	Eilmer of Malmesbury, 11th century Benedictine monk	First documented successful flight, performed with a wooden frame lined with parchment, traveling approximately 200 meter in free fall from a 18 meter elevation.
1206	Al-Jazari (1136–1206) [Turkey]; Badi'al-Zaman Abū al-'Izz ibn Ismā'īl ibn al-Razāz al-Jazarī (بْنُ اَلْعِز أَبُو الزمان بـــديع) بْنُ اَلْعِز أَبُو الزمان بـــديع	Publication of *Book of Knowledge of Ingenious Mechanical Devices* . Description of mechanical devices and mechanism of action.
1245	Thomas Aquinas (1225–1274)	Reformulation of the dynamic concepts of Aristotle (384 BC–322 BC).
1500	Leonardo da Vinci (1452–1519)	Description of early friction concepts, and derivation of the conservation of mass equation for one-dimensional flow. Documented descriptions of wave phenomena, fluid jets, hydraulic pumps, eddy current formation, and low-drag flow as well as high-drag (turbulent flow around an object being pulled though a fluid) flow.
1586	Galileo Galilei (1564–1642)	Investigation on the aspect of drag (friction) on falling objects. The Galilei number is the ratio of the gravitational forces over the viscous forces, yielding a dimensionless number; however, the number was not introduced by Galileo Galilei.
ca. 1660	Edme Mariotte (1620–1684)	First wind tunnel construction to test some of the concepts introduced by Leonardo da Vinci (1452–1519), and his own observations and curiosity.
ca. 1687	Sir Isaac Newton (1643–1727)	Sir Isaac Newton introduced the three laws of motion. His additional contributions in fluid dynamics describe the law of viscosity for linear fluids. Linear fluids (idealized fluid) are referred to as Newtonian fluids.

(Continued)

CHRONOLOGY	NOTEWORTHY PEOPLE	EVENTS AND DISCOVERIES
1699	Guillaume Amontons (1663–1705)	Formal introduction of the concept of friction, based on the rudimentary introduction by Leonardo da Vinci (1452–1519).
1732	Henry de Pitot (1695–1771)	Investigation of the velocity of flow as a function of depth, disproving the leading theory that flow velocity increases with depth. Original design of the "Pitot tube" used to measure the flow velocity.
1738	Daniel Bernoulli (1700–1782)	Demonstration of the Bernoulli's principle: relationship between flow velocity and pressure, for inviscid flow. The Bernoulli principle defines the behavior of flight with respect to light on the airplane wing, as well as the mixing of fluids (combustible and air for a carburetor. Published in *Hydrodynamica*.
1743	Jean-Baptiste le Rond d'Alembert (1717–1783)	Publication on the concepts of forces and accelerating systems: *Traite de Dynamique*. Mathematical description of frictionless flow.
1750	Leonard Euler (1707–1783)	Introduction of the coefficients representing kinetic and static friction; creation of what we consider the Bernoulli equation, differential flow formulation as well as the integral form.
1765	Antoine de Chézy (1718–1798)	Description of steady-state turbulent flow in an open channel, linking the average velocity to the radius of the channel and the depth of the flow.
1781	Charles-Augustin de Coulomb (1736–1806)	Verification of the friction principles that were introduced by Guillaume Amontons (1663–1705).
1797	Giovanni Battista Venturi (1746–1822)	A tube with two tapered ends joining at the narrow ends provides a drop in pressure. This "ventury" can provide suction when a hole is placed in this narrow passage.
1811	Augustin Louis de Cauchy (1789–1857)	Mathematical description of wave phenomena in elastic media and elastic membranes. Cauchy also introduced the concept and definition for stress, which are complementary to those of Siméon Denis Poisson (1781–1840).
1820	Gotthilf Heinrich Ludwig Hagen (1797–1884)	Theoretical design for hydraulic engineering projects.
1838	Jean-Louis Léonard Marie Poiseuille (1799–1869)	Introduction of the Hagen–Poiseuille law describing nonturbulent flow through a compliant system (e.g., blood vessels, primarily applicable to smaller diameter vessels), crediting the influence of Gotthilf Heinrich Ludwig Hagen (1797–1884). The flow applies to steady-state conditions for a Newtonian fluid that is incompressible.

(Continued)

CHRONOLOGY	NOTEWORTHY PEOPLE	EVENTS AND DISCOVERIES
1839–1868	Heinrich Gustav Magnus (1802–1870)	Description of the process of absorption of gases in blood (respiration); vapor pressure for evaporated liquids. A projectile spinning object will veer away from the original trajectory: Magnus effect. This applies, for instance, to rotating propellers and pitched baseballs.
1840	Claude-Louis Navier (1785–1836) and George Gabriel Stokes (1819–1903)	Fluid dynamics based on Newton's second law concepts incorporating friction concepts and pressure gradient: Navier–Stokes equations.
1845	Henry Philibert Gaspard Darcy (1803–1858)	Redisign of the Pitot tube, used to measure the local flow velocity. Still in use to measure the speed of flight for airplanes.
1850	Julius Ludwig Weisbach (1806–1871)	Refined the work of Henry Philibert Gaspard Darcy (1803–1858) and wrote a series of physics textbooks. Weisbach studied under Johann Carl Friedrich Gauss (1777–1855).
1861	William Froude (1810–1879)	Applications to ship design, reducing the roll of a ship by means of a keel. The hydrodynamic behavior of the hull of a ship could be gauged based on the Froude number, derived from a set of experimental obtained data points.
1875	Lord Rayleigh (1842–1919) [John Strutt]	Dimensional analysis technique to provide a theoretical approach with regard to diabatic incompressible flow in a system with a constant cross-sectional area, neglecting the heat exchange aspects.
1877	Ernst Waldfried Josef Wenzel Mach (1838–1916)	Study and description of shock waves, introduced the Mach number for travel velocity with respect to the speed of sound. Additional work of Ernst Mach was in interferometry, Doppler effect aspects and acoustics.
1878	Vincen Strouhal (1850–1922)	Introduction of a dimensionless parameter that describes the tail or wing kinematics of swimming and flying animals in addition to flying object with fixed wings (e.g., airplane). The Strouhal number is the ratio of the characteristic length of the object in the flow, multiplied by the frequency of the observed phenomenon (e.g., vortex; flapping wings) in reference to the velocity of the object with respect to the flow of the medium. The Strouhal number is a function of the Reynolds number, also dimensionless.
1883	Osborne Reynolds (1842–1912)	Friction description with respect to fluid dynamics concepts. Introduction of the Reynolds number defining the ratio of inertial force with respect to viscous forces. The Reynolds number provides a method to compare similar flow patterns under different fluid flow situations.

(Continued)

CHRONOLOGY	NOTEWORTHY PEOPLE	EVENTS AND DISCOVERIES
1889	Robert Manning (1816–1897)	Description of the average flow velocity for free-flow pipe flow based on the incline, and the radius of the pipe and fill area of the tube (jointly providing the wetted area, or hydraulic radius): Manning formula.
1895	Diederik Johannes Korteweg (1848–1941) and Gustav de Vries (1866–1934)	Diederik Korteweg and his student Gustav de Vries derived a nonlinear partial differential equation defining the propagation of waves in shallow water. The Korteweg–de Vries (KdV) equation describes the solitary wave described by John Scott Russell (1808–1882). The KdV equation has had an important implications for the development of the mathematical description of solitons.
1899	Jules Henri Poincaré (1854–1912) and Jacques Salomon Hadamard (1865–1963)	Geodesic flow; mathematical description and physical analysis. With further analysis by George David Birkhoff (1884–1944) in 1927.
1904	Ludwig Prandtl (1875–1953)	Description of the boundary layer for viscous flow, formed at the interface with a solid surface.
1905	Orville Wright (1871–1948) and Wilbur Wright (1867–1912)	First sustained flight with a powered fixed-wing aircraft.
1905	Vito Volterra (1860–1940)	Description of plastic deformation of ductile materials, describing the ability of solid materials to deform under tensile stress, using a theory of dislocations. One example is bending a metal coat hanger.
1907	Edgar Buckingham (1867–1940)	Description on the movement of soil moisture ("capillary action"), as well as gas diffusion in soil.
1910	Moritz Weber (1871–1951)	Analysis of multiphase flow at the boundary interface, in principle Weber compared the inertia of the fluid motion to the surface tension at the interface, described by the Weber number.
1915	Paul Richard Heinrich Blasius (1883–1970)	Description of the net force resulting from fluid flow applied to a fixed body submerged in the flow, using a complex velocity potential defining the flow. The solution of the Blaius theorem uses the Cauchy residue theorem (Augustin Louis de Cauchy [1789–1857]). Student of Ludwig Prandtl (1875–1953).
1923	Sir Geoffrey Ingram Taylor (1886–1975)	Combined contributions to fluid dynamics and wave theory, specifically in a convoluted form applied to vortex formation. Specific topics in his research were with respect to flow through porous surfaces and sheet flow. Taylor contributed to the development of the supersonic aircraft, ca. 1946.
1924	Theodore von Kármán (1881–1963)	Introduction of the Kármán vortex street concept. The Kármán vortex can result in resonance effect and Aeolian sound production.

(Continued)

CHRONOLOGY	NOTEWORTHY PEOPLE	EVENTS AND DISCOVERIES
1931	Georges Jean Marie Darrieus (1888–1979)	Introduction of the wind turbine.
1937	Sir Frank Whittle (1907–1996)	Introduction of the jet engine.
1944	Lewis Ferry Moody (1880–1953)	Friction computation and introduction of the Moody chart, plotting the roughness with respect to Reynolds number of flow and the Darcy–Weisbach friction factor defining the surface contact.
1947	Chuck Yeager (1923–)	Breaking of the sound barrier during level flight.
1957	Owen Martin Phillips (1930–2010), respectively John Wilder Miles (1920–2008)	Gravity wave with respect to either water surface (e.g., ocean waves) or wind flow direction (3D) or capillary wave concept. Theoretical description by means of Stokes wave or Airy wave formulation.
1981	Uri Dinnar (1939–2014)	Theoretical description of periodic turbulent and viscous (non-Newtonian) flow, specifically applicable to blood flow in large (compliant) vessels.

General

CHRONOLOGY	NOTEWORTHY PEOPLE	EVENTS AND DISCOVERIES
6000 BC–2000 BC	Stone Age	Mechanical labor and tool fabrication.
ca. 6000 BC		First recorded use of floatation devices: boats. This illustrated the Archimedes principle (Archimedes [287 BC–212 BC]), but no documented descriptions on the floatation principles from those days.
ca. 4000 BC		First recorded use of wheel for transportation.
ca. 3000 BC		Traceable use of a potter's wheel used for the construction of crockery.
3300 BC–1000 BC	Bronze Age	Smelting and forging of soft metals using low heat: copper, tin, gold. This age also introduces the written documentation.
1000 BC–700 AD	Iron Age	Higher heat requirements and more detailed tool manufacturing, introducing scientific and engineering challenges. Historical tracking of processes and developments and philosophies. Introduction of complicated mechanisms and requiring detailed analytical thinking.
ca. 600 BC	Thales of Miletus (ca. 624 BC–ca. 546 BC; known as Thales: Θαλῆς)	Introduction of metrology, measurements of the height of pyramids with proposed standards. Introduced the concept of logic proof.

(Continued)

CHRONOLOGY	NOTEWORTHY PEOPLE	EVENTS AND DISCOVERIES
430 BC	Socrates (469 BC–399 BC)	Scholar and educator, introducing analytical thinking.
ca. 360 BC	Plato (427 BC–347 BC)	Student of Socrates (469 BC–399 BC). Founder of the principles for modern philosophy and science. The Plato school of teaching included, but not limited to, astronomy, biology, mathematics, philosophy, and political theory.
350 BC	Aristotle (384 BC–322 BC)	Student of Plato (427 BC–347 BC). Founder of the Lyceum school of analytical thinking in Macedonia. Aristotle described the initial concepts of physics, motion, time as well as astronomy concepts. Aristotle hypothesized an external horizontal force (acting during flight) perpetuating the projectile motion of a ballistic object, which is incorrect; only gravity forces the object downward.
ca. 250 BC	Archimedes (287 BC–212 BC)	Revealed the properties that define buoyancy. Developed calculus and algebra and created a system for "abbreviating" large numbers by means of what we now consider exponential expressions.
40 BC	Marcus Vitruvius Pollio [Vitruvius] (ca. 80 BC–10 BC)	Roman engineering architect and civil engineer. Vituvius served under Gaius Julius Caesar (100 BC–44 BC). In the army position he was also charged with the care of the infirmed, where he used early biomedical engineering approaches for novel diagnosis and treatment.
62	Hero of Alexandria [ρων ὁ ᾿Αλεξανδρεύς], (10–70)	Mathematician, physicist, and mechanical engineer who also taught pneumatics. A set of two books: *The Pneumatica* describes mechanical devices that work by air, steam, or water pressure. Also known as Heron of Alexandria. He invented a steam-powered engine called the "Æolipile."
120	Claudius Ptolemy {Ptolemaeus} [Πτολεμαῖος] (90–168)	Geographic recordings of a significant part of the Islamic and western world (i.e., Roman and Persian Empire), living in Egypt, as a Roman with Greek education. His cartography extended all the way out, including parts of China (discovered in the fifteenth century). He specifically developed arithmetical techniques for calculating astronomical phenomena, under the teachings of Babylonian astronomers. Also known as: بطلیموس (Batlaymus; Arabic).
644		Wind-powered devices developed by the Persians.

(*Continued*)

CHRONOLOGY	NOTEWORTHY PEOPLE	EVENTS AND DISCOVERIES
771	Karel de Grote (742–815)	General scientific contributions as the ruler of the Netherlands and associated territories (stretching out over France to the Mediterranean and western Germany). Karel de Grote's scientific contributions, including chemical implementations [e.g., crop-growing circulation/alternation] and encouraged teaching of mathematics and scientific problem solving. Karel de Grote encouraged scientific and cultural engagement, during the period of the "Dark Ages (fourth to thirteenth century)" and his time is considered a predate to the "Renaissance" (fourteenth to seventeenth century), named the "Karolinger Renaissance," after Karel (English: Karl).
1500	Leonardo da Vinci (1452–1519)	The preverbal "Renaissance man," involved in all aspects of cultural evolution, science, engineering, politics, and art.
1503	Gregor Reisch (1467–1525)	Detailed outline of the state-of-the-art science and engineering knowledge to date, including human anatomical drawings in the publication *Margarita Philosophica*. The total works of Gregor Reisch form a series of 12 books compiling an encyclopedia describing topics ranging from Latin grammar, to dialectics, rhetoric, arithmetic, music, geometry, astronomy, physics, natural history, physiology, psychology, and ethics.
1512	Gregorius Reisch (1467–1525)	Introduction of the concept of the theodolite, used for topography and geographic location determination.
1543	Nicolaus Copernicus (1473–1543); Alias of Niclas Koppernigk	Introduction of the heliocentric model for the earth, Sun, and other planets. This follows the statement by the astronomer form Greece: Aristarchus of Samos (ca. 310–ca. 230 BC), made more than 1700 years prior. The scientific observations made by Copernicus were validated by Tycho Brahe (1546–1601) and Johannes Kepler (1571–1630).
1590	Francis Bacon, 1st Viscount of St. Alban (1561–1626)	Regulate the general scientific methodology.
ca. 1600	William Gilbert (1544–1603)	Experimentalist. Description of magnetism, in his work *De magnete, magnetisque corporibus, et de magno magnete tellure*. The compass had been in use since 206 BC (Chinese Han Dynasty: 206 BC–220 AD; maybe even earlier, during the Qin Dynasty: 221 BC–207 BC), in the European and Persian area since the thirteenth century.

(Continued)

CHRONOLOGY	NOTEWORTHY PEOPLE	EVENTS AND DISCOVERIES
ca. 1600	Galileo Galilei (1564–1642)	Major contributor to the scientific revolution and the (re) introduction of analytical thinking in science, engineering, and general thought processes. Galileo Galilei was remanded under house arrest by the Roman Inquisition for his views and teachings where he died after 9 years. This was the trailing end of the Renaissance period.
1614	René Descartes (1596–1650)	Introduction to vortex motion. Introduction of the concept of general corpuscular motion, extending from small (maybe referring to the undefined atom), to planetary orbits. Descartes also made an illustration of the earth's magnetic field configuration in 1644, in his model the moon and celestial objects participated in the formation of the path of the magnetic field lines. Based on the limited experimental observations available in his time the premise was still not bad.
1632	Evangelista Torricelli (1608–1647)	Introduction of the barometer; essential in weather prediction; meteorology.
1650	Blaise Pascal (1623–1662)	Pascal's law, pressure in a container applies an equal force on all surface of the enclosure.
1660	Robert Boyle (1627–1691)	Gas laws, definition of the behavior or gases. Boyle mentioned the compression of gas as a potential "shock-absorber," acting similar to a spring.
1673	Christiaan Huygens (1629–1695)	Construction of a "combustion engine" powered by gun powder. Huygens introduced several concept of mechanical engineering and described the mechanism of shock waves. Christiaan Huygens is most known for his lens manufacturing and optical design of telescopes. The mathematical efforts of Christiaan Huygens in probability theory were far advanced and he collaborated with the mathematician Pierre de Fermat (1601–1665) from France.
1679	Denis Papin (1647–ca. 1712)	Pressure and thermodynamic and mechanical impacts.
1680	Robert Hooke (1635–1703)	Force applied by a compressed spring.
ca. 1687	Sir Isaac Newton (1643–1727)	Sir Isaac Newton introduced several laws of motion. The publication of the *Philosophiæ Naturalis Principia Mathematica* provides detailed definitions regarding ballistic motion, circular motion (centripetal force), laws of action–reaction, gravitational acceleration, inertia, and force with respect to acceleration. Introduction of the three laws of motion.
1698	Thomas Savery (1650–1715)	Construction of the basic steam engine; using information obtained by Denis Papin (1647–ca. 1712).

(Continued)

CHRONOLOGY	NOTEWORTHY PEOPLE	EVENTS AND DISCOVERIES
1705	Edmond Halley (1656–1742)	Discovery of, and mathematical description of the trajectory for "Halley's comet."
1712	Thomas Newcomen (1664–1729)	Construction of a "atmospheric" steam engine.
1714	Brook Taylor (1685–1731)	Fundamental frequency of vibration; string. Additional work on pure mathematics: Taylor series.
1727	Leonard Euler (1707–1783)	Introduction of the concept of the elastic modulus, experimentally verified by Giordano Riccati (1709–1790) in 1782 and mathematically introduced by Thomas Young (1773–1829) in 1807, now known as Young's modulus.
1732	Anders Celsius (1701–1744)	Thermometer scale calibration based on pure water phases.
1733	Daniel Bernoulli (1700–1782)	Acoustics, mechanical vibrations, and fluid dynamic principles introduced. Definition of the fundamental frequency and higher harmonics with supporting elaborate mathematical analysis (solutions to differential equations).
1735	Daniel Gabriel Fahrenheit (1686–1736)	Temperature scale in Fahrenheit based on body temperature and saltwater phases.
1743	Jean-Baptiste le Rond d'Alembert (1717–1783)	Publication on the concepts of forces and accelerating systems: *Traite de Dynamique*.
1752	Benjamin Franklin (1706–1790)	Kite experiment and the documentation of "electric current."
1757–1769	James Watt (1736–1819)	Modern steam engine design and operation with theoretical description of operation.
1762	Joseph Black (1728–1799)	Realization of the concept of latent heat.
1769	Nicolas-Joseph Cugnot (1725–1804)	First operational steam-powered automobile, the predecessor to the internal combustion automobile.
1781	Charles-Augustin de Coulomb (1736–1806)	Definition of the electric field related to electric charge. The electric charge itself was still an elusive concept in those days.
1783	Antoine Laurent de Lavoisier (1743–1794)	Discovery of oxygen and the chemical impact.
1783	Joseph-Michel Montgolfier (1740–1810) and Jacques-Étienne Montgolfier (1745–1799)	Hot-air balloon; buoyancy.
1785	Jacques Alexandre César Charles (1746–1823)	Charles's law, expansion of gases.

(Continued)

CHRONOLOGY	NOTEWORTHY PEOPLE	EVENTS AND DISCOVERIES
1800	Count Alessandro Giuseppe Antonio Anastasio Volta (1745–1827)	Introduction of the battery.
1802	Joseph Louis Gay-Lussac (1778–1850)	Ideal gas law; building on the work by Robert Boyle (1627–1691), more than a century earlier.
1807	Thomas Young (1773–1829)	Formal introduction of the Young's modulus for elastic deformation, tying strain to stress, based on the work by Leonard Euler (1707–1783).
1821	Michael Faraday (1791–1867)	Discovery of electromagnetic rotation, leading to his law on electromagnetic induction in 1831. Meanwhile, in 1923 Michael Faraday experimentally verified the concept of refrigeration, introduced based on the work of John Dalton (1766–1844) in 1802 and William Cullen (1710–1790) in 1756.
1823	Nicéphore Niépce (1765–1833) and Louis Jacques-Mandé Daguerre (1787–1851)	Introduction of photography, using the earlier efforts of Albertus Magnus (1193–1280) with his discovery of silver nitrate, and Georg Fabricius (1516–1571) who discovered silver chloride.
1824	Nicolas Léonard Sadi Carnot (1796–1832)	Refrigerator for general public.
1827	Benoît Fourneyron (1802–1867)	First water turbine.
1831	Michael Faraday (1791–1867) and Joseph Henry (1797–1878)	Law of induction, leading to the development of the electric generator.
1840	Jean Léonard Marie Poiseuille (1799–1869) and Gotthilf Heinrich Ludwig Hagen (1797–1884)	Pressure drop for incompressible fluids with respect to laminar flow.
1848	William Thomson, 1st Baron Kelvin (i.e., Lord Kelvin) (1824–1907)	Absolute temperature scale: Kelvin.
1851	Jean Bernard Léon Foucault (1819–1868)	Foucault pendulum, illustrating the impact of the earth's rotation on motion.
1852	James Prescott Joule (1818–1889) and William Thomson, 1st Baron Kelvin {Lord Kelvin} (1824–1907)	Joule–Thomson effect: rapidly expanding gas leads to a reduction in the temperature of the gas, even offering the potential for a phase change to solid, or liquid. Sometimes also found as the Joule–Kelvin effect.
1854	Robert Wilhelm Eberhard Bunsen (1811–1899)	Bunsen burner.
1859	James Clerk Maxwell (1831–1879)	Description of the distribution law of molecular velocities, also relating to the concept of Brownian motion.

(Continued)

CHRONOLOGY	NOTEWORTHY PEOPLE	EVENTS AND DISCOVERIES
1861	Augustin Mouchot (1825–1911)	Presentation of the use of solar energy as a source for personal energy consumption.
1866	Ludwig Eduard Boltzmann (1844–1906) and Josiah Willard Gibbs (1839–1903)	Statistical mechanics, correlating energy, and heat, to the movement (velocity).
1873	Josiah Willard Gibbs (1839–1903)	Chemical potential, a energy constituent within the Gibbs free energy. Thermodynamic concept describing the energy that can be released or absorbed during a chemical reaction.
1873	James Clerk Maxwell (1831–1879)	Theory of electromagnetic radiation: *Treatise on Electricity and Magnetism*. James Maxwell made use of the prior work by Wilhelm Eduard Weber (1804–1891) and Johann Carl Friedrich Gauss {Gauß} (1777–1855).
1880	Johannes Diederik van der Waals (1837–1923)	Description of the covalent bond. Van der Waals equation.
1887	Heinrich Rudolf Hertz (1857–1894)	Radar development. Detection of electromagnetic radiation (radio waves). Heinrich Hertz also discovered that certain metal plates will generate electricity when exposed to light: photoelectric effect.
1894	Max Karl Ernst Ludwig Planck (1858–1947)	Black body radiation.
1895	Wilhelm Röntgen (1845–1923)	Discovery of X-ray (Röntgen rays).
1897	Joseph John Thomson (1856–1940)	Discovery of the electron; using William Crookes's vacuum tube.
1897	Guglielmo Marconi, 1st Marquis of Marconi (1874–1937)	Introduction of wireless communications and radio.
1896	Manya (Marie) Skłodowska Curie (1867–1934)	General discovery of the concept of radiation and the various levels of energy, particulate and electromagnetic radiation involved in certain decay processes. Discoveries were made with the help of an electrometer that was developed approximately 15 years earlier by her husband Pierre Curie (1859–1906) and his brother Jacques Curie (1856–1941). The first radioactive element they discovered was uranium.
1898	Antoine Henri Becquerel (1852–1908)	Introduction of units for radioactivity radiation. Collaborator with Manya (Marie) Skłodowska Curie (1867–1934). Henri Becquerel, Marie Curie, and Pierre Curie shared the Nobel Prize in Physics for their radioactivity discoveries in 1903.
1900	Ferdinand Adolf Heinrich August Graf von Zeppelin (1838–1917)	Successful dirigible, gas-filled air floatation device with propulsion.

(Continued)

CHRONOLOGY	NOTEWORTHY PEOPLE	EVENTS AND DISCOVERIES
1900	Max Karl Ernst Ludwig Planck (1858–1947)	Inception of quantum mechanics.
1905	Albert Einstein (1879–1955)	Theory of special relativity: relationship between space and time. (1) The laws of physics are invariant in any and all inertial systems, based on a nonaccelerating frame of reference configuration and (2) the speed of light in vacuum is the identical to all observers, regardless of the motion of the frame of reference for the light source. The theory is "special" since it applies to the special case of inertial reference frames.
1913	Niels Henrik David Bohr (1885–1962)	Bohr atomic model.
1916	Albert Einstein (1879–1955)	Theory of general relativity: geometric theory of gravitation. The "general" aspect defines the unified description of gravity as a geometric property of both space and time, also referred to as "space-time." In particular, the curvature of space-time is uniquely related to the momentum and energy of any kind of matter and radiation that are present.
1923	Lester Halbert Germer (1896–1971) and Clinton Joseph Davisson (1881–1958)	Experimental confirmation of the wave–particle duality for electromagnetic radiation.
1926	Erwin Schrödinger (1887–1961)	Quantum mechanical wave equivalence, wave theory for atomic and nuclear energy configurations.
1926	Mark Cowley Lidwell (1878–1969) and Edgar Harold Booth (1893–1963)	Rudimentary, but effective, external cardiac pacemaker design.
1927	Werner Karl Heisenberg (1901–1976)	Uncertainty principle; impossibility to know both the location and the momentum (energy) of a system with absolute accuracy simultaneously. This also removed the causality aspect from events, and substitutes probabilistic distributions.
1930	Richard Buckminster Fuller (1895–1983)	Mechanical engineering and engineering architecture, as well as chemistry; bucky-ball, multipoint connections in both chemical structures and mechanical structures.
1931	Georges Jean Marie Darrieus (1888–1979)	Introduction of the wind turbine.
1940+	Julius Robert Oppenheimer (1904–1967)	Manhattan project: fission reaction. Prominent members: Arthur Compton (1892–1962); Enrico Fermi (1901–1954), Eugene Wigner (1902–1995), and dozens more. One notable result is the creation of nuclear power plants.

(*Continued*)

CHRONOLOGY	NOTEWORTHY PEOPLE	EVENTS AND DISCOVERIES
1937–1959	Chester Floyd Carlston (1906–1968)	Photocopy machine, patented in 1942. The first photocopier was offered for sale by the Haloid company in 1959, later renamed Xerox.
1948	Julian Schwinger (1916–1994), Richard Phillips Feynman (1918–1988), and Sin-Itiro Tomonaga (1906–1979)	Quantum electrodynamics and quantum field theory.
1950	John Alexander Hopps, (1919–1998)	Introduction of the "portable" (45 kg) cardiac pacemaker, based on the earlier work by Mark Lidwell (1878–1969) and Edgar Harold Booth (1893–1963) in 1926. This led, with the development of microprocessors, to the first implantable pacemaker in 1958 by William Chardack (1919–2011) and Wilson Greatbatch (1919–2011).
1956	Paul Winchell {Wilchinsky} (1922–2005)	Artificial heart (Jarvik 7).
1969		First lunar landing; Apollo 11: Neil Armstrong (1930–2012), Michael Collins (1930–) (commander of lunar orbitor module), and Buzz Aldrin {Edwin Eugene Aldrin Jr} (1930–).
1968	Stephen Hawking (1942–), George Francis Rayner Ellis (1939–), and Roger Penrose (1931–)	"Big Bang theory" for the origin of the universe as we know it and how we observe the physical parameters evolve. The concept was introduced by Edwin Hubble (1889–1953) in rudimentary form in 1929.
2008	CERN, Switzerland	Large Hadron Collider, beginning of operations. To date no evidence supporting string theory or supersymmetry has been collected.
2012	François Baron Englert (1932–) and Peter Ware Higgs (1929–)	Higgs boson (126 GeV) discovery in the Large Hadron Collider at CERN, Geneva, Switzerland.

Geo

CHRONOLOGY	NOTEWORTHY PEOPLE	EVENTS AND DISCOVERIES
ca. 600 BC	China; India	Documented use of magnetic compasses; the lodestone. More specific documented use dates to the Han Dynasty (ca. 206 BC).
ca. 600 BC	Thales of Miletus (ca. 624 BC–ca. 546 BC; known as Thales: Θαλῆς)	Introduction of metrology, accurate measurements of objects, phenomena, events, and conditions (e.g., atmospheric conditions).
430 BC	Socrates (469 BC–399 BC)	Scholar and educator, introducing analytical thinking.

(Continued)

CHRONOLOGY	NOTEWORTHY PEOPLE	EVENTS AND DISCOVERIES
350 BC	Aristotle (384 BC–322 BC)	Aristotle described the initial concepts of physics, motion, time as well as astronomy concepts. Aristotle used geological and atmospheric record keeping for the prediction of weather conditions (meteorology). First documented use of a scientific approach to weather forecasting.
ca. 250 BC	Archimedes (287 BC–212 BC)	Revealed the properties that define buoyancy. The base principles relate to the tectonic plate mechanics.
ca. 240 BC	Eratosthenes (ca. 276 BC–ca. 195 BC)	Derivation of the circumference of the earth using trigonometry (round earth was already a concept).
50	Gaius Plinius Secundus (23–79), known as: Pliny the Elder	Publication of the magnetic action of the lodestone in his publication: *Naturalis Historia*. A rather detailed description of the use of magnetism for geographical location determination is described.
62	Hero of Alexandria [ρων ὁ ᾽Αλεξανδρεύς] (10–70)	Mathematician, physicist, and mechanical engineer who also taught pneumatics. The base of this methodology formed the principle understanding of the movement of atmospheric air masses in future years.
120	Claudius Ptolemy {Ptolemaeus} [Πτολεμαῖος] (90–168)	Geographic recordings of a significant part of the Islamic and western world (i.e., Roman and Persian Empire), living in Egypt, as a Roman with Greek education. His cartography extended all the way out, including parts of China (discovered in fifteenth century). He specifically developed arithmetical techniques for calculating astronomical phenomena, under the teachings of Babylonian astronomers. Also known as: بطليمـــوس (Batlaymus; Arabic). Combining the cartography wih the ancient Chinese knowledge of the earth's magnetic field formed early recording of the location of the North and South pole, however rudimentary, only a portion of the earth had been mapped. later documentation with a detailed world map provided an indication of the migration of the magnetic poles.
ca. 132	Zhang Heng (78–139) of China's Han dynasty	Documented construction and operation of the first seismic instrument.
ca. 1000	Abu al-Rayhan al-Biruni (973–1048)	Documented hypothesis of the movement of the tectonic plates, specifically the assumed location of India, which in early history would have been ocean. Realistically: continental drift split the continents from one "continuous" land mass about 200 million years ago, end of Paleozoic era; which is often considered to hold the beginning of animal life.
1,050		Full-scale use of the compass for geographical orientation in the western and far-eastern world.

(Continued)

CHRONOLOGY	NOTEWORTHY PEOPLE	EVENTS AND DISCOVERIES
1,269	Petrus Peregrinus of Maricourt	Formal description of the use of the compass during seafaring expeditions.
1500	Leonardo da Vinci (1452–1519)	The preverbal "Renaissance man," involved in all aspects of cultural evolution, science, engineering, politics, and art.
1535	Joao de Castro (1500–1548)	Recognition of the deviation between the magnetic north and the geographic north.
1543	Nicolaus Copernicus (1473–1543); alias of Niclas Koppernigk	Introduction of the heliocentric model for the earth, sun, and other planets. This follows the statement by the astronomer form Greece: Aristarchus of Samos (ca. 310–ca. 230 BC), made more than 1700 years prior. The scientific observations made by Copernicus were validated by Tycho Brahe (1546–1601) and Johannes Kepler (1571–1630).
1590	Francis Bacon, 1st Viscount of St. Alban (1561–1626)	Regulate the general scientific methodology.
ca. 1600	William Gilbert (1544–1603)	Experimentalist. Description of magnetism, in his work *De magnete, magnetisque corporibus, et de magno magnete tellure*. The compass had been in use since 206 BC (Chinese Han Dynasty: 206 BC–220 AD; maybe even earlier, during the Qin Dynasty: 221 BC–207 BC), in the European and Persian area since the thirteenth century.
ca. 1540		Realization that the magnetic field line running "north to south" (isogones) are not straight lines, but have complex tracks, even loops as a function of the geographical locations. Confirmed by Willem van Bemmelen (1868–1941) based on the magnetic direction recording made by the ships as a function of geographical location traveling for the East India Company (mercantile trips to the Dutch colonies), between the Netherlands and Indonesia (around Cape Horn, South Africa).
ca. 1600	Galileo Galilei (1564–1642)	Major contributor to the scientific revolution and the (re) introduction of analytical thinking in science, engineering, and general thought processes. Galileo Galilei was remanded under house arrest by the Roman Inquisition for his views and teachings where he died after 9 years. This was the trailing end of the Renaissance period.
1614	René Descartes (1596–1650)	Introduction to vortex motion. Introduction of the concept of general corpuscular motion, extending from small (maybe referring to the undefined atom), to planetary orbits. Vortices are found in geological phenomena such as cyclones (hurricanes), maelstrom, and aspects of magma flow.

(Continued)

CHRONOLOGY	NOTEWORTHY PEOPLE	EVENTS AND DISCOVERIES
ca. 1650	Pierre de Fermat (1601–1665)	Developed infinitesimal (elementary) calculus. Instrumental in the development of the mathematical description of the wave refraction principle. Several of Fermat's mathematical efforts in solving polynomial equations extended beyond the two-dimensional plane where most mathematicians were comfortable, which has direct implications in seismic wave propagation, although not investigated in his day to great extent.
ca. 1655	Christiaan Huygens (1629–1695)	Invention of a clockwork mechanism capable of timekeeping while at sea in order to allow for accurate geographical measurements.
1650	Blaise Pascal (1623–1662)	Pascal's law, pressure in a container applies an equal force on all surface of the enclosure. The unit for pressure under atmospheric conditions uses the unit Pascal in his honor.
1660	Robert Boyle (1627–1691)	Gas laws, definition of the behavior or gases. Boyle mentioned the compression of gas relating to partial pressure of atmospheric constituents and barometric values.
1679	Denis Papin (1647–ca. 1712)	Pressure and thermodynamic and mechanical impacts. Denis Papin worked as an assistant to both Christiaan Huygens (1629–1695) and Robert Boyle (1627–1691). His invention of the pressure cooker bears some resemblance to the conditions found in geysers.
1680	Robert Hooke (1635–1703)	Force applied by a compressed spring. The extended implications are in the mechanics of seismic waves.
ca. 1687	Sir Isaac Newton (1643–1727)	The recognition of gravitational force provided one of the essential building blocks in the geological understanding next to.
1705	Edmond Halley (1656–1742)	Discovery of, and mathematical description of the trajectory for "Halley's comet."
1724	George Graham (1675–1751)	Recognition of the concept of diurnal declination, compass needle during the day.
1750–1800		With the advent of more sophisticated measurement instrumentation (thermometer, barometer, wind velocity meter) meteorology became more scientifically rooted, especially with the interest of a broad range of mathematicians in the dynamics of physics; thermodynamics, motion, wave propagation, and pressure perturbations. The methodology for cartography and for geographic orientation (compass) also had evolved significantly.
1714	Brook Taylor (1685–1731)	Fundamental frequency of vibration; string. Additional work on pure mathematics: Taylor series.

(Continued)

CHRONOLOGY	NOTEWORTHY PEOPLE	EVENTS AND DISCOVERIES
1727	Leonard Euler (1707–1783)	Introduction of the concept of the elastic modulus, experimentally verified by Giordano Riccati (1709–1790) in 1782 and mathematically introduced by Thomas Young (1773 – 1829) in 1807, now known as Young's Modulus.
1732	Anders Celsius (1701–1744)	Thermometer scale calibration based on pure water phases.
1733	Daniel Bernoulli (1700–1782)	Acoustics, mechanical vibrations, and fluid dynamic principles introduced. Definition of the fundamental frequency and higher harmonics, with supporting elaborate mathematical analysis (solutions to differential equations). This laid the foundation for seismic imaging using P-wave (primary wave; longitudinal) and S-wave (secondary wave, or shear wave [transverse]).
1735	Daniel Gabriel Fahrenheit (1686–1736)	Temperature scale in Fahrenheit based on body temperature and saltwater phases.
1743	Jean-Baptiste le Rond d'Alembert (1717–1783)	Publication on the concepts of forces and accelerating systems: *Traite de Dynamique*.
1752	Benjamin Franklin (1706–1790)	Kite experiment and the documentation of "electric current."
ca. 1755	Piter van Musschenbroek (1692–1761)	Study of the deviations in the earth's magnetic field lines as a function of altitude, no conclusive data at the time.
1757–1769	James Watt (1736–1819)	Modern steam engine design and operation with theoretical description of operation.
1762	Joseph Black (1728–1799)	Realization of the concept of latent heat.
1769	Nicolas-Joseph Cugnot (1725–1804)	First operational steam-powered automobile, the predecessor to the internal combustion automobile.
1781	Charles-Augustin de Coulomb (1736–1806)	Definition of the electric field related to electric charge. The electric charge itself was still an elusive concept in those days.
1783	Antoine Laurent de Lavoisier (1743–1794)	Discovery of oxygen and the chemical impact.
1783	Joseph-Michel Montgolfier (1740–1810) and Jacques-Étienne Montgolfier (1745–1799)	Hot-air balloon; buoyancy.
1785	Jacques Alexandre César Charles (1746–1823)	Charles's law, expansion of gases.
1800	Count Alessandro Giuseppe Antonio Anastasio Volta (1745–1827)	Introduction of the battery.

(Continued)

CHRONOLOGY	NOTEWORTHY PEOPLE	EVENTS AND DISCOVERIES
1802	Joseph Louis Gay-Lussac (1778–1850)	Ideal gas law; building on the work by Robert Boyle (1627–1691), more than a century earlier.
1807	Thomas Young (1773–1829)	Formal introduction of the Young's modulus for elastic deformation, tying strain to stress, based on the work by Leonard Euler (1707–1783). The Young's modulus plays a significant role in the seismic activity and mechanical deformation as well as the seismic wave propagation in three-dimensional geometry.
1810	Siméon Denis Poisson (1781–1840)	Poisson's analysis of the wave theory of light contributed to the evolution and understanding of interference principles and applications.
1811	Siméon Denis Poisson (1781–1840)	Introduction of the means to quantify the ratio of transverse to axial strain, by means of the Poisson ratio.
1820	William George Horner (1786– 1837)	Introduction of the methodology for solving and calculating polynomials (roots): Horner's method. The methods were actually already described 600 years prior by the Chinese mathematician Qin Jiushao (秦九韶), (ca. 1202–1261).
ca. 1825	Baron Augustin-Louis Cauchy (1789–1857)	Pioneer in mathematical and structural analysis of data. Formally introduced several of the modern concepts of calculus. Cauchy also introduced the concept of convergent series, in order to obtain a finite solution.
1840	Jean Léonard Marie Poiseuille (1799–1869) and Gotthilf Heinrich Ludwig Hagen (1797–1884)	Pressure drop for incompressible fluids with respect to laminar flow. Reference to meteorology, wind formation based on arctic versus topical pressure systems.
1842	James David Forbes (1809–1868)	Measurement of seismic wave with the first seismometer, using a weight hanging from springs. Modern seismometers generally measure vibration amplitude in the frequency range from 0.00118 Hz to 500 Hz. The scale (Richter scale) of the seismic activity was introduced by Charles Francis Richter (1900–1985) and Beno Gutenberg (1889–1960) in 1935.
1843–1848	James Prescott Joule (1818–1889)	Empirical verification of the first law of thermodynamics: stating the equivalence of heat and work. This applies to both the source energy for the persisting liquid core (magma) and the work performed by volcanic eruptions and earthquakes.
1848	William Thomson, 1st Baron Kelvin (i.e., Lord Kelvin) (1824–1907)	Absolute temperature scale: Kelvin. Reference base for geological events and meteorology.

(*Continued*)

CHRONOLOGY	NOTEWORTHY PEOPLE	EVENTS AND DISCOVERIES
1850	Rudolf Julius Emanuel Clausius (1822–1888)	Recognition of two basic principles of thermodynamics, later introduced by means of the first and second law of thermodynamics, respectively: energy is constant and entropy tends toward a maximum. Clausius introduced the parameter U, representing the internal energy. Publication of book *On the Motive Power of Heat, and on the Laws Which Can Be Deduced from It for the Theory of Heat*. Clausius introduced what is now regarded the second law of thermodynamics in 1865 (referred to by William John Macquorn Rankine [1820–1872] as the "thermodynamic function"), as part of any natural thermodynamic process, the sum of the entropies of the participating systems will increase.
1851	Jean Bernard Léon Foucault (1819–1868)	Foucault pendulum, illustrating the impact of the earth's rotation on motion.
1851	Sir George Gabriel Stokes, 1st Baronet (1819–1903)	Creeping flow, partially applicable to seismology, specifically in the treatment of the mathematical solution for tsunami seismic waves. Specific seismic work of Gabriel Stokes was on a "microscopic" scale in earth-sized dimensions, describing vibrational forces and energy related to driven oscillations while crossing bridges, and the resulting bridge collapses in his days. One of the fall-outs from the bridge vibration and collapse is development of studies in metal fatigue. Furthermore, the work of Stokes contributed to the development of the scientific and engineering support for the construction of high-rise buildings in earthquake-prone geographical regions.
1852	James Prescott Joule (1818–1889) and William Thomson, 1st Baron Kelvin {Lord Kelvin} (1824–1907)	Joule–Thomson effect: rapidly expanding gas leads to a reduction in the temperature of the gas, even offering the potential for a phase change to solid or liquid. Sometimes also found as the Joule–Kelvin effect. The Joule–Thomson effect is an isenthalpic process, which entails that the enthalpy of the fluid is constant during the process, which applies to Joule–Thomson inversion temperature, described in the Linde cycle (Carl von Linde [1842–1934]), offering conditions leading to cloud formation.
1859	James Clerk Maxwell (1831–1879)	Description of the distribution law of molecular velocities.
1861	Augustin Mouchot (1825–1911)	Presentation of the use of solar energy as a source for personal energy consumption.
1865	Gabriel Lamé (1795–1870)	Introduction of the shear modulus and another parameter that is linked through the Poisson ratio (Lamé constants), providing the basis for the introduction of the P-wave and S-wave principles, based on the work of Robert Hooke (1635–1703).

(Continued)

CHRONOLOGY	NOTEWORTHY PEOPLE	EVENTS AND DISCOVERIES
1868	Sultan – Abdülaziz (1830–1876) and Grand Vizier: Mehmed Emin Aali Pasha (1815–1871)	Installation of the "first" geophysical and meteorological observatory: "Rasathane-i Amire" in Constantinople (Istanbul, Turkey): Ottoman Empire.
1873	James Clerk Maxwell (1831–1879)	Theory of electromagnetic radiation: *Treatise on Electricity and Magnetism*. James Maxwell made use of the prior work by Wilhelm Eduard Weber (1804–1891) and Johann Carl Friedrich Gauss {Gauß} (1777–1855)
1885	John William Strut, the 3rd Baron Rayleigh (1842–1919)	Introduction of the concept of surface seismic waves. Specifically the surface interface waves, referred to as Rayleigh waves (single surface only), the medium can be of semi-infinite thickness. Also found described under finite thickness plate conditions by Lamb waves (Sir Horace Lamb [1849–1934]).
1887	Heinrich Rudolf Hertz (1857–1894)	Radar development. Detection of electromagnetic radiation (radio waves). Heinrich Hertz also discovered that certain metal plates will generate electricity when exposed to light: photoelectric effect.
1896	Emil Johann Wiechert (1861–1928)	Introduction and verification of the layered model for earth. Emil Johann Wiechert was a pupil of Woldemar Voigt (1850–1919). Emil Wiechert also developed a detailed mathematical model for the seismic activity on earth, with assistance from Beno Gutenberg (1889–1960).
1897	Joseph John Thomson (1856–1940)	Discovery of the electron. The beta particle is one of three decay process that allows for molecular identification and quantification of radioactive activity over time to build a history profile of the geological development processes.
1900	Ludwig Eduard Boltzmann (1844–1906)	Thermodynamic concepts with respect to heat exchange in the earth's volume, specifically defining the entropy. Boltzmann equation for statistical mechanics, introduced by Ludwig Boltzmann between 1872 and 1875, reformulated by Max Karl Ernst Ludwig Planck (1858–1947). For certain systems also addressed as the Gibbs entropy formula, after Josiah Willard Gibbs (1839–1903).
1902	Maurits Snellen	Discovery of the influence of solar activity on the magnetic field lines used for compass orientation (isogones), sunspots.
1905	Albert Einstein (1879–1955)	Alternate theory of gravity, and his theories of relativity shaped the developing field of relativistic astrophysics.
1911	Augustus Edward Hough Love (1863–1940)	Introduction of the "Love wave"; horizontally polarized (elastic) shear waves (SH waves) in a subsurface layer of semi-infinite dimensions, covered by a finite thickness cover layer. These wave will travel faster than Rayleigh waves, which occur in the surface layer.

(Continued)

CHRONOLOGY	NOTEWORTHY PEOPLE	EVENTS AND DISCOVERIES
1912	Alfred Wegener (1880–1930)	Revelation of the tectonic plate concept and description of continental drift.
1910–1935	Alfred Wegener (1880–1930), Maurice Ewing (1906–1974), Bryan L. Isacks (1942?–), Walter C. Pitman, III (1931–), Frederick Vine (1939–), Drummond H. Matthews (1931–1997), S. Keith Runcorn (1922–1995), Xavier Le Pichon (1937–), Harry Hammond Hess (1905–1969), Robert S. Dietz (1914–1995), V. Hugo Benioff (1899–1968), Dan McKenzie (1942–), Edward Bullard (1907–1980), John Tuzo Wilson (1908–1993), and W. Jason Morgan (1935–)	Development and refinement of the tectonic plate model.
1914	Beno Gutenberg (1889–1960)	Confirmation of the layered model for the structure of the earth globe, introduced by his mentor Emil Johann Wiechert (1861–1928).
1917	Sir Horace Lamb (1849–1934)	Introduction of the concept of evanescent waves, referred to as Lamb waves. Elastic waves traveling in the bulk of a finite thickness plate (i.e., tectonic plate).
1919		The observations made during a total solar eclipse in this year by an expedition from the Royal Astronomical Society and the Royal Society of London confirmed the deviation of starlight in the gravitational field of the sun as predicted by the general theory of relativity. The strongest support for this theory came later from the agreement between the calculated and observed values of the precession of the perihelion of Mercury.
1922	Jacob Aall Bonnevie Bjerknes (1897–1975), Vilhelm Friman Koren Bjerknes (1862–1951), Halvor Skappel Solberg (1895–1974), and Tor Bergeron (1891–1977)	Formulation of pressure fronts and the general movement of air masses.

(*Continued*)

CHRONOLOGY	NOTEWORTHY PEOPLE	EVENTS AND DISCOVERIES
1924	Robert Stoneley (1894–1976)	Stoneley wave, Rayleigh wave-type interface wave, at a solid-solid interface, traveling with relatively high amplitude. In case the interface is solid–liquid the wave phenomenon is referred to as the Scholte wave (Johan Gerard Jozef Scholte [1907–1970]. Stoneley waves can be reflected and refracted at sharp impedance contrasts at interfaces such as lithology, fractures, and changes in borehole diameter. Moreover, as formation permeability increases, the propagation velocity for Stoneley wave decreases, resulting in dispersion.
1924	Edward Victor Appleton (1892–1965), Arthur Edwin Kennelly (1861–1939) next to Oliver Heaviside (1850–1925)	Initiation of a series of experiments that established the existence and properties of ionized layers in the upper atmosphere. The existence of this type of layers had been postulated by Arthur Edwin Kennelly (1861–1939) in 1902 and, independently, by Oliver Heaviside (1850–1925) to explain the observed implications for long-distance wireless telegraphy. Edward Appleton received the Nobel Prize for Physics in 1947.
1930	Jacob Clay (1882–1955)	Discovery that cosmic ray intensity decreased in going toward the geomagnetic equator. This latitude effect was investigated exhaustively by Arthur Holly Compton (1892–1962), Robert Andrews Millikan (1868–1953), and others.
1932	Victor Hugo Benioff (1899–1968)	Instrument development leading to the monitoring of the movement of the tectonic plates: Benioff seismograph. Additional instrumentation developed by Hugo Benioff is also capable of measuring strain in the earth's upper layer.
1935	Charles Francis Richter (1900–1985) and Beno Gutenberg (1889–1960)	Introduction of the Richter scale for the determination of the magnitude of seismic activity (earthquake). The scale has a base-10 logarithmic foundation. Prior to the Richter scale earthquakes were defined based on their destructive legacy, primarily pertaining to size of structures affected.
1936	Inge Lehmann (1888–1993)	Description of the numerical assessment of data obtained during earthquakes (seismological data) and the image formation of the structure of the earth's structure, divided in shells with different material phase and composition. The image formation is based on what is referred to as S-waves and P-waves. Inge Lehmann discovered and described the shape, size, and composition (rudimentary) of the earth's inner core.
1938	Guy Stewart Callendar (1898–1964)	Description of the concept of global warming resulting from the insulating layer of carbon diode exhaust in the atmosphere.
1942; 1947	Johan Gerard Jozef Scholte (1907–1970)	Scholte wave, seismic-type wave that has the characteristics of a Rayleigh wave, but is at the interface between a solid and a liquid, or a solid and an elastic (plastic) solid (e.g., sand).

(Continued)

CHRONOLOGY	NOTEWORTHY PEOPLE	EVENTS AND DISCOVERIES
1950		Dedicated studies initiated to observe the developing global warming concepts.
1953	William Maurice Ewing (1906–1974) and Bruce Charles Heezen (1924–1977)	Discovery of the Great Global Rift: oceanic ridge.
1960		Launch of the first weather satellite.
1995	Roger Lee Easton (1921–2014)	Development of the global positioning concept (GPS).

High Energy

CHRONOLOGY	NOTEWORTHY PEOPLE	EVENTS AND DISCOVERIES
13.8 billion years BC	Georges Henri Joseph Édouard Lemaître (1894–1966) and Edwin Powell Hubble (1889–1953)	"The Big Bang"; in 1927 the expanding universe was recognized.
1870	Hermann Ludwig Ferdinand von Helmholtz (1821–1894)	Unofficial introduction to the mechanism of action for nuclear fusion.
1896	Wilhelm Conrad Röntgen (1845–1923)	Discovery of X-ray radiation.
1896	Henri Becquerel (1852–1908)	Emission of "Becquerel rays" from uranium salts, later identified as alpha particles. Becquerel already recognized that this emission was different from X-ray since it was deflected by means of an applied external magnetic field. Conceptual introduction to the field of radioactivity.
1897	Joseph John Thomson (1856–1940)	Discovery of the electron; using William Crookes's vacuum tube.
1897	Marie Skłodowska-Curie (1867–1934)	Discovery of radioactive isotopes. Marie Curie introduced the term "radioactivity."
1899	Ernest Rutherford (1871–1937), 1st Baron Rutherford of Nelson, Lord Rutherford of Nelson	Emission of alpha particle.
1900	Max Karl Ernst Ludwig Planck (1858–1947) and James Clerk Maxwell (1831–1879)	Formal description of the photon and the energy associated with the electromagnetic wave.

(Continued)

CHRONOLOGY	NOTEWORTHY PEOPLE	EVENTS AND DISCOVERIES
1903	Ernest Rutherford (1871–1937), 1st Baron Rutherford of Nelson, Lord Rutherford of Nelson	Discovery of the nuclear decay half-life.
1903	Marie Skłodowska-Curie (1867–1934) and Ernest Rutherford (1871–1937), 1st Baron Rutherford of Nelson, Lord Rutherford of Nelson	Quantification of nuclear decay.
1906	Dmitri Ivanovich Mendeleev (1834–1907)	Periodic Table of Elements.
1908	Johannes Geiger (1822–1945) and Ernest Rutherford (1871–1937)	Development of the Geiger counter, used to measure radioactive radiation.
1909	Francis Aston (1877–1945)	Mass spectrometer mass separation of closely separated isotopes. Highly sensitive mass spectrometer design.
1911	Ernest Rutherford (1871–1937), 1st Baron Rutherford of Nelson, Lord Rutherford of Nelson	Rutherford scattering on nuclear level, indication of the existence of the proton. The proton itself was not mentioned until 1932, this time again by Ernest Rutherford.
1912	Victor Francis Hess (1883–1964)	Recognition of high-energy cosmic radiation, observed during a high altitude balloon ride.
1913	Niels Henrik David Bohr (1885–1962)	Bohr atomic model.
1913	Frederick Soddy (1877–1956)	Formal introduction of the isotope concept.
1914	Niels Henrik David Bohr (1885–1962)	Description of the atomic energy layer model; hydrogen (Bohr atomic model).
1915	Ernest Marsden	Artificial transmutation, associated with radon enclosed by vacuum.
1918	Paul Scherrer (1890–1969)	X-ray diffraction, crystal structure. Nuclear energy development. Established the CERN institute in Switzerland as one of the founders. Directed the construction of the first cyclotron in 1940.
1919	Ernest Rutherford (1871–1937)	Artificial transmutation, hydrogen formation resulting from collisions of alpha particles with nitrogen, also generating oxygen and gamma rays.
1921	James Chadwick (1891–1974) and Étienne Samuel Biéler (1895–1929)	Strong nuclear force.

(Continued)

CHRONOLOGY	NOTEWORTHY PEOPLE	EVENTS AND DISCOVERIES
1923	Arthur Holly Compton (1892–1962)	Description of the deflection of photons by a charge unit, generally an electron, potentially the nucleus: Compton effect.
1925	Johannes Geiger (1822–1945) and Walther Wilhelm Georg Bothe (1891–1957)	Conservation of energy for atomic and nuclear processes.
1925	Werner Karl Heisenberg (1901–1976)	Uncertainty principle.
~1925		Recognition of the "Coulomb barrier" in nuclear collision, providing a "tunneling" effect for the release of alpha particles.
1927	Werner Karl Heisenberg (1901–1976)	Quantum uncertainty principle.
1927	Paul Adrien Maurice Dirac (1902–1984)	Description of antimatter.
1928	Johannes Geiger (1822–1945) and Walther Müller 1905–1979)	Introduction of an improved Geiger counter: the Geiger–Müller counter, using ionization of a confined gas.
1929	Leo Szilard (1898–1964) and Ernest Orlando Lawrence (1901–1958)	Particle accelerator, cyclotron. The cyclotron can accelerate protons to reach kinetic energy in excess of 700 MeV, with respective radius of 4.6 meter (1946). The first cyclotron was built in 1932, at the University of California Berkeley, California: Tevatron. Cyclotrons are specifically and not exclusively used to create isotopes for use in nuclear medicine, in particular for imaging (e.g., PET) and for cancer treatment.
1930	Walther Wilhelm Georg Bothe (1891–1957) and his student Herbert Becker ()	Observation of a puzzling penetrating "radiation" from beryllium bombarded with alpha particles (helium nuclei). Conceptual introduction to the fission process.
1931	Wolfgang Ernst Pauli (1900–1958)	Introduction of an electrically neutral particle, the neutron. Energy when involved in beta decay up to 0.5 MeV. The experimental verification of the existence of the neutrino was not until 1956 by Frederick Reines (1918–1998) and Clyde Cowan Jr. (1919–1974).
1931	Carl David Anderson (1905–1991)	Discovery of the positron, antiparticle for the electron. The "positron" was predicted by Paul Adrien Maurice Dirac (1902–1984) in 1929.
1932	Sir James Chadwick (1891–1974)	Discovery of the neutron. Student of Ernest Rutherford (1871–1937).
1934	Leo Szilard (1898–1964)	Recognition of nuclear decay chain reactions.
1934	Hideki Yukawa [湯川 秀樹], (1907–1981)	Introduction of mesons and the concept of antimatter.

(Continued)

CHRONOLOGY	NOTEWORTHY PEOPLE	EVENTS AND DISCOVERIES
1934	Ida Noddack (1896–1978)	Formal introduction of the concept of "fission"; however, not recognized by her peers at the time. The fission phenomenon was only recognized when announced by Enrico Fermi (1901–1954) later that year.
1934	Enrico Fermi (1901–1954)	Interaction of slow neutron with nuclei and the resulting decay into different elements, including aluminum and uranium.
1935	Arthur Dempster (1886–1950)	Discovery of the lighter uranium isotope: Uranium-235.
1936	Otto Hahn (1879–1968) and Lise Meitner (1878–1968)	Neutron collision of uranium-induced decay examination.
1937	Carl David Anderson (1905–1991), Seth Henry Neddermeyer (1907–1988), Jabez Curry Street (1906–1989), and Edward C. Stevenson (1937–)	Confirmation of the existence of the meson and muon. Subatomic particles are governed by quantum physics principles, and will exhibit a wave–particle duality. The quantum state energy vectors are represented in Hilbert space.
1938	Niels Henrik David Bohr (1885–1962) and John Archibald Wheeler (1911–2008)	Formal description of the nuclear fission process.
1939	Jerome M. B. Kellogg (1905–?)	Discovery of a finite quadruple moment for the deuteron, requiring a noncentral (tensor) nuclear force configuration.
1940	Otto Robert Frisch (1904–1979)	Development of the detonation mechanism for the first atomic bomb.
1940+	Julius Robert Oppenheimer (1904–1967)	Manhattan project: fission reaction. Prominent members: Arthur Compton (1892–1962); Enrico Fermi (1901–1954); Eugene Wigner (1902–1995), and dozens more.
1945	Edwin Mattison Mcmillan (1907–1999) next to Vladimir Iosifovich Veksler (1907–1966)	Independent introduction of the principle of the synchrotron. The synchrotron accelerator produces very high-energy particles, as in the Cosmotron, Brookhaven National Laboratory, USA, or Bevatron, Lawrence Berkeley National Laboratory, USA operating at 10 BeV.
1946		Introduction of the term "Lepton", defining weak nuclear interaction particles; electrons and muons are hence considered leptons.
1947	George Dixon Rochester (1908–2001) and Clifford Charles Butler (1922–1999)	Discovery of the subatomic particle: the "kaon," k-meson. Introduction of the "strangeness" concept for quarks, although the quark concept had not been introduced. In the elementary particle phenomenology the kaon is a bound state of an up- or down quark with a strange quark (anti-quark).

(Continued)

CHRONOLOGY	NOTEWORTHY PEOPLE	EVENTS AND DISCOVERIES
1947	Maria Goeppert-Mayer (Göppert) (1906–1972)	Theoretical concept development for the understanding of nuclear forces, based on a shell model, similar to the atomic electron model.
1947	William Webster Hansen (1909–1949)	Linear accelerator installation at Stanford University, California.
1950	Maria Goeppert-Mayer (Göppert) (1906–1972)	Introduction of the nuclear shell model for atomic nuclei.
ca. 1952	Ludwig von Helmholtz (1821–1894), Lyman Strong Spitzer, Jr. (1914–1997) and Ronald Richter (1909–1991) and Edward Teller (1908–2003)	Nuclear fusion investigation and start of experimentation. The process was in principle described by Hermann Ludwig Ferdinand von Helmholtz (1821–1894), but is continuously in action at the sun's surface.
1954	Chen-Ning Franklin Yang (1922–2004) and Robert Laurence Mills (1927–1999)	Introduction of "Gauge Theories." These gauge theories will eventually form the basis for the "standard model."
1955	Obninsk Nuclear Power Station, Russia	First nuclear power station for energy generation.
1956	Frederick Reines (1918–1998) and Clyde Lorrain Cowan, Jr. (1919–1974)	Experimental confirmation of the neutrino introduced in 1931 by Wolfgang Pauli (1900–1958).
1957	Julian Schwinger (1918–1994), Sidney Bludman (1927–), Sheldon Lee Glashow (1933–), and Hideki Yukawa (1907–1981)	Bosons provide the weak attraction. Initially conceived by Hideki Yukawa (1907–1981) in 1937. These heavy bosons are referred to as W^- and W^+.
1958	Stanley Mandelstam (1928–2016)	Introduction of Mandelstam variables associated with the concept of "crossing symmetry," defining numerical quantities that encode the energy, momentum, and scattering angles of particles in a deflection process described in a Lorentz-invariant fashion.
1958	Lev Davidovich Landau [Russian: Лёв Давидович Ландау] (1908–1968), Arkady Beynusovich Migdal [Russian: Аркадий Бейнусович (Бенедиктович) Мигдал] (1911–1991)	Theory of interacting electrons, specifically with respect to solids; condensed matter physics.

(Continued)

CHRONOLOGY	NOTEWORTHY PEOPLE	EVENTS AND DISCOVERIES
1961	Murray Gell-Mann (1929–)	Description of elementary particles, eight-fold way of defining "strangeness" for the quark. Formal introduction of the elementary particle "quark" concept, the building blocks for protons and neutrons. The "quark" name is based on an expression in the book *Finnegans Wake* by James Joyce.
1964	Charles Hard Townes (1915–2015), Nikolay Gennadiyevich Basov [Николáй Геннáдиевич Бáсов] (1922–2001), and Aleksandr Mikhailovich Prokhorov [Алексáндр Михáйлович Прóхоров] (1916–2002)	Quantum electronics.
1965	Oscar Wallace Greenberg (1932–), Moo-Young Han (1934–), and Yoichiro Nambu [南部陽一郎] (1921–)	Introduction of the concept of "color" change as designation and property for quarks.
1970	Sheldon Lee Glashow (1932–), John Iliopoulos (1940–), and Luciano Maiani (1941–)	Introduction of the charm quark.
1973	Hugh David Politzer (1949–), David Jonathan Gross (1941–), and Frank Anthony Wilczek (1951–)	Discovery associating the quark color theory of the strong interaction to a special property, referred to as "asymptotic freedom." This "color" property is required to describe the data acquired over the prior period from 1968 to 1969 with respect to the substrate of the proton.
1974	Burton Richter (1931–) and Samuel Chao Chung Ting [Chinese: 丁肇中] (1936–)	Description of charm for the quark.
1975	Carlo Rubbia (1934–), Burton Richter (1931–), Frederick Reines (1918–1998), Jack Steinberger (1921–), Leon Lederman (1922–), Richard Taylor (1929–), Jerome Friedman (1930–), and Martin Perl (1927–2014)	Standard model of particle interaction. Interactions between leptons and quarks, interacting by means of bosons. Listing the contributing scientist that led to the discovery of the various elementary particles, respectively: W and Z boson; charm quark; neutrino; muon–neutrino; muon–neutrino, and b-quark; quarks (general); quarks (general); tau.

(Continued)

CHRONOLOGY	NOTEWORTHY PEOPLE	EVENTS AND DISCOVERIES
1975	Martin Lewis Perl (1927–2014)	Discovery of the tau lepton.
1977	Leon Max Ledderman (1922–)	Discovery of the "beauty" and "bottom" designation for quarks.
1978		Discovery of the "gluon" with the assistance of the PLUTO, the first electromagnetic superconductive solenoid located in Hamburg, Germany.
1983	Collider Detector at Fermilab	World's first and at the time highest-energy particle accelerator, colliding antiprotons and protons propelled to center-of-mass energy reaching 2 TeV.
1995	Wolfgang Ketterle (1957–), Eric Allin Cornell (1961–), and Carl Edwin Wieman (1951–)	Experimental verification of Bose–Einstein condensation.
2012	François Baron Englert (1932–) and Peter Ware Higgs (1929–)	Higgs boson (126 GeV) discovery in the Large Hadron Collider at CERN, Geneva, Switzerland. The Large Hadron Collider construction started in 1998 and produces particle acceleration with respective energy levels for protons at up to 4 teraelectronvolts (0.64 microjoules), or lead nuclei: 2.76 TeV per nucleon or 574 TeV per nucleus. The proton energy level was increased to 6.5 TeV in 2015.

Imaging

CHRONOLOGY	NOTEWORTHY PEOPLE	EVENTS AND DISCOVERIES
ca. 410 BC	Mozi (ca. 470 BC– 390 BC)	Chinese philosopher. Description of the use of a pin hole for the projection of an image on a wall of a darkened compartment (room); the initial concept of the camera obscura.
350 BC	Aristotle (384 BC– 322 BC)	Documented recordings of a solar eclipse based on the principles of the camera obscura. His image formation was based on the projection of the sun through gaps between the leaves of a tree.
ca. 300 BC	Euclid of Alexandria (ca. 350 BC–280 BC)	Publication of the treatise on light: Optics ('Οπτικά), describing the principles of the image formation for light traveling in straight lines, the camera obscura, next to general vision aspects.
1480	Leonardo da Vinci (1452–1519)	Experimentation with image formation using an ox eye from which he had scraped the retina, providing a lens with "screen" that forms an image. Additional experimentation with the principles of the camera obscura for image projection.

(Continued)

CHRONOLOGY	NOTEWORTHY PEOPLE	EVENTS AND DISCOVERIES
1560	1560: Bernardino de Sahagún (ca. 1499–ca. 1590), 1565: Nicolás Monardes (1493–1588), 1819: Edward Daniel Clarke (1769–1822), 1822: René Just Haüy (1743–1822), 1833: David Brewster (1781–1868), and 1933: Aleksander Jabloński (1898–1980)	Fluorescence imaging and spectroscopy. The principles of fluorescence are captured by the Jablonski diagram.
1590–1608	Hans Jansen (father of Zacharias) and Zacharias Jansen (1580–1640) and later Hans Lippershey (1570–1619).	Introduction of the optical microscope.
1610	Galileo Galilei (1564–1642)	Improvements to the microscope design by introducing focusing capabilities.
1640	Antonie van Leeuwenhoek (1632–1723)	Refined microscope design. Beginning of microbiology and large-scale microscopic investigations.
1794	Lazzaro Spallanzani (1729–1799)	First documented outline of waves in spatial orientation, forming the foundation for modern ultrasonic imaging.
1816	René Théophile-Hyacinthe Laennec (1781–1826)	Introduction of the stethoscope.
1826	Jean-Daniel Colladon (1802–1893)	Use of ringing a church bell for underwater range finding. Rudimentary "ultrasound" principle.
1864	August Joseph Ignaz Toepler (1836–1912)	Schlieren imaging, refraction of light in a substance as a function of local density or local chemical concentration. Also referred to as "shadow imaging."
1880	Francis Galton (1822–1911)	Construction of a device capable of generating sound waves of 40,000 Hz. Furthering the imaging capabilities with respect to ultrasound, initially attempted to mimic the observation techniques used by bats.
1880	Paul-Jacques Curie (1855–1941) and Pierre Curie (1859–1906)	Discovery of electric charges emerging on the surfaces of certain crystals, which are subjected to pressure or tension (shear or normal stress). This is referred to as the piezoelectric effect. Supporting technology for ultrasound imaging.
1895	Wilhelm Conrad Röntgen (1845–1923)	Primary X-ray imaging feasibility.
1900	Max Karl Ernst Ludwig Planck (1858–1947)	(Planck's) radiation law, describing the concept of black body radiation used in thermographic imaging.

(Continued)

CHRONOLOGY	NOTEWORTHY PEOPLE	EVENTS AND DISCOVERIES
1915	Paul Langevin (1872–1946)	Introduction of "hydrophone" for underwater detection of obstacles.
1922	Erwin Rudolf Josef Alexander Schrödinger (1887–1961) and Hermann Klaus Hugo Weyl (1885–1955)	Introduction of the quantum mechanical principles, which formed the basis for several imaging techniques.
1924	Louis-Victor-Pierre-Raymond, 7th duc de Broglie (1892–1987)	Introduction of the wave phenomenon with respect to all object in motion. Matter wave, propagating with the de Broglie wavelength.
1926	Hans Busch (1884–1973); Leó Szilárd (1898–1964)	Electron microscopy, transmission (TEM), respectively, reflection/scanning (SEM). The resolution principle is based on the wave motion of the moving electron, propagating with the de Broglie wavelength, as a function of the applied energy.
1927	Wolfgang Ernst Pauli (1900–1958), Ralph Kronig (1904–1995), George Eugene Uhlenbeck (1900–1988), Samuel Abraham Goudsmit (1902–1978), and Paul Adrien Maurice Dirac (1902–1984)	Introduction of the electron spin concept and a broad range of relativistic quantum mechanical principles. This formed the foundation for the development of the NMR imaging system: nuclear magnetic resonance (MRI).
1928	Sir Chandrasekhara Ventaka Raman (1888–1970)	Raman spectroscopy.
1937	Karl Dussik (1908–1968)	First recorded event of medical use of ultrasonic imaging.
1946	Felix Bloch (1905–1983) and Edward Mills Purcell (1912–1997)	Fundamental concept introduction providing the mechanism of action for magnetic resonance imaging (MRI).
1951	Erwin Wilhelm Müller (1911–1977)	(Scanning) Helium ion microscopy. The basic principles are very similar to the SEM. The He ion microscope uses both the atomic and molecular interaction of the incident helium ions for "density imaging" on the observed target as well as Rutherford backscattering spectroscopy to derive material properties. In comparison to the SEM, He ion microscope produces 3 to 9 secondary electrons, versus only one for SEM. The work of Erwin Müller on the field ion microscope provided the operational foundation. Erwin Müller first introduced the field emission electron microscope in 1951. The first operational He ion microscope was produced in the first decade of the twenty-first century.

(Continued)

CHRONOLOGY	NOTEWORTHY PEOPLE	EVENTS AND DISCOVERIES
1951+	Douglas Howry (1920–1969) and Joseph H. Holmes (1902–1982)	Pioneering two-dimensional B-mode ultrasound imaging.
1957	Marvin Lee Minsky (1927–)	Confocal microscopy.
1957	Herman P. Schwan (1915–2005)	Bioelectric impedance tomography (electric impedance tomography) and dielectric spectroscopy. Imaging mechanism based on the Maxwell–Wagner effect (polarization); based on the work of James Clerk Maxwell (1831–1879) and Karl Willy Wagner (1883–1953) in the early part of the twentieth century. The Maxwell–Wagner polarization mechanism, which reveals very large effective electric permittivity on scales larger than molecular size. The polarization can be artificially induced and has an associated specific (characteristic) relaxation time. Note: Herman Schwan (Schwann) is sometimes referred to as the "founding father of biomedical engineering." One of the examples of bioelectric impedance tomography outside the use on humans is in the food industry. Impedance tomography is also used in geological investigation; geophysics application.
1957+	David Edmund Kuhl (1929–), Luke Chapman (), and Roy Edwards ()	Positron emission tomography (PET).
1971	Sir Godfrey Newbold Hounsfield (1919–2004) and respectively Allan MacLeod Cormack (1924–1998)	Computed tomography.
1973	Paul Christian Lauterbur (1929–2007)	First operational MRI machine.
1981	Gerd Binnig (1947–) and Heinrich Rohrer (1933–2013)	Design of the scanning tunneling microscope (STM).
1986	Gerd Binnig (1947–), Heinrich Rohrer (1933–), Calvin Quate (1923–), and Christoph Gerber (1942–)	Initial concepts for the atomic force microscope (AFM) were introduced.
1989	Paul K. Hansma (1946–), B. Drake (), O. Marti (), S.A. Gould (), and C.B. Prater ()	Scanning ion-conducting microscope. Imaging technique with close correlation to superconductivity.

(Continued)

CHRONOLOGY	NOTEWORTHY PEOPLE	EVENTS AND DISCOVERIES
1990	Naohiro Tanno () and various groups with refinements by the MIT group consisting of David Huang (), James G. Fujimoto (), Carmen A. Puliafito () , and others.	Optical coherence tomography.

Instrumentation

CHRONOLOGY	NOTEWORTHY PEOPLE	EVENTS AND DISCOVERIES		
6000 BC–2000 BC	Stone Age	Mechanical labor and tool fabrication.		Coherence tomography
				MRI
ca. 6000 BC		First recorded use of floatation devices: boats. This illustrated the Archimedes principle (Archimedes [287 BC–212 BC]), but no documented descriptions on the floatation principles from those days.		PET
				Ultrasound
ca. 4000 BC	Eastern Europe	First recorded drawing of craft with rudimentary wheels.		X-ray
				mass spectrometer
4000 BC	Mesopotamia and Egypt	Documented recording of the construction of shelter, abandoning the nomadic structure.		Geiger counter
				Geiger–Muller
ca. 3500 BC		First documented installation of sewer systems, primarily run-off.		
ca. 3300 BC	Egypt	Drawings of sailboats.		
ca. 3000 BC		Traceable use of a potter's wheel used for the construction of crockery.		
3300 BC–1000 BC	Bronze Age	Smelting and forging of soft metals using low heat: copper, tin, gold. This age also introduces the written documentation.		
2700 BC–2500 BC	Egypt	Construction of pyramids, requiring advanced mechanical engineering efforts and architectural design (civil engineering).		

(Continued)

CHRONOLOGY	NOTEWORTHY PEOPLE	EVENTS AND DISCOVERIES		
ca. 1000 BC	Qanat aqueduct; Perzia	Water supply over a length greater than 71 km, and potential relation with sewer as a secondary use for liquid transport as part of the civil engineering efforts.		
1000 BC–700 AD	Iron Age	Higher heat requirements and more detailed tool manufacturing, introducing scientific and engineering challenges. Historical tracking of processes and developments and philosophies. Introduction of complicated mechanisms and requiring detailed analytical thinking.		
ca. 600 BC	Thales of Miletus (ca. 624 BC–ca. 546 BC; known as Thales: Θαλῆς)	Introduction of standardized and validated metrology.		
ca. 360 BC	Plato (427 BC–347 BC)	Rudimentary astronomy record keeping.		
40 BC	Marcus Vitruvius Pollio [Vitruvius] (ca. 80 BC–10 BC)	Roman engineering architect and civil engineer. Vituvius served under Gaius Julius Caesar (100 BC–44 BC). In the army position he was also charged with the care of the infirmed, where he used early biomedical engineering approaches for novel diagnosis and treatment.		
62	Hero of Alexandria [ρων ὁ ᾽Α λεξανδρεύς] (10–70)	Mathematician, physicist, and mechanical engineer who also taught pneumatics. A set of two books *The Pneumatica* describes mechanical devices worked by air, steam, or water pressure. Also known as Heron of Alexandria. He invented a steam-powered engine called the "Æolipile."		
120	Claudius Ptolemy {Ptolemaeus} [Πτολεμαῖος] (90–168)	Geographic recordings of a significant part of the Islamic and western world (i.e., Roman and Persian Empire), living in Egypt, as a Roman with Greek education. His cartography extended all the way out, including parts of China (discovered in fifteenth century). He specifically developed arithmetical techniques for calculating astronomical phenomena, under the teachings of Babylonian astronomers. Also known as بـ ط لـ يموس. (Batlaymus; Arabic)		

(Continued)

CHRONOLOGY	NOTEWORTHY PEOPLE	EVENTS AND DISCOVERIES		
644		Wind-powered devices developed by the Persians.		
1010	Eilmer of Malmesbury, eleventh century Benedictine monk	First documented successful flight, performed with a wooden frame lined with parchment, traveling approximately 200 m in free-fall from a 18-m elevation.		
1500	Leonardo da Vinci (1452–1519)	The preverbal "Renaissance man", involved in all aspects of cultural evolution, science, engineering, politics and art.		
1503	Gregor Reisch (1467–1525)	Detailed outline of the state-of-the-art science and engineering knowledge to date, including human anatomical drawings in the publication: *Margarita Philosophica*. The total works of Gregor Reisch form a series of twelve (12) books compiling an encyclopedia describing topics ranging from Latin grammar, to dialectics, rhetoric, arithmetic, music, geometry, astronomy, physics, natural history, physiology, psychology, and ethics.		
1512	Gregorius Reisch (1467–1525)	Introduction of the concept of the theodolite, used for topography and geographic location determination.		
1590	Francis Bacon, 1st Viscount of St. Alban (1561–1626)	Regulate the general scientific methodology.		
ca. 1600	William Gilbert (1544–1603)	Experimentalist. Description of magnetism, in his work: *De magnete, magnetisque corporibus, et de magno magnete tellure*. The compass had been in use since 206 BC (Chinese Han Dynasty: 206 BC–220 AD; maybe even earlier, during the Qin Dynasty: 221 BC–207 BC), in the European and Persian area since the thirteenth century.		

(*Continued*)

CHRONOLOGY	NOTEWORTHY PEOPLE	EVENTS AND DISCOVERIES		
ca. 1600	Galileo Galilei (1564–1642)	Major contributor to the scientific revolution and the (re)introduction of analytical thinking in science, engineering, and general thought processes. Galileo Galilei was remanded under house arrest by the Roman Inquisition for his views and teachings where he died after 9 years. This was the trailing end of the Renaissance period.		
1558	Giambattista della Porta (1535–1615)	Incorporation of a lens in the opening of a camera obscura—improved the image formation capabilities.	New	
~1590	Zacharius Janssen (1585–1632)	Constructed a compound microscope with a converging objective lens and a diverging eye lens.		
1604	Johannes Kepler (1571–1630)	In his book *Ad Vitellionem Paralipomena*, Kepler suggested that the intensity of light from a point source varies inversely with the square of the distance from the source, that light can be propagated over an unlimited distance, and that the speed of propagation is infinite. He explained vision as a consequence of the formation of an image on the retina by the lens in the eye and correctly described the causes of long-sightedness and short-sightedness. Conforming the heliocentric model calculated by Nicolaus Copernicus (1473–1543).		
1604	Johannes Kepler (1571–1630)	Formal introduction of the term "camera obscura."	new	
1608	Hans Lippershey (1570–1619)	Constructed a telescope with a converging objective lens and a diverging eye lens.		
1609	Galileo Galilei (1564–1642)	Construction of his own version of the telescope design of Hans Lippershey (1570–1619) and used it for astronomical observations. Galileo documented several astronomical discoveries including the four (4) moons of Jupiter.		

(*Continued*)

CHRONOLOGY	NOTEWORTHY PEOPLE	EVENTS AND DISCOVERIES		
1611	Giovanni Demisiani (?–1614)	Introduced the term "telescope" for his device with three times (3X) magnification.	new	
1611	Johannes Kepler (1571–1630)	In his book *Dioptrice* an explanation is provided for the principles involved in the convergent/divergent lens telescopes and microscopes. The telescope could be constructed using a converging objective and a converging ocular lens. The lens assembly description resembles that for the telephoto lens. Kepler also discovered total internal reflection, but could not effectively describe the optical and geometric relationship between the angle of incidence and the angle of refraction.		
1614	René Descartes (1596–1650)	Introduction to vortex motion. Introduction of the concept of general corpuscular motion, extending from small (maybe referring to the undefined atom), to planetary orbits. Descartes also made an illustration of the earth's magnetic field configuration in 1644, in his model the moon and celestial objects participated in the formation of the path of the magnetic field lines. Based on the limited experimental observations available in his time the premise was still not bad.		
~1618	Christopher Scheiner (1573–1650)	Constructed a telescope of the type suggested by Johannes Kepler (1571–1630) with converging objective lens system. This type of telescope become the standard "astronomical telescope."		
1632	Evangelista Torricelli (1608–1647)	Introduction of the barometer; essential in weather prediction; meteorology.		
1650	Blaise Pascal (1623–1662)	Pascal's law, pressure in a container applies an equal force on all surface of the enclosure		
ca. 1655	Christiaan Huygens (1629–1695)	Invention of a clockwork mechanism capable of timekeeping while at sea in order to allow for accurate geographical measurements.		

(*Continued*)

CHRONOLOGY	NOTEWORTHY PEOPLE	EVENTS AND DISCOVERIES		
1660	Robert Boyle (1627–1691)	Gas laws, definition of the behavior or gases. Boyle mentioned the compression of gas as a potential "shock absorber," acting similar to a spring.		
1673	Christiaan Huygens (1629–1695)	Construction of a "combustion engine" powered by gun powder. Huygens introduced several concepts of mechanical engineering and described the mechanism of shock waves. Christiaan Huygens is most known for his lens manufacturing and optical design of telescopes. The mathematical efforts of Christiaan Huygens in probability theory were far advanced and he collaborated with the mathematician Pierre de Fermat (1601–1665) from France.		
1679	Denis Papin (1647–ca. 1712)	Pressure and thermodynamic and mechanical impacts.		
1680	Robert Hooke (1635–1703)	Force applied by a compressed spring.		
ca. 1687	Sir Isaac Newton (1643–1727)	Sir Isaac Newton introduced several laws of motion. The publication of the *Philosophiæ Naturalis Principia Mathematica* provides detailed definitions regarding ballistic motion, circular motion (centripetal force), laws of action-reaction, gravitational acceleration, inertia and force with respect to acceleration. Introduction of the three laws of motion.		
1698	Thomas Savery (1650–1715)	Construction of the basic steam engine; using information obtained by Denis Papin (1647–c. 1712).		
1705	Edmond Halley (1656–1742)	Discovery of, and mathematical description of the trajectory for "Halley's comet".		
1712	Thomas Newcomen (1664–1729)	Construction of a "atmospheric" steam engine.		
1714	Brook Taylor (1685–1731)	Fundamental frequency of vibration; string. Additional work on pure mathematics: Taylor series.		

(Continued)

CHRONOLOGY	NOTEWORTHY PEOPLE	EVENTS AND DISCOVERIES		
1727	Leonard Euler (1707–1783)	Introduction of the concept of the elastic modulus, experimentally verified by Giordano Riccati (1709–1790) in 1782 and mathematically introduced by Thomas Young (1773–1829) in 1807, now known as Young's modulus.		
1729/1733	Chester Moore Hall (1703–1771)	Construction of achromatic compound lenses using components consisting of glasses with different refractive indices. Construction of first refracting telescope that has chromatic aberration correction.		
1732	Anders Celsius (1701–1744)	Thermometer scale calibration based on pure water phases.		
1733	Daniel Bernoulli (1700–1782)	Acoustics, mechanical vibrations, and fluid dynamic principles introduced. Definition of the fundamental frequency and higher harmonics, with supporting elaborate mathematical analysis (solutions to differential equations).		
1735	Daniel Gabriel Fahrenheit (1686–1736)	Temperature scale in Fahrenheit based on body temperature and saltwater phases		
1757–1769	James Watt (1736–1819)	Modern steam engine design and operation with theoretical description of operation.		
1769	Nicolas-Joseph Cugnot (1725–1804)	First operational steam powered automobile, the predecessor to the internal combustion automobile.		
1783	Joseph-Michel Montgolfier (1740–1810) and Jacques-Étienne Montgolfier (1745–1799)	Hot-air balloon; buoyancy.		
1785	Jacques Alexandre César Charles (1746–1823)	Charles's law, expansion of gases.		
1800	Count Alessandro Giuseppe Antonio Anastasio Volta (1745–1827)	Introduction of the battery.		

(*Continued*)

CHRONOLOGY	NOTEWORTHY PEOPLE	EVENTS AND DISCOVERIES		
1802	Joseph Louis Gay-Lussac (1778–1850)	Ideal gas law; building on the work by Robert Boyle (1627–1691), more than a century earlier.		
1807	Thomas Young (1773–1829)	Formal introduction of the Young's Modulus for elastic deformation, tying strain to stress, based on the work by Leonard Euler (1707–1783).		
1821	Michael Faraday (1791–1867)	Discovery of electromagnetic rotation, leading to his law on electromagnetic induction in 1831. Meanwhile, in 1923 Michael Faraday experimentaly verified the concept of refrigeration, introduced based on the work of John Dalton (1766–1844) in 1802 and William Cullen (1710–1790) in 1756.		
1823	Nicéphore Niépce (1765–1833) and Louis Jacques-Mandé Daguerre (1787–1851)	Introduction of Photography, using the earlier efforts of Albertus Magnus (1193–1280) with his discovery of silver nitrate, and Georg Fabricius (1516–71) who discovered silver chloride.		
1824	Nicolas Léonard Sadi Carnot (1796–1832)	Refrigerator for general public.		
1826	Jean-Daniel Colladon (1802–1893)	Use of ringing a church-bell for underwater range-finding. Rudimentary "ultrasound" principle.		
1827	Benoît Fourneyron (1802–1867)	First water turbine.		
1831	Michael Faraday (1791– 1867) and Joseph Henry (1797–1878)	Law of induction, leading to the development of the electric generator.		
1848	William Thomson, 1st Baron Kelvin (i.e., Lord Kelvin) (1824–1907)	Absolute temperature scale: Kelvin.		
1851	Jean Bernard Léon Foucault (1819–1868)	Foucault pendulum, illustrating the impact of the earth's rotation on motion.		

(Continued)

CHRONOLOGY	NOTEWORTHY PEOPLE	EVENTS AND DISCOVERIES		
1852	James Prescott Joule (1818–1889) and William Thomson, 1st Baron Kelvin {Lord Kelvin} (1824–1907)	Joule–Thomson effect: rapidly expanding gas leads to a reduction in the temperature of the gas, even offering the potential for a phase change to solid, or liquid. Sometimes also found as the Joule–Kelvin effect		
1854	Robert Wilhelm Eberhard Bunsen (1811–1899)	Bunsen burner.		
1861	William Froude (1810–1879)	Applications to ship design, reducing the roll of a ship by means of a keel. The hydrodynamic behavior of the hull of a ship could be gauged based on the Froude number, derived from a set of experimental obtained data points.		
1880	Francis Galton (1822–1911)	Construction of a device capable of generating sound waves of 40,000 Hz. Furthering the imaging capabilities with respect to ultrasound, initially attempted to mimic the observation techniques used by bats.		
1887	Heinrich Rudolf Hertz (1857–1894)	Radar development. Detection of electromagnetic radiation (radio waves). Heinrich Hertz also discovered that certain metal plates will generate electricity when exposed to light: photo-electric effect.		
1895	Wilhelm Conrad Röntgen (1845–1923)	Primary X-ray imaging feasibility.		
1897	Joseph John Thomson (1856–1940)	Discovery of the electron; using William Crookes's vacuum tube.		
1897	Guglielmo Marconi, 1st Marquis of Marconi (1874–1937)	Introduction of wireless communications and radio.		

(Continued)

CHRONOLOGY	NOTEWORTHY PEOPLE	EVENTS AND DISCOVERIES		
1898	Antoine Henri Becquerel (1852–1908)	Introduction of units for radioactivity radiation. Collaborator with Manya (Marie) Skłodowska Curie (1867–1934). Henri Becquerel, Marie Curie, and Pierre Curie shared the Nobel Prize in Physics for their radioactivity discoveries in 1903.		
1900	Ferdinand Adolf Heinrich August Graf von Zeppelin (1838–1917)	Successful dirigible, gas-filled air floatation device with propulsion.		
1904	John Ambrose Fleming (1849–1945)	Application of the Edison effect to make the first thermionic valve ("radio" tube).		
1906	Lee De Forest (1873–1961)	Construction of the first audion (triode) by introducing a grid into a Fleming valve, tube electronics.		
1907–1912	Joseph John Thomson (1856–1940)	Devised methods of positive ray analysis. These processes formed the beginning of mass spectroscopy.		
1909	Guglielmo Marconi (1874–1937) and Carl Ferdinand Braun (1850–1918)	Were jointly awarded the Nobel Prize in Physics—the former for combining the basic knowledge about Hertzian waves to produce wireless telegraphy, and the latter for the study, production, and use of electrical oscillators. Braun also developed the Braun tube, called the "cathode-ray" tube in the United States.		
1911	Charles Thomson Bees Wilson (1869–1959)	Construction of the first expansion cloud chamber, used for particle research. This is one of the most important device in nuclear physics. Charles Wilson was awarded the Nobel Prize in Physics jointly with Arthur Holly Compton (1892–1962) in 1927.		
1915	Paul Langevin (1872–1946)	Introduction of "hydrophone" for underwater detection of obstacles.		

(Continued)

CHRONOLOGY	NOTEWORTHY PEOPLE	EVENTS AND DISCOVERIES		
1918	Paul Scherrer (1890–1969)	X-ray diffraction, crystal structure. Nuclear energy development. Established the CERN institute in Switzerland as one of the founders. Directed the construction of the first cyclotron in 1940.		
1925	Walter M. Elsasser (1904–1991)	Predicted from de Broglie theory illustrating how electrons could be diffracted by crystals.		
1926	Mark Cowley Lidwell (1878–1969) and Edgar Harold Booth (1893–1963)	Rudimentary, but effective, external cardiac pacemaker design.		
1926	Hans Busch (1884–1973); Leó Szilárd (1898–1964)	Electron microscopy, transmission (TEM), respectively, reflection/scanning (SEM). The resolution principle is based on the wave motion of the moving electron, propagating with the de Broglie wavelength, as a function of the applied energy.		
1930	Richard Buckminster Fuller (1895–1983)	Mechanical engineering and engineering architecture, as well as chemistry; Bucky-ball, multipoint connections in both chemical structures and mechanical structures.		
1931	Georges Jean Marie Darrieus (1888–1979)	Introduction of the wind turbine.		
1932	Ernest Orlando Lawrence (1901–1958) and Milton Stanley Livingston (1905–1986)	Construction of the first cyclotron. Ernest Lawrence received the Nobel Prize in Physics in 1939.		
1933	Patrick M. S. Blackett (1897–1974) and Guiseppe P. S. Occhialini (1907–1993)	Obtained the first cloud chamber photographs of electron–positron pair production.		

(Continued)

CHRONOLOGY	NOTEWORTHY PEOPLE	EVENTS AND DISCOVERIES		
1937	Karl Dussik (1908–1968)	First recorded event of medical use of ultrasonic imaging.		
1940	Louis Leprince-Ringuet (1901–2000)	Obtained the first cloud chamber photograph of a collision between a meson and an electron, from which the mass of the meson could be derived.		
1940	Donald William Kerst (1911–1993)	Made the first betatron, an induction type accelerator.		
1940+	Julius Robert Oppenheimer (1904–1967)	Manhattan project: fission reaction. Prominent members: Arthur Compton (1892–1962), Enrico Fermi (1901–1954), Eugene Wigner (1902–1995), and dozens more. One notable result is the creation of nuclear power plants.		
1937–1959	Chester Floyd Carlston (1906–1968)	Photocopy machine, patented in 1942. The first photocopier was offered for sale by the Haloid company in 1959, later renamed Xerox.		
1947	Hartmut Paul Kallmann (1896–1978), next to John Wesley Coltman (1915–) next to Fitz-Hugh Ball Marshall (1912–)	Developed scintillation counters.		
1948	Dennis Gabor (1900–1979)	Description of the principles of wavefront reconstruction, evolving into holography.	c	
1950	John Alexander Hopps, (1919–1998)	Introduction of the "portable" (45 kg) cardiac pacemaker, based on the earlier work by Mark Lidwell (1878–1969) and Edgar Harold Booth (1893–1963) in 1926. This led, with the development of microprocessors, to the first implantable pacemaker in 1958 by William Chardack (1919–2011) and Wilson Greatbatch (1919–2011).		

(*Continued*)

CHRONOLOGY	NOTEWORTHY PEOPLE	EVENTS AND DISCOVERIES		
1951	Erwin Wilhelm Müller (1911–1977)	(Scanning) Helium ion microscopy. The basic principles are very similar to the SEM. The He ion microscope uses both the atomic and molecular interaction of the incident helium ions for "density imaging" on the observed target as well as Rutherford backscattering spectroscopy to derive material properties. In comparison to the SEM the He ion microscope produces 3 to 9 secondary electrons, versus only one for SEM. The work of Erwin Müller on the field ion microscope provided the operational foundation. Erwin Müller first introduced the field emission electron microscope in 1951. The first operational He ion microscope was produced in the first decade of the twenty-first century.		
1951+	Douglas Howry (1920–1969) and Joseph H. Holmes (1902–1982)	Pioneering two dimensional B-mode ultrasound imaging.		
1952		Brookhaven National laboratory was the first to achieve the acceleration of particles to the giga-electron-volt energy range: 2.3-Gev protons.		
ca. 1952	Ludwig von Helmholtz (1821–1894), Lyman Strong Spitzer, Jr. (1914–1997) and Ronald Richter (1909–1991) and Edward Teller (1908–2003)	Nuclear fusion investigation and start of experimentation. The process was in principle described by Hermann Ludwig Ferdinand von Helmholtz (1821–1894), but is continuously in action on the sun's surface.		
1952	Donald Arthur Glaser (1926–2013)	Made the first bubble chamber. He was awarded the Nobel Prize in Physics in 1960. The first large-scale, terrestrial thermonuclear reaction was produced when a "hydrogen fusion device" was tested at Einewetok atoll on November 1.		

(Continued)

CHRONOLOGY	NOTEWORTHY PEOPLE	EVENTS AND DISCOVERIES		
1955	Obninsk Nuclear Power Station, Russia	First nuclear power station for energy generation.		
1956	Paul Winchell {Wilchinsky} (1922–2005)	Artificial heart (Jarvik 7).		
1957	USSR: Soviet Russia	Sputnik-1 [Russian: "Спутник-1]; first satellite.		
1957	Marvin Lee Minsky (1927–2016)	Confocal microscopy.		
1957	Herman P. Schwan (1915–2005)	Bioelectric impedance tomography (electric impedance tomography) and dielectric spectroscopy. Imaging mechanism based on the Maxwell–Wagner effect (polarization); based on the work of James Clerk Maxwell (1831–1879) and Karl Willy Wagner (1883–1953) in the early part of the twentiethth century. The Maxwell–Wagner polarization mechanism, which reveals very large effective electric permittivity on scales larger than molecular size. The polarization can be artificially induced and has an associated specific (characteristic) relaxation time. *Note*: Herman Schwan (Schwann) is sometimes referred to as the "founding father of biomedical engineering." One of the examples of bioelectric impedance tomography outside the use on humans is in the food industry. Impedance tomography is also used in geological investigation; geophysics application.		
1957+	David Edmund Kuhl (1929–), Luke Chapman (?), and Roy Edwards (?)	Positron emission tomography (PET).		
1971	Sir Godfrey Newbold Hounsfield (1919–2004) and respectively Allan MacLeod Cormack (1924–1998)	Computed tomography.		

CHRONOLOGY	NOTEWORTHY PEOPLE	EVENTS AND DISCOVERIES		
1973	Paul Christian Lauterbur (1929–2007)	First operational MRI machine.		
1981	Gerd Binnig (1947–), Heinrich Rohrer (1933–)	Design of the scanning tunneling microscope (STM).		
1986	Gerd Binnig (1947), Heinrich Rohrer (1933–), Calvin Quate (1923–), and Christoph Gerber (1942–)	Initial concepts for the atomic force microscope (AFM) were introduced.		
1989	Paul K. Hansma (1946–), B. Drake (?), O. Marti (?), S.A. Gould (?), and C.B. Prater (?)	Scanning ion-conducting microscope. Imaging technique with close correlation to superconductivity.		
1990	Naohiro Tanno (?) and various groups with refinements by the MIT group consisting of David Huang (?) James G. Fujimoto (?), Carmen A. Puliafito (?), and others.	Optical coherence tomography (OCT).		
1961	Yuri Alekseyevich Gagarin [Russian: Ю́рий Алексе́евич] (1934–1968); USSR: Soviet Russia	First space travel: Vostok spacecraft.		
1983	Collider Detector at Fermilab	World's first and at the time highest-energy particle accelerator, colliding antiprotons and protons propelled to center-of-mass energy reaching 2 TeV.		
2008	CERN, Switzerland	Large Hadron Collider, beginning of operations. To date no evidence supporting string theory or supersymmetry has been collected.		

(*Continued*)

CHRONOLOGY	NOTEWORTHY PEOPLE	EVENTS AND DISCOVERIES		
2012	François Baron Englert (1932–) and Peter Ware Higgs (1929–)	Higgs boson (126 GeV) discovery in the Large Hadron Collider at CERN, Geneva, Switzerland.		

Material

CHRONOLOGY	NOTEWORTHY PEOPLE	EVENTS AND DISCOVERIES
6000 BC–2000 BC	Stone Age	Mechanical labor and tool fabrication
3300 BC–1000 BC	Bronze Age	Smelting and forging of soft metals using low heat: copper, tin, gold. This age also introduces the written documentation.
1000 BC–700 AD	Iron Age	Higher heat requirements and more detailed tool manufacturing, introducing scientific and engineering challenges. Historical tracking of processes and developments and philosophies. Introduction of complicated mechanisms and requiring detailed analytical thinking.
27 BC	Syria	Creation of glass.
400+	Italy	Lycurgus Cup, made with dichroic glass, consisting of early form nanoparticles. The cup shows a different color depending on whether illuminated from within or externally.
600	China	First documented production of ceramics.
1603	Sir Hugh Platt (1522–1608)	Hardening of metal.
1688	France	Construction of plate glass.
1774	Antoine Lavoisier (1743–1794)	Discovery of oxygen; and the chemical process of oxidation.
1782	Josiah Wedgwood (1730–1795)	Mass production of ceramic artifacts.
1811	Lorenzo Romano Amedeo Carlo Avogadro di Quaregna e di Cerreto, Count of Quaregna and Cerreto (1776–1856)	Molecular arrangements; molecular quantity in a mole of substance. Avogadro's law.
1821	Pierre Berthier (1782–1861)	Identification of the corrosion resistance properties for iron–chromium alloys; leading to stainless steel.
1836	Ignace Dubus-Bonnel ()	Introduction of a rudimentary form of fiberglass.
1839	William Hallowes Miller (1801–1880)	Miller indices for lattice configuration, with specific applications to Bravais lattice structures.
1850	Auguste Bravais (1811–1863)	Uncovered lattice structure: Bravais lattice.

(Continued)

CHRONOLOGY	NOTEWORTHY PEOPLE	EVENTS AND DISCOVERIES
1855	Georges Audemars ()	Discovery of the process to produce rayon (cellulose nitrate); sometimes referred to as "artificial silk."
1856	Sir Henry Bessemer (1813–1898)	Carbon steel.
1857	Michael Faraday (1791–1867)	Description of the unique optical properties for nanoparticles.
1874	Jacobus Henricus van't Hoff (1852–1911)	Introduction into the field of polymers.
1886	Friedrich Carl Zinoffsky (1830–??)	Determination of the polymer hemoglobin with molecular weight 16,700, following the work of Felix Hoppe-Seyler (1825–1895).
1887	Thomas Edison (1847–1931)	Advance ceramics processing technology.
1888	Wilhelm Roux (1850–1924)	Preliminary efforts leading to stem-cell research.
1901	Thomas Hunt Morgan (1866–1945)	Introduction of regenerative medicine, transplant research.
1902	Robert Williams Wood (1868–1955)	Surface plasmon resonance.
1906	Dmitri Ivanovich Mendeleev (1834–1907)	Periodic Table of Elements.
1908	William Henry Bragg (1862–1942) and William Lawrence Bragg (1890–1971)	Bragg diffraction law for crystalline lattice structures irradiated by X-ray radiation.
1908	Gustav Mie (1869–1957)	Scattering form nanoparticles, wavelength smaller than the scatter object size; Mie scatter.
1911	Heike Kamerlingh Onnes (1853–1926)	Discovery of superconductivity (metals).
1913	Niels Henrik David Bohr (1885–1962)	Bohr atomic model.
1916	Robert Andrews Millikan (1868–1953)	Experimentally verified Einstein's photoelectric equation.
1916	Peter Joseph Wilhelm Debye (Usa, 1884–1966), Paul Scherrer (B. 1890), next to Albert Wallace Hull (1880-1966)	Obtained the first experimental X-ray powder diffraction patterns.
1925	Wolfgang Ernst Pauli (1900–1958)	Pauli exclusion principle for atomic energy levels.
1929	Otto Stern (1888)	Obtained crystal diffraction of a beam of helium atoms.

(Continued)

CHRONOLOGY	NOTEWORTHY PEOPLE	EVENTS AND DISCOVERIES
1929	Wallace Hume Carothers (1896 – 1937)	Nylon discovered at Du Pont®.
1930	E. J. Williams () and William Lawrence Bragg (1890–1971)	Introduction of solid-state physics.
1931	Carl David Anderson (1905–1991)	Discovery of the positron, anti-particle for the electron. The "positron" was predicted by Paul Adrien Maurice Dirac (1902–1984) in 1929.
1934	Hideki Yukawa [湯川 秀樹], (1907–1981)	Introduction of mesons and the concept of antimatter.
1945	Dorothy Mary Hodgkin (1910–1994)	Protein crystallography, X-ray diffraction studies.
1947	George Dixon Rochester (1908–2001) and Clifford Charles Butler (1922–1999)	Introduction of the "strangeness" concept for quarks.
1953	Karl Ziegler (1898–1973)	Revolutionarized the process of polymerization, supporting mass production.
1958	Lev Davidovich Landau [Russian: Лёв Давидович Ландау] (1908–1968), Arkady Beynusovich Migdal [Russian: Аркадий Бёйнусович (Бенедиктович) Мигдал] (1911–1991)	Theory of interacting electrons, specifically with respect to solids; condensed matter physics.
1960		Introduction of the fiber-optic.
1961	James Edgar Till (1931–) and Ernest Armstrong McCulloch (1926–2011)	Stem cell research and forerunner of tissue engineering and regenerative medicine.
1965		Commercial development of the photovoltaic cell.
1965	Pierre-Gilles de Gennes (1932–2007)	Liquid crystal functionality.
1970	Sheldon Lee Glashow (1932–), John Iliopoulos (1940–), and Luciano Maiani (1941–)	Introduction of the charm quark.
1972	Stephen Hawking (1942–), Jacob Bekenstein (1947–2015)	Thermodynamics of black holes.
1974	Burton Richter (1931–) and Samuel Chao Chung Ting [Chinese: 丁肇中] (1936–)	Description of charm for the quark.

(Continued)

CHRONOLOGY	NOTEWORTHY PEOPLE	EVENTS AND DISCOVERIES
1975	Richard P. Blakemore ()	Magnetotactic bacteria.
1975	Claes-Göran Granqvist (1946–) and Robert A. Buhrman ()	Introduction of the concept and production of the first nanoparticles.
1975	Martin Lewis Perl (1927–2014)	Discovery of the tau lepton.
1977	Leon Max Ledderman (1922–)	Discovery of the "beauty" and "bottom" designation for quarks.
1978		Discovery of the "gluon" with the assistance of the PLUTO, the first electromagnetic superconductive solenoid located in Hamburg, Germany.
1980	Klaus von Klitzing (1943–)	Quantum Hall effect.
1987		Discovery of superconductivity in ceramic oxide, operating at higher temperature than metallic superconductors.
1991	Sumio Iijima [飯島 澄男] (1939–)	Discovery of carbon nanotube.
1995	Wolfgang Ketterle (1957–), Eric Allin Cornell (1961–), and Carl Edwin Wieman (1951–)	Experimental verification of Bose–Einstein condensation.
2012	François Baron Englert (1932–) and Peter Ware Higgs (1929–)	Higgs boson (126 GeV) discovery in the Large Hadron Collider at CERN, Geneva, Switzerland. The Large Hadron Collider construction started in 1998 and produces particle acceleration with respective energy levels for protons at up to 4 teraelectronvolts (0.64 microjoules), or lead nuclei: 2.76 TeV per nucleon or 574 TeV per nucleus. The proton energy level was increased to 6.5 TeV in 2015.

Mechanics

CHRONOLOGY	NOTEWORTHY PEOPLE	EVENTS AND DISCOVERIES
ca. 6000 BC	Egypt	First recorded drawings of rudimentary watercrafts.
ca 4000 BC	Eastern Europe	First recorded drawing of craft with rudimentary wheels.
4000 BC	Mesopotamia and Egypt	Documented recording of the construction of shelter, abandoning the nomadic structure.
ca. 3500 BC		First documented installation of sewer systems, primarily run-off.
ca. 3300 BC	Egypt	Drawings of sailboats.

(Continued)

CHRONOLOGY	NOTEWORTHY PEOPLE	EVENTS AND DISCOVERIES
2700 BC–2500 BC	Egypt	Construction of pyramids, requiring advanced mechanical engineering efforts and architectural design (civil engineering).
ca. 1000 BC	Qanat aqueduct; Perzia	Water supply over a length greater than 71 km, and potential relation with sewer as a secondary use for liquid transport as part of the civil engineering efforts.
ca. 600 BC	Thales of Miletus (ca. 624 BC–ca. 546 BC; known as Thales: Θαλῆς)	Description of the "nature of objects." Thales believed that objects are alive; part of the stream of thought by the "Hylozoists."
430 BC	Socrates (470 BC–399 BC)	School of analytical thinking. Introduction to the base principles of what is currently considered classical mechanics.
350 BC	Aristotle (384 BC–322 BC)	Founder of the Lyceum school of analytical thinking in Macedonia. Aristotle described the initial concepts of physics, motion, time as well as astronomy concepts. Aristotle proposed the concept of an external force (acting during flight) perpetuating the projectile motion of a ballistic object, however incorrect, apart from gravity forcing the object down.
ca. 250 BC	Archimedes (287 BC–212 BC)	Hand operated corkscrew water pump. The philosophies of Archimedes shaped the development process of modern engineering.
ca. 220 BC	China	Civil engineering effort of the architectural and mechanical design and construction of the Great Wall, Ming Dynasty.
40 BC	Marcus Vitruvius Pollio [Vitruvius] (ca. 80 BC–10 BC)	First recorded use and description of the mechanism-of-action of a steam-operated engine to perform work: Æolipile; described in *De Architectura*.
62	Hero of Alexandria [ρων ὁ᾽Αλεξανδρεύς] (10–70)	Second recorded use of steam to provide power to a machine; Æolipile.
650		First recorded use of wind mills and wind energy in the Persian Empire.
800	Persia, the Netherlands; detailed scientific documentation by Simon Stevin (1548–1620)	Wind energy used to pump water, windmill water pump: wind pump. Other use of the windmill was in manufacturing, for example, papermaking, cloth fabrication, wheat processing, and (much) later for the generation of electricity. Jan Adriaanszoon Leeghwater [Leechwater] (1575–1650); draining a significant area of land north from Amsterdam to make it habitable in 1612 (son of carpenter Adriaan Symonszoon [–1618]).

(Continued)

CHRONOLOGY	NOTEWORTHY PEOPLE	EVENTS AND DISCOVERIES
900–1200	Mexico, central America	Construction of temples, which apparently have a close correlation to astronomical observations. Civil engineering.
1206	Al-Jazari (1136–1206) [Turkey]; Badi'al-Zaman Abū al-'Izz ibn Ismā'īl ibn al-Razāz al-Jazarī (Arab: بُنُ اَلْعِز أَبُو الزمـان بـــديع) (الجـزري الرِّزاز بُنُ إِسْماعِيلِ	Publication of *Book of Knowledge of Ingenious Mechanical Devices*. Description of mechanical devices and mechanism of action.
1245	Thomas Aquinas (1225–1274)	Reformulation of the dynamic concepts of Aristotle (384 BC–322 BC).
1500	Leonardo da Vinci (1452–1519)	Formal description of physical phenomena based on the state-of-the-art mathematical definitions. Description of several machines, including "flying machines," and a rudimentary theoretical discourse on the respective mechanism of action for several dynamic systems.
1600	William Gilbert (1544–1603)	Publication about events and scientific exploration of earth's phenomena: *Terrella*. Additional work was on the description of the magnetic field and magnet in *De Magnete, Magneticisque Corporibus, et de Magno Magnete Tellure*.
1617	Johannes Kepler (1571–1630)	Kepler's third law of planetary motion, based on the collected data by Tycho Brahe (1546–1601).
1623	Galileo Galilei (1564–1642)	Experimentation; experimental design, publication: 'Il saggiatore' (*The Assayer; Mechanics*). Galileo described the influence of air as a resistive force in comparison to water for the first time. First principles of mechanics: description of laws of motion (falling bodies; gravitational acceleration), projectile motion (ballistics), and inertia, before Sir Isaac Newton (1643–1727). Invented the pendulum clock and many more engineering feats. By some considered the father of mechanics.
1640	Francesco Maria Grimaldi (1618–1663)	Documentation that the fall of an object traverses a distance that is proportional to the square of the elapsed time, linking it to the gravitational acceleration. Collaborations with Giovanni Battista Riccioli (1598–1671).
1660	Robert Boyle (1627–1691)	Gas laws, definition of the behavior or gases.
1673	Christiaan Huygens (1629–1695)	Huygens introduced several concepts of mechanical engineering and described the mechanism of shock waves.

(Continued)

CHRONOLOGY	NOTEWORTHY PEOPLE	EVENTS AND DISCOVERIES
ca. 1666	Sir Isaac Newton (1643–1727)	Sir Isaac Newton introduced several laws of motion: Newton's three laws of motion. This forms the macroscopic scale of the field of classical mechanics. The publication of the *Philosophiæ Naturalis Principia Mathematica* in 1685 provides detailed definitions regarding ballistic motion, circular motion (centripetal force), laws of action–reaction, gravitational acceleration, inertia, and force with respect to acceleration. Sir Isaac Newton derived the inverse square law for gravitational force in 1666. Formal introduction of the field of classical mechanics.
1698	Thomas Savery (1650–1715)	Construction of the basic steam engine.
1712	Thomas Newcomen (1664–1729)	Construction of a "atmospheric" steam engine.
1757–1769	James Watt (1736–1819)	Modern steam engine design and operation with theoretical description of operation.
	Leonard Euler (1707–1783)	Contributions to the mechanical aspects of civil engineering. Leonard Euler provided a mathematical recourse of the load applied to columns (architecture) and the associated buckling under excessive forces.
1769	Nicolas-Joseph Cugnot (1725–1804)	First operational steam-powered automobile, the predecessor to the internal combustion automobile.
1807	Thomas Young (1773–1829)	Formal introduction of the Young's modulus for elastic deformation, tying strain to stress, based on the work by Leonard Euler (1707–1783).
1830	Joseph Henry (1797–1878)	First electromotor constructed.
1851	Sir George Gabriel Stokes, 1st Baronet (1819–1903)	Creeping flow, partially applicable to seismology. Specific seismic work of Gabriel Stokes was on a human size scale, describing vibrational forces and energy related to driven oscillations while crossing bridges, and the resulting bridge collapses in his days. One of the fall-out from the bridge vibration and collapse is development of studies in metal fatigue.
1877	Ludwig Eduard Boltzmann (1844–1906)	Introduction of the field of statistical mechanics; discrete energy levels. This formed the formal introduction to quantum mechanics. Publication of the paper "On the Relation of a General Mechanical Theorem to the Second Law of Thermodynamics."
1880	Paul-Jacques Curie (1855–1941) and Pierre Curie (1859–1906)	Discovery of electric charges emerging on the surfaces of crystals that are subjected to shear or normal stress. This is referred to as the piezoelectric effect.
1892	Jules Henri Poincaré (1854–1912)	Celestial mechanics.

(Continued)

CHRONOLOGY	NOTEWORTHY PEOPLE	EVENTS AND DISCOVERIES
1897	Joseph John Thomson (1856–1940)	Discovery of the electron; using William Crookes's vacuum tube. Joseph Thompson describes the atom as a "plum pudding" where the raisins in the spherical blob are the electrons.
1900	Max Karl Ernst Ludwig Planck (1858–1947)	Introduction of the premise of quantum theory. The energy of electromagnetic radiation is proportional to the frequency of the electromagnetic wave; discrete quanta with respect to the narrow wavelength bandwidth.
1902	Josiah Willard Gibbs (1839–1903)	Publication of his book *Elementary Principles of Statistical Mechanics*.
1905	Albert Einstein (1879–1955)	Introduction of special theory of relativity.
1909	Robert Andrews Millikan (1868–1953)	Measurement of the mass of the electron.
1916	Niels Henrik David Bohr (1885–1962)	Atomic structure definition (Bohr atomic model) and introduction to quantum theory.
1917	Ernest Rutherford, 1st Baron Rutherford of Nelson (1871–1937)	Discovery of the proton.
1920	Amalie (Emmy) Noether (1882–1935)	Theoretical connection between symmetry and conservation laws. Emmy Noether made significant contributions to a broad field of mathematical applications and the theoretical description of physics concepts. Noether worked closely with David Hilbert (1862–1943) in the early part of her career. Noether introduced two statements, the first regarded as Noether's first theorem, treating conservation laws in a manner of a stress energy tensor, posing that there is a corresponding conservation law corresponding to every differentiable symmetry of the action associated with the physical system. The Noether conservation theorem applies directly to quantum mechanics. Noether's second theorem links the symmetry of an action function for a system to the system's differential equations. The action in this case is an integral defined by the Lagrangian function, from which the behavior of the system can be derived based on the "principles of least action."
1924	Louis-Victor-Pierre-Raymond, 7th duc de Broglie (1892–1987)	Introduction of the wave phenomenon with respect to all objects in motion. Matter wave, propagating with the de Broglie wavelength.

(Continued)

CHRONOLOGY	NOTEWORTHY PEOPLE	EVENTS AND DISCOVERIES
1925	Sir William Hamilton (1788–1856), David Hilbert (1862–1943), Max Planck (1858–1947), Albert Einstein (1879–1955), Niels Bohr (1885–1962), Werner Heisenberg (1901–1976), Louis de Broglie (1892–1987), Erwin Schrödinger (1887–1961), Pascual Jordan (1902–1980), Max Born (1882–1970), Wolfgang Pauli (1900–1958), Paul Dirac (1902–1984), John Wheeler (1911–2008), and John von Neumann (1903–1957)	Introduction of the field of quantum mechanics, the list may be extended, however the main contributors are listed. Quantum mechanics is the field of mechanics, a branch of physics, describing events on a nanoscopic scale, based on the realization that the energy distribution for a system does not always form a continuous spectrum. The work of Erwin Schrödinger (1887–1961) combined quantum mechanics with special relativity, forming a subsection of wave mechanics.
1926	1928: Paul Dirac (1902–1984); 1929 Dmitri Vladimirovich Skobeltsyn (1892–1990); 1932 Carl David Anderson (1905–1991)	Discovery of positron. Generally Carl Anderson is credited with the formal discovery (Nobel Prize).
1926	Jean Baptiste Perrin (1870–1942)	Physical proof providing the existence of molecules.
1927	Wolfgang Ernst Pauli (1900–1958) Ralph Kronig (1904–1995), George Eugene Uhlenbeck (1900–1988), Samuel Abraham Goudsmit (1902–1978), and Paul Adrien Maurice Dirac (1902–1984)	Introduction of the electron spin concept and a broad range of relativistic quantum mechanical principles.
1932	James Chadwick (1891–1974)	Discovery of the neutron.
1941	Richard Phillips Feynman (1918–1988)	Amplitude formulation of the principles of quantum mechanics under the Laplacian approach, or "many paths approach," with equivalence to the "least action" theorem. In principle this combines the matrix formulation and the wave formulation.

Meteorology

CHRONOLOGY	NOTEWORTHY PEOPLE	EVENTS AND DISCOVERIES
3000 BC	India	Description of seasonal cycles and cloud formations, and rudimentary reference to the earth's movement around the sun.
ca. 600 BC	China; India	Documented use of magnetic compasses; the lodestone. More specific documented use dates to the Han Dynasty (ca. 206 BC).
ca. 600 BC	Thales of Miletus (ca. 624 BC–ca. 546 BC; known as Thales: Θαλῆς)	Introduction of metrology, accurate measurements of objects, phenomena, events, and conditions (e.g., atmospheric conditions).
430 BC	Democritus (of Greece) (460 BC–370 BC)	Rudimentary weather prediction processes.
430 BC	Hippocrates of Chios (ca. 470–410 BC)	Publication of the seasonal variabilities and wind velocity and direction profiles.
350 BC	Aristotle (384 BC–322 BC)	Aristotle described the initial concepts of physics, motion, time as well as astronomy concepts. Aristotle used geological and atmospheric record keeping for the prediction of weather conditions (meteorology). First documented use of a scientific approach to weather forecasting.
ca. 250 BC	Archimedes (287 BC–212 BC)	Revealed the properties that define buoyancy. The base principles relate to the tectonic plate mechanics.
50	Gaius Plinius Secundus (23–79), known as: Pliny the Elder	Publication of the magnetic action of the lodestone in his publication: *Naturalis Historia*. A rather detailed description of the use of magnetism for geographical location determination is described.
62	Hero of Alexandria [ρων ὁ'Αλεξανδρεύς] (10–70)	Mathematician, physicist, and mechanical engineer who also taught pneumatics. The base of this methodology formed the principle understanding of the movement of atmospheric air masses in future years.
82	Wang Chong (27–97)	Description of the formation of rain as the result of condensed water vapor (clouds), in contrast to an "extraterrestrial" cause.

(Continued)

CHRONOLOGY	NOTEWORTHY PEOPLE	EVENTS AND DISCOVERIES
120	Claudius Ptolemy {Ptolemaeus} [Πτολεμαῖος] (90–168)	Geographic recordings of a significant part of the Islamic and western world (i.e., Roman and Persian Empire), living in Egypt, as a Roman with Greek education. His cartography extended all the way out, including parts of China (discovered in fifteenth century). He specifically developed arithmetical techniques for calculating astronomical phenomena, under the teachings of Babylonian astronomers. Also known as: بطليمــــوس (Batlaymus; Arabic). Combining the cartography wih the ancient Chinese knowledge of the earth's magnetic field formed early recording of the location of the North and South pole, however rudimentary, only a portion of the earth had been mapped. Later documentation with a detailed world map provided an indication of the migration of the magnetic poles.
500	Varahamihira (505–587) [Devanagari: वराहमिहिर]	Detailed meteorological discourse describing atmospheric events: "Brihatsamhita."
600	Isidore de Seville (560–636)	Description of rainbows, clouds, wind, and rain.
850	Al-Kindi (Alkindus) [Abu Yūsuf Yaʻqūb ibn ʼIshāq as-Sabbāh al-Kindī (Arabic: أبـو يعقــوب يوسـف بـن ,الكنــدي الصبّاح إسـحاق] (801–873)	Description of flow of natural media and a misconceived interpretation that the tides in the oceans are caused as the result of temperature effects, which does apply to the flow of air.
1021	Ibn al-Haytham (Alhazen) [Abū ʻAlī al-Hasan ibn al-Hasan ibn al-Haytham (Arabic: أبـو علـي، الحسـن بـن الحسـن بـن الهيثـــم] (965–1040)	Description of the refraction of light during sunset and sunrise causing the discoloration of the sky. Alhazen uses geometry and his refraction theory to calculate the height of "earth's atmosphere," yielding approximately 80 km, which is close to the currently accepted average altitude of the mesosphere of 80 km.
1027	Avicenna [Arabic: أبـو علـي الحســـين ابـن عبـد الله ابـن ســينا] (ca. 980–1037)	In his *Book of Healing* there is a description of meteorology, how mountains influence the formation of clouds and weather conditions. Additional information about earthquakes and description of a meteor.
1050		Full-scale use of the compass for geographical orientation.
1121	Abu Jafar Muhammad ibn Hasan Khazini (900–971)	Study of the hydrostatic balance.
ca. 1240	Albert the Great (1193–1290)	Description of the refraction of light by an individual raindrop, hence deriving that the rainbow must be produced by little drops of air in the sky.

(Continued)

CHRONOLOGY	NOTEWORTHY PEOPLE	EVENTS AND DISCOVERIES
1269	Petrus Peregrinus of Maricourt	Formal description of the use of the compass during seafaring expeditions.
1441	Prince Munjong of Josen (1414–1452)	Description of the introduction and use of a standardized rain gauge in Korea. The rain gauge served as a tool to estimate the cross yield and from this the tax base was determined.
1450	Leone Battista Alberti (1404–1472)	First conceptual anemometer, the swinging plate wind velocity meter.
1450	Nicolas Cryfts (Nicolas of Cusa) (1401–1464)	Design and experimental verification of the hair hygrometer for the measurement of the humidity. This design is still used, next to other new technology.
1494	Christopher Columbus (1451–1506)	Description of the first experience with a cyclone; encounters with hurricane on the shores of the "Americas."
1500	Leonardo da Vinci (1452–1519)	The preverbal "Renaissance man," involved in all aspects of cultural evolution, science, engineering, politics, and art. Drawing of the design of the first hair hygrometer in his *da Vinci's Codex Atlanticus*. The design was created and tested in 1450 by Nicolas Cryfts (Nicolas of Cusa) (1401–1464).
1543	Nicolaus Copernicus (1473–1543); alias of Niclas Koppernigk	Introduction of the heliocentric model for the earth, sun, and close planets. This follows the statement by the astronomer form Greece: Aristarchus of Samos (ca. 310–ca. 230 BC), made more than 1700 years prior. The scientific observations made by Copernicus were validated by Tycho Brahe (1546–1601) and Johannes Kepler (1571–1630).
1590	Francis Bacon, 1st Viscount of St. Alban (1561–1626)	Regulate the general scientific methodology.
ca. 1600	William Gilbert (1544–1603)	Experimentalist. Description of magnetism, in his work *De magnete, magnetisque corporibus, et de magno magnete tellure*. The compass had been in use since 206 BC (Chinese Han Dynasty: 206 BC–220 AD; maybe even earlier, during the Qin Dynasty: 221 BC–207 BC), in the European and Persian area since the thirteenth century.
ca. 1600	Galileo Galilei (1564-1642)	Major contributor to the scientific revolution and the (re) introduction of analytical thinking in science, engineering, and general thought processes. Galileo Galilei was remanded under house arrest by the Roman Inquisition for his views and teachings where he died after 9 years. This was the trailing end of the Renaissance period.
1611	Johannes Kepler (1571–1630)	Description of the "snow-flake."

(Continued)

CHRONOLOGY	NOTEWORTHY PEOPLE	EVENTS AND DISCOVERIES
1614	René Descartes (1596–1650)	Introduction to vortex motion. Introduction of the concept of general corpuscular motion, extending from small (maybe referring to the undefined atom), to planetary orbits. Vortices are found in geological phenomena such as cyclones (hurricanes), maelstrom, and aspects of magma flow.
1632	Evangelista Torricelli (1608–1647)	Introduction of the barometer; essential in weather prediction; meteorology.
1650	Blaise Pascal (1623–1662)	Pascal's law, pressure in a container applies an equal force on all surface of the enclosure. The unit for pressure under atmospheric conditions uses the unit Pascal in his honor.
1660	Robert Boyle (1627–1691)	Gas laws, definition of the behavior or gases. Boyle mentioned the compression of gas relating to partial pressure of atmospheric constituents and barometric values.
1662	Sir Christopher Wren (1632–1723)	First documented use of rain gauge.
1679	Denis Papin (1647–ca. 1712)	Pressure and thermodynamic and mechanical impacts. Denis Papin worked as an assistant to both Christiaan Huygens (1629–1695) and Robert Boyle (1627–1691). His invention of the pressure cooker bears some resemblance to the conditions found in geysers.
1680	Robert Hooke (1635–1703)	Force applied by a compressed spring.
1686	Edmund Halley (1656–1742)	Study of the cause-and-effect relationship between solar heating and the occurrence of monsoon and trade winds. This work ties to the atmospheric motion. Edmund Halley also described the relationship he found between the measured atmospheric pressure and the observation altitude with respect to the sea level.
ca. 1687	Sir Isaac Newton (1643–1727)	The recognition of gravitational force provided one of the essential building blocks in the geological understanding next to cartography and the physical description of location-specific meteorologic phenomena.
1750–1800		With the advent of more sophisticated measurement instrumentation (thermometer, barometer, wind velocity meter) meteorology became more scientifically rooted, especially with the interest of a broad range of mathematicians in the dynamics of physics; thermodynamics, motion, wave propagation, and pressure perturbations. The methodology for cartography and for geographic orientation (compass) also had evolved significantly.

(*Continued*)

CHRONOLOGY	NOTEWORTHY PEOPLE	EVENTS AND DISCOVERIES
1732	Anders Celsius (1701–1744)	Thermometer-scale calibration based on pure water phases.
1733	Daniel Bernoulli (1700–1782)	Acoustics, mechanical vibrations, and fluid dynamic principles introduced. Definition of the fundamental frequency and higher harmonics, with supporting elaborate mathematical analysis (solutions to differential equations). This laid the foundation for seismic imaging using P-wave (primary wave; longitudinal) and S-wave (secondary wave, or shear wave [transverse]).
1735	Daniel Gabriel Fahrenheit (1686–1736)	Temperature scale in Fahrenheit based on body temperature and saltwater phases.
1743	Jean-Baptiste le Rond d'Alembert (1717–1783)	Publication on the concepts of forces and accelerating systems: *Traite de Dynamique*.
1749	Alexander White (1714–1786) and Thomas Meville (seventeenth century)	Atmospheric data collection by means of weather balloons, replacing the use of kites.
1752	Benjamin Franklin (1706–1790)	Kite experiment and the documentation of "electric current" associated with lightning bolts.
1780	Charles Theodore, Prince-Elector, Count Palatine and Duke of Bavaria (1724–1799)	Introduction of an international network of meteorologic observation stations: *Societas Meteorologica Palatina*.
1781	Charles-Augustin de Coulomb (1736–1806)	Definition of the electric field related to electric charge. The electric charge itself was still an elusive concept in those days. The meteorological implications extend out to the influence of lightning on the environmental conditions: specifically the formation of ozone.
1783	Antoine Laurent de Lavoisier (1743–1794)	Discovery of oxygen and the chemical impact.
1785	Jacques Alexandre César Charles (1746–1823)	Charles's law, expansion of gases.
1802	Luke Howard (1772–1864)	Introduction of the nomenclature for cloud formations.
1802	Joseph Louis Gay-Lussac (1778–1850)	Ideal gas law; building on the work by Robert Boyle (1627–1691), more than a century earlier.
1822	Jean-Baptiste Joseph Fourier (1768–1830)	Introduction of the use of dimensions in mathematical solution and definition of physical quantities.

(Continued)

CHRONOLOGY	NOTEWORTHY PEOPLE	EVENTS AND DISCOVERIES
1824	Nicolas Léonard Sadi Carnot (1796–1832)	Introduction to the second law of thermodynamics, with heat exchange implications providing explanation to natural phenomena.
1827	Robert Brown (1773–1858)	Brownian motion.
1835	Gaspard-Gustave de Coriolis (1792–1843)	Influence of the earth's rotation on the flow movement and direction: Coriolis force.
1840	Jean Léonard Marie Poiseuille (1799–1869) and Gotthilf Heinrich Ludwig Hagen (1797–1884)	Pressure drop for incompressible fluids with respect to laminar flow. Reference to meteorology, wind formation based on arctic versus topical pressure systems.
1843–1848	James Prescott Joule (1818–1889)	Empirical verification of the first law of thermodynamics: stating the equivalence of heat and work. This applies to both the source energy for the persisting liquid core (magma) and the work performed by volcanic eruptions and earthquakes.
1848	William Thomson, 1st Baron Kelvin (i.e., Lord Kelvin) (1824–1907)	Absolute temperature scale: Kelvin. Reference base for geological events and meteorology.
1850	Rudolf Julius Emanuel Clausius (1822–1888)	Recognition of two basic principles of thermodynamics, later introduced by means of the first and second law of thermodynamics, respectively: energy is constant and entropy tends toward a maximum. Clausius introduced the parameter U, representing the internal energy. Publication of book *On the Motive Power of Heat, and on the Laws Which Can Be Deduced from It for the Theory of Heat*. Clausius introduced what is now regarded the second law of thermodynamics in 1865 (referred to by William John Macquorn Rankine [1820–1872] as the "thermodynamic function"), as part of any natural thermodynamic process, the sum of the entropies of the participating systems will increase. The heat exchange applies directly to solar heating and the formation of weather (and environmental) conditions.
1851	Jean Bernard Léon Foucault (1819–1868)	Foucault pendulum, illustrating the impact of the earth's rotation on motion.
1851	Sir George Gabriel Stokes, 1st Baronet (1819–1903)	Creeping flow, partially applicable to air stream Furthermore, the work of Stokes contributed to the development of the scientific and engineering support for the construction of high-rise buildings in earthquake-prone geographical regions.

(Continued)

CHRONOLOGY	NOTEWORTHY PEOPLE	EVENTS AND DISCOVERIES
1852	James Prescott Joule (1818–1889) and William Thomson, 1st Baron Kelvin {Lord Kelvin} (1824–1907)	Joule–Thomson effect: rapidly expanding gas leads to a reduction in the temperature of the gas, even offering the potential for a phase change to solid, or liquid. Sometimes also found as the Joule–Kelvin effect. Cloud formation and the release of rain and snow fall under this topic. The Joule–Thomson effect is an isenthalpic process, which entails that the enthalpy of the fluid is constant during the process, which applies to Joule–Thomson inversion temperature, described in the Linde cycle (Carl von Linde [1842–1934]), offering conditions leading to cloud formation.
1859	James Clerk Maxwell (1831–1879)	Description of the distribution law of molecular velocities; also applies to atmospheric conditions.
1868	William Thomson, 1st Baron Kelvin (i.e., Lord Kelvin) (1824–1907) and Hermann Ludwig Ferdinand von Helmholtz (1821–1894)	Kelvin–Helmholtz wave phenomenon (Kelvin–Helmholtz instability), resulting from a velocity shear in a moving single continuous fluid or at the interface between two fluids. The two fluids may be the same medium at different temperature and hence different respective density. Described separately by Lord Kelvin (1871) and Hermann von Helmholtz (1868). This phenomenon is most clearly observable for rolling cloud formations, but is also experienced in deep water (ocean), the corona of the sun, and applies to Jupiter's "red spot."
1873	James Clerk Maxwell (1831–1879)	Theory of electromagnetic radiation: *Treatise on Electricity and Magnetism*. James Maxwell made use of the prior work by Wilhelm Eduard Weber (1804–1891) and Johann Carl Friedrich Gauss {Gauß} (1777–1855). Solar radiation heats the earth's surface causing gradients in temperature or discontinuities resulting in the movement of air masses, next to local temperature sensation.
1876	Josiah Willard Gibbs (1839–1903)	Chemical potential, an energy constituent within the Gibbs free energy, setting the standard for the energy content and exchange with respect to phase transitions. Thermodynamic concept describing the energy that can be released or absorbed during a chemical process.
1900	Ludwig Eduard Boltzmann (1844–1906)	Thermodynamic concepts with respect to heat exchange in the earth's volume, specifically defining the entropy. Boltzmann equation for statistical mechanics, introduced by Ludwig Boltzmann between 1872 and 1875, reformulated by Max Karl Ernst Ludwig Planck (1858–1947). For certain systems also addressed as the Gibbs entropy formula, after Josiah Willard Gibbs (1839–1903).
1902	Philippe Teisserenc de Bort (1855–1913)	Description of several of the earth's atmospheric layers: stratosphere, tropopause, and troposphere. Additional credit for the outline of the lower part of the atmosphere goes to Richard Assmann (1845–1918).

(Continued)

CHRONOLOGY	NOTEWORTHY PEOPLE	EVENTS AND DISCOVERIES
1903	Vagn Walfrid Ekman (1874–1954)	Discovery of layered structure of the ocean waters, in similar arrangement as the earth's atmosphere.
1904	Vilhelm Friman Koren Bjerknes (1862–1951)	Introduction of the mathematical modeling requirements for weather prediction.
1905	Albert Einstein (1879–1955)	Recognition and description of the mesosphere.
1912	Theodore von Kármán (1881–1963)	Description of the "von Kármán vortex street." Turbulent flow profile, first observed and described by Arnulph Henry Reginald Mallock (1851–1933) and also by Henri Claude Bénard, (1874–1939)
1917	Sir Horace Lamb (1849–1934)	Introduction of the concept of evanescent waves, referred to as Lamb waves. Elastic waves traveling between two superimposed layers: inversion surface, a third layer forcing itself between the two stacked layers. The resulting compression and extension provides a line pattern of cloud formation, formed in the low-pressure parts of the wave pattern; expanding air forms condensation. Also known as "morning glories."
1922	Jacob Aall Bonnevie Bjerknes (1897–1975), Vilhelm Friman Koren Bjerknes (1862–1951), Halvor Skappel Solberg (1895–1974) and Tor Bergeron (1891–1977)	Formulation of pressure fronts and the general movement of air masses.
1926	John Patterson (1872–1956)	Three cup anemometer, improvement on the work of Leone Battista Alberti (1404–1472).
1938	Guy Stewart Callendar (1898–1964)	Description of the concept of global warming resulting from the insulating layer of carbon diode exhaust in the atmosphere.
1941		Introduction of "pulse radar" used for the localization and determination of the geographical extend of precipitation.
1960		Launch of the first weather satellite.
1971	Tetsuya Theodore "Ted" Fujita [藤田 哲也] (1920–1998)	Introduction of the Fujita scale to quantify the magnitude of tornadoes, cyclones, hurricanes, and typhoons.
1994	Andreas Pflitsch (1958–)	Sonic anemometer.
1995	Roger Lee Easton (1921–2014)	Development of the global positioning concept (GPS).

Nuclear

CHRONOLOGY	NOTEWORTHY PEOPLE	EVENTS AND DISCOVERIES
13.8 billion years BC	Georges Henri Joseph Édouard Lemaître (1894–1966) and Edwin Powell Hubble (1889–1953)	"The Big Bang"; In 1927 the expanding universe was recognized.
350 BC	Aristotle (384 BC–322 BC)	The word "energy" has the Greek origin "Enérgeia" [Greek: ἐνέργεια], which was documented by Aristotle, "enérgeia" does not translation directly into English, the meaning resembles "being at work."
ca. 1800	John Dalton (1766–1844)	Introduction of the "law of multiple proportions" describing the atomic concept based on chemical reactions taking place in ratios of small whole numbers.
1870	Hermann Ludwig Ferdinand von Helmholtz (1821–1894)	Unofficial introduction to the mechanism of action for nuclear fusion.
1896	Wilhelm Conrad Röntgen (1845–1923)	Discovery of X-ray radiation.
1896	Henri Becquerel (1852–1908)	Emission of "Becquerel rays" from uranium salts, later identified as alpha particles. Becquerel already recognized that this emission was different from X-ray since it was deflected by means of an applied external magnetic field. Conceptual introduction to the field of radioactivity.
1897	Joseph John Thomson (1856–1940)	Discovery of the electron; using William Crookes's vacuum tube.
1897	Marie Skłodowska-Curie (1867–1934)	Discovery of radioactive isotopes. Marie Curie introduced the term "radioactivity."
1899	Ernest Rutherford (1871–1937), 1st Baron Rutherford of Nelson, Lord Rutherford of Nelson	Emission of alpha particle.
1900	Max Karl Ernst Ludwig Planck (1858–1947) and James Clerk Maxwell (1831–1879)	Formal description of the photon and the energy associated with the electromagnetic wave.
1903	Ernest Rutherford (1871–1937), 1st Baron Rutherford of Nelson, Lord Rutherford of Nelson	Discovery of the nuclear decay half-life.
1903	Marie Skłodowska-Curie (1867–1934) and Ernest Rutherford (1871–1937), 1st Baron Rutherford of Nelson, Lord Rutherford of Nelson	Quantification of nuclear decay.

(Continued)

CHRONOLOGY	NOTEWORTHY PEOPLE	EVENTS AND DISCOVERIES
1906	Dmitri Ivanovich Mendeleev (1834–1907)	Periodic Table of Elements.
1908	Johannes Geiger (1822–1945) and Ernest Rutherford (1871–1937)	Development of the Geiger counter, used to measure radioactive radiation.
1909	Francis Aston (1877–1945)	Mass spectrometer mass separation of closely separated isotopes. Highly sensitive mass spectrometer design.
1911	Ernest Rutherford (1871–1937), 1st Baron Rutherford of Nelson, Lord Rutherford of Nelson	Rutherford scattering on nuclear level, indication of the existence of the proton. The proton itself was not mentioned until 1932, this time again by Ernest Rutherford.
1913	Niels Henrik David Bohr (1885–1962)	Bohr atomic model.
1913	Frederick Soddy (1877–1956)	Formal introduction of the isotope concept.
1914	Niels Henrik David Bohr (1885–1962)	Description of the atomic energy layer model; hydrogen (Bohr atomic model).
1915	Sir Ernest Marsden (1889–1970)	Artificial transmutation, associated with radon enclosed by vacuum.
1918	Paul Scherrer (1890–1969)	X-ray diffraction, crystal structure. Nuclear energy development. Established the CERN institute in Switzerland as one of the founders. Directed the construction of the first cyclotron in 1940.
1919	Ernest Rutherford (1871–1937)	Artificial transmutation, hydrogen formation resulting from collisions of alpha particles with nitrogen, also generating oxygen and gamma rays.
1923	Arthur Holly Compton (1892–1962)	Description of the deflection of photons by a charge unit, generally an electron, potentially the nucleus: Compton effect.
~1925		Recognition of the "Coulomb barrier" in nuclear collision, providing a "tunneling" effect for the release of alpha particles.
1927	Werner Karl Heisenberg (1901–1976)	Quantum uncertainty principle.
1927	Paul Adrien Maurice Dirac (1902–1984)	Description of antimatter.
1928	Johannes Geiger (1822–1945) and Walther Müller (1905–1979)	Introduction of an improved Geiger counter: the Geiger–Müller counter, using ionization of a confined gas.
1931	Wolfgang Ernst Pauli (1900–1958)	Theoretical introduction of the neutrino. The experimental verification of the existence of the neutrino was not until 1956 by Frederick Reines (1918–1998) and Clyde Cowan, Jr. (1919–1974).

(Continued)

CHRONOLOGY	NOTEWORTHY PEOPLE	EVENTS AND DISCOVERIES
1931	Carl David Anderson (1905–1991)	Discovery of the positron, antiparticle for the electron. The "positron" was predicted by Paul Adrien Maurice Dirac (1902–1984) in 1929.
1932	Sir James Chadwick (1891–1974)	Discovery of the neutron. Student of Ernest Rutherford (1871–1937).
1934	Leo Szilard (1898–1964)	Recognition of nuclear decay chain reactions.
1934	Hideki Yukawa [湯川 秀樹], (1907–1981)	Introduction of mesons and the concept of antimatter.
1934	Ida Noddack (1896–1978)	Formal introduction of the concept of "fission," however not recognized by her peers at the time. The fission phenomenon was only recognized when announced by Enrico Fermi (1901–1954) later that year.
1934	Enrico Fermi (1901–1954)	Interaction of slow neutron with nuclei and the resulting decay into different elements, including aluminum and uranium.
1935	Arthur Dempster (1886–1950)	Discovery of the lighter uranium isotope: uranium-235.
1936	Otto Hahn (1879–1968) and Lise Meitner (1878–1968)	Neutron collision of uranium-induced decay examination.
1937	Carl David Anderson (1905–1991), Seth Henry Neddermeyer (1907–1988), Jabez Curry Street (1906–1989), and Edward C. Stevenson ()	Confirmation of the existence of the meson, and muon.
1938	Niels Henrik David Bohr (1885–1962) and John Archibald Wheeler (1911–2008)	Formal description of the nuclear fission process.
1939	J. M. B. Kellogg	Discovery of a finite quadruple moment for the deuteron, requiring a noncentral (tensor) nuclear force configuration.
1940	Otto Robert Frisch (1904–1979)	Development of the detonation mechanism for the first atomic bomb.
1940+	Julius Robert Oppenheimer (1904–1967)	Manhattan project: fission reaction. Prominent members: Arthur Compton (1892–1962), Enrico Fermi (1901–1954), Eugene Wigner (1902–1995), and dozens more.
1947	George Dixon Rochester (1908–2001), Clifford Charles Butler (1922–1999)	Discovery of the subatomic particle: the "kaon," k-meson. Introduction of the "strangeness" concept for quarks, although the quark concept had not been introduced. In the elementary particle phenomology the kaon is a bound state of an up- or down quark with a strange quark (antiquark).

(Continued)

CHRONOLOGY	NOTEWORTHY PEOPLE	EVENTS AND DISCOVERIES
1947	Maria Goeppert-Mayer (Göppert) (1906–1972)	Theoretical concept development for the understanding of nuclear forces, based on a shell model, similar to the atomic electron model.
1947	William Webster Hansen (1909–1949)	Linear accelerator installation at Stanford University, California.
1950	Maria Goeppert-Mayer (Göppert) (1906–1972)	Introduction of the nuclear shell model for atomic nuclei.
ca. 1952	Ludwig von Helmholtz (1821–1894), Lyman Strong Spitzer, Jr. (1914–1997), and Ronald Richter (1909–1991) and Edward Teller (1908–2003)	Nuclear fusion investigation and start of experimentation. The process was in principle described by Hermann Ludwig Ferdinand von Helmholtz (1821–1894), but is continuously in action at the sun's surface.
1955	Obninsk Nuclear Power Station, Russia	First nuclear power station for energy generation.
1956	Frederick Reines (1918–1998) and Clyde Lorrain Cowan, Jr. (1919–1974)	Experimental confirmation of the neutrino introduced in 1931 by Wolfgang Pauli (1900–1958).
1958	Stanley Mandelstam (1928–2016)	Introduction of Mandelstam variables associated with the concept of "crossing symmetry," defining numerical quantities, which encode the energy, momentum, and scattering angles of particles in a deflection process described in a Lorentz-invariant fashion.
1958	Lev Davidovich Landau [Russian: Лёв Дави́дович Ланда́у] (1908–1968), Arkady Beynusovich Migdal [Russian: Арка́дий Бе́йнусович (Бенеди́ктович) Мигда́л] (1911–1991)	Theory of interacting electrons, specifically with respect to solids; condensed matter physics.
1961	Murray Gell-Mann (1929–)	Description of elementary particles, eightfold way of defining "strangeness" for the quark. Formal introduction of the elementary particle "quark" concept, the building blocks for protons and neutrons. The "quark" name is based on an expression in the book *Finnegans Wake* by James Joyce.
1964	Charles Hard Townes (1915–2015), Nikolay Gennadiyevich Basov [Никола́й Генна́диевич Ба́сов] (1922–2001) and Aleksandr Mikhailovich Prokhorov [Алекса́ндр Миха́йлович Про́хоров] (1916–2002)	Quantum electronics.

(Continued)

CHRONOLOGY	NOTEWORTHY PEOPLE	EVENTS AND DISCOVERIES
1970	Sheldon Lee Glashow (1932–), John Iliopoulos (1940–), and Luciano Maiani (1941–)	Introduction of the charm quark.
1974	Burton Richter (1931–) and Samuel Chao Chung Ting [Chinese: 丁肇中] (1936–)	Description of charm for the quark.
1975	Martin Lewis Perl (1927–2014)	Discovery of the tau lepton.
1977	Leon Max Ledderman (1922–)	Discovery of the "beauty" and "bottom" designation for quarks.
1978		Discovery of the "gluon" with the assistance of the PLUTO, the first electromagnetic superconductive solenoid located in Hamburg, Germany.
1983	Collider Detector at Fermilab	World's first and at the time highest-energy particle accelerator, colliding antiprotons and protons propelled to center-of-mass energy reaching 2 TeV.
1995	Wolfgang Ketterle (1957–), Eric Allin Cornell (1961–), and Carl Edwin Wieman (1951–)	Experimental verification of Bose–Einstein condensation.
2012	François Baron Englert (1932–) and Peter Ware Higgs (1929–)	Higgs boson (126 GeV) discovery in the Large Hadron Collider at CERN, Geneva, Switzerland. The Large Hadron Collider construction started in 1998 and produces particle acceleration with respective energy levels for protons at up to 4 teraelectronvolts (0.64 microjoules), or lead nuclei: 2.76 TeV per nucleon or 574 TeV per nucleus. The proton energy level was increased to 6.5 TeV in 2015.

Optics

CHRONOLOGY	NOTEWORTHY PEOPLE	EVENTS AND DISCOVERIES
~300 BC	Euclid (of Alexandria) (323 BC–283 BC)	Description that light travels in straight lines and defines his version of the law of reflection in his publication: *Optica*. Euclid was a proponent of "extramission for vision; believed that vision involves rays going from the eyes to the object observed. Euclid also described the relationship between the apparent sizes of objects and the angles with the optical axis of the eye: angular magnification.
~150 BC–100 BC	Hero (also known as Heron) of Alexandria (10–70)	Hero showed, by a geometrical means, how the actual path outlined by a ray of light reflected from a plane mirror is shorter than any respective other path resulting from reflected that might be drawn between the source and the chosen point of observation, publication *Catoptrica*.

(Continued)

CHRONOLOGY	NOTEWORTHY PEOPLE	EVENTS AND DISCOVERIES
~140 AD	Claudius Ptolemy (ca. 100–ca. 168)	In a translation from an Arabic publication assumed to be by Ptolemy in the twelfth century into Latin Ptolemy presents a study of refraction, which continuous to describe the phenomena of atmospheric refraction. He suggested that the angle of refraction at the interface of two media is proportional to the angle of incidence.
1021	Abū ʿAlī al-Ḥasan ibn al-Ḥasan ibn al-Haytham [Arabic: الحسـن بـن الحسـن، علـي أبـو الهيثـم بـن], Alhazen (ca. 965–1040)	First documented recognition of the refraction mechanism of action. In his investigations, Alhazen used spherical and parabolic mirrors and was aware of spherical aberration. He also investigated the magnification produced by lenses and atmospheric refraction. His work was translated into Latin and became accessible to later European scholars. Publication: "Risala fi l-Daw" (*Treatise on Light*) as a supplement to his *Book of Optics*. He discusses the meteorology of the rainbow, the density of the atmosphere, and various celestial phenomena, including the eclipse, twilight, and moonlight.
1088	Shen Kuo or Shen Gua [Chinese: 沈括] (1031–1095)	In his Dream Pool Essays (梦溪笔谈) a vivid descriptions of tornadoes, that rainbows were formed by the shadow of the sun in rain, occurring when the sun would shine upon it, and the curious common phenomena of the effect of lightning that, when striking a house, would merely scorch the walls a bit but completely melt to liquid all metal objects inside.
~1220	Robert Grosseteste (1175–1253)	Magister scholarum of the University of Oxford and a proponent of the view that theory should be compared with observation, Grosseteste considered that the properties of light have particular significance in natural philosophy and stressed the importance of mathematics and geometry in their study. He believed that colors are related to intensity and that they extend from white to black, white being the purest and lying beyond red with black lying below blue. The rainbow was conjectured to be a consequence of reflection and refraction of sunlight by layers in a "watery cloud" but the effect of individual droplets was not considered. He held the view, shared by the earlier Greeks, that vision involves emanations from the eye to the object perceived.
ca. 1240	Albert the Great (1193–1290)	Description of the refraction of light by an individual raindrop, hence deriving that the rainbow must be produced by little drops of air in the sky.

(*Continued*)

CHRONOLOGY	NOTEWORTHY PEOPLE	EVENTS AND DISCOVERIES
~1267	Roger Bacon (1214–1294)	Roger Bacon was a follower of Robert Grosseteste (1175–1253) at Oxford. Bacon elaborated on Grosseteste's work on optics. He concluded that the speed of light is finite and its propagation is similar to the propagation of sound. In his publication *Opus Maius*, Bacon provides a description of the magnification of small objects by means of rudimentary convex lenses and suggested that the use of external lenses could find application in the correcting defective eyesight. He also recognized the formation of the rainbow due to "reflection" of sunlight from (within) individual raindrops.
~1270	Witelo (ca. 1220–ca. 1278)	Compilation of a standard text on optics: *Perspectiva*, to be used for several centuries. Witelo published a method of machining parabolic mirrors from iron. Witelo also performed and documented observations on refraction. He recognized that the angle of refraction is not equal to the angle of incidence, however he did not report any observation of total internal reflection.
1303	Bernard de Gordon (1270–1330)	A physician, he mentioned the use of spectacles as a way of correcting far-sightedness (hyperopia).
1304–1310	Theodoric (Dietrich) of Freiberg (1250–1310)	Theodoric explained the formation of a rainbow as the result of refraction and internal reflection within individual raindrops. He provided a detailed explanation for the appearance of a primary and secondary rainbow but, following earlier established belief and scientific interpretations, he considered color to rise from a combination of different proportions of darkness and brightness.
1558	Giambattista della Porta (1535–1615)	Incorporation of a lens in the opening of a camera obscura significantly improved the image formation capabilities.
~1590	Zacharius Janssen (1585–1632)	Constructed a compound microscope with a converging objective lens and a diverging eye lens.
1604	Johannes Kepler (1571–1630)	Suggestion that the radiant intensity (radiance) of light from a point source varies inversely with the square of the distance from the source in his book *Ad Vitellionem Paralipomena*. Introduction of the notion that light can be propagated over an unlimited distance and that the velocity of light propagation is supposedly infinite. Kepler also described vision as a consequence of the formation of an image on the retina resulting from light passing through the lens in the eye, and additionally correctly described the causes of "far-sightedness" (hyperopia) and "near-sightedness" (presbyopia).

(*Continued*)

CHRONOLOGY	NOTEWORTHY PEOPLE	EVENTS AND DISCOVERIES
1604	Johannes Kepler (1571–1630)	Formal introduction of the term "camera obscura."
1608	Hans Lippershey (1570–1619)	Construction of a telescope based on a converging objective lens and a diverging ocular lens configuration.
1609	Galileo Galilei (1564–1642)	Constructed his own version of the telescope design introduced by Hans Lippershey (1570–1619) and used it for astronomical observations.
1610	Galileo Galilei (1564–1642)	Using his telescope, Galileo reported a broad scale of astronomical discoveries including the four (4) moons of Jupiter.
1611	Giovanni Demisiani (?–1614)	Introduced the term "telescope" for his optical device with three times (3X) magnification.
1611	Johannes Kepler (1571–1630)	Kepler presents the lens principles involved in the convergent, respectively, divergent properties applied to microscopes and telescopes in his publication *Dioptrice*. Based on this publication the "power" of a lens is expressed in diopters. In the same treatise, Johannes Kepler proposes the construction of a telescope using a converging objective and a converging ocular lens. This concept of the combination of lenses is still known as the telephoto lens. He also described the process and conditions of total internal reflection, but was unable to find a suitable mathematical relationship between the angle of incidence and the angle of refraction. Willebrord Snel (1591–1626) resolved this issue in 1621.
~1618	Christopher Scheiner (1573–1650)	Constructed a telescope of the type suggested by Johannes Kepler (1571–1630) with converging objective and eye lenses. This type of telescope has since become known as the "astronomical telescope". So far no exact date for the construction of the first instrument of this design.
1621	Willebrord Snel (Snellius) van Royen (1591–1626)	Description of the relationship between the angle of incidence and angle of refraction at the interface when light passes from one transparent medium to another: Snell's law.
1647	Bonaventura Francesco Cavalieri (1598–1647)	Derivation of the relationship between the radii of curvature for the respective two surfaces of a thin lens and the resulting focal length.
1657	Pierre de Fermat (1601–1665)	Introduction of the "mathematical" principle of "least time." Based on this, a ray of light follows the path which takes the least amount of time to its destination. This shortest time path-length principle is consistent with Snell's law of refraction.

(Continued)

CHRONOLOGY	NOTEWORTHY PEOPLE	EVENTS AND DISCOVERIES
1663	James Gregory (1638–1675)	Suggested the use of a converging mirror to be used as the objective of a telescope to mitigate for color aberrations, in his 1663 publication *Optica Promota*; design of the "Gregorian reflecting telescope." The Gregorian reflecting telescope was firts build by Robert Hooke (1635–1703) in 1668.
1665	Francesco Maria Grimaldi (1618–1663)	Grimaldi's observations of diffraction in the publication *Physico-Mathesis de lumine, coloribus et iride* (published posthumously). These were his observations regarding the passage of white light through small apertures. Grimaldi expressed his hypothesis that light is a fluid that exhibits wave-like motion.
1665	Robert Hooke (1635–1703)	Publication *Micrographia*, description of a compound microscope having both a converging objective lens and a converging ocular lens. In the same publication Hooke described his observations of the color displays produced in films of oil on water, flakes of mica, an in soap bubbles. He recognized that the color produced by light interaction with mica flakes is related to the thickness of the medium; however, he was unable to establish a specific relationship between thickness and obtained color. Hooke also advocated his own wave theory for the propagation of light.
1666	Sir Isaac Newton (1643–1727)	Description of the splitting up of white light into its spectral component colors when it passes through a prism.
1668	Robert Hooke (1635–1703)	Construction of the Gregorian reflecting telescope after the design by James Gregory (1638–1675) in 1663, using a reflecting converging mirror.
1668	Sir Isaac Newton (1643–1727)	Construction of the first reflecting telescope, in an attempt to compensate for chromatic aberration experienced by a refracting telescope.
1669	Rasmus Bartholinus (1625–1698)	Discovery of the double refraction in calcite.
1672	Sir Isaac Newton (1643–1727)	Documentation of the dispersion of sunlight passing through a prism. Newton concluded that the light emitted by the sun is composed of different colors, which are individually refracted by glass to different extents.
1676	Olaus (Ole) Christensen Rømer (Roemer) (1644–1710)	Deduced that the speed of light is finite based on his and his contemporary researchers' detailed observations of the eclipses of Jupiter's moons. From Rømer's data, a value of about 2×10^8 m.s^{-1} can be obtained.

(Continued)

CHRONOLOGY	NOTEWORTHY PEOPLE	EVENTS AND DISCOVERIES
1678	Christiaan Huygens (1629–1695)	Publication *Traite de Lumiere* in 1690, to the Academie des Science in Paris, introduction of the Huygens wave theory of light. He considered that light is transmitted through an aether, made up of small elastic particles, each of which can act as a secondary wave source based on the wave mechanism Huygens was able to explain the majority of the known propagation characteristics of light, including discovery by Bartholinus regarding the double refraction in calcite.
1704	Sir Isaac Newton (1643–1727)	In his publication *Opticks*, Newton presented his corpuscular view for light, but that the corpuscles are able to perform waves in the aether. The corpuscular nature of light was based on the fact that light travels in straight lines whereas waves can refract (bend) into the shadow region of the object.
1727	James Bradley (1693–1762)	Bradley calculated the speed of light based on observations of the "aberration" of light from stars while attempting to detect stellar parallax, relying on the apparent motion of a star associated with the to be determined value of the speed of light in relation to the speed of the earth in its solar orbit. Explanation of the projection path aberration of light emitted by stars by forming the vector sum of the orbital velocity of the earth "v" next to the free space velocity of light "c", and showed that the angle of aberration was a function of the ratio of these velocities: "v/c". Based on this formulation Bradley showed that the revolution of the earth around the sun correctly accounted for the observed cyclic change in the optical aberration of star light rays. In comparison, the anti-Copernicans, which were still around in large numbers in the first half of the eighteenth century, were unable to refute this explanation of the change. Bradley's work is the first of many instances that seemed to show (erroneously) that the value of the velocity of light depends on the motion of the observer.
1729/1733	Chester Moore Hall (1703–1771)	Construction of achromatic compound lenses using components consisting of glasses with different refractive indices. Construction of first refracting telescope that has chromatic aberration correction.
1752	Thomas Melvill (1726–1753)	Optical spectra imbedded in the light emission from flames, consisting of metals or salts; characteristic lines of representing the elements that define the constituents of the flame.

(Continued)

CHRONOLOGY	NOTEWORTHY PEOPLE	EVENTS AND DISCOVERIES
1801	Thomas Young (1773–1829)	Assisted in the development of the wave theory by demonstration of the interference properties of light.
1802	William Hyde Wollaston (1766–1828)	Discovery of the dark lines in the solar spectrum, but he was unable to interpret them in accordance with contemporary scientific knowledge.
1808	Étienne-Louis Malus (1775–1812)	Observed the light reflecting from the windows of the Palais Luxembourg in Paris through a calcite crystal as it was rotating, Malus uncovered an effect, which was later attributed to the polarization of light resulting from reflection.
1814	Joseph von Fraunhofer (1787–1826)	Rediscovery and description of the dark lines in the solar spectrum, originally noticed and documented by William Hyde Wollaston (1766–1828) in 1802 and determined the respective (not known at the time); "wavelength" locations with improved precision: Fraunhofer lines.
1815	Sir David Brewster (1781–1868)	Described the polarization direction for light resulting from reflection: Brewster angle.
1816	Augustin-Jean Fresnel (1788–1827)	Rigorous mathematical treatment of diffraction and interference phenomena illustrating that these phenomena can be explained based on a wave theory of light.
1816–1817	Augustin-Jean Fresnel (1788–1827) and Dominique François Jean Arago (1786–1853)	Interference of polarized light and the interpretation by Thomas Young (1773–1829), lead to the conclusion that light waves are transverse. Prior to this point in time the general assumption had been that electromagnetic radiation (light) has a longitudinal wave profile.
1819	Joseph von Fraunhofer (1787–1826)	Description of the diffraction of light by gratings. The gratings were initially made by winding rows of fine wires around screws lined up in parallel.
1821	Augustin-Jean Fresnel (1788–1827)	Presented the mathematical laws enabling the calculation of the radiant intensity (radiance) and direction of polarization for light reflected and refracted from an interface.
1823	Joseph von Fraunhofer (1787–1826)	Publication of the theory of diffraction.
1828	William Nicol (1770–1851)	Invention of the prism made from two calcite components, creating polarization of the transmitted light with respect to the two main axes: Nicol prism.

(Continued)

CHRONOLOGY	NOTEWORTHY PEOPLE	EVENTS AND DISCOVERIES
1834	John Scott Russell (1808–1882)	Observation of what is now referred to as a "solitary waves" and "wave of translation" based on his observations of a wave caused by a boat being drawn along the length of the Union Canal in Scotland. John Russell noticed how the wave travelled great distances without apparent change of shape. The study of solitary waves led to the solitons concept for optics, defining the light propagation in fiber-optics.
1835	George Biddell Airy (1801–1892)	Diffraction pattern produced by a circular aperture; associate resolution consequences: Airy disk.
1840	Carl Zeiss (1816–1888)	Lens fabrication initiated in Jena, Germany.
1845	Michael Faraday (1791–1867)	Rotation of the plane of polarization for light that is passed through glass exposed to a magnetic field: Faraday effect.
1847	Carl Zeiss (1816–1888)	Full-scale production of optical microscopes (Carl Zeiss AG, previously Carl Zeiss Jena).
1849	Armand Hypolite Louis Fizeau (1819–1896)	Speed of light measurement using a rotating toothed wheel to create an alternating pulsation of light beam. Fizeau made the first nonastronomical (nonvacuum) determination of the speed of light (in air), deriving a value of 313,300,000 $m.s^{-1}$. Note that the current accepted and verified speed of light in vacuum is 299,792,458 $m.s^{-1}$.
1849	Louis Pasteur (1822–1895)	Investigation of molecular asymmetry, joining his knowledge of crystallography, chemistry, and optics to obtain the optical polarization rotation. In specific, the reaction of tartaric acid derived by chemical synthesis under biological conditions or artificially. The reactions produce two mirror image molecules, with opposing effective rotated angle of polarization for the transmitted light: optical activity. The organic form of the product only has one rotation angle. Pasteur hence concluded that the molecule must ne asymmetric and can have two forms, resembling left versus right hand.
1850	Jean Bernard Léon Foucault (1819–1868)	Foucault determined the speed of light in atmospheric air using a rotating mirror method, deriving a value of 298,000,000 $m.s^{-1}$. In the same year, Foucault used the same rotating mirror method to determine the speed of light in stationary water and found it to be less than in air. In 1851 Léon Foucault also positioned a pendulum with a string length of 67 meter in Paris, France, to illustrate the rotation of the earth, providing an arc rotation of the swing path in clockwise direction by 11 degree per hour; full circle in 37.2 hours.

(Continued)

CHRONOLOGY	NOTEWORTHY PEOPLE	EVENTS AND DISCOVERIES
1855	David Alter (1807–1881)	Description of the spectrum of hydrogen and other gases.
1859	Armand Hippolyte Louis Fizeau (1819–1896)	Experimental observation that the velocity of light in water is affected by flow of the water, the incremental change in the velocity of light being about a half of the velocity of the flowing water.
1860	Robert Wilhelm Eberhard Bunsen (1811–1899) and Gustav Robert Kirchhoff (1824–1887)	Recordings of the emission spectra of alkali metals in flames. Recognition of dark lines in the spectrum arising from absorption when illuminated by a bright light source through the flame. These dark lines are identical to the spectral lines observed in the solar spectrum observed by William Hyde Wollaston (1766–1828) and Joseph von Fraunhofer (1787–1826) in 1803: Fraunhofer lines, and it was argued that these lines in the sunlight are due to the absorption of light by gases in the solar atmosphere that are cooler than those "emitting the light" (not much was known about the mechanism-of-action of the sun, based on contemporary knowledge an oxidizing gas produces light).
1865	James Clerk Maxwell (1831–1879)	Combining his insights in the studies of the equations describing electric and magnetic fields, he derived that the speed of an electromagnetic wave should, within experimental error, be identical to the speed of light. Maxwell concluded from this that light is electromagnetic wave energy.
1869	John Tyndall (1820–1893)	Experimental studies of the light scattering pattern produced by aerosols.
1871	John William Strutt, third Baron Rayleigh (1842–1919)	Introduction of a general law relating the radiance of light scattered from small particles as a function of the wavelength, for particle dimensions smaller than the wavelength: Rayleigh scattering. This stand in contrast to Mie scattering (Gustav Mie [1869–1957]), where the scattering dimensions are larger than the wavelength. He also constructed a "zone plate" which resulted in focusing of light by Fresnel diffraction.
1873	Ernst Karl Abbe (1840–1905)	Detailed theory of image formation under observation by means of the microscope, specifically the resolution: Abbe criterion.
1874	Jacobus Henricus van't Hoff (1852–1911) and Joseph Achille Le Bel (1847–1930)	Each independently observed the optical activity (rotated polarization angle of the transmitted light) for carbon compounds. They both derived that this can be explained by a four (4)-way bound carbon atom (chemical saturation).
1875	John Kerr (1824–1907)	Quadratic electro-optic effect in glass: Kerr effect.

(Continued)

CHRONOLOGY	NOTEWORTHY PEOPLE	EVENTS AND DISCOVERIES
1879	Josef Stefan (1825–1893)	Publication of an empirical relationship defining the total radiant energy emitted from the surface of a body per unit time to be proportional to the fourth power of the absolute temperature of that body.
	Sir Joseph Wilson Swan (1828–1914)	Demonstration of an incandescent light bulb with a carbon filament.
1879	Thomas Alvin Edison (1847–1931)	Development and sale of a working electric lamp using cotton as a carbon filament.
1882	Albert Abraham Michelson (1852–1931)	Michelson interferometer.
1885	Johann Jakob Balmer (1825–1898)	Definition of an empirical formula describing the wavelength position of the emission lines in the visible part of the hydrogen. Spectrum: Balmer series.
1887	Albert Abraham Michelson (1852–1931) and Edward William Morley (1838–1923)	Failure to verify the illusive concept of "luminiferous aether" (in fact, electromagnetic radiation does not require an "aether") by correlation of speed of light to the direction in which the light beam moves: the Michelson–Morley experiment.
1887	Heinrich Rudolf Hertz (1857–1894)	Discovery of the photoelectric effect, primarily by accident. Heinrich Hertz experimentally proved the electromagnetic wave concept, theoretically described by James Clerk Maxwell (1831–1879). Heinrich Hertz is a nephew of the Gustav Ludwig Hertz (1887–1975).
1890	Otto Heinrich Wiener (1862–1927)	Recognition of standing waves produced by light reflecting at normal incidence from a silver mirror. Nodes and antinodes in the standing electromagnetic wave were recorded photographically illustrating a node at the mirror surface, yielding the electric field to be zero (no electric field inside a conductor). From this it was derived that the electric component of the electromagnetic wave carries the more important effect, at least for this time of detection.
1891–1892	Ludwig Mach (1868–1951) and Ludwig Louis Albert Zehnder (1854–1949)	Description of the respective interferometer efforts of Ludwig Mach in 1892 and Ludwig Zehder in 1891 independently, what has become known as the Mach–Zehnder interferometer with the ability to monitor changes in refractive index, and inherent density, with respect to compressible gas flows. The Mach–Zehnder interferometer has found apropos applications in the field of aerodynamics. The optical path for the interferometer is governed by the Fermat principle (Pierre de Fermat [1601–1665]). Ludwig Mach is the son of Ernst Waldfried Josef Wenzel Mach (1838–1916).

(Continued)

CHRONOLOGY	NOTEWORTHY PEOPLE	EVENTS AND DISCOVERIES
1896	Wilhelm Carl Werner Otto Fritz Franz Wien (1864–1928)	Description of the spectral distribution (peak emission wavelength) of radiation from a black body as a function of the temperature of the body.
1896	Pieter Zeeman (1865–1943)	Observation of the broadening of the spectral lines emitted by an atomic source when the source is exposed to an external magnetic field.
1899	John William Strutt, the 3rd Baron Rayleigh (1842–1919)	Explanation of the principles for the blue color of the sky as well as the red sunsets resulting from preferential scattering angle as a function of wavelength for white light by molecules in the earth's atmosphere.
1899	Marie Paul Auguste Charles Fabry (1867–1945) and Charles Fabry and Alfred Pérot (1863–1925)	Description of the Fabry–Perot interferometer, enabling high-resolution observation of spectral features.
1900	Max Karl Ernst Ludwig Planck (1858–1947)	Successful explanation of the spectrum of radiation emitted from a heated black body. Planck introduced a universal constant in his proportionality equation as the "quantum of action," now known as Planck's constant. As a consequence the energy of an oscillator is the sum of small discrete units, each of which has a value that is proportional to the respective oscillation frequency.
1902	Woldemar Voigt (1850–1919)	Discovery of magnetic birefringence, or magnetic double refraction. The Voigt effect has several similarities to the Faraday effect.
1905	Albert Einstein (1879–1955)	Explanation of the photoelectric effect based on the assumption that light is quantized, these electromagnetic energy quanta become known as photons.
1908	Gustav Mie (1869–1957)	Presented a description of light scattering from particles that are not small compared to the wavelength of light, taking account of particle shape and the difference in refractive index between the particles and the supporting medium. This stand in contrast to Rayleigh scattering (John William Strutt, the 3rd Baron Rayleigh [1842–1919]), where the scattering dimensions are smaller than the wavelength.
1908	Walter Ritz (1878–1909)	Announcement of the combination principle for computing the frequencies of spectral lines.
1908	Louis Carl Heinrich Friedrich Paschen (1865–1947)	Experimental verification of the existence of a spectral series of hydrogen in the near infrared predicted by the Rydberg–Ritz relation.

(*Continued*)

CHRONOLOGY	NOTEWORTHY PEOPLE	EVENTS AND DISCOVERIES
1910–1912	Victor Franz Hess (1883–1964) and Werner Kol Hoerster (1887–1945)	Discovery of cosmic rays. Victor Franz Hess was awarded the Nobel Prize in Physics jointly with Carl David Anderson (1905–1991) in 1936.
1913	Neils Henrik David Bohr (1885–1962)	Atom model in which the electrons were presumed to occupy stable orbits demarcated by well-defined energy levels. This theory underwrites the quantum aspect of the absorption and emission of light by an atom resulting from the acceleration of an electron moving from one orbit to another orbit of different energy. This also provides an explanation of the absorption and emission at particular frequencies that are characteristic for that particular atomic energy configuration, depending on the element in question.
1915	William David Coolidge (1873–1975)	Patent on a method for creating tungsten electric lamp filaments.
1916	Albert Einstein (1879–1955)	Proposed stimulated emission of light process, complementing the standard absorption and spontaneous emission.
1919	Sir Arthur Stanley Eddington (1882–1944)	Observation of the solar eclipse on May 29 at Príncipe Island off the west coast of Africa. it was Eddington's intention to determining the apparent position of stars that are visible close to the sun's disk. From this he managed to conclude that the path of light from these stars is bent by the sun's gravitational field, conforming to the predictions of the theory of general relativity by Albert Einstein (1879–1955).
1926	Albert Abraham Michelson (1852–1931)	Determination of the speed of light by means of a rotating mirror with a light path from the observatory at Mount Wilson, Pasadena, California, spanning a distance of 35 km to a reflector on Mount San Antonio. Average value $c = 299,796,000 \ \mathrm{m.s^{-1}}$.
1927	Paul Adrien Maurice Dirac (1902–1984)	Presentation of electromagnetic radiation field in quantized form.
1928	Sir Chandrashekhara Venkata Râman (1888–1970)	Inelastic scattering of light from liquids, weak radiance line shifts. The effect arises from the scattering of light by vibrating molecules and is known as Raman scattering.
1932	Roy James Kennedy (1897–1973) and Edward Moulton Thorndike (1905–)	Experimentally attempted to detect the aether drift with a very stable and refined form of interferometer having arms of unequal length. Both the length and the time transformations of the special theory of relativity had to be used to account for the null result.

(Continued)

CHRONOLOGY	NOTEWORTHY PEOPLE	EVENTS AND DISCOVERIES
1932	Peter Joseph William Debye (1884–1966) with Francis Weston Sears (1898–1975) next to Réne Lucas (1898–1990) and Pierre Biquard (1901–1992)	Description of diffraction of electromagnetic radiation by ultrasonic waves; beginning of acousto-optics.
1932	Edwin Herbert Land (1909–1991)	Invention of the "polaroid" polarizing film.
1934	Frits Zernicke (1888–1966)	Description of the phase-contrast microscope.
1939	Walter H. Geffcken (1904–1995)	Description of the transmission interference filter.
1941	W. Canton Anderson ()	Measured the speed of light using a Kerr cell used to modulate a light beam passing through a Michelson interferometer. Obtained the value $c = 299,776,000$ m.s^{-1}. Note that the current accepted and verified speed of light in vacuum is 299 792 458 m.s^{-1}.
1947	Willis Eugene Lamb, Jr. (1913–2008) and Robert E. Retherford (1882–1939)	During the course of spectral measurements of the fine structure of hydrogen in the microwave region of electromagnetic radiation, made the observation of a small displacement (the "Lamb shift") of an energy level from its theoretical position as predicted by Dirac's quantum theory of the electron (Paul Adrien Maurice Dirac [1902–1984]). Lamb was awarded the Nobel Prize in Physics jointly with Polykarp Kusch (1911–1993) in 1955.
1948	Dennis Gabor (1900–1979)	Description of the principles of wave front reconstruction, evolving into holography.
1954	Charles Hard Townes (1915–2015), James Power Gordon (1928–2013) and Herbert J. Zieger (1925–2011)	Publication: "Molecular microwave oscillator and new hyperfine structures in the microwave spectrum of NH$_3$," describing the maser at Columbia University operating on ammonia producing coherent microwave radiation: MASER. Charles Hard received the Nobel Prize in Physics in 1964.
1958	Arthur Leonard Schawlow (1921–1999) and Charles Hard Townes (1915–2015)	Publication of "Infrared and Optical Masers" in which the maser principle were proposed to be extended into the visible region of the electromagnetic spectrum, creating the "laser" concept.
1958	Gordon Gould (1920–2005)	Arguably one of the first people to design, build, and operate a laser.
1960	Theodore Harold Maiman (1927–2007)	Described the first operational laser, built at the Hughes Research Laboratories, operating a rod of synthetic ruby as the medium: Ruby LASER.
1960	Ali Javan [Persian: جوان ع لی] (1926–)	Construction and operation of the first helium-neon laser.

(Continued)

CHRONOLOGY	NOTEWORTHY PEOPLE	EVENTS AND DISCOVERIES
1961	Peter Alden Franken (1928–1999), Arthur E. Hill (–2014), C. W. Peters () and Gabriel Weinreich (1930?–)	Demonstrated harmonic generation, specifically second harmonic, from laser light by transmission of the ruby laser pulse through a quartz crystal.
1961	Ali Javan (1926–), William Ralph Bennett (1930–2008), and Donald R. Harriott (1928–2007)	First gas laser at the Bell Laboratories. Lasing medium was a helium and neon mixture, emitting in the near infrared, the line with highest radiance at a wavelength of 1153 nm.
1962	Marshall. I. Nathan, Robert H. Rediker, Robert N. Hall, W. Keyes, Ted M. Quist, Nick Holonyak (1928–) and S. F. Bevacqua	Five groups describing the observation of stimulated emission from gallium arsenide semiconductor diodes: inception of the diode laser. Based on the pioneering work of Captain Henry Joseph Round (1881–1966) in 1907 and Rubin Braunstein () in 1955.
1963	Chandra Kumar Naranbhai Patel (1938–)	The first carbon dioxide laser, Bell Laboratories.
1964	William B. Bridges (1934–)	First ion laser built at Hughes Research Laboratories.
1964	Jerome V. V. Kasper () and George Claude Pimentel (1922–1989)	Photodissociation mechanism of action description for the Iodine laser. The laser operated at a wavelength of 1315 nm at the University of California, Berkeley. The population inversion in atomic iodine was induced by the photodissociation of either CH_3I or CF_3I.
1966	Peter P. Sorokin (1931–) and John R. Lankard ()	First organic dye laser
1967–1969	S. L. McCall () and E. L. Hahn ()	Described studies of the propagation of very short optical pulses through a medium consisting of resonant two level atoms, developing in the process the criteria to be satisfied by the shape of the pulse so that it would propagate as an optical soliton (the area theorem) and describing the propagation mechanism of self-induced transparency (SIT).
1971	John M. J. Madey (1943–)	Publication: "Stimulated emission of bremsstrahlung in a periodic magnetic field," Madey describes the principles of the free electron laser.
1976	John M. J. Madey (1943–)	Stanford University group operates the first free electron laser (FEL).
1985	Dennis L. Matthews ()	X-ray laser at the Lawrence Livermore National Laboratory, operating at 20 nm emission wavelength band.
1990		The Hubble space telescope is positioned in a low orbit around Earth on April 25, 1990.

(Continued)

Quantum

CHRONOLOGY	NOTEWORTHY PEOPLE	EVENTS AND DISCOVERIES
1850	Sir William Rowan Hamilton (1805–1865)	Reformulation of Newtonian mechanics: Hamilton mechanics. Hamilton mechanics can be considered an essential building block to the development of quantum mechanics. Sir William Hamilton introduced the principles leading to the formulation of the Hamiltonian operator used in quantum mechanics, defining the total energy of a system.
1916	Niels Henrik David Bohr (1885–1962)	Atomic structure and quantum theory.
1922	Erwin Rudolf Josef Alexander Schrödinger (1887–1961) and Hermann Klaus Hugo Weyl (1885–1955)	Introduction of the quantum mechanical principles, which formed the basis for several imaging techniques.
1924	Louis-Victor-Pierre-Raymond, 7th duc de Broglie (1892–1987)	Introduction of the wave phenomenon with respect to all object in motion. Matter wave, propagating with the de Broglie wavelength.
1927	Wolfgang Ernst Pauli (1900–1958) Ralph Kronig (1904–1995), George Eugene Uhlenbeck (1900–1988), Samuel Abraham Goudsmit (1902–1978), and Paul Adrien Maurice Dirac (1902–1984)	Introduction of the electron spin concept and a broad range of relativistic quantum mechanical principles. This formed the foundation for the development of the NMR imaging system: nuclear magnetic resonance (MRI).
1937	John Archibald Wheeler (1911–2008)	Theoretical physics and relativity. Corrections to the Bohr (Niels Bohr [1885–1962]) liquid drop model.
1948	Richard Phillips Feynman (1918–1988)	Introduction of the Feyman diagrams.
1957	Rudolf Ludwig Mössbauer (1929–2011)	Discovery of atomic recoilless nuclear energy interaction under gamma radiation resulting in resonance fluorescence: Mössbauer effect.
1964	Charles Hard Townes (1915–2015), Nikolay Gennadiyevich Basov [Николай Геннадиевич Басов] (1922–2001), and Aleksandr Mikhailovich Prokhorov [Александр Михайлович Прохоров] (1916–2002)	Quantum electronics.

(Continued)

Solid-state

CHRONOLOGY	NOTEWORTHY PEOPLE	EVENTS AND DISCOVERIES
"Ancient man"		Realization that the following chemical compounds were pure; what we currently consider as elements: gold (8000 BC), silver (<5000 BC), iron (<5000 BC), copper (9000 BC), mercury (<2000 BC), tin (~3500 BC), carbon (3750 BC), and sulfur (2000 BC).
450 BC	Leucippus (fifth century BC)	Argued that the universe consists as a structure of atoms and voids.
430 BC	Democritus (of Greece) (460 BC–370 BC)	Proclamation that the atom is the smallest and simplest unit of all matter. All matter is composed of atoms. The first rudimentary introduction of the elementary build block but with no scientific support. Greek word "atomos" (ἄτομος), meaning indivisible.
350 BC	Aristotle (384 BC–322 BC)	Declaration of only four (4) elements defining the existence on earth: fire, water, air, and earth. Matter only has the following properties: wet, dry, hot, or cold.
300	Alchemists:	Based on the philosophy of Aristotle the alchemists believed that "regular" metals could be converted into precious metal, specifically gold; wishful thinking…The item required to perform this conversion was referred to as the elusive "philosopher's stone."
1615	Jean Beguin (1550–1620)	First diagram expression for a chemical reaction in a notation that we still adhere to today.
1661	Robert Boyle (1627–1691)	First "modern chemist." End of the era of the Alchemists (perpetuated for 2000 years), partially based on the book by Robert Boyle *The Sceptical Chymist*.
1669	Henning Brand (1630–1710)	Documented observation that phosphorus is an element.
ca. 1670	Sir Isaac Newton (1643–1727)	Sir Isaac Newton was one of the prominent proponents and advocates of the atom theory.
1757	William Cullen (1710–1790)	Introduction of the first formula for a chemical reaction.
1774	Antoine Lavoisier (1743–1794)	Discovery of oxygen; and the chemical process of oxidation.
1785	Charles Augustin de Coulomb (1736–1806)	Treatise on electricity: *Premier Mémoire sur l'Électricité et le Magnétisme*. The unit of electric charge is named after him posthumously. The free electric charge is the electron, which was neither fully understood, nor described. The electron does form the basis for strong chemical connections, based on ion formation.

(*Continued*)

CHRONOLOGY	NOTEWORTHY PEOPLE	EVENTS AND DISCOVERIES
1789	William Higgins (1763–1825)	First use of the term molecule describing a chemical compound consisting of multiple atoms. The word molecule can be traced back to 1678. The expression and concept of the molecule has ties to Rene Descartes (1596–1650) and Robert Boyle (1627–1991).
ca. 1800	John Dalton (1766–1844)	Introduction of the "law of multiple proportions" describing the atomic concept based on chemical reactions taking place in ratios of small whole numbers.
1806	Sir Humphry Davy, 1st Baronet (1778–1829)	Discovery of several alkali next to alkaline earth metals, as well as contributions to the description and discovery of the elemental nature of the elements chlorine and iodine.
1804	Christian Samuel Weiss (1780–1856)	Description of crystalline structure as a configuration of attractions and repulsions, based on the work of René Just Haüy (1743–1822).
1807	Thomas Young (1773–1829)	Formal introduction of the Young's modulus for elastic deformation, tying strain to stress, based on the work by Leonard Euler (1707–1783).
1820	Pierre Louis Dulong (1785–1838) and Alexis-Thérèse Petit (1791–1820)	Dulong and Petit law of specific heats; coupled oscillators.
1820	Claude Louis Marie Henri Navier (1785–1836)	Efforts on developing mathematical models describing molecular concepts for elasticity of three-dimensional isotropic bodies, expressed in *Lois de l'équilibre et du mouvement des corps solides*.
1826	Franz Ernst Neumann (1798–1895)	Mathematical description of the "crystalline structure." Franz Neumann additionally described the heat exchange and specific heat concept based on the work of Alexis-Thérèse Petit and Pierre Louis Dulong (Dulong–Petit law). This was published almost 30 years later as the Kopp–Neumann rule, by his student Hermann Franz Moritz Kopp (1817–1892). Student of Christian Samuel Weiss (1780–1856).
1827	Augustin-Louis Cauchy (1789–1857)	Theory of linear elasticity: Cauchy relations.
1850	Sir William Rowan Hamilton (1805–1865)	Sir Hamilton is most known for his reformulation of Newtonian mechanics: Hamilton mechanics. Hamilton mechanics can be considered an essential building block to the development of quantum mechanics. Sir William Hamilton introduced the principles leading to the formulation of the Hamiltonian operator used in quantum mechanics, defining the total energy of a system.

(Continued)

CHRONOLOGY	NOTEWORTHY PEOPLE	EVENTS AND DISCOVERIES
1850	Auguste Bravais (1811–1863)	Uncovered lattice structure: Bravais lattice.
1850	George Boole (1815–1864)	Known for the Boolean algebra and logic. The work of George Boole inspired Claude Shannon (1916–2001).
1852	Wilhelm Eduard Weber (1804–1891)	Molecular model for magnetism, based on the "molecular rotation," which allows alignment of the electrical eddy currents to form a magnetic solid with a defined North and South pole under application of an external magnetic field. Assisted by the work of Sir James Alfred Ewing (1855-1935).
1853	Gustav Heinrich Wiedemann (1826–1899) and Rudolf Franz (1827–1902)	Relationship between electrical conductivity and thermal conductivity for a solid medium.
1857	Hermann Ludwig Ferdinand von Helmholtz (1821–1894)	Introduction of chemical thermodynamics concepts and definitions and electrodynamics.
1860	Georg Friedrich Bernhard Riemann (1826–1866)	The work of Bernhard Riemann was instrumental in the development of the development of the theory of general relativity and the supporting mathematical evaluation.
1864	Augustus Matthiessen (1831–1870)	Description of the specific conductivity of materials as a function of temperature and impurities in the solid medium.
1865	James Clerk Maxwell (1831–1879)	Electromagnetic theory.
1870	Hermann Ludwig Ferdinand von Helmholtz (1821–1894)	Unofficial introduction to the mechanism of action for nuclear fusion.
1873	Josiah Willard Gibbs (1839–1903)	Chemical potential, a energy constituent within the Gibbs free energy. Thermodynamic concept describing the energy that can be released or absorbed during a chemical reaction.
1879	William Crookes (1832–1919)	Cathode rays and realization that single charged particles must be involved.
1879	Edwin Hall (1855–1938)	Description of the "Hall effect": the expression of a transverse force on the electric charges within a conductor carrying a current while exposed to an external magnetic field: polarization resulting in a measurable electric potential between the lateral sides of the conductor.
1880	Pierre Curie (1859–1906) and Jacques Curie (1856–1941)	Discovery of the generation of electricity by mechanical manipulation of crystals: piezoelectric concept.
1884	Ludwig Minnigerode (1773–1839)	Recognition of at least 32 possible crystal classes, based on his mentor's work: Franz Ernst Neumann (1798–1895).

(Continued)

CHRONOLOGY	NOTEWORTHY PEOPLE	EVENTS AND DISCOVERIES
1885	Eugene Goldstein (1850–1930)	Principle discovery of the proton, however not recognized as such.
1888	Heinrich Friedrich Weber (1843–1912)	Discovery that the emitted wavelength band from a heated body changed the peak wavelength location as a function of the measured temperature. This paved the way for the radiation formula released by Max Planck (1858–1947), it also provided the entry into quantum theory.
1890	Jules Henri Poincaré (1854–1912)	Introduction of methods and means for deriving accurate topographical data. Some of the work of Poincaré revolved around defining the geometry of the universe. Poincaré also contributed to fluid dynamic modeling in addition to the description of celestial motion.
1896	Wilhelm Conrad Röntgen (1845–1923)	Discovery of X-ray radiation.
1896	Henri Becquerel (1852–1908)	Emission of "Becquerel rays" from uranium salts, later identified as alpha particles. Becquerel already recognized that this emission was different from X-ray since it was deflected by means of an applied external magnetic field. Conceptual introduction to the field of radioactivity.
1897	Joseph John Thomson (1856–1940)	Discovery of the electron concept; using William Crookes's vacuum tube. The electron itself was at this point not identified.
1897	Joseph John Thomson (1856 – 1940)	Introduction of the concept "ionic bond," also referred to as polar bond.
1897	Marie Skłodowska-Curie (1867–1934)	Discovery of radioactive isotopes. Marie Curie introduced the term "radioactivity."
1899	Paul Karl Ludwig Drude (1863–1906)	Introduction of the "free electron gas" for conduction in metals, based on his work under Woldemar Voigt (1850–1919). Additional work by Paul Drude was in optics, specifically the description of light and interaction with (transparent) object base on the theories of James Clerk Maxwell (1831–1879).
1899	Ernest Rutherford (1871–1937), 1st Baron Rutherford of Nelson, Lord Rutherford of Nelson	Emission of alpha particle.
1900	Samuel Giuseppe Vito Volterra (1860–1946)	Description and formulation of cylindrical waves. Volterra became involved in the biological cause and effect, respectively predator–prey, aspects, pioneering the field of mathematical biology.

(Continued)

CHRONOLOGY	NOTEWORTHY PEOPLE	EVENTS AND DISCOVERIES
1900	David Hilbert (1862–1943)	Hilbert space: vector space designed to accommodate an infinite number of dimensions, with respect to the three-dimensional Euclidean space. The Hilbert spatial interpretation forms an indispensable tools in solving for partial differential equations, as well as pertaining to quantum mechanics, and Fourier analysis. In Fourier analysis this applies to applications in signal processing and heat transfer. Hilbert Space is an ergodic theory, which provides the mathematical foundations of certain thermodynamics topics.
1900	Max Karl Ernst Ludwig Planck (1858–1947) and James Clerk Maxwell (1831–1879)	Formal description of the photon and the energy associated with the electromagnetic wave. Introduction of Planck's radiation law.
1903	Ernest Rutherford (1871–1937), 1st Baron Rutherford of Nelson, Lord Rutherford of Nelson	Discovery of the nuclear decay half-life.
1903	Marie Skłodowska-Curie (1867–1934) and Ernest Rutherford (1871–1937), 1st Baron Rutherford of Nelson, Lord Rutherford of Nelson	Quantification of nuclear decay.
1905	Albert Einstein (1879–1955)	Energy–mass equivalence hypothesis introduced. Einstein also published his theoretical interpretation of the movements of object, specifically approaching the speed of light in his special theory of relativity and general theory of relativity. In 1917 he published his predictions on stimulated emission and hence the preliminary description of the operations of a LASER. Additional mathematical work eludes to quantum theoretical approach.
1906	Dmitri Ivanovich Mendeleev (1834–1907)	Periodic Table of Elements.
1907	Pierre-Ernest Weiss (1865–1940) and Paul Langevin (1872–1946)	Refinement of the local magnetic field in ferromagnetic materials, the early work by Wilhelm Eduard Weber (1804–1891).
1908	Johannes Geiger (1822–1945) and Ernest Rutherford (1871–1937)	Development of the Geiger counter, used to measure radioactive radiation.
1909	Francis Aston (1877–1945)	Mass spectrometer mass separation of closely separated isotopes. Highly sensitive mass spectrometer design.
1909	Robert Andrews Millikan (1868–1953)	Measurement of the mass of the electron.

(Continued)

CHRONOLOGY	NOTEWORTHY PEOPLE	EVENTS AND DISCOVERIES
1910	Amalie Emma Noether (1882–1935)	Master of abstract algebra. Amalie Noether also introduced the concept of conservation laws based on the symmetry in nature and physics and engineering.
1910	Hermann Klaus Hugo (Peter) Weyl (1885–1955)	Weyl studied under David Hilbert (1862–1943) and was also close to Amalie Emma Noether (1882–1935). Hermann Weyl uncovered a gauge invariance and with his interpretation of Riemann surfaces his teachings form the basis of many aspects supporting the theoretical explanation in modern physics concepts. Weyl also contributed to the efforts of Erwin Schrödinger (1887–1961).
1911	Heike Kamerlingh Onnes (1853–1926)	Discovery of superconductivity. Building on the resistance measurements at low temperatures by Sir James Dewar (1842–1923) and J. Andrew Fleming (1846?–1928?) in 1892.
1911	Ernest Rutherford (1871–1937), 1st Baron Rutherford of Nelson, Lord Rutherford of Nelson	Rutherford scattering on nuclear level, indication of the existence of the proton. The proton itself was not mentioned until 1932, this time again by Ernest Rutherford.
1911	Niels Henrik David Bohr (1885–1962)	Elaboration on the "electron gas model" introduced by Paul Karl Ludwig Drude (1863–1906) in 1899.
1912	Max Theodor Felix von Laue (1879–1960)	Established wave nature of X-rays represented by an interference pattern by means of crystal diffraction. Max von Laue received the Nobel Prize in Physics for his discovery in 1914.
1912	Max Born (1882–1970)	Description of the vibration mechanics in (crystalline) lattice structures, providing a fundamental theoretical formulation of the specific heat concept introduced by Albert Einstein (1879–1955) in 1911.
1913	Niels Henrik David Bohr (1885–1962)	Bohr atomic model.
1913	Frederick Soddy (1877–1956)	Formal introduction of the isotope concept.
1913	William Lawrence Bragg (1890–1971) and William Henry Bragg (1862–1942)	Bragg X-ray diffraction for crystal lattice structure: Bragg law. This may often be considered the official beginning of the field for condensed matter physics, respectively, solid-state physics.
1913	Gilbert Newton Lewis (1875–1946)	Introduction of the free electron metallic bond; based on the work by Paul Karl Ludwig Drude (1863–1906).
1914	Niels Henrik David Bohr (1885–1962)	Description of the atomic energy layer model; hydrogen (Bohr atomic model).
1915	Ernest Marsden (1889–1970)	Artificial transmutation, associated with radon enclosed by vacuum.

(Continued)

CHRONOLOGY	NOTEWORTHY PEOPLE	EVENTS AND DISCOVERIES
1916	Niels Henrik David Bohr (1885–1962)	Atomic structure and quantum theory.
1916	Gilbert Newton Lewis (1875–1946)	Description of the shell filling for atomic electrons, and the related covalent bond and the concept of valence electrons.
1917	Ernest Rutherford, 1st Baron Rutherford of Nelson (1871–1937)	Discovery of the proton.
1918	Paul Scherrer (1890–1969)	X-ray diffraction, crystal structure. Nuclear energy development. Established the CERN institute in Switzerland as one of the founders. Directed the construction of the first cyclotron in 1940.
1919	Ernest Rutherford (1871–1937)	Artificial transmutation, hydrogen formation resulting from collisions of alpha particles with nitrogen, also generating oxygen and gamma rays.
1921	Willem Hendrik Keesom (1876–1956)	Keesom theory for degenerate gas. Description of dipole–dipole interaction. William Keesom provided a description of the specific heat at low temperatures. Keesom also managed to freeze helium in 1926.
1921	Alfred Landé (1888–1976)	Mathematician who introduced the Landau factor for an electron with both self-rotation spin and orbital angular momentum.
1922	Erwin Rudolf Josef Alexander Schrödinger (1887–1961) and Hermann Klaus Hugo Weyl (1885–1955)	Introduction of the quantum mechanical principles, supporting the understanding of high-energy physics phenomena such as the atomic structure.
1923	John von Neumann (1903–1957) [original name: Neumann Janos Lajos]	Introduced finite element methodology (also known as Monte Carlo simulation), integration of random number generation. He was also instrumental in the design of thermonuclear bombs as well as significantly advanced the field of hydrodynamics.
1923	Arthur Holly Compton (1892–1962)	Description of the deflection of photons by a charge unit, generally an electron, potentially the nucleus: Compton effect.
1924	Niels Henrik David Bohr (1885–1962)	Introduction of the term: "element". This idea was formed based on Wolfgang Pauli's (1900–1958) exclusion principle. The element concept has been around for millennia.

(Continued)

CHRONOLOGY	NOTEWORTHY PEOPLE	EVENTS AND DISCOVERIES
1924	Satyendra Nath Bose (1894–1974) [সত্যেন্দ্র নাথ বসু] and Albert Einstein (1879–1955)	Introduction of the Bose–Einstein statistics: one of two potential manners of energy occupation for a collection of noninteracting indistinguishable particles with respect to a set of available discrete energy states, this applies to thermodynamic equilibrium only. At extreme low temperatures these energy levels for bosons can result in a joining of states: condensation, the Bose–Einstein condensate.
1924	Sir John Edward Lennard-Jones (1894–1954)	Definition of the attraction between two neutral molecules or atoms: Lennard Jones potential.
1924	Louis-Victor-Pierre-Raymond, 7th duc de Broglie (1892–1987)	Introduction of the wave phenomenon with respect to all object in motion. Matter wave, propagating with the de Broglie wavelength.
1925	Werner Heisenberg (1901–1976)	Introduction of quantum mechanics, specifically in matrix formulation. Heisenberg also introduced the "uncertainty principle"; two parameters describing the same item or phenomenon cannot be known simultaneously with exact accuracy, such as momentum and position, but are inherently linked to each other with a product that yields the reduced-Planck-constant divided by two or greater.
1925	Wolfgang Ernst Pauli (1900–1958)	Pauli exclusion principle for atomic energy levels.
~1925		Recognition of the "Coulomb barrier" in nuclear collision, providing a "tunneling" effect for the release of alpha particles.
~1926	Paul Langevin (1872–1946)	Elaborate work on paramagnetism and diamagnetism with a significant contribution to the development of ultrasound detection based on the piezoelectrics effect discovery by Pierre Curie (1859–1906) and Jacques Curie (1856–1941) in 1888. Paul Langevin introduced the "Twin Paradox" concept with respect to Special Relativity introduced by Albert Einstein (1879–1955).
1926	Paul Dirac (1902–1984) and Enrico Fermi (1901–1954)	Fermi–Dirac statistics.
1926	1928: Paul Dirac (1902–1984); 1929 Dmitri Vladimirovich Skobeltsyn (1892–1990); 1932 Carl David Anderson (1905–1991)	Discovery of positron.

(*Continued*)

CHRONOLOGY	NOTEWORTHY PEOPLE	EVENTS AND DISCOVERIES
1926	Eugene Paul Wigner (1902–1995)	Series publications on the application of group theory in quantum mechanics. Eugene Wigner shared the Nobel Prize in Physics jointly with Maria Goeppert-Mayer (Göppert) and Johannes Hans Daniel Jensen (1907–1973) in 1963.
1926	Jean Baptiste Perrin (1870–1942)	Physical proof providing the existence of molecules.
1927	Werner Karl Heisenberg (1901–1976)	Quantum Uncertainty Principle.
1927	Paul Adrien Maurice Dirac (1902–1984)	Description of antimatter.
1927	Wolfgang Ernst Pauli (1900–1958) Ralph Kronig (1904–1995), George Eugene Uhlenbeck (1900–1988), Samuel Abraham Goudsmit (1902–1978), and Paul Adrien Maurice Dirac (1902–1984)	Introduction of the electron spin concept and a broad range of relativistic quantum mechanical principles. This formed the foundation for the development of the NMR imaging system: nuclear magnetic resonance (MRI).
1928	Arnold Johannes Wilhelm Sommerfeld (1868–1951)	Theory of metals: free electron model that obeys the Fermi–Dirac statistics; Paul Adrien Maurice Dirac (1902–1984) and Enrico Fermi (1901–1954).
1928	Johannes Geiger (1822–1945) and Walther Müller (1905–1979)	Introduction of an improved Geiger counter: the Geiger–Müller counter, using ionization of a confined gas.
1928	Sir Chandrasekhara Ventaka Raman (1888–1970)	Raman spectroscopy; indicating the energy levels in atoms and molecules.
1928	Felix Bloch (1905–1983)	Description of the migration process of electrons in an atomic lattice structure. The electron transport formed what Felix Bloch referred to as a wave process, now referenced as Bloch waves. The wave process (i.e,. wavelength) directly corresponds to the periodic nature of the lattice structure, in particular for a crystal.
1930	Enrico Fermi (1901–1954)	Chemical potential for electrons: Fermi level, equivalent to the thermodynamic work required to add or remove an electron to the energy configuration of the body. This applies in particular to semiconductors and the working of p-type[and n-type-doped materials such as diodes and transistors.
1931	Linus Carl Pauling (1901–1994)	Description of the general and detailed nature of various types of chemical bonds.

(Continued)

CHRONOLOGY	NOTEWORTHY PEOPLE	EVENTS AND DISCOVERIES
1931	Wolfgang Ernst Pauli (1900–1958)	Theoretical introduction of the neutrino. The experimental verification of the existence of the neutrino was not until 1956 by Frederick Reines (1918–1998) and Clyde Cowan Jr. (1919–1974).
1931	Carl David Anderson (1905–1991)	Discovery of the positron, antiparticle for the electron. The "positron" was predicted by Paul Adrien Maurice Dirac (1902–1984) in 1929.
1932	Sir James Chadwick (1891–1974)	Discovery of the neutron. Student of Ernest Rutherford (1871–1937).
1934	Leo Szilard (1898–1964)	Recognition of nuclear decay chain reactions.
1934	Hideki Yukawa [湯川 秀樹], (1907–1981)	Introduction of mesons and the concept of antimatter.
1934	Ida Noddack (1896–1978)	Formal introduction of the concept of "fission," however, not recognized by her peers at the time. The fission phenomenon was only recognized when announced by Enrico Fermi (1901–1954) later that year.
1934	Enrico Fermi (1901–1954)	Interaction of slow neutron with nuclei and the resulting decay into different elements, including aluminum and uranium.
1935	Enrico Fermi (1901–1954)	Developed Fermi–Dirac statistics, although independent from Paul Dirac (1902–1984) but simultaneously. The Fermi–Dirac statistics applies to fermions, while the counterpart that it does not include are referred to as bosons. Fermi worked on X-ray crystallography, as well as energy levels in semiconductor structures. The Fermi level concept for electrons in atomic energy approximating absolute zero ties directly in with the Pauli exclusion principle. Fermi worked with and studied under Max Born (1882–1970), Werner Heisenberg (1901–1976), Pascual Jordan (1902–1980), Paul Ehrenfest (1880–1933), Hendrik Lorentz (1853–1928), Samuel Goudsmit (1902–1978), Jan Tinbergen (1903–1994), and Albert Einstein (1879–1955). Fermi concluded that beta decay from the nucleus formed another energetic particle and determined it to be real and named it a neutrino.
1935	Paul Adrien Maurice Dirac (1902–1984)	Developed Fermi–Dirac statistics, although independent from Enrico Fermi (1901–1954) but simultaneously.
1935	Arthur Dempster (1886–1950)	Discovery of the lighter uranium isotope: Uranium-235.
1936	Otto Hahn (1879–1968) and Lise Meitner (1878–1968)	Neutron collision of uranium-induced decay examination.

(Continued)

CHRONOLOGY	NOTEWORTHY PEOPLE	EVENTS AND DISCOVERIES
1937	Carl David Anderson (1905–1991), Seth Henry Neddermeyer (1907–1988), Jabez Curry Street (1906–1989), and Edward C. Stevenson ()	Confirmation of the existence of the meson, and muon.
1938	Niels Henrik David Bohr (1885–1962) and John Archibald Wheeler (1911–2008)	Formal description of the nuclear fission process.
1939	Jerome M. B. Kellogg (1905–)	Discovery of a finite quadruple moment for the deuteron, requiring a noncentral (tensor) nuclear force configuration.
1940	Otto Robert Frisch (1904–1979)	Development of the detonation mechanism for the first atomic bomb
1940+	Julius Robert Oppenheimer (1904–1967)	Manhattan project: fission reaction. Prominent members: Arthur Compton (1892–1962), Enrico Fermi (1901–1954), Eugene Wigner (1902–1995), and dozens more.
1947	Charles Kittel (1916–)	Elaborate theoretical work on solid-state physics, respectively: condensed matter physics.
1947	George Dixon Rochester (1908–2001), Clifford Charles Butler (1922–1999)	Discovery of the subatomic particle: the "kaon," k-meson. Introduction of the "strangeness" concept for quarks, although the quark concept had not been introduced. In the elementary particle phenomenology the kaon is a bound state of an up- or down quark with a strange quark (antiquark).
1947	Maria Goeppert-Mayer (Göppert) (1906–1972)	Theoretical concept development for the understanding of nuclear forces, based on a shell model, similar to the atomic electron model.
1947	William Webster Hansen (1909–1949)	Linear accelerator installation at Stanford University, California.
1950	Maria Goeppert-Mayer (Göppert) (1906–1972)	Introduction of the nuclear shell model of atomic nuclei.
ca. 1952	Ludwig von Helmholtz (1821–1894), Lyman Strong Spitzer, Jr. (1914–1997), and Ronald Richter (1909–1991) and Edward Teller (1908–2003)	Nuclear fusion investigation and start of experimentation. The process was in principle described by Hermann Ludwig Ferdinand von Helmholtz (1821–1894), but is continuously in action at the sun's surface.
1955	Obninsk Nuclear Power Station, Russia	First nuclear power station for energy generation.
1956	Frederick Reines (1918–1998) and Clyde Lorrain Cowan Jr. (1919–1974)	Experimental confirmation of the neutrino introduced in 1931 by Wolfgang Pauli (1900–1958).

(Continued)

CHRONOLOGY	NOTEWORTHY PEOPLE	EVENTS AND DISCOVERIES
1957	John Bardeen (1908–1991), John Robert Schrieffer (1931–) and Leon N. Cooper (1930–)	Bardeen–Cooper–Schrieffer theory of superconductivity.
1958	Stanley Mandelstam (1928–)	Introduction of Mandelstam variables associated with the concept of "crossing symmetry," defining numerical quantities which encode the energy, momentum, and scattering angles of particles in a deflection process described in a Lorentz-invariant fashion.
1958	Lev Davidovich Landau [Russian: Лёв Давидович Ландау] (1908–1968), Arkady Beynusovich Migdal [Russian: Аркадий Бейнусович (Бенедиктович) Мигдал] (1911–1991)	Theory of interacting electrons, specifically with respect to solids; condensed matter physics.
1961	Murray Gell-Mann (1929–)	Description of elementary particles, eightfold way of defining "strangeness" for the quark. Formal introduction of the elementary particle "quark" concept, the building blocks for protons and neutrons. The "quark" name is based on an expression in the book *Finnegans Wake* by James Joyce.
1964	Charles Hard Townes (1915–2015), Nikolay Gennadiyevich Basov [Николай Геннадиевич Басов] (1922–2001) and Aleksandr Mikhailovich Prokhorov [Александр Михайлович Прохоров] (1916–2002)	Quantum electronics.
1970	Sheldon Lee Glashow (1932–), John Iliopoulos (1940–), and Luciano Maiani (1941–)	Introduction of the charm quark.
1974	Burton Richter (1931–) and Samuel Chao Chung Ting [Chinese: 丁肇中] (1936–)	Description of charm for the quark.
1975	Martin Lewis Perl (1927–2014)	Discovery of the tau lepton.
1977	Leon Max Ledderman (1922–)	Discovery of the "beauty" and "bottom" designation for quarks.

(Continued)

CHRONOLOGY	NOTEWORTHY PEOPLE	EVENTS AND DISCOVERIES
1978		Discovery of the "gluon" with the assistance of the PLUTO, the first electromagnetic superconductive solenoid located in Hamburg, Germany.
1983	Collider Detector at Fermilab	World's first and at the time highest-energy particle accelerator, colliding antiprotons and protons propelled to center-of-mass energy reaching 2 TeV.
1986	Karl Alexander Müller (1927–) and Johannes Georg Bednorz (1950–)	High-temperature superconductivity.
1991	Sumio Iijima [飯島 澄男] (1939–)	Discovery of carbon nanotube.
1992	Kenneth Kin Man Kwong ()	Introduction of "functional MRI." In 2013 the sugar consumption was measured in cancer cells with respect to normal cells for diagnostic verification.
1995	Wolfgang Ketterle (1957–), Eric Allin Cornell (1961–), and Carl Edwin Wieman (1951–)	Experimental verification of Bose–Einstein condensation.
1997	Sir Konstantin Sergeevich Novoselov (1974–) and Sir Andre Konstantin Geim (1958–)	Introduction of nanoscience; in particular the properties of graphene.

Thermodynamics

CHRONOLOGY	NOTEWORTHY PEOPLE	EVENTS AND DISCOVERIES
3300 BC–1000 BC	Bronze Age	Smelting and forging of soft metals using low heat: copper, tin, and gold. This age also introduces the written documentation.
1000 BC–700 AD	Iron Age	Higher heat requirements and more detailed tool manufacturing, introducing scientific and engineering challenges. Historical tracking of processes and developments and philosophies. Introduction of complicated mechanisms and requiring detailed analytical thinking.
500 BC	Heraclitus of Ephesius [Heraclitus: Ἡράκλειτος] (535 BC–475 BC)	Introduction of the concept of "flux"; referring to the flow of energy as well as media. One of the first reference to basic thermodynamic principles.
350 BC	Aristotle (384 BC–322 BC)	The word "energy" has the Greek origin "enérgeia" [Greek: ε'νέργεια], which was documented by Aristotle, "enérgeia" does not translation verbatim into English, the meaning resembles: "performing work."

(Continued)

CHRONOLOGY	NOTEWORTHY PEOPLE	EVENTS AND DISCOVERIES
40 BC	Marcus Vitruvius Pollio [Vitruvius] (ca. 80 BC–10 BC)	Architectural designs that harness the solar energy.
62	Hero of Alexandria [ρων ὁ ᾿Α λεξανδρεύς], (10–70)	Mathematician, physicist, and mechanical engineer who also taught pneumatics. A set of two books, *The Pneumatica*, describes mechanical devices worked by air, steam, or water pressure. Also known as Heron of Alexandria. He invented a steam-powered engine called the "Æolipile," relying on the heat exchange and mechanical conversion; fundamental thermodynamic concepts in practical application.
1500	Leonardo da Vinci (1452–1519)	The preverbal "Renaissance man," involved in all aspects of cultural evolution, science, engineering, politics, and art.
1543	Nicolaus Copernicus (1473–1543); Alias of Niclas Koppernigk	Introduction of the heliocentric model for the earth, sun, and other planets. This follows the statement by the astronomer from Greece: Aristarchus of Samos (ca. 310–ca. 230 BC), made more than 1700 years prior. The scientific observations made by Copernicus were validated by Tycho Brahe (1546–1601) and Johannes Kepler (1571–1630).
1590	Francis Bacon, 1st Viscount of St. Alban (1561–1626)	Statement referring to motion being the essence of heat.
ca. 1600	William Gilbert (1544–1603)	
ca. 1600	Galileo Galilei (1564–1642)	Using a "thermoscope" Galileo Galilei was able to derive that fact that energy is exchanges during the flow of air and as such assign a scale of "heat" to the sensation: hotness vs. coldness. This principle can be traced back to Hero of Alexandria (10–70).
1614	René Descartes (1596–1650)	Introduction to vortex motion. Introduction of the concept of general corpuscular motion, extending from small (maybe referring to the undefined atom), to planetary orbits.
1660	Robert Boyle (1627–1691)	Gas laws, definition of the behavior or gases and phenomenological thermodynamic observations.
1673	Christiaan Huygens (1629–1695)	Construction of a "combustion engine" powered by gun powder. Huygens introduced several concept of mechanical engineering and described the mechanism of shock waves. The mathematical efforts of Christiaan Huygens in probability theory were far advanced and he collaborated with the mathematician Pierre de Fermat (1601–1665) from France.
1676		
1679	Denis Papin (1647–ca. 1712)	Pressure with inherent thermodynamic and mechanical impacts.

(Continued)

CHRONOLOGY	NOTEWORTHY PEOPLE	EVENTS AND DISCOVERIES
1680	Robert Hooke (1635–1703)	Force applied by a compressed spring and associated stored potential energy, which is exerted as kinetic energy upon release of the spring.
ca. 1687	Sir Isaac Newton (1643–1727)	
1687	Guillaume Amontons (1663–1705)	Innovations on hygrometer, thermometer, and barometer. Speculation about the existence of a low enough temperature where all atomic, respectively, molecular motion of a gas will seize, an "absolute zero" temperature, in reference to his experimentation with gases and based on the work of Joseph Louis Gay-Lussac (1778–1850). Additional work of Guillaume Amontons in 1699 describes friction in great detail, later verified by Charles-Augustin de Coulomb (1736–1806) in 1781.
1698	Thomas Savery (1650–1715)	Construction of the basic steam engine; using information obtained by Denis Papin (1647–c. 1712).
1712	Thomas Newcomen (1664–1729)	Construction of a "atmospheric" steam engine.
1724	Herman Boerhaave (1668–1738)	Description of phase changes for media and the associated exchange of energy.
1732	Anders Celsius (1701–1744)	Thermometer-scale calibration based on pure water phases.
1735	Daniel Gabriel Fahrenheit (1686–1736)	Temperature scale in Fahrenheit based on body temperature and saltwater phases.
1738	Daniel Bernoulli (1700–1782)	Hydrodynamics, vibrations, and kinetic theory. Definition of the fundamental frequency and higher harmonics, with supporting elaborate mathematical analysis (solutions to differential equations) in his publication *Hydrodynamica*.
1752	Benjamin Franklin (1706–1790)	Kite experiment and the documentation of "electric current" with associated electric energy content, most visible in the destructive power of lightning bolts.
1783	Antoine Laurent de Lavoisier (1743–1794)	Introduction of the "caloric theory," "substance of heat." Lavoisier constructed the first known calorimeter and measured the heat exchange resulting from a chemical reaction.
1757–1769	James Watt (1736–1819)	Modern steam engine design and operation with theoretical description of operation.
1762	Joseph Black (1728–1799)	Realization of the concept of latent heat; observation that ice is melting (phase change to liquid) without a change in temperature.

(Continued)

CHRONOLOGY	NOTEWORTHY PEOPLE	EVENTS AND DISCOVERIES
1769	Nicolas-Joseph Cugnot (1725–1804)	First operational steam powered automobile, the predecessor to the internal combustion automobile.
1777	Carl Wilhelm Scheele (1742–1786)	Recognized heat transfer as the result of radiation (infrared light) to be a different exchange mechanism than convection and conduction.
1781	Charles-Augustin de Coulomb (1736–1806)	Definition of the electric field related to electric charge. The electric charge itself was still an elusive concept in those days.
1783	Antoine Laurent de Lavoisier (1743–1794)	Discovery of oxygen and the chemical impact.
1783	Joseph-Michel Montgolfier (1740–1810) and Jacques-Étienne Montgolfier (1745–1799)	Hot-air balloon; buoyancy.
1785	Jacques Alexandre César Charles (1746–1823)	Charles's law, expansion of gases.
1791	Pierre Prévost (1764–1823)	Experimentally verifies that all bodies radiate heat, regardless of their temperature. Precursor to Planck's law and Wien's law.
1798	Count Rumford (1753–1814), Benjamin Thompson	Quantitative analysis of the conversion of heat into work by means of his cannon-boring experimentation. This relates kinetic energy to heat and discredits the caloric theory.
1799	Sir Humphry Davy, 1st Baronet (1778–1829)	Experimental quantification of the conversion of work (friction) into heat using ice blocks that were rubbed on a surface and caused a phase change: liquification.
1802	Joseph Louis Gay-Lussac (1778–1850)	Ideal gas law; building on the work by Robert Boyle (1627–1691), more than a century earlier.
1824	Nicolas Léonard Sadi Carnot (1796–1832)	Thesis publication: "Reflections on the Motive Power of Fire," leading to the refrigerator for general public in 1842. Carnot introduced the cyclic process, which could be built into a cyclic machine, operating between two heat reservoirs, using the temperature of the reservoir as the parameter that influences the process, not necessarily the medium that is used in the system.
1827	Benoît Fourneyron (1802–1867)	First water turbine.
1841	Julius Robert von Mayer (1814–1878)	First attempt to define the laws of conservation, but was unsuccessful. Even though Julius Robert von Mayer lacked the mathematical skills to support his hypothesis he is still considered to be one of the founding fathers of thermodynamics.

(Continued)

CHRONOLOGY	NOTEWORTHY PEOPLE	EVENTS AND DISCOVERIES
1843	James Prescott Joule (1818–1889)	Quantitative experimental data collection and theoretical description of principal thermodynamic concepts.
1843–1848	James Prescott Joule (1818–1889)	Empirical verification of the first law of thermodynamics; equivalence of heat and work. This was later rewarded by assigning the heat quantity in unit Joule (J). Publication in 1851: "Remarks on the heat and the constitution of elastic fluids."
1847	Hermann Ludwig Ferdinand von Helmholtz (1821–1894)	Formulation of the principles of conservation of energy.
1848	William Thomson, 1st Baron Kelvin (i.e., Lord Kelvin) (1824–1907)	Absolute temperature scale: Kelvin.
1850	Rudolf Julius Emanuel Clausius (1822–1888)	Recognition of two basic principles (later introduced by means of the first and second law of thermodynamics: energy is constant and entropy tends toward a maximum). Clausius introduced the parameter U, representing the internal energy. Publication of book: *On the Motive Power of Heat, and on the Laws Which Can Be Deduced From It for the Theory of Heat*. According to Josiah Willard Gibbs (1839–1903) Clausius was one of the founding fathers of thermodynamics in the principle manner we currently still use. Clausius introduced what is now regarded the second law of thermodynamics in 1865 (referred to by William John Macquorn Rankine (1820–1872) as the "thermodynamic function"), as part of any natural thermodynamic process, the sum of the entropies of the participating systems will increase.
1852	James Prescott Joule (1818–1889) and William Thomson, 1st Baron Kelvin {Lord Kelvin} (1824–1907)	Joule–Thomson effect: rapidly expanding gas leads to a reduction in the temperature of the gas, even offering the potential for a phase change to solid, or liquid. Sometimes also found as the Joule–Kelvin effect.
1859	William John Macquorn Rankine (1820–1872)	Publication of the book *A Manual of the Steam Engine and Other Prime Movers*, chapter titled "Principles of Thermodynamics," introducing the concept of the "thermodynamic function" later recognized as entropy.
1860	James Clerk Maxwell (1831–1879)	Maxwell statistical distribution of atomic or molecular velocities for idealized gases, allowing for only brief elastic collisions. Published in 1867 as "On the dynamical theory of gases."
1861	Augustin Mouchot (1825–1911)	Presentation of the use of solar energy as a source for personal energy consumption.

(Continued)

CHRONOLOGY	NOTEWORTHY PEOPLE	EVENTS AND DISCOVERIES
1862	Ludwig Eduard Boltzmann (1844–1906)	Refinements to the Maxwell distribution and associated entropy based on additional implementation of kinetic gas theory. This culminated in 1877 in the Maxwell–Boltzmann distribution.
1873	Josiah Willard Gibbs (1839–1903)	Thermodynamic concept describing the energy that can be released or absorbed during a chemical reaction. In 1875 Josiah Gibbs published his *On the Equilibrium of Heterogeneous Substances*, describing the thermodynamic aspects in general form describing chemical reaction and heterogeneous systems. This work included the chemical potential, a energy constituent within the Gibbs free energy.
1879	Joseph Stefan (1835–1893)	Determination that radiation has a quantity: radiance, which is proportional to the fourth power of the temperature of the system.
1893	Wilhelm Carl Werner Otto Fritz Franz Wien (1864–1928)	Black body emission: Wien's displacement law. The peak radiance emitted by a black body (spectral radiance) shifts to shorter wavelengths at higher temperatures.
1895	Wilhelm Röntgen (1845–1923)	Discovery of X-ray (Röntgen rays).
1897	Joseph John Thomson (1856–1940)	Discovery of the electron; using William Crookes's vacuum tube.
1900	Ludwig Eduard Boltzmann (1844–1906)	Boltzmann equation for statistical mechanics, introduced by Ludwig Boltzmann between 1872 and 1875, reformulated by Max Karl Ernst Ludwig Planck (1858–1947) defining the entropy of a system. For certain systems also addressed as the Gibbs entropy formula, after Josiah Willard Gibbs (1839–1903).
1906	Walther Hermann Nernst (1864–1941)	Third law of thermodynamics: "The entropy of a perfect crystal at absolute zero is exactly equal to zero," influenced by Johannes Diederik van der Waals (1837–1923).
1909	Constantin Carathéodory (1873–1950)	Theoretical discourse on thermodynamics, based on axiomatic principles, entirely mathematical in its format.
1912	Peter Joseph William Debye (1884–1966)	Increased accuracy in determination of heat capacity for a body by means of implementation of low frequency acoustics (low frequency phonons) in the analysis process.
1924	Sir John Edward Lennard-Jones (1894–1954)	Definition of the attraction between two neutral molecules or atoms: Lennard-Jones potential.

(Continued)

CHRONOLOGY	NOTEWORTHY PEOPLE	EVENTS AND DISCOVERIES
1924	Satyendra Nath Bose (1894–1974) [সত্যেন্দ্র নাথ বসু] and Albert Einstein (1879–1955)	Introduction of the Bose–Einstein statistics: one of two potential manners of energy occupation for a collection of noninteracting indistinguishable particles with respect to a set of available discrete energy states, this applies to thermodynamic equilibrium only. At extreme low temperatures, these energy levels for bosons can result in a joining of states: condensation, the Bose–Einstein condensate.
1931	Georges Jean Marie Darrieus (1888–1979)	Introduction of the wind turbine.
1931	Subramanyan Chandrasekhar (1910–1995)	Relativistic thermodynamics.
1940+	Julius Robert Oppenheimer (1904–1967)	Manhattan project: fission reaction. Prominent members: Arthur Compton (1892–1962), Enrico Fermi (1901–1954), Eugene Wigner (1902–1995), and dozens more.
1948	Claude Elwood Shannon (1916–2001)	Introduction of information theory, basis is in thermodynamic principles.
1972	Stephen Hawking (1942–) and Jacob Bekenstein (1947–2015)	Thermodynamics of black holes. Specific items of interest are the following. Jacob Bekenstein: the entropy of a black hole is proportional to its surface area; Stephen Hawking: black holes may radiate particle that may lead to the "evaporation" of the black hole.

Index of Names

Note: Names are arranged in chronological order by date of birth. Page numbers followed by f refer to images.

Thales (624–546 BC), 396, 396f

Pythagoras (570–495 BC), 162, 162f

Socrates (469–399 BC), 103–104, 323, 323f

Hippocrates of Cos (460–377 BC), 85

Plato (427–347 BC), 103–104, 104f, 125, 510

Aristotle (384–322 BC), 78

Euclid (325–270 BC), 510

Archimedes (287–212 BC), 140

Hipparchus (190–125 BC), 155

Pollio, Marcus Vitruvius (80 BC–15 AD), 118–119, 119f

Ptolemaeus, Claudius (Ptolemy) (approximately
      90–168 AD), 155, 155f, 322, 328, 510

Sahl, Ibn (Arabic: سهل ابن) (Abu Saʻd al-ʻAlaʼibn Sahl)
      (940–1000), 262, 262f, 322

Al-Bīrūnī (Abū al-Rayḥān Muḥammad ibn Aḥmad
      al-Bīrūnī) (973–1048), 226

De Maricourt, Pierre (Pergrinus, Petri) (1220–1270), 33, 118

de Mondeville, Henri (1260–1320), 71

Da Vinci, Leonardo (1452–1519), 103, 119, 140, 350

Copernicus, Nicolaus (1473–1543), 162, 244, 328, 389

Vesalius, Andreas (1515–1564), 501–502, 502f

Fabricius, Georg (Goldschmidt) (1516–1571), 76, 76f

Gilbert, William, Sir (1544–1633), 501

Brahe, Tycho {Tyge Ottesen Brahe} (1546–1601), 328,
      389, 413

Stevin, Simon (1548–1620), 350, 350f

Galilei, Galileo (1564–1642), 27, 150, 362, 389, 405,
      433, 481, 502

Lipperhey, Hans (Lipperhey) (1570–1619), 389

Praetorius, Michael (original name: Michael Schultheiβ)
      (1571–1621), 140, 140f

Metius, Jacobus (Jacobus Adriaanszoon)
      (1571–1624), 389

Kepler, Johannes (1571–1630), 100, 113, 264, 329, 413

Leeghwater, Jan Adriaanszoon (1575–1650), 347, 453

Van Helmont, Johannes (Jan) Baptista (1579–1644),
      491, 491f

Janssen, Zacharias (1580–1640), 389

Rey, Jean (1583–1645), 405

Snel ("Snell"), Willebrord Snel van Royen (Snellius)
      (1591–1626), 262, 322–323, 322f, 492

Descartes, René (1596–1650), 245, 322, 350

Fermat, Pierre de (1601–1665), 18, 150

Roberval, Gilles Personne de (1602–1675), 244–245, 245f

Guericke, Otto von (1602–1682), 517–518, 518f, 559

Torricelli, Evangelista (1608–1647), 433, 433f, 481

Renaldini, Carlo {Rinaldini} (1615–1698), 227, 227f

Wallis, John (1616–1703), 530, 531f

Picard, Jean-Félix (1620–1682), 86, 127

Pascal, Blaise (1623–1662), 18f, 150, 350, 433, 481

Cassini, Giovanni Domenico (1625–1712), 350

Huygens, Christiaan (1629–1695), 6, 27, 79, 541

Van Leeuwenhoek, Antonie Philips (1632–1723),
      491–492, 492f

Hooke, Robert (1635–1703), 541

Gregory, James (1638–1675), 384

Newton, Isaac, Sir (1642–1727), 16, 78, 147–148, 350,
      362, 475, 541

Roemer {Rømer, also Römer}, Olaus (Ole) (1644–1710),
      247, 247f, 405

Calley, John (1663–1725), 271

Stradivari, Antonio (1644–1737), 421

Papin, Denis (1647–1712), 4, 5f, 144, 271

Savery, Thomas (1650–1715), 5, 271, 271f

Sauveur, Joseph (1653–1716), 270, 270f

Cristofori, Bartolomeo (1655–1731), 85

Seignette, Pierre (1660–1719), 88

Newcomen, Thomas (1664–1729), 271

Gray, Stephen (1666–1736), 125

Riccati, Jacopo Francesco; Count (1676–1754), 239–240,
      239f

Hales, Stephen (1677–1761), 434

Réaumur, René-Antoine Ferchault de (1683–1757), 219,
      219f, 227

Taylor, Brook (1685–1731), 382, 382f, 384

Fahrenheit, Gabriel Daniel (1686–1736), 219, 227, 390,
      405, 532

Van Musschenbroek, Petrus (1692–1761), 492, 492f

Voltaire, François-Marie d'Arouet (1694–1778),
      515, 515f

Pitot, Henri (1695–1771), 93–94, 93f

Maclaurin, Colin (1698–1746), 109

Von Kleist, Ewald Jurgens (1700–1748), 520, 520f

Bernoulli, Daniel (1700–1782), 140–141, 301

Celsius, Anders (1701–1744), 219, 227, 390, 532

Franklin, Benjamin (1706–1790), 125, 501f

Euler, Leonhard (1707–1783), 32, 140

Gordon, Andrew (1712–1751), 359

D'Alembert, Jean-Baptiste le Rond (1717–1783), 350
Canton, John (1718–1772), 501f
Lambert, Johann Heinrich (1728–1777), 350
Black, Joseph (1728–1799), 400, 587
IngenHousz, Jan (Ingen-Housz or Ingen Housz)
    (1730–1779), 80
Wedgwood, Josiah (1730–1795), 545–546, 546f
Priestley, Joseph (1733–1804), 81, 145–146, 146f
Lavoisier, Antoine-Laurent de (1743–1794), 145
Coulomb, Charles-Augustin de (1736–1806), 411
Watt, James (1736–1819), 537–538, 538f
Galvani, Luigi (1737–1789), 514
Lagrange, (Joseph-Louis) Giuseppe Luigi comte de
    Lagrange (1737–1813), 110, 113, 350
De Saussure, Horace-Bénédict (1740–1799), 327
Scheele, Carl Wilhelm (1742–1786), 76, 278–279, 279f
Volta, Alessandro Giuseppe Antonio Anastasio Gerolamo
    Umberto, Count (1745–1827), 514–515, 514f
Venturi, Giovanni Battista (1746–1822), 499–500, 500f
Bennet, Abraham (1749–1799), 501f
Laplace, Pierre-Simon de, Marquis de Laplace
    (1749–1827), 113, 150, 301, 350, 572
Van Marum, Martin (1750–1837), 559
Prévost, Pierre (1751–1839), 145
Legendre, Adrien-Marie (1752–1833), 113, 350
Thomson, Benjamin, Sir (Count Rumford) (1753–1814),
    250, 409, 409f
Gregor, William (1761–1817), 425
Chappe, Claude (1763–1805), 386
Pfaff, Johann Friedrich (1765–1825), 44, 44f, 545
Niépce, Joseph Nicéphore (1765–1833), 77
Bonaparte, Napoléon (1769–1821), 514
Seebeck, Thomas Johann (1770–1831), 292, 292f, 399
Daguerre, Louis-Jacques-Mandé (1787–1851), 292
Young, Thomas (1773–1829), 146–147, 541, 571–573, 571f
Biot, Jean-Baptiste (1774–1862), 270
Malus, Étienne Louis (1775–1812), 113
Ampère, André Marie (1775–1836), 359
Ritter, Johann Wilhelm (1776–1810), 243, 243f, 470
Avogadro, Lorenzo Romano Amedeo Carlo
    (1776–1856), 41
Gauss, Johann Carl Friedrich (German: Gauß)
    (1777–1855), 44, 545
Poinsot, Louis (1777–1859), 110, 110f
Davy, Humphry (1778–1829), 324
Poisson, Siméon Denis (1781–1840), 113–114, 113f
Brewster, David (1781–1868), 88
Sturgeon, William (1783–1850), 359, 359f
Bessel, Friedrich Wilhelm (1784–1846), 553
Navier, Claude-Louis Marie Henri (1785–1836), 141
Dulong, Pierre Louis (1785–1838), 43
Peltier, Jean Charles Athanase (1785–1845), 26, 26f
Prout, William (1785–1850), 153, 153f
Fraunhofer, Joseph von (1787–1826), 316, 517, 517f
Fresnel, Augustin-Jean (1788–1827), 147
Ohm, Georg Simon (1789–1854), 243

Cauchy, Augustin-Louis (1789–1857), 110, 423
Stirling, Robert (1790–1878), 351, 351f
Petit, Alexis Thérèse (1791–1820), 43, 43f
Savart, Félix (1791–1841), 270, 270f
Faraday, Michael (1791–1867), 359, 393
Morse, Samuel Finley Breese (1791–1872), 386
Green, George (1793–1841), 113
Péclet, Jean Claude Eugène (1793–1857), 24, 24f
Weber, Ernst Heinrich (1795–1878), 545
Carnot, Nicolas Leonard Sadi (1796–1832), 113
Steiner, Jakob (1796–1863), 6
Hagen, Gotthilf Heinrich Ludwig (1797–1884), 113
Poiseuille, Jean Leonard Marie (1799–1869), 112, 112f
Plücker, Julius (1801–1868), 104–105, 105f
Wheatstone, Charles (1802–1875), 550–551, 551f
Sturm, Jacques Charles François (1803–1855), 359
Darcy, Henry (1803–1858), 94
Jacobi, Carl Gustav Jacob (1804–1851), 55, 109
Clark, Alvan Graham (1804–1887), 553
Weber, Wilhelm Eduard (1804–1891), 544–545,
    544f, 545f
Hamilton, William Rowan, Sir (1805–1865), 285, 378
Earnshaw, Samuel (1805–1888), 411
Liouville, Joseph (1809–1882), 55, 359, 549
Von Mayer, Julius Robert (1814–1878), 522, 522f
Zeiss, Carl (1816–1888), 583, 583f
Joule, James Prescott (1818–1889), 522
Foucault, Jean Bernard Léon (1819–1868), 342, 541
Fizeau, Armand Hippolyte Louis (1819–1896), 223, 247,
    541, 545
Stokes, George Gabriel, Sir (1819–1903), 141,
    352–353, 352f
Rankine, William John Macquorn (1820–1872),
    209–211, 210f, 390
Becquerel, Alexandre-Edmond (1820–1891), 327
Tyndall, John (1820–1893), 214, 456–457, 457f
Helmholtz, Hermann Ludwig Ferdinand von
    (1821–1894), 336, 407, 518, 518f
Clausius, Rudolf Julius Emanuel (1822–1888), 290
Kirchhoff, Gustav Robert (1824–1887), 179, 218, 243, 546
Carré, Ferdinand Philippe Edouard (1824–1900), 558
Kelvin, 1st Baron (Lord William Thomson, Lord Kelvin)
    (1824–1907), 227, 289, 378, 390, 411, 533
Mouchot, Augustin (1825–1911), 328
Stoney, George Johnstone (1826–1911), 171
Verne, Jules (1828–1905), 288
Raoult, François-Marie (1830–1901), 212, 212f
Maxwell, James Clerk (1831–1879), 189, 284, 378, 444,
    504, 541, 545
Tait, Peter Guthrie (1831–1901), 378, 378f
Wimshurst, James (1832–1903), 558–559, 559f
Crookes, William, Sir (1832–1919), 127
Guthrie, Frederick (1833–1886), 240
Mendeleev, Dmitri Ivanovich [Дмитрий Иванович
    Менделеев] (1834–1907), 35
Stefan, Josef (1835–1893), 348, 348f, 456

Toepler, August Joseph Ignaz (1836–1912), 280, 425–426, 426f, 558

Holtz, Wilhelm (1836–1913), 558

Von Basch, Samuel Siegfried Karl Ritter (1837–1905), 340, 434

Van der Waals, Johannes Diderik (1837–1923), 148, 447, 489, 489f

Mach, Ernst (1838–1916), 582

Gibbs, Josiah Willard (1839–1903), 55

Abbe, Ernst Karl (1840–1905), 583

Ader, Clément (1841–1925), 198

James, William (1842–1910), 288

Reynolds, Osborne (1842–1912), 237, 237f

Rayleigh, Lord, a.k.a. John William Strutt (1842–1919), 214, 214f, 216–218, 275

Boltzmann, Ludwig Eduard (1844–1906), 56, 67, 348, 444, 457

Richard Abmann (Assmann) (1845–1918), 449

Röntgen, Wilhelm Conrad {Roentgen} (1845–1923), 248–249, 249f, 503, 565

Westinghouse, George (1846–1914), 549–550, 550f

Pickering, Edward Charles (1846–1919), 86, 86f

Joukowsky, Nikolay (1847–1921), 587–588, 588f

Tappeiner, Hermann von (1847–1927), 71

Edison, Thomas Alva (1847–1931), 240, 399, 452

Heaviside, Oliver (1850–1925), 386, 387

Putnam, Sarah Gooll (1851–1912), 86f

Schuster, Arthur, Sir (1851–1934), 37, 287–288, 287f

Schott, Otto (1851–1935), 583

Becquerel, Antoine Henri (1852–1908), 81, 179, 199, 254

Van't Hoff, Jacobus Henricus (1852–1911), 345–346, 493, 493f

Poynting, John Henry (1852–1914), 139, 139f

Ramsay, William Mitchell, Sir (1852–1916), 208, 208f

Langley, John Newport (1852–1925), 10

Onnes, Heike Kamerlingh (1853–1926), 364

Lorentz, Hendrik Antoon (1853–1928), 240f

Poincaré, Jules Henri (1854–1912), 109, 109f

Rydberg, Johannes Robert (1854–1919), 256–257, 256f

Eastman, George (1854–1932), 77

Zehnder, Ludwig (1854–1949), 582

Bohr, Christian Harald Lauritz Peter Emil (1855–1911), 84

Teisserenc de Bort, Léon (1855–1933), 449

Laurberg, Julie (1856–1915), 336f

Runge, Carl David Tolmé (1856–1927), 250–251, 250f

Thomson, Joseph John (1856–1940), 73, 127, 189, 254, 410–412, 411f, 443

Allievi, Lorenzo (1856–1941), 484

Curie, Paul-Jacques (1856–1941), 88–89

Tesla, Nikola (1856–1943), 395–396, 396f

Hertz, Heinrich Rudolf (1857–1894), 75, 232, 443

Lyapunov, Aleksandr Mikhailovich [Александр Михайлович Ляпунов] (1857–1918), 150

Thévenin, Léon Charles (1857–1926), 407, 407f

Larmor, Joseph, Sir (1857–1942), 189

Planck, Maxwell Karl Ernst Ludwig (1858–1947), 96, 96f, 172f, 173, 177, 179, 286, 471–472, 554

Curie, Pierre (1859–1906), 88–89, 119, 204

Finsen, Niels Ryberg (1860–1904), 329

Villard, Paul Ulrich (1860–1934), 503, 503f

Wiechert, Emil Johann (1861–1928), 443, 504

Von Lenard, Philipp Eduard Anton (Lénárd Fülöp Philipp Eduard Anton von Lenard) (1862–1947), 521–522, 522f

Trouton, Frederick Thomas (1863–1922), 449–450, 449f

Pérot, Jean-Baptiste Alfred (1863–1925), 40, 40f

Riva-Rocci, Scipione (1863–1937), 243–244, 243f, 340

Kipping, Frederick (1863–1949), 313

Minkowski, Hermann (1864–1909), 423

Wien, Wilhelm Carl Werner Otto Fritz Franz (1864–1928), 189, 254, 554–555, 554f

Pockels, Friedrich Carl Alwin (1865–1913), 73, 108–109, 108f

Zeeman, Pieter (1865–1943), 580–581, 580f

Frank, Otto (1865–1944), 346, 561

Paschen, Friedrich (1865–1947), 19–21, 19f

Starling, Ernest Henry (1866–1927), 345–346, 345f

Fessenden, Reginald Aubrey (1866–1932), 468

Poussin, Baron Charles-Jean Étienne Gustave Nicolas de la Vallée (1866–1962), 137, 137f

Curie, Manya (Marie) Skłodowska (1867–1934), 119, 193, 199, 204

Kutta, Martin Wilhelm (1867–1944), 250–251

Fabry, Maurice Paul Auguste Charles (1867–1945), 40

Sørensen, Søren Peder Lauritz (1868–1939), 46, 336, 336f

Sommerfeld, Arnold Johannes Wilhelm (1868–1951), 218, 333, 333f, 581

Millikan, Robert Andrews (1868–1953), 410, 440

Mie, Gustav Adolf Feodor Wilhelm Ludwig (1868–1957), 214

Townsend, John Sealy Edward, Sir (1868–1957), 20, 439–440, 440f

Liénard, Alfred-Marie (1869–1958), 443

Wilson, Charles Thomson Rees (1869–1959), 557, 557f

Broek, Antonius van den (1870–1926), 35

Perrin, Jean Baptiste (1870–1942), 41, 41f, 410–411

Rutherford, Ernest (1871–1937), 153, 179, 189, 254–255, 254f, 287, 324, 411, 439, 503, 532, 558

Tsvet, Mikhail Semyonovich {Михаил Семёнович Цвет} (1872–1919), 451, 451f

Langevin, Paul (1872–1946), 9, 23f, 254f

Russell, Bertrand Arthur William (1872–1970), 251, 251f

Schwarzschild, Karl (1873–1916), 287–288, 288f

Gad, Franziska (1873–1921), 336f

Carathéodory, Constantin (1873–1950), 44, 290

Korotkov, Nikolai Sergeyevich (Николай Сергеевич Коротков) (1874–1920), 244, 341, 434

Houdini, Harry (1874–1926), 288

Weiss, Ehrich (1874–1926), 288

Bénard, Henri (1874–1939), 217

Stark, Johannes (1874–1957), 344–345, 345f, 581

Lewis, Gilbert Newton (1875–1946), 171

Prandtl, Ludwig (1875–1953), 140–141, 141f

Saunders, Frederick Albert (1875–1963), 252, 269

Raab, Oscar (1876–1986), 71, 187

Barkla, Charles Glover (1877–1944), 566

Aston, Francis William (1877–1945), 189

Jeans, James Hopwood, Sir (1877–1946), 218

Soddy, Frederick (1877–1956), 189, 208, 324, 324f

Russell, Henry Norris (1877–1957), 221, 251–252, 251f, 269

Mandelshtam, Leonid Isaakovich (1879–1944), 207

Burton, Eli Franklin (1879–1948), 443

Pfund, August Herman (1879–1949), 44–45, 45f

Einstein, Albert (1879–1955), 75, 77, 96, 122, 148, 284, 413, 421–422

Richardson, Owen Willans, Sir (1879–1959), 240, 240f

Laue, Max Theodor Felix von (1879–1960), 520–521, 520f

Ehrenfest, Paul (1880–1933), 460

Gans, Richard Martin (1880–1954), 218

Davisson, Clinton Joseph (1881–1958), 410

Back, Ernst Emil Alexander (1881–1959), 21

Von Kármán, Tódor (Theodore) (1881–1963), 518–519, 519f

Eddington, Arthur Stanley, Sir (1882–1944), 362

Franck, James (1882–1964), 232

Blasius, Paul Richard Heinrich (1883–1970), 141

Debye, Petrus (Peter) Josephus Wilhelmus (1884–1966), 218, 581

Busch, Hans (1884–1973), 443

Bohr, Niels Henrik David (1885–1962), 147, 174, 177, 179, 307, 552, 566

Taylor, Geoffrey Ingram, Sir (1886–1975), 383, 383f

Schottky, Walter Hermann (1886–1976), 282, 282f

Moseley, Henry (Harry) Gwyn Jeffreys (1887–1915), 35

Schrödinger, Erwin Rudolf Josef Alexander (1887–1961), 23, 148, 174, 177, 179, 284, 284f, 286

Stern, Otto (1888–1969), 349–350, 349f

Raman, Chandrasekhara Venkata, Sir (1888–1970), 206–207, 207f

Tate, John Torrence Sr. (1889–1950), 381, 381f

Hubble, Edwin Powell (1889–1953), 389

Van der Pol, Balthasar (1889–1959), 488, 488f

Brillouin, Léon Nicolas (1889–1969), 333, 549

Nyquist, Harry Theodor ("Nyqvist") (1889–1976), 264, 302

Gerlach, Walther (1889–1979), 349, 350

Èapek, Karel (1890–1938), 246

Armstrong, Edwin Howard (1890–1954), 198, 198f

Landsberg, Grigory Samuilovich (1890–1957), 207

Scherrer, Paul (1890–1969), 279

Bragg, William Lawrence, Sir (1890–1971), 520

Wolfers, Frithiof (1890–1971), 171

Chadwick, James (1891–1974), 189

Compton, Arthur Holly (1892–1962), 541, 557

Scatchard, George (1892–1973), 273–274, 274f

Schmidt, Ernst Heinrich Wilhelm (1892–1975), 281–282, 281f

Thomson, George Paget, Sir (1892–1975), 410, 410f

De Broglie, Prince Louis Victor Pierre Raymond duc (1892–1987), 175f, 177, 179, 285, 443, 541

Saha, Meghnad (1893–1956), 261, 261f

Weissenberg, Karl (1893–1976), 547, 547f

Urey, Harold Clayton (1893–1981), 479, 479f

Kramers, Hendrik Anthony (Hans) (1894–1952), 549

Tamm, Igor (1895–1971), 426

Sievert, Rolf Maximilian (1896–1966), 310–311, 311f

Tihanyi, Kálmán (1897–1947), 401

Cockcroft, John (1897–1967), 532

Knoll, Maximillion (1897–1969), 443

Krishnan, Kariamanickam Srinivasa (1898–1961), 207

Wentzel, Gregor (1898–1978), 549, 549f

Smyth, Henry DeWolf (1898–1986), 322

Rabi, Isidor Isaac (1898–1988), 187–188, 188f, 433

Zartman, Ira Forry (1899–1981), 580, 580f

Deshpande, Vijay (mid-twentieth century–), 377

Jaklevic, Robert C. (mid-twentieth century–), 363

Lambe, John J. (mid-twentieth century–), 363

Mercereau, James (mid-twentieth century–), 363

Silver, Arnold (mid-twentieth century–), 363

Weir, John B. de V. (? -?, twentieth century), 547

Kuper, Charles Goethe (twentieth century), 25

Edwards, Roy Q. (twentieth century–), 315

Pauli, Wolfgang Ernst (1900–1958), 23, 23f, 173, 177, 460

Slater, John C. (1900–1975), 319

Gagnan, Émile (1900–1979), 288

Uhlenbeck, George Eugene (1900–1988), 460, 460f

Fermi, Enrico (1901–1954), 398

Lawrence, Ernest Orlando (1901–1958), 15

Heisenberg, Werner Karl (1901–1976), 23, 148, 173, 177, 179, 429, 472

Van de Graaff, Robert Jemison (1902–1967), 486, 486f

Goudsmit, Samuel Abraham (1902–1978), 460

Dirac, Paul Adrien Maurice (1902–1984), 2, 23, 96, 173–174, 177–178, 184

Wigner, Eugene (Jenő Pál) (1902–1995), 556, 556f

Powell, Cecil Frank (1903–1969), 137, 137f

Wooster, William Alfred (Peter) (1903–1984), 562

Thomas, Llewellyn Hilleth (1903–1992), 409

Walton, Ernest Thomas Sinton (1903–1995), 532, 532f

Gamow, Georgiy Antonovich (George) (1904–1968), 179

Gray, Louis Harold (1905–1965), 565

Bloch, Felix (1905–1983), 135, 433

Segrè, Emilio Gino (1905–1989), 292, 293f

Anderson, Carl David (1905–1991), 2, 178

Fröhlich, Herbert (1905–1991), 25

Ruge, Arthur Claude (1905–2000), 355

Thorndike, Edward M. (1906–?), 413

Carlson, Chester (1906–1968), 69

Goeppert-Mayer, Maria (Göppert) (1906–1972), 556

Tomonaga, Sin-Itiro (朝永 振一郎) (1906–1979), 429, 429f

Ruska, Ernst (1906–1988), 443

Bethe, Hans Albrecht (1906–2005), 362

Womersley, John Ronald (1907–1958), 561, 561f

Jensen, Johannes Hans Daniel (1907–1973), 556

Yukawa, Hideki (1907–1981), 576, 576f

Peierls, Rudolf Ernst, Sir (1907–1995), 25, 25f

McClung, Fred J. (1907–2014), 168

Dussik, Karl Theodore (1908–1968), 468

Landau, Lev Davidovich (1908–1968), 174

Rytov, Sergei M. [Рытов, Сергей Михайлович] (1908–1996), 258

Weisskopf, Victor Frederick (1908–2002), 548, 548f

Land, Edwin Herbert (1909–1991), 117, 449

Peters, Bernard (1910–1993), 43, 43f

Plunkett, Roy (1910–1994), 386

Chandrasekhar, Subrahmanyan (1910–1995), 287

Cousteau, Jacques-Yves (1910–1997), 288–289

Hertzsprung, Ejnar (1911–1967), 221

Torrey, Henry Cutler (1911–1998), 433

Simmons, Edward E., Jr. (1911–2004), 355

Wheeler, John Archibald (1911–2008), 551–552, 552f

Hall, Cecil Edwin (1912–1991), 443

Purcell, Edward Mills (1912–1997), 161, 161f, 433

Wu, Chien-Shiung (Wú Jiànxióng; 吳健雄) (1912–1997), 564, 564f

Van Allen, James Alfred (1914–2006), 484–485, 484f

Townes, Charles Hard (1915–), 278, 439, 439f

Schiff, Leonard Isaac (1915–1971), 280, 281f

Hofstadter, Robert (1915–1990), 220

Wiegand, Clyde (1915–1996), 292

Hillier, James (1915–2007), 443

Bascom, William Newell (1916–2000), 448

Shannon, Claude Elwood (1916–2001), 264, 301–302, 302f

Prokhorov, Aleksandr M. (1916–2002), 439

Crick, Francis Harry Compton (1916–2004), 537, 556

Wilkins, Maurice Hugh Frederick (1916–2004), 537, 556–557, 557f

Kohman, Truman P. (1916–2010), 11

Skeggs, Leonard T. Jr. (1918–), 318, 318f

Feynman, Richard Phillips (1918–1988), 429, 552, 588

Schwinger, Julian Seymour (1918–1994), 429, 564, 579

Reines, Frederick (1918–1998), 225–226, 226f

Pound, Robert Vivian (1919–2010), 135–136, 136f, 433

Fujita, Tetsuya (1920–1998), 430

Gould, Gordon (1920–2005), 168

Chamberlain, Owen (1920–2006), 292

Rényi, Alfréd (1921–1970), 228, 228f

Sakharov, Andrei (1921–1989), 426

Schawlow, Arthur Leonard (1921–1999), 278, 278f

Yang, Chen Ning (1922–), 569–570

Basov, Nicolay G. (1922–2001), 439

Lattes, César Mansueto Giulio (1924–2005), 576

Perkins, Donald Hill (1925–), 39, 39f

Tate, John Torrence, Jr. (1925–), 381, 381f

Van der Meer, Simon (1925–2011), 487, 487f

Rasmussen, John (1926–), 214, 214f

Salam, Abdus (1926–1996), 546, 579

Bilaniuk, Olexa-Myron (1926–2009), 377

Logan, Benjamin Franklin (1927–), 307

Perl, Martin Lewis (1927–), 226

Mills, Robert Laurence (1927–1999), 570

Watson, James Dewey (1928–), 537, 537f, 556

Gell-Mann, Murray (1929–), 180, 588

Kuhl, David Edmund (1929–), 315

Mössbauer, Rudolf (1929–2011), 220

Hellwarth, Robert W. (1930–), 168

Rebka, Glen Anderson, Jr. (1931–), 135–136

Sudarshan, George (1931–), 377

Verlet, Loup (1931–), 501

Prebus, Albert (1931–2000), 443

Glashow, Sheldon Lee (1932–), 283, 546, 579

Walecka, John Dirk (1932–), 528, 528f

Weinberg, Steven (1932–), 546, 546f, 579

Rubbia, Carlo (1934–), 487

Shepp, Lawrence (Larry) Alan (1936–2013), 307

Zweig, George (1937–), 180, 588, 588f

Tompsett, Michael Francis (1939–), 401

Josephson, Brian David (1940–), 364

Brus, Louis E. (1943–), 172

Ekimov, Alexey (1945–), 172

't Hooft, Gerard {Geradus} (1946–), 377, 377f

Georgi III, Howard Mason (1947–), 283

Schrieffer, Howard Lawrence (1948–), 283–284, 283f

Bradt, Helmut L. (–1950), 43

Reed, Mark (1955–), 172

Index of Subjects

Note: Page numbers followed by f refer to figures, respectively.

Acoustics
Parallel processing, 7
Parametric acoustic array, 9, 9f
Paraxial approximation, 10–11, 11f
Peierls, Rudolf Ernst, Sir (1907–1995), 25, 25f
Peierls–Fröhlich–Kuper ground state, 25
Peierls transition, 25
Period of a cycle (T), 34, 35f
Periodogram, 37, 37f
Phantom, 49, 49f
Phase, 49–50, 50f–51f
Phase cancellation, 51, 51f
Phase noise, 53–54, 54f
Phase rotation, 54, 54f
Phase sequence, 55
Phased array, 58, 58f
Phase velocity, 57
Phase-only imaging, 58
Photoacoustic microscopy, 61–64
Piano, 85–86, 86f
Piezoelectric effect, 87–88, 88f
Piezoelectric resonance, 88, 89f
Piezoelectricity, 89
Piezoelectric transducer, 89, 89f
Point source, 111
Poly(vinylidene) fluoride (PVDF), 122
Power spectrum, 139
Praetorius, Michael (original name: Michael Schultheiβ) (1571–1621), 140, 140f
Pyroelectricity, 162
PZT, 162–163
Q Factor, 165–166, 166f
Quantification, 171
Radiation coupling, 191, 191f
Radiation force, 192, 192f
Rayleigh criterion, 215, 215f
Rayleigh–Sommerfeld diffraction, 218
Refraction, 225, 225f
Resonance, 231, 231f
Resonance frequency, 232, 232f
Reverberation, 236, 236f
Riccati equations, 240
Rician noise, 241, 241f
Robot, 245, 245f

Robotics, 245–246, 246f
Rytov approximation, 258
Rytov, Sergei M. [Рытов, Сергей Михайлович] (1908–1996), 258, 258f
Sabine equation, 259
SAM, 263, 263f
Sampled delay focusing, 263
Sampling, 263–264
Sampling depth, 264
Sauveur, Joseph (1653–1716), 270, 270f
Savart, Félix (1791–1841), 270, 270f
SAW, 271
Scanning acoustic microscope (SAM), 272–273, 273f
Scattering, 275, 275f
Seismic, 293, 293f
Seismic acoustic imaging, 294, 294f
Seismic wave, 294, 294f
Seismic wave, dissipative effects, 295
Seismometer, 296, 296f
Shadowgraph method, 300, 300f
Shear Modulus (G_∞), 304
Shear stress (σ_s), 305, 305f
Shepp-Logan phantom, 307–308, 308f
Signal, 311–312, 312f
Signal-to-noise ratio (S/N or SNR), 312, 312f
Snell's law, 323, 323f
Snel's Law, 323
Soliton, 331, 331f
Sonogram, 334–335, 335f
Sonography, 335
Sonohysterography, 335
Sonoluminescence, 335
Sound, 336–337, 337f
Speaker, 337
STANI, 343
Stereo, 348–349
Surface gravitational wave, 367, 367f
Surface roughness, 368–369, 369f
Tectonics, 385, 385f
Temporal period (T), 391, 391f
Thermal wave, 398–399
Timbre, 421, 421f
Tissue characterization, 424–425, 425f
Tomography, 428, 428f

Acoustics (*Continued*)
Transducer, 441
Tremor, 445
Ultrasonic computerized tomography, 464–465, 465f
Ultrasonics, 467, 467f
Ultrasonograms, 468
Ultrasound, 468–469, 469f–470f
Unified Fourier reconstruction, 474
Velocity ($\vec{v}$), 497
Vibration, 502–503, 503f
Volcano, 514, 514f
$V(z)$ inversion, 525
Wave dispersion, 539–540, 540f
Wentzel–Kramers–Brillouin (WKB) solution method, 549
Astronomy/Astrophysics
Paleomagnetism, 3–4, 4f
Periodogram, 37, 37f
Photosphere, 79–80, 80f
Picard, Jean-Félix (1620–1682), 86
Pickering, Edward Charles (1846–1919), 86, 86f
Pion, 91
Planetary data, 99, 99f
Planetary motion, 99, 99f
Planetary motion, Kepler's laws of, 100
Planetary precession, 100
Poisson, Siméon Denis (1781–1840), 113, 113f
Polytropic process, 121
Positron (β^+), 127
Prandtl, Ludwig (1875–1953), 140–141, 141f
Pressure coefficient ($Pt = (P − P_\infty)/(1/2)\rho_\infty v_\infty^2$), 144
Ptolemaeus, Claudius (approximately 90–168 AD), 155, 155f
Pulsar, 158, 158f
Purcell, Edward Mills (1912–1997), 161, 161f
Quantum liquid, 174
Quantum magnet, 174
Quasar, 182–183, 183f
Quasi-steady state, 184–185, 185f
Radiant energy fluence rate ($E^0(\vec{r},t)$), 189
Radiation belt, 191
Radiative transfer, 196
Radioastronomy, 202–203, 203f
Rayleigh–Taylor instability, 218
Red dwarf, 221, 221f
Red giant, 221–222
Redshift, 223, 223f
Reines, Frederick (1918–1998), 225–226, 226f
Ritter, Johann Wilhelm (1776–1810), 243, 243f
Roemer {Rømer, also Römer}, Olaus (Ole) (1644–1710), 247, 247f
Saha ionization equation, 261
Satellite, 264–265, 265f
Saturn, 269, 269f
Scattering, 275, 275f
Scattering phase function, 277, 277f

Scattering phase function, Henyey–Greenstein, 278
Schuster, Arthur, Sir (1851–1934), 287, 287f
Schwarzschild, Karl (1873–1916), 288, 288f
Sojourner, 327, 327f
Solar wind, 329
Solstice, 332, 332f
Star, 343–344, 344f
Sun, 361–362, 362f
Supernova, 365, 365f
Synchrotron, 374, 374f
Synchrotron radiation, 374
Tectonics, 385, 385f
Telescope, 389, 389f
Three Laws of planetary motion, 413–414, 414f
Time perturbation, colliding black holes, 422–423, 423f
Timocharis, 423
Transport equation, 443–444
Triplet, Wild's, 447
Universal gravitational constant (G), 475
Universal gravitation, law of, 475
Universe, 475–476, 476f
Vacuum field equations, 482
Van Allen, James Alfred (1914–2006), 484, 484f
Van Allen belts, 485
Venus, 500, 500f
Volcano, 514, 514f
Von Guericke, Otto (1602–1682), 517–518, 518f
Von Kármán, Tódor (Theodore) (1881–1963), 518–519, 519f
Wheeler, John Archibald (1911–2008), 551–552, 552f
White dwarf, 552–553, 553f
Wing, 560, 560f
Zenith, 584, 584f
Zenith angle, 585, 585f
Atomic Physics
Pair annihilation, 2
Pairing energy (P_{pair}), 3
Paramagnetism, 9
Parent nucleus, 11
Parity, 12–13, 13f
Parity conservation rule, 14
Particle, 14–15, 15f
Particle accelerator, 15, 15f
Particle accelerators, linear, 16
Paschen, Friedrich (1865–1947), 19, 19f
Paschen law, 20, 20f
Paschen lines, 20
Paschen series, 20, 21f
Paschen–Back effect, 21
Pauli, Wolfgang Ernst (1900–1958), 23, 23f
Pauli exclusion principle, 23
Pauli spin matrix, 23
Periodic table of elements, 35, 36f
Perrin, Jean Baptiste (1870–1942), 41, 41f
Perturbation theory, 42

Peters, Bernard (1910–1993), 43, 43f
Pfund, August Herman (1879–1949), 44–45, 45f
Pfund series, 45, 45f
Phase space, 55–56, 56f
Phase velocity, 57
Phasor, 59
Phosphorescence, 59–60, 60f
Phosphorus (phosphor) $\left(^{30}_{15}P\right)$, 60–61, 61f
Photodisintegration, 71
Photoelectric cells, 73–74, 74f
Photomultiplier tube, 77–78, 78f
Photon, 78–79, 79f
Photovoltaic effect, 81–82, 82f
Physisorption, 85
Pickering, Edward Charles (1846–1919), 86, 86f
Pickering series, 87
Piezoelectric effect, 87–88, 88f
Piezoelectric resonance, 88, 89f
Piezoelectricity, 89
Piezoelectric transducer, 89, 89f
Pinch effect, 90, 90f
Pion, 91
Planck, Maxwell Karl Ernst Ludwig (1858–1947),
    95–96, 96f
Planck's Constant h, 96
Planck's law, 96
Planck's radiation law, 96–97, 97f
Plasma, 100–101, 101f
Plasma frequency, 101
Plasmon, 101
Plücker, Julius (1801–1868), 104–105, 105f
Plutonium $\left(^{244}_{94}Pu\right)$, 105, 105f
Polonium $\left(^{84}_{209}Po\right)$, 119
Pool, M. L., 122
Positive ions, 126, 126f
Positive rays, 127
Positron (β^+), 127
Positron annihilation, 127–128, 128f
Positron emission tomography (PET), 128–129, 129f
Positronium, 129, 129f
Potential barrier, 130, 130f
Potential well, 133–134, 134f
Pound, Robert Vivian (1919–2010), 135–136, 136f
Powell, Cecil Frank (1903–1969), 137, 137f
Poynting vector ($\vec{S}$), 140
Precession, 142, 142f
Prévost theory of heat exchange, 145
Primary cosmic ray particles, 147
Principal moments, 147
Principal quantum number, 147
Probability, 149–150, 150f
Prompt neutron, 151
Proton, 153
Prout, William (1785–1850), 153, 153f
p-type doping, 155–156, 156f
Purcell, Edward Mills (1912–1997), 161, 161f

Pyroelectricity, 162
Q Equation, 165, 165f
Q of reaction, 166
Quadrupole moment, 170, 170f
Quanta, 171
Quantum electrodynamics (QED), 173
Quantum number, 176–177, 176f
Quantum orbital angular momentum, 177
Quantum physics, electron shells, 177–178
Quantum spin angular momentum, 178
Quantum state, 178, 178f
Quantum theory, 179
Quantum total angular momentum, 179
Quark, 180–181, 180f
Quasiparticle, 184
Rabi, Isidor Isaac (1898–1988), 187–188, 188f
Radiation, 189–190, 190f
Radiation hazards, 192–193, 193f
Radiation units, 194–195, 195f
Radiative capture, 196, 196f
Radioactive decay, 199, 199f
Radioactive decay constant (λ_{decay}), 200, 200f
Radioactive decay law, 201
Radioactive isotope, 201, 201f
Radioactive transformation, 201
Radioactive waste, 202, 202f
Radioactivity, 202, 202f
Radioastronomy, 202–203, 203f
Radioisotope, 204
Radionuclide, 204
Radium $\left(^{226}_{88}Ra\right)$, 204
Radius of gyration (R_g), 204
Radon $\left(^{222}_{86}Rn\right)$, 205, 205f
Raman spectroscopy, 208
Rayleigh–Jeans equation, 218
Reflectance, 223, 223f
Reflection, 224, 224f
Reproduction factor, 228
Residual nucleus, 229
Resonance, 231, 231f
Resonance absorption, 232
Resonance potential, 232–233, 233f
Resonance states, 234
Rest mass, 235
Richardson's equation, 240
Roentgen, Röntgen, 248
Roentgen, W. C., 248
Röntgen, Wilhelm Conrad {Roentgen} (1845–1923),
    248–249, 249f
Russell–Saunders coupling, 252, 253, 253f
Rutherford cross section, 255
Rutherford scattering, 255, 255f
Rydberg, Johannes Robert (1854–1919), 256, 256f
Rydberg constant, 257
Rydberg series, 257, 257f
Rydberg state, 258

Atomic Physics (*Continued*)

Saint-Elmo's fire, 262, 262f

Scherrer, Paul (1890–1969), 279, 279f

Schrödinger, Erwin Rudolf Josef Alexander (1887–1961), 284, 284f–285f

Schrödinger's cat, 286–287, 287f

Second law of Faraday, 290

Second-generation of matter, 291

Selection rule and, 296

Self-consistent field, 297

Semiconductors, 298

Shape factor, 302

Sharp series, 304

Shell model, 307, 307f

Sigma particle, 311

Singlet state, 317, 317f

Slater determinant, 319–320

Smyth report, 322

Soddy, Frederick (1877–1956), 324, 324f

Solid-state, 331

Solid-state physics, 331

Sommerfeld, Arnold Johannes Wilhelm (1868–1951), 333, 333f

Spectroscopy, 338–339, 339f

Spin, 341–342, 342f

Star, 343–344, 344f

Stefan–Boltzmann law, 348

Stern, Otto (1888–1969), 349, 349f

Stern-Gerlach experiment, 350

Stimulated emission, 350

Stokes, George Gabriel, Sir (1819–1903), 352, 352f

Stokes' Law, 353–354

Subshell, 361

Sun, 361–362, 362f

Superconductivity, 364

Superfluid, 365

Synchrotron, 374, 374f

Synchrotron radiation, 374

Tensor, 394

't Hooft, Gerard (1946–), 377, 377f

Thermal neutrons, 398

Thermionic emission, 399

Thermonuclear energy, 402

Thermonuclear fission, 402–403, 403f

Thermonuclear fusion, 403–404, 404f

Thomas precession, 409

Thomson, George Paget, Sir (1892–1975), 410, 410f

Thomson, Joseph John (1856–1940), 410–411, 411f

Thomson scattering, 412, 412f

Thorium radioactive series, 412–413, 413f

Thyratron, 416

Time dilation, 422

Torrey, Henry Cutler (1911–1998), 433

Total angular momentum, 437

Townsend, John Sealy Edward, Sir (1868–1957), 439–440, 440f

Tracers, 440

Transistor, 442, 442f

Transuranic element, 444–445

Triplet state, 447, 447f

Trouton, Frederick Thomas (1863–1922), 449, 449f

Trouton's rule, 450

U-234 $\left(^{234}_{92}\text{U}\right)$, 459

U-235 $\left(^{235}_{92}\text{U}\right)$, 459, 459f

U-238 $\left(^{238}_{92}\text{U}\right)$, 460, 460f

Uhlenbeck, George Eugene (1900–1988), 460, 460f

Ultrahigh pressure, 463

Ultraviolet catastrophe, 471, 471f

Unbestimmtheitsprinzip, 472

Uncertainty principle, 472–473, 473f

Unified atomic mass units (u), 474

Unstable equilibrium state, 476, 476f

Up antiquark, 478

Up quark, 478

U-quark, 478

Uranium $\left(^{238}_{92}\text{U}\right)$, 478, 478f

Urey, Harold Clayton (1893–1981), 479, 479f

Valence band, 483, 483f

Van de Graaff generator, 486–487, 487f

Van der Waals, Johannes Diderik (1837–1923), 489, 489f

Van der Waals equation of state, 490

Van der Waals force, 491

Vapor pressure equation, 494

Viscosity (η), 505–506, 506f

Viscosity, dynamic (η_{dyn}), 506

Von Lenard, Philipp Eduard Anton (Lénárd Fülöp Philipp Eduard Anton von Lenard) (1862–1947), 521–522, 522f

V particles, 481

Walton, Ernest Thomas Sinton (1903–1995), 532, 532f

Wavelength, de Broglie, 543

Wave number (k), 541

Weak interaction, 543–544, 544f

Weisskopf half-life, 548

Weisskopf single particle transition probability, 548

Weisskopf, Victor Frederick (1908–2002), 548, 548f

Wheeler, John Archibald (1911–2008), 551–552, 552f

Wiedemann–Franz ratio, 554

Wien, Wilhelm Carl Werner Otto Fritz Franz (1864–1928), 554, 554f

Wien–Planck law, 554–555, 555f

Wien's displacement law, 555, 555f

Wigner distribution, 556

Wigner, Eugene (Jenő Pál) (1902–1995), 556, 556f

Wilson, Charles Thomson Rees (1869–1959), 557, 557f

Wilson cloud chamber, 558, 558f

Work function (φ_{elec}, in electron volt: eV), 562

Wu, Chien-Shiung (Wú Jiànxióng; 吴健雄) (1912–1997), 564, 564f

X-ray, characteristic, 566, 567f
X-rays diffraction in crystals, 567, 567f–568f
Zartman, Ira Forry (1899–1981), 580, 580f
Zeeman, Pieter (1865–1943), 580, 580f
Zeeman and Stark effect, 581
Zeeman effect, 581–582, 582f
Zero-point energy, 587, 587f
Biomedical Physics
Pacemaker, 1–2, 2f
Parabola, 5, 5f
Paracrine signaling, 5–6, 6f
Parasympathetic nerve system, 10, 10f
Parent nucleus, 11
Partition coefficient, 17
Paxillin, 24
PDT, 24
Penumbra, 28–29, 29f
Perception, 29–30, 30f
Perceptron, 30
Perfusion, 32, 33f
Period doubling, 34, 34f
Peristaltic motion, 38, 38f
Permeability (μ_{mag}), 39
Permittivity (ε_{elec}), 39
Persistence time, 42
PET tracer, 42
pH, 46–47, 47f
Phagocyte, 47, 47f
Phagocytosis, 48, 48f
Phase encoding, 52–53, 53f
Phased array, 58, 58f
Photinus-luciferin 4-monooxygenase, 61
Photoacoustic microscopy, 61–64
Photobiological process, 64
Photobleaching, 64
Photochemical effect, 64
Photochemical reaction, 64
Photocoagulation, 64–69, 69f
Photodynamic therapy (PDT), 71–72, 72f
Photoelectric effect, 74, 75f
Photography, 77, 77f
Photopic vision, 79, 79f
Photosynthesis, 80–81, 81f
Phototoxicity, 81
Physiologic dead space, 83–84, 84f
Physiology, 84–85, 85f
Physisorption, 85
Pinocytosis, 91, 91f
Plasma, 100–101, 101f
Plasticity, 102, 102f
Plasticizers, 103
Pneumotachometer, 106, 106f
Po$_2$, 108, 108f
Poiseuille's law, 112–113
Poisson, Siméon Denis (1781–1840), 113, 113f
Poisson equations, 114

Poisson noise, 114
Polar coordinates, 114, 114f
Polar moment of inertia, 115
Polar nature of a medium, 115, 115f
Polydimethylsiloxane (PDMS), 119–120
Polymer, 120, 120f
Polymethylmethacrylate (PMMA), 120, 120f
Polypeptide, 121, 121f
Polyvinyl chloride (PVC), 121–122, 122f
Poly(vinylidene) fluoride (PVDF), 122
Porphyrins, 124–125, 125f
Positron annihilation, 127–128, 128f
Positron emission tomography (PET), 128–129, 129f
Potassium $\left(^{19}_{39}\text{K}\right)$, 130
Potassium chloride (KCl), 130
Potential difference, 131, 131f
Potential energy of a liquid surface, 132
Precession, 142, 142f
Pressure (P), 142–143, 143f
Principal stress, 147
Prout, William (1785–1850), 153, 153f
Pseudo plastics, 154, 154f
Pulmonary system, 157–158, 158f
Pulsatile flow, 159, 159f
Pulse oximeter, 159–160, 160f
Purcell, Edward Mills (1912–1997), 161, 161f
P-wave, 161, 161f
PZT, 162–163
Q Factor, 165–166, 166f
Q–T Interval, 169, 169f
Quantum dot (QD), 172, 172f
Quantum magnet, 174
Quartz, 182, 182f
Raab, Oscar (1876–1986), 187, 187f
Radiance $\left(\Phi(\vec{r},\vec{s})\right)$, 188, 189f
Radiant energy fluence rate $\left(E^0(\vec{r},t)\right)$, 189
Radiation dose, 192, 192f
Radiation therapy, 193–194, 194f
Radiative power, 196
Radiative transfer, 196
Radio frequency (RF), 197, 197f
Radioactive decay law, 201
Radioisotope, 204
Radionuclide, 204
Radiopharmaceutical, 204, 204f
Radius of gyration (R_g), 204
Random walk, 209, 209f
Rankine, 209
Rapid prototyping, 212, 213f
Rayleigh scattering, 216–217, 217f
Rayleigh screening, 217
Reabsorption, 218
Redox potential, 222
Redox reaction, 222, 222f
Relaxation time, 227
Reserve volume (RV), 228–229, 229f

Biomedical Physics (*Continued*)

Residual volume, 229

Resistance, 229–230

Resonance frequency, 232, 232f

Respiration, 234, 234f

Resting potential, 235

Retina, 235, 235f

Reverse osmosis, 236, 236f

Reynolds, Osborne (1842–1912), 237, 237f

Reynolds number, 238

Rheobase, 238

Rheobasic current, 238

Rheology, 239

Rician noise, 241, 241f

Riva-Rocci cuff, 244, 244f

Rods, 247, 247f

Röntgen, Wilhelm Conrad {Roentgen} (1845–1923), 248–249, 249f

Rouleaux formation, 250, 250f

S, M, and L responses of the human eye, 259

Sabine equation, 259

Saccade, 260, 260f

SAM, 263, 263f

Sarcomere, 264, 264f

Saturation, 265–266, 266f–267f

Saturation curve, 267–268, 268f

Scaffold, 271–272, 272f

Scanning acoustic microscope (SAM), 272–273, 273f

Scatchard, George (1892–1973), 273–274, 274f

Scatchard equation, 274

Scatchard plot, 274, 274f

Scatchard–Rosenthal plot, 275

Scattering phase function, Henyey-Greenstein, 278

Schlieren imaging for concentration, 281, 281f

Schwarzschild, Karl (1873–1916), 288, 288f

Scuba gear, 288–289, 289f

Sediment equilibrium, 291

Sediment equilibrium in a density gradient, 291

Sedimentation velocity, 292

Selectin, 296

Selectively permeable, 297

Semipermeable membrane, 299, 299f

Shape memory alloys (SMAs), 302–303, 303f

Shark, 303, 303f

Shear force, 304, 304f

Shear Modulus (G_∞), 304

Shear strain (μ_s), 305, 305f

Shear stress (σ_s), 305, 305f

Shear-thickening fluid, 306, 306f

Shear-thinning fluid, 306, 306f

Shepp-Logan phantom, 307–308, 308f

Sherwood number (Sh = $h_m L / D_{AB}$), 308

Shunt, 310, 310f

Sievert (*Sv*), 310

Sievert, Rolf Maximilian (1896–1966), 310–311, 311f

Signal, 311–312, 312f

Signal-to-noise ratio (S/N or SNR), 312, 312f

Silastic™, 313

Silicone rubber, 313–314, 314f

Silicon nitride, 313

Single photon emission computed tomography (SPECT), 315

Skeggs, Leonard T. Jr. (1918–), 318, 318f

Skeletal muscle, 318

Skin, 318–319, 319f

Sodium ($^{22}_{11}\text{Na}$), 324–325, 325f

Sodium chloride (NaCl), 325

Solar therapy, 329

Somesthesis, 333

Sonogram, 334–335, 335f

Specific heat (c_{sp}), 337

Specific resistance, 338

Sphygmomanometer, 340–341, 341f

Stochastic process, 352

Strouhal number (Sr = $\nu L / \nu_p$), 358

Student's *t*-test, 358–359

Surface Potential Energy, 367–368, 368f

Surface tension, 370, 370f

Surfactant, 372, 372f

Synapse, 372–373, 373f

Synaptic signaling, 373, 373f

Systolic pressure, 374–375, 375f

Taylor dispersion, 383–384

Teflon®, 385–386

Telegraph equation, 387–388

Telemetry, 388, 388f

TEM, 390

Thermodynamics, 399–400

Thermodynamics, second law, 400

Thermodynamics, third law, 400

Tidal breathing, 416–417, 417f

Tidal volume, 419, 419f

Tissue characterization, 424–425, 425f

Titanium, 425

Toepler, August Joseph Ignaz (1836–1912), 425–426, 426f

Tomographic slices, 427, 427f

Tomography, 428, 428f

Tonicity, 429–430, 430f

Total lung capacity (TLC), 438, 438f

Tracers, 440

Transcytosis, 440

Transmission electron microscope, 443, 443f

Tremor, 445

Tsvet, Mikhail Semyonovich {Михаи́л Семёнович Цвет} (1872–1919), 451, 451f

Ultimate stress, 461

Ultracentrifuge, 461–462, 462f

Ultrafast biological events, 462–463, 463f

Ultrasonic ablation, 464, 464f

Ultrasonic imaging, 466

Ultrasonograms, 468

Ultrasound, 468–469, 469f–470f
Umbilical cord, 472, 472f
Van der Pol equation, 488
Van der Pol oscillator, 488
Van der Waals bonding, 489–490, 490f
Van Leeuwenhoek, Antonie Philips (1632–1723), 491–492, 492f
Van't Hoff, Jacobus Henricus (1852–1911), 493, 493f
Van't Hoff equation, 493
Van't Hoff law, 494
Vein, 497
Velocity ($\bar{v}$), 497
Ventilation, 498
Ventilator, 498–499, 499f
Vesalius, Andreas (1515–1564), 501–502, 502f
Viscoelastic, 504, 504f
Viscosity (η), 505–506, 506f
Viscosity, dynamic (η_{dyn}), 506
Viscosity model, 509, 509f
Vision, 510–511, 511f
Visual acuity, 512, 512f
Vital capacity (VC), 512
Vitreous humor, 512–513, 513f
Voice, 513, 513f
Volta, Alessandro Giuseppe Antonio Anastasio Gerolamo Umberto, Count (1745–1827), 514, 514f
Von Helmholtz, Hermann Ludwig Ferdinand (1821–1894), 518, 518f
Wall, 528–529, 529f
Water (H_2O), 532–533, 533f
Wave dispersion, 539–540, 540f
Wave propagation speed, 541–542
Weber, Ernst Heinrich (1795–1878), 544, 544f
Weir, John B. de V., 547
Weir equation, 547
Wilkins, Maurice Hugh Frederick (1916–2004), 556–557, 557f
Womersley, John Ronald (1907–1958), 561, 561f
Womersley number, ($\alpha_{Wo} = r\sqrt{\rho\omega/\eta}$), 562
Work function (φ_{elec}, in electron volt: eV), 562
X-ray, 565–566, 566f
Young–Laplace equation, 572

Chemical Physics
Paracrine signaling, 5–6, 6f
Parasympathetic nerve system, 10, 10f
Partition coefficient, 17
Paxillin, 24
PDT, 24
Perception, 29–30, 30f
Percolation, 31, 31f
pH, 46–47, 47f
Phase, 49–50, 50f–51f
Phase diagram, 51–52, 52f
Phosphorus (phosphor) ($^{30}_{15}P$), 60–61, 61f
Photinus-luciferin 4-monooxygenase, 61

Photobiological process, 64
Photobleaching, 64
Photochemical effect, 64
Photochemical reaction, 64
Photodynamic therapy (PDT), 71–72, 72f
Photographic plate, 76, 76f
Phototoxicity, 81
Physiology, 84–85, 85f
Plasticity, 102, 102f
Plasticizers, 103
Plastics, 103, 103f
Po_2, 108, 108f
Poisson equations, 114
Polarization selective film, 117
Polar nature of a medium, 115, 115f
Polaroid™ film, 117, 117f
Polydimethylsiloxane (PDMS), 119–120
Polymer, 120, 120f
Polymethylmethacrylate (PMMA), 120, 120f
Polypeptide, 121, 121f
Polyvinyl chloride (PVC), 121–122, 122f
Poly(vinylidene) fluoride (PVDF), 122
Porphyrins, 124–125, 125f
Potassium ($^{19}_{39}K$), 130
Potassium chloride (KCl), 130
Potential energy of a liquid surface, 132
Potential well, 133–134, 134f
Q Equation, 165, 165f
Q Value, 169, 169f
Radiopharmaceutical, 204, 204f
Raoult, François-Marie (1830–1901), 212, 212f
Reabsorption, 218
Reciprocity rule, 220
Redox potential, 222
Redox reaction, 222, 222f
Resting potential, 235
Retina, 235, 235f
Reverse osmosis, 236, 236f
Rheobase, 238
Rheobasic current, 238
Rods, 247, 247f
Salt, 263
Sarcomere, 264, 264f
Saturation, 265–266, 266f–267f
Scatchard, George (1892–1973), 273–274, 274f
Scatchard equation, 274
Scatchard plot, 274, 274f
Scheele, Carl Wilhelm (1742–1786), 278–279, 279f
Sediment equilibrium, 291
Sediment equilibrium in a density gradient, 291
Sedimentation velocity, 292
Selectin, 296
Semipermeable membrane, 299, 299f
Silastic™, 313
Silicon (Si), 313, 313f
Silicone rubber, 313–314, 314f

Chemical Physics (*Continued*)
Silicon nitride, 313
Skeggs, Leonard T. Jr. (1918–), 318, 318f
Skin, 318–319, 319f
Slater determinant, 319–320
Soddy, Frederick (1877–1956), 324, 324f
Sodium $\left(_{11}^{22}Na\right)$, 324–325, 325f
Sodium chloride (NaCl), 325
Solar therapy, 329
Solution, 332
Sørensen, Søren Peder Lauritz (1868–1939), 336, 336f
Stark, Johannes (1874–1957), 344–345, 345f
Starling, Ernest Henry (1866–1927), 345, 345f
Starling's law, 346, 346f
Stoichiometric coefficient, $\left(v_i^{(j)}\right)$, 352
Stoichiometry, 352
Surface energy, 366–367
Surface phenomena of Liquids, 367
Surface Potential Energy, 367–368, 368f
Surface tension, 370, 370f
Surfactant, 372, 372f
Synapse, 372–373, 373f
Synaptic signaling, 373, 373f
Tate, John Torrence Jr. (1925–), 381, 381f
Tectonics, 385, 385f
Teflon®, 385–386
Thermodynamics, 399–400
Thermokinetic oscillator, 402
Tonicity, 429–430, 430f
Ultrafast biological events, 462–463, 463f
Umbilical cord, 472, 472f
Van't Hoff, Jacobus Henricus (1852–1911), 493, 493f
Van't Hoff equation, 493
Van't Hoff law, 494
Ventilator, 498–499, 499f
Vision, 510–511, 511f
Volcano, 514, 514f
Water (H$_2$O), 532–533, 533f
Weir, John B. de V., 547
Weir equation, 547
Young–Laplace equation, 572
Computational Physics
Parabola, 5, 5f
Parallel processing, 7
Parametric acoustic array, 9, 9f
Paraxial approximation, 10–11, 11f
Parity, 12–13, 13f
Partition function, 17
Pauli, Wolfgang Ernst (1900–1958), 23, 23f
Peierls–Fröhlich–Kuper ground state, 25
Perceptron, 30
Percolation, 31, 31f
Pergrinus, Petri, a.k.a. Pierre de Maricourt (1220–1290), 33, 33f
Period doubling, 34, 34f
Periodogram, 37, 37f

Permeability (μ_{mag}), 39
Persistence time, 42
Perturbation theory, 42
Pfaffian, 44
Pfaff, Johann Friedrich (1765–1825), 44, 44f
Phantom, 49, 49f
Phase, 49–50, 50f–51f
Phase cancellation, 51, 51f
Phase diagram, 51–52, 52f
Phase encoding, 52–53, 53f
Phased array, 58, 58f
Phase noise, 53–54, 54f
Phase rotation, 54, 54f
Phase sequence, 55
Phase space, 55–56, 56f
Phase transition, 56–57
Phase-locked loop, 58
Phasor, 59
Piano, 85–86, 86f
Piezoelectric resonance, 88, 89f
Pipe, 91–92, 92f
Pitot theorem, 94, 94f
Planck, Maxwell Karl Ernst Ludwig (1858–1947), 95–96, 96f
Planck's Constant *h*, 96
Planetary data, 99, 99f
Planetary orbits, 100
Pockels effect, 108–109, 109f
Poincaré, Jules Henri (1854–1912), 109, 109f
Poincaré section, 110
Point charges, 111
Point vortex, 111, 111f
Poisson, Siméon Denis (1781–1840), 113, 113f
Poisson brackets, 113
Poisson distribution, 113
Poisson noise, 114
Polar coordinates, 114, 114f
Polar moment of inertia, 115
Potential well, 133–134, 134f
Poussin, Baron Charles-Jean Étienne Gustave Nicolas de la Vallée (1866–1962), 137, 137f
Power law, 139
Power method, 139
Power spectrum, 139
Poynting, John Henry (1852–1914), 139, 139f
Poynting vector ($\vec{S}$), 140
Prandtl, Ludwig (1875–1953), 140–141, 141f
Probability, 149–150, 150f
Probability, theory of, 150
Pyroelectricity, 162
Pythagoras (c. 570–c. 495 BC), 162, 162f
Pythagorean theorem, 162
PZT, 162–163
Q Factor, 165–166, 166f
Q Space, 167, 167f
Quantification, 171

Quantized Dirac equation, 171
Quantum electrodynamics (QED), 173
Quantum field theory, 173
Quantum fluids, 173
Quantum liquid, 174
Quantum magnet, 174
Quantum mechanics, 174–175, 175f–176f
Quantum number, 176–177, 176f
Quantum optics, 177
Quantum tunneling, 179–180, 180f
Radiance ($\Phi(\vec{r}, \vec{s})$), 188, 189f
Radioactive decay, 199, 199f
Random walk, 209, 209f
Rayleigh–Gans theory, 217
Rayleigh–Gans–Debye scattering, 218
Rayleigh–Taylor instability, 218
Reciprocal space, 219–220, 220f
Red, 221
Redshift, 223, 223f
Relaxation time, 227
Rényi entropy, 228
Residuals, 229
Resonance, 231, 231f
Rheology, 239
Riccati, Jacopo Francesco; Count (1676–1754), 239, 239f
Riccati equations, 240
Richardson, Owen Willans, Sir (1879–1959), 240, 240f
Richardson's equation, 240
Roberval, Gilles Personne de (1602–1675), 244–245, 245f
Robot, 245, 245f
Robotics, 245–246, 246f
Rotational (divergence-free) vector field, 249
Runge, Carl David Tolmé (1856–1927), 250, 250f
Runge–Kutta method, 251
Russell–Saunders coupling, 252–253, 253f
Rytov, Sergei M. [Рытов, Сергей Михайлович] (1908–1996), 258, 258f
Rytov approximation, 258
Sahl, Ibn (Arabic: سهل ابن) (Abu Sa'd al-'Ala'ibn Sahl) (940–1000), 262, 262f
Sampled delay focusing, 263
Sampling, 263–264
Sampling depth, 264
Saunders, Frederick Albert (1875–1963), 269
Sauveur, Joseph (1653–1716), 270, 270f
Savart, Félix (1791–1841), 270, 270f
Scalar, 272
Scattering phase function, 277, 277f
Scattering phase function, Henyey-Greenstein, 278
Schrieffer, Howard Lawrence (1948–), 283, 283f
Schrieffer Unified Theory, 284
Schrödinger, Erwin Rudolf Josef Alexander (1887–1961), 284, 284f–285f
Schrödinger equation of motion, 285–286, 286f

Schrödinger's cat, 286–287, 287f
Schrödinger Wave Equation, 286
Schuster, Arthur, Sir (1851–1934), 287, 287f
Schwarzschild, Karl (1873–1916), 288, 288f
Second law of thermodynamics, Carathéodory's statement of the, 290
Second order differential equations, 290
Second order phase transition, 290–291, 291f
Seebeck effect, 292
Selection rule and, 296
Self-avoiding walk, 297, 297f
Self-consistent field, 297
Self-excited vibration, 297–298
Self-inductance (L_{ind}), 298
Separation of variables, 299
Sextant, 299–300, 300f
Shannon, Claude Elwood (1916–2001), 301–302, 302f
Shannon sampling law, 302
Shannon sampling theorem, 302
Shear Modulus (G_∞), 304
Shedding frequency (ν_v), 307
Shepp-Logan phantom, 307–308, 308f
Shunt, 310, 310f
Simpson's rule, 315
Simulated annealing, 315
Singularity, 317, 317f
Solar system, 328–329, 329f
Solid angle, 330, 330f
Soliton, 331, 331f
Sommerfeld, Arnold Johannes Wilhelm (1868–1951), 333, 333f
Stark, Johannes (1874–1957), 344–345, 345f
Stark effect, 345
Stochastic process, 352
Stokes, George Gabriel, Sir (1819–1903), 352, 352f
Stokes' Law, 353–354
Strong nuclear force, 358, 358f
Student's t-test, 358–359
Sturm, Jacques Charles François (1803–1855), 359, 359f
Sturm–Liouville technique, 359–360
Surface Potential Energy, 367–368, 368f
Taylor, Brook (1685–1731), 382, 382f
Taylor, Geoffrey Ingram, Sir (1886–1975), 383, 383f
Taylor expansion, 384
Tectonics, 385, 385f
Telegraph, 386–387, 387f
Telegraph equation, 387–388
Thermocouple, 399
Tomography, 428, 428f
Torsion, 434–435, 435f
Trace, 440
Transformer, 441, 441f
Traveling salesman problem, 445
Triplet state, 447, 447f

Computational Physics (*Continued*)
Turbulence, 455, 455f
Unbestimmtheitsprinzip, 472
Uncertainty principle, 472–473, 473f
Unified theories of the weak and electromagnetic
interactions, 474
Unified theory, 475, 475f
Vacuum field equations, 482
Van Allen, James Alfred (1914–2006), 484, 484f
Van Allen belts, 485
Van der Pol, Balthasar (1889–1959), 488, 488f
Van der Pol equation, 488
Van der Pol oscillator, 488
Variance (σ^2), 496, 496f
Velocity (v), 497
Verlet method, 501
Viscosity (η), 505–506, 506f
Viscosity, dynamic (η_{dyn}), 506
Volcano, 514, 514f
Voltmeter, 516, 516f
Von Helmholtz, Hermann Ludwig Ferdinand
(1821–1894), 518, 518f
Von Laue, Max Theodor Felix (1879–1960), 520, 520f
Von Laue's method, 521, 521f
Vortex, 522–523, 523f
Vortex shedding, 524
Voxel, 524, 524f
Wave dispersion, 539–540, 540f
Wave energy, 540
Wave particle duality, 541
Weak interaction, 543–544, 544f
Weber (Wb), 544
Weisskopf, Victor Frederick (1908–2002), 548, 548f
Wentzel, Gregor (1898–1978), 549, 549f
Wentzel–Kramers–Brillouin (WKB) solution
method, 549
Wheeler, John Archibald (1911–2008), 551–552, 552f
Wigner distribution, 556
Wigner, Eugene (Jenő Pál) (1902–1995), 556, 556f
XY model, 568
Yang, Chen Ning (清华大学) (1922–), 569, 569f
Yang–Mills field, 569–570, 570f
Yang–Mills theory, 570
Yukawa, Hideki (1907–1981), 576, 576f
Yukawa potential, 576–577, 577f
Zeeman effect, 581–582, 582f
Zenith, 584, 584f
Zenith angle, 585, 585f
Zero-equation model, 586
Zhukovsky, Nikolay Yegorovich (also: Joukowsky;
Николая Егорович Жуковский)
(1847–1921), 587–588, 588f
Dynamics
Planetary vorticity, 100
Self-excited vibration, 297–298
Unified theory, 475, 475f

Van der Waals bonding, 489–490, 490f
Velocity ($\vec{v}$), 497
Electronics
Parallel-plate capacitor, 7–8, 8f
Pérot, Jean-Baptiste Alfred (1863–1925), 40, 40f
Phased array, 58, 58f
Photocathode, 64
Photodetector, 70–71, 71f
pn-junction, 106–107, 107f
Poisson noise, 114
Polarity of emf (electromotive force), 115
p-type doping, 155–156, 156f
p-type semiconductor, 156, 156f
Q Factor, 165–166, 166f
Radio, 196–197, 197f
Radio frequency (RF), 197, 197f
Radio station, 198, 198f
R–C Circuits, 218
Reactance (χ_L), 219
Rectifier, 220–221
Resistance, 229–230
Resistor, 230, 230f
Reverse-biased diode, 237
Rheobase, 238
Rheobasic current, 238
Robot, 245, 245f
Robotics, 245–246, 246f
Saccade, 260, 260f
Saha, Meghnad (1893–1956), 261, 261f
Saha ionization equation, 261
Schottky, Walter Hermann (1886–1976), 282, 282f
Schottky barrier, 282–283
Schottky diode, 283
Schottky effect, 283
Shannon, Claude Elwood (1916–2001),
301–302, 302f
Sievert (*Sv*), 310
Sievert, Rolf Maximilian (1896–1966), 310–311, 311f
Signal, 311–312, 312f
Signal-to-noise ratio (S/N or SNR), 312, 312f
Speaker, 337
Specific resistance, 338
Thermistor, 399
Thévenin, Léon Charles (1857–1926), 407, 407f
Thévenin's theorem, 407, 407f
Thyratron, 416
Thyristor, 416
Transducer, 441
Transformer, 441, 441f
Transistor, 442, 442f
Ultrasonics, 467, 467f
Ventilator, 498–99, 499f
Volta, Alessandro Giuseppe Antonio Anastasio
Gerolamo Umberto, Count (1745–1827),
514, 514f
Voltage (V), 515

Water wave, 534–535, 535f
Wave, 538–539, 539f
Wimshurst, James (1832–1903), 558–559, 559f
Wimshurst machine, 559–560, 560f
Work function (φ_{elec}, in electron volt: eV), 562

Energy
Paleomagnetism, 3–4, 4f
Paracrine signaling, 5–6, 6f
Parasympathetic nerve system, 10, 10f
Pauli spin matrix, 23
Péclet, Jean Claude Eugène (1793–1857), 24, 24f
Péclet number (Pe), 24
Péclet number, mass transfer (Pe$_m$), 24
Peltier coefficient, 26
Peltier, Jean Charles Athanase (1785–1845), 26, 26f
Peltier effect, 26, 27f
Permeability (μ_{mag}), 39
Permittivity (ε_{elec}), 39
Persistence time, 42
Photodynamic therapy (PDT), 71–72, 72f
Photoelectric effect, 74, 75f
Physisorption, 85
Piezoelectric effect, 87–88, 88f
Piezoelectricity, 89
Piezoelectric transducer, 89, 89f
Pion, 91
Planck, Maxwell Karl Ernst Ludwig (1858–1947), 95–96, 96f
Planck's Constant h, 96
Pockels effect, 108–109, 109f
Positron emission tomography (PET), 128–129, 129f
Potential barrier, 130, 130f
Potential difference, 131, 131f
Power number ($N_p = c_{Np} (P_w/\omega_N{}^3\rho L^5)$), 139
Poynting, John Henry (1852–1914), 139, 139f
Quantized Dirac equation, 171
Quantum concentration, 172
Quantum electrodynamics (QED), 173
Quantum field theory, 173
Quantum fluids, 173
Quantum gas, 173–174
Quantum liquid, 174
Quantum mechanics, 174–175, 175f–176f
Quantum optics, 177
Quark, color of, 182
Quark, flavor of, 182
Radiant energy fluence rate $\left(E^0 (\vec{r},t) \right)$, 189
Radiation therapy, 193–194, 194f
Radiative transfer, 196
Radioactive decay, 199, 199f
Radioactive decay law, 201
Rain, 205
Rain gauge, 206, 206f
Raman, Chandrasekhara Venkata, Sir (1888–1970), 206, 207f
Rayleigh–Taylor instability, 218

Redox potential, 222
Redox reaction, 222, 222f
Saint-Elmo's fire, 262, 262f
Savart, Félix (1791–1841), 270, 270f
Schrödinger, Erwin Rudolf Josef Alexander (1887–1961), 284, 284f–285f
Schrödinger's cat, 286–287, 287f
Seebeck, Thomas Johann (1770–1831), 292, 292f
Seismology, 295
Sonoluminescence, 335
Stanton number (St $= h/\rho v c_p = $ Nu$_L$/Re$_L$Pr), 343
Stanton number, mass transfer (St$_m = h_m/v = $ Sh$_L$/Re$_L$Sc), 343
Star, 343–344, 344f
Stark effect, 345
Stratosphere, 355–356, 356f
Strong nuclear force, 358, 358f
Superconductivity, 364
Supernova, 365, 365f
Synaptic signaling, 373, 373f
Synchrotron, 374, 374f
Synchrotron radiation, 374
Telegraph equation, 387–388
Thermodynamics, first law of, 400
Thermodynamics, second law, 400
Thermodynamics, third law, 400
Thermokinetic oscillator, 402
Thermometer, 402, 402f
Thermosphere, 405–406, 406f
Thomson, Joseph John (1856–1940), 410–411, 411f
Tip angle, 424, 424f
Toepler, August Joseph Ignaz (1836–1912), 425–426, 426f
Triplet state, 447, 447f
Troposphere, 448–449, 449f
Turbine, 453, 453f
Ultraviolet catastrophe, 471, 471f
Valence band, 483, 483f
Van de Graaff generator, 486–487, 487f
Van Musschenbroek, Petrus (1692–1761), 492, 492f
Volta, Alessandro Giuseppe Antonio Anastasio Gerolamo Umberto, Count (1745–1827), 514, 514f
Von Helmholtz, Hermann Ludwig Ferdinand (1821–1894), 518, 518f
Von Kleist, Ewald Jurgens (1700–1748), 520, 520f
Weir, John B. de V., 547
Wheatstone, Charles (1802–1875), 550–551, 551f
Wheatstone bridge, 551, 551f
Yukawa, Hideki (1907–1981), 576, 576f
Yukawa potential, 576–577, 577f
Zweig, George (1937–), 588, 588f

Engineering
Paxillin, 24
Q Factor, 165–166, 166f
Rapid prototyping, 212, 213f

Engineering (*Continued*)

Stevin, Simon (1548–1620), 350, 350f

Tensile (ultimate) strength, 392–393, 393f

Thermal equilibrium, 397

Thermal expansion, 397–398, 398f

Thermodynamics, 399–400

Ultrasonic imaging, 466

Variance (σ^2), 496, 496f

Velocity ($\vec{v}$), 497

Vibration, 502–503, 503f

Wave dispersion, 539–540, 540f

Fluid Dynamics

Parallel-plate fluid flow, 8, 8f

Particle imaging velocimetry (PIV), 16, 16f

Particle tracking velocimetry (PTV), 17

Pascal, Blaise (1623–1662), 18, 18f

Pascal (Pa), 18

Pascal's law, 18

Pascal's principle, 18–19, 19f

Passenger car, drag coefficient, 21–22, 22f

Péclet, Jean Claude Eugène (1793–1857), 24, 24f

Péclet number (Pe), 24

Péclet number, mass transfer (Pe_m), 24

Perfect gas, 32

Perfect incompressible behavior, 32

Perfusion, 32, 33f

Periphractic region, 38

Phase, 49–50, 50f–51f

Phase cancellation, 51, 51f

Physiologic dead space, 83–84, 84f

Piezoelectric effect, 87–88, 88f

Piezoelectric resonance, 88, 89f

Piezoelectric transducer, 89, 89f

Piezoelectricity, 89

Pipe, 91–92, 92f

Pipeline parameter ($\rho^n = \varpi_{gr}\varpi_0/2gH$), 92

Pitot, Henri (1695–1771), 93, 93f

Pitot tube, 94, 94f

Pneumotachometer, 106, 106f

Po_2, 108, 108f

Point vortex, 111, 111f

Poise (P), 112

Poiseuille, Jean Leonard Marie (1799–1869), 112, 112f

Poiseuille flow, 112

Poiseuille number ($Ps = v_{ph}\eta/gd_p^2\,(\rho_s - \rho_f)$), 112

Poiseuille's law, 112–113

Poisson's ratio (ν_p), 114

Polar coordinates, 114, 114f

Polar nature of a medium, 115, 115f

Positive displacement pump, 126, 126f

Potential energy of a liquid surface, 132

Potential flow, 132

Potential head, 133, 133f

Power number ($N_p = c_{Np}\,(P_w/\omega_N^3\rho L^5)$), 139

Prandtl, Ludwig (1875–1953), 140–141, 141f

Prandtl–Meyer expansion, 141–142

Prandtl number ($Pr = (\eta/\alpha_{dif}) = c_p\eta/\kappa$), 141

Prandtl–Meyer function, 142

Pressure (P), 142–143, 143f

Pressure coefficient ($Pt = (P - P_\infty)/(1/2)\rho_\infty v_\infty^2$), 144

Principle of conservation of mass, 148

Principle of corresponding states, 148

Propeller, 151–152, 152f

Pseudo plastics, 154, 154f

Pulmonary system, 157–158, 158f

Pulsatile flow, 159, 159f

Pump, 160, 160f

Pyroelectricity, 162

Quantum fluids, 173

Quantum liquid, 174

Quasi-steady state, 184–185, 185f

Radius of gyration (R_g), 204

Rain, 205

Rain gauge, 206, 206f

Rankine–Hugoniot equations, 211

Rayleigh–Bénard flow, 217

Rayleigh flow, 216

Rayleigh line, 216, 216f

Rayleigh number ($Ra = L^3\rho^2 g\alpha_{exp}\Delta Tc_p/\eta\kappa = GrPr$), 216

Rayleigh–Taylor instability, 218

Relative permeability, 226

Reserve volume (RV), 228–229, 229f

Residuals, 229

Residual volume, 229

Resistance, 229–230

Resonance, 231, 231f

Reverberation, 236, 236f

Reynolds, Osborne (1842–1912), 237, 237f

Reynolds experiment, 237

Reynolds number, 238

Reynolds number, magnetic ($Re_m = \mu\sigma v_{fl}L$), 238

Reynolds stress, 238

Rheological diagram, 238, 239f

Rheology, 239

Riccati, Jacopo Francesco; Count (1676–1754), 239, 239f

Riccati equations, 240

Ripple, 242

Riva-Rocci cuff, 244, 244f

Riva-Rocci, Scipione (1863–1937), 243, 243f

Robot, 245, 245f

Robotics, 245–246, 246f

Rotational (divergence-free) vector field, 249

Roughness, 249

Roughness, relative, 249

Rouleaux formation, 250, 250f

Saberian number (Sa =), 259

Schlieren imaging, 280, 280f

Schmidt, Ernst Heinrich Wilhelm (1892–1975), 281, 281f

Schmidt number, ($Sc = \eta/\rho D_{AB}$), 282

Scuba gear, 288–289, 289f
Seismology, 295
Self-excited vibration, 297–298
Separation boundary layer, 299
Shadowgraph method, 300, 300f
Shaft horsepower, 301
Shallow-water tides, 301, 301f
Shear flow, 304
Shear Péclet number, 305
Shear strain (μ_s), 305, 305f
Shear stress (σ_s), 305, 305f
Shear-thickening fluid, 306, 306f
Shear-thinning fluid, 306, 306f
Shedding frequency (ν_v), 307
Sherwood number (Sh = $h_m L / D_{AB}$), 308
Shock wave, 309, 309f
Shunt, 310, 310f
Sink and source, 318
Smoke method, 321–322, 322f
Soliton, 331, 331f
Sommerfeld, Arnold Johannes Wilhelm (1868–1951), 333, 333f
Sound, 336–337, 337f
Speaker, 337
Specific viscosity, 338
Speed of wave propagation in a confined liquid, 340
Sphygmomanometer, 340–341, 341f
Stanton number (St = $h / \rho v c_p$ = $Nu_L / Re_L Pr$), 343
Stanton number, mass transfer ($St_m = h_m / v = Sh_L / Re_L Sc$), 343
Star, 343–344, 344f
Starling, Ernest Henry (1866–1927), 345, 345f
Starling's law, 346, 346f
Static head, 347, 347f
Stokes, George Gabriel, Sir (1819–1903), 352, 352f
Stokes drift, 353, 353f
Stokes' Law, 353–354
Stream function, 356–357
Stress (σ_s), 357, 357f
Strouhal number (Sr = $\nu L / \nu_v$), 358
Supersonic flow, 366, 366f
Surface energy, 366–367
Surface gravitational wave, 367, 367f
Surface phenomena of Liquids, 367
Surface Potential Energy, 367–368, 368f
Surface roughness, 368–369, 369f
Surface tension, 370, 370f
Surface waves, 371, 371f
Surfaces of discontinuity, 372
Surfactant, 372, 372f
Tangential stress, 379–380, 380f
Taylor, Geoffrey Ingram, Sir (1886–1975), 383, 383f
Taylor dispersion, 383–384
Tectonics, 385, 385f
Telegraph equation, 387–388
Tension, surface, 394

Tensor, 394
Thermodynamics, first law of, 400
Thermodynamics, second law, 400
Thermodynamics, third law, 400
Thermography, 400–401, 401f
Thermometer, 402, 402f
Thixotropic liquid, 408
Throttle, 415, 415f
Thrust, 415–416, 416f
Tidal breathing, 416–417, 417f
Tidal volume, 419, 419f
Tidal waves, 419–420, 420f
Tide-generating forces, 420
Tornado, 430–431, 431f
Torricelli, Evangelista (1608–1647), 433, 433f
Torricelli's barometer, 433–434, 434f
Torsional oscillations, 436, 436f
Torsion wave, 435, 435f
Total loss, 437–438, 438f
Total lung capacity (TLC), 438, 438f
Tracers, 440
Transport equation, 443–444
Trochoidal waves, 448, 448f
Tsunami, 450, 450f
Tuft flow, 451–452, 452f
Turbine, 453, 453f
Turbo machine, 454, 454f
Turboprop engine, 454, 454f
Turbulence, 455, 455f
Ultrasonic flow meter, 466, 466f
Umbilical cord, 472, 472f
Unsteady flow, 477, 477f
Valve, 483–484, 484f
Valves closure, Allievi's equations, 484
Van't Hoff factor, 493
Vapor pressure equation, 494
Velocity potential, 497–498, 498f
Ventilation, 498
Ventilator, 498–499, 499f
Venturi, Giovanni Battista (1746–1822), 500, 500f
Venturi, 499, 499f
Viscoelastic, 504, 504f
Viscoplastic, 505, 505f
Viscosity, 505
Viscosity (η), 505–506, 506f
Viscosity, dynamic (η_{dyn}), 506
Viscosity, intrinsic, 506
Viscosity, kinematic, 507, 507f
Viscosity, reduced, 507
Viscosity index, 508
Viscosity meter, 508
Viscosity model, 509, 509f
Viscosity of deformable spherical particles (η_{sph}), 509
Viscosity, relative, 508
Viscosity, specific, 508
Viscosity, static, 508

Fluid Dynamics (*Continued*)

Viscosity, structural, 508, 508f

Viscous lubrication, 509

Vital capacity (VC), 512

Volcano, 514, 514f

Von Kármán, Tódor (Theodore) (1881–1963), 518–519, 519f

Von Kármán vortex street, 519, 519f

Vortex, 522–523, 523f

Vortex, Kármán, 524

Vortex shedding, 524

Vorticity (ϖ), 524

Voxel, 524, 524f

Wake, 527, 527f

Wall, 528–529, 529f

Wall attachment phenomenon, 529, 529f

Wall factor 1 ($K_2 = 2(d_{pv}/D_C)$), 530, 530f

Wall factor 2 ($K_3 = (d_{pv}/D_C)(Z/D_C)$), 530, 530f

Wall-tracing method, 531, 531f

Water (H_2O), 532–533, 533f

Water clock, 533, 533f

Water hammer, 534

Water wheel, power, 535–536, 536f

Waterspout, 536, 536f

Wave, 538–539, 539f

Wave dispersion, 539–540, 540f

Wave energy, 540

Wave propagation speed, 541–542

Weber number (We = Const($\rho v^2 L/\sigma$)), 545

Weissenberg, Karl (1893–1976), 547, 547f

Weissenberg number, (Wi = $t_f |\vec{v}|/D$), 547–548

Wentzel–Kramers–Brillouin (WKB) solution method, 549

Wing, 560

Womersley, John Ronald (1907–1958), 561, 561f

Womersley number, ($\alpha_{Wo} = r\sqrt{\rho\omega/\eta}$), 562

Worthington jet, 563, 563f

Yield stress (τ^*), 570–571, 571f

Young–Laplace equation, 572

Zero-equation model, 585

Zhukovsky, Nikolay Yegorovich (also: Joukowsky; Николая Егорович Жуковский) (1847–1921), 587–588, 588f

General

p (linear momentum), 1

Papin, Denis (1647–1712), 4, 5f

Paracrine signaling, 5–6, 6f

Parallel axis theorem, 6

Parallel circuit, 6, 7f

Parallel-plate capacitor, 7–8, 8f

Parallel processing, 7

Paramagnetic substances, 9

Parent nucleus, 11

Particle, 14–15, 15f

Particle accelerator, 15, 15f

Particle theory of light, 16–17, 17f

Pascal (Pa), 18

Pascal's principle, 18–19, 19f

Paschen–Back effect, 21

Paschen lines, 20

Paschen series, 20, 21f

Pauli, Wolfgang Ernst (1900–1958), 23, 23f

Pendulum, 27–28, 28f

Penumbra, 28–29, 29f

Perception, 29–30, 30f

Perfect diamagnetism, 32

Periodic waves, 37

Period of a cycle (T), 34, 35f

Permanent magnet, 39

Permeability (μ_{mag}), 39

Permittivity (ε_{elec}), 39

Perpetual motion, 40, 41f

Perrin, Jean Baptiste (1870–1942), 41, 41f

Persistence time, 42

Phase, 49–50, 50f–51f

Phase cancellation, 51, 51f

Phase diagram, 51–52, 52f

Phase encoding, 52–53, 53f

Phase-locked loop, 58

Phase rotation, 54, 54f

Phasor, 59

Photocopy, 69–70, 70f

Photocurrent, 70

Photoelectric equation, 75

Photoelectron, 76

Photographic plate, 76, 76f

Photon, 78–79, 79f

Physics, 82–83, 83f

Physics constants, 83

Physics laws, 83

Physiology, 84–85, 85f

Picture, 87, 87f

Piezoelectric effect, 87–88, 88f

Piezoelectric resonance, 88, 89f

Piezoelectricity, 89

Piezoelectric transducer, 89, 89f

Pion, 91

Pitch, 92, 93f

Pixel, 95, 95f

Planck, Maxwell Karl Ernst Ludwig (1858–1947), 95–96, 96f

Plane of incidence, 97

Plane of polarization, 97, 97f

Plane-polarized waves, 98, 98f

Planet, 98, 98f

Planetary motion, 99, 99f

Planetary motion, Kepler's laws of, 100

Planetary precession, 100

Planetary vorticity, 100

Plane wave, 97

Plasma, 100–101, 101f

Plato (427–347 BC), 103–104, 104f

Plücker, Julius (1801–1868), 104–105, 105f
Plutonium Project, 106
pn-junction, 106–107, 107f
Pnp transistor, 107, 107f
Po_2, 108, 108f
Pockels, Friedrich Carl Alwin (1865–1913), 108, 108f
Pockels effect, 108–109, 109f
Poincaré, Jules Henri (1854–1912), 109, 109f
Point charges, 111
Poise (*P*), 112
Polarity of emf (electromotive force), 115
Polarization, 115–116, 116f
Polarization of light, 116, 116f
Polarization selective film, 117
Polaroid™ film, 117, 117f
Poles, 118, 118f
Pollio, Marcus Vitruvius (c. 80 BC–c. 15 AD), 118–119, 119f
Polycrystalline solids, 119
Polymethylmethacrylate (PMMA), 120, 120f
Population inversion, 122–124
Positive charge, 125
Positive lens, 126–127, 127f
Positron (β^+), 127
Positron emission tomography (PET), 128–129, 129f
Potential (V), 130
Potential difference, 131, 131f
Potential energy (PE), 131–132, 132f
Potentiometer, 135, 135f
Pound (lb), 135
Pound–Rebka experiment, 136
Power (*P*), 138, 138f
Power factor, 138
Poynting, John Henry (1852–1914), 139, 139f
Poynting vector ($\vec{s}$), 140
Pressure (*P*), 142–143, 143f
Pressure cooker, 144, 144f
Prévost, Pierre (1751–1839), 145, 145f
Priestley, Joseph (1733–1804), 145–146, 146f
Primary colors, 146, 146f
Principia of Newton, 147
Principle of complementarity, 147–148
Principle of least action, 148
Principle of relativity, 148–149
Projectile, 150–151, 151f
Propulsion, 152, 152f
Ptolemy (approximately 90–168 AD), 155
p-type doping, 155–156, 156f
p-type semiconductor, 156, 156f
Pulley, 156–157, 157f
Pulsar, 158, 158f
Pyroelectricity, 162
Pythagoras (c. 570–c. 495 BC), 162, 162f
Pythagorean theorem, 162
PZT, 162–163
Q Space, 167, 168f

Quanta, 171
Quantized Dirac equation, 171
Quantum chromodynamics, 172
Quantum electrodynamics (QED), 173
Quantum field theory, 173
Quantum fluids, 173
Quantum jump, 174
Quantum level, 174
Quantum mechanics, 174–175, 175f–176f
Quantum of action (*h*), 177
Quantum physics, electron shells, 177–178
Quantum randomness, 178
Quantum state, 178, 178f
Quantum theory, 179
Quark, 180–181, 180f
Quark, color of, 182
Quark, flavor of, 182
Quasicrystalline solid, 183
Quasimonochromatic light, 183
Radiance ($\Phi(\vec{r},\vec{s})$), 188, 189f
Radiant flux, 189
Radiation, 189–190, 190f
Radiation belt, 191
Radiative power, 196
Radio, 196–197, 197f
Radioactive decay, 199, 199f
Radioisotope, 204
Radio receiver, 197–198, 198f
Radio station, 198, 198f
Radium ($^{226}_{88}Ra$), 204
Radon ($^{222}_{86}Rn$), 205, 205f
Rain, 205
Rain gauge, 206, 206f
Raisin-pudding atom, 206
Ramsay, William Mitchell, Sir (1852–1916), 208, 208f
Rankine, William John Macquorn (1820–1872), 210, 210f
Rapid prototyping, 212, 213f
Rarefaction, 213, 213f
Rayleigh, Lord, a.k.a. John William Strutt (1842–1919), 214, 214f
Rayleigh emission law, 215, 215f
Rayleigh scattering, 216–217, 217f
R–C Circuits, 218
Reactance (χ_L), 219
Réaumur, René-Antoine Ferchault de (1683–1757), 219, 219f
Reciprocal space, 219–220, 220f
Rectifier, 220–221
Reduced mass, 223
Reflectance, 223, 223f
Reflecting telescope, 224, 224f
Reflection, 224, 224f
Refraction, 225, 225f
Refraction, index of (*n*), 225

General (*Continued*)

Refraction, law of, 225

Reines, Frederick (1918–1998), 225–226, 226f

Relative density, 226

Renaldini, Carlo (1615–1698), 227, 227f

Rényi, Alfréd (1921–1970), 228, 228f

Rényi entropy, 228

Resistor, 230, 230f

Resolution, 230

Resolving power, 230–231, 231f

Resonance, 231, 231f

Resonance states, 234

Rest energy (E_0), 234

Reverberation, 236, 236f

Reverse osmosis, 236, 236f

Reverse-biased diode, 237

Right-hand current rule, 242, 242f

Right-hand force rule, 242, 242f

Ritter, Johann Wilhelm (1776–1810), 243, 243f

RMS value, 244

Roberval, Gilles Personne de (1602–1675), 244–245, 245f

Rock salt, 246, 246f

Roemer {Rømer, also Römer}, Olaus (Ole) (1644–1710), 247, 247f

Rolling friction, 248, 248f

Röntgen, Wilhelm Conrad {Roentgen} (1845–1923), 248–249, 249f

Rumford, Count (1753–1814), 250

Runge, Carl David Tolmé (1856–1927), 250, 250f

Runge–Kutta method, 251

Russell, Bertrand Arthur William (1872–1970), 251, 251f

Rutherford, Ernest (1871–1937), 254, 254f

Rutherford's atom, 256, 256f

Rydberg constant, 257

Rydberg state, 258

s, 259, 259f

S, M, and L responses of the human eye, 259

Saccade, 260, 260f

Salt, 263

Satellite, 264–265, 265f

Saturable nuclear force, 265

Saturated vapor pressure, 265

Saturn, 269, 269f

Sauveur, Joseph (1653–1716), 270, 270f

Savart, Félix (1791–1841), 270, 270f

Savery, Thomas (1650–1715), 271, 271f

Scalar, 272

Scattering, 275, 275f

Scattering cross section, Rayleigh, 275–276, 276f

Schmidt, Ernst Heinrich Wilhelm (1892–1975), 281, 281f

Schriefer, Howard Lawrence (1948–), 283, 283f

Schriefer Unified Theory, 284

Schrödinger, Erwin Rudolf Josef Alexander (1887–1961), 284, 284f–285f

Schrödinger's cat, 286–287, 287f

Schrödinger Wave Equation, 286

Schwarzschild, Karl (1873–1916), 288, 288f

Second, 289, 289f

Second law of Faraday, 290

Second law of thermodynamics, 290

Second law of thermodynamics, Clausius formulation, 290

Seismic, 293, 293f

Seismic wave, 294, 294f

Seismology, 295

Seismometer, 296, 296f

Self-excited vibration, 297–298

Self-induced electromotive force, 298

Self-inductance (L_{ind}), 298

Semiconductors, 298

Sextant, 299–300, 300f

Shannon, Claude Elwood (1916–2001), 301–302, 302f

Shannon entropy (H_S), 302

Shark, 303, 303f

Shear Modulus (G_∞), 304

Shear strain (μ_s), 305, 305f

Shear stress (σ_s), 305, 305f

Shepp-Logan phantom, 307–308, 308f

Shock absorber, 308–309, 309f

Shock wave, 309, 309f

Shunt, 310, 310f

Signal, 311–312, 312f

Signal-to-noise ratio (S/N or SNR), 312, 312f

Simple harmonic motion, 314, 314f

Simultaneity, 315

Single photon photoelectric effect, 316

Single-slit diffraction, 316, 316f

SI units, 310

Skin, 318–319, 319f

Snell's law, 323, 323f

Snel's Law, 323

Socrates (469–399 BC), 323, 323f

Sojourner, 327, 327f

Solar wind, 329

Solenoid, 329–330, 330f

Solstice, 332, 332f

Sommerfeld, Arnold Johannes Wilhelm (1868–1951), 333, 333f

Sonic boom, 333–334, 334f

Sonogram, 334–335, 335f

Sonography, 335

Sonohysterography, 335

Sound, 336–337, 337f

South geographic pole, 337

South magnetic pole, 337

Special theory of relativity, 337

Specific heat (c_{sp}), 337

Specific heat capacity (c_{sp}), 337

Specific weight, 338
Spectroscopy, 338–339, 339f
Speed (v), 340
Spherical wave, 340
Spin, 341–342, 342f
Star, 343–344, 344f
Stark, Johannes (1874–1957), 344–345, 345f
Stark effect, 345
Stefan, Joseph (1835–1893), 348, 348f
Stereo, 348–349
Stevin, Simon (1548–1620), 350, 350f
Stokes, George Gabriel, Sir (1819–1903), 352, 352f
Stokes' Law, 353–354
Strain (ε_s), 354, 354f
Strain gauges, 354–355, 355f
Stratosphere, 355–356, 356f
Stress (σ_s), 357, 357f
Stress birefringence, 357, 357f
Strong nuclear force, 358, 358f
Sturgeon, William (1783–1850), 359, 359f
Subatomic particles, 360, 360f
Sublimation, 361, 361f
Sun, 361–362, 362f
Superconducting quantum interference device
       (SQUID), 363–364, 364f
Supercritical mass, 365
Superheated steam, 365
Supernova, 365, 365f
Surface charge density (σ_{elec}), 366, 366f
't Hooft, Gerard (1946–), 377, 377f
Tachyon, 377
Tacoma Narrows Bridge, 377–378, 378f
Tait, Peter Guthrie (1831–1901), 378, 378f
Tangential acceleration (a_T), 379, 379f
Tate, John Torrence Sr. (1889–1950), 381, 381f
Tate, John Torrence Jr. (1925–), 381, 381f
Tate's law, 381
Tau lepton, 382, 382f
Telegraph, 386–387, 387f
Telemetry, 388, 388f
Telescope, 389, 389f
Temperature (T), 390–391, 391f
Temporal period (T), 391, 391f
Tensile force, 392
Tensile (ultimate) strength, 392–393, 393f
Tension (F_T or τ), 394, 394f
Terminal velocity, 395, 395f
Tesla, Nikola (1856–1943), 395–396, 396f
Tesla (T), 395
Thales (c. 624–546 BC), 396, 396f
Theodolite, 397, 397f
Thermal energy, 397
Thermal equilibrium, 397
Thermal expansion, 397–398, 398f
Thermistor, 399
Thermocouple, 399

Thermodynamics, first law of, 400
Thermodynamics, second law, 400
Thermodynamics, third law, 400
Thermodynamics, zeroth law of, 400
Thermometer, 402, 402f
Thermonuclear energy, 402
Thermonuclear fission, 402–403, 403f
Thermonuclear fusion, 403–404, 404f
Thermoscope, 405, 405f
Thin lenses, combinations of, 408, 408f
Thomas precession, 409
Thompson, Benjamin, Sir (1753–1814), 409, 409f
Thomson, George Paget, Sir (1892–1975), 410, 410f
Thomson, Joseph John (1856–1940), 410–411, 411f
Thomson, William (1824–1907), 411–412
Thorndike, Edward M. (1906?–), 413
Three Laws of planetary motion, 413–414, 414f
Tidal Forces, 417–418, 418f
Tidal motion, 418, 418f
Timbre, 421, 421f
Time (t), 421–422, 422f
Time dilation, 422
Time perturbation, colliding black holes, 422–423, 423f
Timocharis, 423
Toepler, August Joseph Ignaz (1836–1912),
       425–426, 426f
Tokamak Fusion Reactor, 426, 426f
Tomonaga, Sin-Itiro (朝永 振一郎) (1906–1979),
       429, 429f
Torque (τ), 432, 432f
Torr, 432
Torricelli, Evangelista (1608–1647), 433, 433f
Torsion, 434–435, 435f
Torsion wave, 435, 435f
Torsional oscillations, 436, 436f
Total internal reflection, 437
Transducer, 441
Transformer, 441, 441f
Transistor, 442, 442f
Transport equation, 443–444
Transverse electromagnetic (TEM) waves, 445
Transverse waves, 445, 445f
Triboelectric sequence, 445–446, 446f
Triple point, 446, 446f
Triplet state, 447, 447f
Triple-twin domain, 447–448
Tsunami, 450, 450f
Tungsten filament, 452, 452f
Twin "paradox", 455–456, 456f
Two-photon absorption, 456
Tyndall, John (1820–1893), 456–457, 457f
U-234 ($^{234}_{92}\text{U}$), 459
U-235 ($^{235}_{92}\text{U}$), 459, 459f
U-238 ($^{238}_{92}\text{U}$), 460, 460f
Ultimate stress, 461
Ultimate tensile strength, 461, 461f

General (*Continued*)

Ultrafast phenomena, 463

Ultrahigh pressure, 463

Ultrasonic levitation, 466–467, 467f

Ultrasound, 468–469, 469f–470f

Ultraviolet catastrophe, 471, 471f

Unbestimmtheitsprinzip, 472

Uncertainty principle, 472–473, 473f

Underdamped system, 473–474, 474f

Unequal-arm balance, 474

Unified atomic mass units (*u*), 474

Unified theories of the weak and electromagnetic interactions, 474

Unified theory, 475, 475f

Universal gravitational constant (*G*), 475, 475f

Universal gravitation, law of, 475, 475f

Universe, 475–476, 476f

Up antiquark, 478

Up quark, 478

U-quark, 478

Vacuum, 481–482

Vacuum pump, 482–483

Van de Graaff, Robert Jemison (1902–1967), 486, 486f

Van der Meer, Simon (1925–2011), 487, 487f

Van der Pol, Balthasar (1889–1959), 488, 488f

Van der Pol oscillator, 488

Van der Waals bonding, 489–490, 490f

Van Helmont, Johannes (Jan) Baptista (1579–1644), 491, 491f

Van Musschenbroek, Petrus (1692–1761), 492, 492f

Variable capacitor, 495

Variable resistor, 495, 495f

Vector boson, 497

Velocity ($\vec{v}$), 497

Venus, 500, 500f

Versorium, 501, 501f

Vesalius, Andreas (1515–1564), 501–502, 502f

Villard, Paul Ulrich (1860–1934), 503, 503f

Viscoplastic, 505, 505f

Viscosity, 505

Viscosity, apparent, 506

Viscosity, intrinsic, 506

Viscosity, reduced, 507

Viscosity meter, 508

Viscosity, relative, 508

Viscosity, specific, 508

Viscosity of deformable spherical particles (η_{sph}), 509

Voice, 513, 513f

Volta, Alessandro Giuseppe Antonio Anastasio Gerolamo Umberto, Count (1745–1827), 514, 514f

Voltage (V), 515

Voltaic pile, 515, 515f

Voltaire, 515, 515f

Voltmeter, 516, 516f

Volume (V), 516, 516f

Volume charge density (ρ_e), 517s

Von Guericke, Otto (1602–1682), 517–518, 518f

Von Kármán vortex street, 519, 519f

Von Kleist, Ewald Jurgens (1700–1748), 520, 520f

Von Leibniz, Gottfried Wilhelm, 521

Von Mayer, Julius Robert (1814–1878), 522, 522f

Wall, 528–529, 529f

Wallis, John (1616–1703), 530, 531f

Water (H_2O), 532–533, 533f

Water wave, 534–535, 535f

Watson, James Dewey (1928–), 537, 537f

Watt, James (1736–1819), 537–538, 538f

Watt (W), 537

Wave, 538–539, 539f

Wave dispersion, 539–540, 540f

Wavefront, 542

Wavelength (λ), 542–543, 543f

Wave motion, 540

Weak force, 543

Weak interaction, 543–544, 544f

Weber, Ernst Heinrich (1795–1878), 544, 544f

Weber, Wilhelm Eduard (1804–1891), 545, 545f

Weber (Wb), 544

Wedgwood, Josiah (1730–1795), 545–546, 546f

Weight (F_w), 546

Weinberg, Steven (1932–), 546, 546f

Weisskopf, Victor Frederick (1908–2002), 548, 548f

Wentzel, Gregor (1898–1978), 549, 549f

Westinghouse, George (1846–1914), 549–550, 550f

White, 552, 552f

White dwarf, 552–553, 553f

White light, 553

White noise, 553, 553f

Wien, Wilhelm Carl Werner Otto Fritz Franz (1864–1928), 554, 554f

Wilkins, Maurice Hugh Frederick (1916–2004), 556–557, 557f

Wimshurst, James (1832–1903), 558–559, 559f

Wimshurst machine, 559–560, 560f

Wollaston prism, 561, 561f

Wooster, William Alfred (Peter) (1903–1984), 562

Work (*W*), 562, 562f

Work function (φ_{elec}, in electron volt: eV), 562

Work–energy theorem, 563

Yield length, 570, 570f

Young's modulus (Y_n), 572, 572f

Yukawa, Hideki (1907–1981), 576, 576f

Yukawa potential, 576–577, 577f

Z Boson, 579, 579f

Zeeman, Pieter (1865–1943), 580, 580f

Zeeman and Stark effect, 581

Zeeman effect, 581–582, 582f

Zero-G, 586

Zero-mass particles, 586

Zeroth law of thermodynamics, 587

Zweig, George (1937–), 588, 588f

Geophysics
  Paleomagnetism, 3–4, 4f
  Penumbra, 28–29, 29f
  Percolation, 31, 31f
  Perfect incompressible behavior, 32
  Peters, Bernard (1910–1993), 43, 43f
  Phase, 49–50, 50f–51f
  Phased array, 58, 58f
  Photosphere, 79–80, 80f
  Photosynthesis, 80–81, 81f
  Planetary motion, 99, 99f
  Planetary motion, Kepler's laws of, 100
  Planetary orbits, 100
  Planetary precession, 100
  Planetary vorticity, 100
  Plastic strain, 102, 102f
  Poisson's ratio (ν_p), 114
  Poles, 118, 118f
  Ptolemaeus, Claudius (approximately 90–168 AD), 155, 155f
  Quasi-steady state, 184–185, 185f
  Rain, 205
  Rain gauge, 206, 206f
  Reynolds number, magnetic ($\mathrm{Re}_m = \mu\sigma v_{fl}L$), 238
  Rheology, 239
  Seismic, 293, 293f
  Seismic wave, 294, 294f
  Seismic wave, dissipative effects, 295
  Seismology, 295
  Seismometer, 296, 296f
  Sextant, 299–300, 300f
  Solstice, 332, 332f
  Star, 343–344, 344f
  Stratosphere, 355–356, 356f
  Sun, 361–362, 362f
  Sun spot, 362, 363f
  Sundog, 363, 363f
  Surface gravitational wave, 367, 367f
  Tectonic plates, 384, 384f
  Tectonics, 385, 385f
  Theodolite, 397, 397f
  Thermometer, 402, 402f
  Thermosphere, 405–406, 406f
  Tidal waves, 419–420, 420f
  Tide-generating forces, 420
  Tornado, 430–431, 431f
  Torricelli, Evangelista (1608–1647), 433, 433f
  Tracers, 440
  Tremor, 445
  Triplet, Wild's, 447
  Troposphere, 448–449, 449f
  Tsunami, 450, 450f
  Turbulence, 455, 455f
  Tyndall, John (1820–1893), 456–457, 457f
  Ultrahigh pressure, 463
  Universe, 475–476, 476f
  Unstable equilibrium state, 476, 476f
  Van der Pol equation, 488
  Van der Pol oscillator, 488
  Van't Hoff factor, 493
  Velocity ($\vec{v}$), 497
  Velocity potential, 497–498, 498f
  Volcano, 514, 514f
  Waterspout, 536, 536f
  Wave dispersion, 539–540, 540f
  Zenith, 584, 584f
  Zenith angle, 585, 585f
High-Energy Physics
  Perkins, Donald Hill (1925–), 39, 39f
  Quantum chromodynamics, 172
  Quark, 180–181, 180f
  Quasiparticle, 184
  Second-generation of matter, 291
Imaging
  PET tracer, 42
  Phased array, 58, 58f
  Phase-only imaging, 58
  Photoacoustic microscopy, 61–64
  Photocathode, 64
  Photography, 77, 77f
  Pixel, 95, 95f
  Positron emission tomography (PET), 128–129, 129f
  Pound, Robert Vivian (1919–2010), 135–136, 136f
  Quantification, 171
  Radiography, 203, 203f
  Rayleigh screening, 217
  Reciprocal space, 219–220, 220f
  Rényi, Alfréd (1921–1970), 228, 228f
  Rényi entropy, 228
  Resonance frequency, 232, 232f
  Rician noise, 241, 241f
  Schlieren imaging for concentration, 281, 281f
  Shannon, Claude Elwood (1916–2001), 301–302, 302f
  Shannon entropy (H_S), 302
  Shape factor, 302
  Shepp-Logan phantom, 307–308, 308f
  Single photon emission computed tomography (SPECT), 315
  Slice, 320, 320f–321f
  Sonography, 335
  Sonohysterography, 335
  Spectroscopic ellipsometry, 338
  TEM, 390
  Temporal width, 391–392
  Thermography, 400–401, 401f
  Tissue characterization, 424–425, 425f
  Tomographic slices, 427, 427f
  Tomography, 428, 428f
  Torrey, Henry Cutler (1911–1998), 433
  Transmission electron microscope, 443, 443f
  Two-photon absorption, 456

Imaging (*Continued*)
 Ultrasonograms, 468
 Voxel, 524, 524f
 V(*z*) inversion, 525
 Weissenberg, Karl (1893–1976), 547, 547f
 Wilkins, Maurice Hugh Frederick (1916–2004), 556–557, 557f
Material sciences
 Pressure (*P*), 142–143, 143f
 Spectroscopic ellipsometry, 338
Mechanics
 p (linear momentum), 1
 Papin, Denis (1647–1712), 4, 5f
 Parallel axis theorem, 6
 Partition function, 17
 Passenger car, drag coefficient, 21–22, 22f
 Paxillin, 24
 Péclet number, mass transfer (Pe$_m$), 24
 Peierls, Rudolf Ernst, Sir (1907–1995), 25, 25f
 Peierls–Fröhlich–Kuper ground state, 25
 Peierls transition, 25
 Perception, 29–30, 30f
 Perfect incompressible behavior, 32
 Period of a cycle (*T*), 34, 35f
 Periodogram, 37, 37f
 Peristaltic motion, 38, 38f
 Persistence time, 42
 Phagocyte, 47, 47f
 Phagocytosis, 48, 48f
 Phase, 49–50, 50f–51f
 Phase cancellation, 51, 51f
 Phase noise, 53–54, 54f
 Phase rotation, 54, 54f
 Phase sequence, 55
 Phase velocity, 57
 Photoelasticity, 72–73, 73f
 Piezoelectric effect, 87–88, 88f
 Piezoelectric resonance, 88, 89f
 Piezoelectric transducer, 89, 89f
 Piezoelectricity, 89
 Pipeline parameter ($\rho^n = \varpi_{gr}\varpi_0/2gH$), 92
 Plastic strain, 102, 102f
 Plasticity, 102, 102f
 Plasticizers, 103
 Plastics, 103, 103f
 Poinsot, Louis (1777–1859), 110, 110f
 Poinsot motion, 110, 111f
 Point source, 111
 Poise (*P*), 112
 Poisson's ratio (v_p), 114
 Polar coordinates, 114, 114f
 Polar moment of inertia, 115
 Polar nature of a medium, 115, 115f
 Polyvinyl chloride (PVC), 121–122, 122f
 Poly(vinylidene) fluoride (PVDF), 122
 Potential energy (PE), 131–132, 132f

Potential energy of a liquid surface, 132
Power number ($N_p = c_{Np} (P_w/\omega_N^3\rho L^5)$), 139
Praetorius, Michael (original name: Michael Schultheiß) (1571–1621), 140, 140f
Precession, 142, 142f
Pressure (*P*), 142–143, 143f
Principal moments, 147
Principal plane, 147
Principal stress, 147
Principle of least action, 148
Probability, theory of, 150
Projectile, 150–151, 151f
Propulsion, 152, 152f
Pulley, 156–157, 157f
Pyroelectricity, 162
PZT, 162–163
Q Factor, 165
Quanta, 171
Quantum liquid, 174
Quantum physics, electron shells, 177–178
Quasi-steady state, 184–185, 185f
Rapid prototyping, 212
Relaxation time, 227
Resistance, 229–230
Resonance, 231, 231f
Rheology, 239
Robot, 245, 245f
Robotics, 245–246, 246f
Roughness, 249
Roughness, relative, 249
Rytov, Sergei M. [Рытов, Сергей Михайлович] (1908–1996), 258, 258f
Sarcomere, 264, 264f
Saturation, 265–266, 266f–267f
Saturation curve, 267–268, 268f
Saturn, 269, 269f
Sauveur, Joseph (1653–1716), 270, 270f
Savart, Félix (1791–1841), 270, 270f
Savery, Thomas (1650–1715), 271, 271f
Scaffold, 271–272, 272f
Scanning acoustic microscope (SAM), 272–273, 273f
Schrödinger, Erwin Rudolf Josef Alexander (1887–1961), 284, 284f–285f
Schrödinger's cat, 286–287, 287f
Sediment equilibrium, 291
Sediment equilibrium in a density gradient, 291
Sedimentation velocity, 292
Seismic, 293, 293f
Seismic wave, 294, 294f
Seismic wave, dissipative effects, 295
Seismology, 295
Seismometer, 296, 296f
Self-excited vibration, 297–298
Shape memory alloys (SMAs), 302–303, 303f
Shear force, 304, 304f
Shear Modulus (G_∞), 304

Shear Péclet number, 305
Shear strain (μ_s), 305, 305f
Shear stress (σ_s), 305, 305f
Shedding frequency (ν_ν), 307
Shock absorber, 308–309, 309f
Signal, 311–312, 312f
Signal-to-noise ratio (S/N or SNR), 312, 312f
Silastic™, 313
Silicone rubber, 313–314, 314f
Skeletal muscle, 318
Slater determinant, 319–320
Soliton, 331, 331f
Somesthesis, 333
Sonogram, 334–335, 335f
Speaker, 337
Specific heat (c_{sp}), 337
Specific viscosity, 338
Spin, 341–342, 342f
Spring force, 342
Stirling, Robert (1790–1878), 351, 351f
Stress (σ_s), 357, 357f
Surface energy, 366–367
Surface gravitational wave, 367, 367f
Surface phenomena of Liquids, 367
Surface Potential Energy, 367–368, 368f
Surface roughness, 368–369, 369f
Surface tension, 370, 370f
Surfactant, 372, 372f
Tangential acceleration (a_T), 379, 379f
Tangential stress, 379–380, 380f
Tate, John Torrence Sr. (1889–1950), 381, 381f
Tate, John Torrence Jr. (1925–), 381, 381f
Tate's law, 381
Tectonic plates, 384, 384f
Tectonics, 385, 385f
Teflon®, 385–386
Telemetry, 388, 388f
Tensile force ($\overrightarrow{F_T}$), 392
Tensile strain, 392, 392f
Tensile stress, 393, 393f
Tension (F_T or τ), 394, 394f
Tension, tangential, 394
Terminal velocity, 395, 395f
Thermodynamics, 399–400
Tidal forces, 417
Titanium, 425
Tornado, 430–431, 431f
Torsion, 434–435, 435f
Torsional oscillations, 436, 436f
Torsion wave, 435, 435f
Transcytosis, 440
Transducer, 441
Transport equation, 443–444
Tremor, 445
Triplet state, 447, 447f
Triplet, Wild's, 447

Tsunami, 450, 450f
Turbo machine, 454, 454f
Turboprop engine, 454, 454f
Ultimate stress, 461
Ultimate tensile strength, 461, 461f
Ultracentrifuge, 461–462, 462f
Ultrafast biological events, 462–463, 463f
Ultrasonic ablation, 464, 464f
Ultrasonic imaging, 466
Ultrasonics, 467, 467f
Ultrasound, 468–469, 469f–470f
V particles, 481
Van der Pol equation, 488
Van der Pol oscillator, 488
Ventilation, 498
Ventilator, 498–499, 499f
Vibration, 502
Viscoelastic, 504, 504f
Viscoplastic, 505, 505f
Viscosity, 505
Viscosity (η), 505–506, 506f
Viscosity, dynamic (η_{dyn}), 506
Viscosity, static, 508
Volcano, 514, 514f
Vortex, 522–523, 523f
Vortex shedding, 524
Wall, 528–529, 529f
Water wave, 534–535, 535f
Wave, 538–539, 539f
Wave dispersion, 539–540, 540f
Wave energy, 540
Wave equation, 540
Wave motion, 540
Wave propagation speed, 541–542
Wavelength (λ), 542–543, 543f
Wentzel–Kramers–Brillouin (WKB) solution
    method, 549
Wing, 560, 560f
Work (W), 562, 562f
Work–energy theorem, 563
Yield length, 570, 570f
Yield stress (τ^*), 570
Young, Thomas (1773–1829), 571, 571f
Young–Laplace equation, 572
Young's modulus (Y_n), 572, 572f
Meteorology
    Quasi-steady state, 184–185, 185f
    Saturation curve, 267–268, 268f
    Telemetry, 388, 388f
    Tornado, 430–431, 431f
    Torricelli, Evangelista (1608–1647), 433, 433f
    Tracers, 440
    Waterspout, 536, 536f
Nuclear Physics
    Packing fraction, 2
    Pair annihilation, 2

Nuclear Physics (*Continued*)
Pair formation, 2–3, 3f
Pairing energy (P_{pair}), 3
Paramagnetism, 9
Parent nuclide, 11–12, 12f
Parity, 12–13, 13f
Parity conservation rule, 14
Particle accelerator, 15, 15f
Particle accelerators, linear, 16
Particle in potential well, 16
Paschen, Friedrich (1865–1947), 19, 19f
Paschen law, 20, 20f
Paschen series, 20, 21f
Paschen–Back effect, 21
Pauli, Wolfgang Ernst (1900–1958), 23, 23f
Pauli exclusion principle, 23
Periodic table of elements, 35, 36f
Perkins, Donald Hill (1925–), 39, 39f
Perrin, Jean Baptiste (1870–1942), 41, 41f
Peters, Bernard (1910–1993), 43, 43f
Pfund, August Herman (1879–1949), 44–45, 45f
Pfund series, 45, 45f
Phase space, 55–56, 56f
Phase velocity, 57
Phosphorus (phosphor) ($^{30}_{15}P$), 60–61, 61f
Photodisintegration, 71
Photoelectric cells, 73–74, 74f
Photoelectric effect, 74, 75f
Photoelectric nuclear effect, 76
Photomultiplier tube, 77–78, 78f
Photovoltaic effect, 81–82, 82f
Pickering series, 87
Pickup reaction, 87
Pinch effect, 90, 90f
Pion, 91
Planck, Maxwell Karl Ernst Ludwig (1858–1947),
    95–96, 96f
Planck's law, 96
Planck's radiation law, 96–97, 97f
Plasma, 100–101, 101f
Plasma frequency, 101
Plasmon, 101
Plücker, Julius (1801–1868), 104–105, 105f
Plutonium ($^{244}_{94}Pu$), 105, 105f
Polarization, 115–116, 116f
Polonium ($^{84}_{209}Po$), 119
Pool, M. L., 122
Positive ions, 126, 126f
Positive rays, 127
Positron (β^+), 127
Positron decay, 128
Positron emission tomography (PET),
    128–129, 129f
Positronium, 129, 129f
Potential energy (PE), 131–132, 132f
Potential well, 133–134, 134f

Pound, Robert Vivian (1919–2010), 135–136, 136f
Powell, Cecil Frank (1903–1969), 137, 137f
Power (*P*), 138, 138f
Precession, 142, 142f
Prévost, Pierre (1751–1839), 145, 145f
Prévost theory of heat exchange, 145
Primary cosmic ray particles, 147
Principal quantum number, 147
Probability, 149–150, 150f
Prompt neutron, 151
Proton, 153
Prout's hypothesis, 153
Prout, William (1785–1850), 153, 153f
Purcell, Edward Mills (1912–1997), 161, 161f
Q Equation, 165, 165f
Q Factor, 165–166, 166f
Q of reaction, 166
Quality factor, 170–171, 171f
Q Value, 169, 169f
Quantum, 172, 172f
Quantum mechanics, 174–175, 175f–176f
Quantum number, 176–177, 176f
Quantum physics, electron shells, 177–178
Quantum state, 178, 178f
Quantum theory, 179
Rabi, Isidor Isaac (1898–1988), 187–188, 188f
Radial quantum number, 188
Radial wave equation, 188
Radial wave function, 188
Radiance ($\Phi(\vec{r}, \vec{s})$), 188, 189f
Radiation dose, 192, 192f
Radiation hazards, 192–193, 193f
Radioactive decay, 199, 199f
Radioactive decay chain, 199–200, 200f
Radioactive decay constant (λ_{decay}), 200, 200f
Radioactive decay law, 201
Radioactive isotope, 201, 201f
Radioactive transformation, 201
Radioactive waste, 202, 202f
Radioactivity, 202, 202f
Radioisotope, 204
Radionuclide, 204
Radium ($^{226}_{88}Ra$), 204
Radon ($^{222}_{86}Rn$), 205, 205f
Raman scattering, 207–208, 208f
Raman spectroscopy, 208
Rasmussen, John (1926–), 214, 214f
Rayleigh–Jeans equation, 218
Rayleigh scattering, 216–217, 217f
Reactor, 219
Recoil energy, 220
Reflection, 224, 224f
Refraction, 225, 225f
Reines, Frederick (1918–1998), 225–226, 226f
Relaxation time, 227
Reproduction factor, 228

Residual nucleus, 229
Resolving power, 230–231, 231f
Resonance reactions, 233, 233f
Rest mass, 235
Richardson's equation, 240
Roentgen rays, 248
Roentgen, Röntgen, 248
Roentgen, W. C., 248
Röntgen, Wilhelm Conrad {Roentgen} (1845–1923),
    248–249, 249f
Russell, Henry Norris (1877–1957), 251, 251f
Russell–Saunders coupling, 252–253, 253f
Rutherford, Ernest (1871–1937), 254, 254f
Rutherford cross section, 255
Rutherford's atom, 256, 256f
Rydberg constant, 257
Rydberg, Johannes Robert (1854–1919), 256, 256f
Saha, Meghnad (1893–1956), 261, 261f
Saturable nuclear force, 265
Saunders, Frederick Albert (1875–1963), 269
Scattering, 275, 275f
Scattering length, singlet, 277
Scattering length, triplet, 277
Scherrer, Paul (1890–1969), 279, 279f
Schiff, Leonard Isaac (1915–1971), 280, 280f
Schrödinger, Erwin Rudolf Josef Alexander
    (1887–1961), 284, 284f–285f
Schrödinger equation of motion, 285–286, 286f
Schrödinger's cat, 286–287, 287f
Schrödinger Wave Equation, 286
Second law of Faraday, 290
Second-generation of matter, 291
Segrè, Emilio Gino (1905–1989), 292, 293f
Selection rule and, 296
Self-energy, coulomb, 297
Semiconductors, 298
Separation of variables, 299
Shape factor, 302
Sharp series, 304
Shell model, 307, 307f
Sievert, Rolf Maximilian (1896–1966), 310–311, 311f
Sievert (Sv), 310
Sigma particle, 311
Simultaneity, 315
Singlet scattering length, 316
Singlet state, 317, 317f
Smyth report, 322
Soddy, Frederick (1877–1956), 324, 324f
Sodium $\left(^{22}_{11}\text{Na}\right)$, 324–325, 325f
Sodium cooled reactor, 326, 326f
Sodium iodide detector, 326
Solid angle, 330, 330f
Solid-state, 331
Solid-state physics, 331
Sommerfeld, Arnold Johannes Wilhelm (1868–1951),
    333, 333f

Special theory of relativity, 337
Specific heat, 337
Star, 343–344, 344f
Stefan–Boltzmann law, 348
Stern, Otto (1888–1969), 349, 349f
Stern-Gerlach experiment, 350
Strong nuclear force, 358, 358f
Sun, 361–362, 362f
Superfluid, 365
Synchrotron, 374, 374f
Synchrotron radiation, 374
Taylor, Geoffrey Ingram, Sir (1886–1975), 383, 383f
Telescope, 389, 389f
TEM, 390
Thermal energy, 397
Thermal expansion, 397–398, 398f
Thermal neutrons, 398
Thermionic emission, 399
Thomson, George Paget, Sir (1892–1975), 410, 410f
Thomson, Joseph John (1856–1940), 410–411, 411f
Thomson scattering, 412, 412f
Thorium radioactive series, 412–413, 413f
Thyratron, 416
Torrey, Henry Cutler (1911–1998), 433
Total angular momentum, 437
Townsend, John Sealy Edward, Sir (1868–1957),
    439–440, 440f
Tracers, 440
Transient equilibrium, 441–442
Transistor, 442, 442f
Transmission electron microscope, 443, 443f
Transuranic element, 444–445
Triplet state, 447, 447f
Tunneling, 452
U-234 $\left(^{234}_{92}\text{U}\right)$, 459
U-235 $\left(^{235}_{92}\text{U}\right)$, 459, 459f
U-238 $\left(^{238}_{92}\text{U}\right)$, 460, 460f
Uhlenbeck, George Eugene (1900–1988), 460, 460f
Ultraviolet catastrophe, 471, 471f
Unbestimmtheitsprinzip, 472
Uncertainty principle, 472–473, 473f
Up antiquark, 478
Up quark, 478
U-quark, 478
Uranium $\left(^{238}_{92}\text{U}\right)$, 478, 478f
Urey, Harold Clayton (1893–1981), 479, 479f
Van de Graaff generator, 486–487, 487f
Van der Waals bonding, 489–490, 490f
Van der Waals equation of state, 490
Vapor pressure, 494
Viscosity (η), 505–506, 506f
Viscosity, dynamic (η_{dyn}), 506
Viscosity, intrinsic, 506
Viscosity of deformable spherical particles (η_{sph}), 509
Viscosity, reduced, 507
Viscosity, relative, 508

Nuclear Physics (*Continued*)

    Viscosity, specific, 508

    Von Laue, Max Theodor Felix (1879–1960), 520, 520f

    Von Laue's method, 521, 521f

    Von Lenard, Philipp Eduard Anton (Lénárd Fülöp Philipp Eduard Anton von Lenard) (1862–1947), 521–522, 522f

    V particles, 481

    Walecka, John Dirk (1932–), 528, 528f

    Walton, Ernest Thomas Sinton (1903–1995), 532, 532f

    Water reactor, 534

    Wave equation, 540

    Wave number (k), 541

    Wave particle duality, 541

    Wavefunction, 542

    Wavelength, de Broglie, 543

    Weisskopf, Victor Frederick (1908–2002), 548, 548f

    Wheeler, John Archibald (1911–2008), 551–552, 552f

    Wiedemann–Franz ratio, 554

    Wien, Wilhelm Carl Werner Otto Fritz Franz (1864–1928), 554, 554f

    Wien–Planck law, 554–555, 555f

    Wien's displacement law, 555, 555f

    Wigner, Eugene (Jenő Pál) (1902–1995), 556, 556f

    Wigner distribution, 556

    Wilson, Charles Thomson Rees (1869–1959), 557, 557f

    Wilson cloud chamber, 558

    Work (W), 562, 562f

    Work function (φ_{elec}, in electron volt: eV), 562

    W-Particle, 564, 564f

    Wu, Chien-Shiung (Wú Jiànxióng; 吳健雄) (1912–1997), 564, 564f

    X-ray, 565–566, 566f

    X-ray, characteristic, 566, 567f

    Yrast line, 574, 574f

    Yrast region, 574–575, 575f

    Yrast state, 575, 575f

    Zartman, Ira Forry (1899–1981), 580, 580f

    Zeeman, Pieter (1865–1943), 580, 580f

    Zeeman and Stark effect, 581

    Zeeman effect, 581–582, 582f

    Zero-point energy, 587, 587f

Optics

    Paraxial approximation, 10–11, 11f

    Particle theory of light, 16–17, 17f

    PDT, 24

    Perception, 29–30, 30f

    Period of a cycle (T), 34, 35f

    Periodogram, 37, 37f

    Pérot, Jean-Baptiste Alfred (1863–1925), 40, 40f

    Phantom, 49, 49f

    Phase velocity, 57

    Phase-only imaging, 58

    Phosphorescence, 59–60, 60f

Photinus-luciferin 4-monooxygenase, 61

Photoacoustic microscopy, 61–64

Photobiological process, 64

Photobleaching, 64

Photochemical effect, 64

Photochemical reaction, 64

Photocoagulation, 64–69, 69f

Photodetector, 70–71, 71f

Photodynamic therapy (PDT), 71–72, 72f

Photoelasticity, 72–73, 73f

Photoelectric effect, 74, 75f

Photographic plate, 76, 76f

Photography, 77, 77f

Photon, 78–79, 79f

Photopic vision, 79, 79f

Phototoxicity, 81

Plane wave, 97

Pockels, Friedrich Carl Alwin (1865–1913), 108, 108f

Pockels effect, 108–109, 109f

Point source, 111

Polarization, 115–116, 116f

Power spectrum, 139

Prism, 149, 149f

Ptolemy (approximately 90–168 AD), 155

Pulse oximeter, 159–160, 160f

Q Switching, 168, 168f

Quality factor, 170–171, 171f

Quanta, 171

Quantum optics, 177

Quartz, 182, 182f

Quasimonochromatic light, 183

Quasiparticle, 184

Raab, Oscar (1876–1986), 187, 187f

Radiance ($\Phi(\vec{r},\vec{s})$), 188, 189f

Radiation, 189–190, 190f

Radiation coupling, 191, 191f

Raman, Chandrasekhara Venkata, Sir (1888–1970), 206, 207f

Raman scattering, 207–208, 208f

Raman spectroscopy, 208

Rayleigh, Lord, a.k.a. John William Strutt (1842–1919), 214, 214f

Rayleigh criterion, 215, 215f

Rayleigh emission law, 215, 215f

Rayleigh–Gans theory, 217

Rayleigh screening, 217

Rayleigh–Jeans equation, 218

Rayleigh–Gans–Debye scattering, 218

Reflectance, 223, 223f

Reflection, 224, 224f

Refraction, 225, 225f

Refraction, index of (n), 225

Retina, 235, 235f

Ritter, Johann Wilhelm (1776–1810), 243, 243f

Robot, 245, 245f

Robotics, 245–246, 246f

Rods, 247, 247f

Roemer {Rømer, also Römer}, Olaus (Ole) (1644–1710), 247, 247f

S, M, and L responses of the human eye, 259

Sahl, Ibn (Arabic:) (Abu Sa'd al-'Ala'ibn Sahl) (940–1000), 262, 262f

Sampling, 263–264

Sampling depth, 264

Saturation, 265–266, 266f–267f

Scattering, 275, 275f

Scattering cross section, Rayleigh, 275–276, 276f

Scattering phase function, 277, 277f

Scattering phase function, Henyey-Greenstein, 278

Schawlow, Arthur Leonard (1921–1999), 278, 278f

Scheele, Carl Wilhelm (1742–1786), 278–279, 279f

Schlieren imaging for concentration, 281, 281f

Schuster, Arthur, Sir (1851–1934), 287, 287f

Schwarzschild, Karl (1873–1916), 288, 288f

Shadowgraph method, 300, 300f

Signal, 311–312, 312f

Signal-to-noise ratio (S/N or SNR), 312, 312f

Single-slit diffraction, 316, 316f

Snel ("Snell"), Willebrord Snel van Royen (1591–1626), 322, 322f

Snell's law, 323, 323f

Snel's Law, 323

Solar therapy, 329

Spectroscopic ellipsometry, 338

Spectroscopy, 338–339, 339f

Spherical wave, 340

Stereo, 348–349

Stimulated emission, 350

Stokes, George Gabriel, Sir (1819–1903), 352, 352f

Stress birefringence, 357, 357f

Sun, 361–362, 362f

Sun spot, 362, 363f

Sundog, 363, 363f

Telescope, 389, 389f

Temporal period (T), 391, 391f

Temporal width, 391–392

Thermoacoustic imaging, 399

Thick lens, 408

Thin lenses, combinations of, 408, 408f

Toepler, August Joseph Ignaz (1836–1912), 425–426, 426f

Total internal reflection, 437

Townes, Charles Hard (1915–), 439, 439f

Transport equation, 443–444

Triplet, Wild's, 447

Trouton, Frederick Thomas (1863–1922), 449, 449f

Tsvet, Mikhail Semyonovich {Михаил Семёнович Цвет} (1872–1919), 451, 451f

Two-photon absorption, 456

Two-slit diffraction, 456

Ultrafast biological events, 462–463, 463f

Ultraviolet, 470–471, 471f

Vacuum field equations, 482

Van Leeuwenhoek, Antonie Philips (1632–1723), 491–492, 492f

Van Royen, Willibrord Snel (1591–1626), 492

Velocity ($\bar{v}$), 497

Vision, 510–511, 511f

Visual acuity, 512, 512f

Vitreous humor, 512–513, 513f

Von Fraunhofer, Joseph (1787–1826), 517, 517f

Wave dispersion, 539–540, 540f

Wave number (k), 541

Wave particle duality, 541

Wheatstone, Charles (1802–1875), 550–551, 551f

White, 552, 552f

Wollaston prism, 561, 561f

Young, Thomas (1773–1829), 571, 571f

Young's slit experiment, 573, 573f

Zehnder, Ludwig (1854–1949), 582, 582f

Zeiss, Carl (1816–1888), 583, 583f

Quantum Physics

    Parity, 12–13, 13f

    Parity conservation rule, 14

    Paschen, Friedrich (1865–1947), 19, 19f

    Paschen–Back effect, 21

    Phase, 49–50, 50f–51f

    Phase cancellation, 51, 51f

    Photon, 78–79, 79f

    Piezoelectric effect, 87–88, 88f

    Piezoelectric resonance, 88, 89f

    Piezoelectricity, 89

    Piezoelectric transducer, 89, 89f

    Pion, 91

    Positron (β^+), 127

    Potential barrier, 130, 130f

    Potential well, 133–134, 134f

    Precession, 142, 142f

    Pyroelectricity, 162

    Q Switching, 168, 168f

    Quanta, 171

    Quantum, 172, 172f

    Quantum dot (QD), 172, 172f

    Quantum liquid, 174

    Quantum magnet, 174

    Quantum number, 176–177, 176f

    Quantum physics, electron shells, 177–178

    Quantum total angular momentum, 179

    Quantum tunneling, 179–180, 180f

    Quark, color of, 182

    Quark, flavor of, 182

    Radiation, 189–190, 190f

    Radioactivity, 202, 202f

    Recoil energy, 220

    Resonance, 231, 231f

    Riccati equations, 240

    Rician noise, 241, 241f

    Russell–Saunders coupling, 252–253, 253f

Quantum Physics (*Continued*)
Rutherford scattering, 255, 255f
Schrödinger, Erwin Rudolf Josef Alexander
 (1887–1961), 284, 284f–285f
Schrödinger's cat, 286–287, 287f
Second law of Faraday, 290
Selection rule and, 296
Signal, 311–312, 312f
Signal-to-noise ratio (S/N or SNR), 312, 312f
Soliton, 331, 331f
Special theory of relativity, 337
Specific heat (c_{sp}), 337
Spin, 341–342, 342f
Stern, Otto (1888–1969), 349, 349f
Stern-Gerlach experiment, 350
Stochastic process, 352
Strong nuclear force, 358, 358f
Sun, 361–362, 362f
Tachyon, 377
Temporal width, 391–392
Thermal wave, 398–399
Thermodynamics, 399–400
Thomson, Joseph John (1856–1940), 410–411, 411f
Triple-twin domain, 447–448
Two-photon absorption, 456
Unified theories of the weak and electromagnetic
 interactions, 474
Unified theory, 475, 475f
Valence band, 483, 483f
Van der Waals bonding, 489–490, 490f
Variance (σ^2), 496, 496f
V particles, 481
Walecka, John Dirk (1932–), 528, 528f
Wave equation, 540
Weak interaction, 543–544, 544f
Wentzel, Gregor (1898–1978), 549, 549f
Wentzel–Kramers–Brillouin (WKB) solution
 method, 549
Wigner, Eugene (Jenő Pál) (1902–1995), 556, 556f
Zeeman effect, 581–582, 582f
Zero-mass particles, 586
Zweig, George (1937–), 588, 588f
Solid-state Physics
Parity, 12–13, 13f
Parity conservation rule, 14
Particle, 14–15, 15f
Peierls, Rudolf Ernst, Sir (1907–1995), 25, 25f
Peierls–Fröhlich–Kuper ground state, 25
Peierls transition, 25
Periodic law, 35
Phase, 49–50, 50f–51f
Phosphorescence, 59–60, 60f
Phosphorus (phosphor) ($^{30}_{15}P$), 60–61, 61f
Positron annihilation, 127–128, 128f
Positron emission tomography (PET), 128–129, 129f
Primary electron, 147

Principal moments, 147
Principle of corresponding states, 148
Pyroelectricity, 162
Quantum dot (QD), 172, 172f
Quantum magnet, 174
Quartz, 182, 182f
Quasicrystalline solid, 183
Q Value, 169, 169f
Radius of gyration (R_g), 204
Raman scattering, 207–208, 208f
Rankine, William John Macquorn (1820–1872),
 210, 210f
Relaxation time, 227
Richardson, Owen Willans, Sir (1879–1959), 240, 240f
Rock salt, 246, 246f
Röntgen, Wilhelm Conrad {Roentgen} (1845–1923),
 248–249, 249f
Rutherford, Ernest (1871–1937), 254, 254f
Rutherford's atom, 256, 256f
Rydberg constant, 257
Rydberg state, 258
Schawlow, Arthur Leonard (1921–1999), 278, 278f
Schottky, Walter Hermann (1886–1976), 282, 282f
Schottky barrier, 282–283
Schottky diode, 283
Schottky effect, 283
Second-generation of matter, 291
Shell model, 307, 307f
Silicon (Si), 313, 313f
Spectroscopic ellipsometry, 338
Stark, Johannes (1874–1957), 344–345, 345f
Stark effect, 345
Strong nuclear force, 358, 358f
Student's *t*-test, 358–359
Subshell, 361
Superconductivity, 364
't Hooft, Gerard (1946–), 377, 377f
Tectonics, 385, 385f
TEM, 390
Temperature (*T*), 390–391, 391f
Tensor, 394
Thermal wave, 398–399
Titanium, 425
Townes, Charles Hard (1915–), 439, 439f
Transmission electron microscope, 443, 443f
Triplet state, 447, 447f
Ultimate stress, 461
Ultimate tensile strength, 461, 461f
Ultrafast phenomena, 463
Unbestimmtheitsprinzip, 472
Uncertainty principle, 472–473, 473f
Unified atomic mass units (*u*), 474
Unstable equilibrium state, 476, 476f
Van der Waals bonding, 489–490, 490f
Van der Waals, Johannes Diderik (1837–1923),
 489, 489f

Vibration, 502–503, 503f
Viscoelastic, 504, 504f
Viscosity (η), 505–506, 506f
Viscosity, dynamic (η_{dyn}), 506
Volcano, 514, 514f
Wavelength (λ), 542–543, 543f
Wedgwood, Josiah (1730–1795), 545–546, 546f
Thermodynamics
Papin, Denis (1647–1712), 4, 5f
Partial pressure, Dalton's law of, 14
Partial pressure of a constituent, 14, 14f
Partition function, 17
Pascal, Blaise (1623–1662), 18, 18f
Pascal, law of, 18
Passive resistance, 22
Passive state, 23
Péclet number (Pe), 24
Péclet number, mass transfer (Pe_m), 24
Peierls–Fröhlich–Kuper ground state, 25
Peltier, Jean Charles Athanase (1785–1845), 26, 26f
Peltier coefficient, 26
Peltier effect, 26, 27f
Perfect gas, 32
Perfect incompressible behavior, 32
Permeability (μ_{mag}), 39
Permittivity (ε_{elec}), 39
Petit, Alexis Thérèse (1791–1820), 43, 43f
Pfaffian, 44
Phase, 49–50, 50f–51f
Phase cancellation, 51, 51f
Phase diagram, 51–52, 52f
Phase rotation, 54, 54f
Phase rule, 55, 55f
Phase sequence, 55
Phase transition, 56–57
Photinus-luciferin 4-monooxygenase, 61
Photobiological process, 64
Photochemical reaction, 64
Photosynthesis, 80–81, 81f
Physisorption, 85
Pinch temperature, 90, 90f
Pion, 91
Planck, Maxwell Karl Ernst Ludwig (1858–1947), 95–96, 96f
PMM1, 106
PMM2, 106
Pockels effect, 108–109, 109f
Poincaré, Jules Henri (1854–1912), 109, 109f
Polar nature of a medium, 115, 115f
Polytropic process, 121
Positron (β^+), 127
Potential energy of a liquid surface, 132
Potential well, 133–134, 134f
Power (P), 138, 138f
Power cycle, 138
Poynting correction, 140

Prandtl, Ludwig (1875–1953), 140–141, 141f
Prévost, Pierre (1751–1839), 145, 145f
Principle of highest entropy, 148
Principle of lowest energy, 148
Probability, 149–150, 150f
Propulsion, 152, 152f
Prout, William (1785–1850), 153, 153f
Psychrometry, 154
Pump, 160, 160f
Pyroelectricity, 162
Q Phase, 166, 167f
Quantized Dirac equation, 171
Quantum concentration, 172
Quantum electrodynamics (QED), 173
Quantum field theory, 173
Quantum fluids, 173
Quantum gas, 173–174
Quantum liquid, 174
Quantum mechanics, 174–175, 175f–176f
Quasi-steady state, 184–185, 185f
Radiant energy fluence rate ($E^0(\vec{r}, t)$), 189
Radiation therapy, 193–194, 194f
Rankine, William John Macquorn (1820–1872), 210, 210f
Rankine, 209
Rankine cycle, 210–211, 211f
Raoult, François-Marie (1830–1901), 212, 212f
Raoult's law, 212
Rayleigh flow, 216
Rayleigh line, 216, 216f
Rayleigh number ($Ra = L^3\rho^2 g\alpha_{exp}\Delta T c_p / \eta\kappa = GrPr$), 216
Rayleigh–Taylor instability, 218
Réaumur, René-Antoine Ferchault de (1683–1757), 219, 219f
Refrigeration cycle, 225
Relative humidity (RH), 226
Relative permeability, 226
Relative permittivity, 227
Rényi, Alfréd (1921–1970), 228, 228f
Rényi entropy, 228
Reynolds, Osborne (1842–1912), 237, 237f
Rheology, 239
Richardson–Dushman equation, 240
Rutherford, Ernest (1871–1937), 254, 254f
Rutherford's atom, 256, 256f
Rydberg constant, 257
Saha, Meghnad (1893–1956), 261, 261f
Saha ionization equation, 261
Saturated state, 265
Saturation, 265–266, 266f–267f
Saturation curve, 267–268, 268f
Saturation dome, 268, 268f
Saturation pressure, 269
Schmidt, Ernst Heinrich Wilhelm (1892–1975), 281, 281f
Schrödinger equation, 285

Thermodynamics (*Continued*)

Schrödinger equation of motion, 285–286, 286f
Schrödinger Wave Equation, 286
Second law, 289
Second law, Kelvin–Planck's statement, 289
Second law of Faraday, 290
Second law of thermodynamics, Carathéodory's statement of the, 290
Second law of thermodynamics, Clausius formulation, 290
Second order phase transition, 290–291, 291f
Seebeck effect, 292
Seebeck, Thomas Johann (1770–1831), 292, 292f
Semipermeable membrane, 299, 299f
Shannon sampling law, 302
Shannon sampling theorem, 302
Shedding frequency (v_v), 307
Shell model, 307, 307f
Solar power, 327–328, 328f
Solid form of aggregation, 330
Solidification, 331
Solid-state, 331
Solid-state physics, 331
Solute, 332
Solution, 332
Solvent, 333
Specific heat (c_{sp}), 337
Spin, 341–342, 342f
Stirling, Robert (1790–1878), 351, 351f
Stirling cycle, 351, 351f
Stoichiometric coefficient, $\left(v_i^{(j)}\right)$, 352
Stoichiometry, 352
Stratosphere, 355–356, 356f
Strong nuclear force, 358, 358f
Sublimation, 361, 361f
Subshell, 361
Supercritical fluid state, 364
Superheated steam, 365
Superheated vapor state, 365
Surface energy, 366–367
Surface phenomena of Liquids, 367
Surface Potential Energy, 367–368, 368f
Surface tension, 370, 370f
Surfactant, 372, 372f
Tectonics, 385, 385f
Temperature (T), 390–391, 391f
Thermal conductivity, 397
Thermal diffusivity ($\alpha_{dif} = \kappa/\rho c_p$), 397
Thermal energy, 397
Thermal equilibrium, 397
Thermal expansion, 397–398, 398f
Thermal wave, 398–399
Thermoacoustic imaging, 399
Thermocouple, 399
Thermodynamics, 399–400
Thermodynamics, first law of, 400

Thermodynamics, second law, 400
Thermodynamics, third law, 400
Thermodynamics, zeroth law of, 400
Thermography, 400–401, 401f
Thermokinetic oscillator, 402
Thermometer, 402, 402f
Thermophysical properties, 404–405
Thermoscope, 405, 405f
Thermosphere, 405–406, 406f
Thermostatics, 406
Third law of thermodynamics, 408
Thompson, Benjamin, Sir (1753–1814), 409, 409f
Thomson, William (1824–1907), 411–412
Throttle, 415, 415f
Total potential, 438
Triple point, 446, 446f
Troposphere, 448–449, 449f
Trouton, Frederick Thomas (1863–1922), 449, 449f
Turbine, 453, 453f
Ultrahigh pressure, 463
Uncorrelated states, 473
Unstable equilibrium state, 476, 476f
Unsteady state, 478
Valve, 483–484, 484f
Van der Waals, Johannes Diderik (1837–1923), 489, 489f
Van der Waals bonding, 489–490, 490f
Van der Waals equation of state, 490
Van Laar equations, 491
Van't Hoff equation, 493
Van't Hoff factor, 493
Van't Hoff, Jacobus Henricus (1852–1911), 493, 493f
Van't Hoff law, 494
Vapor, 494, 494f
Vapor pressure, 494
Variance (σ^2), 496, 496f
Vibration, 502–503, 503f
Volcano, 514, 514f
Von Helmholtz, Hermann Ludwig Ferdinand (1821–1894), 518, 518f
Von Mayer, Julius Robert (1814–1878), 522, 522f
Vortex, 522–523, 523f
Vortex shedding, 524
Water reactor, 534
Wet-bulb temperature, 550
Wiedemann–Franz ratio, 554
Wien, Wilhelm Carl Werner Otto Fritz Franz (1864–1928), 554, 554f
Wien–Planck law, 554–555, 555f
Wien's displacement law, 555, 555f
XY model, 568
Young–Laplace equation, 572
Yukawa, Hideki (1907–1981), 576, 576f
Yukawa potential, 576–577, 577f
Zero-entropy state, 585
Zero-temperature state, 587
Zeroth law of thermodynamics, 587